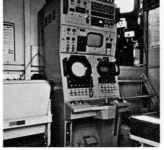

FIRE CONTROL SYSTEM

NA 10 Mod. 1 is the fire control system suiting light vessels armed with S/S missiles and one or two small calibre guns.

The ORION 10X radar and TV and IR sensors are used in it.

Chosen by the Italian Navy for its hydrofoil project. Installed on fast patrol boats of foreign Navies.

SELENIA, INDUSTRIE ELETTRONICHE ASSOCIATE S.p.A.
00131 Rome, Italy, Via Tiburtina km 12.400

ELSAG, ELETTRONICA SAN GIORGIO S.p.A.
16154 Genoa Sestri, Italy, Via Hermada 6

NAVAL SYSTEMS DIVISION

[iv]

JANE'S
SURFACE SKIMMERS
Hovercraft and Hydrofoils

Compiled and Edited by **Roy McLeavy**

Order of Contents

World Sales Distribution

Jane's Yearbooks,
Paulton House, 8 Shepherdess Walk,
London N1 7LW, England

All the World
except

United States of America and Canada:
Franklin Watts Inc.,
730 Fifth Avenue,
New York, NY 10019, USA

Editorial communication to:

The Editor, Jane's Surface Skimmers
Jane's Yearbooks, Paulton House, 8 Shepherdess Walk
London N1 7LW, England
Telephone 01- 251 1666

Advertisement communication to:

Jane's Advertising Department
Jane's Yearbooks, Paulton House, 8 Shepherdess Walk
London N1 7LW, England
Telephone 01-251 1666

Jane's Yearbooks
for international coverage.

Established for over three-quarters of a century, Jane's Yearbooks are internationally recognized as authoritative works of reference in their respective fields. Each of the Jane's Yearbooks is in effect an international encyclopedia of factual information on its own particular subject. The emphasis is on accurate and up-to-date facts checked and re-checked. Accuracy and comprehensiveness on a world-wide scale, give the books their reliability as works of reference. Dimensions are given in both British and metric units, and almost all the entries are illustrated with either photographs or drawings. Jane's Yearbooks are indispensible to all professional servicemen – be they naval, military or air-force – as well as to government departments.

Jane's Fighting Ships
Edited by Captain J. E. Moore, R.N.
Unrivalled as a reference book on the world's navies, the latest edition has extensive revisions, and incorporates important changes including the reclassification of all ships. The book covers 15,000 ships in more than 110 countries. There are over 3,000 photographs, plans, silhouettes and line drawings in approximately 760 pages.

Jane's Weapon Systems
Edited by R. T. Pretty
Recognised as an important catalogue of military systems, equipment and armament, each entry is revised and updated as necessary each year. Sections with changes of particular significance include those on strategic missiles, naval missiles, drones and remotely piloted vehicles. There are over 1,000 photographs and diagrams in about 920 pages.

Jane's All The World's Aircraft
Edited by J. W. R. Taylor
Produced with the fullest possible co-operation of the aerospace industries of the world, this volume provides all the details of every aircraft, military as well as civil, in production or development in 38 countries. The book contains about 900 pages and 1,500 photographs and 3 view drawings.

Jane's Surface Skimmers
Hovercraft and Hydrofoils.
Edited by Roy McLeavy
With the growing world-wide acceptance of skimmer-craft for military besides commercial use, Jane's Surface Skimmers becomes increasingly valuable for all those with interests in this field. In this young industry new developments are constantly being recorded in all areas covered by the publication. There are about 500 photographs and diagrams in approximately 450 pages.

Jane's Infantry Weapons
Edited by Major F. W. H. Hobart (Retd.)
This latest addition to the Jane's 'family' follows logically from the success of 'Jane's Weapon Systems' to which it is largely complementary. The book has four main sections i.e.: Point Target Weapons; Area Weapons; Anti-aircraft and Anti-tank Weapons, and Electronics. Each section is sub-divided according to the nature of the subject and entries give standardised, detailed descriptions and specifications. Illustrated with diagrams and photographs in about 800 pages.

Typical presentation of information in Jane's Yearbooks. Top: 'Jane's Fighting Ships'; centre: 'Jane's Weapon Systems' and bottom: 'Jane's All the World's Aircraft

JANE'S YEARBOOKS
Paulton House
8 Shepherdess Walk, London N1
Telephone 01-251 1666
Telex 946893. Beeney Bromley
Cables MACJANES LDN

RADAR SYSTEMS FOR SHIPS, HELICOPTERS AND GROUND STATIONS - RADARS FOR NAVIGATION AND AIR-NAVAL SEARCH - DISPLAYS - MISSILE ASSIGNMENT CONSOLLES - HOMING RADARS - SIGNAL PROCESSING AND DATA HANDLING TECHNIQUES.

SMA

SEGNALAMENTO MARITTIMO ED AEREO

P. O. BOX 200 - FIRENZE (ITALIA) - TELEPHONE: 705651 - TELEX: SMARADAR 57622 - CABLE: SMA FIRENZE

JANE'S SURFACE SKIMMERS
ALPHABETICAL LIST OF ADVERTISERS
1975/76 EDITION

strikepower

BRITISH HOVERCRAFT

Take missile strikepower right inshore and onshore.
Cross minefields, submerged defences, swamps,
sand and shallows at 50 knots.
Carry supporting combat troops and you'll
have a beach head in no time.
How? Only by British Hovercraft.

british hovercraft corporation

East Cowes Isle of Wight England Telephone Cowes 4101 Telex 86190

*A Member of the Westland Group of Companies—
7 times winner of the Queen's Award to Industry.*

1975

JANE'S SURFACE SKIMMERS
CLASSIFIED LIST OF ADVERTISERS
1975/76 EDITION

The companies advertising in this publication have informed us that they are involved in the fields of manufacture indicated below

ACV MANUFACTURERS
Bell Aerospace
Bertin
British Hovercraft Corporation
Vosper Thornycroft

ACV OPERATORS
British Rail Hovercraft

ACV RESEARCH AND DESIGN
Bell Aerospace
Bertin
British Hovercraft Corporation
Selenia
Vosper Thornycroft

DIESEL ENGINES
Motoren-und Turbinen-Union
Zahnradfabrik

ELECTRONIC EQUIPMENT
Selenia

FINISHED MACHINE PARTS
Rose Bearings

GLASS FIBRE RESINS
British Hovercraft Corporation

HOVERCRAFT COMMAND STAFF TRAINING
Bell Aerospace
British Hovercraft Corporation
British Rail Hovercraft

HOVERCRAFT CONSULTANTS
Bell Aerospace
British Rail Hovercraft
Vosper Thornycroft

HOVERCRAFT FERRY SERVICE
British Rail Hovercraft

HOVERCRAFT INTERIOR DESIGN
Bell Aerospace
British Hovercraft Corporation
Vosper Thornycroft

HOVERCRAFT INTERIOR FURNISHINGS
British Hovercraft Corporation
Vosper Thornycroft

HOVERCRAFT MANUFACTURERS
Bell Aerospace
Bertin
British Hovercraft Corporation
Vosper Thornycroft

HOVERCRAFT OPERATORS
British Rail Hovercraft
Hoverwork

HOVERPALLET MANUFACTURERS
Bertin
British Hovercraft Corporation

HYDROFOIL BOATS AND SHIPS
Cantiere Navaltecnica
Supramar
Vosper Thornycroft

HYDROFOIL INTERIOR DESIGN
Cantiere Navaltecnica
Vosper Thornycroft

HYDROFOIL INTERIOR FURNISHING
Cantiere Navaltecnica
Vosper Thornycroft

HYDROFOIL MISSILE/GUN BOATS
Cantiere Navaltecnica
Supramar
Vosper Thornycroft

HYDROFOIL RESEARCH & DESIGN
Cantiere Navaltecnica
Supramar
Vosper Thornycroft

INSTRUMENTS—ELECTRONIC
Bell Aerospace
British Hovercraft Corporation

INSTRUMENTS—NAVIGATION
Bell Aerospace

INSTRUMENTS—TEST EQUIPMENT
British Hovercraft Corporation

PATROL BOATS
Bell Aerospace
Cantiere Navaltecnica
Supramar
Vosper Thornycroft

PUBLICATIONS
British Hovercraft Corporation
Vosper Thornycroft

RADAR FOR NAVIGATION, WARNING INTERCEPTION, FIRE CONTROL
Bell Aerospace
Selenia
SMA

RADIO NAVIGATION EQUIPMENT
Bell Aerospace
Selenia

REVERSE-REDUCTION GEARS
Vosper Thornycroft
Zahnradfabrik

SKIRT MATERIALS
Bell Aerospace
British Hovercraft Corporation
Northern Rubber

TRANSMISSION SYSTEMS
British Hovercraft Corporation

331/396

538

652

956

400 to 6000 horses mtu diesel power

mtu

Motoren- und Turbinen-Union Friedrichshafen GmbH · M. A. N. Maybach Mercedes-Benz · 799 Friedrichshafen · W.-Germany

[8]

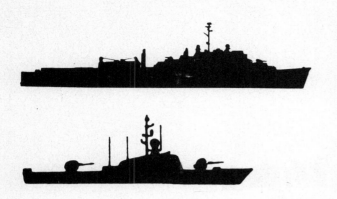

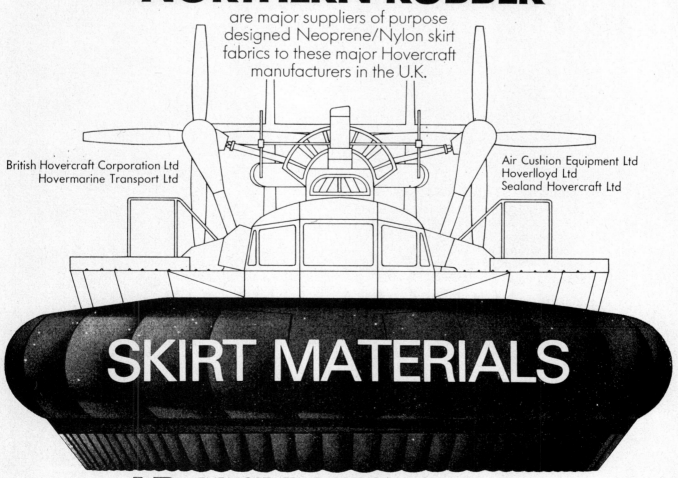

Floating wings.

JANE'S SURFACE SKIMMERS

Hovercraft and Hydrofoils

NINTH EDITION

COMPILED AND EDITED BY
ROY McLEAVY

1975-76

I.S.B.N. 0 354 00525 1

JANE'S YEARBOOKS

LONDON

FLAGSTAFF MK II

a stable platform by Grumman

With capability for a wide variety of mission applications
- Missile carrier ▪ Coastal patrol ▪ Search & rescue ▪ Crew boat
- Gun platform ▪ Anti-submarine warfare ▪ Fast transport ▪ Cargo carrier

Offering these design features:
- Open ocean habitability ▪ Operational economy ▪ Rugged construction
- Proven technology ▪ High–speed performance ▪ 65,000 lbs. of useful payload

Grumman's 67-ton Flagstaff (PG(H)-1) was the first of a new class of U. S. Navy gunboats designed to offer an excellent high speed stable gun platform in rough water.

For further information:
Mr. Joseph Barbetta, Marine Systems Requirement
Grumman Aerospace Corporation,
Bethpage, New York 11714
Telephone: (516) 575-2735, Telex: 961430

GRUMMAN AEROSPACE CORPORATION

CONTENTS

"JANE'S" is a registered trade mark

Built in 1958 and still going strong, one of SUPRAMAR's PTL 28 Hydrofoils
serving SHELL's offshore platforms on the Lake of Maracaibo in Venezuela.

HYDROFOILS=SUPRAMAR

Supramar=Hydrofoil: Simple as it sounds but basically factual ● Hydrofoils came to this world, first by Supramar, both militarily and commercially ● Nearly 40 years of painstaking research, testing, development and accumulated experience in Hydrofoil technology ● Over 20 years of production and licensing major shipyards around the world ● Over 18 years of solid and continuous operations with some 160 Hydrofoils operating the world's rivers, lakes, coastal waters and rough seas ● Over two billion passenger kilometers without a single fatality ● Supramar Hydrofoils could have an important and profitable place in your plan of operation ● They are used by over 100 scheduled ferry services using different types of Supramar Hydrofoils ● Shell Oil have used Supramar hydrofoils for over 15 years to service offshore drilling rigs ● Several Navies use Supramar Hydrofoils for coastal patrol duties ● Supramar Hydrofoils are now fully developed with a simple system of air stabilization, another revolutionary technique exclusively developed and patented internationally by Supramar ● If your business is water transportation, we have an experienced team to handle your purchase, long-term financing, leasing, operational or equity participation requirements ● You should get the facts from Supramar before making any decision ● Write on your letterhead to:

SUPRAMAR AG, DENKMALSTR 2, 6006 Lucerne, Switzerland
Telephone: 041-369636   Telex: 78228

FOREWORD

UP, UP AND AWAY!

For the hovercraft industry the road to recognition has been long and hard. But in the space of the past twenty months it has been acquiring an air of stability which has the unmistakable look of permanency about it.

One of the biggest factors in the industry's change of fortune is that inflation, devaluation and rising costs have so eroded the economics of new displacement ferryboats that hovercraft, which are smaller, faster and often less expensive, are rapidly emerging as the "better buy". Within the industry it is confidently predicted that the first large orders for new hoverferries will be placed within the next two years, and that by the early 1980s, robust annual sales levels running into millions of pounds will have been reached.

However, profits are as much sought by shipping operators today as at any time in seafaring history. Currently the economic recession has hit traffic, competition is stiffer, and the overheads are unprecedented. By now there can be few major car ferry operators who have not directed their accountants and EDP teams to compare the potential profitability of mixed-traffic hovercraft with that of new conventional displacement ferries. Those who have completed the exercise recently are firmly in favour of hovercraft.

The key to the stimulus in sales is the hoverferry's greater flexibility in terms of design, capacity, performance and handling requirements. Traditionally, displacement car ferries have been designed to cater for peak season traffic volumes. Off-peak and during shoulder seasons, their operating costs remain the same, but the revenue they produce is often minimal. Restricted by their speed, draught and very often by their loading arrangements, with bow and stern doors which may match the facilities in only two ports, they cannot be diverted to other, more profitable routes or activities in the lean months.

On occasions when ferry operators have tried to seek out alternative routes, they have been confronted immediately with the need to invest in costly berths, loading facilities and terminals, not forgetting expensive back-up services like dredging, to ensure that the berths can accommodate the ferries, no matter what the tidal state.

Initially, operating companies were slow to appreciate that hovercraft economics, in common with those of other "zero draft" skimming craft, are more akin to those of commercial aviation and have little in common with shipping practice. Now they are spelling out the advantages for themselves.

One big attraction is that the craft could be smaller. A hoverferry need have only one-third of the payload capacity of the vessel replaced, but being three to four times faster, it would be able to convey at least the same volume daily over the same route, or an even greater load if required. This is because the passenger/freight mileage per hour is increased by the ratio of its speed to that of the comparable displacement boat. An operator can therefore purchase a hoverferry, albeit smaller than the vessel it replaces, but at a lower price, without reducing his available capacity at peak periods. Moreover, since the building time is generally shorter, the escalation in cost while awaiting delivery is reduced.

Then there is a range of other important inducements: crewing requirements are much lower, 12-15 for an ACV compared with over 100 for a conventional car ferry, due to the smaller number of passengers to be catered for and the greater degree of automation employed; fewer maintenance staff are needed; fuel bills are reduced and, finally, the operator is freed of all restrictions imposed on him by the limited speed range and design features inherent in the conventional ferryboat, from its car-loading arrangements to its draught.

In low season, the ferry operator can utilise the full performance capability of the hoverferry, which normally cruises at only 55-60 per cent of its maximum service-speed, on an alternative but longer route. Or, he can withdraw one or more of his fleet from the summer routes, leaving one craft only to maintain the service, but running this at increasing speed to provide an acceptable frequency. In this way he avoids harnessing peak season capacity to low season traffic, and can either restrict his losses or sidestep them completely.

In the case of the conventional car ferries, the loading/off-loading facilities at the ports of call have to match their own, otherwise the loading ramps, whether at the bow, stern or sides, cannot be operated. If the facilities do not exist, they have to be built at a cost probably running into millions of pounds. Inadequate port facilities present no problems to hovercraft. Firstly, their roll-on, roll-off loading/off-loading arrangements are the most efficient devised, and secondly, the craft require only a simple concrete apron on a conveniently sited beach for a base. The terminal buildings, which are primarily for administration, customs and passport control, are relatively simple and inexpensive to build, and the only other need is for a reasonably good access road within reach, from which a spur can be laid to the hoverport. In other words the basic requirements for setting up alternative hoverferry routes during the low season are by no means complex or expensive.

Apart from these considerations, the hovercraft is also capable of operating in conditions which may force the ordinary ferry to stop. One such case is provided by a projected hoverferry service recently examined in Scandinavia. During the winter, this stretch of the Baltic becomes heavily iced, which means the existing 3,000-ton ferry can operate only when preceded by a 6,000-8,000-ton merchantman acting as an icebreaker. Apart from building a bridge or tunnel or setting up an air ferry service, which would be uneconomical, the hovercraft is the only means of providing an all-year-round uninterrupted service, and it can operate faster across ice than water.

The simplicity of their handling facilities has encouraged operators to propose them for a variety of new routes around the Mediterranean and also between Europe and North Africa. The use of displacement ferries on these routes would have been out of the question because of the need to sink millions of pounds into building permanent port installations.

There can no longer be any doubt about the popularity of large hovercraft ferries with the public. During the first nine months of 1975, the joint average load factors of British Rail Seaspeed's two SR.N4s and Hoverlloyd's three SR.N4 Mk IIs on the English Channel routes were 60.1 per cent for passengers and 73.05 per cent for cars.

"NEW GENERATION" HOVERCRAFT

Another stimulus for the commercial hovercraft market is that BHC's figures for its "new generation" BH.88 hovercraft, the SR.N4 replacement, show that it will be cheaper to operate than the conventional ferries. At present, BHC is awaiting a contract from British Rail Seaspeed for "stretching" its two standard SR.N4s. In lengthened form, the SR.N4 Mk 3 will provide much of the operational data for the design of the BH.88, which will be approximately the same size and carry a similar payload, 400 passengers and 59 cars. However there would be many improvements in the overall design. It would employ Rolls-Royce Marine Tyne gasturbines to achieve a 25 per cent improvement in fuel consumption, an improved propulsion system by using the latest large propellers or ducted fans, a modified skirt and hull to reduce hydrodynamic resistance and an improved lift fan design. BHC predicts that not only will the new craft be five knots faster than the SR.N4, but it will show a 40 per cent reduction in power requirements and a 60 per cent saving in fuel! The latter figure is one of the most significant of all, since it will mean that the fuel used by the BH.88 will be about 2.0 lb/payload ton-mile, some 15 per cent less than orthodox ships per unit of payload.

With figures like these in view, few ferry operators will be able to afford to ignore hovercraft.

BHC states that the BH.88, which requires no totally new technology, could be in service by 1981, providing the first of the class is ordered no later than 1978. Estimated cost of the craft will be about £6m at today's prices, but at the same time a research and development investment of about £0.5m is considered necessary.

Operation of the BH.88 would by no means be limited to European waters. The craft, which would be capable of operating safely and with reasonable comfort in conditions up to Force 9, would be ideal for many routes in the Pacific, North and Central America and Canada, including among others a highway/water connection across Lake Michigan. In winter in North America, it would offer double value because of its effectiveness as an ice-breaker. Operation from Canada and other non-American bases would avoid the problems of the Jones Act.

Interest in large hovercraft continues to grow in other countries also. In

Voyageur sets the pace...

Commercial uses in amphibious service and military trials have combined to show the adaptability of these craft.

Ever since a prototype Voyageur participated in the U.S. Army/U.S. Navy OSDOC II exercises, Bell Aerospace has widened its lead in development of amphibious logistic support vehicles. Bell craft are supplying transport service to remote areas in Alaska and Canada. The unique and proven capabilities of these craft give them overwater speeds of up to 50 MPH plus four-foot obstacle clearance over land, swamp, ice, beaches, sand, snow or tundra. Canadian Coast Guard Voyageur operations include search-and-rescue, aids-to-navigation and icebreaking.

Work is underway to adapt the commercial Voyageur to an improved military air cushion vehicle. A hull stretch will increase the payload capability to 30 tons. An improved air filtration system will also be incorporated using proven off-the-shelf hardware.

Voyageur can be carried as deck cargo in a condition of full military readiness, or dismantled into modules for air or land transport. The craft and its five-ton-payload sister ACV, Viking, are operational vehicles. They are providing the technology and hardware base for high-confidence commercial and military craft.

textron Bell Aerospace Canada

Grand Bend, Ontario

[16]

France, SEDAM has started work on the N.500, a 240-tonne mixed traffic hoverferry; in the United States, Bell and Rohr are preparing the final details for their 2,000-ton SES projects—the industry's first "giant"—and in the Soviet Union, work is reported to be well advanced on a substantially larger version of the 200-ton "Aist" air cushion assault landing craft.

Firm orders have been placed for two SEDAM N.500s by SNCF (French National Railways), which will employ them on a service between Boulogne and Dover starting in 1977, in addition to which an option on two further craft is held by Compagnie Générale Transmediterranée, which is planning a service between Nice and Corsica. Assembly of the N.500 prototype began during the summer of 1975 at SEDAM's new plant at Pauillac, on the Gironde estuary where the capacity is sufficient to permit the construction of four N.500s a year. The N.500's payload of 85 tonnes can comprise 400 passengers and 45 medium-size cars or 280 passengers, 10 cars and 5 coaches. Passengers are accommodated in two saloons on the two upper half-decks located one each side of a central longitudinal bow girder structure containing the coach passageway. Trials of the prototype are expected to begin during the late summer of 1976. SEDAM's design team expects to achieve a payload/total weight ratio of more than 35% in the N.500, plus a carrying capacity of 11,050 t.km/h, a substantial advance on today's capabilities, and a performance which is leading to increasing interest being shown in the craft from both existing and new operators.

WAR GAMES

Development of the US Navy's surface effect ships continues apace, the ultimate goal being the construction of ocean-going ships of up to 10,000 tons, capable of speeds of 80-100 knots. Naval planners are looking to the SES to regain the edge in speed that has gone to the submarine with the advent of nuclear power. War games have shown that the speed of the SES can make a substantial contribution to existing ASW techniques, particularly when employed on convoy screening work in conjunction with helicopters. One series of exercises demonstrated that an SES carrying an ASW helicopter can increase the helicopter's range by 20-40 per cent and its time on station while searching for hostile submarines by as much as 100 per cent.

During Phase 1 of the SES programme, the US Navy's two 100-ton testcraft demonstrated the validity of the concept and provided the design data needed before proceeding to larger ships. The Aerojet-General SES-100A, which now has variable-geometry waterjet inlets flush with the hull instead of the original pod-like ram inlets, has attained speeds well over 70 knots, while the Bell Aerospace SES-100B set up a new SES world speed record on May 23rd, 1975 when it streaked across St. Andrews Bay, Florida at 82.3 knots, nearly 95 mph.

Phase II is concerned with the design, development, construction and testing of a single test ship, the 2,000-ton 2KSES. Contracts for the development of critical sub-systems and parallel ship design were awarded to Bell Aerospace and Rohr Industries in July 1974. Concern had been expressed about the need to develop and test components including transmission, waterjet systems, lift fans and skirts, as well as heave alleviation systems to control the vessel's ride characteristics, and the additional data being gathered under these contracts will undoubtedly minimise the risk in the design and construction of the large open-ocean prototype.

Although two prototypes had been planned at the onset, R & D constraints introduced in late 1974 led to a decision to develop one SES prototype only. The current subsystem and ship design contracts are due to be completed by June 1976, and by that time one contractor is expected to have been selected to design and build the 2KSES.

Construction will take approximately three years and the vessel is expected to be completed by mid-1981. After contractor's demonstrations, it will undergo trials with the US Navy for approximately one year, during which it will be employed as a weaponised test ship while its suitability for a variety of anti-submarine, anti-aircraft and surface warfare roles is determined.

If the prototype proves effective, one of the US Navy's initial aims is the establishment of a class of 2,000-3,000-ton surface effect warships for use as escorts, small helicopter and V/STOL aircraft platforms and as missile armed surface combatants. Concepts for very much larger SESs of 6,000-10,000-tons are being examined with a view to their use as sea control ships, small carriers and high value cargo lift vessels. One interesting point is that a great deal of thought is being concentrated upon vessels with a high length-to-beam ratio with lengths up to seven times their beam. An important limitation on the beam of large SESs is dictated by the ability of the vessels to navigate the Panama Canal. To obtain data on the operational characteristics of the high length to beam ration concept,

the Surface Effect Ship Project Office has added the 46 ft long XR-5 to its small but highly effective flotilla of free-running manned test craft.

Soviet engineers have been quick to criticise the large, aerostatic type ACV as being too slow and having too limited a range. However, early successes with its Russian aerodynamic equivalent do not seem to have deterred the Soviet Navy from continuing to examine the hovercraft for its military potential. The biggest example to leave its Leningrad shipyards so far is the 200-ton "Aist" which is similar in configuration, lift, propulsion, skirts and loading arrangements to the SR.N4. "Aist" was revealed to the Russian public in one of a series of television films devoted to the 20th anniversary of the ending of World War II. The film compared the weapons of that time with those in use by the Soviet armed forces today, and "Aist", preceded by two "Gus" ACVs, demonstrated a beach landing. While the latter unloaded two parties of marine infantry, "Aist" lowered its bow door and out came a main battle tank. The craft, which appears to be a "one-off" design for research and development, can also carry mechanised infantry. The angled temporary structure above the longitudinal centreline suggests that amongst its occasional cargoes are Frog, Scud or Scaleboard battlefield missiles on their heavy duty transporters. Unlike the tanks, which require less headroom, the missile transporters would have to back out through the rear. It is reported that work is now progressing on a vessel which is substantially larger than "Aist" but which retains the same general lines.

MINESWEEPERS

Military duties are also foreseen for BHC's SR.N4 Mk.2, which is currently being offered as a minesweeper or hunter, together with a variant of the BH.7 and Vosper Thornycroft's new VT.2. All three are fully amphibious and their low pressure accoustic, and magnetic underwater signatures render them virtually immune to all types of mines. Other factors in their favour are that their transit time to and from minefields is very much quicker than that of orthodox minesweepers, their crew requirement less, and they can be employed for rescuing survivors in mined waters.

In the small to middleweight ACV field, the British Hovercraft Corporation is still discovering fresh markets for its ubiquitous SR.N6 Winchester class, and sales of Hovermarine's HM.2 continue to increase. Negotiations are currently under way for the sale of military, twin-propeller and standard models of the SR.N6 to countries in the Middle East. Both the Mk.6, the twin-propeller model, and the variant incorporating Air Vehicles' ducted propeller are proving appreciably quiter than their predecessors. During noise level tests, the Mk.6 prototype registered 105dBA while climbing a steep slope under full power, and operating over a level surface registered only 80dBA, the normal roadside noise level. Although thoughts are being directed towards second generation craft of N6 size, the first generation models still appear to have plenty of wear in them. Those employed on utility tasks are very often treated no differently from a tug or dredger, yet continue to operate satisfactorily, day in, day out, in the most rugged of terrain and climatic conditions. At least one SR.N6 has logged in excess of 25,000 hover-hours.

In July 1975 Hovermarine Transport Ltd, announced plans to manufacture and market the HM.2 and HM.5 in Japan and other areas of the Far East through a new company, Hovermarine Pacific Ltd, a joint venture company established by Hovermarine Corporation, Taiyo Fishery Co Ltd, Sasebo Heavy Industries and Fairfield Maxwell Ltd. In 1976, HM.2 manufacturing facilities will be set up by Sasebo on the island of Kyushu, and in 1977 they will be expanded to accommodate production of the HM.5. The HM.2 continues to rank as the world's fastest selling hovercraft, with more than forty either on order or delivered by October 1975. Recent models include a variant for fire-fighting. The new HM.5, which is likely to repeat the success of the HM.2, will seat from 160-200 passengers, according to the route requirements, and is designed to cruise at 35 knots in waves up to 1 m high. Like HM.2 it will be diesel-powered and propelled by twin marine propellers. Military versions are envisaged, and it is intended that these should be powered by gas-turbines. Enquiries for the HM.5 from Europe, the Mediterranean, Far East and Pacific have confirmed that a need exists for a craft of this size and performance.

In Canada, the Bell Aerospace Canada Voyageur is proving an invaluable workhorse, both as a heavy freight vehicle for oil companies and in its more recent and unexpected guise of icebreaker. It has been particularly effective in clearing channels in shallow waters, inaccessible to orthodox icebreaking vessels. Bell is now building a stretched Voyageur, the LACV/30, for the US Army. The chief modifications are the lengthening of the decks by 11 ft to facilitate the carriage of additional 10-ton Milvan containers and the siting of a mobile gantry at the bow to position the

BERTIN
air cushions

have reached very high standards in:

performances
reliability
and economy

The AEROTRAIN	is ready to insure efficiently urban, suburban and intercity transports, improving speed, comfort and economics (*see Aérotrain entry*)
The NAVIPLANE N 500	the first second generation marine air cushion vehicle, will cross the channel as from 1977. (*see SEDAM entry*)
Industrial AIR CUSHION	platforms based upon a wide range of standard air pads are used in most industrial areas more and more extensively. (*see Bertin entry*)

BERTIN & Cie

B.P. 3 — F. 78370 PLAISER (France)
Tél: 462.25.00 — Télex 692471 F

cargo. Vessels of this type will be employed in LOTS (Logistics-Over-The-Shore) operations and there is a strong possibility that thirty will be required. The first two will be completed in early 1976.

In Japan, orders continue to be placed for the Mitsui MV-PP5, twelve of which are in service with six operators. The first three MV-PP15s have been delivered to Ryuku Kauin Co Ltd and are operating between Naha and the Expo' 75 Port at Okinawa.

Few details of commercial ACVs have emerged from the Soviet Union during the past twelve months. The prototype Orion, the 80-seat sidewall craft developed from the Zarnitsa, has completed its trials on a narrow and shallow tributary of the Volga. It is stated that the vessel, which has a speed of over 30 knots, promises to be a great success in Siberia, a vast hinterland, covered with virgin forest and tundra, which offers nothing but rivers for transport. Both the Orion and another new Soviet hovercraft, the Chayka, will be built at the Sosnovskiiy Shipbuilding Yard in Kirovskaya Oblast. The Chayka-1, at present under construction, is the first of thirty to be built for the Black Sea Shipping Line and will operate between resorts in the Crimea and Caucasus.

AERODYNAMIC SKIMMERS

One of the current problems besetting the British government and its NATO allies is how to move British Royal Marine Commandos to Northern Norway, where in an emergency, they would be required to reinforce NATO's northern front. Because successive defence cuts have deprived them of suitable naval vessels, the Commandos may have to depend upon requisitioned car ferries for transport.

Since the kind of situation likely to develop in Norway requires an immediate response, delay while the commercial vessels were modified for the task would be fatal to the cohesion of the defence plan.

Assuming that the folly of penny-pinching in such vital matters is recognised before long, and the money made available for new ships, the question is—has any type of displacement vessel the performance potential required for this kind of work? More and more nations are beginning to doubt it. Military planners in the United States, the Soviet Union, France, Iran and other countries are beginning to regard the wing-in-ground-effect machine as the craft closest to their requirements for high speed troop and cargo carrying. Since these vessels would cruise at a height above the water equal to approximately half their beam or wing span, they would be invulnerable to torpedo attacks and mines, and could approach coastlines beneath defensive surveillance radar screens. In addition, their speed of 200-300 mph, coupled with the multiterrain capability provided by an air cushion landing system, would give them an operational flexibility previously unknown in warship design.

An introduction to the free-flying ram-wing surface effect vehicle was given in the 1974-75 edition by Dr. Alexander M. Lippisch, FRAeS, designer of the delta-wing Aerofoil Boat, a highly successful configuration which is under development, not only in the United States and the German Federal Republic, but also in the Soviet Union. In this edition baseline configurations for several aerodynamic naval vessels are discussed in a paper specially written by Dr. John H. Masters and Richard R. Greer of Water Research Co, Phoenix, Arizona. Apart from high speed troop and low-density cargo transports, these include highly mobile ASW systems, air defence and missile launching platforms and quick response, long-range carrier/support vessels for helicopters, coastal patrol craft and SEV patrol and landing craft.

NORTH SEA DEFENCES

An obvious requirement for the defence of the North Sea oil rigs is the provision of a number of 200-ton, all-weather patrol hydrofoils, armed to combat both surface and underwater craft. Large winged surface effect vehicles (WSEVs) could carry a pair of hydrofoils, together with their crews, weapons, support personnel and fuel to the area to be patrolled. As 'mother' craft they would provide weapons replacement, maintenance and refuelling facilities. Cruising speed of the WSEVs would be in excess of 200 knots and they would have the range to reach any part of the North Sea.

In their paper, Dr Masters and Mr Greer describe and illustrate how the two hydrofoils would be carried in the underside of the WSEVs in wells which would completely enclose their superstructure and retracted struts. Air cushion assault landing craft could be carried in exactly the same way, with troops and their assault weapons accommodated inside the wings.

Tests of the giant Soviet experimental wing-in-ground-effect machines, with a span of 131 ft 3 in (40 m) and a length of nearly 400 ft (122 m) are continuing on the Caspian Sea. Trials, which began in 1965, are being undertaken in the company of proportionally smaller models.

The machine, which operates at a height of 24.43 ft (7.14 m) above the water, has a speed of 300 knots. Applications of this type of craft include the transport of troops and military equipment, and ASW patrol, in which its considerable range and endurance will be an advantage.

In the meantime, the designers of the little Eska-1 utility craft, have broadened their approach and are now experimenting with the idea of applying Rogallo-type flexible delta wings to light ekranoplans. The parawing, well known for its outstanding aerodynamic qualities and stability, is also convenient for transporting and storage. Encouraged by the results of flight tests with a converted Let L-13J Blanik powered sailplane, the team has designed a number of small ekranoplan projects incorporating flexible wings, including a modified version of the An-2V, a floatplane version of the Antonov An-2 single-engine general-purpose biplane. Realisation of the project would give the 27-year-old design a completely new lease of life and provide a much faster form of surface transportation in underdeveloped areas for a relatively low investment. A great many uses for small inexpensive vehicles of this type are foreseen, especially in underdeveloped countries.

HYDROFOILS

Faced with growing order books for both commercial and military craft, the outlook for hydrofoil manufacturers continues to look extremely favourable. Supramar's two new licencees, Supramar Pacific Shipbuilding Co Ltd, Hong Kong and Vosper Thornycroft Private Ltd, Singapore, are both completing their first craft, PTS 75 Mk 111s and PT 20s respectively, while Hitachi Shipbuilding in Japan has completed the first of the improved PT 50 Mk IIs. Hitachi has now built a total of twenty-three PT 50s and fourteen PT 20s, with another two PT 50s under construction.

Supramar's latest designs include the PT 100, a short-range, commuter variant of the PTS 75 Mk III, with seats for 200 passengers, and a new version of the PT 150D, the PTS 150 Mk III, with improved air-stabilisation and a higher cruising speed. The first three PT 150Ds, built by Westermoen, are currently in service on the route Malmö-Copenhagen and carried record traffic during the summer of 1975. The company is continuing the development of its air-stabilisation system for both its existing designs and "new generation" craft with fully submerged foils.

Among the major events of the past twelve months was the entry into service in Hong Kong and the Pacific of Boeing's 106-ton Jetfoil, and the start of the trials of the 230-ton Boeing NATO/PHM. The first Jetfoil service was successfully initiated on April 25th by Far East Hydrofoil Co with Jetfoil 002 Madeira. The craft, which carries 284 passengers on the Hong Kong-Macao route at speeds of up to 45 knots, completed the 38-mile run in 50 minutes. The second Jetfoil service, operated by Pacific Sea Transport of Honolulu, was inaugurated by the Kamehameha, a 190-seat Model 929-100, on June 15th, 1975. Known as the SeaFlite service, PST's route network operates out of Honolulu to the islands of Kauai, Maui and Hawaii. The three stage lengths are 98, 85 and 76 nautical miles respectively and each takes two to two-and-a-half hours.

The Jetfoils have been received enthusiastically in both Hong Kong and the Hawaiian Islands. The cabins are quieter than those of commercial jet aircraft and the large, spray-free windows are excellent for sightseeing. Far East Hydrofoils has ordered two Jetfoils and Pacific Sea Transportation three. Boeing has another five Jetfoils under construction and has ordered long lead items on boats 11-25.

Consideration is being given by Boeing to the marketing of Jetfoils on a modular basis. One approach would be to supply operators, both commercial and military, with the basic hull, complete with powerplant, foils and control system, and the purchaser would arrange to install his own superstructure. Such an arrangement would give the operator access to craft embodying the latest developments in hydrofoil technology and allow him to add superstructure tailored to his own needs. Variants would range from passenger ferries to utility craft for off-shore mineral operations to coastguard patrol vessels and missile gunboats.

The modular concept is likely to appeal in particular to lesser developed countries since, by completing the craft locally, a useful saving in hard currency could be realised.

The Boeing NATO/PHM-1 Pegasus performed its first foilborne run on February 25th 1975, and testing is reported to be progressing satisfactorily. Pegasus achieved its designed speed, completed the Navy-conducted phase of testing its weapons and then began operational evaluation in the San Diego area in the summer of 1975. It is now undergoing missile firing tests on the Pacific Missile Range. A production decision is expected in late 1975 or early 1976, followed by a number of overseas procurement orders. The US Navy contract calls, tentatively, for twenty-three craft to follow and these are expected to become operational over the next seven years.

During the year both the Boeing PCH-1 High Point and the Grumman PGH-1 Flagstaff were employed by the US Coast Guard in Puget Sound and off San Francisco. They undertook a number of duties from fisheries patrol to search and rescue missions as part of a programme to evaluate high speed water craft for possible Coast Guard use.

In March 1975 Grumman announced the addition of two new designs to its range, a second developed version of the Dolphin 1, known as the Dolphin III and the Flagstaff Mk III. Both are "stretched" models: the former is intended primarily as a utility and crew boat for offshore operations and the latter for long-range, low payload military operations. Both have an overall length of 83 ft, and the full load displacement of each is 83.5 tons. A choice of powerplants is offered: either a 4,480 hp Rolls-Royce RM2B Tyne or a 4,250 hp Allison 501K20A.

In July 1974, the Leopoldo Rodriquez Shipyard of Messina, the first company in the world to undertake the series production of hydrofoil craft, changed its name to Cantière Navaltecnica SpA. Since completing its first PT.20 in 1956, the company has built a total of 120 hydrofoils and currently has another ten on order. Much of the credit for overcoming the shipping industry's initial scepticism towards hydrofoils was due to the efforts of the indefatigable Carlo Rodriquez and his two nephews, Leopoldo and Franco. May they long continue building their superb craft under their new 'banner'.

MAFIUS MISSILE CRAFT

Latest additions to the Navaltecnica range are a search and rescue model of the RHS 140 with facilities for fire-fighting and wreck marking; the RHS 160 Hydroil for off-shore oil-rig supply and the Mafius 300 and 600 hydrofoil missilecraft. Though differing in size—85 tons and 118 tons, respectively—the two latter vessels are almost identical in terms of overall design, construction and internal arrangements. Both are equipped with the SAS stability augmentation system, which stabilises the vessels in bad weather, and the Breda-Bofors twin 40 mm L70 rapid-fire cannon. In addition the Mafius 300 will mount two Otomat or similar missiles and the Mafius 600 four.

Another name change in Italy, Alinavi is now a jointly-owned company with Cantieri Navali Riuniti holding 90 per cent, and the Boeing Company 10 per cent. The new company is known as CNR-Alinavi, and under the terms of the licensing agreement it has access to Boeing technology in the fields of military fully-submerged foil hydrofoil craft only. Tests of the first P 420 Sparviero class hydrofoil missilecraft have been completed successfully and the vessel is now in service with the Italian Navy. It is understood that the Italian Navy is ordering another three craft.

In the Soviet Union today, there are hydrofoil services on the Volga, Dneiper, Sozh, Don and Neva, on the rivers of Siberia, and alpine lakes in almost every Soviet republic. This year, during the navigation season, they will have carried about 20 million passengers and it is forecast that this figure will increase year by year.

The hydrofoils operate at three times the speed of orthodox craft and where they compete with trains, they often move passengers faster than the trains do. They are, moreover, economical to operate and display one important ecological advantage over displacement riverboats—they do not erode river banks.

Over the past fifteen years, the mainstays of the hydrofoil fleet have been the 64-seat Raketa, the 116-seat Meteor and the 116-seat Kometa. On various routes they have been supplemented by experimental craft like the Sputnik, Vikhr, and Burevestnik, and on very shallow rivers and canals, by the waterjet-propelled Byelorus. All of the main types are now being redesigned.

The Raketa is being replaced by the new Voskhod 2, a quieter, more seaworthy craft powered by a stern-mounted M-401A diesel driving a marine propeller through a vee-drive. The latest Kometa variants will also have their engines aft and are likely to incorporate an air-stabilisation system or other form of automatic lift variation for a more comfortable ride in the higher sea states.

A new version of the 15-seat Nevka hydrofoil launch will be introduced and plans are being finalised for the construction of the 140-ton Cyclone, a 250-seat seagoing vessel powered by gas-turbine-driven waterjets. According to the designers, it will cruise at 42 knots and have a range of 300 miles.

Overseas interest in Soviet hydrofoils is focused chiefly on the little Volga runabout, which has been sold in nearly 40 different countries, and the 116-seat Kometa-M. Once international passenger certificate problems have been overcome, there is little doubt that the Kometa could be in great demand.

Russia's latest military hydrofoil, the Turya, is based on the hull of the "Osa" missile-firing fast patrol boat. It has a single main foil of trapeze or vee configuration only, which is set back one-third of the hull length from the bow. At 20-23 knots in relatively calm conditions, the foil generates sufficient lift to raise the greater part of the hull clear of the water, providing a "sprint" speed of 40-45 knots. The arrangement is similar to that employed on the earlier Soviet "P8" Class and the Chinese "Hu Chwan" Class. An obvious attempt to gain a substantially improved "sprint" performance at minimum cost, this approach has proved far more effective than it looks.

The installation of a small variable-depth sonar at the transom suggests that the primary duty of Turya is anti-submarine patrol. The main armament appears to comprise four 21 in single AS torpedo tubes, a forward 25 mm twin mount and a twin 57 mm AA mount aft. A substantial production programme is underway, with more than one yard in the Western USSR involved and one in the Soviet Far East.

INDUSTRIAL APPLICATIONS

ACV activity in the industrial field is increasing continually, with more and more companies employing hovertrailers and large hoverplatforms to traverse marshy or ice-bound terrain. Among recent developments has been the introduction by Alyeska Pipeline Service Co of the world's first scheduled chain hoverferry on the Yukon River. Between October and April each year the Yukon is completely frozen. The provision of hover-transporters was necessary to continue the operation during the winter months. The two vessels, converted from modular flat-deck barges by Mackley Ace, each have a payload capacity of 160 tons and have carried between them up to 230 vehicles a day. The craft are winched across and at the point of the crossing the Yukon is one mile wide, with a current of 8 knots. During the first five months they carried 25,000 vehicles and achieved an operating efficiency of 95 per cent.

Newcomers to the hoverplatform/hoverbarge field are Sedam and Mitsui. Sedam is developing two amphibious hoverbarges, one of 50 t, of 100 t capacity to off-load cargo ships in ports which, because of the vast growth of sea traffic, have become almost permanently congested. The Amphibarges, as they are called, would unload the vessels and carry the cargo to warehouses close to the port, but clear of the main areas of congestion. Their amphibious capability will enable them to make the transition from water to land and carry their loads up to the warehouses where conventional fork lift trucks, mobile cranes and other freight handling equipment would be employed for off-loading. Among the alternative methods of propulsion proposed are small tugs, outboard motors, a ship-to-shore cable system and, for onshore work, tractors or crawler tracks. Mitsui has designed a 310-ton hoverbarge, the SEP-1, which is equipped with jack-up legs similar to those employed on some offshore oil rigs. This enables the craft to be located above test or survey sites in shallow waters or in areas of marsh or tundra.

A hoverplatform intended for a completely new application—that of icebreaking—is being developed by Bell Aerospace Canada. Experiments with models, the ACT-100 and the Voyageur, have demonstrated the potential of ACVs as icebreakers and the new platform will be used for full-scale evaluation of the concept. Water would be pumped into the platform's ballast tanks giving it an operating weight ranging from 170,300-365,000 lb. It would be attached to the bow of the Canadian Coast Guard ship Montcalm.

Air Cushion Equipment's hover flotation system continues to be employed throughout the world to move heavy loads, the biggest of which was a 700-ton storage tank. The operation was undertaken at Pauillac for Shell France. While the tank was being moved, the roof was floated on a second cushion of air to limit the possibility of damage to the roof and to reduce the pressure differential developed across the bottom of the tank. Air Cushion Equipment and Aero-Go have both introduced fluid handling systems employing water instead of air as the cushion liquid, to move large and dense loads. The first two shipyards to employ fluid bearings to lift and move ship modules are Todd Shipyard, Seattle and Vancouver Shipyard, British Columbia.

The rapid growth of commercial and military applications will continue to improve the competitive position of both the ACV and hydrofoil with other forms of transport. Executives of manufacturing and operating companies alike are confident that the lean, formative years are now over, and that radical improvements in the industry's fortunes lie ahead.

Roy McLeavy
November, 1975

strong, steady, swift and sure
SWORDFISH type
all-weather, sea superiority hydrofoil

ACV MANUFACTURERS AND DESIGN GROUPS

ARGENTINA

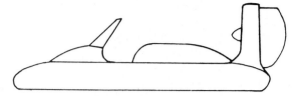
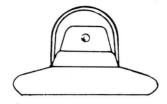

BRUZZONE

ADDRESS:

Peru 327, Buenos Aires, Republic of Argentina, South America

Jorge Oscar Bruzzone, an Argentinian aeronautical engineer, has designed an amphibious craft, the Guaipo BMX-1, which has been built and tested by the Argentine Navy. (Described in JSS 1971-72 edition).

Mr. Bruzzone has experimented with ACVs for nearly fifteen years. At the present time he is building privately a light two-seater and a three-seater. Preliminary details of his Yacare JOB-3 two-seat recreational craft are given below.

YACARE JOB-3

The prototype of this new amphibious runabout is undergoing trials.

LIFT AND PROPULSION: Lift air is provided by a Citroen 30 hp automotive engine driving a centrifugal fan. Propulsive thrust is supplied by a 30 hp engine driving a ducted, two-bladed propeller.

CONTROLS: Twin aerodynamic rudders control craft heading.

HULL: Moulded glass reinforced plastic structure.

DIMENSIONS:

Length	14 ft 5¼ in (4·40 m)
Beam	7 ft 10½ in (2·40 m)

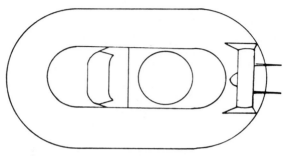

Bruzzone JOB-3 single-seat recreational craft

Height	3 ft 11¼ in (1·20 m)	Normal payload	397 lb (180 kg)
WEIGHT:		PERFORMANCE:	
Normal all-up weight	992 lb (450 kg)	Max speed	49·71 mph (80 km/h)
Normal empty weight	595 lb (270 kg)	Vertical obstacle clearance	11¾ in (0·30 m)

AUSTRALIA

FAIREY AUSTRALASIA PTY LTD

HEAD OFFICE:

Box 221, Elizabeth, South Australia 5112

TELEPHONE:

(08) 255192

CABLES:

Fairey, Adelaide

DIRECTORS:

F. R. Green, BE, CEng, FRAeS, FAIM, Chairman and Managing Director

A. Moffatt, FASA, ACIS

Fairey Australasia, incorporated in New South Wales, was founded in August 1949. Its Operations Division is located within the Weapons Research Establishment area in Salisbury, South Australia.

The primary activities of the Company are the design, development and manufacture of mechanical, optical, electro-mechanical, and electronic equipment for the aircraft and missile industry and the armed services.

Under a licencing agreement concluded in the autumn of 1972 between the company and Taylorcraft Transport Pty Ltd, it will build, develop and market the Skimaire range, which currently includes the Skimaire I 3-seater, the Skimaire II, a 6-seat, twin-engined craft, and the Skimaire III, a utility version of the Mk II with a 1,000 lb (453·59 kg) load capacity.

Trials of a modified version of the Skimaire II were underway during 1975.

SKIMAIRE I

A small amphibious ACV of glass fibre and ply construction, the Skimaire seats three in an enclosed, pressurized and ventilated cabin. Power is supplied by an adapted Volkswagen industrial engine and the maximum speed over calm water is 50 mph (80·46 km/h).

The Skimaire, a 2-3 seat amphibious ACV, powered by a single 68 bhp Volkswagen engine

The production prototype Skimaire was completed in September 1969, and trials were completed in February 1970. The craft is in production. Skimaires have been supplied to purchasers in Australia, Canada, Taiwan, Indonesia and Japan.

LIFT AND PROPULSION: Immediately aft of the cockpit is a single, internally mounted 68 bhp Volkswagen 127V air-cooled four-cylinder, four-stroke petrol engine which drives via a gear box a 2 ft (609 mm) diameter aluminium alloy centrifugal lift fan, and a 4 ft 2 in (1·27 m) diameter, 4-bladed, fixed-pitch propeller. The propeller is surrounded by a metal guard.

Fuel is carried in two external 5 gallon tanks with amidships refuelling points. Recommended fuel is super grade automotive gasoline.

CONTROLS: Twin rudders mounted on the

propeller guard are operated via Bowden cables by the steering wheel. A set of louvre doors mounted below the lift fan controls the supply of air to the plenum and these can be employed as a braking control. Engine speed is controlled by a hand throttle linked to a foot pedal set so that the hand throttle sets the lower limit of engine speed.

HULL: Built in three grp sections—cabin top and deck, hull bottom and cabin interior —bonded together to form a rigid cell. The lower part of the hull is filled with closed cell structure foam and is reinforced below the cabin by a corrugated section. All mechanical components are mounted on a tubular steel frame which can be removed for major servicing.

SKIRT: Closed bag type, attached around the hull periphery where the outer flange joins top and bottom components. Drainage holes provided at rear.

ACCOMMODATION: Access to the cabin is through either of two gullwing doors, located amidships, one each side. The normal seating arrangement places the driver forward, centrally, and there are removable seats for two passengers at the rear. 300 lb (136 kg) of cargo can be carried with the passenger seats removed. The cabin is heated and ventilated.

SAFETY EQUIPMENT: 2 lb fire extinguisher amidships and Spot-a-Fire system.

SYSTEMS: Electrical: 12 volt, 77Ah battery, with 240 w generator for starting and lights.

COMMUNICATIONS: Provision is made for the installation of a marine type transmitter/receiver.

DIMENSIONS, EXTERNAL:
Length   17 ft 0 in (5·18 m)
Beam   8 ft 0 in (2·43 m)
Height overall, power off
                      5 ft 10 in (1·77 m)
Height overall, skirt inflated
                      6 ft 0 in (1·82 m)
Draft afloat   2½ in (63 mm)
Skirt depth   1 ft (304 mm)

WEIGHTS:
Normal empty weight   1,200 lb (544·28 kg)
Normal all-up weight 1,850 lb (839·10 kg)
Normal payload   650 lb (294·82 kg)

PERFORMANCE:
Max speed over calm water
                      50 mph (80·46 km/h)
Cruising speed over calm water
                      35 mph (56·32 km/h)
Turning circle diameter at 30 knots
                      130 ft (39·62 m)
Max wave capability
                      2-3 ft waves (·609-·914 m)
Still air range and endurance at cruising
  speed   170 miles (273·58 km)
Max gradient, static conditions   6 in 1
Vertical obstacle clearance
                      1 ft 0 in (304 mm)

PRICE AND TERMS:
Approximate cost of craft, ex works, Aust. $18,000·00.

A Fairey Australasia Pty Ltd Skimaire I on the Coorong. The vehicle, a fully amphibious three-seater is powered by a single 68 bhp Volkswagen 127V air-cooled engine, and has a top speed over calm water of 50 mph (80·46 km/h)

Above and below: The Fairey Australasia Skimaire II is a "scaled-up" model of the Skimaire I with twice the seating capacity. Seen in these photographs is the latest variant of this amphibious six-seater, with revised cabin entry doors/windows and various other refinements

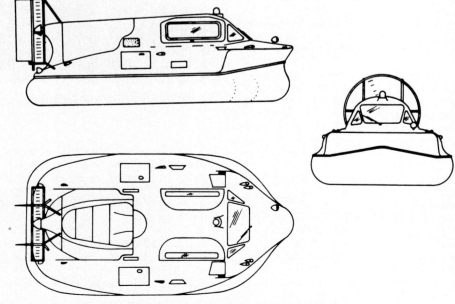

The Skimaire I light amphibious ACV

SKIMAIRE II

This is a 60 mph (96·60 km/h) twin-engined six-seat derivative of the Skimaire Mk I. Trials were in progress as this edition went to press.

LIFT AND PROPULSION: Motive power for the integrated lift/propulsion system is supplied by two internally-mounted 68 hp Volkswagen 127V air-cooled four-cylinder, four-stroke piston engines, each of which drives a 2 ft 0 in (·61 m) diameter centrifugal lift fan and a 4-bladed fixed pitch propeller. Two 4-bladed reversible-pitch propellers can be supplied as optional extras. Each propeller is surrounded by a metal guard. Cushion area is 190 sq ft (17·65 m²), and cushion pressure is 21 lbs/sq ft. Fuel capacity is 27 Imp gallons (122·85 l). Recommended fuel is super grade automotive gasoline.

CONTROLS: Twin rudders hinged to the rear of the two propeller guards and differential thrust control craft heading. A set of louvre doors mounted below the lift fans controls the supply of air to the plenum and these can be employed as a braking control.

HULL: Basically glass reinforced plastic with aluminium and stainless steel reinforcement.

DIMENSIONS:

Length overall	23 ft 3 in (7·086 m)
Beam, power on	13 ft 9 in (4·19 m)
power off	12 ft 9 in (3·89 m)
Height overall, power on	6 ft 6 in (1·98 m)
power off	5 ft 6 in (1·68 m)

WEIGHTS:

Empty weight, with fuel	2,800 lb (1,271·2 kg)
Payload	1,200 lb (544·8 kg)
Gross weight	4,000 lb (1,816 kg)

PERFORMANCE:

Max speed over land	60 mph (96·60 km/h)
over calm water	50 mph (80·50 km/h)
Max gradient	1 in 8
Vertical clearance	1 ft 6 in (457 mm)

Range and endurance
app 220 miles (355 km), 4 hours

PRICE: Ex works, standard fittings, Aust. $44,000·00.

SKIMAIRE III

This light utility ACV has a cargo deck aft of the driver and is designed to transport general freight loads weighing up to 1,200 lb (544·8 kg).

The amidship load deck has a large removable hatch to facilitate loading.

The specification is similar in most respects to that of Skimaire II.

PRICE: Ex works, standard fittings. Aust. $42,000·00.

Fairey Skimaire II amphibious six-seater, powered by two 68 bhp Volkswagen air-cooled engines and capable of 60 mph (96·60 km/h) over land and 50 mph (80·50 km/h) over water

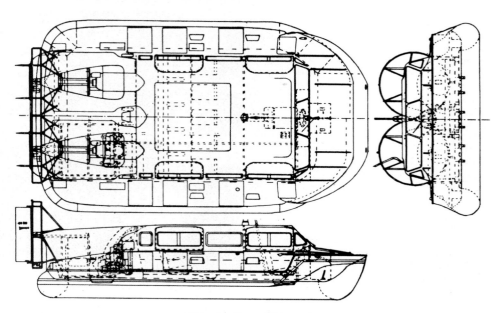

Skimaire II amphibious six-seater

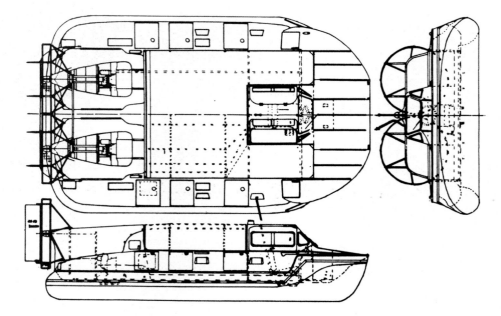

A utility model of the twin-engined Skimaire, the Mk III carries up to a 1,200 lb (544.8) kg payload on its amidship load deck

NEOTERIC ENGINEERING AFFILIATES LTD

HEAD OFFICE:
9 Queen Street, Melbourne, Australia 3000
TELEPHONE:
Melbourne 623917
TEST FACILITY:
11 Beach Drive, Long Island, Hastings, Victoria, Australia 3915
EXECUTIVES:
Chris Fitzgerald, President
Rob Wilson, Technical Director
Dave Atkins, Design and Planning
Laurie Fair, Production
Arthur Boyd, Operations
Bernhard Sucker, Design
Denis Markham, Supply
Sam Cilauro, Electronics
Ken O'Connor, Sales
Allan Fitzgerald, Accountant

Neoteric Engineering Affiliates Pty Ltd specialises in the research and development of industrial and commercial ACV systems as well as the design and marketing of small recreational hovercraft. Many of its executives have been active in ACV research in Australia since 1960, and before forming the present company, conducted a business under the name Australian Air Cushion Vehicles Development.

The company is at present concentrating on marketing single and two-seat models of the Neova amphibious hovercraft, which are available in kit or ready-built form. A three-seat model, also available in a light utility configuration, is under development.

The craft is suited to production line manufacture and can be substantially scaled-up for greater load capacity. International patents are pending and the company is seeking licensing agreements with overseas manufacturers.

NEOVA 1 and 2

A highly-manoeuvrable light ACV, the Neova is an amphibious single-seater, intended primarily for recreational use. Both the Neova I and the larger, two-seat Neova II are being marketed in kit form, but a limited number of factory-built Neova IIs are available. The kit-built models are of ply construction, with steel attachments at highly stressed areas.

Hulls of factory-built craft are fabricated in glass fibre and thermoplastic sheet mouldings.

The overall dimensions of the machine— 7 ft (1·23 m) by 13 ft (3·96 m)—allow it to be transported by road on a flat trailer.

LIFT AND PROPULSION: Integrated system powered by a single 46 hp Volkswagen engine driving two axial fans. Airflow is ducted into the plenum for lift and two outlets aft for thrust. The engine, transmission and axial-flow fans are mounted on a rubber-seated platform, secured to the main hull by three bolts. A large hatch provides ready access to the engine and all components.

CONTROLS: Back and forward movement of a dual stick control column operates two thrust buckets which vary the power and the direction of the thrust. The column is pulled back for reverse thrust and moved ahead for forward thrust. Differential use of the two columns, with one stick forward and the other back, is used for changing craft direction. The aerodynamic rudders at the

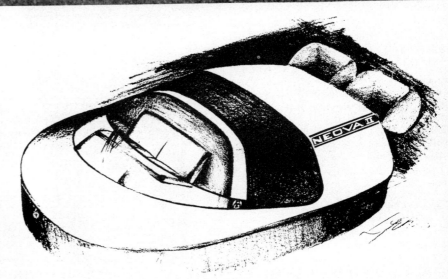

Top: Neova I clearing an 18 in (457 mm) high ledge at 15 mph (24·14 km/h) while demonstrating its multi-terrain capability. Centre: Neova I, with both thrust buckets raised, climbing a bank at the side of the Yarra river in the City of Melbourne. Bottom: Impression of the enlarged Neova II, a two-seater. The roll-bar, aft of the cockpit, is stressed to withstand three times the vehicle's weight

rear of the propulsion ducts are normally used only for small corrections in heading at cruising speed.

HULL: Home-built models are of ply construction, with steel attachments at lifting and towing points. Skid pads on the underside protect the structure from damage by abrasion. An inflatable fender is attached to the periphery to prevent structural damage

when travelling at low speeds. An integral siphon system prevents the collection of excessive water within the hull. Buoyancy is 150%.

ACCOMMODATION: Driver sits forward in an open cockpit. Side-by-side seating for two in Neova II. Safety features include a cockpit roll bar which is stressed to withstand three times the vehicle's weight. Family models will be equipped with a detachable canopy.

DIMENSIONS:

Length overall	13 ft 0 in	(3·96 m)
Beam overall	7 ft 0 in	(2·13 m)
Height overall, skirt inflated		
	5 ft 0 in	(1·54 m)

WEIGHTS:

Normal all-up weight	1,000 lb	(453 kg)
Payload, maximum	99·78 lb	(45·5 kg)

PERFORMANCE:

Cruising speed (at 75% power setting)		
	25 mph	(40·23 km/h)
Turning radius at 20 mph (32·18 km/h)		
	200 ft	(60·96 m)
Max gradient from standing start	1 : 10	
Vertical obstacle clearance	6 in	(152 mm)
Endurance on full power	1½ hours	

PRICES:
Neova I. Price ex-factory complete, $A4,500. Complete (kit excluding engine) $A2,000. Plan pack $A35.

Neova II. Two-seat model, with similar specification to Neova I. Price ex-factory, complete $A4,500. Complete kit (excluding engine) $A2,000. Plan pack $A40.

NEOVA 3

Two versions of this enlarged and more powerful model are under development—a 3-seat sports model and a high-performance utility craft. Power will be supplied by a 100 hp flat-four aircraft engine.

STOLKRAFT PTY LTD

HEAD OFFICE:
52 Hilltop Road, Clareville Beach, NSW 2107, Australia

TELEPHONE:
918 3620

CABLES:
Stolcraft Sydney

DIRECTORS:
Leo D. Stolk, Managing Director/Designer
Clive M. Backhouse, Chairman
Rhoda Gladys Stolk, Director/Company Secretary

CONSULTANT:
James Eken, Commercial Marine Design, 24, Thomas Street, Chatswood, NSW 2067, Australia

OVERSEAS REPRESENTATIVE:
UNITED KINGDOM:
Richard M. Jones,
61 Grayling Road, Stoke Newington, London N.16

Mr. L. D. Stolk's Stolkraft concept is a new approach to the air-lubricated planing hull. His main objectives have been to overcome the basic pitch instability apparent in some earlier designs and to eliminate bow wash.

The basic Stolkraft hull is of trimaran configuration and is designed to roll the waves beneath the hull to provide hydrodynamic lift at speeds below 30 mph (40·28 km/h).

At speed an appreciable amount of aerodynamic lift is built up by a ram-air cushion at the bow, and this, combined with air fed through twin bow intakes and vented from a transverse step beneath the hull aft, lifts the craft in order to reduce frictional resistance.

A feature of the concept is the absence of trim variation. During trials undertaken on the torpedo range of the Royal Australian Navy at Pittwater, near Sydney, it was demonstrated that the craft rises bodily, parallel to the surface and has no tendency to porpoise. At speed it creates neither bow-wash nor hull spray.

The aerodynamic lift on the prototype is about 65% and the maximum load draft is reduced by 80%.

The hull design is applicable to a wide range of vessels from passenger ferries for inland waterways to seagoing craft.

STOLKRAFT PLEASURE CRAFT

The prototype of the company's first production runabout, the fibreglass-hulled SKI-16 Mk 1, was nearing completion as this edition went to press in July 1975. Location of the rear-air intakes and the vented transverse step is seen in the accompanying drawing.

If, through wave action, a gust of wind or an increase in speed, the forward hull lifts clear of the water as far back as the transverse step, the aerodynamic lifting forces ahead of the step will rapidly decrease. At the same

Interceptor prototype at 50 mph (80 km/h) during trials. The twin bow intakes (below) feed pressurised air to a ventilated transverse step and thence to a second air cushion created beneath the hull aft

time, the lifting forces at the rear of the hull will increase because of the greater volume of air being rammed through the step. Because of the decrease in lift forward, and the increased lift aft, the centre of pressure moves towards the rear of the boat. A constant trim angle is maintained automatically in this manner without the use of instrumentation.

PROPULSION: A Volvo Aquamatic, of either 170 or 225 hp, drives a water screw for propulsion. Fuel is carried in two 20-gallon tanks located amidships, port and starboard.

HULL: Stepped trimaran configuration. Moulded fibreglass construction.

ACCOMMODATION: Open cockpit for driver and up to six passengers.

DIMENSIONS, EXTERNAL:

Length overall	16 ft 3 in	(4·95 m)
Beam overall	8 ft 0 in	(2·43 m)
Draft, static	1 ft 6 in	(457 mm)
Draft, under way	3 in	(76 mm)

WEIGHTS:

Normal empty weight	1,800 lbs	(816·42 kg)
Normal gross weight	3,300 lb	(1,451·49 kg)
Normal payload	1,200 lb	(544·28 kg)

INCEPTOR

The prototype Inceptor is of grp construction and features a trimaran hull, the bow of which is designed to contain a ram-air cushion. An air-vented step, halfway along the hull, produces a second air cushion aft.

At speed, the aerodynamic lift generated by the inclined surface at the bow and the air-vented tunnel surfaces aft reduce the hull draft by 85%.

The craft, which seats three, is powered by a 125 hp Mercury outboard driving a 3in (330 mm) diameter propeller.

DIMENSIONS:
Length   14 ft 3 in (4·34 m)
Beam   6 ft 3 in (1·90 m)

WEIGHTS:
Gross weight (3 passengers plus ballast)
                     2,660 lbs (1,206·54 kg)

PERFORMANCE:
Max speed   50 mph (80·46 km/h)

Preliminary specifications for three Stolkraft design project are given below:

HARBOUR FERRY OR RIVER FREIGHTER
Length overall   65 ft 0 in (19·81 m)
Width   26 ft 0 in (7·92 m)
Displacement   65 tons
Passengers   135
Powerplant (diesel) 2,650 shp
Speed   45 mph plus (72·42 km/h)
Draught at 45 mph, waves not
  exceeding 5 ft (1·52 m) 1 ft 3 in (381 mm)

CRUISER OR WATER TAXI
Length overall   33 ft 0 in (10·05 m)
Beam   13 ft 6 in (4·11 m)
Displacement (payload 30 pass)   9 tons
Speed (full load)   50 mph (80·46 km/h)
Powerplant 2 × 300 shp petrol
  or diesel   600 shp
Draught at rest (full load) 2 ft 6 in (0·76 m)
Draught at approximately 50 mph,
                     6 in (152 mm)

Stolkraft's first production craft is this 16 ft long, seven-seat water-taxi or runabout, powered by a Volvo Aquamatic outboard

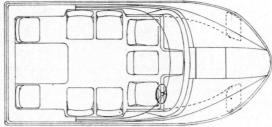

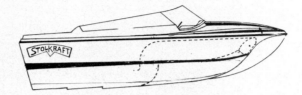
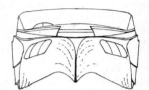

General arrangement of the Stolkraft seven-seat fibreglass-hulled runabout

TAYLORCRAFT TRANSPORT (DEVELOPMENT) PTY LTD
HEAD OFFICE:
Parafield Airport, South Australia 5106
TELEPHONE:
258 4944
DIRECTORS:
R. V. Taylor, Managing Director
J. Taylor

Taylorcraft has been active in ACV research and development since 1966. It is currently developing and marketing machines ranging from the Kartaire, a light single-seater for home builders, to a mixed-traffic sidewall craft designed to carry ten cars and up to 100 passengers.

Other additions to the company's range are the Islander IA for coastal medical work and the Islander IV freighter.

The Skimaire range is licensed to Fairey Australasia Pty Ltd by a holding company, Taylorcraft Transport Pty Ltd.

KARTAIRE Mk I and II
This is a single-seat vehicle for home builders and initial training. It is supplied in partial kit form in the interests of safety. The engines, engine mounting and wooden

The Taylorcraft Kartaire II a light single-seater for home builders

components are found by the constructor.

The craft will carry its driver—either adult or child—over flat terrain, sand or water, and if required to traverse deep water, the

hull can be fitted with an expanded polystyrene buoyancy block. The latest production model, the Kartaire Mk II has a grp hull and a top speed of 35 mph (56·32 km/h) over water.

LIFT AND PROPULSION: Lift power is furnished by a Victa 160cc two-stroke driving a 1 ft 6 in (457 mm) diameter centrifugal, alloy lift fan. Propulsive thrust on both versions is supplied by a second Victa 160cc two-stroke driving a 3-bladed fixed-pitch, 2 ft 10 in (863 mm) diameter Taylorcraft propeller.

Mk III will be propelled by a 15 bhp two-stroke engine driving a 2-bladed plastic propeller when a suitable engine is available in Australia.

CONTROL: An aircraft-type control column operates twin aerodynamic rudders set in the airscrew slipstream for directional control.

HULL: Kit parts are in ¼ in (6·35 mm) marine plywood; in assembled form the components are in marine ply and glassfibre reinforced plastics.

SKIRT: Bag type skirt in Linatex rubber or Neolon.

The following details apply to the Kartaire Mk. II.

DIMENSIONS:

Length overall	9 ft 0 in (2·74 m)
Beam overall	4 ft 0 in (1·21 m)
Height overall	4 ft 0 in (1·21 m)

WEIGHTS:

Normal empty weight	120 lb (54·42 kg)

PERFORMANCE:

Max speed over calm water	35 mph
Max gradient	1 in 8
Vertical obstacle clearance	6 in

PRICES:

Kartaire I, single-seat ultra-light recreational craft in kit form, $180·00.

Kartaire. II, with grp hull, assembled, $95·00.

KARTAIRE IV

The Kartaire IV is an ultra-light air cushion vehicle designed for use over water, mud flats and sand. It may be used as emergency transport in flooded areas or as a dinghy in sheltered waters. Its useful hard-structure clearance allows it to operate over fairly rough surfaces.

LIFT AND PROPULSION: Lift power is supplied by a single Fuji 167cc two-stroke driving a 2 ft (609 mm) diameter 6-bladed axial fan. Propulsive thrust is furnished by an 8 hp Robin driving a 6-bladed, fixed-pitch 2 ft (609 mm) diameter axial fan. The lift and thrust fan ducts are of alloy construction.

CONTROLS: Stick-operated rudder and throttle levers for lift and thrust engines. Both engines are fitted with pull starters.

HULL: The hull is a simple inflatable raft, from which is suspended a finger type skirt. All fabric parts are made from neoprene and hypalon-coated nylon. The hull side and end members are inflated by hand bellows. A light alloy frame with plug-in side stringers supports the two engines.

ACCOMMODATION: The open cockpit is 5 ft (1·52 m) long and 1 ft 10 in (0·55 m) wide and is provided with a single inflated seat which is adjustable to ensure correct trim. Although designed as a single-seater, a passenger may be carried under overload conditions.

DIMENSIONS:

Length, hardstructure	10 ft 0 in (3·04 m)
Beam	5 ft 0 in (1·52 m)
Height	4 ft 6 in (1·37 m)

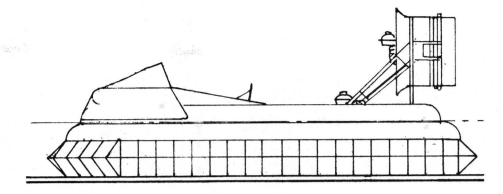

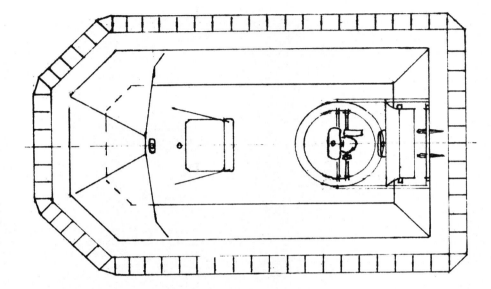

Taylorcraft Kartaire IV, with lift system powered by a Fuji 167 cc two-stroke and propulsive thrust furnished by an 8 hp Robin engine

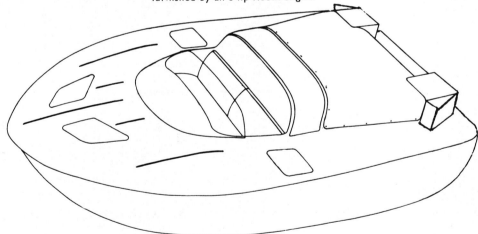

Taylorcraft Interceptaire air-jet propelled two-seater. Two hinged thrust vanes operated by a control column provide directional control

WEIGHTS:

Empty	100 lb (45·35 kg)
Gross	280 lb (127·00 kg)

PERFORMANCE (Still Air):

Max speed over land	45 mph (72·42 km/h)
over water	40 mph (64·37 km/h)

INTERCEPTAIRE

This new 17 ft (5·18 m) long, airjet propelled two-seater was due to enter production during 1974.

The hull is of glassfibre construction and power is supplied by an adapted Volkswagen engine. A single control column operates two hinged thrust vanes for directional control. Speed over land is expected to be

about 60 mph (96·56 km/h) and over water about 35 mph (65·32 km/h).

Retail price will be $A3,500.

PUFFAIRE II

This small, sturdily built utility vehicle is intended for operation over land, rivers and sheltered waters. It has an open cockpit with two seats and an open deck which can accommodate bulky loads of up to 1,000 lb (453 kg). Various alternative accommodation arrangements can be made, including the installation of a folding awning to protect both the crew and cargo, or a 5-seat modular passenger cabin, which fits into the well deck immediately aft of the control cabin.

A Trailaire ACV trailer unit (see company's entry in section covering ACV Trailers, Tractors and Heavy Lift Systems) can be towed by the craft, increasing the payload capacity to two tons.

LIFT AND PROPULSION: Integrated system powered by a Ford 351 V8 water cooled automotive engine. Mounted inboard, the engine drives two centrifugal fans through a torque convertor. Both fans are totally enclosed in ducts to eliminate any danger from rotating parts. A high thrust unit can be supplied for special applications.

SKIRT: 1 ft 6 in (457 mm) high skirt with 100% segments. Fingers and groups of fingers are easily replaced when necessary.

CONTROLS: Directional control is effected by a skirt shift system and supplemented by differential use of airjet thrust. A single control column, on which is mounted the throttle lever, is located on the right hand side of the cockpit. This also controls reverse thrust.

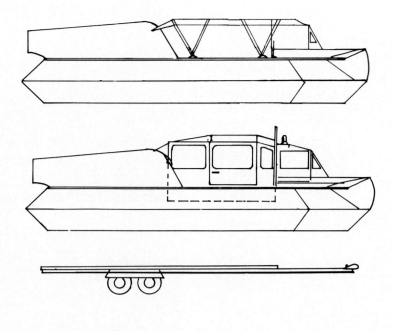
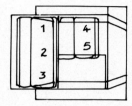
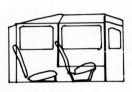

DIMENSIONS:
Length overall:	
on cushion	22 ft 0 in (6·7 m)
hard structure	19 ft 0 in (5·8 m)
Beam overall:	
on cushion	14 ft 0 in (4·27 m)
hard structure	8 ft 2 in (2·09 m)
Height overall:	
on cushion	7 ft 0 in (2·13 m)
hard structure	5 ft 7 in (1·69 m)
Draft afloat	9 in (229 mm)
Cargo deck size	
7 ft 0 in × 6 ft 3 in (2·13 m × 1·83 mm)	

WEIGHTS:
Empty	2,630 lb (1,193 kg)
Payload	1,000 lb (453 kg)

General arrangement of the Taylorcraft Transport Puffaire 11 open deck utility vehicle, showing optional configurations including the addition of a 5-seat cabin module. A 200 hp Holden V8 petrol engine powers the integrated lift/propulsion system. Payload is 1,000 lb (453 kg)

Fuel and driver	370 lb (168 kg)	Hump speed	12 mph (20 km/h)
Gross weight	4,000 lb (1,814 kg)	Hard structure clearance	1 ft 6 in (457 mm)
PERFORMANCE:		Max wave height	3 ft 0 in (·914 m)
Max speed over land	45 mph (70 km/h)		
over water	35 mph (55 km/h)		
Max gradient	1 : 6		

ISLANDAIRE IV

This is a new multi-purpose amphibious ACV, powered by three 245 hp automotive

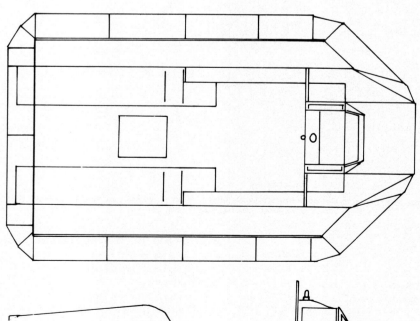

Taylorcraft Transport Puffaire 11

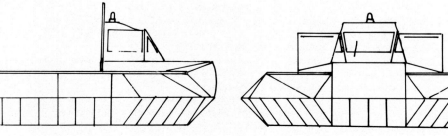

engines. Four variants are projected, the Islandaire 1A ambulance and search and rescue craft; Islandaire II, a twelve-seater; Islandaire III, a 20-seat passenger ferry, and the Islandaire IV, a freighter with a payload/fuel capacity of 5,800 lb (2,630 kg).

Half the load deck is enclosed and the remaining area can be protected by a canopy. Bulky items up to 20 ft (6·09 m) long may be carried subject to weight distribution requirements.

LIFT AND PROPULSION: Cushion air is supplied by a single V8 water cooled automotive engine driving two 3 ft 8 in (1·11 m) diameter centrifugal, double intake fans, via a torque converter and bevel gears. Propulsive thrust is furnished by two pylon-mounted engines of identical type, each driving a 6 ft (1·82 m) diameter, reversible-pitch propeller.

CONTROLS: Directional control is effected by twin aerodynamic rudders and supplemented by differential propeller thrust. A skirt control system provides low speed manoeuvrability.

HULL: Access to the well deck is via a rear loading door, 7 ft 0 in (2·13 m) wide.

ACCOMMODATION: Elevated control cabin forward with seats for driver, engineer and third crew member.

DIMENSIONS:
Length overall on cushion
48 ft 6 in (14·78 m)
Length overall, off cushion
44 ft 3 in (14·17 m)
Beam overall, on cushion
24 ft 0 in (7·31 m)
Beam overall, off cushion
20 ft 0 in (6·09 m)
Height (excl mast):
on cushion   12 ft 0 in (3·65 m)
off cushion   8 ft 6 in (2·59 m)
Freight deck, width   7 ft 0 in (2·13 m)
        length   14 ft 0 in (4·26 m)
DIMENSIONS, INTERNAL:
Cabin, 3 seats:
length   7 ft 9 in (2·36 m)
width   8 ft 0 in (2·43 m)
Cabin, single-seat:
length   6 ft 0 in (1·82 m)
width   4 ft 0 in (1·21 m)

Model of the Taylorcraft Puffaire II, showing the location of the centrifugal fans and load deck. The removable passenger module has five seats

WEIGHTS:
				long sea
Gross weight	12,700 lb (5,760 kg)	Gradient, standing start		1 : 7·5
Fuel and payload	5,800 lb (2,630·8 kg)	Isolated obstacle		3 ft (0·91 m)

PERFORMANCE:
Fuel consumption
Cruising speed	45 mph (72·42 km/h)		19 gph (81·8 b/ph) at cruising speed
Max speed	65 mph (104·37 km/h)	Endurance	5 hours
Max wave length	6 ft-8 ft (1·82-2·43 m),		

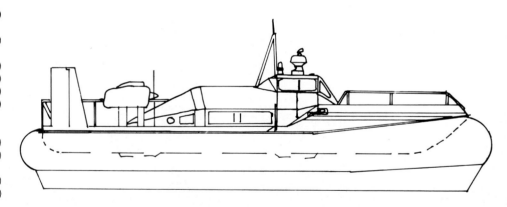

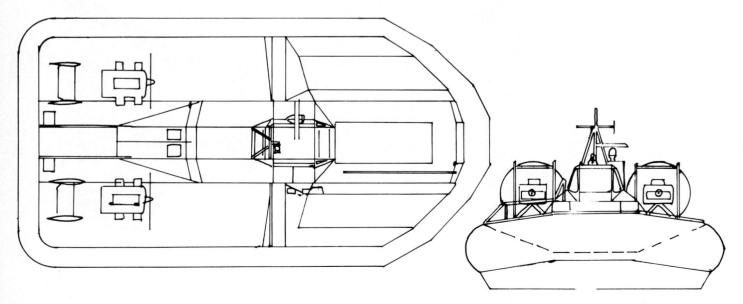

Taylorcraft Islandaire IA, ACV ambulance and Search and Rescue craft

PRICE (approx only):

Islandaire I (8 seat)	$A120,000
Islandaire II (12 seat)	$A150,000
Islandaire III (20 seat)	$A175,000
Islandaire IV (2 ton payload)	$A160,000

SPORTAIR

This inflatable-hulled three-seater is intended for pleasure and utility applications. It combines a useful payload with a large, open cockpit, making it ideal for activities ranging from skin diving to flood rescue and light police patrol duties.

LIFT AND PROPULSION: Integrated system powered by a single 30 hp, 2-cylinder, 2-stroke engine. Mounted aft of the cockpit, the engine drives via vee belts, a single ducted fan for lift and two reversible-pitch ducted fans for forward or reverse thrust. Cushion area is 127 sq ft (11·78 m²) and the cushion pressure is 6·5 lb/sq ft (311 Pa).

CONTROLS: Steering is by a conventional wheel. Levers control the thrust reversing mechanism.

HULL: The hull is inflated by a car-type vacuum cleaner. Special bellows are provided to bring the pressure up to 2½ lb/sq in before use. Features include separate buoyancy compartments for safety and built-in handgrips around the hull. A simple drainage system and a bow canopy are provided.

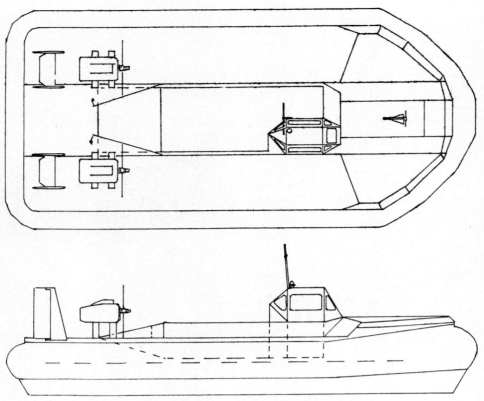

Taylorcraft Islandaire IV multi-duty ACV freighter

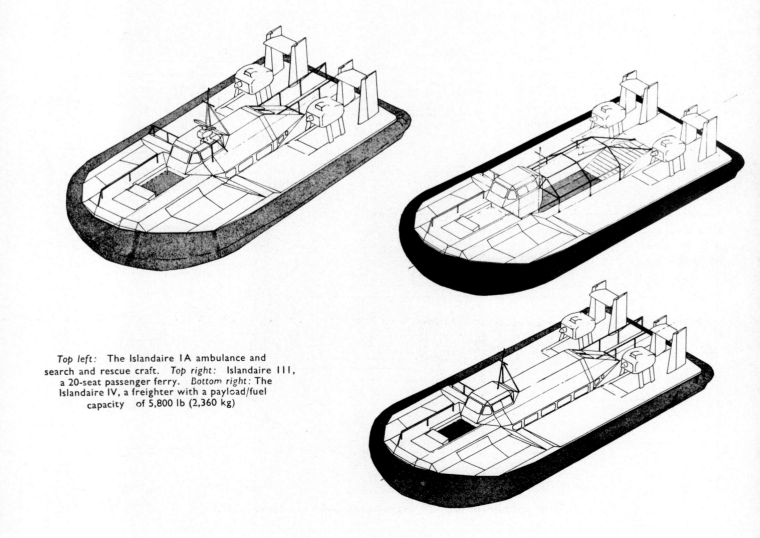

Top left: The Islandaire IA ambulance and search and rescue craft. *Top right:* Islandaire III, a 20-seat passenger ferry. *Bottom right:* The Islandaire IV, a freighter with a payload/fuel capacity of 5,800 lb (2,360 kg)

SKIRT: Segmented skirt with easily replaced segments. Skirt includes a protective web below the hull floor.

DIMENSIONS, EXTERNAL:

Length overall	17 ft 0 in (5·18 m)
Beam overall	9 ft 0 in (2·74 m)
Hull length	14 ft 0 in (4·27 m)
Hull beam	7 ft 4 in (2·23 m)
Tube diameter	1 ft 6 in (45 cm)
Thwarts	1 ft 0 in (0·30 m)
Height, off cushion	3 ft 6 in (1·06 m)
Height, on cushion	5 ft 0 in (1·52 m)

WEIGHTS:

Tare	280 lb (127 kg)
Payload	350 lb (159·9 kg)
Driver and fuel	190 lb (86 kg)
Gross	800 lb (363 kg)

PERFORMANCE:

Cruising speed, calm water	40 mph (64 km/h)
Range	60 miles (96 km)
Obstacle clearance	1 ft 6 in (45 cm)
Gradient	1:6

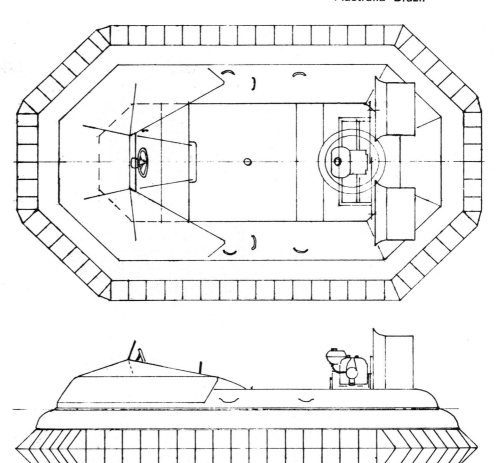

Taylorcraft's new Sportaire, a three-seater powered by a single 30 hp two-cylinder engine and featuring reversible-pitch thrust fans

BRAZIL

FEI
FACULTY OF INDUSTRIAL ENGINEER-ING

ADDRESS:
Research Vehicle Department (DEPV), Faculty of Industrial Engineering, São Bernado do Campo, Avenido Oreste Romano 112, São Paulo

TELEPHONE:
443 1155

SENIOR EXECUTIVE:
Eng. Rigoberto Soler Gisbert, Director of Vehicle Research

The Vehicle Research Department of the FEI was founded in 1968. Its first major task was to conduct a full-scale investigation into Brazil's transport problems and its likely future requirements. An outcome of this was the design and construction by students and faculty of a 51 ft (15·54 m) long prototype of a tracked ACV, the TALAV, which was exhibited during the 150th anniversary of Brazilian Independence in August 1972 (see Tracked Skimmers).

Since then the Department, under the direction of Eng. Rigoberto Soler Gisbert, has designed, built and tested a number of light amphibious ACVs, including the VA and the VA-1, which it is expected, will be put into production by a Brazilian industrial concern.

VA

A glassfibre-hulled amphibious two-seater, the VA is powered by a single Volkswagen VW 1300 automotive engine and has a top speed of about 50 mph (80 km/h).

LIFT AND PROPULSION: Integrated

FEI VA two-seat light sports ACV during trials.

system powered by a single 50 hp VW 1300 automotive engine driving a ducted fan. Air from the fan feeds into the plenum below for lift and aft propulsion. Total fuel capacity is 6·6 gals (30 litres).

CONTROLS: Single aerodynamic rudder, hinged to rear of fan duct, provides heading control.

HULL: Moulded grp structure.

SKIRT: Bag-type, 6 in (15 cm) deep.

ACCOMMODATION: Open cockpit with seating for two, side-by-side.

DIMENSIONS:

Length overall	13 ft 5⅝ in (4·10 m)
Beam	6 ft 10⅝ in (2·10 m)
Height	4 ft 11 in (1·5 m)

WEIGHTS:

Empty weight	882 lb (400 kg)
Loaded weight	1,654 lb (750 kg)

PERFORMANCE:

Maximum speed:	
over land	50 mph (80 km/h)
over water	31 mph (50 km/h)
Maximum gradient, static conditions	1 : 10
Vertical obstacle clearance	6 in (15 cm)

VA-1

The VA-1 is designed for use in a variety of projects aimed at opening up and developing areas of the Amazon and traversing the swamps of the Matto Grosso.

LIFT AND PROPULSION: Cushion lift is provided by a single 40 hp Volkswagen 1300 automotive engine driving twin fans located on the centre line, one each end of the open load deck. Thrust is supplied by two 90 hp Volkswagen 2000 engines, each driving a ducted 2-bladed propeller aft. Cushion area is 13·5 m², and cushion pressure 11 gr/cm². Total fuel capacity is 22 gal (100 l).

CONTROLS: A single aerodynamic rudder provides directional control.

HULL: Moulded fibreglass.

SKIRT: Bag type flexible skirt, 10 in (25 cm) deep.

ACCOMMODATION: Enclosed cabin, forward, seats a driver and three passengers. Access is via two hinged doors, one port, one starboard.

DIMENSIONS:

Length overall	21 ft 7⅞ in (6·60 m)
Beam	10 ft 1⅛ in (3·05 m)
Height	7 ft 8½ in (2·35 m)

WEIGHTS:

Empty weight	1,764 lb (800 kg)
Loaded weight	3,308 lb (1,500 kg)

PERFORMANCE:

Maximum speed:

over water	43·5 mph (70 km/h)
over land	74·5 mph (120 km/h)
Max gradient, static conditions	20%
Vertical obstacle clearance	10 in (25 cm)

Top: Power for the VA is supplied by a single 50 hp VW 1300 automotive engine which gives it a top speed over water of 43.5 mph (70 kmh)

Bottom: A model of VEI's VAI four-seat utility vehicle for operation over land, rivers and sheltered water.

BULGARIA

OKRUJNAYE POLYTECHNIC
Plovdiv, Bulgaria
ICARUS II

Relatively little news has been forthcoming over the years on hovercraft activities in the smaller countries of the Eastern bloc. That interest is probably just as keen in these parts as it is in the West, is indicated by the accompanying photograph. Described as "an automobile that rides on an air-cushion", Icarus II was designed and built by students of the Okrujnaye Polytechnic, Plovdiv, Bulgaria, under the guidance of Mr. Christel Christov.

Icarus II

CANADA

BELL AEROSPACE CANADA
(A division of Textron Canada Ltd)
DIRECTORS:
William G. Gisel, President
Norton C. Willcox, Vice-President
Joseph R. Piselli, Vice-President
James G. Mills, Managing Director
HEAD OFFICE:
P.O. Box 160, Grand Bend, Ontario, NOM 1TO, Canada
TELEPHONE:
Area Code 519 238-2333

In January 1971, Bell Aerospace Canada acquired facilities at Grand Bend, Ontario, for the development and production of its Voyageur heavy haul ACV, and the smaller 17-ton Viking multi-duty craft.

The facilities at Grand Bend Airport include two buildings with a total of 30,000 sq ft (3,350 m²) of floor space on a 52-acre (21 Ha) site.

The company has worked closely with the Canadian Department of Industry, Trade and Commerce in planning a programme which has led to the establishment in Canada of a commercially viable air cushion industry to meet the growing requirements for Coast Guard, remote area cargo hauling, high speed passenger ferry services and other specialised applications.

The first two 40-ton Voyageurs were built under a joint agreement between the company and the Canadian Department of Industry, Trade and Commerce. The prototype, Voyageur 001, differs from later craft insofar as it is fitted with two GE LM-100 engines, as opposed to the ST6T-75 Twin-Pac gas-turbines which are now standard.

The newer Viking, a smaller but similar multi duty craft was completed under a one-prototype cost-sharing programme similar to that under which the Voyageur was developed.

Both Voyageur and Viking feature a basic flatbed hull of all-welded extruded marine aluminium that can be adapted to a variety of operational needs by adding the required equipment and superstructure.

Construction of Voyageur 001 started in March 1971. It began operational trials and certification testing in November 1971.

Since early 1973, Voyageur 001 has been operating extensively in the Mackenzie Delta region of Northern Canada on oil industry exploration logistics support. Voyageur 002 is owned and operated by the Canadian Coast

Guard and since March 1975 has been undergoing trials as an ACV icebreaker. Ice in excess of 1 ft 5 in (431 mm) thick has been successfully broken.

Voyageur 003 has been employed in Alaska in a petroleum industry logistics support role since July 1974. Since March 1975, the craft has been under charter to Alyeska/Bechtel as a pipeline logistics ferry across the Yukon river, where it has operated in temperatures as low as —65°F.

Craft 004 has been under charter to Agence Maritime Inc. since October 1974 as a ship-to-shore and coastal lighter, supplying remote areas of the St. Lawrence North Shore. Nos. 005 and 006 are in various stages of completion and have been sold. Craft 007 is scheduled for completion in mid-1976.

MODEL 7380 VOYAGEUR

The Bell Model 7380 is a twin-engined fully amphibious hovercraft designed to haul payloads of up to 25 tons over Arctic and other terrain at speeds up to 87 km/h (54 mph).

The 25 ton payload is equal to that of most transport aircraft engaged in regular supply operations in the North and other remote regions, including the C-130 Hercules. The Model 7380 therefore provides a direct transport link from the airstrips to settlements and support bases for the movement of men, equipment and supplies.

The craft has been tested extensively by the Canadian Coast Guard and the US Army for a variety of high speed amphibious missions.

Modular construction is employed and the craft can be dismantled into easily handled units, plus skirts, for ease of transportation by road, rail or air.

Estimates indicate that ton-mile operating costs will be less than 25% of those experienced with heavy lift helicopters and 50% that of existing small ACVs.

By adding superstructure to the basic flatbed hull, the craft can be used for various alternative roles from a 140 seat passenger ferry to military weapons platform.

LIFT AND PROPULSION: Two 1,300 hp Pratt & Whitney ST6T-75 Twin-Pac gas-turbines mounted aft, one each side of the roll-on/roll-off cargo deck, power the integrated lift/propulsion systems, which employ fans, propellers and transmissions similar to those of the Bell SK-5 and BHC SR-N6. Each engine has two separate gas-turbine sections which drive into a combining gearbox, providing twin-engine reliability for each integrated lift fan and propeller. The second gearbox employed in the Twin-Pac installation is a strengthened version of the integrated drive used in the SR.N5, developed by the SPECO Division of Kelsey-Hayes. The output of each engine is absorbed by a three-bladed Hamilton Standard 43D50 reversible-pitch propeller of 9 ft (2·74 m) diameter and by a 12-bladed 7 ft (2·13 m) diameter light alloy centrifugal lift fan. The fans deliver air to the cushion via a 4 ft (1·21 m) deep peripheral skirt which incorporates stability trunks. Air drawn by the engines first enters a Donaldson filter that traps and removes dust particles. It then passes through a fine knitmesh filter and into a Peerless Vane filter that gathers water droplets. Lift fans and propellers are linked mechanically and the power output of each engine can be apportioned between the

Above: Voyageur 002, operated by the Canadian Coast Guard, breaking up a 3½-mile long ice jam on the Riviere des Prairies, north of Montreal. The craft was operated at a speed of 10 knots to create a series of trailing waves, one of which was allowed to precede the Voyageur into the ice pack, breaking the surface ice into pieces
Below: The Voyageur compressing and cracking the jammed ice into smaller segments. The gaps between the segments increase as they move downstream, carried by the river's three-knot current

Voyageur 003, completely assembled, being transported by flat bed truck from Prudhoe Bay, down the Alyeska Pipeline road, to the Yukon river. It is now under charter to the Alyeska Pipeline Service Company as a pipeline logistics ferry

propellers and lift fans allowing speed and hoverheight to be varied to suit prevailing operating conditions. The engines have multifuel capability and can be started in extremely low temperatures (—65°F). Two fuel tanks, each consisting of three interconnected bays containing flexible rubber cells, are built into the aft end of the port and starboard forward flotation boxes. Total fuel capacity is 15,000 litres (3,300 Imp gal), sufficient for a range of approximately 550 nautical miles with a 15-ton payload. Types of fuel which may be used are kerosene, AVTUR, JETA, JP4, JP5 and Arctic diesel. CONTROLS: Steering is by means of two aerodynamically-balanced rudders hinged to

the rear of propeller, supplemented by the
use of differential propeller pitch control.
Side-located bow thrusters aid low-speed
manoeuvring.   All controls are located in the
raised cab, which seats a crew of two plus
four passengers.   Propeller pitch controls are
located on the starboard side of the operator's
seat, so that they can be operated by the
right hand, while power can be controlled
with the left hand.   A conventional foot-
operated control bar is provided for rudder
actuation.

HULL: Exceptionally rugged all-metal structure, fabricated in corrosion-resistant 6,000
series extruded aluminium alloys, with double
wall skinning and multiple watertight compartments.   The design of the modular
structure incorporates hollow-core, thin-
walled aluminium extrusions similar to those
employed in the superstructures of commercial and naval ships.   Use of this material,
with extruded corners for constructing joints,
produces a structural box of great strength
and stiffness.   The hull design is based on
flat surfaces, thus eliminating the need for
formed parts and simplifying repairs.   The
structural modules are welded using gas-
shielded metal arc and gas shielded tungsten
arc processes.

The basic craft hard structure is broken
down for transportation into twelve sections.
These consist of three forward flotation boxes,
two forward and two aft side decks, two
power modules, an aft centre flotation box,
a cabin support pedestal and the control
cabin.

The three forward flotation boxes are almost
identical in appearance and measure 40 ft
long, 8 ft wide and 3 ft 1½ in deep (12·19 ×
2·43 × 0·952 m).   The port and starboard
boxes each contain a fuel tank and a landing
pad support structure.

The aft centre flotation box is of similar

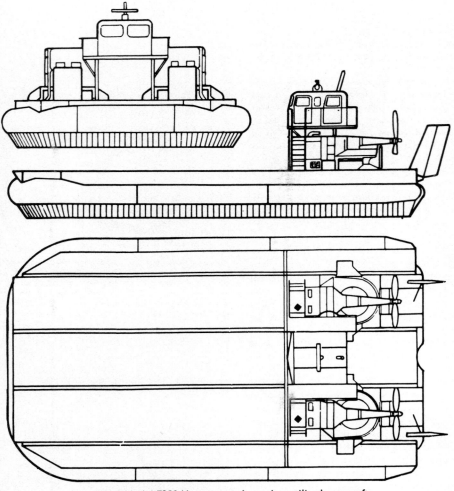

Bell Model 7380 Voyageur twin-engine utility hovercraft

construction, but shorter in length.   Scallops
are formed in each side to prevent airflow

blockage around the perimeter of the lift fans,
which are contained in the power modules

Upper left and right: Since early 1973, Voyageur 001 has been operated by KAPS Transport in the Mackenzie Delta region of northern Canada
in oil exploration logistics support missions.   Typical loads are a Caterpillar tractor and a Nodwell seismic driller weighing   46,000 lb, a 3,300
Imperial gallon fuel tank (filled) and miscellaneous items of earth-moving equipment *Bottom left:* Voyageur 001 during military lighterage operations
in the joint US Army/Navy/ Marine Corps exercise OSDOC II *Bottom right:*   003 carrying oil tanks to a drilling site in north Alaska

located on either side of the centre box. This module, together with the three forward boxes, forms the structural backbone of the craft. Loads from the side decks and power modules are transmitted into this primary structure.

The main deck is designed to accept loadings of up to 4,882 kg/m² (1,000 lb/sq ft.) Cargo tiedown-rings and craft handling gear are provided. Off-cushion, the cargo deck is sufficiently low to permit rapid loading and unloading from trucks and fork lifts.

The craft is completely amphibious and has a reserve buoyancy in excess of 100%.

SKIRT: 1·22 m (4 ft) deep neoprene nylon skirt developed from that of BHC SR.N6. 50% peripheral fingers. High attachment line at bow, similar to that employed on the BH.7. Airflow to the side and bow skirts is supplied through the duct formed by the side hulls. The transverse stability trunks are also supplied from the side hull airflow, via a duct built into the outboard forward flotation boxes immediately forward of the fuel tanks. The port and starboard rear trunks are supplied by rearward airflow from the respective fans. The longitudinal keel is fed by ducts leading from each fan forward to the centre of the aft centre flotation box, then downwards into the keel bag.

ACCOMMODATION: The control cabin is supported on a raised platform aft of the deck between the power modules. It is raised sufficiently to provide 1·93 m (6 ft 4 in) of headroom for personnel or cargo and provides the operator with a 360 deg view. The unit is basically a modified four door truck cab, measuring 2·64 × 2·38 m (8 ft 8 in long by 7 ft 10 in wide). The operating crew of two are seated forward. The operator's position is on the starboard side, and the relief driver or radar operator is at the port position. The control console is located between the two seats and contains the control levers for the engines.

A full-width bench seat is located across the back of the cab, with access provided by the two rear doors. Seat belts are provided for four passengers. Cabin heating and window defrosting is provided by a dual heater, operating on vehicle fuel, and located at the forward end, beneath the port walkway to the control cabin. Electronically heated windows are also installed. Thermal insulation and double glazing are provided throughout the cab and this also attenuates engine noise.

Additional features provided in the cab design are structural provisions for roof mounted radar, air-conditioning and the provision of space in the control console for radio communications and navigation equipment.

SYSTEMS: Electrical: Four gearbox-driven brushless generators, each supplying 28 volts dc, and two 28 volt Nickel-Cadmium batteries. External power: 28 volts dc.

The Viking on patrol near Parry Sound, Ontario

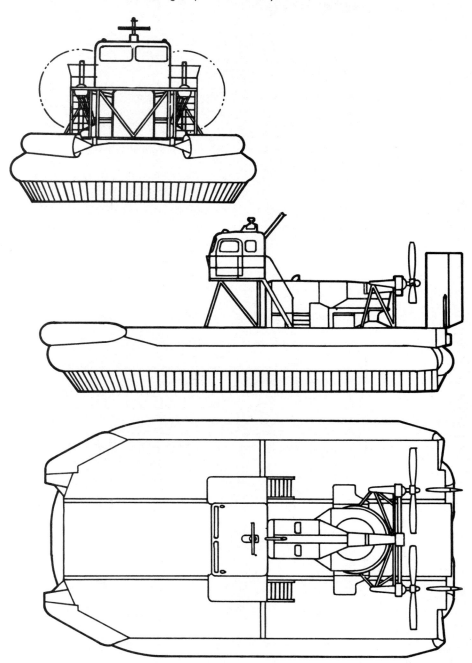

Power for the Viking multi-purpose ACV is provided by a single 1,300 hp Twin-Pac T75, coupled to two variable-pitch propellers via a V-drive transmission. Maximum speed, calm water, is 92 km/h (57 mph)

DIMENSIONS:

Length overall	20 m (65·7 ft)
Beam overall	11·2 m (36·7 ft)
Height verall, power on	6·7 m (22·0 ft)
Height overall, power off	5·74 m (18 ft 10 in)
Height of cargo deck, power off	1·17 m (3 ft 10 in)
Skirt height	1·22 m (4 ft 0 in)
Cushion area	166 m² (1,789 sq ft)
Cushion loading at 41,277 kg (91,000 lb)	248·92 kg/m² (50·88 lb/sq ft)
Buoyancy reserve at 41,277 kg (91,000 lb)	125%
Cargo deck size	40 × 32 ft (1,280 sq ft) (12·19 m × 9·75 m) (119 m²)

WEIGHTS:

Basic weight, empty	16,202 kg (35,720 lb)
Design gross weight	40,823 kg (90,000 lb)
Max permissible gross weight	41,277 kg (91,000 lb)

PERFORMANCE:
Max speed over calm water, still air conditions, at a sea level standard day temperature of 59 deg F (15 deg C) with a 20 ton payload.
At 78,000 lb (35,381 kg) gross, 2,600 shp
54 mph (87 km/h)
Endurance at cruise power with 600 US gallons (2,280 l) and 30-ton payload
3 hours
Endurance can be extended to 10-13·5 hours by trading off payload for fuel, with maximum fuel of 15,000 litres (3,300 Imp gal) the payload will be in the region of 18 tons at the maximum permissible gross weight of 41,277 kg (91,000 lb).

MODEL 7501 VIKING

Evolved from the 40-ton Voyageur, the 17-ton Viking has been designed to meet the need for a smaller but similar multi-purpose craft capable of hauling a 6-7-ton payload at a speed of 92 km/h (57 mph).

The Viking prototype, equipped to meet Canadian Coast Guard requirements for an inshore search-and-rescue craft, was completed in early 1974. A study has been made of a lighterage variant for the US Marine Corps and the craft also has applications as a seismic survey/hydrographic vehicle.

Features of the Viking include a tapered skirt, a more effective bow thrust-port system and a vee-drive transmission operable collectively and differentially to provide a high degree of manoeuvrability. A number of mechanical components are interchangeable with those of the Voyageur, simplifying maintenance and spares holdings. Modular construction features of the Voyageur have

The Bell Viking prototype, equipped to meet Canadian Coast Guard requirements for an inshore search and rescue craft

been retained to facilitate transport by road, rail and air, and speedy reassembly and maintenance on site.

LIFT AND PROPULSION: A single UACL ST6T-75 Twin-Pac gas-turbine, delivering 1,300 shp continuous and 1,700 shp intermittent, powers the integrated lift/propulsion system, which employs a number of components identical to those used on the Voyageur. Engine output is transferred to a single 2·13 m (7 ft 0 in) diameter light alloy centrifugal lift fan and, via a V-drive transmission, to two 2·74 m (9 ft 0 in) diameter Hamilton Standard 3-blade variable-pitch propellers for thrust. Maximum cushion pressure is 193·2 kg/sq m (39·6 lb/sq ft). Total fuel capacity is 6,954 l (1,530 Imp gals. 1,837 US gals). Types of fuel allowed are kerosene, JP4, JP5, JETA, AVTUR or Arctic diesel.

CONTROLS: Craft heading is controlled by twin aerodynamically balanced rudders, supplemented by differential propeller thrust. Bow thrust-ports, port and starboard, assist directional control at low speeds.

HULL: All-metal structure fabricated in 6,000 series corrosion-resistant extruded marine aluminium. Basic craft hard structure comprises six modules which are unbolted for transportation. Cargo deck has a total area of 76·2 sq m (820 sq ft).

SKIRT: 1·22 m (4 ft 0 in) deep neoprene-

nylon tapered skirt developed from that of BHC SR.N6. with 50% peripheral fingers and a high attachment line at the bow.

ACCOMMODATION: Operating crew of two (commander/operator; navigator/relief operator), seated in a cabin supported on a raised platform amidships. Basic flat-deck configuration will accommodate a wide range of payloads, or superstructure and/or special equipment.

SYSTEMS:
ELECTRICAL: Two gearbox-driven brushless generators, each supplying 28 volts dc, and two 28 volt Nickel-Cadmium batteries. External power 28 volts dc.

DIMENSIONS:

Length overall	13·6 m (44·5 ft)
Beam overall	7·9 m (26·0 ft)
Height overall	6·1 m (20·0 ft)
Cargo deck area	76·2 sq m (820 sq ft)
Deck height, off cushion	1·2 m (3·9 ft)

WEIGHTS:

Empty weight	9,383 kg (20,685 lb)
Max permissible gross weight	14,742 kg (32,500 lb)

PERFORMANCE:

Max speed, calm water	92 km/h (57 mph)
Continuous gradient capability, standing start	10%
Vertical obstacle clearance	1·2 m (4 ft)
Ditch crossing width	2·1 m (7 ft)
Endurance with maximum fuel	13 hours
Max wave height	in excess of 1·8 m (6 ft)
Max range	680 nautical miles

CANADIAN CUSHION CRAFT LTD

HEAD OFFICE:
Octagon Pond, PO Box 8534, Station A, St. John's, Newfoundland A1B 3N9, Canada

TELEPHONE:
(709) 368-1023

TELEX:
016-4675

WORKS:
Beclin Building, Topsail Road, St. John's, Newfoundland

DIRECTORS:
R. E. Good, President
R. C. Fishlock, Vice-President, Technical Director
J. Halley, Secretary-Treasurer

In August 1975, Canadian Cushion Craft Ltd began the series production of the Canair 2, an amphibious two-seater intended for a range of utility applications, from patrol and survey to light transport duties. A feature of the company's marketing is the offer of free basic training in the operation

of the craft by a qualified ACV instructor.

CANAIR 2

Development of the Canair 2 has been supported by the Newfoundland and Labrador Development Corporation, which may participate in the production and marketing of the machine. Its features include a planing hull to reduce the risk of overturning, a single engine and fan installation for reduced maintenance and an HDL skirt with easily replaceable segments.

Canair 2, an amphibious two-seater designed for a range of utility applications. Development of the vehicle, which is powered by a single 35 bhp Kohler air-cooled engine, was supported by the Newfoundland and Labrador Development Corporation

LIFT AND PROPULSION: Power for the integrated lift/propulsion system is provided by a single Kohler 440 2AS air-cooled 2-cycle engine delivering 35 bhp at 6,000 rpm. Power is transmitted to a 2 ft 6 in (0·726 m) diameter, 10-bladed multi-wing fan aft. The primary air flow is directed aft, and the secondary, for cushion lift, passes down into the plenum. The engine is completely enclosed to reduce the intake of dust, sand and salt-water spray. The engine is cooled by its own fan, in addition to which a main drive fan extracts air out of the compartment via side ducts and forward intake vents. Total fuel capacity is 5 gallons.

CONTROLS: A simple twist grip mounted on a central control stick operates the engine throttle. Movement of the stick operates twin rudders hinged to the rear of the fan duct to control craft heading.

HULL: Built in moulded grp. Buoyancy is provided by six watertight compartments, each with an individual inspection hatch.

SKIRT: HDL type loop and segment skirt fabricated in lightweight neoprene-coated nylon. All segments are readily replaceable with simple plastic stud and strap fasteners designed to fail under excessive snatch loads, leaving the segments undamaged.

ACCOMMODATION: Side-by-side seating for driver and passenger in an open cockpit. Room provided behind the seat for baggage or equipment. Seat moves forward or backward for trim change.

DIMENSIONS (engine off):

Length	14 ft 0 in (4·26 m)
Width	7 ft 3 in (2·20 m)
Height	4 ft 6 in (1·37 m)
Cushion depth	10 in (254 mm)

WEIGHTS:

Dry weight	450 lb (204·10 kg)
Normal payload (including two occupants)	450 lb (204·10 kg)

PERFORMANCE:

Max speed	30 mph (48·28 km/h)
Cruising speed	25 mph (40·23 km/h)
Endurance at 80% full power	2 hours

The craft has operated successfully in 25 mph (40·23 km/h) winds, and seas slightly in excess of 1 ft 6 in (0·457 m) high with a payload of 400 lb (181·429 kg).

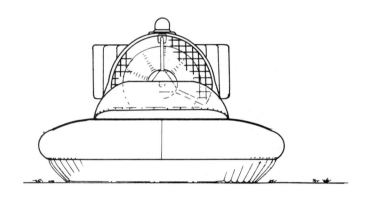

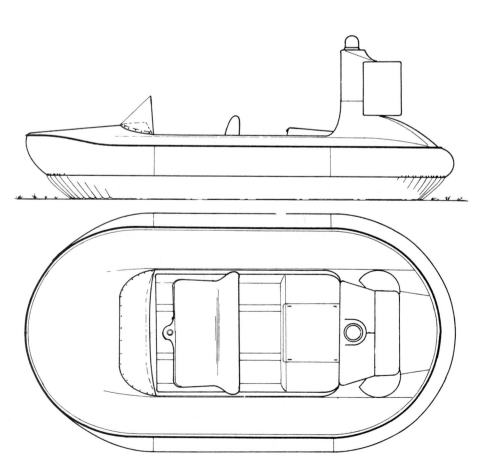

General arrangement of the Canair 2, two-seat, light amphibious hovercraft

FLYLO CORPORATION LTD

HEAD OFFICE:
King Street, W. Ingersoll, Ontario
TELEPHONE:
(519) 485-3003
DIRECTORS:
J. D. Loveridge, President
J. D. Duncan, Secretary Treasurer
Michael Herling
Paul Ivanier

Flylo Corporation, a subsidiary of Ingersoll Machine and Tool Co Ltd, was formed in July 1969 to design, construct and market ACVs in North America. The company is now building the Caliban fibreglass-hulled two-seater for which it has exclusive worldwide manufacturing rights.

CALIBAN

This is a direct descendent of the lightweight sporting craft designed and built by Geoffrey Kent for the first International Hovercraft Rally held at Appethorpe in 1967. One of the most successful craft in the competition field in the United Kingdom, it was also the first amateur-built machine to cross the Solent.

Extended marketing of the Caliban revealed a demand for fibreglass rather than a plywood hull, and also a preference for a two-seater with an enclosed cabin.

The Flylo Caliban, which incorporates these features, is now in production.

LIFT AND PROPULSION: Lift engine is a 12·5 hp Canadian Curtiss Wright two-stroke. Thrust is provided by a 23 hp twin Canadian

Two-seat, fibreglass-hulled variant of the Caliban, built in Canada by Flylo Corporation

Curtiss Wright driving a 2-bladed, fixed-pitch metal propeller at half engine speed through a timing belt. A centrifugal clutch is fitted.
HULL: Fibreglass construction.
ACCOMMODATION: Side-by-side seating for driver and one passenger in enclosed cabin with sliding canopy. At the rear of the cabin is a protective roll bar, which is also used as a handhold when stepping into the craft.

DIMENSIONS:
Length overall 13 ft 6 in (4·11 m)
Beam overall 6 ft 9 in (2·05 m)
Vertical obstacle clearance 9 in (228 mm)
WEIGHTS:
Unladen weight, complete with canopy, battery, and electric starter for both engines 490 lb (222 kg)
Carrying capacity 450 lb (204 kg)
PRICE: C$3,595·00.

HOVER CENTRE OF CANADA

HEAD OFFICE:
Box 656, Maple, Ontario
TELEPHONE:
677 4518
CABLES:
Hovercentre Toronto

OFFICERS:
Dean McCulloch, Vice-President

The Hover Centre of Canada supplies ACV kits and spares. Since 1972 it has acted as

the North American representative for various purchasers of ACVs in the Near and Middle East. The company is also the official agent in Canada for all the main United Kingdom ACV publications.

HOVER-JAK LIMITED

HEAD OFFICE:
169 Centre Street East, Richmond Hill, Ontario, Canada L4C IA5
TELEPHONE:
Area Code 416-884-7735 and 884-6650
OFFICERS:
G. Grass, President

J. Flett, Vice-President
C. Flinders, General Manager
C. P. Kirwan, Marketing Manager
This company was registered by the Ontario Provincial Government to manufacture, sell and service air cushion vehicles, including those designed by Jones Kirwan and Associates.

The Company, is the Canadian licence holder for the manufacture of craft employing the Bertin system of independently fed multiple plenum chambers.

The company's HJ-15 air cushion trailer is illustrated in the section devoted to Heavy Load Carrying Systems.

HOVERJET INC

HEAD OFFICE:
58 Glen Cameron Road No. 21, Thornhill, Ontario, Canada
TELEPHONE:
(416) 881-0737
DIRECTORS AND SENIOR EXECUTIVES:
Ralph Schneider, President
Bruce Halliwell, Vice-President
E. De Asis, Chief Engineer
D. Epp, Plant Superintendent
SUBSIDIARIES AND AFFILIATED COMPANIES:
Alpha Aerospace Corporation Ltd, Continental Hoverjet Ltd, Kamloops BC, Canada (manufacturer of HJ-100).
Hoverjet Inc is, currently producing the HJ-1000, 5-seat passenger and utility craft, the prototype of which completed its trials

in April 1974. The company is engaged primarily in ACV research and development and undertakes contract design, consultancy and prototype construction for other companies. Ralph Schneider, formerly director of research and development at Hoverair Corporation and Airfloat Ltd, is responsible for Hoverjet's development and engineering programmes.

HOVERJET HJ-1000

An amphibious "workhorse" designed to meet the needs of exploration parties, the HJ-1000 is of frp construction and carries a payload of up to 1,000 lb (453·59 kg). Power is provided by three 42 hp Kohler engines.

The craft has been designed to permit transport by air, sea and road. It will fit into a transport aircraft with an 8 ft (2·43 m)

door opening; it can be accommodated in a standard 8 ft × 8 ft × 20 ft (2·43 m × 2·43 m × 6·09 m) container for delivery by sea, or it can be loaded onto an 8 ft × 20 ft (2·43 m × 6·09 m) boat trailer.

LIFT AND PROPULSION: Lift is supplied by a single 42 hp Kohler K440-2AS two-cycle aircooled engine driving two 1 ft 8 in (0·50 m) diameter 10-bladed aluminium fans mounted vertically at the opposite ends of a transverse shaft. Cushion pressure is 15·9 lb sq ft. Propulsive thrust is supplied by two duct-mounted, 42 hp Kohler K440-2AS two-cycle aircooled engines, each driving a single 2 ft 6 in (0·762 m) diameter 10-bladed axial fan. For manoeuvring and hullborne operation over water a 7 hp outboard motor on a remotely-operated swing mount can be fitted as an optional extra. Fuel is carried in two 10-gallon (45·46 litre) tanks, one port, one starboard, each with a refuelling neck located on deck. Recommended fuel is 2-cycle mix, 40 : 1.

CONTROLS: Craft heading is controlled by a column which activates twin rudders at the rear of the thrust ducts via push-pull cables.

HULL: Two-piece construction, comprising upper and lower bodies in colour impregnated fibreglass on welded steel inner frame. Engine and fan mounts are of tubular, welded steel construction.

SKIRT: Segmented loop in laminated 16 oz nylon/neoprene.

ACCOMMODATION: Driver sits forward and up to four passengers are accommodated in a wide cabin aft. Access is via a large door and roof opening on the port side. The passenger seats fold against the sides of the cabin to provide a cargo hold measuring 4 ft wide × 8 ft 0 in long by 4 ft 4 in high (1·21 m × 2·43 m × 1·32 m). Safety equipment includes "pop-out" emergency exit windows, built-in buoyancy, a fire extinguisher and an electric bilge pump.

SYSTEMS, Electrical: 12 volts for starting and generating. 75 W engine generators, 30 amp/hr battery.

OPTIONAL EQUIPMENT: Navigation lights, flashing beacon, spotlight, radio, lifejacket.

DIMENSIONS:

Length overall, power off	18 ft 0 in (5·48 m)
Length overall, skirt inflated	19 ft 2 in (5·84 m)
Beam overall, power off	7 ft 10 in (2·38 m)
skirt inflated	8 ft 11 in (2·71 m)
Draft afloat	4 in (101 mm)
Cushion area	142 sq ft (13·19 sq m)
Height overall, power off	5 ft 4 in (1·62 m)
skirt inflated	6 ft 5 in (1·95 m)

HJ-1000, 5-seat utility craft, powered by three 42 h.p. Kohler engines

DIMENSIONS, INTERNAL:

Main cabin:

Length	8 ft 0 in (2·43 m)
Max width	4 ft 0 in (1·21 m)
Max height	4 ft 4 in (1·32 m)
Floor area	32·5 sq ft (3·01 sq m)

WEIGHTS:

Normal empty weight	970 lb (439·96 kg)
Normal all-up weight	2,000 lb (907·185 kg)

Normal gross weight	2,000 lb (907·185 kg)
Normal payload	1,000 lb (453·59 kg)
Maximum payload	1,200 lb (544·28 kg)

PERFORMANCE:

Details of speed and range not available at time of going to press.

Vertical obstacle clearance

1 ft 1 in (330 mm)

PRICE: C$7,500, FOB, Toronto, Canada.

HOVERLIFT SYSTEMS LTD.

HEAD OFFICE:

1201, 603 Seventh Avenue, S.W. Calgary, Alberta T2P 2T5

TELEPHONE:

263-3983 or 263-7686

OFFICERS:

R. D. Hunt, President

Dale M. Simmons, Executive Vice-President & Secretary

K. W. Crowshaw, Vice-President

V. H. Redekop, Treasurer

Hoverlift Systems Ltd was incorporated in

April 1975 as a member of the Simmons Group of Companies which is active in the resource and energy fields. Its member companies are: Simmons Drilling Ltd., Kandex Research and Development Ltd., McMurray Operators, Ltd., Rudale Resources Ltd., Western Underground Contractors Ltd. and Hoverlift Systems Ltd. Simmons Drilling in particular has worked for fifteen years in the Canadian North, and is well aware of the many problems posed by operation and maintenance of equipment in the intense cold and darkness of the Canadian Winter.

Hoverlift Systems Ltd. aims to provide aircushion equipment and services developed especially for these conditions, to those companies operating in the Canadian Arctic and Sub-Arctic regions where mineral exploration, civil engineering, construction, hydro-electric, forestry and manufacturing projects are hampered by climate and difficult terrain.

Hoverlift Systems Ltd. is currently building a small ten ton air-cushion system designed to be rapidly despatched and put into emergency operation in remote areas where no support equipment exists.

HOVERTEC INC

HEAD OFFICE:

Unit One, 250 Rayette Road, Concord, Ontario, L4K 1BI

TELEPHONE:

416-669-9801

DIRECTORS:

Jim McCurdy, President

Peter Roberts, Works Director

The first craft to be marketed by Hovertec Inc is the Chinook miniature ACV runabout. The vehicle is in production and is being sold through a national dealer network. Sales began in the USA in late 1974. By March 1975, 150 of the Mk 1 version and five Mk 2s

had either been built or were on order.

The company is at present completing a new amphibious runabout seating two side-by-side.

CHINOOK I

This is a lightweight amphibious single seater with a maximum payload capacity of about 325 lb (147·41 kg). Built in fibreglass reinforced plastics it is 11 ft 3 in long and sufficiently small and light to be transported on the roof of a family car.

Maximum speed over water is 30 mph (48·28 km/h).

LIFT AND PROPULSION: Cushion air is supplied by a 5 hp Tecumseh 2-cycle engine

driving a 2 ft 0 in (0·60 m) diameter ten bladed polypropelene fan. A 20 hp Kohler 295-1, 2 cycle engine drives a 2 ft 0 in (0·60 m) diameter, 10-bladed ducted fan for thrust. Fuel capacity is 5 Imp gallons (22 litres). Fuel recommended is high octane automotive spirit.

HULL: Moulded in fibreglass reinforced plastic.

SKIRT: Bag type in neoprene impregnated nylon.

ACCOMMODATION: Open cockpit with single-seat for driver.

DIMENSIONS:

Length overall   11 ft 3 in (3·42 m)

Beam overall 5 ft 0 in (1·52 m)
Height overall 3 ft 7 in (1·09 m)
Hoverheight, hard structure
to ground 8 in (203 mm)
WEIGHTS:
Normal empty weight 285 lb (129·26 kg)
Normal payload 325 lb (147·41 kg)
PERFORMANCE (at normal operating weight):
Max speed over calm water
30 mph (48·28 km/h)
Max speed overland
up to 40 mph (64·37 km)
over ice and snow
up to 45 mph (72·42 km)
Still air range and endurance at
cruising speed 4·5-5 hours
Max gradient, static conditions 20°
Vertical obstacle clearance 8 in (203 mm)
PRICE: Mk 1: C$ 1,550·00, c.o.d. (FOB for overseas orders).

CHINOOK II

The prototypes of the Chinook completed trials in March 1975. The chief difference between the model and its predecessor is in the installation of a more powerful propulsion engine, the 26 hp Kohler 295-2AX, for improved performance. Basic hull structure, weights and dimensions are unchanged.
PERFORMANCE:
Max speed over calm water
40 mph (64·37 km/h)
Still air range and endurance 4·5-5 hours
Max gradient, static conditions 30 degrees
Vertical obstacle clearance 8 in (203·20 mm)
PRICE AND TERMS:
C $ 1,750·00 c.o.d. (FOB for overseas orders).

HOVERTEC TWO-SEATER

Construction of this amphibious fibreglass-hulled two-seater, derived from the earlier Chinook, began in April 1975. Trials were due to start in the late summer of 1975.
LIFT AND PROPULSION: A single 8 hp Chrysler engine installed immediately ahead of the cockpit drives a 5-bladed polypropelene axial-flow fan for lift. Thrust is supplied by two 26 hp Kohler 2AX 295 engines mounted aft and driving two, 10-bladed polypropelene ducted fans. Fuel is carried in a single 10 Imp gallon (45·46 l) capacity tank located in the engine compartment aft of the cockpit.
CONTROLS: Craft heading is controlled by twin aerodynamic rudders hinged to the rear of the propulsion fan ducts. Tabs are provided for pitch and roll trim.
HULL: Monocoque structure in moulded fibreglass reinforced plastics.
SKIRT: Bag type, in neoprene impregnated nylon.
ACCOMMODATION: Open cockpit with bench seat for driver and passenger side-by-side.
DIMENSIONS:
Length overall 12 ft 6 in (3·81 m)
Length overall, skirt inflated
14 ft 0 in (4·26 m)
Beam overall, power off 6 ft 6 in (1·98 m)
Beam overall, skirt inflated
8 ft 9 in (2·66 m)
Height overall on landing pads,
power off 3 ft 9 in (1·14 m)
Height overall, skirt inflated
4 ft 6 in (1·37 m)

Hovertec's light amphibious single-seater, the 30 mph (48 km/h) Chinook, The craft measures 11 ft 3 in (3·42 m) by 5 ft (1·52 m) and can be carried on the roof of a family car

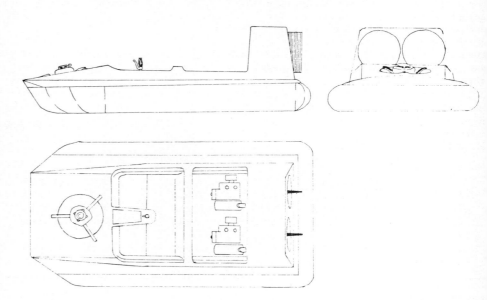

Above and Below: The Hovertel two-seater

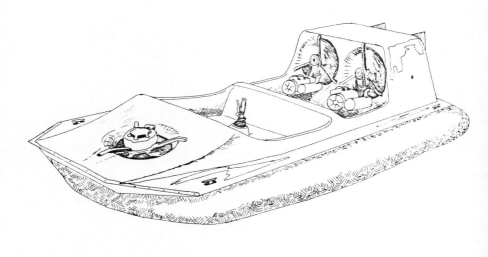

Draft afloat 12 in (304·80 mm)
WEIGHTS:
Normal empty weight 350 lb (158·75 kg)
Normal gross weight 900 lb (408·21 kg)
Normal payload 550 lb (249·46 kg)

PERFORMANCE:
Details not available
PRICE AND TERMS:
Retail prices, standard model C $2,500 de luxe model C $2,900·00.

KOMAR ENGINEERING LTD

HEAD OFFICE:
42 Dundas Street, W Trenton, Ontario

TELEPHONE:
613-392-4477

DIRECTORS:
Gordon J. Komar, MSc, PEng, MEIC,
AMCASI, President
J. W. Tuck, BSc, PEng, Secretary
Erla Komar, Treasurer
H. A. Komarechka

SENIOR EXECUTIVE:
G. Komar, General Manager

Komar Engineering was formed in June 1969 as a mechanical engineering consultancy and also to design and develop air cushion vehicles. The company's first production design is the Aquaterra 65T, a 14 ft (3.26 m) long 3-seater with a moulded fibreglass hull. Development of the craft is continuing and arrangements for production are underway.

AQUATERRA

Recent modification to this fully amphibious 3-seater includes the provision of an enclosed cockpit for all-weather operation and a more powerful thrust engine, raising the top speed to 60 mph (96.56 km/h) over ice. The craft is designed primarily for recreational use and is stated to be an ideal vehicle for sportsmen in hunting and fishing areas.

LIFT AND PROPULSION: The craft is of plenum type, with a single 36 hp Canadian Curtiss Wright 2-cycle air-cooled engine mounted ahead of the cabin and driving a 3 ft (914 mm) 12-bladed axial-flow fan in cast aluminium for cushion lift. Aft of the cockpit is a 65 hp air cooled Volkswagen engine driving a 2-bladed Banks-Maxwell propeller for thrust. Fuel capacity is 12.5 gallons (56.82 l).

CONTROLS: Craft heading is controlled by twin aerodynamic rudders operated by a steering wheel. Other operating controls include a hand-operated locking lift throttle, foot operated thrust accelerator, push button starters and a dual manual choke.

HULL: Moulded fibreglass structure mounted on a tubular aluminium frame. Peripheral bag skirt, 1 ft 0 in (304 mm) deep, fabricated in nylon reinforced neoprene.

ACCOMMODATION: Operator and up to two passengers sit side by side in an enclosed cabin in the centre of the craft. The enclosed cabin is standard. A heater-defroster is supplied as an optional extra.

SYSTEMS: Electrical: 12 volts for engine starting, internal and external lights, windshield wiper.

DIMENSIONS, EXTERNAL:

Length overall:
power off	14 ft 0 in (4.26 m)
skirt inflated	15 ft 0 in (4.57 m)

Aquaterra 65T, an amphibious 3-seater built by Komar Engineering Ltd. Maximum speed over water is 50 mph (80.46 km/h)

Beam overall:
power off	6 ft 6 in (1.98 m)
skirt inflated	7 ft 6 in (2.28 m)

Height overall:
power off	6 ft 6 in (1.98 m)
skirt inflated	7 ft 4 in (2.23 m)

WEIGHTS:
Normal empty weight	750 lb (340.17 kg)
Normal all up weight	1,250 lb (566.96 kg)
Normal gross weight	1,450 lb (657.67 kg)
Max payload	600 lb (272.14 kg)
Normal payload	400 lb (181.42 kg)

PERFORMANCE:

Max-speed:
calm water	50 mph (80.46 km/h)
ice	60 mph; (96.56 km/h)
Cruising speed	45 mph (72.42 km/h)
Max gradient	20%
Vertical obstacle clearance	
	1 ft 0 in (304 mm)

Price   App C$8,100, fob Trenton, Ontario

MINISTRY OF TRANSPORT
AIR CUSHION VEHICLE DIVISION

HEAD OFFICE:
Tower "C", Place de Ville, Ottawa, Ontario
K1A 0N5

CHIEF, ACV DIVISION:
J. Doherty

The Air Cushion Vehicle Division, Ministry of Transport was established in 1968 as part of the Marine Administration.

The Division is responsible to the Director of Marine Safety for all aspects of Air Cushion Vehicle regulation. This includes the establishment of vehicle fitness standards, certification of pilots and maintenance engineers and registration of Air Cushion Vehicles.

On the operations side, the Division has direct responsibility to the Director of the Coast Guard to advise and assist the Coast Guard in its Air Cushion Vehicle activities. Included in this is the use of air cushion technology for ice-breaking and the Division has been instrumental in developing this new and exciting air cushion technology. The Coast Guard Air Cushion Vehicle Evaluation and Development Unit is also a responsibility of the ACV Division.

There is also close collaboration with the Ministry of Transport's Policy and planning Branch, Surface Administration and the Transportation Development Agency. The advice of the Division is constantly sought by other federal departments and provincial governments. The Division also participates actively on the National Research Council Associate Committee of Air Cushion Technology.

WESTON AIR CUSHION VEHICLES INC

HEAD OFFICE:
PO Box 515, Parry Sound, Ontario,
P2A-2X4

TELEPHONE:
(705) 342-5242

PLANT:
Murray Point Road, Nobel, Ontario

DIRECTORS:
Geoffrey Hatton, President
James Walsh, Q.C.
Duncan Smith

Weston Air Cushion Vehicles Inc was founded in March 1973 by Geoffrey Hatton,

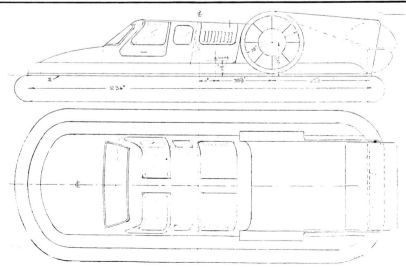

General arrangement of the Whirl-Wind V. Motive power is provided by a single 132 hp 6- cylinder, water-cooled 300 CID Ford engine. Cruising speed over snow and ice is 40-45 mph

formerly of the well-known Hatton & Bass partnership, one of the leading builders of light ACVs in the United Kingdom until 1972. The primary aim of Weston Air Cushion Vehicles is to produce multi-duty vehicles capable of operating in the underdeveloped areas of the Canadian North. The Whirl-Wind V, its first production craft, seats five or alternatively can carry a payload of up to 800 lb.

For the past year, the craft has undergone trials in ice and snow, and has stood up well to a rigorous test programme. The company is at present embarking on a marketing programme to back its production capacity of eight vehicles a month. At the beginning of August 1975, four Whirl-Winds were in service in various parts of Canada and it was anticipated that a further ten units would be in operation by the end of the year.

WHIRL-WIND V

This is a new multi-purpose amphibious ACV, designed to carry a driver and four passengers, or up to 800 lb (362·85 kg) of freight. Built in moulded, reinforced fibreglass, it is powered by a single 132 hp Ford water-cooled engine and cruises over ice and snow at a speed of 40-45 mph (64-72·42 km/h). The width of the craft allows it to be trailed on the road or packed in a standard container.

LIFT AND PROPULSION: Integrated system powered by a single 132 hp, 6-cylinder 300 CID Ford water-cooled engine. Mounted inboard, the engine, which is run at 2,850 rpm, absorbing 120 hp, drives two 7-bladed axial steel fans, rotating at 1,850 rpm and delivering 80,000 cfm. Both fans are mounted at opposite ends of a transverse shaft and are enclosed in ducts to eliminate any danger from moving parts. Airflow is ducted beneath the craft for lift and via outlets aft for thrust. Fuel capacity is 18 gallons (81·82 litres), sufficient for a still air range of 75 (120 km) miles. An auxiliary tank can be fitted to increase the range to 200 miles.

CONTROLS: Craft heading is controlled by twin aerodynamic rudders. Driving controls comprise a steering wheel, engine throttle and a hydraulic lever which operates the reverse thrust buckets.

INSTRUMENTS: Tachometer, oil pressure gauge, ammeter, hour meter, fuel gauge, water temperature meter. Panel mounted switches operate the flashing beacon, windshield wipers and washers and the ventilation controls.

HULL: Semi monocoque structure in coloured, moulded reinforced fibreglass. Moulded urethane collar in the hull gives 150% buoyancy.

SKIRT: Continuous hypalon bag skirt, giving a 12 in (304 mm) hard structure clearance. Skirt configuration varied according to operating conditions.

ACCOMMODATION: Access to the enclosed cabin is through two gull-wing doors, one port, one starboard. Cool air is provided during summer operation by a ventilation unit that can be isolated during winter. The cabin is fitted with a 13,000 btu cab heater which supplies hot air to the cabin and windscreen.

OPTIONAL EXTRAS: Snow deflector; auxiliary petrol tank to increase range to 200 miles; heating system and panel controls; cushion pressure gauge; spotlight or headlights; compass; trailer.

Above: Three views of Whirl-Wind V, a new Canadian craft designed and built by Weston Air Cushion Vehicles Inc, of Parry Sound, Ontario. The craft is designed to carry an 800 lb payload, or five people, including the driver and fuel

SYSTEMS, ELECTRICAL: Engine-driven 12 volt dc, 42 amp alternator, and 12 volt 70 Ah capacity battery. Provides power for engine starting, all lights, windscreen wipers and optional equipment.

DIMENSIONS:

Length overall	19 ft 6 in (5·94 m)
Beam	7 ft 4 in (2·35 m)
Height	4 ft 6 in (1·37 m)

WEIGHTS:

Normal all-up weight 2,900 lb (1,415·39 kg)

Empty weight	2,100 lb (952·50 kg)
Normal payload	800 lb (362·85 kg)

PERFORMANCE:

Cruising speed,
  calm water   30-35 mph (48-52·32 km/h)
  ice and snow   40-45 mph (64-72·42 km/h)
Vertical obstacle clearance   12 in (305 mm)
Still air range at cruising speed,
  18 gallon fuel capacity
                 75 miles (120·70 km.)
With auxiliary fuel tank
                 200 miles (221·86 km)

CHANNEL ISLANDS

T. S. GOOCH

ADDRESS:

La Genètière, Route Orange, St. Brelade, Jersey, C.I.

TELEPHONE:

Central (0534) 42980

Mr T. S. Gooch has designed and built a number of lightweight air cushion vehicles, the latest of which is the J-5. In May 1969, his J-4 became the first home-built ACV to make a Channel crossing to France under its own power. The craft completed the 18-mile (28·96 km) outward crossing from Gorey, C.I., to Carteret in Brittany in 65 minutes and the return journey in 40 minutes.

The J-4 won first place in the Thames Hover Race in 1970 in the under 500 cc class, and has since been acquired by Hovercraft Development Ltd for research and development applications.

Mr Gooch is now concentrating on the development of the J-5 four-seater with almost double the cushion area of the J-4.

Plans of the J-4 are available for amateur construction and are selling well.

GOOCH J-4

This distinctive 13 ft (3·96 m) long amphibious two-seater has been designed with quiet operation and safety in mind. Instead of the more usual propeller, therefore, two axial fans mounted in a transverse duct across the stern are employed for propulsive thrust. The craft is of ply and aluminium construction and cruises at 40 mph (64·37 km/h). To facilitate storage or towing, the two ply sidewings carrying the skirt periphery and running the full length of the main hull structure hinge upwards to reduce the overall beam (power off) from 7 ft (2·13 m) to 4 ft (1·21 m).

The prototype J-4 was finished in June 1968 and the craft completed its trials in July of that year. No variants of the basic design are being contemplated at present, but alternative engines may be fitted.

LIFT AND PROPULSION: Lift is supplied by a Villiers 8E 197 cc two-stroke motor-cycle engine mounted in the bow and driving a 24 in (0·609 mm) diameter 10-blade axial multiwing fan attached directly to its crankshaft. The propulsion engine is a 250 cc Ariel Arrow, twin two-stroke which drives, via a timing belt or vee belt, two 24 in (0·609 mm) diameter 5-bladed Multiwing axial fans mounted vertically on a common shaft inside a transverse duct. Propulsive air is drawn in by the fans from each side of the duct and expelled through a rectangular outlet at the stern. An aluminium reverse thrust/braking bucket is fitted above the air-jet aperture. Total fuel capacity is 4 gallons, carried in two 2-gallon tanks, one each side of the craft on the CG. A filter cap is fitted to each tank. Recommended fuel is two-stroke mixture or regular grade petrol with 20 : 1 fuel/oil ratio.

CONTROLS: Craft direction is controlled by deflection of the thrust from the air-jet propulsion system by four rudders which are operated by a tiller in the cockpit. A foot pedal controls the raising and lowering of the broaking/reverse thrust bucket.

The Gooch J-4 air-jet propelled, two-seat recreational hovercraft

Bow on view of the new Gooch J-5 showing the bow thrust ports and the 3 ft (0·91 m) wide sidewings which hinge upwards to reduce the overall beam for transport

HULL: Construction is primarily of 4 mm exterior grade ply skinning with spruce frame members. Buoyancy compartments are provided fore and aft. Fan intakes are in glass fibre and the reverse/braking bucket is constructed in aluminium. A 9 in (228·6 mm) deep segmented skirt in 4 oz (124 gr) neoprene-coated nylon is attached to the hull periphery.

ACCOMMODATION: Side-by-side seating is provided for two on a bench type seat with foam rubber cushions. A small fire extinguisher is carried in the cockpit.

SYSTEMS: ELECTRICAL: 6V battery, charged by an alternator on the propulsion engine via a rectifier for starting.

DIMENSIONS, EXTERNAL:

Length overall, power off

13 ft 0 in (3·96 m)

Length overall, skirt inflated

13 ft 0 in (3·96 m)

Beam overall, power off 7 ft 0 in (2·13 m)

Beam overall, skirt inflated

7 ft 10 in (2·38 m)

Height overall, power off 3 ft 4 in (1·01 m)

Height overall, skirt inflated

4 ft 0 in (1·21 m)

DIMENSIONS, INTERNAL:

Cabin

4 ft × 4 ft × 1 ft 9 in

(1·21 m × 1·21 × 0·533 m)

WEIGHTS:

Normal empty weight   310 lb (140·60 kg)

Normal all up weight   470 lb (213·17 kg)

Normal gross weight   630 lb (285·75 kg)

Normal payload   320 lb (145·14 kg)

Max payload   680 lb (308·42 kg)

PERFORMANCE:

Max cruising speed over land and water

40 mph (63·74 km/h)

Endurance   2 hours

Max survival sea state

1 ft waves (304 mm)

Max gradient, static conditions   1 in 8

Vertical obstacle clearance   8 in (203 mm)

PLANS:

Plans available, price £5·00, cash with order.

J-5

This new four-seat recreational craft, a derivative of the J-4, is under development. The new design may be made available either in plan or kit form.

LIFT AND PROPULSION: Motive power for the integrated lift/propulsion system is provided by a single 900 cc Hillman Imp engine which develops about 30 hp. Power is transmitted via a chain drive to two pairs of 1 ft 11 in (0·58 m) diameter, double-entry centrifugal fans, mounted on a common shaft, with each pair located in a transverse duct aft of the cockpit. Air is drawn from both sides of each fan housing and expelled forward through the side bodies to pressurise the cushion, and aft through rectangular ducts for propulsion. Cushion pressure is about 10 lb/sq ft. Air can also be ejected through thrust ports forward for braking and manoeuvring at low speeds. Two pedal-operated, aluminium braking/reverse buckets are fitted above each air-jet duct. Total fuel capacity is 10 gallons (45·56 l) carried in tanks under the rear passenger seats on C/P.

CONTROLS: Heading is controlled by differential thrust and by twin sets of rudders operating in the air-jets.

ACCOMMODATION: Seats are provided for an operator and three passengers. The cockpit, which can be open or closed, is sufficiently large to accommodate a standard hospital stretcher, should craft of this type be employed for beach rescue.

HULL: Wooden construction, similar to that employed for J-4. Structure consists primarily of 1 in square spruce frame members glued and screwed to 4 mm marine ply sheet. Hull base is in 6 mm ply sheet. Buoyancy compartments are provided fore and aft. Fan intakes are in glassfibre and the braking buckets are in aluminium.

SKIRT: Loop-and-segment type in 4 oz Briflon. The skirt is attached to the outer edges of the two 3 ft (0·91 m) wide ply sidewings which run the full length of the hull structure and hinge upwards to reduce the overall beam for transport.

One application forseen for the J-5 is that of beach rescue craft. The cockpit, which can be enclosed by a plexiglas canopy, is large enough to accommodate a standard stretcher

UNDERCARRIAGE: Two retractable, independently sprung trailing wheels can be fitted. In the retracted position they can be employed as landing skids.

DIMENSIONS:

Length overall, skirt inflated

15 ft 0 in (4·57 m)

Beam overall:

skirt inflated   12 ft 4 in (3·75 m)

sideways folded   6 ft 2 in (1·87 m)
Height overall, skirt inflated

4 ft 6 in (1·37 m)

WEIGHTS:
Empty weight   410 lb (185·96 kg)

PERFORMANCE:
Maximum speed:
over water   about 35 knots
over land   40 mph (64·37 km/h)

WINFIELD HOVERCRAFT LTD

HEAD OFFICE:
    Belle View Pleasure Park, St. Brelade, Jersey C.I.

DIRECTORS:
    W. D. W. Knight
    J. Knight
    E. Bisson

Winfield Hovercraft Ltd builds and operates single-seat hovercraft "bumper cars" at the Hoverdrome, Belle Vue Pleasure Park, Jersey. The original Hoverdrome at Belle Vue has now been reconstructed to form a 63 ft 0 in (19·20 m) diameter arena contoured like a saucer and with a 7 ft (2·13 m) × 2 ft (0·60 m) outer lip. This allows customers to fly round the outer edge, but come back to rest on the level section in the centre.

The company has devised a system by which a signal, automatically controlled by a time switch, is received by each craft at the end of the specified running time, reducing the 4,000 rpm necessary for hovering to about 700 rpm for tickover. This stops the craft but leaves all the engines running for the next customers.

The Winfield circular hovercraft for amusement centres

WINFIELD AMUSEMENT HOVERCRAFT

This small, sturdily constructed single-seat vehicle has been designed primarily as a bumper car for amusement centres. The chassis, built on racing car principles, is of light tubular steel, and the circular body, 6 ft 0 in (1·82 m) in diameter, is in fibreglass. Around the periphery is a 4 in (101 mm) wide pneumatic bumper.

Power for the integrated lift/propulsion system is provided by a single 150 cc engine. The control system permits the craft to travel forwards, backwards, sideways or spin around its own axis.

On a smooth level ground, such as a beach it will exceed 40 mph (64·37 km/h), but at the Hoverdrome the maximum speed is limited to around 7 mph (11·26 km/h).

CHINA

An ACV research programme is being undertaken by a shipyard in the Shanghai area. Two small amphibious ACVs are currently employed as test craft, it is reported, one imported from Australia, the other built at the yard.

FINLAND

ERKKI PERI

ADDRESS:
    Karjakatu 15, 49400 Hamina, Finland

LICENSER:
    Keksintösäätiö (Foundation of Finnish Inventions), Hämeentie 6 A8, 00530 Helsinki 53, Finland

TELEPHONE:
    90-717 299

Since 1959, Mr Erkki Peri has been developing multi terrain vehicles capable of operating in the severe snow, ice and flood conditions found in northern latitudes. His latest approach combines the advantages of the ACV with those of an aerosled. One of the major design objectives has been to decrease the weight carried by the pontoon-type skis without raising the vehicle from the ground.

Because of the contact between the vehicle's skis and the supporting surface beneath, directional control is a great improvement on that of most conventional skirted ACVs. The forward skis and the air rudder aft move simultaneously to control craft heading.

Additional design features are the improved stability offered by the skirt/ski arrangement and the mounting of the skis on a spring suspension system to ensure a smooth ride.

The project, which covers two prototypes, is offered for licensing and exploitation by the Foundation of Finnish Inventions, an organisation supported by the Finnish Ministry of Trade and Industry, the Finnish Fund for Research & Development and the Finnish Cultural Foundation.

The first prototype is the larger of the two. The second has been designed and built in an endeavour to offer a lighter and less expensive vehicle and also to provide a test bed for technical innovations. Both vehicles are constructed in light aluminium.

FIVE-SEAT HOVERSLED

The designer's principal objective has been to provide an easily controlled vehicle capable of carrying relatively heavy loads at high speed across snow, ice, inland waterways, slush and sludge. This has been achieved by raising the hull with the aid of an air cushion while retaining a percentage of the load on pontoon-like skis which maintain full contact with the supporting surface beneath. The vehicle is steered by turning the front pontoons and the air rudder simultaneously. All four pontoons are buoyant and support the vehicle and its load on water, lift engine off.

The craft has been tested extensively over water, ice and snow.

LIFT AND PROPULSION: Cushion air is supplied by a single 55 hp Renault R8TS driving a centrifugal fan at the base of a cylindrical intake aft of the cabin. From the plenum the air is fed into a bag and finger skirt system fitted to the front and rear of the vehicle and above and between the pontoon/skis at the sides. The bag skirt areas above the pontoons act as pneumatic springs. Thrust is supplied by 92 hp Renault TS driving an 80 m (204 cm) diameter McCauley propeller. Max static thrust is 500 lb (230 kg). Fuel is carried in three tanks, each with a capacity of 6·6 gal (30 l).

CONTROLS: Craft direction is controlled by turning forward pontoons and the air rudder simultaneously.

HULL: Frame and cabin of conventional construction in light aluminium. Ski/pontoons are fabricated in aluminium filled with polyurethane foam.

ACCOMMODATION: Heated cabin seating driver and four passengers, plus room for casualty on a stretcher.

DIMENSIONS:
Length overall	23 ft 0 in (7 m)
Beam overall	9 ft 10 in (3 m)
Cushion area	150 sq ft (14 m²)

WEIGHTS:
Normal gross weight	3,300 lb (1,500 kg)

PERFORMANCE (Design):

Prototype of the Peri Hoversled a new vehicle designed for service in northern latitudes—a combination ACV and aerosled. The forward ski/pontoons and the air rudder aft move simultaneously to control craft heading. The designer, Erkki Peri, has provided the pontoons with both sprung and pneumatic suspension for a smooth ride.

Smaller and of lighter construction than the first Peri Hoversled, this new test craft was awaiting the installation of a lift engine and skirt when this photograph was taken. The four ski/pontoons are in foam-filled ABS plastic and provide sufficient buoyancy to support the vehicle and its load when off-cushion.

Max speed, calm water	45 mph (75 km/h)
Cruising speed	25 mph (40 km/h)
Fuel consumption	3-4½ gal/hr (15-20 l/hr)

HOVERSLED UTILITY

Smaller than the Peri Hoversled prototype this model is of lighter construction than its predecessor and is less expensive to build. At the time of going to press it was still incomplete. After the installation of the lift engine and skirt, the total basic weight was expected to be in the region of 1,170 lb (430 kg).

LIFT AND PROPULSION: Propulsive thrust is supplied by a 25 hp Sachs SA 360 2 cyl engine driving a 6 ft 11 in (2·10

m) diameter wooden two-bladed propeller.

CONTROLS: Craft heading controlled by turning forward pontoons and air rudder simultaneously.

HULL: Frame and cabin built in light aluminium. Ski/pontoons in ABS-plastic and filled with polyurethane foam plastic for buoyancy.

DIMENSIONS:
Length overall	19 ft 0½ in (5·8 m)
Beam	9 ft 10 in (3 m)
Beam with skirt and pontoons removed for transport	8 ft 2½ in (2·5 m)

WEIGHTS:
Gross weight	2,205 lb (1,000 kg)

FRANCE

BERTIN & CIE

OFFICE AND WORKS:
 BP No. 3, 78370 Plaisir, France
TELEPHONE:
 462.25.00
Telex: Aviatom 692471 F
DIRECTORS:
 Jean Bertin, President Director General
 Benjamin Salmon, Director General
 Michel Perineau, Director General
 Société Bertin & Cie has been engaged in developing the Bertin principle of separately

fed multiple plenum chambers surrounded by flexible skirts since 1956. A research and design organisation, the company employs a staff of more than 500, mainly scientists and design engineers who are involved in many areas of industrial research, including air cushion techniques and applications.

Société de l'Aérotrain is responsible for the construction and development of Bertin tracked air cushion vehicles (Aérotrain) and the SEDAM is responsible for developing the

Naviplane and Terraplane vehicles. Designs based upon the Bertin technique are described under the entries for these two companies in this volume.

The Bertin principle for air cushions has also led to numerous applications in the area of industrial handling and aeronautics. These applications, developed by Bertin, are described in the sections devoted to Air Cushion Applicators, Conveyors and Pallets; and Air Cushion Landing Systems.

The company's designers are also under-taking studies in the field of long-range, transocean marine vehicles combining the features of freightplanes and wing-in-ground-effect machines. Preliminary details of the Bertin Cygn concept are given below:

CYGNE PROJECT

Studies conducted by Bertin designers for a number of years have led to the design of a new form of low-flying, transoceanic freighter which will combine the speed of a freight plane with the cargo space and low operating costs of a conventional ship.

The project involves two machines, Cygne 10 and Cygne 14, of 1,000 and 1,400 tonnes all-up weight, and gross payloads of 550 tonnes and 867 tonnes, respectively. They will be capable of operating at any height from zero level up to 10,000 ft at a speed of 200 knots. Much of their journey would be completed while operating in ground effect. They would complete Atlantic crossings in about 20 hours.

Landing or alighting on water becomes economically feasible with this type of machine, and since refuelling in mid-route is possible, they could totally revise the economics of airfreighting by reversing the payload/fuel ratio. Thus freight aircraft, in the opinion of the Bertin design team, would no longer be flying tankers but would become freighters in the full sense of the word, with payload rather than fuel becoming preponderant.

One of the limits on the tonnage increase for conventional aircraft is caused by the limitations of the wheeled undercarriage. The Bertin designs would overcome this by the use of an air-cushion landing system, which would have the additional advantage of permitting these machines to operate from land or water. The Bertin philosophy has been to build the aircraft around the idea of a giant truck, moderate in speed, but still ten times faster than a ship. For this reason, and also because of the relatively limited output of the turbojets at the present time, it seemed essential to return to pro-pellers.

Each craft will have either eight or twelve propeller turbines, some mounted forward above the mainplane and the remainder

Above: The Bertin Cygne 14, a project for a combined aircraft, wing-in-ground-effect freight plane with an all-up weight of 1,400 tonnes. Cruising speed would be 200 knots and the payload 867 tonnes. *Below:* Based on an alternative configuration, the Cygne 10 is a flying-wing with an all-up weight of 1,000 tonnes. Due to the limited output of today's gas-turbines, multiple engines will be installed in the manner of the pre-war Do.X

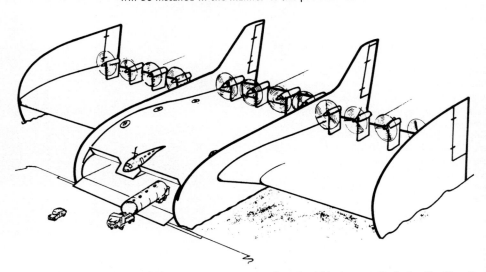

above an aerofoil-shaped hull.

Bertin compares the use of multiple engines with the formula employed by many large seaplanes and flying boats in the late 'twenties and early 'thirties, particularly the Dornier Do. X, which several times, carried remark-ably high payloads over long ranges while flying in its ground cushion.

CLUB FRANCAIS DES AEROGLISSEURS

HEAD OFFICE AND WORKS:
85 Rue Republique, 92150 Suresnes, France
WORKS:
41 and 43 Rue Aristid Briande, 95130 Meung sur Loire, France
OFFICERS:
Jacques Beaudequin, Director
Gabriel Vernier, Chief Designer

M. Jacques Beaudequin, President of the Club Francais des Aeroglisseurs has designed a number of successful lightweight amphib-ious ACVs, including the Moise III and the Skimmercraft, described in the 1971-72 edition.

His latest design is the Motoglisseur V Beach, preliminary details of which are given below.

MOTOGLISSEUR V BEACH

Derived from the earlier Skimmercraft, the V Beach is a lightweight amphibious two-seater with an inflatable catamaran hull.

Club Francais des Aeroglisseurs is to build this new amphibious two-seater in series. The pro-duction model will be powered by two Citroen engines and have a top speed of 62 mph (100 km/h)

LIFT AND PROPULSION: Cushion lift is supplied by a 22 hp 425 cc Citroen air-cooled 4-stroke driving a 24.4 in (620 mm) Multiwing fan.

Propulsive thrust is provided by an adapted Citroen AMI 8 602 cc 4-stroke driving a 4 ft 7⅛ in (1.40 m) diameter four-bladed Merville propeller via a reduction and reverse gearbox.

CONTROLS: Craft direction is controlled by twin aerodynamic rudders aft and operated by a steering wheel. Elevators operating in the propeller slipstream provide trim.

HULL: Basic structural member is the central load carrying deck on which the lift and propulsion units are mounted. The inflatable hull is of catamaran configuration and features flexible bow and stern skirts.

The two inflatable hulls are in polyester coated with neoprene and hypalon.
ACCOMMODATION: Open cockpit for three side-by-side with individual seats.

DIMENSIONS:

Length overall	21 ft 0 in (6.40 m)
Beam overall	9 ft 4¼ in (2.85 m)
Height	5 ft 11 in (1.80 m)

WEIGHTS:

Loaded weight	926 lb (420 kg)
Payload	529 lb (240 kg)

PERFORMANCE:

Max speed	62 mph (100 km/h)
Range	124 miles (200 km)
Turning radius	82 ft at 37 mph (25 m at 60 km h)

GEORGES HENNEBUTTE
Societe d'Exploitation et de Developpement des Brevets Georges Hennebutte

HEAD OFFICE:
43 Avenue Foch 64200, Biarritz
WORKS:
23 Impasse Labordotte, Biarritz
TELEPHONE:
24.22.40
SENIOR DIRECTOR:
M. Ellia
CHIEF EXECUTIVE.
G. Hennebutte

Ets G. Hennebutte was founded in 1955 to design and build inflatable dinghies. Its Espadon series of sports craft is used extensively by French lifeguard patrols and the French Navy.

Development of the Espadon to meet a range of special requirements led to the construction of a number of experimental craft, including one equipped with foils, one with hydroskis and a third with an inflatable parasol delta wing for aerodynamic lift.

The success of the latter has resulted in the adaptation of a standard Espadon 542 dinghy by adding a pair of wings, one of which is of half-venturi configuration, and air propulsion.

The wings have been designed by M. Clement, President of the Basque Flying Club, and the prototype, a single-seater, was due to begin tests during the summer of 1975. Construction of two and four-seat prototypes, were due to start as soon as the trials of the first machine were completed.

The company hopes to start production of the single-seater by the end of 1975, and the four-seater by mid-1976

FLYING BOAT No. 1
This is the first of a new series of lightweight ram-wings based on the Espadon series of inflatable hulls built by Ets. Georges Hennebutte. The wings comprise a variable-incidence lifting surface forward, and a fixed, half-venturi, U-channel wing aft.

Features of the craft are shown in the accompanying three-view.

The company's principal objective is the development of a small, high-speed marine craft for offshore and inter-island travel, able to match the average family car in price and cruising speed.
PROPULSION: Motive power is provided by a 32 hp automotive engine driving a two-

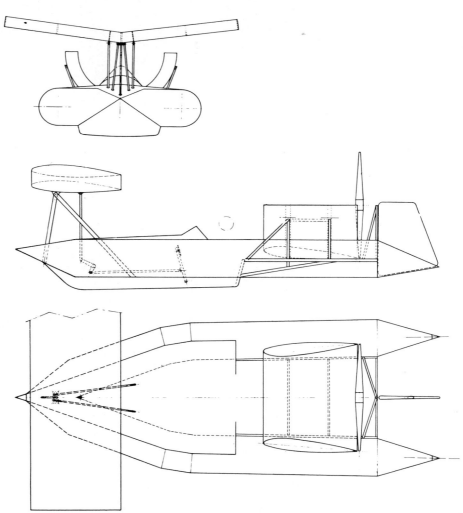

General arrangement of the Hennebutte Flying Boat No. 1, ram-wing ACV research vehicle. Features include a variable-incidence wing forward and a channel-flow wing aft. Thrust is supplied by a 32 hp engine driving a two-bladed propeller aft. Two- and four-seat versions are planned

bladed propeller. The two-seat model will have a 60 hp engine and the four-seater, will have an 82 hp car engine driving twin propellers.
CONTROLS: Craft heading is controlled by a combined aerodynamic and water rudder aft. Incidence of the forward wing is varied by fore and aft movement of the control column.
HULL: Rigid central hull frame in polyester with inflatable nylon-coated neoprene outer sections based on those of the Espadon 542.

Struts are provided to support the forward parasol wing, and a special cradle is fitted aft for the propulsion engine.

ACCOMMODATION: Open cockpit for driver only.
DIMENSIONS:

Length overall	17 ft 9½ in (5.42 m)
Beam overall	6 ft 10⅛ in (2.10 m)

PERFORMANCE:
Estimated cruising altitude
9 ft 10 in - 16 ft 5 in (3-5 m)

Z. O. ORLEY
ADDRESS:
21 Rue Mademoiselle, 75 Paris 15ème
TELEPHONE:
828-2949

Mr. Z. O. Orley and Mr. Ivan Labat have designed a range of lightweight recreational craft employing the glider-craft air cushion system invented by Mr. Orley. The object of the system is to reduce the loss of cushion air by fully skirted vehicles when crossing uneven surfaces.

Beneath the hard structure of the glider craft is an air cushion chamber in rubberised fabric, the base of which is divided into a number of small cell compartments.

Each cell is equipped at the lower end with a perforated shutter, pivoted around a shaft across the cell bay, and linked with a lid which fits tightly into the aperture of an air-supply duct.

A short surface sensor protruding beneath each shutter is designed to open up the delivery of cushion air fully whenever the cell encounters an obstacle rising above the general plane of the reaction surface, and reduce cushion air delivery when crossing a hollow.

A design study is being undertaken for a small commercial craft for operations in South America to carry 12 passengers and freight.

Mr Orley and his partner will build to order commercial and military prototypes employing his system for use over arctic and tropical terrain. Illustrations of a dynamic model incorporating the glider-craft air cushion system appears in JSS 1973-74 and earlier editions.

SEDAM
SOCIETE D'ETUDES ET DE DEVELOPPEMENT DES AEROGLISSEURS MARINS, TERRESTRES ET AMPHIBIES

HEAD OFFICE:
  80 Avenue de la Grande Armée, 75 Paris 17eme
TELEPHONE:
  380-17-69
TELEX:
  29-124 Paris
OFFICERS:
  Bernard Guillain, President Director General
  Benjamin Salmon, Director General
  Paul Guienne, Director Technique
  Admiral J. R. Evenou, Conseil de Direction

SEDAM was incorporated on July 9th 1965, to study, develop and test the Naviplane series of amphibious ACVs based on principles conceived by Bertin & Cie. In April 1968, the company was vested with similar responsibilities for the Terraplane wheeled ACVs based on identical principles. The company holds the exclusive world licence for Bertin patents involving both the Naviplane and Terraplane series.

In 1965, the 5-ton Naviplane BC 8 was completed, after which SEDAM built several small research craft, including the N 101, a quarter-scale manned research model of the 27-ton 90-passenger N 300. Two N 300s were completed in the winter of 1967/68 and operated along the Cote d'Azur during the summer of 1969. One has since been operated by the Department of Gironde as a passenger/car ferry across the Gironde estuary and is available for charter operation.

Following its reorganisation in late 1972, the company has been concentrating on four main objectives: the final design, construction and marketing of the 240t N 500 Naviplane series; incorporation of improvements on the N 300; the development and construction of a new Terraplane and the introduction of a series of air cushion barges. Details of the latter are to be found in this edition in the section devoted to ACV Trailers and Heavy Lift Systems.

Two firm orders have been received for the N 500 from SNCF, who will operate the first two craft across the English Channel on the route Boulogne-Dover. The craft, which will be assembled in a new plant at Pauillac, on the Gironde estuary near Bordeaux, are due to enter service in 1977. SEDAM is responsible for all design studies (lift, stability, manoeuvrability etc) and for the trials. It will also undertake the assembly of the craft. Major sub-contracts have been let to Lorient Dockyard (main hull structure) and UTA at Le Bourget (tail unit.) Options on two more craft are held by Compagnie Générale Transmediterranée

The aim of the new N 300 programme is to design a production model which will incorporate various improvements felt necessary in the light of the operations conducted by

Naviplane N 102C 14 seat ferry or light utility craft, powered by a single 700 hp Astazou XIV gas turbine. Pitch trim is provided by a variable incidence elevator mounted on the fin

N102L with revised planform

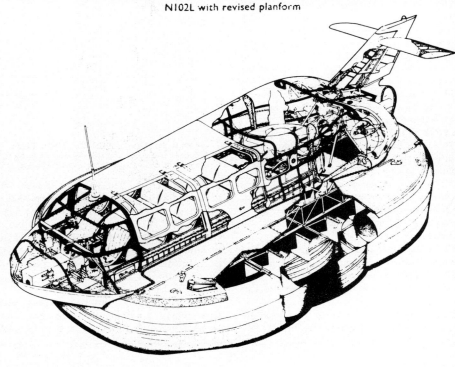

Cutaway of the N102L showing internal arrangements

the two prototypes since 1969. Modification will be introduced in the interests of both economy and ease of production.

A completely new Terraplane, based on the T3S, was completed in 1973. A combined ACV and wheeled vehicle, it is designed for use in under-developed territory, regardless of season or state of the soil. The primary market is French-speaking Black Africa.

In September 1972, Sedam and Fiat SpA. Turin, signed an agreement under which Fiat received exclusive rights for the manufacture in Italy of Naviplane vehicles employing patents evolved by Bertin et Cie and Sedam. Within the agreement is the right to market these craft in Italy, the Soviet Union, Poland, Yugoslavia, Egypt and other countries in the Near East, Africa and South America.

The company is also undertaking feasibility studies for surface effect warships of up to 4,000 tons for the French Navy.

In July 1972, in response to an E.E.C. request, Sedam completed a study for a 2,000 metric ton mixed-traffic sidewall vessel propelled by waterjets. Designed for fast ferry services between the main European and Mediterranean ports, the vessel would carry 2,000 passengers and up to 500 cars at a cruising speed of 50 knots.

NAVIPLANE N 102C

A 13-14 seat, single engine ACV employing a plenum chamber enclosed by a labyrinth skirt developed from Bertin's patents, the Naviplane 102C is designed for a wide range of civil and military applications, including customs and police patrol, water-taxi, light cargo and ambulance work, military reconnaissance and dual-control training for the commanders of large Naviplanes.

Two prototypes were completed during 1959 and the first N 102C production craft was launched in 1970. In June 1970 the craft was flown to Kinshasa, in the Congo, for trials and demonstrations. Ten N 102s have since been built, including one 'stretched' variant, the Naviplane N 102L, with its length increased from 33 ft 6 in (10·20 m) to 35 ft 9 in (10·90 m). Two are being employed by the Departments of Montpellier and Perpignan, two have been supplied to the French Navy, one has been sold to Fiat, two are being used by Sedam for research, and the remaining craft are for sale.

LIFT AND PROPULSION: A single 700 hp Turboméca Astazou XIV or 565 hp Astazou XI shaft turbine powers the integrated lift propulsion system. Mounted at the rear of the cabin, the engine drives a 5 ft 3 in (1·60 m) variable-pitch axial lift fan and two five-bladed variable and reversible pitch shrouded propellers for propulsion.

CONTROL: Directional control at cruising speed and above is maintained by an aerodynamic rudder hinged to the rear of the tail fin and differential pitch of the two propellers. At low speeds, steering is assisted by pneumatically-operated side thrust ports. Pitch trim at cruising speed is controlled by a manually operated variable-incidence elevator mounted on the fin.

HULL: The basic hull structure comprises a doughnut-shaped inflated buoyancy chamber in neoprene nylon fabric, surrounding a corrosion resistant light alloy sandwich platform. The buoyancy chamber is

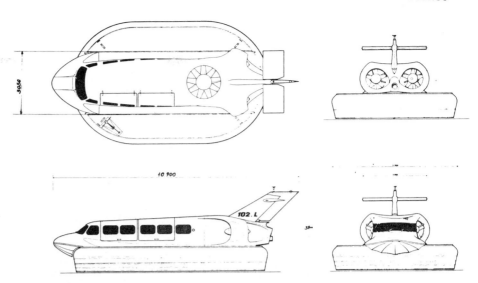

"Stretched" version of the N102—the model L—with revised planform

The N.300 Naviplane, a 27-ton multi-purpose hoverferry, one of which is operated by the Bordeaux Port Authority

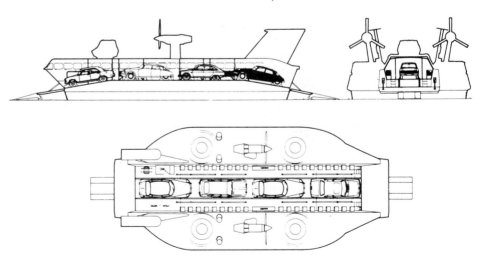

Mixed ferry version of the N 300, accommodating thirty-eight passengers and four cars

divided into twelve watertight compartments for safety. Reserve buoyancy is in excess of 200%. The main components of the superstructure—the shaped bow, cockpit, passenger/freight cabin, engine housing, fan and propeller ducts—are in moulded glass reinforced plastics. The side-

wings can be removed to facilitate transport by road, rail or air.

The cabin seats a crew of either one or two and either thirteen or twelve passengers. There are two bucket seats forward and three bench-type seats behind accommodating three or four passengers each, according to

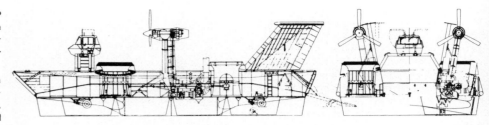

traffic requirements.   Access is through two wide gull-wing doors.   The central section of the cabin superstructure can be quickly removed to provide a freight deck for pallets, containers or military equipment.

OVERLAND USE: Provision is made on the underside of the main hull structure for the attachment of a three-legged, retractable undercarriage.   The front wheel is steered hydraulically to provide precise directional control.   Lowering of the undercarriage facilitates repairs to the hull underside and skirt maintenance.   The arrangement also allows an extra 1 ton payload to be carried over land.   Speed over relatively smooth ground, with undercarriage lowered, is close to 40 mph (64·37 km/h).

DIMENSIONS, EXTERNAL (N 102C):

Length overall	33 ft 5⅞ in (10·20 m)
Beam	25 ft 3⅛ in (7·70 m)
Height overall on landing pads	
	13 ft 1½ in (4·00 m)
Skirt depth	2 ft 7½ in (0·80 m)

DIMENSIONS, INTERNAL:

Cabin length	11 ft 9¾ in (3·60 m)
Max width	7 ft 3 in (2·20 m)
Size of gull-wing doors, one each side:	
Height	2 ft 9½ in (0·85 m)
Width	6 ft 2 in (1·90 m)

WEIGHTS:

Empty weight	6,600 lb (3,200 kg)
Normal gross weight	8,800 lb (4,200 kg)
Normal payload	2,200 lb (1,000 kg)
Fuel load	1,100 lb (600 l)
Normal load over water	
	2-2,400 lb (900-1,100 kg)
over land	4,200-4,600 lb (1,900-2,100 kg)

PERFORMANCE: (Normal all-up weight):

Max speed, max power, over calm water	
	54 knots
Max speed, max continuous power	55 knots
Cruising speed (IAS) in 2 ft 6 in (0·75 m)	
waves	40-45 knots

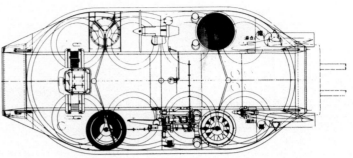

Internal arrangements of the N300. The drawings show the craft in open deck freighter configuration. The all-passenger version seats 90 in a lightweight cabin structure which is attached to the freight deck

Model of the 240 tonne SEDAM N.500 double deck, mixed-traffic ferry, two of which have been ordered by SNCF for services across the English Channel, starting in 1977.   Each craft will carry up to 400 passengers and 45 medium-size cars, or 280 passengers, 10 cars and 5 coaches

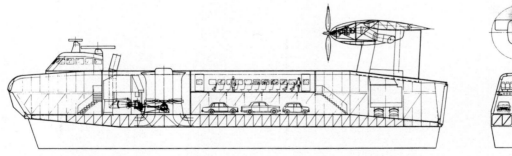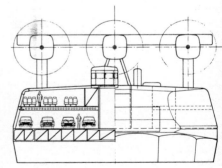

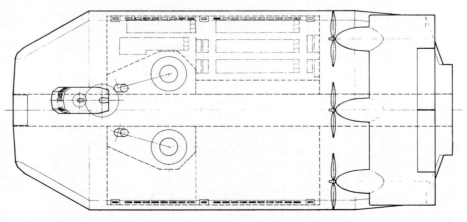

General arrangement of the N.500, which will be powered by five 3,200 hp Avco Lycoming TF 40 marinised gas-turbines, two for lift and three for propulsion

Endurance (max continuous power)
	3-4 hours
Max gradient	12-18%
Acceptable wave height	3 ft (1 m)

DIMENSIONS, EXTERNAL (N 102L):
Length overall	35 ft 9 in (10·90 m)
Beam overall, on cushion	19ft 4¼ in (5·90m)
Beam overall, hardstructure	
	10 ft 0 in (3·05 m)
Height overall, on cushion	
	12 ft 9½ in (3·90 m)

NAVIPLANE N 300

A 27-ton multi-purpose transport for amphibious operation, the N 300 was the first full-scale vehicle in the Naviplane series designed for commercial use.

The first two N 300s were built at Biarritz at the Breguet factory and started tethered hovering and preliminary handling trials in December 1967. Afterwards they were transported by sea to the Sedam test centre at l'Etang de Berre. In September 1968 N 300-01 and -02 went to Nice for a series of experimental services and tests conducted by the French armed services.

During the summer of 1970 the two craft operated a scheduled passenger service along the Cote d'Azur. One N 300 was later acquired by the Gironde Department for the operation of a passenger/car ferry service across the Gironde estuary between Blaye and Lamarque. The craft, which was operated by the Bordeaux Port Authority

carried up to four cars and thirty-five passengers per crossing. It operated thirty crossings per day, seven days a week.

The passenger version seats 90 in a lightweight cabin structure above the open deck. Possible military uses of the N 300 include coastal patrol, salvage, rescue, landing craft, assault craft and logistic supply vehicle.

A production model is under development one variant of which has its wheelhouse built onto the cabin superstructure forward instead of being located on a bridge structure spanning the foredeck.

LIFT AND PROPULSION: Motive power is provided by two Turboméca Turmo IIIN3 gas turbines located in separate engine rooms, port and starboard and drawing filtered air from plenum compartments behind the forward fan ducts. Each engine is coupled via a main gearbox located directly beneath each propeller pylon to a 3-bladed Ratier-Figeac 11 ft 10 in (3·60 m) diameter, variable and reversible pitch propeller and via a secondary gearbox to a two 11-blade 6 ft 3 in (1·90 m) diameter axial lift fans. The main gearboxes are cross-connected by a shaft so that in the event of one engine failing or malfunctioning the four fans and two propellers can all be driven by the remaining engine. The fans deliver air to eight individual Bertin skirts, each 6 ft 7 in (2 m) deep and with a hemline diameter of 10 ft 2 in (3·09 m). These are in turn surrounded by a single

wrap-round skirt.

CONTROLS: The wheelhouse, which seats a captain and navigator, is located above a bridge spanning the foredeck to provide a 360° view. The main driving controls and the instrumentation are positioned in front of the port seat.

The wheel of a control column varies the pitch of the two propellers differentially and fore and aft movement of the column alters pitch collectively.

HULL: The hull is a raft-like structure built in marine corrosion resistant aluminium alloys. Main buoyancy compartments are beneath the freight deck. Fans and machinery are installed in separate structures on either side of the freight/passenger deck, port and starboard.

ACCOMMODATION: Aircraft-type seats are provided for 100-120 passengers. Baggage areas are provided in the centre of the passenger saloon, port and starboard, and at the rear of the saloon where there is also a dinghy stowage area. Access to the passenger compartment is by steps built into the bow and stern ramp/doors.

DIMENSIONS:
Length overall	78 ft 9 in (24 m)
Beam	34 ft 5 in (10·5 m)
Height overall	24 ft 7 in (7·5 m)
Skirt depth	6 ft 7 in (2·0 m)
Cabin floor area	861 sq ft (80 m²)
Cushion area	1,722 sq ft (160 m²)

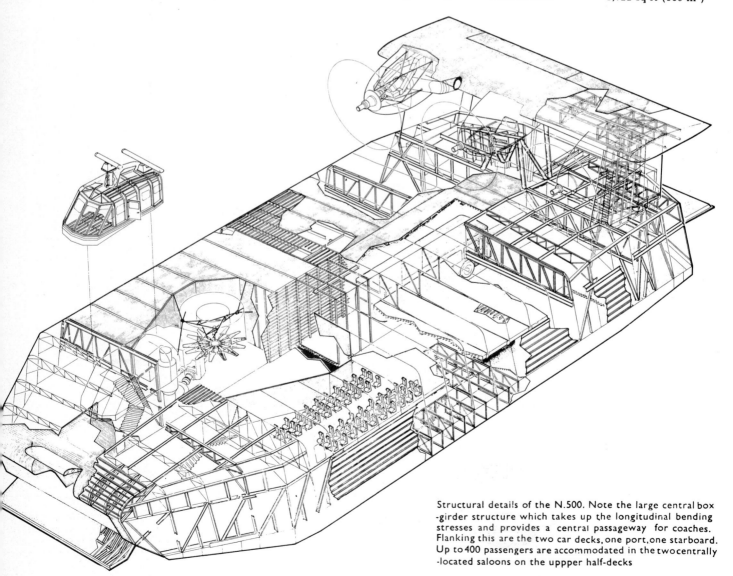

Structural details of the N.500. Note the large central box-girder structure which takes up the longitudinal bending stresses and provides a central passageway for coaches. Flanking this are the two car decks, one port, one starboard. Up to 400 passengers are accommodated in the two centrally-located saloons on the upper half-decks

WEIGHTS:

Basic weight	14 tons
Passenger version	100-120 passengers
Freight version	13 ton
Normal all-up weight	27 tons

PERFORMANCE:

Max speed	57/62 knots
Cruising speed	44/50 knots
Endurance	3 hours

NAVIPLANE N500

Two firm orders have been placed for the N500, a 240-tonne, mixed-traffic hoverferry with a payload capacity of 85 tonnes and a maximum speed of 70 knots (130 km/h) in calm conditions. The first two craft will be built for SNCF (French National Railways) which will employ them on a service across the English Channel, between Boulogne and Dover, starting in 1977.

The French government is contributing half the development and production costs of the first two craft, a total of Fr. 74 million.

An option on two further craft is held by Compagnie Générale Transmediterrancé, which plans to operate a service between Nice and Corsica. Interest in the N500 is also being shown by Hoverlloyd.

Assembly of the first N500 is due to start at Pauillac, near Bordeaux, on the Gironde estuary, at the end of 1975. The assembly shop, currently nearing completion, is of sufficient size to permit the construction of up to four craft a year. The trials will also be conducted from the base at Pauillac, which will have a staff of 80-100. The first craft is due to be completed by mid-1976.

LIFT AND PROPULSION: Motive power is supplied by five 3,200 hp Avco Lycoming TF 40 marinised gas-turbines, two for lift and three for propulsion. Each lift engine drives via a reduction system and bevel gear a 13 ft 1½ in (4 m) diameter, 13-bladed, axial-flow fan of laminate construction. The fans, built by Ratier-Forest, are based on experience gained with the N300 series, and the blades can be adjusted, when stopped, to suit flight conditions. Revolution speed is 900 rpm and the tip speed is limited to 200 m/s to avoid excessive noise. Each fan weighs 1,764 lbs (800 kg) and their rated input power is 2,150 kW.

Fan air intakes are located immediately aft of the wheelhouse, one each side of the longitudinal centreline. Cushion air is drawn into two wells reaching down through the passenger and car decks, into a plenum beneath the latter, from which it is fed to the multiple skirts. The flow of air to each group of skirts is controlled by air valves.

Both fans deliver air to a common plenum and in the event of either having to be shut down, the remaining unit has sufficient capacity to enable the craft to take-off and operate in waves up to 8 ft 3 in (2·5 m) high.

Lift and propulsion systems are totally independent of each other in order to reduce gearing to a minimum. The three propulsion engines, each contained in a separate nacelle, are mounted on a horizontal stabiliser aft, where each TF40 drives a 20 ft 8 in (6·3 m) diameter, 4-bladed variable- and reversible-pitch propeller at 620 rpm. The propellers, designed and built by Hawker-Siddeley

Dynamics, are similar to those used on the BH.7. The blades consist of a duralumin spar, forged and machine-finished, and covered with a glass fibre and epoxy resin shell to NACA Series 16 and 64 modified profiles. Tractive power is 15 t at zero speed and 11·5 t at 36 m/s.

The horizontal stabiliser is designed to counteract pitching during take-off and create sufficient lift to compensate the tail-load moment induced by the aerodynamic forces acting on the craft.

The craft can take-off and operate with one propulsion unit out of action in waves 8 ft 3 in (2·5 m) high.

CONTROLS: Craft directional control is provided by pedal-operated aerodynamic rudders and differential propeller pitch. In the event of either outboard propeller being stopped, yawing moment is compensated by the use of rudders. Pitch control is provided by elevators on the horizontal stabiliser, and fuel is transferred between forward and aft tanks to adjust fore and aft static trim.

HULL: Modular structure built in simple light alloy units. The main platform structure is made up of welded longitudinal and transverse girder boxes which also form buoyancy chambers. The main longitudinal box girder is the central lane for coaches and heavy vehicles. Beneath each car deck is a structure made up by welded trellis-type lateral beams. The main hull platform supports the box-like coach compartment on the longitudinal centreline and the two car decks, one each side of the coach deck.

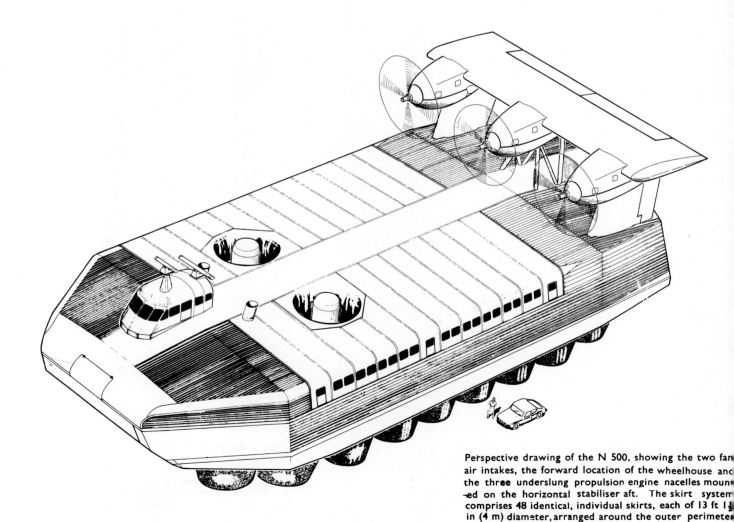

Perspective drawing of the N 500, showing the two fan air intakes, the forward location of the wheelhouse and the three underslung propulsion engine nacelles mount-ed on the horizontal stabiliser aft. The skirt system comprises 48 identical, individual skirts, each of 13 ft 1½ in (4 m) diameter, arranged around the outer perimeter of the hull base in a continuous double ring

n land, off-cushion, the craft rests on small
lindrical inflated pads. Lifting jacks are
nployed to raise the craft off the ground for
spection and servicing. Both the forward
ld aft load door/ramps can accommodate
ree vehicles abreast for loading and off-
ading.

KIRTS: Arrangement based on that
lopted for the N300. Planform of the
500's hull is a rectangle, elongated at
e bow by a semicircle. The skirt system
mprises 48 identical skirts, each of 13 ft
in (4 m) diameter, arranged around the
ter perimeter of the hull base in a contin-
us double ring. The skirts are in Tergal
erylene) covered with synthetic rubber.
r is fed to the skirts in groups, giving a
byrinth effect. It is also fed into the
ntral cushion area direct.

CCOMMODATION: In the mixed-traffic
rsion, passengers are accommodated in
o saloons on two upper half-decks on either
le of the box structure containing the
ach passageway. The arrangement is
imed to give passengers greater safety,
ice they are on a different level from the
hicles; as well as greater comfort as their
cation is in the centre of the craft. Since
eir seats are sited above the spray they will
so have a better view. The payload of 85
nnes would comprise 400 passengers and
medium-size cars, or 280 passengers, 10
rs and 5 coaches. The wheelhouse, located
ove the forward end of the longitudinal
ach box, accommodates a crew of three—
ptain, co-pilot and radio operator/nav-
ator. Access is via a companionway at
e base of the starboard lift engine com-
rtment and a vertical ladder from the
ssenger saloon.

STEMS, ELECTRICAL: Electrical supply
provided by two turbo-alternators, each
mprising a Deutz T216 gas-turbine driving
Auxilec 1602 alternator.

AVIGATION: Two Decca radars, one 10
, one 3 cm plus one gyro and one magnetic
mpass.

MENSIONS, EXTERNAL:
Length overall   164 ft 1 in (50 m)
Beam overall   75 ft 1½ in (23 m)
Height overall, on cushion   55 ft 9 in (17 m)
Cushion length   147 ft 8 in (45 m)
Cushion beam   72 ft 2 in (22 m)

The SEDAM MN.2 manned, 1:7 dynamic model of the N.500, undergoing tests on the Berre flats.
The propellers and fans are driven by piston engines. This particular model has been used chiefly
for gathering data on handling and manoeuvrability

DIMENSIONS, INTERNAL:
Cargo deck length, inboard
                        150 ft 11 in (46 m)
Cargo deck width, inboard
                        72 ft 2 in (22 m)
Cargo deck area   10,332 ft² (960 m²)
WEIGHTS:
Total loaded weight   240 tonnes
PERFORMANCE:
Max speed, calm water   70 knots
Cruising speed, 1·50 m waves   58 knots
Cruising speed, 2·50 m waves   48 knots
Endurance over 2·5 m waves   5 hours
Max wave height   13 ft 2 in (4 m)

MN.2 RESEARCH CRAFT

While conducting design studies for the
N500, SEDAM made extensive use of data
gathered from models. Wind tunnel tests
were undertaken at the Eiffel research centre
with a 1 : 50 scale model, and a 1 : 20 model
was tested at the Carèsnes tank to measure
aerodynamic and hydrodynamic resistance.
Two manned, dynamic research craft
employed were the MN.1 and the MN.2.
The former, a 1 : 9 scale, 19 ft 8 in (6 m) long
model was designed for testing the fans and
multiple skirt system, while the latter was

built for handling and manoeuvrability trials.
In addition, a number of tests were conducted with scale model skirts, singly and
in groups.

2,000 TON NAVIPLANE

A study for a 2,000-ton sidewall-type
Naviplane was completed for the European
Economic Community in July 1972.

The project called for a cost assessment
of a high speed vessel capable of providing
mixed-traffic ferry services between the main
European and Mediterranean ports.

Sedam's proposal covers a vessel capable
of carrying 2,000 passengers and 500 cars.
Four gas-turbine driven waterjets, two in
each sidewall, aft, would give the craft a
cruising speed of 50 knots. The lift system
would comprise two 6,250 hp gas-turbines,
each driving two 13 ft 1 in (4m) diameter,
contrarotating axial fans.
DIMENSIONS:
Length overall   328 ft 1 in (100 m)
Beam overall   131 ft 3 in (40 m)
Height on cushion   50 ft 10 in (15·50 m)
Height, vehicle compartment
                       18 ft 0 in (5·50 m)
Height, passenger cabin   7 ft 3 in (2·20 m)

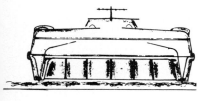

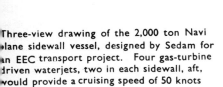

Three-view drawing of the 2,000 ton Navi
plane sidewall vessel, designed by Sedam for
an EEC transport project. Four gas-turbine
driven waterjets, two in each sidewall, aft,
would provide a cruising speed of 50 knots

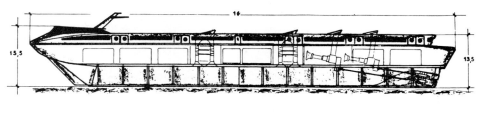

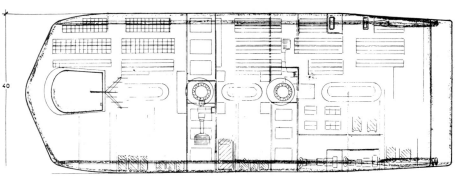

WEIGHTS:

Empty weight	1,010 metric tons
Payload	700 metric tons
Gross weight	2,000 metric tons

PERFORMANCE:

Maximum continuous cruising speed	50 knots
Endurance	10 hours, plus 10% reserve
Gross weight	382,000 lb (174 tonnes)

TERRAPLANE T3S

The Terraplane T3S is a combined ground effect machine and wheeled vehicle, driven like a car or truck, but with the essential difference that it can be run at speeds up to 31 mph (50 km/h) over uneven ground, water or liquid mud.

It is designed for use over unprepared land in underdeveloped territories regardless of the season or the state of the soil. A hydraulic system allows selection of weight transference to the road wheels ranging from 20-50% of the total weight of the ground surface and gradient.

On roads the entire weight can be supported by the wheels and the vehicle is then operated in a similar way to the traditional lorry. The air cushion only can be employed when crossing rivers and when manoeuvring the craft in a confined space.

LIFT AND PROPULSION: The front wheels are fitted with heavy duty tyres and are steered by a normal steering wheel from the driver's cab.

Motive power for the lift/propulsion system is provided by an adapted 250 hp Chevrolet V8 petrol engine. This drives an axial fan for lift and a hydrostatic transmission circuit which provides either two-

The Terraplane T3S, combined ground effect machine and wheeled vehicle for off-the-road transport in underdeveloped areas

or four-wheel drive. Cushion air is ducted into seven individual neoprene-coated tergal skirts, six of which are surrounded by a lightweight wrap-round skirt. Transmission to the four wheels is via an engine-mounted pump circulating fluid through lines to four hydraulic motors which drive the wheels.

Special paddle vanes which can be attached to the wheels allow travel over water at speeds up to 4·35 mph (7 km/h).

WEIGHTS:

Weight empty	2 tons
Weight loaded	3·6 ton

DIMENSIONS:

Length	20 ft 8 in (6·3 m
Width	8 ft 2¼ in (2·5 m

PERFORMANCE:

Speed over flat surfaces	43·5 mph (70 km/h
Speed over uneven ground	31 mph (50 km/h
Speed over water	4·35 mph (7 km/h
Endurance	3 hours
Gradient capability	8-20 %
Vertical obstacle clearance	1 ft 4 in (0·40 m

GERMAN FEDERAL REPUBLIC

RHEIN-FLUGZEUGBAU GmbH

(Subsidiary of VFW-Fokker GmbH)

HEAD OFFICE AND MAIN WORKS:
405 Mönchengladbach, Flugplatz, Postfach 408

TELEPHONE:
02161/62031

TELEX:
08/52506

EXECUTIVE DIRECTORS:
Dipl-Volkswirt Wolfgang Kutsher
Dipl-Ing Alfred Schneider

TECHNICAL AND SCIENTIFIC MANAGER, X-113 AM AEROFOIL PROJECT:
Dr A. M. Lippisch FRAeS

HEAD OF TESTS:
Ing. D. Schönfelder

RFB is engaged in the development and construction of airframe structural components, an emphasis being placed on wings fabricated entirely in glass fibre reinforced plastics. Research and design activities include studies for the Federal German Government, which is also providing assistance for the development of the X-113 Am Aerofoil boat.

The company is currently building a 6-seat version of the Aerofoil Boat which will have a range in excess of 621 miles (1,000 km) when operating within the ground effect envelope. First flight of the new craft, which is designated X-114, is scheduled for May 1976.

Dr Alexander Lippisch's X-113 Am Aerofoil boat during demonstrations in the Waser estuar North Sea. Built by VFW-Rhein-Flugzeugbau, GmbH, this is one of the world's first wi in-ground effect machines capable of full flight. It takes off and begins to skim above its suppo ing surface at 31 mph (50 km/h)

RFB (LIPPISCH) X-113 Am AEROFOIL BOAT

The Aerofoil Boat was conceived in the United States by Dr A. M. Lippisch. The first wing-in-ground-effect machine built to Lippisch designs was the Collins X-112, which was employed by Lippisch to examine the stability problems likely to be encountered in the design of larger machines of this type.

Since 1967 further development of t concept has been undertaken by RF with government backing. The single-se X-113 has been built as a test craft to provi data for the design of larger craft of the sam type.

The X-113 Am underwent its first a worthiness test from Lake Constance October 1970.

During the first series of tests, the cr

emonstrated its operating ability on water
s well as flight capability at very low
ltitudes. These tests were followed in the
autumn of 1971 by a second series of trials
uring which performance measurements
ere taken. A cine camera built into the
ockpit recorded instrument readings and a
amera built into the lateral stabilisers took
ictures of small threads on the upper wing
urface for current flow analysis.

The earlier trials on the Bodensee were
ollowed in November/December 1972 by a
aird series of tests in the North Sea in the
Veser estuary area.

Apart from various performance measure-
ents, the aim of these trials was to invest-
ate the machines' capabilities in roughish
eather conditions. Although the machine
as originally designed only for a brief
eneral demonstration on calm water, the
tention undertook take-offs and landings
a moderate sea.

Remarkably good sea behaviour was
own from the outset. Taking-offs and
ndings in wave heights of about 2 ft 6 in
·75 m) presented no problem. During the
ourse of these tests, flights were made in the
oastal region, and sometimes on the Watten-
eer, in wind forces of up to 25 knots, without
ny uncontrollable flying tendencies being
oserved in low-level flight.

The flight performance measurements gave
gliding angle of 1:30, which cannot be
reatly improved by enlarging the machine.
t is also of interest to note that the relatively
in outer laminate of the GFR wing sand-
ich, with a thickness of 0.4 mm, stood up to
he loads involved in taking off in a roughish
a and also remained watertight throughout
he whole period of trials.

Towards the end of the trials, in order to
duce noise and give the airscrew better
otection from spray, the machine was
nverted to pusher propulsion.

Flight performance could not be invest-
ated because of the weather.

It is now planned to enlarge the machine
to a 2-seater. Trials are due to be under-
ken in 1974.

According to the speed selected, the Aerofoil
oat can perform three functions. At very
w speeds it corresponds to an ordinary
oat; at 9 mph (15 km/h) it operates like a
droplane and starting from about 31 mph
0 km/h) it begins skimming the surface.
will also climb out of ground effect.
uring its first series of tests it was reported
have made several flights of up to 328 ft
00 m).

Operating in ground effect, the craft is
ated by its designers to exceed in effective-
ess any other form of water transport, and
ave power requirements 30% less than that
similar water craft. The craft is
perated at a height above the surface of up
one-half the hull beam (wing span) for
ptimum performance.

The company envisages a range of Aerofoil
raft for a variety of civil and military
urposes, from single-seat runabouts to cargo
ansporters with payloads of up to 10 tons.
s transports they could be employed on
oastal, inter-island and river services.
ilitary variants could be used as assault
aft, FPBs and ASW vessels.

Flight tests, including a series performed
ver rough water in the North Sea near
remmerhaven, have established that 50%

Underside of the X-113 Am, showing the anhedral reversed delta wing which overcomes the
problem of pitch instability during the transition from surface effect to free- flight and back again

Model of the new six-seat Lippisch X-114 Aerofoil Boat. A 200 hp engine drives a ducted fan
designed by Rhein-Flugzeugbau

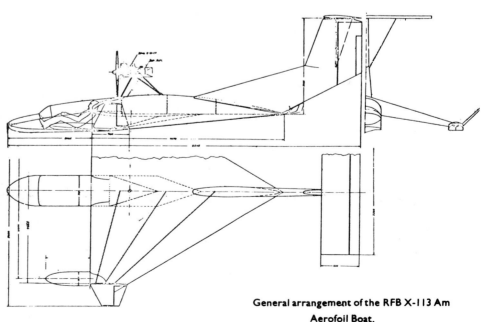

General arrangement of the RFB X-113 Am
Aerofoil Boat.

less power is required in ground effect,
enabling operations in excess of 50-ton-miles
per gallon of fuel at speeds in the 90-180
knot range.

POWER PLANT: Thrust is supplied by a
48 hp (derated to 40 hp) Nelson H63-CP
horizontally-opposed four-cylinder, two-
stroke engine driving a 3 ft 10 in (1·17 m)

diameter 2-bladed wooden propeller.

STRUCTURE: Glassfibre sandwich construction with a core of tubular or foam plastic. Tailplane and rudder are made in cloth-covered wood, and wing floats are in styrofoam. Side walls of the hull are of Conticell sandwich construction. Wing is of sandwich construction with a 0·4 mm covering laminate.

DIMENSIONS, EXTERNAL:

Wing span   19 ft 3¾ in (5·89 m)

Length overall	27 ft 8 in (8·43 m)
Height overall	6 ft 9½ in (2·07 m)

WEIGHTS:

Weight empty	562 lb (255 kg)
Max T-O weight	760 lb (345 kg)

RFB X-114 AEROFOIL BOAT

Evolved from the X-113, this new six-seater has a maximum take-off weight of 2,977 lb (1,350 kg) and is fitted with a retractable wheel undercarriage, enabling it to operate from land or water.

Power is provided by a 200 hp engine driving a specially-designed Rhein-Flugzeugbau ducted fan. Range, with a driver, five passengers and 220 lb (100 kg) of fuel is more than 621 miles (1,000 km). Operational speed is 46-124 mph (75-200 km/h).

The prototype is due to make its first flight in May 1976.

ISRAEL

NATHAN KIRPITZNIKOFF LTD

HEAD OFFICE:

11 David Hamelech Blvd., Tel-Aviv, Israel

TELEPHONE:

265067/249945

Nathan Kirpitznikoff, the Israeli architect and exhibition designer, has been active in the ACV field since 1964. He has built and tested a number of plenum-chambered development craft, including the NX-1 Orale, the NX-2 and N-2 Lady Bird, described in JSS 1971-72 and earlier editions.

More recently his experiments have centered on the overland use of AVCs, employing the Lady Bird 2 hull.

RESEARCH HOVERCRAFT

Preliminary details of this amphibious utility craft were received as this edition went to press. The vehicle is based on the lower hull of the N-2 with a flat deck aft of the lift air intakes, modified for the carriage of freight. Features include a special skirt designed for a 200 hour life span and landing wheels for precise directional control for overland operation.

Research hovercraft based on the hull of the Kirpitznikoff N-2 Lady Bird

The vehicle has logged over 30 hours of operation, mostly over land, but including some water crossings. Maximum speed of the vehicle, under calm conditions, is 54 mph (87 km/h), maximum payload is 3,969 lb (5,800 kg) and the maximum turning radius is 105 ft (32 m).

ITALY

FIAT SpA

HEAD OFFICE:

Direzione Centrale Ricerca e Sviluppo, Corso Giovanni Agnelli 200, Turin, Italy.

TELEPHONE:

33331

TELEX:

Fiat MRFR 21022

OFFICERS:

Dr. Ing. Oscar Montabone

Fiat has been licensed by Sedam, the French ACV company, for the manufacture of Sedam Naviplane vehicles, and has been granted exclusive rights for their sale in Italy, Argentina, Egypt, Yugoslavia, Poland, Turkey, the Soviet Union and other countries.

Fiat's "Direzione Centrale Ricerca Sviluppo", is currently undertaking a research programme in this field.

HOVERCRAFT ITALIANA SRL

HEAD OFFICE:

Via A. Borelli, 5, 00161 Rome, Italy

TELEPHONE:

4956148—5127308

EXECUTIVES:

Captain Tito Bettocchi, Technical Manager
M. Ilo Roberto Bruschina, Production Manager

BT.4-74

This new fibreglass-hulled three-seater, based on the earlier BT-3-72, is about to go into series production. The prototype was completed with the assistance of the Italian Air Force and has been undergoing trials on Lake Bracciano. Captain Bettocchi reports that his latest machine is capable of carrying six people instead of three, as was intended, and that the overall performance is well in excess of expectations.

The craft is the first Italian design hovercraft to be available commercially. The skirt and certain other features are covered in Italian patent 47918A/71. Possible uses include family runabout and patrol craft.

LIFT AND PROPULSION: A 21 hp JLO 295 two-stroke engine located behind

First hovercraft of Italian design to go into production, the BT.4-74 is a fibreglass-hulled 3-seater employing a patented double skirt. The prototype was completed with the assistance of the Italian Air Force and has been undergoing trials on Lake Bracciano. The two vanes outboard of the single rudder are employed as air brakes.

the cockpit and mounted in an open plastic duct drives a 2 ft 1½ in (64·8 cm) fan at 3,200 rpm for cushion lift. Thrust is provided by a 3 ft 6 in (107 cm) diameter wooden 2-bladed propeller driven by a 50 hp JLO LR 760/Z engine mounted aft of the lift fan duct. Production models will be fitted with a 72 hp McCulloch Model 438.

CONTROLS: Twin aerodynamic rudders hinged to the rear of the propeller duct provide directional control. Twin vanes aft for braking,

HULL: Two piece moulded grp structure with upper and lower hulls bolted together at skirt line.

SKIRT: Double "Italian" style skirt of new design, fabricated in 17 oz nylon neoprene and 10 in (25 cm) deep.

ACCOMMODATION: Driver and up to two passengers seated side-by-side in a pressurised cabin.

SYSTEMS, ELECTRICAL: 12 volt battery for starting, navigation lights and headlamps.

DIMENSIONS:

Length overall	17 ft (5·20 m)
Beam	8 ft 6 in (2·60 m)
Height on landing pads	4 ft 9 in (1·45 m)
Height, skirt inflated	5 ft 6 in (1·68 m)

WEIGHTS:

Empty	860 lb (390 kg)
Useful load	460 lb (210 kg)
Gross weight	1,320 lb (600 kg)

PERFORMANCE:

Max speed	41 mph (66 km/h)
Cruising speed	34 mph (55 km/h)
Speed in 1 ft (30 cm) waves and 15 knot wind	20 mph (30 km/h)

Vertical obstacle clearance	10 in (25 cm)
Acceptable wave height	2 ft (0·60 m)
Max gradient	12-18%
Endurance, max cont power	2 hr + 15 min reserve

PRICE AND DELIVERY:

Approx cost, basic craft $12,000, including 10% tax, FOB, Rome, Italy. Delivery time from acceptance of order, 4 months.

FAN-JET 6-SEATER

In June 1974, the company announced that plans were underway for the development of a fan-jet propelled six-seater.

JAPAN

Pastoral single-seat research ACV

ASHIKAGA INSTITUTE OF TECHNOLOGY

ADDRESS:

Mechanical Design Study Group, Institute of Technology, 268 Ohmae cho, Ashikagishi, 26326, Japan

DIRECTORS:

T. Imamura

E. Sakai

S. Suzuku

The Mechanical Design Study Group at the Ashikaga Institute of Technology is conducting an ACV research programme in conjunction with the Aerodynamics Section of the Physical Science Laboratory, Nihon University. It has recently taken over the Pastoral, constructed at Nihon University in 1970, and introduced various modifications. In its new form the craft is some 35% lighter, and has been redesignated Pastoral 2.

PASTORAL 2

This is a light amphibious single-seater employed to gather data for research and development projects. At the time of going to press the modified craft had completed nearly five hours of tests over sand, grass and mud and had attained a speed of 55 mph (98 km/h).

LIFT AND PROPULSION: A single 8 hp Fuji Heavy Industries 2-cycle single-cylinder air-cooled engine installed immediately aft of the cockpit drives a 5-bladed 1 ft 9¼ in (540 mm) diameter axial-flow fan for lift. Propulsion is supplied by a 36 hp Toyota 2U-B 4-cycle, 2-cylinder engine driving a 3 ft 11¼ in (1,200 mm) diameter two-bladed propeller.

CONTROLS: Twin aerodynamic rudders operated by a wheel in the cockpit control craft heading .

HULL: Moulded glassfibre, with inflatable fabric-reinforced neoprene sidebody/skirt.

DIMENSIONS:

Length overall, skirt inflated	13 ft 9¼ in (4·20 m)
Beam overall, skirt inflated	5 ft 11 in (1·80 m)
Height, skirt inflated	5 ft 1 in (1·55 m)

WEIGHTS:

Normal all-up weight	706 lb (320 kg)

PERFORMANCE:

Max speed over land	56 mph (90 km/h)
over water	37 mph (60 km/h)

HOVERMARINE PACIFIC LTD

In July 1975 it was announced that Hovermarine Transport Ltd, the U.K. subsidiary of Hovermarine Corporation, is to begin manufacturing and marketing Hovermarine products in Japan and other nearby areas in the Far East through a new company, Hovermarine Pacific Ltd.

Hovermarine Pacific will be a joint venture by Hovermarine Corporation, Taiyo Fishery Co. Ltd., Sasebo Heavy Industries Ltd. and Fairfield-Maxwell Ltd. Taiyo is the world's biggest fish processing company, with an annual sales revenue in excess of US $2 billion and Sasebo is the world's tenth largest shipbuilder. Fairfield-Maxwell, based in New York, is a private company with extensive interests in shipping.

Initial activities of Hovermarine Pacific will be focused on the marketing of the Hovermarine HM.2, 60-passenger, 35-knot sidewall hoverferry. The company was expecting to receive new orders from the Far East for HM.2s at the time of going to press. These will be met from Hovermarine's existing facilities in Southampton, England and Titusville, Florida. In 1976 HM.2 manufacturing facilities will be established at Sasebo, on the Japanese island of Kyushu. A year later, the Sasebo facilities will be expanded to accommodate production of the 200-seat Hovermarine HM.5.

Hovermarine is licensed by Hovercraft Development Ltd., an agency of the National Research Development Corporation, under various world-wide patents relating to air cushion technology. The license excludes the Japanese market, and therefore Hovermarine products have not previously been available there. Hovermarine Pacific will be licensed directly to engage in this business.

MITSUBISHI HEAVY INDUSTRIES LTD

HEAD OFFICE:

5-1, Marunouchi 2-chome, Chiyoda-ku, Tokyo, Japan

TELEPHONE:

Tokyo (212)-3111

WORKS:

Kobe Shipyard & Engine Works, 1, 3-chome Wadasaki-cho, Hyogo-ku, Kobe

TELEPHONE:

Kobe (671) 5061

CABLES:

Dock Kobe

PRESIDENT:

G. Moriya

MANAGING DIRECTOR & SENIOR MANAGER OF SHIPBUILDING DIVISION:

I. Takezawa

SENIOR EXECUTIVES:

Y. Terada, Manager of Domestic Ship Department (Head Office)

T. Katayama, Manager of Warship Department (Head Office)

K. Kai, General Manager of Kobe Shipyard & Engine Works

M. Muto, Manager of Hovercraft Section Kobe Shipyard and Engine Works

Mitsubishi completed a 3 ton experimental ACV in 1962 and is now engaged in technical studies for large commercial craft for Japanese inland sea services.

The company concluded a licence agreement with British Hovercraft Corporation and

Hovercraft Development Ltd in 1964. In February 1965 the company imported for evaluation and demonstration an SR.N5 which was returned in August of that year.

The company imported an SR.N6 in November 1966. A trial passenger ferry service was undertaken by Kyushu Shosen, a Japanese Shipping Company, in Kyushu, between Kumamoto and Shimabara, and Kumamoto and Hondo during the nine month period from September 1, 1967 until May 31, 1968.

The craft was also operated as a pleasure craft on Lake Biwa, Shiga Prefecture, from September to November, 1968.

The craft was also operated as a passenger ferry between Toba and Gamagohri in Ise Bay.

Descriptions of the SR.N5-M and SR.N6-M appeared in JSS 1971-72 and earlier editions.

Mitsui Shipbuilding & Engineering Co. Ltd.

HEAD OFFICE:
6-4, Tsukiji 5-chome, Chuo-ku, Tokyo, Japan
TELEPHONE:
544-3450
TELEX:
J22821, J22924
CABLE:
Mituizosen Tokyo
BOARD OF DIRECTORS:
Isamu Yamashita, President
Sobei Kudo, Senior Managing Director
Masami Fukuyama, Senior Managing Director
Jiro Komatsu, Senior Managing Director
Kyoichi Kato, Managing Director
Shoji Massaki, Managing Director
Kazuo Hamano, Managing Director
Kazuo Nagai, Managing Director
Kazuo Maeda, Managing Director
Ryoji Kawazura, Managing Director
Teiji Asano, Director
Yasuhisa Sawada, Director
Tatsuhiko Ueno, Director
Masahiko Irie, Director
Michio Sugimoto, Director
Takeharu Sueoka, Director
Takeo Takayanagi, Director
Hiromasa Kikuchi, Director
Hideo Matsushima, Director
Masataro Takami, Director
Yoshio Ishitani, Director
Kakuro Tsukamoto, Director
Koji Arase, Director
Saburo Sakamoto, Auditor
Nobuo Yashima, Auditor
Yoshinori Takahashi, Auditor
Tetsujiro Tomita, Deputy Director
Masatomo Ishibashi, Manager, Hovercraft Department

Mitsui's Hovercraft Department was formed on May 1st 1964, following the signing of a licencing agreement in 1963 with Hovercraft Development Ltd and Vickers Ltd, whose ACV interests were later merged with those of British Hovercraft Corporation. In addition, the company was licenced by Westland S.A. in 1967, following the formation of BHC.

The company has built two eleven-seat MV-PP1s, one of which has been supplied to the Thai Customs Department, fourteen MV-PP5s and four MV-PP15s.

The MV-PP5 is now in production at the initial rate of four craft a year. In the summer of 1969 the craft was put into service by Meitetsu Kaijo Kankosen Co, Ltd, between Gamagoori and Toba, Ise Bay.

Since October 1971 three MV-PP5s designated Hobby 1, 2 and 3 have been operated by Oita Hoverferry Co., Ltd on a coastal route linking Oita airport with the cities of Oita and Beppu. The three craft complete a total of sixteen round trips per day to link with flight schedules at the airport.

Other PP5 operators include Japanese National Railways (two craft), Kagoshima Airport Hovercraft Co Ltd (four craft), Yaeyama Kanko Ferry Co Ltd (one craft)

Mitsui's MV-PP15 50-ton passenger ferry, powered by twin 1,950 hp Avco Lycoming TF25 gas turbines. The craft seats 155 passengers and has a top speed of 65 knots. Seen in these photographs are the raised control cabin, the pylon mounted propellers, lift fan air intakes and the thrust ports beneath the passenger door entrances, port and starboard

and Nippon Hoverline (two craft). The craft has now been joined in production by the bigger, 155-seat MV-PP15.

The company is also building the prototype MV-PP05, a 5-seater, and has started the design of a 200-ton mixed-traffic ferry.

MV-PP15

Developed from the earlier PP5, the Mitsui MV-PP15 is designed for high speed passenger ferry services on coastal and inland waterways. Accommodation is provided for 155 passengers and a crew of 5.

The prototype was completed in the autumn of 1972. At the time of going to press three MV-PP15s were under construction for Ryukyu Kaiun K, which was planning a fast

ferry service for visitors to Oceanexpo '75 at Okinawa.

LIFT AND PROPULSION: Two Avco Lycoming TF25 gas-turbines, each with a maximum continuous output of 2,200 hp at 15°C, drive the integrated lift/propulsion system. Each turbine drives a 7 ft 6 in (2·3 m) diameter, 13-bladed centrifugal fan and a 10 ft 6 in (3·2 m) diameter, 4-bladed variable-pitch propeller. Power is transmitted via a main gearbox, propeller gearbox, fan gearbox and an auxiliary gearbox, all connected by shafting and flexible couplings. Auxiliary systems, such as hydraulic pumps for propeller pitch and lubricating oil pumps are driven directly by auxiliary gears. Fuel is carried in two flexible tanks located immediately ahead of the lift fan assemblies. Total volume of the fuel tanks is 21·2 ft³ (6 m³).

CONTROLS: Twin aerodynamic rudders in the propeller slipstream and differential propeller pitch provide directional control. The rudders are operated hydraulically by a wheel from the commander's position. In addition, two retractable wheels, located aft, one each side of the main buoyancy tank, can be extended downwards into the water to prevent drift when turning and assist braking at high speeds. On land, the wheels assist manoeuvring and help to reduce skirt wear.

A thrust port air bleed system provides lateral control at slow speeds. Four ports are located beneath the passenger door entrances, port and starboard. A water ballast system is provided for longitudinal and transverse cg adjustment.

HULL: Construction is primarily in corrosion resistant aluminium alloy. The basic structure is the main buoyancy chamber which is divided into watertight sub-divisions for safety, and includes the fore and aft ballast tanks. Overall dimensions of the main buoyancy raft structure are 64 ft 10½ in (19·8 m) long by 23 ft 3½ in (7·1 m) wide by 2 ft 4 in (0·7 m) high. Sidebodies of riveted construction are attached to the sides of the main buoyancy structure. The outer shell of the main buoyancy chamber, machinery deck space, the forward deck and passageways around the cabin interior, are all constructed in honeycomb panels with aluminium cores. The lift fan air intake, inner window frames and hood for the electric motor that rotates the radar scanner are in glassfibre reinforced plastics.

Six rubber-soled landing pads are fitted to the hull base, together with jacking pads. Four lifting eyes for hoisting the craft are provided in the buoyancy chamber.

SKIRT: 5 ft 3 in (1·60 m) deep fingered-bag skirt of Mitsui design, fabricated in nylon-based sheet and coated both sides with synthetic rubber. Two transverse stability bags are included in the skirt system to minimise pitch and roll.

ACCOMMODATION: The passenger cabin, containing 155 seats, is located above the forward part of the main buoyancy chamber. The seats are arranged in three groups and divided by two longitudinal aisles. Seats in the two outer sections are arranged in rows of three abreast, and in the centre section, six abreast.

The four cabin entrance doors, two port, two starboard, are divided horizontally, the top section opening upwards and the lower section opening sideways. A lavatory, toilet unit, pantry and luggage room are provided aft, and a second luggage room is located forward. Lockers are sited close to the forward entrance doors. The control cabin is located above the passenger cabin superstructure and provides a 360 deg. view. It is reached from the passenger saloon by a companion ladder. An emergency exit is provided on the starboard side.

The cabin has a total of four seats, one each for the commander and navigator, plus two spare ones of the flip-up type. The wheel for the air rudders, the two propeller pitch-

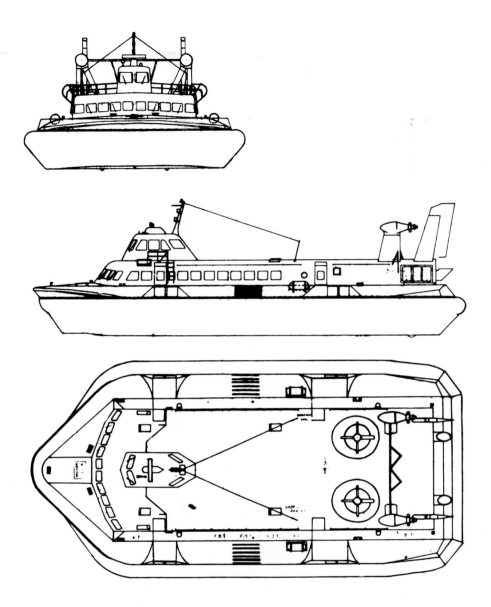

Mitsui MV-PPI5 155-seat hoverferry. Twin Avco Lycoming TF25 gas-turbines power the integrated lift propulsion system and give the craft a maximum speed of 60 knots

control levers, instrument panel and switches are arranged on a console ahead of the commander; and the radio, fuel tank gauge, water ballast gauge and fire warning system are arranged ahead of the navigator.

On the cabin roof are the radar-scanner, mast for navigation lights, a siren and a searchlight.

SYSTEMS:

ELECTRICAL: 28·5 volts dc. Two 9kw generators are driven directly by the main engines. One 24 volt 175 Ah battery is employed for starting, and another for control. Both are located in the engine room and are charged by the generators when the main engines are operating. A shore-based power source is used for battery charging when the main engines are not in use.

RADIO/NAVIGATION: Equipment includes one 10 in radar, compass, radio and one 20 cm, 250 W searchlight.

AIR CONDITIONING: Two Daikin RKA 1000R-PP15 air coolers, each with a capacity of 20,000 Kcal/hr. Compressors are driven by belts from the auxiliary gearboxes and cooled air is supplied via air-conditioning ducts. Four ceiling ventilators are provided,

each equipped with a 40W fan.

SAFETY: Remotely-controlled BCF or BTM fire extinguishers provided in the engine room. Portable extinguishers provided in the passenger cabin. Inflatable life boats, life jackets, automatic SOS signal transmitter and other equipment carried according to Japanese Ministry of Transport regulations.

DIMENSIONS, EXTERNAL:
Length overall on cushion
86 ft 8 in (26·40 m)
Length overall on landing pads
82 ft 4 in (25·09 m)
Beam overall on cushion 45 ft 7 in (13·90 m)
Beam overall on landing pads
36 ft 5 in (11·10 m)
Height on cushion 25 ft 11 in (7·90 m)
Height on landing pads to tip of propeller
blade 22 ft 8 in (6·90 m)
Skirt depth 5 ft 3 in (1·60 m)
DIMENSIONS, INTERNAL:
(Passenger cabin including toilet, pantry and locker rooms):
Length 46 ft 5 in (14·14 m)
Maximum breadth 23 ft 2 in (7·06 m)
Maximum height 6 ft 11 in (2·10 m)

Floor area	1,001 sq ft (93 m²)

WEIGHTS:

All-up weight	about 50 tons

PERFORMANCE:

Max speed	about 65 knots
Cruising speed	about 50 knots
Fuel consumption	
	about 280 gr/shp/hr at 15 deg C
Endurance	about 4 hours

MV-PP5

Mitsui's first large hovercraft, the 50-seat MV-PP5, is a gas-turbine powered craft intended primarily for fast ferry services on Japanese coastal and inland waters. The craft is now in production at the rate of four a year.

LIFT AND PROPULSION: All machinery is located aft to reduce to a minimum the noise level in the passenger cabin. A single IHI IM-100 gas-turbine (license-built General Electric LM100) with a maximum continuous rating of 1,050 hp at 19,500 rpm drives the integrated lift/propulsion system. Its output shaft passes first to the main gearbox from which shafts extend sideways and upwards to two 3-bladed Hamilton/Sumitomo variable-pitch propulsion propellers of 8 ft 6 in (2·59 m) diameter. A further shaft runs forward to the fan gearbox from which a drive shaft runs vertically downwards to a 7 ft 7 in (2·27 m) 13-bladed lift fan mounted beneath the air intake immediately aft of the passenger saloon roof. The fan is constructed in aluminium alloy and the disc plate is a 1½ in (40 mm) thick honeycomb structure.

To prevent erosion from water spray the propeller blades are nickel plated.

Fuel is carried in two metal tanks, with a total capacity of 416 gallons (1,900 litres), located immediately ahead of the lift fan assembly.

CONTROLS: Twin aerodynamic rudders in the propeller slipstream and differential thrust from the propellers provide directional control. The rudders are controlled hydrau-

lically from the commander's position. In addition two retractable water rods, located slightly aft of amidships on each side of the main buoyancy tank, can be extended downwards to prevent drift when turning and these also assist braking at high speeds. The water rods are operated hydraulically by foot-pedals. When used in conjunction with the rudders, the turning radius is reduced to about a third of that taken when only air rudders are used.

A thrust-port air bleed system provides lateral control at slow speeds. The thrust ports are actuated by air extracted from the engine compressor and are located beneath the passenger door entrances, port and starboard.

HULL: Construction is primarily of high strength AA502 aluminium alloy suitably protected against the corrosive effects of sea water. The basic structure is the main buoyancy chamber which is divided into eight watertight sub-divisions for safety, and includes fore and aft trimming tanks. Two further side body tanks, each divided into three watertight compartments, are attached to the sides of the main buoyancy chamber. To facilitate shipment the side body tanks can be removed, reducing the width to 12 ft 4 in (3·75 mm).

The outer shell of the main buoyancy chamber, the machinery deck space, the forward deck and the passage decks around the cabin exterior are all constructed in honeycomb panels with aluminium cores.

The lift fan air intake, radar cover, part of the air conditioning duct, and inside window frames are in glass-fibre reinforced plastic.

Design loads are as required by the Provisional British ACV Safety Regulations.

SKIRT: The flexible skirt was designed by Mitsui in the light of research conducted with aid of the RH-4 (MV-PP1 prototype) It is made of 1/32 in (0·8 mm) thick chloroprene-coated nylon sheet. A fringe of finger type nozzles is attached to the skirt base at

the bow and on both sides. At the stern a D-section bag skirt is used to avoid scooping up water.

Two transverse and one longitudinal stability bags are fitted.

ACCOMMODATION: The passenger cabin is sited above the forward end of the main buoyancy chamber. Seats for the two crew members are on a raised platform at the front of the cabin. All controls, navigation and radio equipment are concentrated around the seats. The windows ahead are of reinforced tempered glass and have electric wipers.

The two cabin entrance doors are divided horizontally, the lower part opening sideways, the top part upwards. The standard seating arrangement is for 42 passengers but ten additional seats can be placed in the centre aisle.

In accordance with Japanese Ministry of Transport regulations a full range of safety equipment is carried, including two inflatable life rafts, 54 life jackets, one automatic, manually activated fire extinguisher for the engine casing and two portable fire extinguishers in the cabin. Other standard equipment includes ship's navigation lights, marine horn, searchlight and mooring equipment, including an anchor. The twelve side windows can be used as emergency exits and are made of acrylic resin.

SYSTEMS:

ELECTRICAL SYSTEM: Two 2 kW, 28·5 volt ac/dc generators driven by belts from the main gearbox. One 24 volt, 100 Ah battery for engine starting.

HYDRAULIC AND PNEUMATIC SYSTEM: A 99·56 lb/in² (7·0 kg/cm²) hydraulic system pressure for water rods and 56·8-99·5 lb/in² (4·7-7 kg/cm²) pneumatic system for thrust port operation.

COMMUNICATION AND NAVIGATION: Equipment includes a radio and radar.

DIMENSIONS, EXTERNAL:

Length overall	52 ft 6 in (16·0 m)
Beam overall	28 ft 2 in (8·6 m)

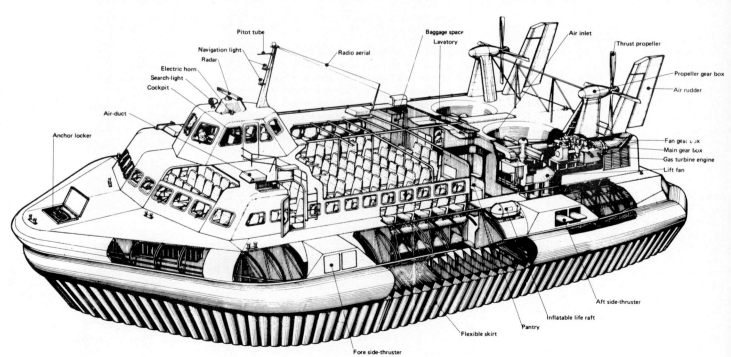

Cutaway of the Mitsui MU-PP15, showing the seating arrangements for the 155 passengers. Seats are arranged in three groups, divided by two longitudinal aisles. In the two outer sections they are arranged in rows of three abreast, and in the centre, six abreast

Height overall on landing pad

	14 ft 5 in (4·4 m)
Skirt depth	3 ft 11 in (1·2 m)
Draft afloat	11 in (0·2 m)
Cushion area	741 sq ft (88· m²)

DIMENSIONS, INTERNAL:

Cabin:

Length	23 ft 4 in (7·1 m)
Max width	12 ft 6 in (3·8 m)
Max height	6 ft 3 in (1·9 m)
Floor area	280 sq ft (26 m²)

Doors:

Two (0·65 m) × (1·4 m), one each side of cabin

Baggage-hold volume	24 cu ft (0·6 m³)

WEIGHTS:

Normal all-up weight	14 tons
Normal payload	5·5 tons

PERFORMANCE:

Max speed, calm water 55 knots (102 km/h)

Cruising speed, calm water
45 knots (83 km/h)

Still air range and endurance at cruising speed of about 160 nautical miles, 4 hours approximately

Vertical obstacle clearance 2 ft (0·6 m) approximately.

MV-PP1

The MV-PP1 is a small peripheral jet ACV built for river and coastal services and fitted with a flexible skirt. It seats a pilot and ten passengers and cruises at 40 knots.

Two craft of this type have been built to date—the prototype, which was completed in July 1964 and has been designated RH-4,

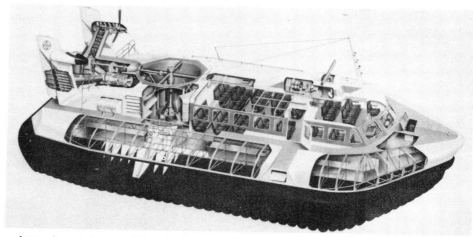

Internal arrangement of the MV-PP5 showing passenger accommodation and the gas-turbine powered lift/propulsion system aft of the cabin

and the first production model, the PP1-01.

The latter was sold to the Thai Customs Department, for service in the estuary of the Menam Chao Phya and adjacent waters, and has been named Customs Hovercraft 1.

It has been in service with the Thai Customs Department since September 1967.

Details of construction weights, performance, etc will be found in JSS for 1970-71 and earlier editions.

Mitsui MV-PP5 50-seat hovercraft, designed for fast ferry services on Japanese coastal and inland waters

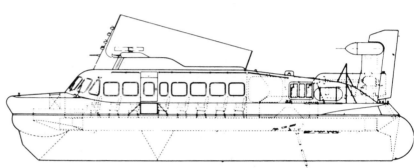

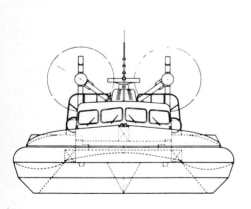

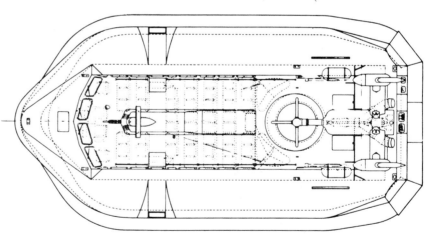

Mitsui has built fourteen MV-PP5s, eleven of which are currently in service. The three craft above are operated by Kagoshima Airport Hovercraft Co Ltd (*left*), Yaeyama Kanko Ferry Cc Ltd (*centre*) and Japanese National Railways

NAKAMURA SEISAKUSHO CO LTD

HEAD OFFICE:
2-13 2-Chome, Tamagawa, Ota-ku, Tokyo 144, Japan
TELEPHONE:
03-759-2311
CABLES:
Gamecreator, Tokyo
DIRECTORS:
Masaya Nakamura, President
Hazime Yamauchi, General Director
Takeharu Daira, Sales Director
Tadashi Manabe, Director
Shigeru Yamada, Director
SENIOR EXECUTIVES:
Tadanori Yanagidaira, General Manager, NAMCO Group
Tatuo Ichisi, Sales Manager
Hiromichi Kuroda, Designer
Noboru Horii, Designer
Fumio Tatumi, Designer

Nakamura Seisakusho Co of Tokyo is a leading Japanese manufacturer of amusement and recreational equipment. The company's first venture into the ACV field is a battery-powered single-seater, the Namco-1. Designed initially as an amusement novelty, the vehicle is now undergoing development as a hand-propelled pallet, capable of lifting loads of up to 120 kg (265 lb).

NAMCO-1

This novel, battery-powered single-seater is intended for amusement only and is designed for use over relatively smooth surfaces. A feature of the craft is the use of a diaphragm-type industrial air bearing system for lift.

A pedestrial-propelled pallet version has been built.

LIFT AND PROPULSION: Motive power is supplied by five Hitachi 12v 50AL automobile storage batteries. Three of the batteries power three National 12v dc 0·125W blowers which operate at 19,000 rpm to provide pressurised air to inflate the diaphragm, which is in 0·04 in thick neoprene rubber. Air then passes through holes in the base of the diaphragm to form a continuous air film between the diaphragm and the surface beneath.

Thrust is supplied by two National 24v dc, 0·6 kW electric motors (powered by the remaining two batteries) each driving a 1 ft 11 in (0·6 m) diameter, 5-bladed, 30° pitch Multi-wing fan made by Yashima Kogyo. Total propulsive thrust available is 22·05 lb (10 kg).

CONTROL: Craft heading is controlled by differential use of the thrust fans. It can travel forward, backwards or sideways, or spin around on its own axis.

HULL: Hull of prototype is in steel plate with bumper in polyethylane. Production models will be in fibreglass with pneumatic bumpers.

DIMENSIONS:

Height overall on landing pads, power off
3 ft 1 in (0·94 m)
Height overall, diaphragm inflated
3 ft 3·4 in (1·00 m)
Diameter overall   5 ft 3 in (1·60 m)
Diameter of diaphragm 3 ft 1·2 in (1·20 m)
Cushion area   11·02 sq ft (0·95 m²)

WEIGHTS:

Normal empty weight   264·6 lb (120 kg)
Total battery weight   137·3 lb (60 kg)

Above and below: Nakamura Seisakusho's battery-powered Namco-1 amusement ACV is raised above its supporting surface on a diaphragm-type industrial air bearing

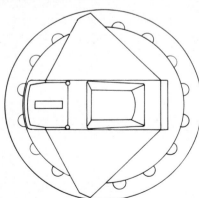

General arrangement of the Namco-1

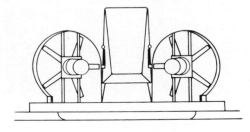

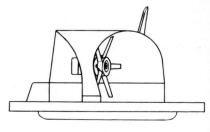

NIHON UNIVERSITY, NARASHINO

ADDRESS:
Aerodynamics Section, Nihon University at Narashino, 7-1591 Narashinodai; Funabashi, Chiba-Ken, Japan

TELEPHONE:
0474-66-1111-4

EXECUTIVES:
Masahira Mino, Senior Director
Toyoaki Enda, Director

The Aerodynamics Section of the Physical Science Laboratory, Nihon University, is conducting an extensive ACV research programme, which includes the construction and test of four small experimental craft: the Pastoral light amphibious single-seater, the Mistral, propelled by either water-screw or waterjet, the Floral, a two-seat sidewall craft and the N73.

An air boat, the Ripple, is employed as a "chase" craft to record on film the behaviour of these light ACVs over water.

Nihon University's ACV design group works in close co-operation with similar groups at the Institute of Technology, Ashikaga, and the University of Aoyama-Gakuin. Pastoral, in modified form, is now being employed in a research programme conducted by the Institute of Technology, Ashikaga.

A new design, the LJ-10 Jimny, a combined ground effect machine and wheeled vehicle, has been completed by Nihon in conjunction with Aoyama Gakuin University.

FLORAL 1

This experimental two-seater was completed in February 1971, and was the first sidewall craft to be built in Japan. In calm water the performance has proved to be superior to that of standard displacement runabouts of similar size and output. The craft was reconstructed in 1972 when the twin outboard propulsion units were replaced by a single unit, and a new stern skirt and trim flaps were introduced. Instrumentation includes trim, roll angle and speed indicators and gauges for measuring pressure in the plenum chamber.

LIFT AND PROPULSION: Lift is provided by a single 8 hp ZD-305 2 cycle single-cylinder air-cooled engine, located aft of the open cockpit and driving an F. S. Anderson 710-20-3L plastic fan. Propulsion is provided by a single Penta 550 outboard engine driving a waterscrew.

CONTROL: Engine/propeller unit turns for steering.

DIMENSIONS:
Length overall	17 ft 1 in (5·2 m)
Beam overall	5 ft 11 in (1·8 m)
Height overall	2 ft 7½ in (0·8 m)

WEIGHTS:
Normal gross weight	1,191 lb (540 kg)

PERFORMANCE:
Max speed over calm water
39 mph (62·7 km/h)
Max speed, 16 in (·40 m) waves
32 mph (52·1 km/h)

MISTRAL 2

Developed jointly by Nihon University, Masahiro Mino and the Institute of Technology, Ashikaga, the Mistral 2 is an experimental water-screw propelled single-seater derived from the SEA-NAC.

LIFT AND PROPULSION: A single 8 hp Fuji ES-162DS- 2-cycle single-cylinder air-cooled engine mounted immediately aft of the cockpit drives a 22⅞ in (580 mm) S11-03-FS03 5-bladed aluminium alloy fan for lift.

Floral I, two-seater sidewall ACV, built by students of the Aerodynamics Section of Nihon University, Narashino, Japan

Mistral 2 single seat research ACV

LJ-10 Jimny a combined ground effect machine and wheeled vehicle. Designed for use over terrain normally unpassable to wheeled or crawler-equipped tractors the vehicle comprises a Suzuki Auto Co LN-360 Jimny—a counterpart to the US Army's jeep—equipped with a sidebody to support the skirt system and two lift fan assemblies. Cushion air is supplied by a 55 hp Nissan engine driving two 10-bladed centrifugal fans

Propulsion is supplied by either a 22 hp Fuji KB-2 or 50 hp Mercury 500 driving a waterscrew.

HULL: Moulded glass fibre, with inflated fabric-reinforced neoprene side-body/skirt.

CONTROLS: Engine/propeller unit turns for steering.

DIMENSIONS:

Length overall	13 ft 5 in (4·10 m)
Beam overall	5 ft 11 in (1·80 m)
Height overall	3 ft 7 in (1·09 m)

WEIGHTS:

Normal gross weight	664 lb (310 kg)

PERFORMANCE:

Max speed over calm water	42 mph (67·5 km/h)
Max speed, 2 ft (0·6 m) waves	28 mph (45·5 km/h)

LJ-10 JIMNY

Based on a reconditioned Suzuki Auto Co LN-360 Jimny—a jeep counterpart—this is a combined ground effect machine and wheeled vehicle, and can be driven like a car or truck. It was built by the Aerodynamics Section of Nihon University, headed by Masahiro Minot, in conjunction with the Traffic Engineering Dept, Aoyoma Gakuin University, headed by Eiji Tonokura. The vehicle is designed for use over uneven ground, and, marshes, and other terrain which cannot be traversed by wheeled or tracked cars and trucks. During 1973, the craft successfully completed running tests over normal road surfaces, unprepared tracks and stretches of water.

LIFT AND PROPULSION: Motive power for the lift system is provided by a single 55 hp Nissan A-10 988 cc engine which drives two 23½ in (595 mm) diameter 10-bladed centrifugal fans mounted on a common shaft to the rear of the driving position. Air is drawn through two inward facing metal ducts and expelled downwards into a fingered-bag skirt system. The vehicle has a four wheel drive system, powered by a Suzuki FB 395 cc petrol engine developing 27 hp at 6,000 rpm. Heading is controlled by a normal steering wheel located ahead of the driver.

DIMENSIONS

Length	17 ft 8 in (5,390 mm)
Width	10 ft 11 in (3,440 mm)
Height	5 ft 11 in (1,820 mm)

WEIGHTS:

All-up weight	2,200 lb (998 kg)

PERFORMANCE:

No details received

N 73

This experimental single-seater has attained 55 mph (90 km/h) over water and 37 mph (60 km/h) during trials over land.

LIFT AND PROPULSION: A single 13 hp Daihatsu 2-cycle, single-cylinder air-cooled engine immediately ahead of the cockpit

N 73 amphibious runabout during trials. Built by the Aerodynamics Section, Nihon University, the craft has attained 55 mph (90 km/h) over water

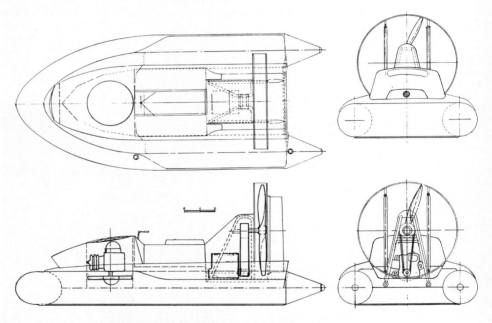

General arrangement of the N 73 single-seat amphibious runabout

drives a 22 in (560 mm) diameter Multiwing fan for lift. Propulsion is supplied by a 40 hp Xenoax G44B 2-cycle twin-cylinder engine driving a 3 ft 11¼ in (1,200 mm) diameter 2-bladed propeller.

CONTROLS: Craft heading is controlled by twin aerodynamic rudders hinged to the rear of the propeller shroud and operated by a handlebar.

HULL: Moulded glass fibre with inflated fabric-reinforced neoprene sidebody/skirt.

DIMENSIONS:

Length overall	14 ft 9 in (4·50 m)
Beam overall	5 ft 10⅞ in (1·80 m)
Height	5 ft 1 in (1·55 m)

WEIGHTS:

Normal empty weight	750 lb (340 kg)
Normal payload	474 lb (215 kg)

PERFORMANCE:

Max speed over water	55 mph (90 km/h)
Max speed over land	37 mph (60 km/h)
Range	93·2 miles (150 km)

KUWAIT

AL-RODHAN TRADING AND CONTRACTING EST

HEAD OFFICE:

P.O. Box 5020, Kuwait, Arabian Gulf

Al-Rodhan is the representative for Eglen Hovercraft Inc in Kuwait, United Arab Emirates, Bahrain, Oman and Muscat, Yemen and Saudi Arabia.

NETHERLANDS

MACHINEFABRIEK ENBE BV

Air Cushion Vehicle Design and Manufacturing Subsidiary:

B. V. LUCHTKUSSENVOERTUIGEN FABRIEK

HEAD OFFICE:
Industrieterrein, Asperen, Netherlands

TELEPHONE:
03451-2743/2744

TELEX:
ENBE NL 47864

WORKS:
LKV Fabr. Industrieterrein, Asperen

DIRECTORS:
W. A. G. v. Burgeler
N. C. Nap

SHAREHOLDERS, (BV ENBE)
N. C. Nap
A. H. Nap
W. A. G. v. Burgeler

ENBE has built three light amphibious ACV prototypes, the B-1, B-2 and B-3, all designed by Mr. W. A. G. v. Burgeler.

Since January 1st, 1974, the company has been the distributor in the Netherlands for the Air Vehicles AV.2 light utility ACV.

B3

The B3 is an unusual combination of ground effect machine and tracked vehicle, driven like a tractor or tank, but capable of negotiating high gradient slopes, rough country, ice, snow and marshes at speeds up to 20 km/h (12·42 mph). The prototype illustrated seats 16-18 passengers but a projected utility version, intended for operations ranging from dredging to oil survey support services, will mount a small hydraulic crane and/or excavating equipment.

LIFT AND PROPULSION: Motive power is supplied by a water-cooled NSU-Wankel

Prototype of the B.3 tracked utility vehicle, designed for operation across marshes and rough country and capable of negotiating 30 deg gradients

rotary engine delivering 135 bhp at 6,000 rpm. Transmission is via an engine-mounted pump circulating fluid through lines to three hydraulic motors, one driving an axial lift fan, the other two driving crawler-type tracks. Fuel is carried in a single rear tank with a capacity of 120 l (26 Imp gals).

CONTROLS: Vehicle heading controlled by differential variance of track speeds.

HULL: Metal construction.

ACCOMMODATION: Cabin is heated and ventilated and provides seats for a driver and up to 18 passengers. Access is via a rear door. An emergency exit is provided at the front of the cabin. In the utility role the vehicle will carry up to two tons of freight.

SYSTEMS: Electrical: An engine-operated generator supplied 12 volts to an aircraft-type battery for the operation of lights and engine starting.

DIMENSIONS, EXTERNAL:
Length overall, skirt inflated
6·70 m (20 ft 4⅛ in)
Beam overall, skirt inflated
3·30 m (10 ft 9⅞ in)
Height overall, power off 1·95 m (5 ft 1¼ in)
Height overall, skirt inflated
1·87 m (6 ft 2 in)
Skirt depth 30 cm (11¾ in)
DIMENSIONS, INTERNAL:
Cabin length 4 m (13 ft 1⅛ in)
Cabin width 3 m (9 ft 10⅛ in)
Max height 1·5 m (4 ft 11 in)
PERFORMANCE:
Max speed, forward and reverse
20 km/h (14·42 mph)
Gradient up to 30 deg
TERMS:
Terms of payment, 50% with order, remainder on delivery. Export orders: 25% on order. 75% irrevocable L.O.C.

NEW ZEALAND

HOVER VEHICLES (N.Z.) LTD

ADDRESS:
PO Box 10, Ohau, New Zealand

TELEPHONE:
80792 LEVIN

EXECUTIVES:
Roy Blake
David Clemow
Jim Pavitt
Ron Wadman
Brian Shaw
Mel Douglas
Don Murray, Managing Director

Hover Vehicles (N.Z.) Ltd has been formed by a group of New Zealand pilots, engineers and businessmen in association with Roy Blake, winner of the "Hovernaut of the Year" title in the United Kingdom in 1968, who afterwards emigrated to New Zealand.

The company plans to build vehicles which can be employed either on light utility applications or as recreational craft. The first craft under development is the H.V.4, a 6·4 m (21 ft) long amphibious six-seater, the final design for which has been completed. Static tests took place early in 1975, and a major test programme was expected to be underway by June 1975.

Model of the Hover Vehicles H.V.4. A single 185 Rover V8 3,500 cc hp automobile engine drives a 3 ft (914 mm) diameter centrifugal lift fan and two 3 ft (914 mm) diameter variable pitch shrouded airscrews. Maximum speed is expected to be about 45 mph (72·42 km/h)

Future plans are uncertain and will depend on the performance of the prototype. It is envisaged that several pre-production models will be built before consideration is given to putting the craft into full-scale production.

Apart from the design and construction of the H.V.4 the company has built and tested its own variable- and reversible-pitch fibre-glass airscrew which will be used for ACV

propulsion.

Government financial assistance was provided for the first prototype. Preliminary details of the company's first craft are given below.

H.V.4

The prototype of this attractive six-seat recreational ACV is complete and a major test programme was scheduled to begin by

June 1975. It is intended as a quiet, easily controlled craft which can be driven by an "above average" car driver after two hours training.

LIFT AND PROPULSION: Power for the integrated lift/propulsion system is provided by a single 185 hp Rover V8 automobile engine which drives a 3 ft (914 mm) diameter centrifugal lift fan and two 3 ft (814 mm) diameter variable-pitch shrouded airscrews.

ACCOMMODATION: Seats are provided for a driver and five passengers in a fully enclosed cabin.

WEIGHTS:
Normal loaded weight
1,360·77 kg (3,000 lb)

DIMENSIONS:
Length overall	6·4 m (21 ft 0 in)
Beam overall	3·04 m (10 ft 0 in)
Reduced for transport by road	2·43 m (8 ft 0 in)
Ground clearance	609 mm (2 ft 0 in)

PERFORMANCE:
Max speed   72·42 km/h (45 mph)

COMMERCIAL HOVERCRAFT INDUSTRIES LTD

HEAD OFFICE:
23 Selwyn Street, Onehunga, New Zealand

This company is currently engaged in the manufacture of the C.H.700, a 4-5 seater powered by three 18 hp Wankel rotary engines. Six craft of this type were built by the company in 1972.

C.H.700

This is a fully amphibious recreational craft with a payload capacity of 680 lb (308·42 kg). The enclosed cabin is pressurised to prevent the ingestion of dust and spray.

LIFT AND PROPULSION: Immediately aft of the cabin is an 18 hp Wankel K.M. 419 rotary engine which drives a centrifugal fan for lift. Propulsive thrust is supplied by twin Wankel engines of identical type driving two fixed-pitch propellers. Fuel capacity is 11 gallons (50 l); consumption, 3·5 gph (15·19 l/ph).

CONTROLS: Craft heading is controlled by twin aerodynamic rudders hinged to the rear of the propeller ducts and by differential thrust.

HULL: Mixed construction, employing a combination of marine ply, glass fibre and anodised aluminium. Buoyancy is provided by ten watertight compartments and poly-styrene foam blocks.

ACCOMMODATION: Enclosed, pressurised cabin with seats for driver and 3-4 passengers.

PERFORMANCE:
Max speed over land   35 mph (56·32 km/h)
Max speed over water 25 mph (40·23 km/h)

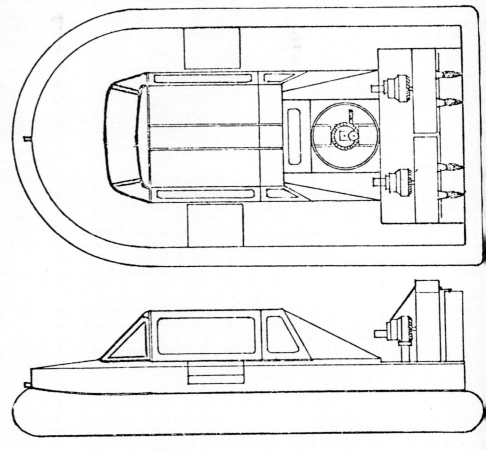

C.H.700, a 4-5 seater powered by three 18 hp Wankel engines

Endurance		3 hours
Vertical clearance	8-12 in (203·304 mm)	
WEIGHTS:		
Empty weight	1,100 lb (498·92 kg)	
Gross weight	1,780 lb (807·35 kg)	
Useful load	680 lb (308·42 kg)	

SYSTEMS: Electrical: 12 volts for engine starting, lights etc.

DIMENSIONS:
Length	15 ft 9 in (4·80 m)
Beam	8 ft 0 in (2·43 m)
Height	4 ft 6 in (1·37 m)

SWEDEN

FLYGTEKNISKA FORSOKSANSTALTEN THE AERONAUTICAL RESEARCH INSTITUTE OF SWEDEN

HEAD OFFICE:
PO Box 11021, S-161 11 Bromma 11

TELEPHONE:
08.26 28 40

TELEX:
107 25

TELEGRAMS:
Flygtekniska

EXECUTIVE RESPONSIBLE FOR ACV DEVELOPMENT:
Einar Bergström,

FAA has conducted an ACV research programme for several years and is now working on designs for a series of full-size craft.

The FAA concept, described as a "semi-hovercraft", has three flexible, inflated rubber keels, a bow cushion seal and one or

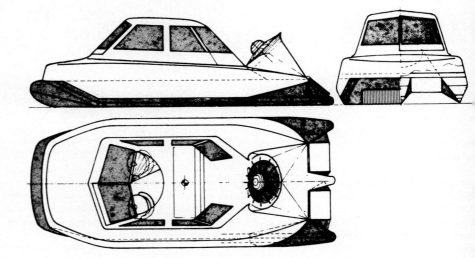

A 50-knot, four-seat runabout designed by FFA

more fans situated aft.

The fans produce both propulsive thrust and cushion pressure. Air from the fans is blown rearwards beneath two adjustable flaps. These control the pressure in the two halves of the cushion, which is divided into two by a central keel. The hover gap is normally zero, hovering being limited to that necessary to clear stretches of ice and shallow water, and for parking on concrete terminals, beaches and pontoons. Hovering, turns, side thrust and reverse thrust are controlled by the operation of two adjustable side keels aft and the bow seal.

The concept is aimed towards lower initial and operating costs, reduced noise, and improved manoeuvrability.

A small dynamic test vehicle with a 10 hp engine was followed in 1971 by a larger test craft which has successfully completed a major trials programme. Development of a 4-seat recreational ACV based on the test craft and a 41-seat hoverferry started in 1972. Negotiations for the construction of prototypes are complete. Development of the FFA ACV system is continuing and a production prototype of a two-seat sportscraft was due to be completed in September 1974.

Preliminary details of FFA's initial range of commercial designs are given below.

FFA SPORTSCRAFT

This glassfibre hulled lightweight ACV is projected in single and two-seat versions, the latter being available with either tandem or side-by-side seating. It will operate across water, snow and ice and can be parked on beaches.

LIFT/PROPULSION: Integrated system powered by a single 18-20 hp Wankel engine or suitable two-stroke, mounted aft in an inclined nacelle and driving a two-bladed fan in a circular entry duct. Air from the fan is fed into a divided plenum chamber for lift and blown rearwards beneath a single aft flap for propulsion.

CONTROLS: Fore and aft movement of single control column operates aft propulsion flap. Craft direction is controlled by asymmetric discharge of cushion air.

HULL: Basic structure comprises two main components: a glassfibre upper shell, to which are attached the side keels and open cockpit, and a lower shell comprising the cockpit base and the engine nacelle/fan duct. Lower sections of the central and outer keels and forward seal are of thin, steel reinforced rubber material.

ACCOMMODATION: Single-seat model has an open cockpit. Two-seat versions are available with either tandem or side-by-side seating. Folding cabin hood will be fitted to latter model.

DIMENSIONS (TWO-SEAT MODEL):

Length overall	11 ft 9¾ in (3·6 m)
Beam overall	5 ft 10¾ in (1·8 m)

WEIGHTS:

Empty	220 lb (100 kg)
Loaded	573 lb (260 kg)

PERFORMANCE:

Cruising speed	30 knots plus

FFA TEST VEHICLE

FFA's second test vehicle is also the prototype of the organisation's four-seat runabout. During its initial trials programme it attained an overwater speed of 50 mph (80·46 km/hr)

FFA's test vehicle at 34 knots, while accelerating at 1·3 knots per second. Powered by a 57 hp Volkswagen engine, it has attained 56 knots on half-power

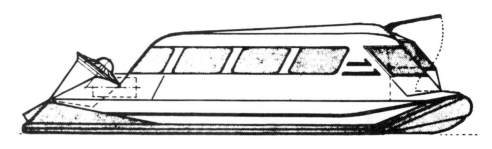

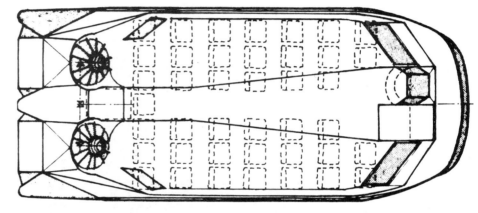

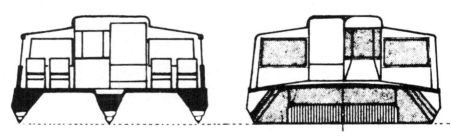

FFA's high-speed hover-bus, designed to link outlying areas with the heart of Stockholm by operating along the city's waterways. Seats are provided for 41 passengers and the top speed is expected to be about 80 knots

The craft is fully amphibious and operates over ice, snow and water. It can be parked on any suitable flat beach.

LIFT AND PROPULSION: Motive power for the integrated lift/propulsion system is provided by a single VW 57 hp automotive engine driving via rubber belts two 23⅝ in (0·60 m) 6-bladed Bahco axial fans.

CONTROLS: Directional control was provided initially by the differential setting of two flaps, operating in the port and starboard propulsion airjet slots aft. This form of control has now been replaced by an improved system in which fan air is discharged asymmetrically.

Clearance height, roll angle, pitch and trim are controlled by adjusting the thrust port flaps.

DIMENSIONS:

Length overall	17 ft 8½ in (5·4 m)
Cushion area	96 ft² (9·0 m²)

WEIGHT:

Total test weight	1,609 lb (730 kg)

PERFORMANCE:

Max speed at full power, estimated	76 knots
Max speed with half power	56 knots
Normal test speed	23-35 knots
Acceleration at 34 knots, tested	1·3 knots/sec

FFA FOUR-SEAT RUNABOUT

LIFT AND PROPULSION: Integrated system powered by a 35 hp two-stroke driving a two-bladed duct-mounted fan. Immediately below the fan, the duct is divided to feed the two halves of the cushion which are separated by a central keel. Aft airjet flap ends are connected to the outer and central keels by triangular webs, which limit up and down flap movement and eliminate side flow.

HULL: The basic hull structure, including the rigid upper sections of the three keels, fan ducting and canopy, are fabricated in glass reinforced plastics. The upper grp keel sections are filled with foam plastic for buoyancy. The lower sections, in textile reinforced neoprene, are inflated by fan air. The contours of the keels when inflated are maintained by an internal stay system employing nylon ropes located in six positions along each keel.

The forward flexible seal is made in a single piece in textile reinforced rubber.

HULL: Similar structure to that of the test craft.

ACCOMMODATION: Entry to the fully enclosed four-seat cabin is through a hinged door at the front. The driver's position is on the starboard side, and the cabin roof section immediately above swings to one side permitting the craft to be steered from a standing position. Both front seats can be turned to face inwards. The two passengers at the rear sit side-by-side on a single seat.

DIMENSIONS:
Similar to those of the FFA testcraft.

PERFORMANCE:
Max speed over water   50 knots

FFA HOVER BUS

FFA's 41-seat Hover Bus is designed to provide high frequency links between towns on the outskirts of Stockholm and an underground station located by the waterside in the heart of the city, from which trains leave every two minutes to all parts of the metropolis. The proposed Hover Bus services are intended to open new areas for population growth, and will provide connections to the city centre at intervals of 5-20 minutes during the morning and evening rush hour periods.

The craft is designed for year-round operation across archipelagos, rivers and lakes. It will traverse ice, snow, shallow water and beaches.

LIFT AND PROPULSION: Integrated system with motive power supplied by a single 400 hp Avco Lycoming 10-720 piston engine located above the central keel aft and driving two ducted fans via shafts and bevel gears.

HULL: Mixed construction employing marine aluminium alloy and glass reinforced plastics. Lower (inflatable) sections of the three keels are in a synthetic rubber material; similar

ACCOMMODATION: Seats are provided for 41 passengers, most of whom sit three abreast in twelve rows either side of a central aisle. An additional four seats are provided forward and there is a single seat at the end of the aisle aft. The driver sits forward on the port side, with the passenger entry door to his immediate right.

material is also used for the bow seal.

DIMENSIONS:
Length overall   36 ft 9 in (11·2 m)

WEIGHTS:
Empty   3·4 tons
Loaded   6·9 tons

PERFORMANCE:
Max speed, calm water   80 knots

SAAB-SCANIA
Saab-Scania Aktiebolag

HEAD OFFICE:
S-581 88 Linköping

TELEPHONE:
013-13 00 20

TELEX:
64940 SAABLGS

OFFICERS AND EXECUTIVES
Curt Mileikowsky, President
T. Arnheim, Executive Vice-President
T. Lidmalin, Executive Vice-President

AEROSPACE DIVISION:
T. Gullstrand, Head of Division
H. Schroder, Head of Aircraft Section
I. K. Olsson, Head of Missile and Avionics Section
Hans G. Anderson, Head of Information Division

Interest in amphibious hovercraft has been growing in Sweden for some time, chiefly because of the potential of this type of vehicle for maintaining year-round communications between the mainland and islands in the Swedish archipelago. In 1964, with the intention of developing a range of air cushion craft suitable for operations of this kind, Saab-Scania and Kockums formed a joint hovercraft study group which, since then, has been conducting theoretical studies, model tests and project analyses.

In 1972, work began on a 4-ton experimental ACV, which will provide data on skirt design, trim systems, stability and control. Craft operating in the Swedish archipelago would need to have rapid and precise response to controls while operating at high speed over ice, and a basic requirement of the skirt system is that it should be easily repairable after being torn by broken ice. Construction of the research craft described below was undertaken by Marinkonsult AB, a Swedish consulting company.

4-TON EXPERIMENTAL ACV

LIFT AND PROPULSION: A centrally-mounted Saab V4 100 hp automotive engine drives, via a V-belt, two AB Ventilatorverken centrifugal fans mounted vertically at opposite ends of a transverse shaft. Volutes for the two fans are on the sidedecks outside the main cabin superstructure. Fan air is directed downwards into the plenum, but

Above and below: A 4-ton experimental ACV developed jointly by Saab-Scania Kockums and Marinkonsult. Lift is provided by a 100 hp Saab V4 car engine driving two centrifugal fans mounted vertically at opposite ends of a transverse shaft. A 180 hp Lycoming flat-four aero-engine driving a 2-bladed fixed pitch propeller provides thrust. Craft heading at low speeds is provided by airjet apertures at the front and rear of both lift fan volutes. The bow thruster, which rotates, is driven by a 23 hp Wankel engine and used in conjunction with the aerodynamic rudder for controlling yaw at cruising speed and above

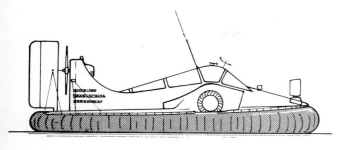
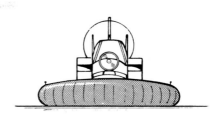
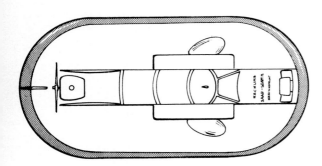

General arrangement of the 30 ft (9·2 m) long Kockums—Saab-Scania research hovercraft

ust/braking apertures are provided ward and aft on the fan volutes to permit ssurised air to be bled off as required for trol at low speeds. Propulsive thrust supplied by a single 180 hp Lycoming craft "flat-four" engine mounted aft, ving a two-bladed fixed-pitch propeller. a later stage this will be replaced by an omotive engine, mounted inboard, and ving a reversible pitch-propeller. NTROLS: Craft heading at cruising speed d above is controlled by an aerodynamic lder operating in the propeller slipstream. w control is provided by a rotating, nkel-driven ducted fan at the bow on the in superstructure. At low speeds craft pulsion and heading control is provided airjet apertures forward and aft on the fan volutes. These are used collectively differentially, port and starboard. Bow ff ports provide yaw control. Pitch is mmed by the use of a transverse stability nk which divides the cushion into two and mits a higher cushion pressure to be

maintained beneath the rear of the cushion for normal operation. A trim valve, adjacent to the lift fans, increases the volume of air entering the cushion forward to provide a quick bow-up trim. This and most other controls are operated electropneumatically. HULL: Built in glassfibre reinforced polyester, employing a sandwich-type structure with vinylcell foam as a core. Trimaran-type buoyancy structure with two parallel vertical walls extending upwards to form sides of cabin superstructure and fins. Horizontal deck surface provides top of buoyancy structure. SKIRT: 1 ft 11 in (0·6 m) deep, fingered-bag type skirt, fabricated in material supplied by Trelleborgs Gummifabrik. Fingers are designed for ease of replacement and each is individually attached to the deck by two wires. Length of the wires is adjustable, also the point of attachment to the deck. The wires are attached to the deck at points three to ten times further apart than the width of the fingers, forming a web pattern between the fingers and the deck. The bag skirt,

fabricated in a lightweight material, is pressed against this wire web by the cushion pressure. Since the web absorbs most of the forces from its fingers to the deck, the bag skirt can be made in lightweight material.

DIMENSIONS:
Length overall, hard structure
        30 ft 2¼ in (9·2 m)
Beam overall, hard structure
        15 ft 5 in (4·7 m)
Height on cushion, cabin top
        9 ft 6 in (2·9 m)
Skirt depth   1 ft 11⅝ in (0·6 m)
Cushion area   306·89 sq ft (28·5 m²)

WEIGHTS:
Starting all-up weight   3 tons
Payload and fuel   1 ton

PERFORMANCE:
No details available at the time of going to press

TRINIDAD

ELACANTH GEMCO LTD

AD OFFICE:
Richardson Street, Point Fortin, Trinidad, W.I.
LEPHONE:
oint Fortin 2439
BLES:
oelacanth, Trinidad
RECTORS:
Nigel Seale
Kelvin Corbie
RETARY:
. Varma
oelacanth Gemco Ltd, the first company pecialise in the design and construction of cushion vehicles in the West Indies, has n granted Pioneer Status for the manuture of hovercraft in Trinidad by the ernment-controlled Industrial Develop-

Pluto Mk II, a manned test model of Coelacanth Gemco Pluto series, puts to sea for a test run off Point Fortin, Trinidad

ment Corporation. The company has obtained the approval of the Town and Country Planning Commission to construct an ACV

factory and a hoverport at Guapo beach, Trinidad. Guapo Bay and the neighbouring Antilles Bay will be used by the company for sea tests and a disused runway adjacent to the site will be used for overland tests.

The company also plans to build a two-mile long, 100 ft wide ACV roadway between Guapo Beach and the Point Fortin Industrial Estate.

Meetings have been held with the Trinidad Government to negotiate a right-of-way over Government owned land.

A freight operation is planned with ACVs taking aboard finished goods from the factories, and delivering them to Port-of-Spain, 40 minutes away at a speed of 60 knots.

Craft at present under development by the company are the Pluto, Jupiter, Venus, Arcturus and Mars, a military ACV, A manned test model of the latter is expected to be ready for trials in 1975.

Progress is also being made with the development of a hover truck, with a payload of 3 tons, for carrying sugar cane from the Trinidad cane fields in wet weather.

PLUTO Mk. I and II

The Pluto is a two-seat test vehicle, built in marine ply, and designed to provide data for a sport and recreational craft which will be marketed under the same name.

The production prototype, which is based on the existing hull and designated Pluto Mk II is undergoing trials. A four-seat version, Pluto Mk III, is due to go into production in 1975.

Two and four-seat versions are planned. A standard feature of the production models will be a two-berth cabin and cooking facilities, which will allow the craft to be used for cruising to the northwest of Trinidad in the Gulf of Paria.

LIFT AND PROPULSION: Lift power on Pluto Mk II is supplied by two 6 hp Briggs and Stratton motor-mower engines driving two Rotafoil fans. Thrust is supplied by two 250cc Velocettes driving two 2 ft 3 in (0·685 m) diameter ducted Hordern-Richmond propellers at 5,000 rpm.

DIMENSIONS, EXTERNAL:

Length	16 ft 0 in (4·87 m)
Width	7 ft 10 in (2·38 m)
Height	6 ft 0 in (1·82 m)

WEIGHTS:

Empty weight	1,100 lb (498·92 kg)
Loaded weight, 2 seat model	
	1,500 lb (680·35 kg)

PERFORMANCE:

Speed over water	22 mph (35·40 km/h)
Speed over land (with one person)	
	39 mph (62·76 km/h)
Vertical obstacle clearance	8 in (203 mm)

PLUTO Mk III

Developed from Pluto Mk. II, Mk. III is a four-seater runabout and yacht.

The first production model is now complete and was due to make the first test runs at the end of June, 1975.

LIFT AND PROPULSION: Lift is provided by a single 20 hp Sachs Wankel rotary engine driving two Rotafoil fans, and propulsion by two 250cc Velocettes driving two 2 ft 3 in (0·685 m) diameter ducted Hordern Richmond propellers at 5,000 rpm.

All series production craft will be powered by three Sachs Wankel engines—one for lift and two for propulsion. Fuel is carried in two standard marine power boat tanks, mounted amidships on the outer hull periphery.

Plans are being made to power a de luxe model with a 120 hp engine driving a hydraul-

Nigel Seale, designer of Pluto III, stands at the controls as the craft is put through static hovering tests in Coelacanth Gemco's workshop.   Hatches in the cabin roof and at the bow enable mooring lines to be handled more easily.   The vessel was due to undergo overwater trials at the end of June 1975

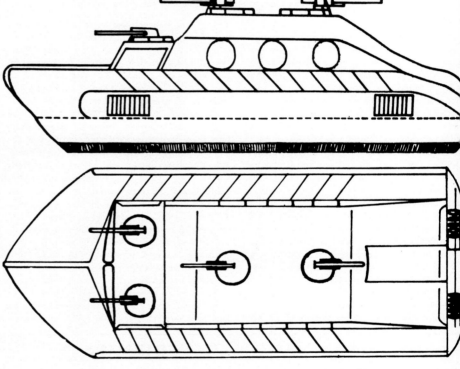

Provisional three-view drawing of the Mars light patrol craft

ic pump which will, in turn, drive three hydraulic motors, Two of these will power the propulsion system and the third will power the lift system.

CONTROLS: Craft heading is controlled by twin rudders aft operating in the slipstreams of the two propellers. Thrust ports are fitted port and starboard, fore and aft, to provide additional control at slow speeds when approaching and leaving jetties.

HULL: First production craft will be in $\frac{3}{16}$ in mahogany marine ply, with the bottom and sides sheathed to 6 in (152 mm) above the waterline in glassfibre.

ACCOMMODATION: The cabin accommo-dates a family of four—two adults and two children—and stores for an overnight stay. The seats are removable and can be used on the beach.   On board the craft, the position of the seats can be altered if necessary to adjust craft trim.   Built-in steps are provided on each side of the hull to simplify access craft after bathing. A hatch is provided for baggage items and stores and another ward to facilitate the handling of mooring s and the anchor. The cabin windows, $\frac{3}{16}$ in plexiglass, slide rearwards in their mes for access to the cabin.

DIMENSIONS, EXTERNAL:

ength	18 ft 0 in (5·48 m)
idth	7 ft 10 in (2·38 m)
eight, inflated skirt	6 ft 0 in (1·82 m)
ushion depth	1 ft 3 in (381 mm)
reeboard in displacement mode	2 ft 6 in (0·76 m)

DIMENSIONS, INTERNAL:

Cabin floor area (total usable area)	40 sq ft (3·71 m²)

WEIGHTS:

ormal gross weight (4 passengers and 20 gallons of petrol)	1,950 lb (884·5 kg)
mpty weight	1,250 lb (566·90 kg)

PERFORMANCE:

peed over water	25 mph (40·23 km/h)
peed over land	40 mph (64·37 km/h)

ST: Estimated price, g.r.p. model £3,500 est Indies $16,800).

NUS

his craft has been designed principally carrying oil company executives to and n wells in the Gulf of Paria, in Soldado t other areas in the West Indies. Ten and een seat versions will be built, and like the

Jupiter, the craft will be available in either amphibious form with a continuous skirt or as a rigid sidewall type with bow and stern skirts.

A manned scale model hull of the craft was completed in November 1968. This craft is also being used as a test bed for the two and four-seat Pluto series.

JUPITER

A projected four-seat ACV runabout, Jupiter is designed around the basic hull of the company's Super Bee cabin cruiser, and will be available either as an amphibious craft, with a continuous peripheral skirt, or as a rigid sidewall type with bow and stern skirts.

Lift will be provided by a 75 hp modified outboard driving two Rotafoil fans, and propulsive thrust by a 90 hp modified outboard driving a reversible pitch-ducted propeller.

DIMENSIONS:

Length	18 ft 0 in
Beam	10 ft 0 in
Height	7 ft 0 in

WEIGHT:

Weight, incl fuel	2,810 lb

PERFORMANCE:

Max speed (est)	50 knots

ARCTURUS

The Arcturus is a 35-seat amphibious ACV

designed by Nigel Scale. Motive power for the lift and propulsion system will be supplied by high speed diesel generators driving Lear Siegler Electric Motors.

Work has started on a manned scale model but activity has been suspended temporarily while the company concentrates its resources on the development of the Pluto series.

MARS

Coelacanth Gemco's first military design is the 35 ft (10·66 m) long Mars, a 10-ton patrol craft designed to operate in sheltered waters. It will carry seven fully armed men.

A manned scale model capable of testing hovering performance is being built and is expected to be ready for trials in 1975.

Construction will be in g.r.p., with aluminium extrusions and panels. Six Rotafoil fans will be employed in the integrated lift/propulsion system.

A feature of the craft will be the employment of stabilisers to reduce drift.

DIMENSIONS:

Length	35 ft 0 in (10·66 m)
Beam	15 ft 0 in (4·57 m)
Height	15 ft 0 in (4·57 m)

WEIGHTS:

Normal all-up weight	10 tons

PERFORMANCE:

Cruising speed	35 knots

UNITED KINGDOM

R BEARINGS LTD

AD OFFICE AND WORKS:
uay Lane, Hardway, Gosport, Hampshire PO12 4LJ

LEPHONE:
70) 17-87421

LEX:
7674

LEGRAMS:
IR BEAR—GOSPORT

RECTORS:
. Murray-Jones, Chairman
E. Cook, Managing
M. Grant, A.C.A., Finance
C. Nicholson
R. Hawker

OCIATE DIRECTORS:
H. Arrow, Engineering
J. Eadie, TD MInstM, Marketing

ir Bearings Ltd was formed in March 1965 manufacture light ACVs employing the mpany's own integrated lift/propulsion tem and skirt design. Production of the 11 Crossbow three-seater began in '4 and at the time of going to press 12 ve been sold. The first sale was to Mitsui second to King Hussein of Jordan for on the Gulf of Akaba; five are being built the Nigerian police force and a further r have been ordered by a customer in the ited States. The twelfth has been ordered operation in Venezuela.

n 1975, the company began the design of 'stretched' version, the 9-seat AB 12 gbow, the prototype of which is due for pletion in 1976. Power for the integrated propulsion system will be provided by 130 hp Wankel rotary engines, either of ch will enable the craft to return to base the event of the other failing. Simple

e-production prototype of the Airbearings 11 Crossbow during trials on the Solent

The Air Bearings Crossbow, a three-seat general purpose amphibious ACV

defects on the dead engine can be rectified while the craft is under way as both engines are accessible from the cabin. It is stated that considerable interest in the new design has been shown by companies in the USA, South America and the Middle East.

AB 11 CROSSBOW

This general purpose amphibious ACV is based on the company's experience with the HC 9, HC 10, and earlier prototypes. Luxury, commercial and lightly armoured military variants are available.

LIFT AND PROPULSION: Motive power for the integrated lift/propulsion system is provided by a 135 hp Johnson (OMC) 135 ESL 74 V4 two-stroke, driving a single four- or six-bladed axial fan. The fan, 32½ in (812 mm) in diameter, is built in laminated wood and mounted on top of the engine crankshaft. Thrust is provided by ejecting fan air horizontally from the rear of the hull. Fuel is carried in two 16 gallon bagged tanks located in the sides of the hull close to the c of g. Refuelling points are provided port and starboard, amidships. Fuel recommended is 4 star petrol/oil mix 45:1.

CONTROLS: Triple rudders operating in the airjet exit provide directional control. Two elevators aft of the thrust ducts provide trim control at speed. Reverse thrust is by a shutter and vane system. Two 4 gallon ballast tanks are provided for fore and aft trim.

Driving controls consist of a steering wheel and three hand-operated levers, console mounted, which control engine throttle, reverse thrust mechanism and craft pitch.

INSTRUMENTATION: Instruments include tachometer, air speed indicator, trim indicator, static ballast gauge, fuel and water temperature and battery condition gauges, clock and hours-run indicator. Panel mounted switches operate flashing beacon, navigation and headlights and ballast pump controls.

HULL: The hull and superstructure are constructed in grp throughout. Longitudinal members and bulkheads are in aluminium aeroweb. A continuous 100% finger skirt of HDL design in Polyurethane/Nylon is fitted giving a 12 in (30 cm) hard structure clearance.

ACCOMMODATION: Single bench seat for driver and up to two passengers abreast or two bucket seats. Entry is through two gullwing doors, one port, one starboard.

SYSTEMS, ELECTRICAL: Two 12 v alternators, 35 amp/hr and 6 amp/hr. Two 12 v batteries, 60 amp/hr and 30 amp/hr.

COMMUNICATIONS: Radio, optional extra.

DIMENSIONS:

Length overall	18 ft 9 in	(5·72 m)
Beam (skirt inflated)	11 ft 6 in	(3·50 m)
Beam (power off)	7 ft 8 in	(2·33 m)
Height on landing pads	4 ft 3 in	(1·27 m)
Cushion area	147 sq ft	(13·65 m²)

DIMENSIONS, INTERNAL:

Cabin:

Length	4 ft 8 in	(1·42 m)
Max width	4 ft 8 in	(1·42 m)
Max height	3 ft 2 in	(91·5 cm)
Floor area	22 sq ft	(2·04 m²)

WEIGHTS:

Normal empty weight	1,340 lb	(607 kg)
Normal all-up weight	2,100 lb	(952 kg)
Normal gross weight	2,100 lb	(952 kg)
Normal payload	400 lb	(181·42 kg)
Maximum payload	600 lb	(272·14 kg)

Interior of Crossbow's cabin showing the instrument layout and controls. The bench seat accommodates the driver and two passengers

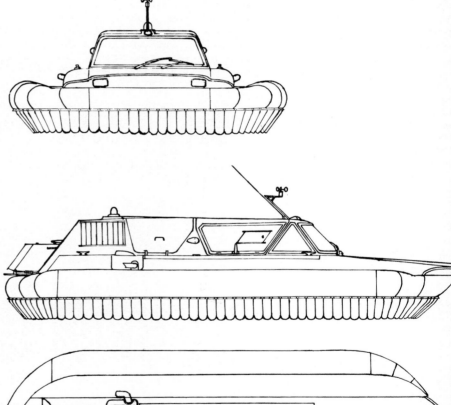

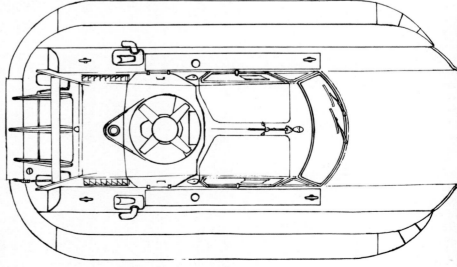

General arrangement of the AB II Crossbow

PERFORMANCE (normal operating weight, calm water):

Max speed	35 knots
Cruising speed	30 knots
Endurance at cruising speed	4 hours
Max gradient, static conditions	1:10
Vertical obstacle clearance	1 ft (30 cm)

AB 12 LONGBOW

An enlarged and more powerful version of the elegant Crossbow, Longbow is fitted with twin engines to provide an adequate power reserve to cope with difficult terrain or sea conditions. At the same time, the arrangement ensures that the occupants can return to base in the event of one engine failing.

Two 130 hp Wankel rotary engines power the integrated lift/propulsion system. In the event of either being shut down, the craft can return to its base or the safety of the shore on its remaining engine.

The vehicle retains the ease of handling of Crossbow and employs a similar system of controls and reverse thrust. It also incorporates bow thrust ports to aid manoeuvring at slow speed.

A para-military model, equipped with a machine gun, a searchlight and a loudhailer, is being developed.

LIFT AND PROPULSION: Power for the integrated lift/propulsion system is supplied by two 130 hp Wankel rotary engines mounted aft of the cabin. Access to the engine bay is provided to allow any simple defect to be rectified while the craft is underway. Power is transmitted from each engine to a single 3 ft 2 in (0·96 m) diameter Dowty Rotol six-bladed axial-flow fan, which provides pressurised air for both lift and thrust. Split ducting channels two-thirds of the air to an airjet aperture aft, and one-third to the lift ducts. Some lift air is bled off for engine cooling. Fuel is carried in three tanks, two located in the sides of the hull amidships, and one central collector tank. Total fuel capacity is 60 Imp gallons (272·75 l). Fuel recommended is 87 octane. Refuelling necks are located amidships.

CONTROLS: Twin rudders operating in each of the twin airjet thrust exists provide heading control at cruising speed and above. Low speed directional control is provided by bow thrust ports. Elevators aft of the thrust apertures provide trim control at speed. Reverse thrust is by shutter and vane system. Water ballast tanks give static longitudinal trim. A battery shift system provides lateral trim.

HULL: Hull and superstructure are built in grp. Longitudinal members and cabin bulkheads are in aluminium aeroweb.

SKIRT: 3 ft (0·914 m) deep loop and segment skirt of HDL design in polyurethane/nylon.

ACCOMMODATION: Enclosed cabin, with three rows of three seats for driver and eight passengers. Alternative configuration with four rows of three seats, for driver and eleven passengers. Access is via two sets of gull wing doors, two port, two starboard. Standard model is heated and ventilated. Air conditioning optional extra. The engine bay has an automatic fire extinguisher system.

Impression of the AB 12 Longbow, a twin-engined derivative of Crossbow, designed to carry a driver and eight passengers

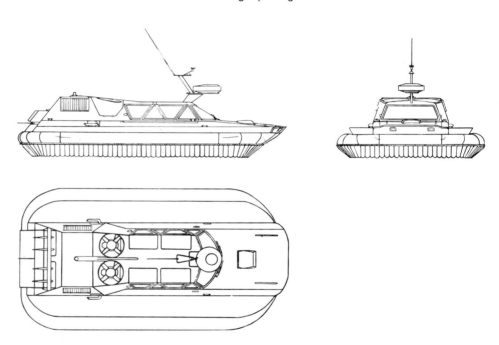

AB 12 Longbow (two 130 hp Wankel rotary engines)

SYSTEMS: Electrical: Two 12 V alternators (55 Ah) and two or four 12 V batteries (60 Ah). Communications: Radio optional. Navigation: Radar optional. Armament: Can mount light automatic weapon on cabin-roof if required for para-military duties.

DIMENSIONS, EXTERNAL:

Length overall, power off	28 ft 0 in (8·53 m)
Length overall, skirt inflated	28 ft 0 in (8·53 m)
Beam overall, power off	14 ft 6 in (4·41 m)
Beam overall, skirt inflated	18 ft 6 in (5·63 m)
folded for transportation	8 ft 10 in (2·69 m)
Height overall, on landing pads (without radar and radio aerial	5 ft 2 in (1·57 m)
Height overall, skirt inflated (without radar and aerial)	7 ft 6 in (2·28 m)

DIMENSIONS, INTERNAL:

Cabin length	9 ft 0 in (2·74 m)
Max width	4 ft 2 in (1·27 m)
Floor area	56·25 sq ft (5·22 m²)

WEIGHTS:

Normal empty weight	2,970 lb (1,347·14 kg)
Normal all-up weight	3,370 lb (1,528·59 kg)
Normal gross weight	5,070 lb (2,298 kg)
Normal payload	1,700 lb (771 kg)

PERFORMANCE (at normal operating weight):

Max speed over calm water, max cont power	35 knots
Crusing speed, calm water	30 knots
Max wave capability	2 ft 6 in (0·762 m)
Still air endurance at cruising speed	5 hours
Max gradient, static conditions	1:10
Vertical obstacle clearance	2 ft 0 in (0·609 m)

AIRHOVER LTD

HEAD OFFICE:
Hoverplane Works,
Main Road,
Arlesford,
Colchester, CO7 8DB
Essex

TELEPHONE:
Boxted 356

DIRECTORS:
R. P. Wingfield, Managing Director
V. A. Johnson
V. E. Andrews, Secretary

Airhover Ltd is marketing the Aero Sabre Mk I and Mk II light hovercraft—both open single or two seaters—and the more sophisticated Aero Sabre III, high performance sports ACV.

AERO SABRE Mk I

The new Aero Sabre Mk I is a high performance amphibious light sports hovercraft. It is in production and is available either complete or in kit form. Two models are offered: Mk 1, with a single engine and lift/propulsion duct assembly, and Mk 1SP, a modified version, produced for youth training organisations and schools with workshop facilities as an educational project machine.

LIFT AND PROPULSION: Power for the integrated lift/propulsion system can be provided by a wide choice of engines ranging from a 9 bhp or 13 bhp Stihl to a 12 bhp Kyoritsu. The primary airflow from the eight-bladed axial-flow fan is ejected through a propulsive slot aft of the fan duct, and the secondary airflow, for the cushion, passes downwards into the plenum chamber.

HULL: Mixed aluminium, glassfibre and wooden construction. Laminated wooden outer frame amd similar inner frame. The engine, aluminium duct and outlet, moulded glassfibre seat and streamlined nose fairing are all carried on the two longitudinals and can be detached as one separate unit. Upper surface covered with lightweight nylon, impregnated on both sides with pvc. Fuel tank is integral with glassfibre superstructure with filler neck aft of driver's seat. Fuel capacity is 2 gals (9·09 l).

SKIRT: Made in extra strong nylon fabric and reinforced with double skin of pvc. Skirt is in eleven segments and is stitched with rot-proofed thread. Skirt attachment rails provided.

ACCOMMODATION: Open motor-cycle type upholstered seating for one or two in tandem.

CONTROLS: Throttle twist grip control, with dummy grip opposite and ignition cut-out switch. Steering is by kinesthetic control (body movement). The manufacturer points out that as the performance is "very lively," experience at low speeds is desirable before attempting high speed runs.

DIMENSIONS:

Length	9 ft (2·74 m)
Beam	6 ft (1·82 m)
Height	3 ft (91·44 m)

WEIGHTS:

Unladen	100 lb (45·35 kg)
Max payload	400 lb (181·43 kg)

PERFORMANCE:

Designed speed,	
land	35 mph (56·33 km/h)
water	20 mph (32·18 km/h)
Fuel consumption	1 gph (4·5 lph)
Obstacle clearance	6 in (15·24 cm)

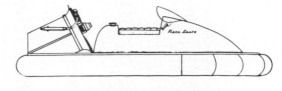
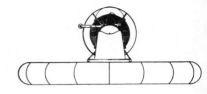
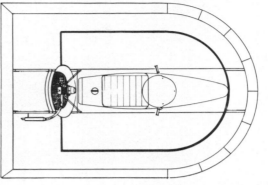

General arrangement of the Aero Sabre Mk I

Above: The Aero Sabre Mk I SP, now available in partially assembled kit form for education authorities for school educational projects including hovercraft theory. *Below:* The standard Aero Sabre Mk. I high performance light sports ACV

AERO SABRE Mk 1 SP

This is a modified version of the Mk 1, produced for Education Authorities which are planning to include hovercraft design theory among their educational projects. Export orders for the machine have been received from overseas authorities, including one from the Government of Western

Australia.

The company was approached with the suggestion that the Aero Sabre Mk 1 would be ideal for such projects, and as a result, a special kit has been developed from which it can be constructed without complicated equipment. It can be completed with simple hand tools and some assistance from a small engineering workshop.

The full kit is divided into seven individual assemblies, five of which are supplied complete. The remaining two, the airframe and the engine, occupy about 60% of the construction time.

The materials used in the airframe are normally available in the school stock room or are readily available locally. Any small two-cycle industrial or motor cycle engine can be installed, providing it develops a minimum of 7 bhp.

If difficulties are experienced in obtaining either materials for the airframe or a suitable engine, these items can also be supplied by Airhove Ltd.

AERO SABRE Mk III

The prototype of this exceptionally elegant two-seater is undergoing tests. One of the aims of the designers has been to produce a high-performance light ACV which combines the lines of a racing aircraft with the comfort of a modern sports car. Various alternative layouts are available to suit commercial applications. Performance depends upon the power installed: but the designed maximum speed is 60 mph (95·56 km/h)
LIFT AND PROPULSION: The lift engine, a 20 hp MAG type 1031 two-stroke is located forward of the cabin beneath a protective metal mesh panel and drives a 1 ft 9 in

Aero Sabre, a 60 mph (96·56 km/h) amphibious two-seater, combines elegance and high performance with the comfort of a modern sports car

(0·53 m) diameter fan with blades set at 30 deg. Each blade is detachable to facilitate replacement. Located aft of the cabin, the propulsion engine, a 33 hp MAG 2062-SRB twin cylinder two-stroke, drives a 3 ft 0 in (0·914 m) diameter two-bladed variable-pitch propeller. The entire thrust unit will be surrounded by a plated protective mesh guard. Both engines have electric starters.
CONTROLS: Heading is controlled by a single, swept back aerodynamic rudder operating in the propeller slipstream. Aircraft-type wheel, instrumentation, switches and throttles.
HULL: Built in high grade marine ply and incorporating three watertight buoyancy compartments. In the event of either one or two of these sustaining damage, the remaining compartments will keep the craft afloat. The superstructure, which includes the canopy, forward, decking and air intake is a one-piece moulding in grp. Windows and wind-

shields are in perspex. Cabin access is via two light alloy gull-wing doors which are raised electrically.
SKIRT: Conventional bag-type, 1 ft 0 in (304 mm) deep.
CABIN: Access is via gull-wing doors. Semi-reclining, upholstered seats are provided side-by-side for driver and passenger. Panels and pillars are finished in matching colours.
DIMENSIONS:

Length overall	17 ft (5·18 m)
Beam overall	8 ft (2·43 m)
Height to top of rudder (on landing pads)	5 ft (1·52 m)
Skirt depth	1 ft 4 in (406 mm)

WEIGHTS:
Not available at time of going to press.

PERFORMANCE:

Obstacle clearance	12 in (304 mm)
Max speed	60 mph (96·56 km/h)

AIR VEHICLES LIMITED

HEAD OFFICE AND WORKS:
1 Sun Hill, Cowes, Isle of Wight
TELEPHONES:
Cowes 3194 and 4439
TELEX:
86513 (Hoverwork, Ryde)
DIRECTORS:
P. H. Winter, MSc
C. D. J. Bland
C. B. Eden
Since its inception in 1968, Air Vehicles Ltd has concentrated on the development of a small 5/6 seater amphibious hovercraft, the AV2. The prototype was completed in 1970 and development has continued during 1971 and 1972. The first pre-production AV2 was completed in 1973. This machine has performed well and the company has launched a marketing programme for this design.

The second and third machines have been purchased by LKV in the Netherlands who will also take delivery of the next four machines for various customers. AV2-002 has been tested extensively by the Rijks-waterstaat, Netherlands, by the British army and by the British Interservices Hovercraft Unit. In 1974 it was demonstrated at the Jakarta Trade Fair, Indonesia.

A developed model of AV.2, with increased seating capacity and reduced fuel consumption, is nearing completion and will be ready for operation in late 1975.

Air Vehicles also undertakes modifications to the British Hovercraft Corporation range of SR.N5 and SR.N6 hovercraft. These

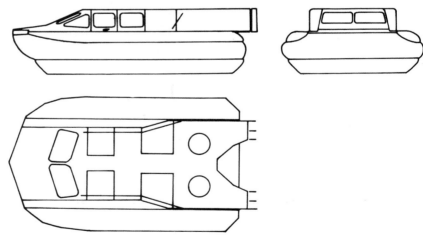

General arrangement of the Air Vehicles Ltd. AV 2-002

include flat deck conversions (see photo), power assisted rudder packs and various other units designed to assist commercial and military users, in particular, the new ducted propeller installation designed and built by the company.

Air Vehicles Ltd has recently undertaken several studies on the transport of very heavy loads on towed hoverbarges in many parts of the world. The first hoverbarge to be built for operation across the Yukon River in Alaska was designed by the company and completed in November 1974.

AV.2

A feature of this twin-engined amphibious

5-6 seater is the use of fan-jet propulsion to minimise noise. The prototype, built in 1970, has completed several hundred hours of development testing to prove the basic reliability of the machine and its components. This was followed by various operations, charters and tests undertaken with AV2-002. As a result production craft—AV.2-003 and subsequent machines—embody various improvements in terms of construction, payload and control. The craft is suitable for both civil and para-military roles. It can operate on either of its two engines enabling it to return to base in the event of one engine failing.

LIFT AND PROPULSION: Two converted outboard engine powerheads drive two centrifugal fans for lift and propulsion. Kits will be available to convert the engines from petrol to kerosene fuel.

CONTROLS: Rudder vane control and throttles for the two engines, auxiliary control systems for trim and reverse thrust.

HULL: 001 and 002, robust foam/fibreglass structure. 003 and subsequent craft, fibreglass internal and external production mouldings. Hull sidebodies are inflated for buoyancy but can be deflated for transport.

ACCOMMODATION: Enclosed cabin for driver and up to five passengers.

SKIRT: Pressurised bag with separate segments.

DIMENSIONS:

Length overall	19 ft 0 in (5·79 m)
Beam overall	11 ft 2 in (3·40 m)
Beam, sidebodies deflated for transport	
	7 ft 10½ in (2·39 m)

WEIGHTS:

Empty weight	200 lb (907·12 kg)
Loaded weight	3,000 lb (1,360·8 kg)

PERFORMANCE:

Cruising speed, calm water	35 knots
Fuel consumption (petrol) at full throttle	
	15 gal/hr (68 l/hr)
Fuel consumption, cruising	
	10 gal/hr (45 l/hr)

PRICE: Standard craft, £18,000, ex-works.

AV.2D

A developed version of AV.2 is being constructed which utilises the well-tried hull, skirt system and inflatable sidebodies but incorporates a single Rover V8 engine to give increased seating capacity, improved performance in wind and better fuel consumption. This craft will be completed in October 1975 and will be available for charter from the end of the year. Future craft of this type will be available for charter also.

POWER PLANT: One Rover V8 3·5 litre petrol engine.

ACCOMMODATION: Driver and up to eight passengers or equivalent payload.

DIMENSIONS:

Length overall	22 ft 6 in (6·85 m)
Beam overall	11 ft 2 in (3·40 m)

WEIGHTS:

Empty weight	2,200 lb (997·85 kg)
Loaded weight	3,700 lb (1,678·277 kg)

PERFORMANCE:

Cruising speed in calm water	30 knots
Fuel consumption	6 gal/hr (27·27 l/hr)

Above: First production AV.2—the 003—has a slightly longer cabin equipped with sliding access doors. The hull is in moulded fibreglass. *Below:* Seen clearly in this photograph are AV.2-002's segmented bag skirt and the sidebodies, which are deflated for transport. Calm water cruising speed is 35 knots

N5 HOVERFREIGHTER

Converted by Air Vehicles Ltd from the original N5 craft, this provides a fast personnel and supply carrier for application anywhere in the world.

It has been employed on civil engineering and survey contracts in the Wash and on Maplin Sands. On January 1st 1975, it began operating from Thursday Island, North Queensland, providing services and communications between offshore islands for the Department of Aboriginal Affairs.

Accommodation is provided for up to 19 passengers.

DIMENSIONS:

Length overall	38 ft 9 in (11·80 m)
Beam overall	23 ft 0 in (7·01 m)
Deck area	450 sq ft (41·81 sq m)

WEIGHTS:

Max deck load	6,700 lb

A military SR.N6 equipped with an Air Vehicles' ducted propeller, reducing the noise level by more than 10dBA

DUCTED PROPELLER N6

A ducted propeller installation has been designed and built by Air Vehicles Ltd for the SR.N6 hovercraft. The propeller, 6 ft 10 in (2·08 m) in diameter, is designed to maintain the original thrust of the N6 but to reduce the noise level by more than 10dBA. The unit can be fitted very simply to any standard N6 or N5 and the first installation has been made on a military N6. Ground running tests have been completed with sea trials scheduled to take place in the summer of 1975.

N6 HOVERFREIGHTER

Converted from a standard SR.N6 by Air Vehicles Limited this craft was first operated by Hoverwork in the Arctic in 1971. In one operation undertaken in heavy fog it carried up to ten tons per hour between ships and a shore base over floating ice.

It has since been used on several overseas charters, including one of long duration in 1975, when it was employed on seismic survey work in Saudi Arabia.

ACCOMMODATION: Front cabin: 8 men or 3 plus stretcher; rear cabin: 2 men.

AUXILIARY EQUIPMENT: Heavy duty air conditioner, Kelvin Hughes Type 17 radar, long-range fuel tanks (7 hours duration), vhf radio, mf radio.

DIMENSIONS:

Length overall	48 ft 5 in (14·76 m)
Beam overall	23 ft 0 in (7·01 m)
Deck area	500 sq ft (46·4 m²)
Underfloor storage	650 cu ft (18·0 m³)

WEIGHTS:

Normal payload	7,000 lb (3,175 kg)
Maximum payload	10,000 lb (4,536 kg)
Gross overload	15,000 lb (6,804 kg)

Two craft modified by Air Vehicles Ltd for freighting operations. *Above:* an SR.N6 and *below,* SR.N5 GH-2009

AJAX HOVERCRAFT

HEAD OFFICE:
967 Stockport Road,
Levenshulme,
Manchester M19 3NP
TELEPHONE:
061 224 5422
HOME TELEPHONE:
061 432 6636
DIRECTORS:
Donald Woolley
David Woolley

Harold Poyser Ltd is continuing the activities of Ajax Hovercraft, which had been engaged in ACV research and development since January 1971. The company's activities are centred chiefly on the production of the two-seat AH 5. It also offers a spares service for enthusiasts, including basic materials, skirts, fans, engines, ducts and complete thrust and lift modules.

AH 5

Features of this fibreglass-hulled two-seater include an enclosed luggage space fore and aft, and a wide, comfortable cabin for the driver and passenger.

LIFT AND PROPULSION: Lift air is provided by an 8·62 bhp Rowena Stihl single-cylinder two-stroke driving a 2 ft 0 in (609 mm) diameter, 10-bladed multiwing fan at 3,220 rpm. The fan blades are set at 30 degrees, and the hub has a steel bush mounted on a keyed, stainless steel shaft. At maximum auw, the cushion pressure is 12·52 lb sq ft. Cushion area is 67·88 sq ft. Propulsive thrust is supplied by two identical 8·62 hp Rowena Stihl 6507-JL single-cylinder two strokes, each of which drives a 2 ft 0 in (609 mm) diameter, 5-bladed multiwing fan with blades set at 45 degrees. Fuel is carried in two interconnected metal tanks installed in the sidebodies. Total capacity is 11 gallons (50 l). Manufacturer recommends 90-93 octane mixed 20 : 1 with outboard motor oil.

CONTROLS: Triple rudders hinged to the rear of each of the two thrust ducts control craft heading.

HULL: moulded grp structure.

SKIRT: 11 in (279 mm) deep bag-type skirt in 15 oz neoprene on nylon.

ACCOMMODATION: Driver and passenger

sit side-by-side on a bench-type seat. Canopy is in grp and slides forward on nylon rails. Manual screen washer and electric wipers are standard. Plastic side windows can be pushed out in an emergency. Front screen is of laminated safety glass.

SYSTEMS: 6v lighting coils on each engine rectified to dc.

DIMENSIONS, EXTERNAL:

Length overall:	
power off	13 ft 7 in (4·14 m)
skirt inflated	14 ft 4½ in (4·39 m)
Beam overall:	
power off	6 ft 7 in (2·00 m)
skirt inflated	7 ft 11 in (2·41 m)
Height overall:	
on landing skids	3 ft 6¾ in (1·08 m)
skirt inflated	4 ft 4 in (1·32 m)
Draft afloat	2½ in (63 mm)
Skirt depth	11 in (279 mm)

DIMENSIONS, INTERNAL:

Cabin and forward stowage
  4 ft wide by 5 ft 8 in long (1·21 m wide
            by 1·72 m long)

Aft stowage
  19½ in by 23 in × 12 in deep (495 mm by
            584 mm × 304 mm)

WEIGHTS:

Normal empty weight	350 lb (158·75 kg)
Normal all-up weight	850 lb (385·53 kg)
Recommended max payload	
	500 lb (226·78 kg)

PERFORMANCE:

Speed, calm water	about 35 knots
sand, ice, short grass	
	about 60 mph (96·56 km/h)
Max gradient	1 · 10

Power for the Ajax AH5 amphibious two-seater is provided by three 8 bhp Rowena Stihl two-strokes, one for lift and two for propulsion. Built into the hull, aft of the cabin, is a hold for small items of baggage. Top speed over calm water is about 35 knots

BRITISH HOVERCRAFT CORPORATION

HEAD OFFICE:
  East Cowes, Isle of Wight
TELEPHONE:
  Cowes 4101
TELEX:
  86190
TELEGRAMS:
  BRITHOVER COWES TELEX
DIRECTORS:
Sir Christopher Hartley, KCB, CBE, DFC, AFC, BA, Chairman
R. Stanton-Jones, MA, DCAe, CEng, AFRAeS, Managing Director
J. McGarity, Works Director
T. Bretherton, Finance Director and Secretary
R. L. Wheeler, MSc, DIC, CEng, AFRAeS, Technical Director
J. M. George, BSc(Eng), DCAe, Sales Director
W. A. Oppenheimer, FCA
G. S. Hislop, PhD, BSc, ARCST, CEng, FIMechE, FRAeS, FRSA
B. D. Blackwell, MA, BSc(Eng), CEng, FIMechE, FRAeS, FBIM

The British Hovercraft Corporation is the world's largest hovercraft manufacturer. It was formed in 1966 to concentrate the British hovercraft industry's major technical and other resources under a single management.

The corporation deals with a wide variety of applications of the air cushion principle,

Swift, the first 200-ton SR.N4 Mk 2 mixed traffic hovercraft. Converted by BHC from a standard craft for Hoverlloyd Ltd., the Mk 2 carries up to 280 passengers and 37 vehicles compared with 254 passengers and 30 vehicles on the standard craft

the emphasis being on the development and production of amphibious hovercraft. Other activities include the investigation of industrial applications of the air cushion principle.

The capital of the corporation is £5 million, which is wholly owned by Westland Aircraft Ltd.

BHC established the world's first full-scale hovercraft production line in 1964. Currently it is producing the 10-ton Winchester (SR.N6) Class craft, the 50-ton Wellington (BH.7) Class craft and the 190-ton Mountbatten

(SR.N4) Class craft at East Cowes.

At present five Mountbatten Class craft are in service as passenger/car ferries on the Dover/Boulogne and Ramsgate/Calais routes; two with British Rail Hovercraft, and three with Hoverlloyd Ltd.

One BH.7 is in service with the Royal Navy's Naval Hovercraft Trials Unit and six have been delivered to the Imperial Iranian Navy. Three additional BH.7 Mk.5s have been ordered by the Imperial Iranian Navy and are under construction.

Military and general duty variants of the Warden and Winchester Class hovercraft are now in service with the Naval Hovercraft Trials Unit, Imperial Iranian Navy, Italian Interservice Hovercraft Unit and the Canadian and Saudi Arabian Coast Guard.

Winchesters have been employed since 1967 in trials and sales demonstrations in Africa, Canada, Denmark, Finland, India, South America and the middle and Far East, logging well over 160,000 operating hours.

Commercial general purpose variants of the Warden and Winchester are in service with British Rail Hovercraft Ltd, Dept. of Civil Aviation, New Zealand, Department of Transport, Canada, Hovertravel Ltd, Hoverwork Ltd and Mitsubishi Heavy Industries Ltd. In recent years the Winchester has been used increasingly for general purposes roles including hydrographic and seismic survey, freighting and search and rescue duties.

MOUNTBATTEN (SR.N4) CLASS Mk. 1

The world's largest hovercraft, the Mountbatten is a 190-ton passenger car/ferry designed for stage lengths of up to 100 n miles (184 km) on coastal water routes. It has an average service speed of 40-50 knots in waves up to 10 ft (3·04 m) in height and is able to operate in 12 ft (3·7 m) seas at a speed of about 20 knots.

The first craft entered commercial service with British Rail Hovercraft Ltd. in August 1968 on the Dover/Boulogne route and British Rail took delivery of a second craft for service on the same route late in the summer of 1969.

Two further craft entered service with Hoverlloyd Limited in April 1969 on the Ramsgate/Calais route—and a third craft joined this operation in 1972.

LIFT AND PROPULSION: Power is supplied by four 3,400 shp Rolls-Royce Marine Proteus free-turbine, turboshaft engines located in pairs at the rear of the craft on either side of the vehicle deck. Each has a maximum rating of 4,250 shp, but usually operates at 3,400 shp when cruising. Each engine is connected to one of four identical propeller/fan units, two forward and two aft. The propulsion propellers, made by Hawker Siddeley Dynamics, are of the 4-bladed, variable and reversible pitch type 19 ft (5·79 m) in diameter. The lift fans, made by BHC, are of the 12-bladed centrifugal type, 11 ft 6 in (3·5 m) in diameter.

Since the gear ratios between the engine, fan and propeller are fixed, the power distribution can be altered by varying the propeller pitch and hence changing the speed of the system, which accordingly alters the power absorbed by the fixed pitch fan. The power absorbed by the fan can be varied from almost zero shp (i.e. boating with minimum power) to 2,100 shp, within the propeller and engine speed limitations. A

During 1974, British Rail's two SR.N4s carried between them 580,000 passengers and 83,000 cars on the Dover-Boulogne, Dover-Calais Seaspeed services.

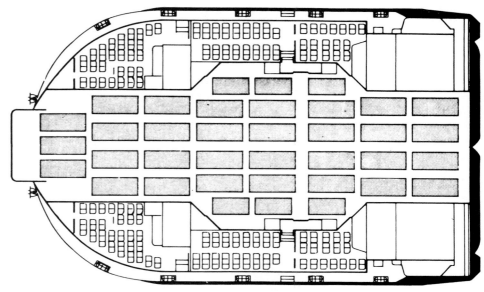

In most respects, the SR.N4 Mk. 2 is identical to the standard version. The increased capacity of 282 passengers and 37 cars was achieved by removing two inner passenger cabins to increase the car deck area and by widening the outer passenger cabins

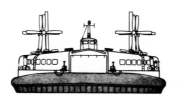
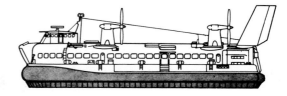
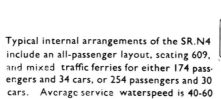
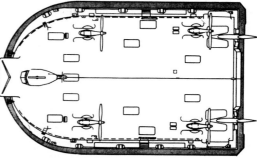

Typical internal arrangements of the SR.N4 include an all-passenger layout, seating 609, and mixed traffic ferries for either 174 passengers and 34 cars, or 254 passengers and 30 cars. Average service waterspeed is 40-60 knots

typical division on maximum cruise power would be 2,000 shp to the propeller and 1,150 shp to the fan; the remaining 250 shp can be accounted for by engine power fall-off due to the turbine rpm drop, transmission losses and auxiliary drives.

The drive shafts from the engines consist of flanged light-alloy tubes approximately 7ft 6 in (2·28 m) long supported by steady bearings and connected by self-aligning couplings. Shafting to the rear propeller/fan units is comparatively short, but to the forward units is approximately 60 ft (18·27 m).

The main gearbox of each unit comprises a spiral bevel reduction gear, with outputs at the top and bottom of the box to the vertical propeller and fan drive shafts respectively. The design of the vertical shafts and couplings is similar to the main transmission shafts, except that the shafts above the main gearbox are of steel instead of light alloy to transmit the much greater torque loads to the propeller. This gearbox is equipped with a power take-off for an auxiliary gearbox with drives for pressure and scavenge lubricating oil pumps, and also a hydraulic pump for the pylon and fin steering control.

The upper gearbox, mounted on top of the pylon, turns the propeller drive through 90° and has a gear ratio of 1·16 : 1. This gearbox has its own self-contained lubricating system.

Engines and auxiliaries are readily accessible for maintenance from inside the craft, while engine, propellers, pylons and all gearboxes can be removed for overhaul without disturbing the main structure.

The fan rotates on a pintle which is attached to the main structure. The assembly may be detached and removed inboard onto the car deck without disturbing the major structure.

CONTROLS: The craft control system enables the thrust lines and pitch angles of the propellers to be varied either collectively or differentially. The fins and rudders move in step with the aft pylons. The pylons, fins and rudders move through $\pm 35°$, $\pm 30°$ and $\pm 40°$ respectively.

Demand signals for pylon and fin angles are transmitted from the commander's controls electrically. These are compared with the pylon or fin feed-back signals and the differences are then amplified to actuate the hydraulic jacks mounted at the base of the pylon or fin structure. Similar electro-hydraulic signalling and feed-back systems are used to control propeller pitches.

The commander's controls include a rudder bar which steers the craft by pivoting the propeller pylons differentially.

For example, if the right foot is moved forward, the forward pylons move clockwise, viewed from above, and the aft pylons and fins move anti-clockwise, thus producing a turning movement to starboard. The foregoing applies with positive thrust on the propellers, but if negative thrust is applied, as in the case of using the propellers for braking, the pylons and fins are automatically turned to opposing angles, thus maintaining the turn. A wheel mounted on a control column enables the commander to move the pylons and fins in unison to produce a drift to either port or starboard as required. The control of the distribution of power between each propeller and fan is by propeller pitch lever. The pitch of all four propellers can be adjusted collectively over a limited range by a fore-and-aft movement of the control wheel.

HULL: Construction is primarily of high strength, aluminium-clad, aluminium alloy, suitably protected against the corrosive effects of sea water.

The basic structure is the buoyancy chamber, built around a grid of longitudinal and transversal frames, which form twenty-four watertight sub-divisions for safety. The design ensures that even a rip from end-to-end would not cause the craft to sink or overturn. The reserve buoyancy is 250% the total available buoyancy amounting to more than 550 tons.

Top and bottom surfaces of the buoyancy chamber are formed by sandwich construction panels bolted onto the frames, the top surface being the vehicle deck. Panels covering the central 16 ft (4·9 m) section of the deck are reinforced to carry unladen coaches, or commercial vehicles up to 9 tons gross weight (max axle load 13,000 lb (5,900 kg)), while the remainder are designed solely to carry cars and light vehicles (max axle load 4,500 lb (2,040 kg)). An articulated loading ramp, 18 ft (5·5m) wide, which can be lowered to ground level, is built into the bows, whilst doors extending the full width of the centre deck are provided at the aft end.

Cars being unloaded from the SR.N4 via the 31 ft (9.45 m) wide stern doors

Panels covering the central 16 ft (4·9 m) of the vehicle decks are reinforced to carry unladen coaches or commercial vehicles up to 9 tons gross weight while the remainder is designed solely to carry cars and light vehicles

Passenger seating in one of the side cabins flanking the car deck on a Hoverlloyd SR.N4

Similar grid construction is used on the elevated passenger-carrying decks and the roof, where the panels are supported by deep transverse and longitudinal frames. The buoyancy chamber is joined to the roof by longitudinal walls to form a stiff fore-and-aft structure. Lateral bending is taken mainly by the buoyancy tanks. All horizontal surfaces are of pre-fabricated sandwich panels with the exception of the roof, which is of skin and stringer panels.

Double curvature has been avoided other than in the region of the air intakes and bow. Each fan air intake is bifurcated and has an athwartships bulkhead at both front and rear, supporting a beam carrying the transmission main gearbox and the propeller pylon. The all-moving fins and rudders behind the aft pylons pivot on pintles just ahead of the rear bulkhead.

The fans deliver air to the cushion via a peripheral fingered bag skirt.

The material used for both bags and fingers is nylon, coated with neoprene and/or natural rubber, the fingers and cones being made from a heavier weight material than the trunks.

ACCOMMODATION: The basic manning requirement is for a commander, an engineer/radio operator and a radar operator/navigator. A seat is provided for a fourth crew member or a crew member in training. The remainder of the crew, i.e. those concerned with passenger service or car handling, are located in the main cabins. The arrangement may be modified to suit individual operator's requirements.

The control cabin is entered by either of two ways. The normal method, when the cars are arranged in four lanes, is by a hatch in the cabin floor, reached by a ladder from the car deck. When heavy vehicles are carried on the centre section, or if for some other reason the ladder has to be retracted, a door on the side of the port forward passenger cabin gives access to a ladder leading onto the main cabin roof. From the roof an entrance door gives access into the control cabin.

The craft currently in service carry 254 passengers and 30 cars but the basic design permits variations from an all-passenger craft (609 seats) to one carrying 174 passengers and 34 cars.

The car deck occupies the large central area of the craft, with large stern doors and a bow ramp providing a drive-on/drive-off facility.

Separate side doors give access to the passenger cabins which flank the car deck. The outer cabins have large windows which extend over the full length of the craft. The control cabin is sited centrally and forward on top of the superstructure to give maximum view.

DIMENSIONS, EXTERNAL:
Overall length   130 ft 2 in (39·68 m)
Overall beam   78 ft 0 in (23·77 m)
Overall height on landing pads
                      37 ft 8 in (11·48 m)
Skirt depth   8 ft 0 in (2·44 m)
DIMENSIONS, INTERNAL:
Passenger/vehicle floor area
                      5,800 sq ft (539 m²)
Vehicle deck headroom-centre line
                      11 ft 3 in (3·43 m)
Bow ramp door aperture size (height ×
width) 11 ft 6 in × 18 ft (3·51 × 5·48 m)
Stern door aperture size (height × width)
      11 ft × 31 ft (3·51 m × 9·45 m)

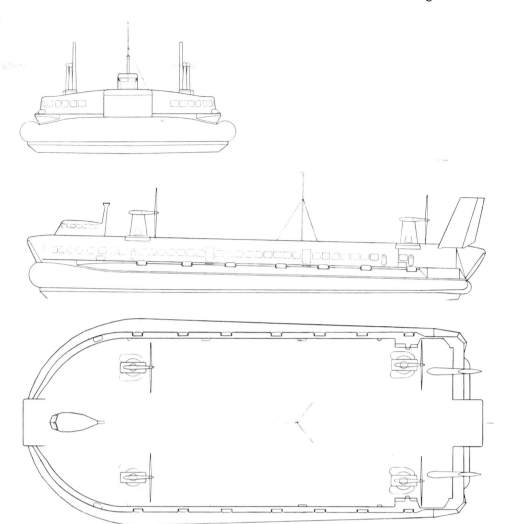

General arrangement of the SR.N4 Mk. 3

Impression of the "stretched" SR.N4 Mk. 3, a design study undertaken for British Rail, The craft, which would have a normal gross weight of about 265 tons, would carry up to 396 passengers and 53 vehicles

WEIGHTS:
Normal gross weight   180 tons
Fuel capacity
    4,500 Imp gallons (20·456 litres)
PERFORMANCE (at normal gross weight at 15°C):
Max waterspeed over calm water, zero wind
    (cont power rating)   70 knots
Average service waterspeed   40-60 knots
Normal stopping distance from 50 knots
                           525 yards (480 m)
Endurance at max cont power on 2,800 Imp
    gallons   2-5 hours
Negotiable gradient from standing start
                                    1 : 11

SR.N4 Mk.2
To cope with the increasing public demand for their cross-Channel service, Hoverlloyd has increased the capacity of its craft from 254 passengers and 30 vehicles to 280 passengers and 37 vehicles.

Modification of the first of these craft was completed in January 1973, and the remaining two craft underwent similar conversions during the winter 1973/74.

This increase in capacity has been achieved by the removal of the two inner passenger cabins on the car deck level to accommodate more vehicles. Passenger capacity has been increased by widening the outer cabins to the periphery of the craft structure.

At a maximum gross weight of 200 tons, the SR.N4 Nk.2 is heavier than the standard craft, but the effect of this increase in weight on performance is minimal ensuring that high frequency schedules continue to be met. The craft is also fitted with a 'tapered' skirt which is now standard for all SR.N4 craft.

SR.N4 Mk 3

This is a design study for a 'stretched' model undertaken for British Rail. It would be capable of carrying 410 passengers and up to 54 vehicles.

This is a design study for a 'stretched' model undertaken for British Rail. It would be capable of carrying 396 passengers and up to 53 vehicles.

The four marine Proteus gas-turbines would be up-rated to 3,800 shp each, and each would drive a propeller/fan unit with a 21 ft (6·40 m) diameter propeller. The additional power would ensure that the performance of the current craft is maintained.

Craft motion would be less than that experienced on the standard SR.N4, and for similar comfort levels the larger craft should be capable of operating in waves up to 2 ft (0·61 m) higher than the present craft.

DIMENSIONS:

Length overall	186 ft 0 in (56·69 m)
Beam, hard structure	87 ft 0 in (26·52 m)
Cushion depth, mean	10 ft 0 in (3·05 m)
Height on landing pads	44 ft 0 in (13·41 m)

WEIGHTS:

Basic weight	168 tons
Max disposable load (incl. fuel etc)	112 tons

WINCHESTER (SR.N6) CLASS

Designed primarily as a fast ferry for operation in sheltered waters, the Winchester can accommodate either 38 passengers or 3 tons of freight.

Fully amphibious, it can operate from relatively unsophisticated bases above the high water mark, irrespective of tidal state.

Directional control is achieved by twin rudders and a thrust port system. Two manually actuated elevators provide pitch trim at cruising speed.

Winchesters have been in regular commercial service since 1965 and current operators include: British Rail Hovercraft Ltd., Hovertravel Ltd, Hoverwork Ltd, and Mitsubishi. A further Winchester is in service with the Civil Aviation Department, Ministry of Transport, New Zealand, as a crash rescue craft at Auckland International Airport. Its smaller, 7-ton predecessor, the SR.N5 (see JSS 1971-72 and earlier editions) is in service with the Canadian Coast Guard.

Military variants are in service with the Royal Navy's Hovercraft Trials Unit, the Imperial Iranian Navy and the Saudi Arabian Frontier Force and Coast Guard.

LIFT AND PROPULSION: Power for the intergrated lift/propulsion system is provided by a Rolls-Royce Marine Gnome gas turbine with a maximum continuous rating at 15°C of 900 shp. This drives a BHC 12-blade centrifugal 7 ft (2·13 m) diameter lift fan, and a Dowty Rotol 4 blade variable pitch 9 ft (2·14 m) diameter propeller for propulsion.

DIMENSIONS, EXTERNAL:

Overall length	48 ft 5 in (14·76 m)
Overall beam (solid structure)	23 ft (7·01m)
Overall height on landing pads	15ft (4·57m)
Skirt depth	4 ft (1·22 m)

DIMENSIONS, INTERNAL:

Cabin size (length × width)
    21 ft 9 in × 7 ft 8 in (6·62 m × 2·34 m)
Cabin headroom-centre line   6 ft (1·83 m)
Door aperture size (height × width)
    5 ft 9 in × 3 ft 3 in (1·75 m × 0·99 m)

WEIGHT:

Normal gross weight	10 tons

PERFORMANCE (at normal gross weight at 15°C.):

One of four SR.N6s operated by the Royal Navy's Hovercraft Trials Unit, Lee-on-Solent.   This particular variant is a Mk. 2

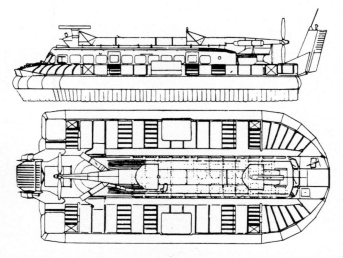
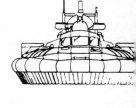

General arrangement of the SR.N6 Mk. IS (one 1,000 shp Rolls-Royce Marine Gnome gas-turbine

Max water speed over calm water zero wind (cont power rating)   52 knots (96 km/hr)
Average service waterspeed in sheltered coastal waters 30·35 knots (55·65 km/hr)
Endurance at max cont power rating on 265 Imp gall of fuel   3·6 hours

WINCHESTER (SR.N6) CLASS— PASSENGER FERRY/GENERAL PURPOSE

Since the SR.N6 first entered service as a passenger ferry in 1965, it has carried well over three million fare-paying passengers and is now firmly established in certain areas as an integral part of surface transportation networks.

The popularity of these services subsequently led to the introduction of an SR.N6 with a larger carrying capacity, designated the SR.N6 Mk.1S. At 58 ft in length, the Mk.1S is 10 ft longer than the standard craft and can carry up to 58 passengers as opposed to 35/38 in the standard SR.N6.

Other modifications to this craft include additional baggage panniers, emergency exits and improved cabin ventilation. An additional bonus is a significant increase in ride comfort.   To ensure that performance is maintained, the rating of the Rolls-Royce Marine Gnome gas turbine engine has been increased by 100 shp to 1,000 shp.

Two Mk.1S craft, Sea Eagle and Sea Hawk are in service with British Rail Hovercraft Ltd, on the Seaspeed service linking Cowes and Southampton and one Mk 1S is in operation on the Ryde/Southsea route with Hovertravel Limited.

Apart from passenger services, commercial SR.N6s have also made successful inroads into other fields of operation in recent years and typical examples of such applications include freight-carrying, hydrographic/seismographic survey, offshore support operations, general communications, crash rescue and firefighting.

To undertake these duties, craft have been modified either with the fitting of specialised equipment or by structural alterations such as flat-decks.

WINCHESTER (SR.N6) CLASS— MILITARY

Currently, variants of the SR.N6 are in

rvice with eight of the world's military and
aramilitary forces on coastal defence and
gistic support duties.

The SR.N6 Mk.2/3, for logistic support,
atures a roof loading hatch and strengthened
de-decks for carrying long loads of up to
ton. Lightweight armour may be fitted
protect troops being carried in the cabin,
e engine and other vital systems. Defensive
mament is provided by a roof-mounted
ht machine gun (7·62 mm or 0·5 in).

The craft can carry upwards of 20 fully-
quipped troops or supply loads of up to
tons. A small auxiliary generator is in-
alled to provide power when the main
gine is stopped.

The SR.N6 Mk.4 for coastal defence duties
ay be fitted with 20 mm cannon or short-
nge wire-guided surface/surface missiles.
ommunications equipment is concentrated
ehind the rear cabin bulkhead.

The SR.N6 Mk 5A, with a length of 60 ft
in (18·5 m) is 12 ft longer than the standard
R.N6 and differs greatly externally. Its
ain feature is a long central well-deck,
rengthened for carrying vehicles including
V 202 Snocats and Landrovers and weapons
cluding howitzers. A bow ramp is provided
r loading. Twin cabins flank the well-deck,
at on the starboard side housing the
aptain, navigator and controls, and that on
e port the observer and vehicle driver.

To maintain high performance at the heavier
ading—33,000 lb maximum gross weight—
e Marine Gnome gas turbine has been
prated to 1,400 shp

R.N6 Mk. 5A, leading particulars:
IMENSIONS:

Overall length	60 ft 8 in ((18·5 m)
Overall beam	25 ft 4 in (7·7 m)
Overall height (on landing pads)	14 ft 2 in (4·3 m)
Engine	R.R. Gnome GN 1301
Maximum power	1,400 shp
All-up weight	33,000 lb (15,000 kg)
Capacity	Up to 4 persons and 1 vehicle and trailer; 1 m/c gun
Maximum speed	47 knots
Endurance	3 hr
Long range endurance	6 hr

WINCHESTER (SR.N6) CLASS—Mk.6

The SR.N6 Mk. 6 is the latest development
f the successful Winchester series and
presents a significant step forward in terms
f increased payload, all weather performance
nd a substantial reduction in external noise.
hese advances have been achieved by the
troduction of twin-propeller propulsion, a
ore powerful engine, a redesigned skirt and
n increase of 10 ft (3·04 m) in overall length.
The twin 10 ft (3·04 m) diameter propellers
ith which the craft is fitted turn at reduced
m, resulting in lower external noise levels.
he pitch of each can be varied independently
ving the pilot greatly improved directional
ontrol at high and low speeds.

Power is supplied by a Rolls-Royce Gnome
301 gas-turbine rated at 1,400 shp maximum
nd 1,285 shp continuous.

R.N6 Mk 6A FAST INTERCEPTOR

A fast patrol version of the SR.N6, the
lk 6A is designed primarily for coastal
efence, but alternative roles include coastal
atrol, fast escort and search and rescue. A
ull range of navigation aids provide it with
4-hour operating capability.

The craft is amphibious, with good rough
ater performance and has low-speed pro-
ellers to ensure low external noise.

One of two SR.N6 Mk. IS hovercraft operated on the Seaspeed service between Cowes and South-ampton. This 'stretched' variant, 10 ft longer than the standard craft seats up to 58 passengers, compared with 35/38 in the earlier models

SR.N6 Mk 6 prototype, showing the twin-propeller arrangement and tapered skirt

Impression of the 50-knot SR.N6 Mk 6A gunship, equipped with a BMARC 30 mm twin gyro-stabilised cannon. The craft will be capable of engaging targets at high speeds in rough water

Dependent upon the role for which it is required, the craft can either be fitted with a 20 mm GAM B.O.1 mounting, or a 30 mm A32 mounting. With the former weapon, which is manually operated and independent of electrical supplies, the vessel is capable of fulfilling all coastguard duties. With the latter, it is able to engage targets while operating at high speeds in rough water. It can also track fast-moving targets.

Each system can be augmented by small arms operated from the cabin top, providing covering fire for boarding parties.

If required, the craft can be adapted for various armed logistic support roles, including that of vehicle carrier, with troops in the main cabin, or troop-carrier with a soft extension above the well deck. Capacity is provided for up to 11 persons and one vehicle and trailer.

LIFT AND PROPULSION: Motive power is supplied by a single 1,400 shp Rolls Royce Gnome GN.1301 gas-turbine driving a single centrifugal lift fan and two 10 ft (3·05 m) diameter variable-pitch propellers.

HULL: Marine corrosion-resistant aluminium alloys. Flat side decks accommodate auxiliary power units air-conditioning system and servicing equipment.

SKIRT: Tapered, BHC fingered bag type.

ACCOMMODATION: Cabin access is from the well deck via a watertight door in the forward bulkhead. Radio racks, power generation equipment and small arms lockers are located in the forward cabin areas. Seating is provided on each side of the central area. Above are the command and navigation stations. All accommodation is air-conditioned. A galley and toilet are located aft, with doors separating them from the main cabin area.

SYSTEMS, WEAPONS: Alternative arrangements: Single Oerlikon 20 mm manually operated G.A.M.-B.O.1 rapid fire cannon operated by one man. Twin B.M.A.R.C. 30 mm gyro-stabilised type A32 Mounting—this weapon system incorporates two-axis gyro stabilisation which gives high accuracy in adverse weather conditions.

APU: A Lucas 15/90 gas-turbine APU provides electrical power for full air conditioning and all equipment when engine is stopped.

COMMUNICATIONS: HF, VHF and UHF radio installed, together with radar and Decca Navigator.

DIMENSIONS:

Craft length over hard structure

	63 ft 0 in (19·2 m)
Beam, skirt inflated	26 ft 0 in (7·92 m)
Height on landing pads	21 ft 9 in (6·63 m)
Height hovering	29 ft 2 in (8·89 m)

WEIGHTS:

Max A.U.W.　　　38,000 lb (17,240 kg)

With Oerlikon single 20 mm cannon on manually operated GAM-BO1 mounting:

Craft basic weight	27,000 lb (12,250 kg)
Normal max operating weight	
	35,000 lb (15,880 kg)
Disposable load	8,000 lb (3,630 kg)
Total fuel	5,300 lb (2,400 kg)
Ammunition	500 lb (227 kg)
Boarding Party (Seven Troops)	
	1,400 lb (635 kg)
Overload Capability	3,000 lb (1,360 kg)
Maximum Operating	38,000 lb (17,240 kg)

With B.M.A.R.C. twin 30 mm cannon on

SR.N6 Mk 5, with a central well-deck for small armoured vehicles and weapons, including howitzers The starboard cabin houses the controls and hovercraft crew and the port cabin accommodates the vehicle crews. Payload is 7 tons

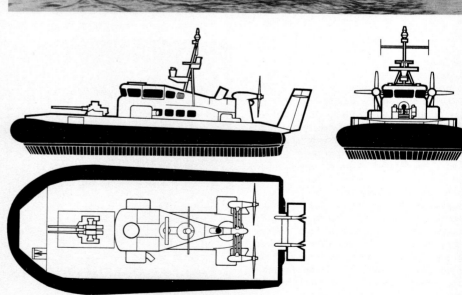

General arrangement of the SR.N6 Mk 6A gunship, powered by a single 1,400 shp Rolls-Royce GN.1301 gas-turbine

gyro-stabilised type A32 mounting:

Craft basic weight	31,200 lb (14,150 kg)
Normal max operating weight	
	38,000 lb (17,240 kg)
Disposable load	6,800 lb (3,080 kg)
Total fuel	3,400 lb (1,540 kg)
Ammunition	900 lb (408 kg)
Boarding party (Seven troops)	
	1,400 lb (635 kg)

PERFORMANCE:

Max speed, calm water	50 knots
Endurance	3 hours
Long range endurance	8 hours

SR.N6 6B LOGISTIC

The Mark 6B is designed for the fast transport of military loads. It is fitted with a bow ramp for vehicle 'drive on/ drive off' to a strengthened well-deck (9·44 m × 2·33 m

...ich provides unobstructed stowage space. ...ere are two cabins, one on each side deck. ...e starboard cabin is for the commander and ...vigator, the port for additional crewmen. ...fensive armament consists of a ring-...ounted machine gun mounted in the port ...bin roof.

...his craft has a carrying capacity of 45 ...ly equipped troops or one ¾ ton Land ...ver with trailer or a Land Rover and ...5 mm field gun. Alternatively it can be ...ded with up to 6 tons of mixed stores.

...MENSIONS:

...verall length	63 ft (19·2 m)
...verall beam	26 ft (7·92 m)
...verall height (on landing pads)	
	21 ft 9 in (6·63 m)
...ngine	R.R. Gnome GN 1301
...aximum power	1,400 shp
...ll-up weight	38,000 lb (17,237 kg)
...apacity	Up to 7 persons and 1 vehicle and trailer; 1 m/c gun
...aximum speed	50 knots
...ndurance	3 hours
...ong range endurance	8 hours

...N6 MARK 6C GENERAL PURPOSE AND ...MMAND VEHICLE

...he Mark 6C is a development of the ...rk 1. It is suitable for military and para-...itary roles and general coastal security ...rk, and can carry up to 40 fully equipped ...ops or 5 tons of military stores.

...ELLINGTON (BH.7) CLASS

...H.7 is a 50-ton hovercraft which was ...igned specifically for naval and military ...es. The prototype, designated BH.7 ...2, has been in service with the Royal ...vy since 1970 where it has been evaluated ...a number of roles including Fishery ...tection, ASW and MCM work.

...he second and third craft, designated ...4 and the fourth and fifth which are ...5As, are all in service with the Imperial ...nian Navy. A further two Mk 5As are ...eduled for delivery to Iran in 1975.

...FT AND PROPULSION: Power for the ...egrated lift propulsion system on the Mk. 2 ...d Mk. 4 is provided by a Rolls Royce/BS ...rine Proteus 15M541 gas-turbine with a ...ximum rating at 23°C of 4,250 shp. On ...Mk. 5A, a 15M549 is installed with a ...ximum rating of 4,250 shp. In both ...es the engine drives, via a light alloy ...veshaft and bevel drive gearbox, a BHC ...blade, centrifugal 11 ft 6 in (3·5 m) dia-...er lift fan and an HSD 4-blade, variable-...h pylon-mounted propeller. Propeller ...meter on the Mk. 4 is 19 ft (5·79 m) and ...ft (6·40 m) on the Mk. 2 and Mk. 5A. ...mal fuel capacity is up to 3,000 Imp ...ons.

...NTROLS: Craft direction is controlled ...swivelling the propeller pylon angle by ...otpedal. Thrust ports are fitted at each ...rter to assist directional control at low ...ed, and a hydraulically-operated skirt-...t system helps to bank the craft into ...as, thereby reducing drift.

...uel is transferred between forward and ...tanks via a ring main to adjust for and ...trim.

...LL: Construction is mainly of corrosion ...stant light alloy. Extensive use is made ...omponents which were designed for the ... The bow structure is a Plasticell base ...ered with glass fibre.

...RT SYSTEM: The fan delivers air to ...cushion via a continuous peripheral

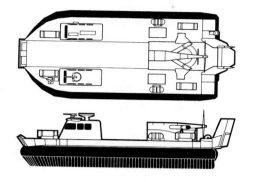

SR.N6 Mk 5A

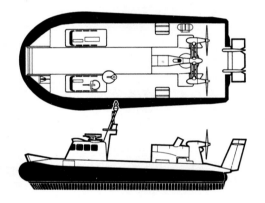

The twin-propeller version, the Mk.6B.

One of two BH.7 Mk. 4s operated by the Imperial Iranian Navy. The craft are employed on logistics duties and have bow loading doors.

fingered bag skirt made in neoprene coated nylon fabric. The skirt provides an air cushion depth of 5 ft 6 in (1·68 m). The cushion is divided into four compartments by a full length longitudinal keel and by two transverse keels located slightly forward of amidships.

ACCOMMODATION: The raised control cabin, located slightly forward of amidships on the hull centre line, accommodates a crew of three, with the operator and navigator in front and the third crew member behind. The driver sits on the right, with the throttle and propeller pitch control lever on his right, and the pylon angle footpedal and skirt-shift column in front.

The navigator, on the left, has a Decca radar display (Type 914 on the Mk. 5) and compass in front and Decometers in an overhead panel.

The large cabin area permits a variety of

operational layouts. In a typical arrangement, the operations room is placed directly beneath the control cabin and contains communication, navigation, search and strike equipment and associated displays.

The craft has an endurance of up to 11 hours under cruise conditions but this can be extended considerably as it can stay 'on watch' without using the main engine.

Provision can be made for the crew to live aboard for several days.

SYSTEMS: Electrical: Two Rover IS/90 APUs provide via two 55kVA generators 3-phase 400Hz ac at 200 volts for ac and dc supplies.

DIMENSIONS, EXTERNAL:
Length overall   78 ft 4 in (23·9 m)
Beam overall   45 ft 6 in (13·8 m)
Overall height on landing pads
     34 ft 0 in (10·36 m)
Skirt depth   5 ft 6 in (1·67 m)

DIMENSIONS, INTERNAL (Mk 4 only):
Bow door size
     13 ft 9 in × 7 ft 3 in (4·18 m × 2·20 m)
Headroom centre line   7 ft 10 in (2·38 m)

WEIGHT:
Normal gross weight   50 tons
Payload   14 tons

PERFORMANCE (at max operating weight at 15°C)
Max waterspeed over calm water (cont power rating)   60 kts
Average water speed in 4½ ft (1·37 m) seas
     35·50 knots

WELLINGTON (BH.7) Mk 4 LOGISTIC SUPPORT

ACCOMMODATION: In this role, the main hold floor area of 600 sq ft (56m²) of the Mk.4 provides an unobstructed space suitable for loading wheeled vehicles, guns and military stores.

Two side cabins, filled with paratroop-type seats, can accommodate up to 60 troops and their equipment.

Access at the bow is through a 'clamshell' door.

Machine guns can be fitted in gun rings on the roof on either side of the cabin and provision can be made for armour plating to protect personnel, the engine and vital electrical components.

SYSTEMS: Two Rover IS/90 gas turbine APUs provide electrical power independently of the main engine.

TYPICAL MILITARY LOADS: 170 fully equipped troops or 3 field cars and trailers plus 60 troops or two armoured scout cars or up to 20 NATO pallets.

DIMENSIONS, EXTERNAL:
Overall length   78 ft 4 in (23·85 m)
Overall beam   45 ft 6 in (13·8 m)
Overall height on landing pads
     33 ft (10·06 m)

DIMENSIONS, INTERNAL:
Main cabin floor area   600 sq ft (56 m²)
Main cabin headroom—centreline
     7 ft 10 in (2·38 m)
Access door aperture (height × width)
     7 ft 3 in (2·20 m) × 13 ft 9 in (4·2 m)

WEIGHTS:
Normal gross weight   45 tons
Fuel load at 45 tons AUW   9 tons
Max fuel capacity   12·5 tons

PERFORMANCE (at normal gross weight at 15°C):
Max waterspeed, calm water, zero wind cont power rating   65 knots (120 km/hr)
Rough waterspeed in 4½ ft (1·37 m) seas

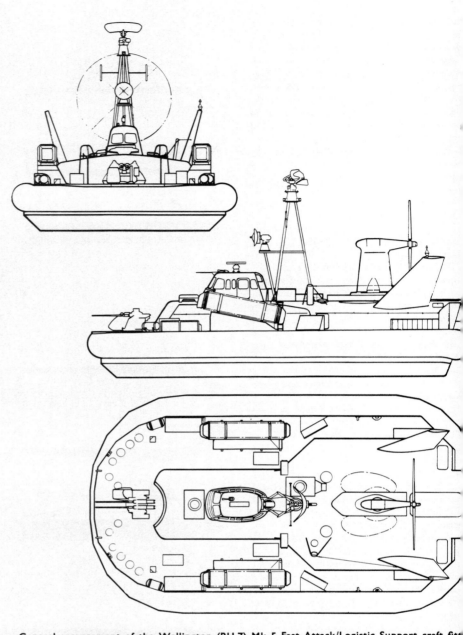

General arrangement of the Wellington (BH.7) Mk 5 Fast Attack/Logistic Support craft fitted with Exocet launchers and a twin 30 mm dual purpose mounting

Wellington Mk 5A fast attack/logistic support craft. This particular variant carries medium range ship-to-ship missiles, such as Exocet, on its sidedecks and retains the bow loading door of the Mk

depending on heading and wave length
35-50 knots (65-92 km/hr)
Endurance at max cont power rating with a
9 tons of fuel (with 10% reserve) 8 hours

WELLINGTON (BH.7) MK. 5 FAST ATTACK

Designed for coastal defence operations, the
BH.7 Mk.5 carries medium-range surface/
surface missiles, such as Exocet, on its sidedecks. Secondary armament consists of a
twin 30 mm surface/AA radar controlled
mounting situated on the foredeck forward
of the main centre cabin.

The main central cabin, employed on the
BH.7 Mk.4 for load-carrying, is equipped
as an operations and fire control room.
Since it is fully amphibious, the BH.7 Mk.5
can be operated from relatively unprepared
bases on beaches and can head directly
towards its target on interception missions
regardless of the tidal state and marginal
terrain. Also, since none of its solid
structure is immersed, it is invulnerable
to underwater defences such as acoustic,
magnetic and pressure mines and to attack
by torpedoes.

A full range of electronic navigational aids
permit the craft to operate by day or night
ensuring 'round-the-clock' availability.

WELLINGTON (BH.7) MK.5A FAST ATTACK/LOGISTICS

Similar to the Mk 5 above, with the
exception that the bow door is retained,
giving the craft a dual fast attack/logistic
capability. Secondary armament can consist of 2 roof-mounted single 20 mm guns.

LEADING PARTICULARS:

Overall length	78 ft 4 in (23·9 m)
Overall beam	45 ft 6 in (13·9 m)
Overall height (on landing pads)	
	34 ft (10·7 m)
Engine	R.R. Proteus (15M 549)
Maximum power	4,250 shp
All-up weight	55 ton (55·88 tonnes)
Capacity	Up to 5 persons and 7 ton weapon payload
Maximum speed	58 knots
Endurance	8 hours
Long range endurance	10 hours

WELLINGTON (BH.7) MK.6 FAST ATTACK/PATROL

This craft is designed to be powered by
two 3,000 hp gas turbines driving a centrifugal
lift fan and a 21 ft (6·40 m) diameter variable-
pitch propeller. The craft illustrated is
armed with four General Dynamics ARM
(anti-radiation missile) or Active Standard
surface-to-surface missiles and a single 76 mm
Oto Melara dual-purpose cannon. If required
it can be adapted for use as a hunter/killer
ASW vessel or for employment as a mine-
countermeasures craft, in conjunction with
the Edo Mk 105 mine countermeasures
system and other similar equipment.

ACCOMMODATION:

Air-conditioned working and living quarters
for crew of 12.

WEAPON SYSTEMS:

4 ARM Standard surface-to-surface missiles,
plus 76 mm Oto Melara radar-controlled
dual-purpose gun. HSA combined fire control
and surveillance radar. Alternative systems: Semi-active variant of Standard,
Exocet, Harpoon, Penguin or Seakiller, 35
mm twin Oerlikon or 30 mm twin Hispano
Suiza.

Wellington Mk 5A Fast Attack/Logistic Support Craft

Impression of the BH.7 Wellington Mk. 6 fast attack/patrol craft, equipped with a 76 mm Oto
Melara cannon and four Exocet ship-to-ship missiles. Maximum speed of the craft, which will have
an all-up weight of 90 tons, will be 68 knots under calm conditions

DIMENSIONS:
Length overall, hard structure
108 ft 3 in (33·0 m)
Beam overall, hard structure
45 ft 6 in (13·9 m)
Height on cushion   36 ft 6 in (11·5 m)

WEIGHTS:
Starting all-up weight   90 tons
Weapons payload   17 tons
Fuel, including ballast   15 tons

PERFORMANCE:
Both engines running at max continuous rating of 6,000 shp.
Max speed, calm conditions   68 knots
Endurance   10 hours
Range of operation   400-550 nm
One engine running at 3,000 shp
Cruising speed (depending on weight and conditions)   16-40 knots
Endurance   18 hours
Cruising range   290-700 nm

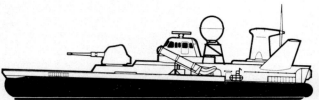

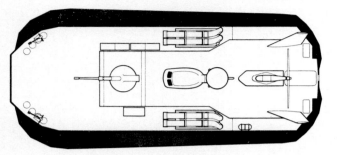

General arrangement of the 108 ft long BH.7 Mk. 6, powered by two 3,000 shp gas-turbines

---

CYCLONE HOVERCRAFT
ADDRESS:
5 Lordsmead, Cranfield, Bedfordshire
EXECUTIVES:
N. Beale

This organisation has developed a low-cost single-seat sports hovercraft designed by two of the most successful designers and builders of light hovercraft. Two prototypes of the Hoverfly have been completed and the second of these was undergoing final trials at the time of going to press. It is planned to manufacture Hoverfly in quantity at a price of approximately £400.00 per craft.

HOVERFLY
A simple single-seat design Hoverfly meets all the safety requirements of the Hover Club of Great Britain. It is capable of speeds of up to 25 mph (40·23 km/h) over land or water and employs an integrated lift/thrust propulsion system.

LIFT & PROPULSION: A single JLO 250 cc two stroke engine rated at 15 hp at 5,500 rpm drives via a toothed belt a 24 in dia, (609 mm) five-bladed, 45° pitch ducted fan. This unit supplies air for both lift and thrust, with about 40% of the fan duct diameter scooping air for the cushion and the remainder being used for thrust. With this system a static thrust of about 45 lb is achieved. Cushion pressure is about 9 lb/sq ft and the craft has a fuel capacity of 1½ gallons.

CONTROLS: A simple twist grip mounted on the steering handlebars operates the throttle for the single engine and an air rudder mounted in the fan duct gives directional control.

HULL: The complete hull structure is constructed from glass-reinforced plastics with polyurethane foam, providing about 150% buoyancy, contained in the underside of the hull. It is also possible to fit marine buoyancy bags along the open wells on the sides of the craft to give additional buoyancy if the craft operates with an overload weight.

SKIRT SYSTEM: A simple bag skirt giving about 6 in obstacle clearance is fitted to the hull. The skirt is made from polyurethane coated nylon fabric weighing 4 oz/sq yd.

ACCOMMODATION: Hoverfly is a single-seater with the driver sitting astride a central bench.

Hoverfly, single-seat sports ACV

DIMENSIONS:
Length overall	9 ft 0 in	(2·74 m)
Width overall	5 ft 0 in	(1·52 m)
Height overall	3 ft 6 in app.	(1·06 m)
Height at rest	3 ft 0 in app.	(·91 m)

WEIGHTS:
Weight empty (dry)	120 lb	(54·42 kg)

Normal payload	200 lb	(90·71 kg
Normal all-up	350 lb	(158·75 kg

PERFORMANCE:
Maximum speed over land
25 mph (40·23 km/h) approx
over water   20 kt approx

HOVERCRAFT DEVELOPMENT LTD

HEAD OFFICE:
Kingsgate House, 66-74 Victoria Street, London SW1E 6SL

TELEPHONE:
01-828 3400

TELEX:
23580

DIRECTORS:
T. G. Fellows (Chairman)
M. W. Innes
Prof. W. A. Mair
J. E. Rapson
T. A. Coombs

SECRETARY:
P. N. Randell

TECHNICAL OFFICE:
Forest Lodge West, Fawley Road, Hythe, Hants. SO4 6ZZ

TELEPHONE:
Hythe (Hants) 842178 STD Code 0703

Hovercraft Development Ltd. (HDL) was formed in January 1959 by the National Research Development Corporation (NRDC) to develop, promote and exploit the hovercraft invention. The company uses its large portfolio of patents as the basis of licensing agreements with the principal hovercraft manufacturers in the United Kingdom and overseas, and allows licensees access to work undertaken by its original Technical Group and the current Technical Office at Hythe. HDL may, in certain cases, provide financial backing to assist projects, such as the Hovermarine HM.5, the BHC SR.N4 and the Vosper VT.1.

The small technical team employed by the company makes assessments of new hovercraft designs and projects in addition to regional and route studies for proposed hovercraft operations. HDL's Technical Office at Hythe also provides a source of unbiased but informed technical information for government departments, official bodies, potential manufacturers, operators and backers of hovercraft enterprises.

Currently, various programmes are being undertaken with a manned test hovercraft, designated HD-4, to evaluate new and improved control and cushion systems for hovercraft of all sizes. This work, together with other investigations, is aimed towards improving the control, skirt and propulsion aspects of modern hovercraft and assist the company's licensees to manufacture increasingly effective products for civil, military and industrial uses.

Patents held by the company largely result from the work undertaken by Christopher Cockerell and the HDL Technical Group, which investigated a wide range of marine, industrial and medical applications. The former Technical Group also operated three research hovercraft.

HD-4

This is a new 14 ft (426 m) long two-seat test vehicle employed by HDL to evaluate new and improved hovercraft control and cushion systems. The prototype was completed in July 1975 and preliminary trials were in progress at the time of going to press.

LIFT AND PROPULSION: Lift is supplied by a single 197 cc Villiers 8E two-stroke driving a single 2 ft 0 in (0·609 m) diameter axial-fan fitted with ten blades each set at 35° pitch. Propulsive thrust is provided by a single 250 cc Aerial Arrow driving two 2 ft 0 in (0·609 m) diameter 5-bladed axial fans mounted on a common transverse shaft. Fuel is carried in two 2-gallon (9·09 l) tanks, one each side of the cockpit. Recommended fuel is two-stroke mixture, 20:1.

CONTROLS: Craft heading is controlled by four rudders operating in the air-jets. Braking/reverse buckets are fitted above each air-jet duct. Pitch and roll are controlled by a balanced skirt-shift system.

HULL: Wooden construction. Craft has a framework of 1 in sq spruce and ½ in sq Ramin, overlaid with sheets of 4 mm and 1·5 mm exterior grade ply.

SKIRT: HDL loop and segment type in 4 oz/yd² and 2 oz/yd² lightweight coated fabric.

ACCOMMODATION: Open cockpit with seating for driver and one passenger.

DIMENSIONS, EXTERNAL:
Length overall, power off 14 ft 0 in (4·26 m)
Beam overall, power off 6 ft 6 in (1·98 m)
Height overall, power off 3 ft 10 in (1·68 m)
Height overall, hovering 5 ft 0 in (1·52 m)

HOVERKING LTD

HEAD OFFICE:
12, Clarendon Place, Leamington Spa, Warwickshire

TELEPHONE:
Leamington Spa 25766 and 28469

WORKS:
Hoverking, Ullesthorpe, Lutterworth, Leics LE17 5AG

DIRECTORS:
C. Knight
P. M. Knight
R. T. Jackson
D. Crowther

CONSULTANTS:
F. Cooton
D. Walters DCAe, C.Eng, AFRAES, MCASI, FBIS
Cdr. Th. Pellinkhof, C.Eng., FIMarE

Hoverking Ltd was formed in 1970 to design and develop the Ranger series of light hovercraft, initially for the amateur builder. The aim was to produce a luxury sports racing hovercraft that could be manufactured commercially to meet the wide demand for racing ACVs.

Ranger 1 has been intensively tested and developed to achieve the right combination of high performance, reliability, safety and stability. This included a series of tests conducted by Loughborough University which confirmed the machine's outstanding pitch and roll stability.

An amateur-built version of the Ranger 1, built by David Ibbotson, won the Hovercraft of the Year Award and David Ibbotson himself was Joint Hovernaut of the Year in 1973. The manoeuvrability of the craft were tested to the full on the canals in Birmingham, where it featured in location shots for the film "Take Me High", starring Cliff Richard.

Ranger I, winner of the 1973 Hovercraft of the Year Award, followed by an experimental version of the Ranger with twin Wankel thrust engines

Widespread interest has been shown in the principles embodied in the design of the Ranger 1. A world-wide network of agents with complete spares and technical support is in the process of being established.

RANGER 1

A single-seater sports/racing hovercraft, Ranger 1 is easy to handle and its components are both simple and functional to ensure low maintenance and running costs.

LIFT AND PROPULSION: Lift air is provided by an 8 hp Sachs Wankel Rotary KM48 engine driving a 22 in (·55 m) diam. 8 blade Multiwing fan. Thrust is provided by a 21 hp Sachs Rotary MK914 engine driving a 27 in (0·68 m) diam. ducted Permali propeller. The fuel capacity is from 2 gal (9·02 l) (for racing) up to 8 gal (36·3 l) for cruising. The fuel tank is mounted inboard in a compartment behind the driver.

CONTROLS: Twin rudders mounted in the propeller slipstream provide directional control. The rudders are linked by teleflex cable to an ergonomically designed control column with handgrips set at 45%, permitting single or two-handed control. The thrust throttle lever can be operated by either hand.

HULL: Box-section, wood-laminated internal structure bonded into a light grp external skin. The four corners are foam filled to provide buoyancy and impact resistance.

SKIRT: Twin bag of lightweight polyurethane impregnated terylene/nylon. Skirt system permits safe operation of the craft even with extensive damage to the outer skirt. The lightweight material permits temporary repairs to be undertaken by hand. System maintains a higher pressure in the skirt than in the plenum, combining the advantages of a low cushion pressure with resistance to skirt decay at high speeds.

ACCOMMODATION: Single-seat located just forward of the centre of gravity. Seating position is adjustable from a normal upright to full 'racing prone' position for maximum safety at high speeds. Adjustable footrest provided.

DIMENSIONS:

Length	11 ft 9 in (9·58 m)
Width	6 ft 7 in (2·00 m)
Height	4 ft 0 in (1·21 m)

WEIGHTS:

Weight empty	400 lb (181·42 kg)
Payload	400 lb (181·42 kg)

PERFORMANCE:

Max speed	55 mph (88·57 km/h)
Fuel consumption	1½-2 gal/hr (6·81-9·0 l/hr)
Maximum cont. gradient	1 : 6
Obstacle clearance	9 in (228 mm)

PRICE: £1,400-£1,800 ex works subject to specification.

RANGER II

This is a new version of the Ranger, with a specification similar to that for Ranger I, but with a modified hull and improved guard for the ducted propeller.

COMMODORE 1

Plans for the development of this two/three-seat, sports/cruising craft, were released as this edition went to press. Details of the production model are expected to be available in early 1976.

LIFT AND PROPULSION: Power for the lift and propulsion systems will be supplied by either three 21 hp Sachs Wankel Mk 914 air-cooled rotary engines or by a 60 bhp water-cooled automotive engine.

HULL: Box section wood laminate interior, bonded to a grp external skin. Multicell buoyancy and impact resistance. Basic hull is designed to accept various cockpit and engine installations to suit environmental requirements.

SKIRT: Hoverking twin bag skirt.

ACCOMMODATION: Seats for driver and up to two passengers. Wrap round windscreen or detachable hard top with sliding canopy.

Top: Ranger II, showing the modified hull

Bottom: New guard for the ducted propeller on Ranger II

DIMENSIONS:

Length overall	14 ft 0 in (4·26 m)	Beam overall	7 ft 0 in (2·13 r
		Height	4 ft 6 in (1·37 n

HOVERMARINE TRANSPORT LIMITED

HEAD OFFICE AND WORKS:
Hazel Wharf, Hazel Road, Woolston, Southampton SO2 7GB

TELEPHONE:
Southampton (0703) 446831

TELEX:
47141

DIRECTORS:
Edward F. Davison, Chairman
Michael R. Richards, Managing Director
David W. Nicholas, Marketing Director
Peter J. Hill, Manufacturing Director
Edward G. Tattersall, Technical Director
William A. Zebedee

Hovermarine Transport Limited, a subsidiary of Hovermarine Corporation (USA),

One of the four Hovermarine HM.2 Mk IIIs operating across Hong Kong harbour

produce the HM.2 rigid sidewall craft and are currently engaged in the manufacture of the HM.5 Hoverferry. Several configurations of HM.2 are available: a 62-65 seat passenger ferry; a general purpose model; and an armed patrol craft, each capable of carrying a 5 ton payload. There is also available a luxury 'Pullman' craft designed to carry 30 passengers. At the time of going to press, thirty vessels had been sold and a further six were under construction.

HM.2 Mk III

A rigid sidewall craft designed for ferry operations, the HM.2 Mk III carries 62-65 passengers or 4·8 tons of freight at speeds up to 35 knots. The craft has a reinforced plastic hull, and is powered by three marine diesel engines.

Its features include an extended bow skirt which permits operations in waves up to 1·6 m (5 ft), mixed flow fans to provide improved cushion characteristics; a new propulsion transmission system, modified engine components and the provision of sound insulation in the cabin to reduce internal noise levels.

HM.2 is type approved in the UK for Certificates of Construction and Performance and Hovercraft Safety Certificates issued by the Civil Aviation Authority, also for Operating Permits issued by the Department of Trade. In addition, the HM.2 has been certified by Lloyds Register of Shipping as a Class A1 Group 2 Air Cushion Vehicle.

In 1975 fleet services were operating in Setubal, Portugal, Rio de Janeiro, Brazil and Hong Kong harbour. In addition, HM.2s are operating in Australia, Belgium, Brazil, Greece, Italy, India, USA and the United Kingdom.

LIFT AND PROPULSION: Two Cummins turbocharged VT8-370 M eight-cylinder V marine diesels, each developing 320 bhp at 2,800 rpm, provide propulsive power, and a single Cummins V8-504m diesel rated at 185 bhp at 2,800 rpm drives the lift fans. The lift engine drives two pairs of forward fans through toothed belts and one aft fan through a hydraulic system. Air for the forward fans is drawn through inlets at each forward cabin quarter and in the base of the wheelhouse structure while the air for the aft fan is drawn through an inlet in the rear companionway. The lift fans are of glass fibre construction.

The two propulsion engines drive two 15 in (381 mm) diameter stainless steel propellers through a reversing gearbox and 1 : 1 ratio Vee box. Short skegs projecting from the base of the sidewalls protect the propellers from driftwood and grounding. Fuel is carried in reinforced rubber tanks, two beneath the aft companionway, holding 640 litres (140 Imperial gallons), and one under the main lift fan holding 182 litres (40 Imperial gallons). Two refuelling points are provided on the transom and one on the starboard side of the main air intakes.

CONTROLS: Craft direction is controlled by twin balanced stainless steel rudders which are operated hydraulically by a car type steering wheel. Additional control is provided by differential use of the water propellers.

HULL: Built in glass reinforced plastic and grp sandwich panels. Hull is one homogeneous laminate into which are bonded grp panel frames.

Interior of the HM.2 Mk III's 62-65 seat passenger saloon

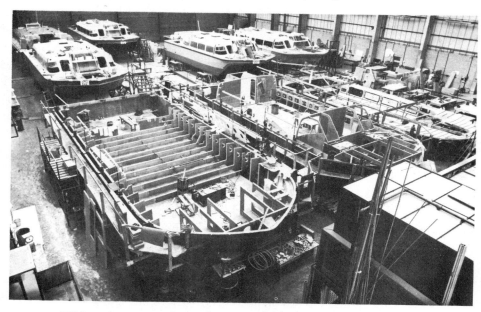

HM.2s under construction at the company's plant at Woolston, Southampton

ACCOMMODATION: The craft is operated by a crew of two. Controls are all sited in an elevated wheelhouse with a 360° view, located at the forward end of the passenger compartment. The captain is seated on the starboard side with the principal instrumentation. Radar and auxiliary equipment is located on the port side.

Accommodation is normally for 62 seated passengers, with a maximum of 65. Seats are normally three abreast in banks of three. Toilet and luggage compartments are located aft.

Passenger access is via a double width door aft. Crew and emergency access is provided forward via two hatch doors, one each side of the wheelhouse.

"Knock-out" emergency windows are provided in the passenger saloon. Safety equipment includes: Beaufort life rafts, aircraft-type life jackets under the seats, and Graviner fire detectors and extinguishers.

Heating for the passenger saloon and wheelhouse is from the fresh water circuits of the engine cooling system, via two heat exchanger blowers through ducts at floor level. Optional air conditioning units can be fitted at the customer's request.

SYSTEMS: Electrical: 24 volt dc from engine driven alternators (2 × 60 amp) with 128 Ah Daganite batteries. Supplies instruments, radio, radar and external and internal lights.

HYDRAULICS: Systems used for the steering and rear fan operate at 800 lb sq in and 2,500 lb sq in maximum respectively.

SKIRT: Front and rear skirts are of loop and segment form and designed for a cushion height of 3 ft (914 mm).

COMMUNICATIONS AND NAVIGATION: Decca Super 101 radar and Redifon GR674 vhf radio. Other navigational equipment includes a Smith E2B Compass and remote reading compass.

DIMENSIONS, EXTERNAL:

Length overall	51 ft 0 in (15·54 m)
Beam overall	20 ft 0 in (6·10 m)
Height overall	13 ft 9 in (4·19 m)
Draft floating with water-screws	
	4 ft 10½ in (1·49 m)
Draft hovering with water-screws	
	2 ft 10½ in (0·87 m)
Cushion area	627 sq ft (584 m²)

DIMENSIONS, INTERNAL:

Cabin (excluding wheelhouse, galley and toilet):

Length	22 ft 0 in (6·7 m)
Max width	16 ft 0 in (4·8 m)
Max height	6 ft 6 in (1·9 m)
Floor area	352 sq ft (32·7 m²)

DOOR SIZES:

Rear door: 4 ft 0 in (1·2 m) wide × 6 ft 3 in (1·9 m) high

Two forward doors:
2 ft 0 in (0·60 m) wide × 6 ft 3 in (1·9 m) high

BAGGAGE HOLDS:

Basic craft 60 cu ft (1·69 m³) aft of cabin

FREIGHT HOLDS:

None on standard passenger version.
Freight carried in main cabin on freight version.

WEIGHTS:

Normal all-up weight, including normal payload	42,500 lb (19,300 kg)
Normal payload	
62 passengers or 4·8 tons (4,900 kg)	
Max gross weight	44,500 lb (20,185 kg)

PERFORMANCE (at normal operating weight):

Max service speed	35 knots
Water speed in 4 ft waves and 15 knot head wind	25 knots
Max wave capability	5 ft (1·52 m)
Endurance	4 hours

HM.2 'PULLMAN'

This craft was developed during the latter end of 1974 as a luxury version of the successful 65 passenger version. Customers had indicated that there would be a ready market for this latest adaptation of the HM.2 high speed ferry, and Hovermarine Transport Limited, in co-operation with design consultants, developed the 'Pullman' concept to meet this demand.

HM.2 Mk III general purpose sidewall craft equipped for hydrographic survey and operated on the River Scheldt by the Belgian Ministry of Public Works

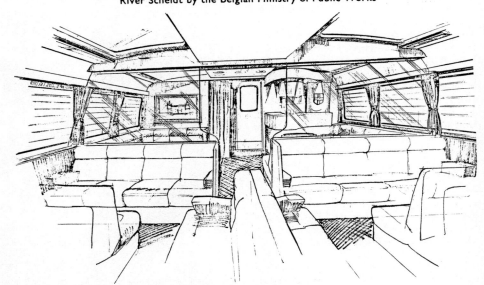

Sketch of the interior of the HM.2 Pullman

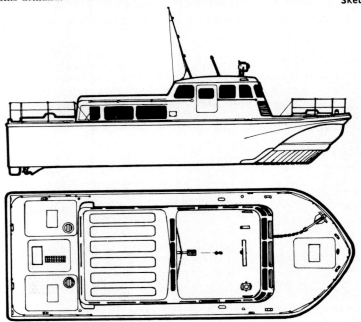

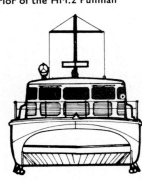

Hovermarine HM.2 Mk III, general purpose craft

The interior utilises the same basic saloon area as the HM.2 65-seater craft, but the interior design and fitting gives the craft a much higher degree of comfort. The saloon is divided into two main areas, an aft bar/saloon and a forward lounge, separated by an engraved 'Plexiglas' screen, and luxury seating can be provided for up to 30 passengers and arranged to give maximum all round visibility. Controllable air-conditioning makes temperature control possible giving maximum passenger comfort. Combined with the seating in the aft saloon are free-standing tables. The toilet compartment, fitted with an electric WC and sanitory unit, is located at the rear end of this saloon.

The forward lounge has first-class aircraft seating and a film projector can be installed. A stereo sound track is available and can be played through eight room-mounted speakers.

Fitted perspex roof lights and sidelights combined with interior curtains or adjustable louvres allow interior lighting to be adjusted.

HM.2 MARK III GENERAL PURPOSE CRAFT

Similar in basic design, construction and power plant to the HM.2 passenger craft, the general purpose version is suited to a variety of roles from police and customs patrol to hydrographic survey, and search and rescue duties.

The craft is equipped with a revised superstructure to suit these applications. For para-military roles, the craft can be equipped with a range of conventional automatic weapons.

DIMENSIONS, EXTERNAL:

Length overall	51 ft 0 in (15·54 m)
Beam overall	20 ft 0 in (6·09 m)
Height above hovering water line is	
	10 ft 8 in (2·35 m) wheelhouse top
Draft hovering	2 ft 10 in (0·86 m)
Draft afloat	4 ft 10 in (1·47 m)

WEIGHTS:

Maximum all up weight (fully equipped)
42,500 lb (19,300 kg)
Normal disposable load 12,300 lb (5,830 kg)

HM.2 TROJAN CLASS—MILITARY SUPPORT

HM.2 Trojan is the military version of the HM.2 Mk III passenger craft, and is similar in basic construction. Designed to undertake a wide variety of support roles, including counter-insurgency, logistic support, troop transport, etc, these craft normally have plastic armour and two machine guns forward.

In the personnel carrier variant, 55 troops may be carried at speeds of up to 35 knots. With the more heavily armed patrol craft layout, however, the main cabin will be sub-divided to provide living accommodation and extra fuel tanks will increase the vessel's range.

The general specification is as shown for the standard passenger version.

HM.5

Plans to develop the HM.5 were announced in February 1975.

The craft will be a little over 50% larger than HM.2, but the capacity will be between 160 to 200 passengers, depending on layout and operator's choice of engines.

This craft is being designed to operate at 35 knots in 1 m waves as its cruise condition. Commercial versions of the craft will be equipped with high speed diesel engines, but for military applications gas-turbines can be installed that will give speeds up to 50

Trojan military support craft

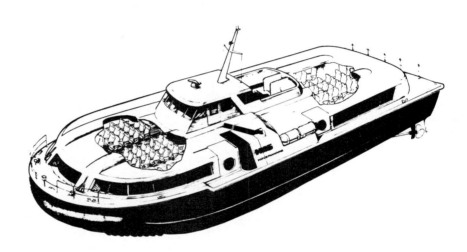

Impression of the HM.5 200-seat hoverferry

Model of the HM.5 undergoing tank tests

knots. Normal installed power will be 3,000 hp using diesel engines.

The craft has been under development for some time and the prototype is scheduled for launching early in 1977. The hull will be manufactured in glass reinforced plastic and may be strengthened locally by use of carbon fibre.

DIMENSIONS:

Length overall	88 ft 7 in (27 m)
Beam overall	32 ft 9¾ in (10 m)
Draught hovering	4 ft 11 in (1·5 m)
Draught afloat	8 ft 2¾ in (2·5 m)

WEIGHTS:

Craft all up weight	73,000 kg (73 tons)
Normal maximum payload	20,000 kg (20 tons)

PERFORMANCE:

Cruising speed
35 knots in waves up to 1 m
Maximum speed
40-50 knots, according to application and choice of engines

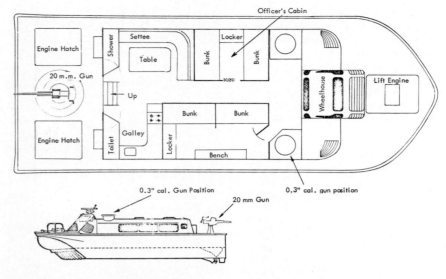

A patrol craft variant of the Hovermarine Trojan, showing the deck arrangement and gun mountings

LIGHT HOVERCRAFT COMPANY

HEAD OFFICE:
Felbridge Hotel & Investment Co Ltd, London Road, East Grinstead, Sussex

TELEPHONE:
East Grinstead 24424

EXECUTIVES:
L. H. F. Gatward, Proprietor

Light Hovercraft Company has been active in the field of hoverpallets since 1969. It has entered the light sports ACV field with a fibreglass hulled-variant of Nigel Beale's Cyclone, which won the British National Hovercraft Championships in 1971 and was joint winner of this event in 1972. In August 1972 a production Cyclone crossed the English Channel from Pegwell Bay hoverport to Calais, a total open sea distance of 35 miles (56·32 km). In late 1973, the company introduced the Wasp, an ultralight runabout, and in April 1974, it introduced the Buzzard, a development of the Cyclone and available in two and four seat models. At the time of going to press in June 1974, the company had sold five Buzzards and four Wasps.

BUZZARD

This lightweight amphibious sports craft is derived from the earlier Cyclone 274 (JSS 1973-74). Two and four seat and one light cargo model are available. The four basic variants are as follows:

Buzzard I. Two seats, one lift unit, one thrust unit.

Buzzard II. Two seats, one lift unit, two thrust units.

Buzzard III. Four seats, one lift unit, two thrust units.

Buzzard IV. Two seats, one lift unit, two thrust units, plus a cargo well.

LIFT AND PROPULSION: Lift is provided by a Rowena Stihl 137 cc engine rated at 9 bhp driving a 1 ft 7 in (482 mm) diameter fan. On the Buzzard Mk I a single Rowena Stihl 137 cc engine of identical type and output drives a ducted multiwing fan for thrust. On the Mk II, III and IV twin Rowena Stihl thrust units are fitted. Fuel capacity is 2·5 gals (12 litres).

CONTROLS: A single rudder hinged to the rear of the thrust fan provides directional control. A lever throttle operates the lift

The light Hovercraft Buzzard IV light utility ACV seats two and has a small cargo well aft of the tandem seat. Maximum payload is 550 lb (250 kg)

The Wasp ultralight hovercraft runabout

engine and a twistgrip throttle controls propulsion.

HULL: Single piece foam-filled glassfibre hull. Rigid structure. Light weight construction for roof rack or trailer.

SKIRT: Bag-type skirt in polyurethane nylon, 1 ft 9 in (·5 m) deep at bow, and 1 ft 4 in (·4 m) at sides.

ACCOMMODATION: Open tandem seating for driver and up to three passengers.

WASP

This is a new ultralight runabout, based on the company's experience with the earlier

Cyclone. The aim has been to produce a small craft of simple design which is both easy to operate and maintain.

LIFT AND PROPULSION: Integrated system, powered by a single Rowena Stihl 9 hp, 173 cc 2-cycle engine. This drives a 1 ft 7 in (482 mm) diameter axial fan, air from which is used for both lift and propulsion, at the ratio of 1:3. Total fuel capacity is ¾ gal (4 litre).

CONTROLS: Heading is controlled by a single aerodynamic rudder aft of the fan duct and operated by a handlebar. Engine out-

DIMENSIONS:	BUZZARD 1	BUZZARD II	BUZZARD III	BUZZARD IV
Length	10 ft 8 in (3·3 m)	As I	14 ft 8 in (4·5 m)	As III
Width	6 ft 2 in (1·9 m)	As I	As I	As I
Height	3 ft 5 in (1·0 m)	As I	As I	As I
WEIGHT	180 lbs (80 kg)	220 lbs (100 kg)	250 lbs (115 kg)	260 lbs (120 kg)
Payload Normal	250 lbs (114 kg)	350 lbs (160 kg)	500 lbs (230 kg)	As III
Overload	350 lbs (160 kg)		700 lbs (320 kg)	As III
PERFORMANCE				
Speed (Optimum)	25 knots (50 khp)	40 knots (80 kph)	As II	As II
Range (Approx)	60 miles (100 km)	As I	As I	As I

PRICES—EXPORT	£	£	£	£
Hovercraft Complete	1,000·00	1.300·00	1,600·00	1,700·00
Hovercraft Kit	950·00	1.250·00	1,550·00	1,650·00
Roof Rack	22·00			

TYPICAL FREIGHT COSTS (KIT & COMP.)		I & II	III & IV
Trailer (Flat deck) 198·00	Case and Packing	100·00	120·00
	Freight in G.B.	40·00	50·00
	F.O.B. Costs	60·00	70·00
	Freight to European Ports	120·00	140·00
	Freight to Other Ports	240·00	280·00
	Air Freight to U.S.A.	450·00	550·00

put is controlled by a twist-grip throttle.

HULL: Single-piece foam-filled glassfibre structure.

SKIRT: Bag-type skirt in polyurethane nylon, 6 in (15 cm) deep.

ACCOMMODATION: Saddle-type seat in grp for driver.

DIMENSIONS:

Length	9 ft 1 in (2·8 m)
Beam	6 ft 1 in (1·85 m)
Height	2ft 10 in (·85 m)

WEIGHTS:

Empty weight	110 lb (50 kg)
Payload	175 lb (80 kg)

PERFORMANCE:

Speed	20 knots (40 km/h)
Range (app)	30 miles (50 km)

EXPORT PRICE: Craft complete £495.00.

Light Hovercraft's latest design is the Fantasy, an amphibious two-seater with a top speed over water of 40 knots

MISSIONARY AVIATION FELLOWSHIP

ADDRESS:
3 Beechcroft Road, South Woodford, London E18 1BJ

TELEPHONE:
01-989 0838

DIRECTORS:
S. Sendall-King
B.Sc., C.Eng., A.F.R.Ae.S., F.S.L.A.E.T.
General Director
T. S. Frank, B.A. UK Director

EXECUTIVE HOVERCRAFT PROJECT:
T. J. R. Longley, A.R.Ae.S.

The Missionary Aviation Fellowship is an international, interdenominational Christian organisation which operates a total of 75 light aircraft in support of missionary work in some of the world's more remote areas.

In the belief that a suitable hovercraft could make a valuable contribution to missionary work, M.A.F. began the design of a craft to its own specification, early in 1970. Design assistance was given voluntarily by several specialists in the field of hovercraft and aircraft engineering.

As a result of two years of intensive trials,

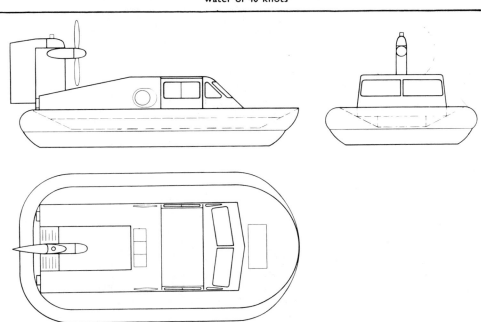

General arrangement of the Missionary Aviation Fellowship hovercraft prototype

the Missionaire has been developed into an efficient and reliable craft. To demonstrate its capability, it was driven around the Isle of Wight with a 1,100 lb payload in 2 hrs 13 minutes. Block cruising speed was 27 knots and the total fuel consumption was only 2·7 gallons per hour.

At the time of going to press the craft was awaiting shipment to Lake Chad, where African and foreign missionaries are together undertaking medical, evangelistic and famine-relief work. Difficulties of transportation, together with the extreme shallowness of the Lake, provide ample scope for evaluating the usefulness of a hovercraft.

MISSIONAIRE Mk I

This is a lightweight amphibious hovercraft powered by two Volkswagen engines. Although originally designed as a five-seater, the craft has a spacious cabin and has demonstrated its ability to carry seven adults over hump speed into a 12 knot headwind without any difficulty. Cruising speed over calm water is 35 knots.

LIFT AND PROPULSION: An air-cooled Volkswagen 1,500 cc automotive engine, developing 53 bhp at 4,200 rpm, drives two 2 ft 0 in (609 mm) diameter aluminium centrifugal impellers for lift. Thrust is provided by a 68 bhp Volkswagen 1,700 cc engine driving a 5 ft 8 in (1·72 m) diameter fixed-pitch Sensenich airboat-type propeller. Power transmission and speed reduction on both units is by Stephens Miraclo-Meteor high-speed belting. Total fuel capacity is 35 Imp gallons (195 l), carried in a single welded aluminium tank located amidships. Recommended fuel is 95 octane automotive grade petrol.

CONTROL: An aerodynamic rudder operating in the propeller slipstream provides directional control under cruising conditions. Forward-located puff-ports are provided for low-speed directional control, though they can be used at high speed. This combination of controls has been found to aid manoeuvrability and facilitate handling. The craft also possesses good high-speed ditching characteristics, with no tendency to plough-in.

Longitudinal trim and a certain amount of lateral trim is provided by two 8 gallon integral water-ballast tanks located side by side in the bows. Water can be pumped aboard while the craft is floating, and can be off-loaded on or off cushion. No ballast is required when maximum payload is carried in the cabin.

HULL: The prototype hull is built in marine ply and spruce. For greater durability and ease of construction, a hull of composite GRP/aluminium alloy construction is planned for future craft. The hull incorporates ample reserve bouyancy.

SKIRT: Segmented type, 1 ft 6 in (458 mm) deep in neoprene/nylon.

ACCOMMODATION: Seats are provided in a fully enclosed cabin for a driver and four passengers. Access is via car-type doors (one each side) hinged to the forward doorposts. The entire cabin roof is hinged at its forward edge, providing unrestricted headroom for entry and loading. The three-place bench-type rear seat can be quickly converted into a stretcher, situated athwartships. A sizeable compartment for hand baggage and medical supplies is located behind the rear bench-seat. Cabin ventilation is provided by cushion air bleed ducts controlled by louvres.

Above and below: Missionary Aviation Fellowship's general purpose amphibious five-seater, the Missionaire. Powered by two Volkswagen engines, the craft has a top speed of 38 knots. The rear passenger seats can be replaced by a stretcher carried athwartships

SYSTEMS: Electrical: generator on the lift engine supplies 12 volts to a 60 a/hr battery for engine starting and other services.

Fire-detection and extinguishing: The engine bay is equipped with flame switches giving visual and audible warning on the instrument panel. A Graviner "Swordsman" BCF fire extinguisher adjacent to the driver's seat is plumbed into a distribution manifold in the engine bay. A quick-release connection makes it instantly useable as a hand-held extinguisher in the event of cabin, or other fires.

COMMUNICATIONS AND NAVIGATION: Provision for radio communications equipment. Magnesyn remote-reading compass.

DIMENSIONS, EXTERNAL:

Length overall, power off	22 ft 0 in (6·70 m)
Length overall, skirt inflated	22 ft 0 in (6·70 m)
Beam overall, power off	10 ft 6 in (3·20 m)
Beam overall, skirt inflated	12 ft 6 in (3·81 m)
*Height overall, on landing pads	7 ft 10 in (2·38 m)
*Height overall, skirt inflated	9 ft 4 in (2·84 m)
Draft afloat	10 in (254 mm)
Cushion area	170 sq ft (15·79 m²)
Skirt depth	1 ft 6 in (458 mm)

*Propeller horizontal.

DIMENSIONS, INTERNAL:

Cabin:

Length	6 ft 3 in (1·90 m)
Max width	7 ft 0 in (2·13 m)
Max height	4 ft 2 in (1·26 m)
Floor area	43·75 sq ft (4·06 m²)
Baggage hold behind rear seats	15 cu ft (0·425 m³)
Freight hold (in place of rear seats)	45 cu ft (1·27 m³)
Door width	3 ft 6 in (1·06 m)

WEIGHTS:

Normal empty weight	2,200 lb (998 kg)
Normal all-up weight	3,200 lb (1,451 kg)
Maximum all-up weight	3,600 lb (1,633 kg)
Normal payload (with full tank)	1,000 lb (453 kg)
Maximum payload	1,400 lb (635 kg)

PERFORMANCE (at normal operating weight):

Max speed over calm water (max power) at 60 deg F	38 knots
Cruising speed, calm water	35 knots
Turning circle diameter at 30 knots	2,200 ft (670 m)
Max wave capability	2-3 ft (609-914 mm)
Still air range at cruising speed (without reserves)	280 nm
Max gradient, static conditions	1:10
Vertical obstacle clearance	1 ft 4 in (407 mm)

PINDAIR LIMITED

HEAD OFFICE AND WORKS:
Quay Lane, Hardway, Gosport PO12 4LJ
TELEPHONE:
Gosport (070 17) 87830
DIRECTORS:
M. A. Pinder, Bsc, CEng, MIMechE, (Managing)
A. M. Pinder
J. Holland, FCA
EXECUTIVES:
M. A. Pinder, Design and Development
M. Rutland, Sales
B. M. Oakley, Testing and Demonstrations
D. McClunan, Production
V. A. Wells, Administration and Accounts
CONSULTANTS:
D. Robertson
E. Gifford

Pindair Limited was formed in May, 1972. It is currently engaged in the design, development, manufacture and sales of a range of inflatable light hovercraft for recreation, commercial and military use as well as supplying amateur hovercraft constructors in the United Kingdom with engines, fans, ducts, skirt materials and many other specialised components.

Five amphibious models are currently in production; one model is at the prototype stage. Production capacity for the smaller models is currently 10 per week and the larger models are custom built.

The use of folding inflatable hulls for the Pindair Skima range offers a number of advantages including ease of transport and storage, low weight, and resistance to icing. Special attention has been paid to simplicity of owner maintenance and use of components with worldwide spares availability.

The smaller models use Husqvarna/Valmet 160 cc 2-stroke engines coupled to ducted multiwing axial fans with replacement polypropylene blades. The larger models use 4-stroke automotive engines. The Skima 12 has been developed with assistance from Hovercraft Development Limited.

In all cases HDL loop segment skirts are used. Prices generally compare with boats having similar payload and performance.

SKIMA 1

This has been designed as a low cost one-man hovercraft which can be stowed in the luggage compartment of most cars, be light enough for easy portability by one man yet be capable of carrying one man on land or water in reasonable conditions. It is suitable for hovercraft familiarisation, amusement parks, exploration or class competitions.

In 1972 three single-seat inflatable hovercraft designed by Pindair reached an altitude of 10,000 ft in the Himalayas by travelling along turbulent rivers.

SKIMA 2

This was the first craft marketed by the company, Examples are now in use on every continent. It is light enough to be carried by two people and can carry two people under reasonable conditions. It has separate lift and propulsion systems and can be folded to fit onto a car roof rack on a small estate car.

The Skima 2 can be used as an amphibious yacht tender runabout, for exploration or for class competitions.

SKIMA 3

This is derived from a special version of the Skima 2 which was raced successfully by Barry Oakley in the 1973, 1974 and 1975 Hover Club of Great Britain Championships, winning a number of open races and also speed, manoeuvrability and free style competitions outright.

Although capable of operating as a three-man hovercraft it is mainly used for two

---

SKIMA PERFORMANCE DATA

Craft	Units of	Skima 1	Skima 2		Skima 3			Skima 4				Skima 6/9 (estimated)			Skima 12			
Payload	80 kg or 1 person	1	1	2	1	2	3	1	2	3	4	3	6	9	3	6	9	12
Max speed over water	km/h	40	45	40	60	50	40	55	55	50	40	60	50	40	70	60	55	50
Max speed over grass	km/h	40	45	40	60	50	40	55	55	50	40	60	50	40	70	60	55	50
Max speed over tarmac	km/h	45	50	45	70	60	45	60	60	50	45	70	60	45	90	70	60	50
Max speed over ice	km/h	50	65	50	90	70	60	70	70	65	60	100	70	60	110	90	70	60
Hump speed	km/h	3	5	8	5	6	8	3	5	6	8	3	6	8	4	6	8	10
Max wind force	Beaufort	3	4	2	6	5	4	6	5	4	3	8	4	2	8	6	4	2
Fuel consumption	litre/h	4	7	7	9	9	9	9	9	9	9	25	25	25	25	25	25	25
Max range	km	50	150	130	150	130	100	150	140	130	100	130	100	80	300	240	220	200
Turning circle (low speed)	m	3	3	3	5	5	5	6	6	6	6	8	8	8	10	10	10	10
Turning circle (high speed)	m	25	35	50	25	35	50	35	50	70	90	35	160	100	35	60	100	120
Max short slope	%	100	100	60	100	70	60	100	80	70	60	100	60	30	60	45	30	15
Max continuous slope	%	15	20	13	25	20	13	30	25	20	13	30	25	15	30	25	20	15

SKIMA SPECIFICATIONS

Craft	Skima 1	Skima 2	Skima 3	Skima 4	Skima 6/9 (estimated)	Skima 12
Length	2·74 m	3·20 m	3·20 m	4·07 m	4·80 m	7·53 m
Width	1·53 m	1·93 m	1·93 m	1·93 m	2·29 m	3·61 m
Height off cushion	91 cm	1·22 m	1·22 m	1·22 m	1·53 m	2·44 m
Dry weight kg	165 kg					
Skirt	HDL	HDL	HDL	HDL	DHL	HDL
Skirt depth	12 cm	15 cm	15 cm	20 cm	30 cm	40 cm
Obstacle clearance	23 cm	30 cm	30 cm	35 cm	50 cm	38 cm
Folded dimensions	76cm × 91cm × 35 cm	91 cm × 1·52m × 61 cm	1·22m × 1·52m × 61 cm	1·22m × 1·52m × 61 cm	not determined	3m × 2·44m × 1·22 m
Pack dimensions	76cm × 91cm × 35 cm	84cm × 1·07m × 61 cm	84cm × 1·07m × 84 cm	84cm × 1·7m × 84 cm	not determined	
Assembly time, mins	15	30	40	40	60	120
Thrust kg	88 kg	132 kg	242 kg	242 kg	440 kg	1,320 kg
Engines	1 Valmet	2 Valmet	3 Valmet	3 Valmet	2 Kohler	Jaguar
Fans	1 Multiwing axial	2 Multiwing axial	3 Multiwing axial	3 Multiwing axial	2 Multiwing axial	1 cent. axial
Total engine power	10	15	25	25	80	200

The Skima 3, powered by three Rowena Stihl 137 cc 2-stroke engines, and capable of 35 mph (56·32 km/h) over water.

The Skima 4, capable of carrying four people under favourable conditions, and recommended as an alternative to the Gemini inflatable boat where amphibious capability is required

  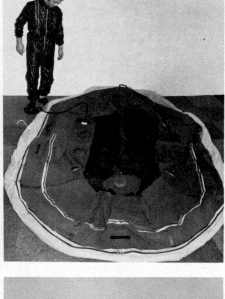

 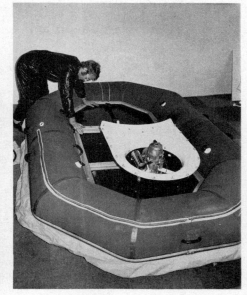 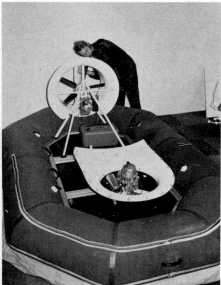

Above, left to right, top and bottom: Six stages in the assembly of the Pindair Skima 2. Packed dimensions of the craft are 2 ft 6 in × 3 ft 6 in × 2 ft, and the total assembly time is 30 minutes

people or by one person in competitions.

SKIMA 4

During proving trials in 1973 this hovercraft covered the longest journey so far by a light hovercraft on inland and coastal waters. The Naval Hovercraft Trials Unit has recommended it as an alternative to the Gemini inflatable boat used by the British armed services, particularly in cases where its amphibious qualities would be an advantage.

Examples of the Skima 4 are in use in various parts of the world as amphibious transport for two people plus their equipment in most conditions or four people in good conditions. The rear inflatable seat is instantly removable for stowing freight or equipment. Users include missionaries on Lake Chad, an aluminium company in the Arabian Gulf, a Pest Research Organisation, a Marine Biology research group, defence forces, subaqua organisations, and flood and beach rescue organisations.

SKIMA 6/9 (PROTOTYPE)

An inflatable hovercraft capable of carrying nine persons in open configuration or six persons when fitted with a light cab. Suitable for general personal transport as well as military, rescue, ambulance, pest control, freight, survey and exploration duties. Capable of being transported complete by road ready for use or folded.

SKIMA 12 (20 PROJECTED)

A semi-inflatable utility hovercraft capable of carrying 12 people in an enclosed cabin. A version capable of carrying 20 people i.e. one Jeep or equivalent freight is under development.

The outer hull can be deflated to allow transportation by road or shipping. Since this hovercraft generates exceptionally low noise and can cope with severe conditions it is particularly suitable for freight, passenger or tourist service, or police, customs, pilots, rescue and military applications.

ROTORK MARINE LIMITED

HEAD OFFICE:
Westbury, Wilts, BA13 4JT, England
DIRECTORS:
J. J. Fry
J. S. Fry
M. F. Briggs
A. J. F. Garnett
A. J. Percy
G. Rushton
MARKETING COMPANY:
Rotork Technical Services Limited
2 Halkin Street, London SW1X 7DJ
TELEPHONE:
01-235-9681
TELEX:
916053
CABLES:
Rotorktech

Rotork Marine is building and marketing a series of fast, flat bottom, multi-purpose workboats, the best known of which is the Sea Truck. A key feature of the design is the use of air lubrication to reduce hydrodynamic drag. A ram-air cushion, contained by shallow side skegs, raises the bow clear of the water at speed. As the pressurised air flows aft it generates air/foam lubrication for the remainder of the hull, permitting speeds of up to 50 mph (80·46 km/h) to be achieved. The performance depends upon the payload, installed power and sea conditions. A wide choice of power plants is available, and cabin modules can be supplied for passenger and work crew accommodation. Bow loading ramps are fitted for ease of access and operation from beaches.

The company offers a series of fast assault craft and patrol boats, tactical personnel carriers and logistic support craft, together with a range of general purpose short haul passenger and vehicle ferries, 8 m (25 ft 3 in) or 12 m (39 ft 4½ in) in length. Since June 1972, when the Mk 4 Sea Truck was introduced, nearly 300 craft have been sold, 90% of which were delivered to overseas markets.

ROTORK 8M SEA TRUCK Mk 4

This is a heavy duty, multi-purpose workboat designed for high performance and low running costs. It can operate safely in only 1 ft (304 mm) of water and is equipped with a bow ramp to facilitate the loading of passengers, freight or light vehicles from beaches. The maximum payload is 3 tons.

POWER PLANT: Dependent upon payload and performance requirements and whether the craft is to be employed for sheltered water or open sea operation. Engines recommend-

Above: A Rotork 12m logistic support craft at speed. *Below:* A Land Rover of the Royal Navy being loaded onto an 8m Rotork Sea Truck

ed are: Outboard: 135 hp OMC OBMs, or 150 Mercury OBMs. These can be fitted as twin or triple installations. Inboard (diesel): 106 hp Volvo AQD 32/270, installed as either single or twin installations. Supplied as standard with these units are the control console, and depending on the type of power unit, 50 gal (220 l) or 100 gal (440 l) bulwark or saddle tanks in welded mild steel, fuel lines, fittings and batteries.

HULL: Heavy duty glass fibre reinforced plastics. Star frame chassis integral with hull structure. 'Top hat' section. Bottom is in double thickness heavy duty grp and has five reinforced rubbing strips. Buoyancy is provided by closed cell polyurethane foam of TD 1 type. The skegs are in prestressed cold drawn stainless steel tube. The ramp, which is manually operated, is in 1 in (25·4 mm) thick, polyurethane-coated marine ply. It is housed in a galvanised steel frame with galvanised steel capping, and is counter-balanced by a torsion bar.

ACCOMMODATION: Up to four moulded grp cabin modules can be installed, together with passenger seats.

SYSTEMS, ELECTRICAL: Heavy duty 12 volt batteries housed in acid-resistant reinforced plastic battery box mounted at deck level

FUEL: Fuel is carried in one or more 50 or 100 gallon pannier type tanks, carried between the upper and lower fender tubes, port or starboard.

SCUPPERS: Scuppers for the removal of deck water are located in the transom. Discharge capacity is 180 gal/min (818·27 litres/min).

DIMENSIONS:

Length overall	24 ft 2 in (7·36 m)
Length at waterline	20 ft 0 in (6·09 m)
Beam	9 ft 10 in (2·74 m)

Freeboard:

unladen, to deck level	5 in (127 mm)
to top of bulwarks	3 ft 0 in (0·914 m)
max load, to deck level	2 in (50·80 mm)
to top of bulwarks	2 ft 7 in (0·787 m)

Deck area (with outboard power)
170 sq ft (15·79 m²)

Draft:
unladen, outboard drive up 7 in (177·8 mm) outboard drive down 1 ft 11 in (0·584 m)

Max load, outboard drive up
11 in (279 mm)

outboard drive down 2 ft 3 in (0·685 m)

WEIGHTS:
Basic hull, less engine 3,200 lb (1,451·49 kg)

Total integral foam buoyancy
11,500 lb (5,216·31 kg)

Payload, inshore 6,000 lb (2,721·55 kg)
sea conditions 3,000 kg

PERFORMANCE (8m):
Performance varies with rig, type of load, installed power and operating conditions. An approximate guide, based on the standard open deck-hull, is provided by the accompanying performance graph. This applies to the STW8 Sea Truck 8m workboat configuration.

ROTORK 12 M SEA TRUCK Mk 4

HULL: Glass-fibre reinforced plastic. Reinforcement: E glass chopped strand mat. E glass woven roving. Silane finish. Matrix: Isophthalic polyester resins meeting Admiralty DG 180 specification for large ships, integrally coloured. Resins: Cellobond A2785 CV or Scott Bader 625 TV.

BUOYANCY: Closed cell polyurethane foam of the TDI type. Nominal density 43·64 kgf/cu m (2·4lb/cu ft) 98% closed cell. Method of manufacture: auto proportioning machine mix foamed in situ.

DECK: Non-slip bonded grit surface applied to special point load resisting composite structure.

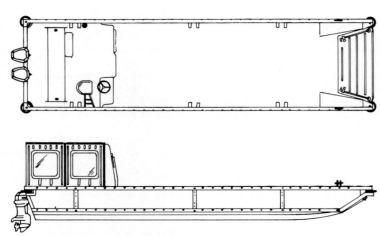

The Rotork 12 Metre Sea Truck in this configuration gives a clear open working deck area of over 6 m × 2·4 m

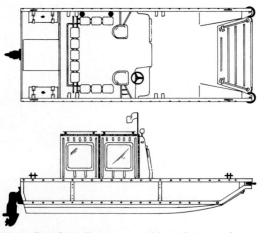

Layout of a Rotork 8 Metre Fast Crew Boat, powered by either a single or twin Volvo Penta AQD 32/270 diesel engines of 106 hp

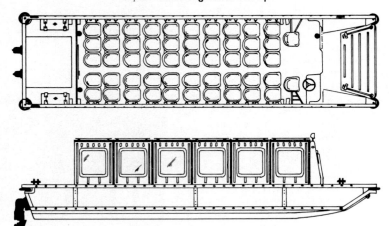

Rotork 12 metre diesel powered shorthaul passenger vehicle with seating for up to 50 passengers plus helmsman and observer. Seating capacity may be reduced according to operational requirements

CHASSIS: 'Star frame' chassis integral with hull structure. 'Top hat' section.

GLAZING: 6 mm perspex acrylic sheet. Triplex where wipers are used.

FENDER FRAMES: Hot-dip galvanized welded mild steel tube 101·6 mm (4 in) diam.

SKEGS: Prestressed cold drawn seamless steel tube. Anti-corrosion coated.

FENDERS: Rotating fender wheels are fitted as standard at bow and stern.

RAMP: 25·4 mm (1 in) thick marine plywood ramp. Polyurethane coated and grit bonded. Housed in galvanized steel frame with galvanized steel capping. Ramp counter-

balanced by torsion bar.

RAMP LOCK: Ramp opened and closed by galvanized mild steel levers. Manually operated.

RAMP SEAL: 50·8 mm (2 in) diam neoprene tube in compression.

SCUPPERS: Scuppers for the removal of water from the deck are located in the transom.

TANKS: Welded mild steel, phosphate conversion coated, epoxide primed, 2-pack polyurethane finish enamelled. Pressure tested.

FITTINGS: ¼ in and ⅜ in BSP

FUEL LINES: 9·5 mm (⅜ in) ID rubber hose with integral steel braiding.

CAPACITY AND MOUNTING: Type 1— 220 litre (50 gallon imperial) pannier for bulwark mounting. Type 2—440 litre (100 gallon imperial) saddle tank for athwartship mounting.

DIMENSIONS:

Length
Overall	11·27 m (37 ft)
At waterline	9·8 m (32 ft 2 in)
Beam	2·74 m (9 ft 10 in)

Freeboards:
Unladen to deck level	127 mm (5 in)
Unladen to top of bulwarks	814·4 mm (36 in)
With max load to deck level	50·8 mm (2 in)
With max load to top of bulwarks	838·2 mm (33 in)

Height:
Of top rail from deck	787·2 mm (31 in)
Of metacentre above centre of gravity	5·51 m (18 ft 1 in)

Deck area:
overall	30·85 sq m (287 sq ft)

Draft:
Unladen, outdrive up	177·8 mm (7 in)
Unladen, outdrive down	584·2 mm (23 in)
With max load, outdrive up	279·4 mm (11 in)
With max load, outdrive down	685·8 mm (27 in)

Weights:
Less engine	2405 kg (4,500 lbs)
Total integral foam buoyancy	886 kg (1,968 lbs)

ROTORK STW 12 SEA TRUCK WORKBOAT

HULL: Standard Rotork 12 metre hull.

COLOUR: Hull—high visibility orange. Metalwork—bright galvanized finish.

FIXING POINTS: Rotork military pattern eye bolts at modular fixing points on upper and lower mainframe.

ELECTRICAL: Navigation lights, klaxon and searchlight mounted on mast operable from helmsman's position are standard equipment.

FUEL: 445 litre (100 gallon imperial) capacity. Mild steel welded and pressure tested tanks fitted with drain cocks, quick release filler caps and sight gauges.

FIRE FIGHTING EQUIPMENT: 1·1 kg (2½ lb) rechargeable CO_2 hand extinguisher.

TOTAL WEIGHT: 2,045 kg (4,500 lb).

Optional items include:

NAVIGATION: Illuminated and fully gimballed compass mounted next to helmsman. Approx weight 2.7 kg (6 lb).

COMMUNICATIONS: VHF 8-channel transmitter/receiver. Approx weight 5·7 kg (13 lb) Small ship radar with range of 16 nm at 3kw. Approx weight 40 kg (88 lb).

CREW PROTECTION: GRP covered after-control position with all round vision. Nylon reinforced PVC dropscreen at rear. Approx weight: 143 kg (315 lb).

INSULATION: Heat resistant safari roof for service in particularly high ambient temperatures. Approx weight 25 kg (55 lb).

SUPPLEMENTARY CREW AREA: 4 ft forward extension of control position providing additional covered crew space and GRP stowage lockers. Approx weight 65 kg (143 lb). Additional extension of cabin

An 8 metre patrol craft in service with the Medway Ports Authority

12m shorthaul passenger ferries are in service in Africa, the Far East and South America

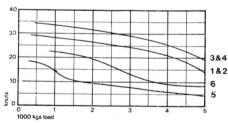

Performance graph for Rotork 12 metre Sea Truck workboat

Propulsion
1 Two 135 hp OMC OBM's 282 kg (620 lb)
2 Two 150 Mercury OBM's 282 kg (620 lb)
3 Three 135 hp OMC OBM's 424 kg (932 lb)
4 Three 150 Mercury OBM's 424 kg (932 lb)
5 One 106 hp Volvo AQD 32/270 inboard 391 kg (861 lb)

forming an enlarged crew compartment. Approx weight 130 kg (286 lb).

MOBILITY: Detachable short haul wheels for launching and landing. Approx weight 151 kg (333 lb).

PROPULSION: (Alternative power plants and weights)
1 Two 135 hp OMC OBM's
282 kg (620 lb)
2 Two 150 Mercury OBM's
282 kg (620 lb)
3 Three 135 hp OMC OBM's
424 kg (932 lb)

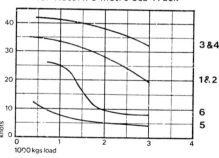

Approximate performance graph for Rotork 8 metre Sea Truck

6 Two 106 hp Volvo AQD 32/270 inboards 782 kg (1,721 lb)

Payload: Maximum normal loading in the 8 metre Sea Truck Workboat is 3,000 kg. This figure is dependent on choice of optional equipment and propulsion system. Individual weights are as indicated.

4 Three 150 Mercury OBM's
424 kg (932 lb)
5 One 106 hp Volvo AQD 32/270 inboard
391 kg (861 lb)
6 Two 106 hp Volvo AQD 32/270 inboards
782 kg (1,721 lb)

PAYLOAD: Maximum normal loading in the 12 metre Sea Truck Workboat is 5,000 kg. This figure is dependent on choice of optional equipment and propulsion system. Individual weights are as indicated.

See accompanying graph for approximate performance figures.

SEALAND HOVERCRAFT LTD.

HEAD OFFICE:
2-5 Old Bond Street, London W1X 3TB
TELEPHONE:
01-493-7681
TELEX:
Dolphmart London 24620
WORKS:
Devonshire Road, Millom, Cumbria
TELEPHONE: Millom 2233
TELEX: Sealhov Millom 65146
DIRECTORS:
E. Wise, Chairman
L. Landau, AICF, Managing Director
A. P. Freeman, MBIM, Works Director
L. M. Wise, FCA
J. A. Joseph
S. Marcelis
SENIOR EXECUTIVES:
B. A. M. Sewell, Works Manager
I. Malcolm, Production Supervisor
L. D. Ackerley, Commercial Manager
P. H. Widdowson, Sales Service Manager
P. Segger, Production Planning
M. Elliot, New Projects Manager
D. Long, Design Office Manager
R. Spours, Materials Controller.

Sealand Hovercraft was formed in 1968 and completed the SH1 two-seater the following year. In 1971 the company produced its first six-seater, the SH2, which was displayed at many exhibitions, including the International Boat Show, Oceanology International, Europort Amsterdam and the Hovering Craft and Hydrofoil Exhibition, Brighton, 1974.

Thirty SH2 craft have been built and supplied to customers in the USA, Soviet Union, Australia, Nigeria, Pakistan, South America, Hong Kong, Middle East and Zaire.

In late 1974 the company introduced the SH2-4, a 9-12 seater which is identical both structurally and mechanically to the SH2, but with the cabin length "stretched" by 6 ft 0 in (1·82 m). Twelve SH2-4s have been built. The company is currently concentrating on the production of the SH2-5, a description of which appears below.

SH2-5

An amphibious, multi-duty hovercraft with a payload of one ton (1,106 kg), the SH2-5 is designed to fit a variety of roles, from a 12-seat waterbus and ambulance to an armed patrol craft.

It is now in production at a rate of two craft per month.

LIFT AND PROPULSION: Integrated system powered by a single 200 hp Chrysler eight-cylinder automobile engine. Cushion air is supplied by a 3 ft (0·914 m) diam. Sealand Hovercraft grp fan, driven via a clutch, shafting and a right-angled gearbox. Thrust is supplied by four 2 ft 8 in (0·81 m) diameter, four-bladed Permali axial-flow fans, mounted in pairs on a common shaft in each of the two propulsion air ducts. Each pair is driven via a toothed belt by a pulley on the power take-off shaft, aft of the clutch assembly. Air for the lift fan, located at the end of the hull, is drawn through an intake located between the two propulsion duct outlets. From the fan it is fed via a bag to individual fingers. Engine, fans and transmission are built onto a steel subframe to form a single, easily removed unit.

Sealand's latest amphibious hovercraft—the SH2-5, a multi-purpose vehicle with a payload of one ton. As a light ferry, it carries a driver and eleven passengers. Maximum speed over calm water is 42 knots

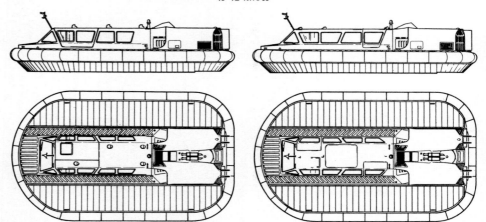

The Sealand SH2-4 9-12 seater, and *right*, the SH2-5 12-seater

Fuel is carried in two stainless steel tanks located in the pannier sections, port and starboard, outboard of the main beams. Total capacity is 100 galls (455 ltr). Refuelling points are provided at the centre of the craft, port and starboard. Fuel recommended, 91 octane. Oil capacity is 13 pints (7·38 ltr.).

CONTROLS: Directional control is maintained by twin aerodynamic rudder vanes hinged to the rear of each of the propulsion ducts. Reverse thrust for braking is obtained by opening out the paired rudder vanes in opposing directions to block the propulsion duct outlets, forcing the air forward through louvres. The craft can be steered by use of the braking system. A water ballast system is used for longitudinal trim.

HULL. Main members are of sandwich form, employing Airex pvc foam cores faced with grp polyester. Hinged sidebodies are in grp laminate. Structure is stressed to withstand forward impact loads of up to 6g.

SKIRT: 1 ft 6 in (457 mm) deep, 50% fingered-bag type, fabricated in pvc-coated nylon.

ACCOMMODATION: Basic version seats a driver and 11 passengers. A choice of seating layout for smaller numbers of passengers or mixed freight/passenger vehicles are available. The cabin is fitted with a fresh air heating and ventilation system. Access is provided through two gull-wing doors and a large freight hatch is provided as standard in the roof. Electrically-operated fire detection and extinguishing equipment is fitted. Stowage is provided for an inflatable liferaft which can be fitted as an optional extra.

SYSTEMS: Electrical: 12 volt alternator. 45 amp hr battery.

COMMUNICATIONS AND NAVIGATION: Optional extras: Viking Princess 10-channel marine radio; Decca 050 radar; Type E2A compass.

ARMAMENT: 7·65 mm machine gun and wire-guided missile to order.

DIMENSIONS, EXTERNAL:

Overall length, power off	26 ft 3¼ in (8 m)
Length, power on	28 ft 4¼ in (8·6 m)
Beam overall, power off	7 ft 7½ in (2·8 m)
Beam, sidebodies and skirt inflated	16 ft 8 in (5·08 m)
Height overall on landing pads	5 ft 5¾ in (1·65 m)
Height overall, skirt inflated	7 ft 0 in (2·1 m)
Draft afloat	10 in (0·25 m)
Cushion area	305 sq ft (28·33 m²)
Skirt depth	1 ft 6 in (0·46 m)

DIMENSIONS, INTERNAL:

Length	13 ft 9 in (4·19 m)
Max width	5 ft 1 in (1·55 m)
Max height	4 ft 1 in (1·24 m)
Floor area (excluding driver's seat area)	approx 56 sq ft (5·2 m²)

WEIGHTS:

Normal gross weight	6,800 lb (3,084 kg)
Payload including driver	2,240 lb (1,016 kg)

PERFORMANCE:

Max speed over calm water	42 knots
Cruising speed	25 knots
Turning circle diameter at 30 knots	300 yds (274 m)
*Still air range and endurance at cruising speed	150 miles (241 km)
Vertical obstacle clearance	1 ft 6 in (0·46 m)

*With ferry fuel tanks range is increased to 300 miles (483 km).

PRICE AND TERMS: On application, according to specification.

SURFACE FLIGHT LTD

HEAD OFFICE:
147/149 London R9ad, East Grinstead,
Sussex

TELEPHONE:
0342 28386

EXECUTIVES:
G. R. Nichol
P. V. McCollum
N. A. Old

Surface Flight Ltd is concentrating on the development of low-cost, two-seat amphibious hovercraft, the first of which, the Sunrider, is now in production. Although designed for recreational use, the craft is suitable for a range of utility roles from light transport and rescue boat, to water-taxi and port and harbour inspection vehicle.

SUNRIDER

The Sunrider is a glass-fibre-hulled two-seater with a maximum speed of 35 mph (56 km/h). Ruggedly constructed, it is easy to operate and has an extremely low noise level.

LIFT AND PROPULSION: A 9·5 bhp Rotax two-stroke, single-cylinder engine located ahead of the open cockpit drives a 7-bladed fan for cushion lift. Thrust is provided by a 38·5 bhp Rotax 2-cylinder two-stroke driving a ducted 20-bladed fan aft of the cockpit. Fuel recommended is 93 octane. Tank capacity is 6 Imp gallons (27 litres).

CONTROLS: Single control column operates twin rudder hinged to rear of fan duct. Column incorporates twist-grip throttle for

Production model of Surface Flight's Sunrider two-seater, which is being employed for a number of light transport and liaison duties

lift fan. Electric starter provided for thrust engine.

HULL: Moulded glass-reinforced plastics.

SKIRT: Loop and segment skirt in polyurethane nylon. Replaceable segments.

ACCOMMODATION: Single, two place bench-type seat in open cockpit

DIMENSIONS:

Length overall	13 ft 4 in (4·06 m)
Beam overall	6 ft 6 in (1·98 m)
Height	3 ft 8 in (1·117 m)

WEIGHTS:

All up weight	1,060 lb (480 kgs)
Payload	420 lb (190 kg)

PERFORMANCE:

Max speed	35 mph (56 km/h)
Range	100 miles (160 km)
Endurance	4 hours approximately

VOSPER THORNYCROFT LTD

HEAD OFFICE:
Vosper House, Southampton Road, Paulsgrove, Portsmouth, England

TELEPHONE:
Cosham 79481

TELEX:
86115

CABLES:
Repsov, Portsmouth

DIRECTORS:
Sir David Brown, Chairman
John Rix, MBE, Managing Director
Commander Christopher W. S. Dreyer, DSO, DSC, RN
Alan A. C. Griffith, OBE
Alan D. Worton
The Hon. Sir Clive Blossom, Bt
Kenneth D. C. Ford
John E. C. Grant, MBE

EXECUTIVE BOARD:
John Rix, MBE, Chief Executive
K. D. C. Ford, Financial Director
J. E. C. Grant, MBE, Secretary
P. D. P. Kemp, Managing Director Shipbuilding Division
L. Peacock, Executive Director Personnel
A. P. Shaw, Director Products Division
D. P. E. Shepherd, OBE, Sales and Commercial Executive Director
P. J. Usher, Deputy Managing Director Shipbuilding Division
J. A. Wilde, CBE, Managing Director Repairs Division
D. E. Wilson, Executive Director Ship Sales

SENIOR EXECUTIVES (Hovercraft):
A. E. Bingham BSc., (Tech), MIMechE, AFRAeS, Chief Hovercraft Designer

A 270-seat Vosper Thornycroft VT I hoverferry

Arnaud de Cosson, Hovercraft Sales Manager

Vosper Thornycroft Limited is the holding company for a number of companies throughout the world, the most important of which is Vosper Thornycroft Private, Ltd. in Singapore.

Vosper Thornycroft has a high reputation as builder of warships including fast patrol craft, corvettes and frigates powered by diesel and gas-turbine machinery singly or in combination. Warships built by the company are in service with the Royal Navy and the navies of more than a dozen foreign and commonwealth countries. It also has a major ship repair facility in Southampton Docks.

With an annual turnover in the region of £56 million, derived mainly from building warships, Vosper Thornycroft also has a number of prosperous ancillary activities. These include the design and production of ship stabilisers, specialised electrical and electronic control equipment for marine and industrial use, oil burning equipment and furnishing.

In 1968, the decision was taken to enter the hovercraft field and shortly afterwards an order was received for the VT 1—an 87 ton hoverferry designed to carry 146 passengers and ten cars at speeds up to 40 knots. The VT 1 has been subjected to exhaustive trials to evaluate every aspect of its commercial viability and particularly its reliability and seakeeping, both in the English Channel and in the notoriously rough waters between the Channel Islands and the French coast. The first two all-passenger craft built by the company were operated in Scandinavian waters between Malmo, Sweden and Copenhagen, Denmark in 1972.

Operationally, the craft proved extremely successful. They carried more than 310,000 passengers and travelled more than 61,000 miles, with a mechanical reliability of 98·73 per cent.

In 1973 the company announced that it was building the VT 2, the first of a new class of fully amphibious hovercraft intended primarily for military applications. The prototype is expected to begin trials in late 1975. Design studies have covered a range of larger vessels, including a 170-ton ASW or MCM vessel and a 500-ton convoy escort.

VT 1

The VT 1 is an 87 ton ACV designed for fast, low-cost passenger/car/operation. It is built to the standards required by the British Civil Air Cushion Vehicle Safety Requirements. Power is supplied by two Avco Lycoming TF25 marine gas-turbines each driving four fixed-pitch lift fans and one controllable-pitch water propeller.

Cruising speed is 35-38 knots (65-70 km/h) and the craft will operate in complete safety in wave heights up to 10-12 ft (3-3·7 m). The VT 1 can be operated from existing terminals or alternatively, simple low-cost slipways or pontoon terminals can be established on beaches.

VARIANTS: Typical layouts include a car/passenger version for 146 passengers and 10 vehicles and a 250/270 passenger version which can be fitted with facilities for serving refreshments on route.

LIFT AND PROPULSION: Motive power is provided by two Avco Lycoming TF 25 marine gas-turbines, with power ratings between 1,675 and 2,000 hp for ambient temperatures between 80°-60°F. These are located in separate engine rooms amidships, port and starboard. Each engine is directly coupled via a transfer gearbox to four 5 ft diameter centrifugal lift fans and thence to a skeg-mounted water propeller via a Vee-drive gearbox.

The eight fans deliver air to the cushion via a continuous peripheral segmented skirt made in lightweight neoprene-proofed nylon material with full cushion depth segments. There are neither stability skirts nor other compartmentation arrangements. The skirt provides an air cushion depth of about 5½ ft (1·68 m).

The propellers are Stone KaMeWa 3-bladed controllable-pitch units and have a diameter of 2·1 ft (640 mm).

Fuel is contained in four integral tanks, located two each side in the raft structure amidships, beneath the lift fan rooms. Total fuel capacity is 3,480 Imp gallons (15,280 litres). One pressure refuelling point is fitted, on the starboard side forward. Types

Interior of one of the four corner passenger cabins flanking the VT 1's central deck area

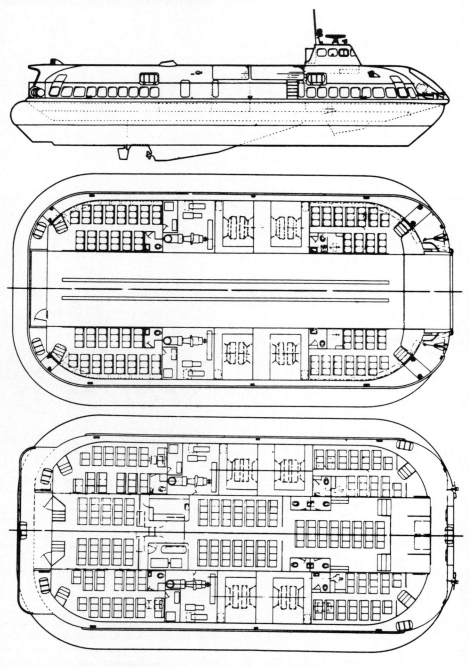

Profile of the VT 1 and (below) interior arrangements of the standard version for 146 passengers and 10 cars and the cruise variant for 270 passengers

Above and below: Operational bases for the 60-knot plus VT 2 fast patrol hovercraft can be established on any gently sloping beach.   Equipped with missiles, it carries an armament load comparable to that of a much larger conventional patrol boat.   Armament would normally comprise two or four anti-ship missiles and either an Oto Melara 76 mm general-purpose automatic cannon, or a Bofors 57 mm cannon, together with their associated control equipment.   Armament and crew weight is 23·5 tons, and with 10·5 tons of fuel the range at 60 knots is 300 nm.   The crew consists of 12 officers and men, served from a common galley.   Principal dimensions of the VT 2 fast patrol hovercraft are: Length, 99 ft 0 in (30·17 m), Beam 43 ft 6 in (13·25 m), and Cushion Depth 5 ft 6 in (1·67 m)

The main driving controls for course and attitude are positioned in front of the port seat, and duplicated in front of the starboard CONTROLS: The control cabin is located above the port side of the superstructure and provides a 360° view.   Provision is made for two craft control positions abreast of each other forward, with radar located at a third seat position behind.   Engine controls are on a central console within easy reach of both front seat positions.

of fuel recommended are: Kerosene, AVTUR and Widecut; diesel, gas oil.

seat.   Directional control is provided by power-operated twin water rudders, controllable-pitch propellers and twin skegs.   A water ballast system is provided for longitudinal and transverse CG adjustments.

OPERATING TECHNIQUES: The VT 1 is designed to operate like a conventional ship when at sea and when berthing alongside piers and moles.   It can operate from simple concrete ramps or slips laid on any reasonably steep beach, an ideal arrangement for loading and off loading vehicles.   By employing this technique for passenger car/ferry services, simple, inexpensive terminals can be built on beaches of suitable gradient (between 1 in 8 and 1 in 12) from which the craft can be operated in all tide states.

At its maintenance base, the beach landing technique is used to land the craft onto a trolley on which it is hauled out of the water for maintenance.

HULL: Construction is mainly in marine corrosion-resistant aluminium alloys.   Both the bottom and deck structures are of conventional stiffened plate.   The craft bottom is designed to resist water impact pressures with closed-up framing in the bow where higher impact pressures are likely to be encountered.   The deck structure in the central car bay will support axle loads up to 4,000 lb (1,814 kg)—an approximate gross vehicle weight of 3 tons (3·1 tonnes)—with lighter structure in the deck's side bays where only foot traffic is anticipated.   Alternatively standard ISO 20 ft (6·1 m) containers of average weight (up to ½ ton per ft run) can be carried, using the car, guide tracks.   The containers would be mounted on weight distributing rollers.

The bottom and deck structure are separat-

ed by longitudinal and transverse web frames which form a buoyancy raft of 31 separate watertight compartments including oil and fuel tanks.   The raft provides the entire torsional strength of the craft.   Reserve buoyancy is more than 100%.

Two main longitudinal vertically stiffened bulkheads run the length of the craft separating the central car bay from the outer machinery and the passenger bays.   These provide the craft's resistance to overall longitudinal bending and shear.   The outer bays are subdivided by four transverse bulkheads of similar construction linked across the central car bay by beams to provide the overall transverse strength of the craft.

The superstructure covering is of light gauge sheet with longitudinal stiffeners.   It is supported on transverse roof and vertical side beams which are designed to resist aerodynamic loading in airspeeds up to 80 knots.   The hull is designed for a maximum disposable load of 35 tons and a normal payload of 21 tons.

LANDING SKEGS: These are of stiffened plate construction similar to that of the buoyancy raft bottom.   Loads due to beaching are diffused into the craft's longitudinal bulkheads via several main transverse frames.

ACCOMMODATION: The car/passenger version has four passenger compartments, one at each corner of the craft, and seats a total of 146 passengers.   Each compartment has a toilet/washroom.   There are two main entrances to each passenger compartment.

For operations from a beach, passengers enter over the main ramp or may use the external superstructure doors via mobile embarkation steps.

The car bay, designed for 10 cars, has full width doors at the bow, which form an access ramp for loading and unloading.   The craft always beaches bows-to, and cars must be driven off in reverse.   To simplify the control and positioning of cars a guide track is provided for each lane of cars and runs the full length of the bay.   This enables vehicles to be disembarked quite satisfactorily.   As an alternative to cars, up to three ISO 20 ft containers can be carried.

Each passenger compartment has a sufficient number of approved emergency exits according to the numbers carried.   A full range of safety equipment is carried.   Both main engine rooms have individual fire warning and extinguishing systems monitored and controlled from the control cabin.   The control cabin and each passenger compartment have hand-operated extinguishers.

One inflatable lifejacket of approved type is stowed under each seat in the passenger saloons, and in addition. liferafts catering for at least 100% of passengers and crew are stowed externally.

HEATING AND VENTILATION: Fresh air heating and ventilating is provided for the four passenger compartments and control cabin only.   The heating plant is a separate combustion heater and blower unit.   It supplies fresh air at ambient or higher temperatures and is thermostatically controlled. Complete air-conditioning can be fitted if required.

SYSTEMS:

ELECTRICAL: 240 volt 50 HZ single-phase AC: 115 volt 400 HZ single-phase AC; 24 volt DC.

Provision for shore supply.

The 240 volt 50 HZ AC supplies are derived from diesel-driven alternators rated at 28 kVA continuous, giving 22·4 kW at 0·8 power factor, lagging. Other supplies are those met from transformer/rectifiers and solid state inverters. The medium voltage service supplies the following: lighting and heating; pumps for the fuel, propeller blade pitch and bilge systems; the transformer/rectifiers for the 115 volt single-phase AC and main 24 volt DC supplies. The 115 volt. 400 HZ AC provides power for the following control systems: steering, speed (propeller blade pitch-adjustment), turbine power (throttle controls).

HYDRAULICS: A 3,000 lb/sq in (14,647 kgt/m²) hydraulic system is installed to operate the rudders, bow door and ramp when fitted. Propeller pitch is actuated by a separate system.

COMMUNICATIONS AND NAVIGATION: Standard equipment includes the following: VHF and standby VHF radio; crew intercom and public address system.

NAVIGATION: Decca 202 radar, Sperry CL.2 gyro compass and two repeaters standby magnetic compass, waterspeed indicator and log, and echo sounder.

Decca Navigator and Flight Log is optional. Alternative equipment can be fitted to customer specification.

DIMENSIONS, EXTERNAL:

Length overall	95 ft 6 in (29 m)
Beam	43 ft 6 in (13·26 m)
Base of skegs to masthead	
	41 ft 9 in (12·73 m)
Calm water level to masthead on hover	
	37 ft 5 in (11·41 m)

Cushion depth	5 ft 6 in (1·67 m)
Draft afloat	9 ft 9 in (2·97 m)
Draft hovering	3 ft 9 in (1·14 m)
Cushion area	3,487 sq ft (324 m²)

DIMENSIONS, INTERNAL:

Four passenger cabins with toilets, each with the following dimensions:

Length	24 ft 0 in (7·3 m)
Max width	13 ft 6 in (4·1 m)
Max height	7 ft 6 in (2·3 m)
Floor area	320 sq ft (29·8 m²) app

Vehicle bay (may also be used for passenger accommodation):

Length	79 ft 6 in (24·2 m)
Width, clear	16 ft 0 in (4·85 m)
Height, clear	9 ft 8 in (2·95 m)
Max axle load	4,000 lb (1,820 kg)

SIZE AND POSITION OF DOORS:

Forward loading door, 17 ft (5·1 m) wide × 9 ft 8 in (2·97 m) high. Four passenger external access doors to saloons, four further doors from saloons to car bay.

WEIGHTS:

Empty weight	55 tons
Normal maximum operating weight	87 tons
Normal operating weight	83 tons
Normal disposable load	27·5 tons
Normal payload	22 tons

PERFORMANCE (At maximum continuous power and normal operating weight), at ambient temperatures of 60°F:

Normal service speed	38 knots (70 km/h)
Turning circle diameter at 38 knots entry speed	2,000 ft (610 m)
Water speed in 4 ft waves and 15 knot headwind	35 knots (64 km/h)
Max wave capability at 15 knots	12 ft (3·6 m)
Max wave capability on scheduled runs	8 ft (2·44 m)

Still air range and endurance:

at normal fuel load   150 n miles, 4 hours

at maximum fuel load

340 n miles, 9 hours

VOSPER THORNYCROFT HOVERCRAFT FOR NAVAL AND MILITARY USE

Based on the VT 1, this gas-turbine powered hovercraft patrol boat has a floating displacement of 100 tons and a speed of 46 knots. Typical armament would comprise Exocet anti-ship missile launchers, and a twin-barrelled 35 mm Oerlikon cannon designed primarily for rapid and accurate fire against aircraft and guided missiles, but which is also extremely effective when directed against light surface craft. The missiles and cannon will be controlled by a Contraves fire control system or a similar system.

The craft offers a number of important advantages over conventional fast patrol boats of comparable size. In particular, due to the depth and flexibility of its fully peripheral skirt, the craft can maintain a high speed and provide a stable weapons platform in sea conditions in which many patrol boats would scarcely be able to operate.

LIFT AND PROPULSION: Motive power is provided by two Avco Lycoming TF 35 gas-turbines each rated at 2,750 shp at 60°F ambient temperature located in separate engine rooms amidships port and starboard. Each engine is coupled via a transfer-gearbox to four grp lift fans and thence to a water propeller via a vee-drive gearbox. Total fuel capacity is 20 tons.

ARMAMENT: One 35 mm twin Oerlikon cannon and four Exocet missile launchers. Search radar, fire control radar, fire control systems for guns and missiles and electronic countermeasures equipment. Other suitable combinations can be installed.

HULL: Construction is mainly in marine corrosion-resistant light alloys.

ACCOMMODATION: Captain, three officers, three senior ratings and seven junior ratings are accommodated in air conditioned spaces, furnished to modern standards.

CONTROLS: The control cabin is located above the superstructure on the longitudinal

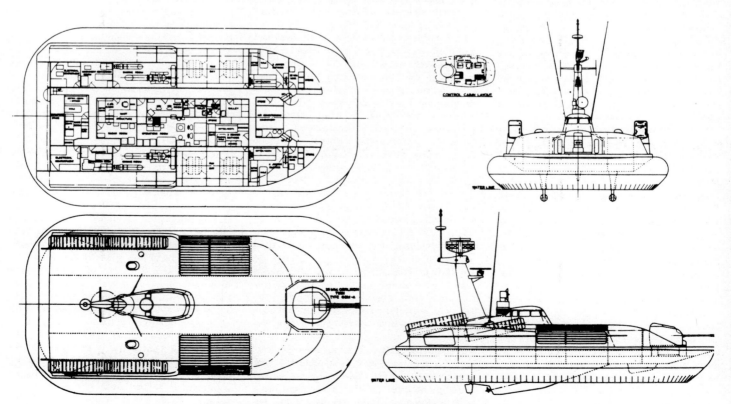

General arrangement of the Vosper Thornycroft hovercraft FPB equipped with four exocet antiship missile launchers and a twin-barrelled 35mm oerlikon cannon.

centreline amidships and provides a 360° view. The control position is forward to port, with an engineer's position to starboard and navigator's and observer's positions behind.

Directional control is provided by power operated twin water rudders, controllable-pitch propellers and twin skegs.

OPERATING TECHNIQUE: As for Vosper VT 1.

COMMUNICATIONS AND NAVIGATION: Decca TM626 navigational radar and full craft-to-air, craft-to-ship and craft-to-shore communications

DIMENSIONS:

Length overall	93 ft 6 in (28·05 m)
Beam (hard structure)	43 ft 6 in (13·25 m)
Draft hovering	3 ft 6 in (1·07 m)
Draft hullborne	10 ft 0 in (3·05 m)

WEIGHTS:

Basic weight	66 tons
Armament and crew	24 tons
Fuel	20 tons
Total (in half fuel condition)	100 tons

PERFORMANCE:

Max speed	46 knots
Endurance	

With 20 tons of fuel, the endurance is 14 hours at 43 knots, or 600 nautical miles

THE VT2 HOVERCRAFT

First fully amphibious hovercraft to be built by Vosper Thornycroft, the VT 2 is intended for military applications. It employs air propulsion instead of water propellers, enabling the vessel to traverse shallows and operate from small coves and beaches. In overall size, configuration and payload, it is similar to the earlier VT 1 mixed-traffic ferry. Externally, the feature which immediately identifies the craft is the presence above the stern superstructure of two 13 ft 6 in (4·11 m) diameter ducted fans, which are powered by Proteus marine gas-turbines.

A number of variants are projected, ranging from a 65-knot logistic support vessel to a patrol craft armed with two surface-to-surface missile launchers and a rapid-fire cannon.

Normal load capacity of the logistic support variant is about 32 tons, but considerable overloading is acceptable, and with suitable deck reinforcing, a 50-ton Chieftain battle tank could be carried.

The ducted fans are designed to maintain a noise level far lower than that of earlier air-propelled craft. Its negligible water noise signature, combined with a low surface pressure and slight magnetic signature will render it less vulnerable to mines.

The vessel can either be shipped to a theatre of operations, or if required by a NATO country, it could be deployed to any point on the coastline of Europe or the Mediterranean under its own power. The longest 'stage' would be from the United Kingdom to Gibraltar, a distance of approximately 1,100 nautical miles, and to allow an adequate reserve en route for rough seas, the craft would carry an additional 10 tons of fuel, starting out at an all-up weight of 115 tons.

LIFT AND PROPULSION: Motive power for the integrated lift/propulsion system is supplied by two Rolls Royce Proteus marine gas-turbines rated at 4,500 shp maximum and 3,800 shp continuous. The gas turbines are installed in port and starboard engine rooms, amidship, and each powers two drive

Above and below: Logistic support version of the new fully-amphibious VT 2. Two massive ducted fans, each 13 ft 6 in (4·11 m) in diameter, dominate the stern superstructure

Impression of the Vosper Thornycroft 170 ton ASW or MCM vessel. Maximum speed would be in excess of 50 knots

shafts via a David Brown gearbox. One shaft transmits power to a bank of four centrifugal lift fans, which absorbs about one third of the output, the other drives a ducted propulsion fan via an inclined shaft.

The 13 ft 6 in (4·11 m) diameter propulsion fans, made by Dowty Rotol, have variable-pitch blades and are housed in ducts manufactured by Vosper Thornycroft. Each engine/fan unit provides sufficient power to maintain the craft on full cushion and ensure adequate controllability in the event of a single engine failure.

The blade tip speed will be low so that the noise commonly associated with open air propellers will be substantially reduced.

CONTROLS: Control surfaces for vectoring

thrust are fitted aft of the fans for normal steering, but differential pitch is used for steering at low speeds. Thrust can be varied for manoeuvring the craft without altering the engine speed or cushion depth. HULL: Structure similar to that of VT 1. Built mainly in marine, corrosion-resistant aluminium alloys.

Preliminary details of the four main variants are summarised below, together with weights.

DIMENSIONS (all variants):

Length overall	99 ft 0 in (31·17 m)
Beam overall	43 ft 6 in (13·10 m)
Cushion height	5 ft 6 in (1·67 m)
Hand structure clearance when hovering	
	3 ft 7 in (1·09 m)

Draft in deployment condition

2 ft 10 in (0·86 m)

Height (hovering to top of propulsion fan
ducts)   30 ft 3 in (9·15 m)

PERFORMANCE:

Max speed, calm conditions

in excess of 60 knots

Max speed in 5 ft (1·52 m) waves 55 knots

VARIANTS:

VT 2 LOGISTIC SUPPORT HOVERCRAFT

Designed to carry a company of 130 fully-
armed troops and their vehicles.   The vehicle
bay is approximately 16½ ft (5·02 m) wide,
9½ ft (2·89 m) high and 70 ft (21·33 m) long.
It has a full width bow ramp and door
together with an 8 ft (2·43 m) wide stern
ramp and door for the through loading and
unloading of vehicles.   The craft can carry
payloads of 30-33 tons, together with fuel
for five hours.   Considerable overloading of
the craft is acceptable at reduced performance
so that with suitable deck and entrance
ramp reinforcing, a 50 ton Chieftain battle
tank could be carried.

WEIGHTS:

Operating weight	62·5
Payload	32·0
Fuel	10·5
Starting auw	105·0 tons

VT 2 MULTI-ROLE LOGISTIC SUPPORT AND GP PATROL HOVERCRAFT

Fitted with a rear loading door and ramp,
enabling four 1-ton Landrovers and 60 troops
to be loaded in the aft section of the central
bay.   The bow is the same as that of the
lightly armed fast patrol version.   The
forward area of the central bay and the
forward cabins on each side would be fitted
out as a small operations room and crew
quarters.

WEIGHTS:

Operating weight	65·5
Armament and crew	5·0
Payload	19·0
Fuel	10·5
Starting auw	100·0 tons

VT 2 FAST PATROL HOVERCRAFT, HEAVILY ARMED

This version can be equipped with two
Otomat missiles and a 57 mm Bofors cannon
or alternatively four Otomat missiles may be
fitted in conjunction with a smaller rapid-fire
cannon.   Other armament of similar weight
could be fitted to meet individual specifications.   Armament and crew weight is 23½
tons, and with 10½ tons of fuel, the endurance
is five hours or 300 nm at 60 knots.   An
additional 10½ tons of fuel for the overload
case (giving a half fuel weight of 100 tons)
results in a range of 600 nm.

WEIGHTS:

Operating weight	66·0
Armament and crew	23·5
Fuel	10·5
Starting auw	100·0 tons

VT 2 FAST PATROL, LIGHTLY ARMED

Armed with a twin Hispano-Suiza 30 mm
cannon.   At a starting weight of 100 tons,
it has 24½ tons of fuel, providing a range of
700 nm or 11½ hours endurance at a speed of
60 knots.   An additional 10½ tons of fuel
(a total of 35 tons), increases the range to
1,000 nm.

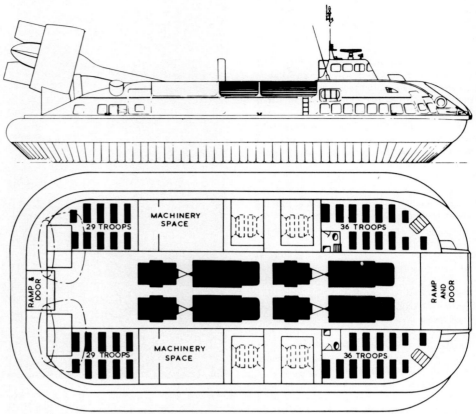

Outboard profile and accommodation plan of the VT 2 in logistic support configuration

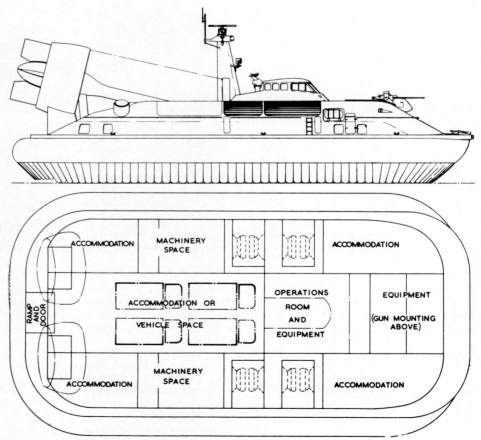

VT 2 equipped for lightly armed patrol and general purpose roles

WEIGHTS:			Fuel	24·5
Operating weight	70·5			
Armament and crew	5·0		Starting auw	100·0 tons

170-TON ASW OR MCM VESSEL

This design for a 170-ton anti-submarine or mine countermeasures vessel is based on that of the 100-ton fast patrol boat. An increase in installed horsepower and length provides off-shore capability, and the larger deck area permits the installation of a wider range of weapons.

Motive power is supplied by three Rolls-Royce Proteus gas-turbines driving lift fans and three axial-flow waterjet units. Alternatively the designers propose a CODAG arrangement in which diesel engines can be coupled to the integrated lift/propulsion system to provide increased range.

DIMENSIONS:
Length overall	37·1 m
Beam (hard structure)	12·25 m
Height, power on (sea level to top of control cabin)	8·1 m
Cushion depth	2·3 m
Hovering draught	1·0 m
Floating draught (gear retracted)	1·5 m

WEIGHTS:
All-up weight	170 tonnes
Armament load	29 tonnes

PERFORMANCE:
Range full power	700 nm
With diesels fitted for low speed cruising—at AUW 182 tonnes—15 knots	1,500 nm
Speed, maximum continuous	In excess of 50 knots

500-TON ASW OR CONVOY ESCORT

The main role for which this vessel has been designed is that of ocean convoy escort. Lift fans and waterjet units would be driven by a Rolls-Royce Olympus and two Avco Lycoming TF45 gas turbines.

DIMENSIONS:
Length overall	66 m
Beam (hard structure)	19 m
Height (sea level to top of control cabin—on cushion)	13·5 m
Cushion depth	3·5 m
Hovering draught	1·7 m
Floating draught (skeg folded)	2·8 m

WEIGHTS:
All-up weight	500 tonnes
Armament load	50 tonnes

PERFORMANCE:
Range full power	1,200 nm
Range at 23 kts	2,000 nm
Speed—maximum continuous	In excess of 50 knots

VT 1M

Built as a manned scale model of the VT1 hovercraft, the VT 1M has now completed its programme of development trials, including a test programme with waterjet propulsion.

A 500-ton ocean-going escort designed by Vosper Thornycroft. A helicopter landing pad and hangar can be provided aft of the superstructure

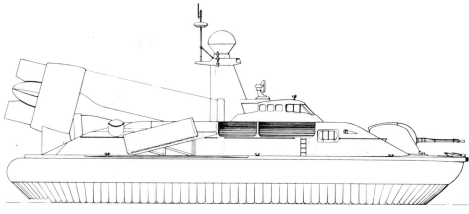

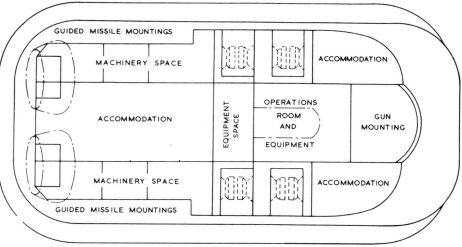

The VT 2 heavily-armed patrol craft carries either two Otomat missiles and a 57 mm Bofors cannon, or alternatively four Otomat missiles and a smaller gun

VT 1M-001 equipped with a waterjet propulsion system

UNITED STATES

AEROJET-GENERAL CORPORATION
(Subsidiary of the General Tire and Rubber Co)

CORPORATE OFFICE:

J. H. Vollbrecht, President

9100 East Flair Drive, El Monte, California 91734

TELEPHONE:

(213) 572-6000

AEROJET ENERGY CONVERSION COMPANY:

J. L. Heckel, President

PO Box 13222, Sacramento, California 95813

TELEPHONE:

(916) 355-1000

AALC OPERATIONS, AEROJET ENERGY CONVERSION COMPANY:

PO Box 2173, Tacoma, Washington 98401

F. F. Herman, Program Manager

A. E. Rose, Director, Operations

Aerojet-General began research and development programmes on both rigid sidewall and skirted amphibious air cushion configurations in June 1966. The company's research and development programmes include lift system development, skirt and structural materials investigations and development sub-scale and full-scale dynamic model testing, test laboratory development and full-scale vehicle operation. In addition, Aerojet has conducted government and company funded design and application studies on many rigid sidewall and skirted air cushion vehicle designs for military, non-military government and commercial roles. Work is at present concentrated on a US Navy contract for the development of the AALC Jeff(A) amphibious assault landing craft.

SES-100A

Earlier contracts for preliminary design of a "less than 100-ton" SES craft and for the dynamic test programme for the US Navy's XR-3 research craft led to the award of a contract, in January 1969, for the detailed design, construction and test of a 100-ton rigid sidewall testcraft—the SES-100A—under the sponsorship and management of the Surface Effect Ships Programme Office (SESPO), an agency of the US Navy.

Dockside testing began in August 1971 and deep water trials began in May 1972. Official US Navy test and evaluation trials began in September 1972 and were completed in 1974.

Subsequently the craft was moved from the Seattle, Washington, area to the US Navy's SES Test Facility at the Naval Air Station, Patuxent River, Maryland, where tests have been resumed.

A description of the vessel appears in the entry for Rohr Industries, which under navy contract, provides maintenance, engineering, test planning and data handling support for the test programme.

AALC JEFF(A)

In 1970, Aerojet-General was awarded a contract by US Naval Ship Systems Command for the preliminary design of an experimental 160-ton 50-knot amphibious assault landing craft. This was followed in March 1971 by a further contract for the detail design, construction and test of the

Above and below: Aerojet-General's SES-100A during a series of high-speed test runs. The craft is powered by four 3,500 hp Avco Lycoming TF 35 gas-turbines and has a maximum speed of about 80 knots. Shown in these photographs are the forward skegs, used for directional control at high speeds, and the two engine air inlets on the topside, aft. The cabin accommodates four crew members and up to six test observers

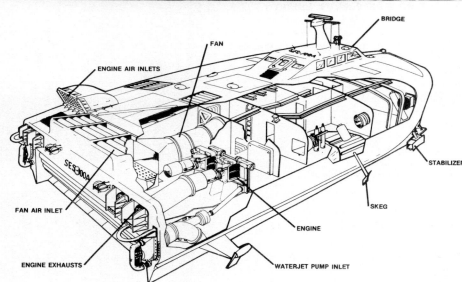

Cutaway drawing showing the positions of the waterjet pump inlets, skegs and bow stabilisers on the SES-100A

craft, which is designated AALC Jeff(A) Construction of the hull was initiated by Todd Shipyards Corporation, Seattle, Washington, in 1974. Manufacturer's and US Navy trials will be undertaken during 1976 and 1977.

The craft is designed to operate at a nominal speed of 50 knots in Sea State 2 and accommodate up to 75 tons in palletised supplies and/or equipment. It is designed primarily for use by the US Marine Corps, and will carry tanks, trucks, half-trucks

and other equipment from an LPD, LSD or LHA mother ship to a point inland.

To ensure adequate world-wide operational capability, the specification calls for operation in temperatures from 0°-100°F.

LIFT AND PROPULSION: Cushion lift is provided by two 3,750 hp Avco Lycoming TF40 gas-turbines, one in each of the two sidestructures, driving two sets of four 4 ft 0 in (1·21 m) diameter fans through lightweight transmission and shafting connections.

Thrust is supplied by four 3,750 hp Avco Lycoming TF40 gas-turbines each driving a 7 ft 5 in (2·26 m) diameter pylon-mounted shrouded propeller, located above the side-structure, and outside the cargo deck area to provide free access and uninterrupted air flow. Each propeller pylon rotates to provide both propulsion and directional control.

HULL: Constructed in marine aluminium with maximum use of corrugated structures to minimise total craft weight. The main hull is formed by a buoyancy raft with port and starboard side structures. Each side-structure contains three Avco Lycoming gas-turbines with associated air intakes, exhausts, shrouded propellers, lift fans, transmissions and auxiliary power systems.

The bottom and deck structures of the hull are separated by longitudinal and transverse bulkheads to form a number of watertight flotation compartments. The cargo deck area is 2,280 sq ft (211·82 m²); the bow ramp opening width is 21 ft 6 in (6·55 m) and the aft ramp width is 27 ft 4 in (8·33 m).

SKIRT: 5 ft (1·52 m) deep "Pericell" loop and cell type.

ACCOMMODATION: Two air-conditioned and sound-insulated compartments, each seating three crew members or observers. Access to each compartment is via the cargo deck.

DIMENSIONS:
Length overall, on cushion
                  96 ft 1 in (29·30 m)
  on landing pads   92 ft 0 in (28·04 m)
Beam overall, on cushion
                  48 ft 0 in (14·63 m)
  on landing pads   44 ft 0 in (13·41 m)
Height overall, on cushion
                  23 ft 1 in (7·03 m)
  on landing pads   18 ft 9 in (5·71 m)
Bow ramp opening width
                  21 ft 6 in (6·55 m)
Stern ramp opening width
                  27 ft 4 in (8·33 m)
Cargo deck area   2,280 sq ft (211·82 m²)

WEIGHTS:
Gross weight   334,000 lb (154,221 kg)
Empty weight   180,000 lb (81,697 kg)
Fuel   40,000 lb (18,144 kg)
Design payload   120,000 lb (54,431 kg)
Design overload 150,000 lb (68,038 kg)

PERFORMANCE:
Max speed with design payload   50 knots
Range   200 nm
Max gradient, standing start   11½%
Nominal obstacle clearance
                  4 ft 0 in (1·21 m)

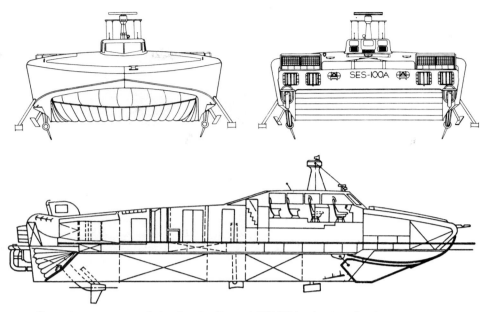

General arrangement of the Aerojet-General SES-100A, showing the loop-and-segment bow seal design

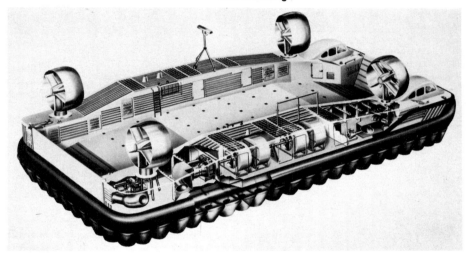

Above and below: The Aerojet-General Jeff(A) amphibious assault landing craft under construction for the US Navy. Designed primarily to meet the US Marine Corp's requirements in the 1980s, it will carry tanks, trucks, half tracks and other equipment from LPD, LSD or LHA mother ships to the shore at a speed of 50 knots

AIRCUSHION BOAT COMPANY INC

HEAD OFFICE:
    401 Alexander Avenue, Building 391,
      Tacoma, Washington 98421

TELEPHONE:
    (206) 272 3600

EXECUTIVES:
    W. W. Buckley, President
    F. C. Gunter, Vice-President

The Aircushion Boat Company is responsible for the development of the Airboat—a concept described by the company as an air-cushion-assisted catamaran. Vessels of this series of sidewall craft are based on conventional fibreglass hulls and employ water propeller or waterjet propulsion. Lift is supplied by an independent engine/fan system and flexible skirts are fitted fore and aft to contain the air cushion.

The company states that the cushion supports 75% of the loaded weight of the Airboats, and that as a result of the reduced drag the prototype uses 20% less fuel per mile. Another advantage is that when travelling at high speed, the air cushion softens the ride by preventing heavy slamming. Vessels of this type are being marketed by the company for a variety of applications including fast crew boats, water taxis, patrol boats, survey and sports fishing craft.

AIRBOAT III

Airboat III is employed as a development craft and began trials in Puget Sound in January 1974.

It has performed in short 4 ft (1·21 m) waves at speeds up to 35 knots without undue discomfort to the crew due to slamming. Another characteristic is that it generates very little wash when executing full speed runs on smooth water in protected waterways.

LIFT AND PROPULSION: Two 330 Chrysler petrol engines driving twin water screws propel the craft. A third engine powers a centrifugal fan for cushion lift.

HULL: Fine retardant foam and fibreglass sandwich construction.

DIMENSIONS:
Length	38 ft (11·58 m)
Beam	13 ft 6 in (4·11 m)

WEIGHTS:
All-up weight	16,000 lb (7,257 kg)
Normal payload	3,000 lb (1,360 kg)

PERFORMANCE:
Cruising speed	35 knots
Maximum speed	40 knots plus

42 FT AIRBOAT

The 42 ft (12·8 m) long Airboat is a high speed passenger ferry/freighter capable of operating in 4·5 ft waves. In passenger configuration seating is provided for 21 plus a crew of two.

A feature of the design is the extension of the bow well ahead of the air cushion. When rough water forces the bow down at speed the broad area forward of the cushion planes and raises the bow without slamming.

With the lift fan system off, the craft operates as a conventional displacement catamaran and has a top speed of 15 knots. With the lift system on, acceleration to the cruising speed of 30 knots is easily attained in ten boat lengths. In 8-10 ft (2·4-3·04 m) following seas a stable, near horizontal attitude is maintained while contouring swells and no tendency to broach or lose directional control is experienced.

LIFT AND PROPULSION: Motive power is supplied by three diesels, one for lift and

Airboat III during trials on Puget Sound

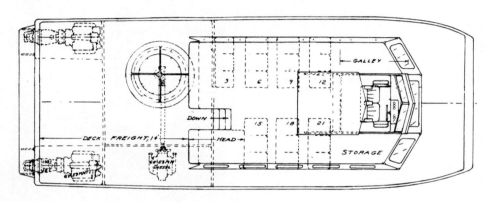

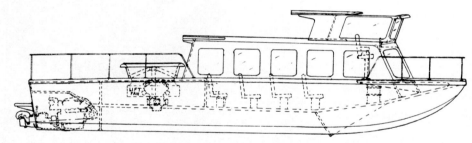

General arrangement of the waterjet-propelled 42 ft Airboat

two for propulsion. The lift engine drives a large low rpm centrifugal fan contained in a reinforced box which is an integral part of the hull structure. Power is transmitted via a clutch and Spicer shaft to a heavy duty, lightweight right-angle gearbox. Power delivered to the fan at cruise condition pressure and airflow is 180 hp. Each of the propulsion engines is turbocharged and drives a waterjet. The standard fuel tank capacity is 300 gallons, providing a cruising range of more than 250 miles at 30 knots.

Marine propellers can be fitted to the vessel instead of waterjets if required. The powerplant remains the same, but the propulsion engines supply power through reversing gearboxes to shafts and marine propellers. Hydraulically operated twin rudders are mounted on the transom of each of the hulls. The propeller-driven version is capable of the same top speed, with slightly improved fuel economy.

HULL: Robust, fire-retardent foam and fibreglass sandwich structure, with unitised beam tying the catamaran hulls. High freeboard, wide buoyant hull and low profile for seaworthiness in rough seas and gale force winds.

ACCOMMODATION: In passenger/crew boat configuration, accommodation is provided for 21 seat passengers and a crew of 2. The passenger saloon is completely enclosed with 6 ft 6 in (1·98 m) high headroom throughout. The cabin contains a galley, head and large storage area. The bridge is elevated for 360° view and is located slightly aft of the bow. A sliding hard top provides upward visibility if required.

DIMENSIONS:
Length	42 ft (12·80 m)
Beam	17 ft (5·18 m)

PERFORMANCE:
Service speed	30 knots
Maximum speed	in excess of 33 knots
Max speed, displacement condition	15 knots
Fuel consumption at 30 knots	34 gph (154·56 l/ph)
Cruising range at 30 knots	over 250 miles (402 km)

AIR CUSHION VEHICLES, INC

HEAD OFFICE:
R.D.5., Box 85, Troy, New York 12180
TELEPHONE:
518 283-6200
EXECUTIVE:
William W. Haney, National Sales Manager
Air Cushion Vehicles Inc, is marketing a
lightweight, amphibious runabout, the Model
410 Air Cycle.

AIR CYCLE MODEL 410

LIFT AND PROPULSION: Power for the
integrated lift/propulsion system is provided
by a single, 33 hp twin-cylinder Rockwell
JLO engine, mounted immediately ahead of
the cockpit and driving a 3-bladed, ducted
axial fan. Air from the fan feeds into the
plenum below for lift and aft for propulsion.
CONTROL: Craft direction is controlled by
the movement of multiple rudder vanes.
operating in the fan slipstream. Thrust
spoilers are provided for speed control, and
horizontal stabilisers for trim.
ACCOMMODATION: Open cockpit with
single seat. Craft will carry two sitting in
tandem, but with reduced performance.
SYSTEMS: Electrical: 12 volts for engine
starting and navigation lights.
DIMENSIONS:

Controls on the Air Cycle include multiple rudders, thrust spoilers to vary the speed of the
craft and horizontal stabilisers for trim

Length	10 ft 6 in (3·20 m)		
Beam	5 ft 6 in (1·67 m)	in excess of 40 mph (64·37 km/h)	
Height	3 ft 6 in (1·06 m)	Max gradient	
WEIGHTS:		Climbs 20% continuous gradient with one	
Weight empty	350 lb (158·75 kg)	170 lb (77·10 kg) adult aboard	
Load capacity	300 lb (136·07 kg)	PRICE:	
PERFORMANCE:		Recommended retail price, FOB factory:	
Max speed over land, water, snow and ice		$1,495·00	

AIRSEAMOBILE COMPANY

HEAD OFFICE:
24706 Evereve Circle, El Toro, California
92630
TELEPHONE:
714 836-1192
714 586-4419
PROPRIETOR:
Arthur M. Jackes
AirSeaMobile Company was established by
Arthur M. Jackes and a group of aircraft

engineers to undertake on a part-time basis
the design and development of ACV sports
craft. Mr. Jackes' design concept is based
on an integrated lift/propulsion system with
a straight-through flow. Various aspects are
incorporated in US patent 3,486,577. Several
preliminary designs have been completed,
two dynamic models have been tested, and
the prototype of a two-seat sports ACV, the
ASM-6, is undergoing trials.
Development of the ASM-6 is being under-

taken in association with Palm Enterprises
of Midland, Texas.
Northrop Corporation has sponsored a
preliminary design study by the company of
a 200-knot, 250-ton SES. A wind tunnel
model of this design has been built and
tested and has confirmed the high-speed
characteristics predicted for this craft.
Technical papers based on this work have
been prepared and will be presented as
opportunity permits.

BEARDSLEY AIR CAR CO

HEAD OFFICE:
40, Windward Drive, Severna Park, Maryland
TELEPHONE:
301-647 0526

PRESIDENT:
Melville W. Beardsley

The Beardsley Air Car Co is basically a
research and development operation con-

ducted by Melville Beardsley. Details of
the Fan-Jet Skimmer a small single-seater
designed by Melville Beardsley, will be found
in the entry for Skimmers Incorporated, the
company marketing these products.

BELL AEROSPACE
Division of Textron Inc.

HEAD OFFICE:
Buffalo, New York 14240
TELEPHONE:
Area Code 716 297-1000
OFFICERS:
William G. Gisel, President
Lawrence P. Mordaunt, Executive Vice-
President—Operations
Norton C. Willcox, Executive Vice-President
—Administration
Joseph R. Piselli, Vice-President—Market-
ing
Dr. C. F. Berninger, Vice-President—
Research and Engineering
Adolph Kastelowitz, Vice-President—Manu-
facturing
John F. Gill, Vice-President—Product
Assurance
Delmar E. Wilson, Vice-President—Western
Region
John R. Clark, Jr. Vice-President—Eastern
Region (Washington, D.C.)
John W. McKinney, Controller

BELL NEW ORLEANS OPERATIONS

P.O. Box 29307, New Orleans, Louisiana
70189
TELEPHONE:
Area Code 504 255-5901

John J. Kelly, Vice-President and General
Manager
Donald F. Bonhardt, Director of Product
Assurance
Joseph A. Cannon, Director of Marketing
John B. Chaplin, Director of Engineering
Roland Decrevel, 2KSES Project Manager
Hugh F. Farabaugh, Director of Employee
Relations and Services
Clarence L. Forrest, Director, Full-Scale
Test and Project Manager, SES-100B
Donald E. Kenney, Director of Administra-
tion
Clifford F. Lennon, Director of Manufactur-
ing
Robert S. Postle, LC JEFF(B) Project
Manager
Murray Shabsis, Director of Materiel
Albert W. Spindler, Director of Public
Relations

Bell Aerospace began its air cushion vehicle
development programme in 1958. Craft
built by the company range in size from the
18 ft XHS3 to the SES-100B, 105-ton
surface effect ship test craft which is undergoing sea trials.
The company has rights to manufacture and
sell in the United States, machines employing
the hovercraft principle through a licencing
arrangement with the British Hovercraft
Corporation and Hovercraft Development
Ltd.
In addition to importing seven BHC
SR.N5s, three of which were employed by
the US Navy and later by the US Coast
Guard for use and evaluation, Bell built
three SK-5 Model 7255s—the company's first
production ACVs—to a US Army specification. The craft were airlifted to Vietnam,
where they performed a variety of missions,
including high speed troop/cargo transportation and patrol. One SK-5 Model 7255 is
employed in a research programme being
conducted by the US Army's Weapons
Command, St Louis Missouri.

An astonishingly high rate of turn is demonstrated by the Bell SES-100B in this dramatic US Navy photograph. On its second circuit the vessel appears to be banking round an inclined track of water created by the wash of its first circular run

In January 1969, the US Surface Effect Ships Project Office awarded Bell a contract for the detailed design of a 100-ton surface effect ship test craft. Construction began in September 1969 and the preparation of the craft for trials began early in 1971. An extensive test and evaluation programme began in February 1972 on Lake Pontchartrain, Louisiana.

In May 1973, the SES-100B was transferred to the Naval Coastal Systems Laboratory at Panama City, Florida, for deep water and high sea state testing in the Gulf of Mexico. In January 1974 the company announced that the SES-100B had successfully completed the testing necessary to confirm and expand the technology necessary for the design of a 2,000-ton ocean-going surface effect ship.

In March 1971 the company was awarded a Phase II contract by the US Navy authorising it to start work on a programme covering the detail design, construction and test of an experimental 160-ton AALC (amphibious assault landing craft), designated L. C. JEFF(B).

This work is being undertaken at the company's New Orleans Division, where all its SEV programmes have been consolidated. Construction of the prototype began in 1972.

In March 1972 the Advanced Research Projects Agency of the US Department of Defense awarded Bell a contract under which the company will produce studies of nine different aspects of the ARPA's projected 1,000 ton, 120-knot arctic-based logistics vehicle.

In November 1972, it was announced that Bell had been awarded a $2·9 million contract by US Naval Ship Systems Command to conduct a preliminary design study for a 2,000 ton operational prototype surface effect ship. This study, completed in mid-1973, resulted in preliminary plans for an all-aluminium vessel, designed for speeds in excess of 80 knots.

In July 1974, Bell was awarded a $36 million contract to conduct an advanced development programme for a 2,000-ton, high-speed ocean-going, operational warship—the 2KSES. The 18-month contract awarded by the Naval Material Command covers the design, development and testing

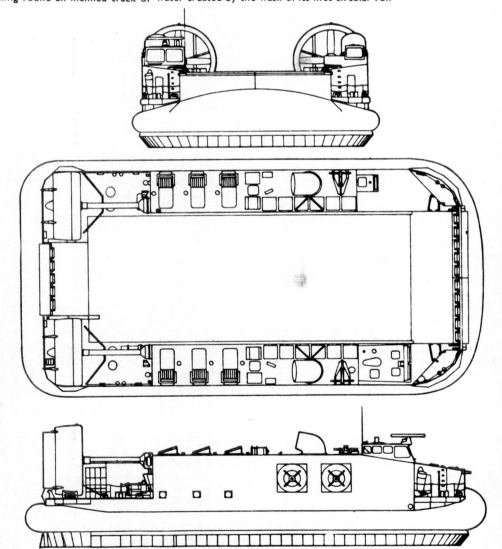

General arrangement of Bell's Amphibious Assault Landing Craft (AALC) JEFF (B). Power is supplied by six 2,800 hp Avco Lycoming gas-turbines driving four centrifugal impellers for lift and two 4-bladed ducted propellers for thrust

of full-scale sub-systems and components including transmission, waterjet systems, lift fans and skirts, as well as a method of controlling the vessel's ride characteristics in a variety of sea states.

Bell Aerospace Canada (see Canadian section) has built two prototypes of the Bell Model 7380 Voyageur heavy haul ACV, the second of which has been purchased by the Canadian Ministry of Transport for use by the Canadian Coast Guard. Production of additional Voyageurs is in hand. At the time of going to press Voyageurs 005 and 006 were nearing completion and 007 was due to be completed in mid-1976. The company is also testing the prototype of a new craft, the 15-ton Viking, which has been designed to meet the need for a smaller but similar multi-purpose vehicle capable of handling a 5-ton payload. The prototype, equipped for in-shore search-and-rescue duties, was completed early in 1974 and is operating with the Canadian Coast Guard.

The company also initiated a programme for the USAF that covers the design, development, installation and test of an air cushion landing system aboard a De Havilland XC-8A Buffalo transport aircraft. The first ACLS landing of the XC-8A took place at Wright-Patterson AFB, Dayton, Ohio on April 11th, 1975 and additional tests are being planned.

SK-5 Model 7255

Details of the SK-5 Model 7255 and its predecessor, the Model 7232, will be found in JSS 1972-73 and earlier editions.

AALC JEFF(B)

In March 1971, US Naval Ship Systems Command awarded Bell's New Orleans Operations a contract for the detail design, construction and testing of an experimental 160-ton, 50-knot air cushion assault landing craft.

Two companies are developing ACV test craft to the 150,000 lb (68,038 kg) payload. 50 knot specification—Bell and Aerojet-General. The Bell project is designated L.C. Jeff(B). Both craft will operate from the well-decks of landing ships and also alongside cargo ships.

The Bell contract involves mathematical and scale model investigations, interface and support system design, subsystem and component testing and design and systems analysis.

Detailed engineering design began in 1971 and is now complete. Fabrication of the prototype started in 1972 at New Orleans and the main hull (buoyancy box) has been completed. Installation of welded outer trusses and inboard and outboard side-structure framing is in progress. Cargo deck plating is undergoing final installation. On completion the company will conduct a programme of technical trials and contractor's engineering tests. The craft will then be delivered to the US Navy, which will conduct a series of tests and trials with an emphasis on operational use.

A $\frac{1}{6}$th dynamic scale model has been constructed and began an extensive series of engineering tests on Lake Pontchartrain in 1972. The model, which allows "free-flight" testing with radio control of all major craft functions, was used to confirm the final detailed design. A description of the craft, designated B-23, appears later in this entry.

L.C. JEFF(B) is designed to operate at a nominal speed of 50 knots in Sea State 2, and accommodate up to 75 tons in palletised supplies and/or equipment, up to the size of the 60-ton US Army main battle tank.

To ensure adequate world-wide operational capability, the specification calls for operation in temperatures from 0°-100°F and requires that the performance criteria can be met with a 25 knot headwind on a 100°F day.

Top: The helmsman's platform on the JEFF(B) amphibious landing assault craft is manned by two of the four-member operating crew and includes accommodation for an observer or wave commander. Helmsman and relief helmsman are located forward and occupy the right and left seats respectively. In addition to a set of controls and primary instruments that duplicate those of the helmsman, the relief helmsman's console also monitors radar information
Centre: Designed to fit within the dry well decks of the US Navy's LSD and LPD assault ships. JEFF(B) has fore and aft loading ramps for rapid on- and off-loading of troops, equipment and vehicles such as the 60-ton main battle tank. A typical LSD well deck can accommodate four JEFF(B)s and an LPD can take two
Bottom: Impression of a JEFF(B) coming ashore through surf with skirt inflated and bow and stern ramps raised

LIFT AND PROPULSION: Motive power is supplied by six 2,800 hp Avco Lycoming gas-turbines, driving four 5 ft 0 in (1·52 m) diameter double-entry centrifugal impellers for lift, and two 4-bladed 11 ft 9 in (3·58 m) diameter, Hamilton-Standard variable pitch, ducted propellers, for thrust. Fuel capacity is 6,400 gallons (29,094 l).

CONTROLS: Deflection of two aerodynamic rudders hinged at the rear of the propeller duct exits, differential propeller pitch, and the deflection of bow thrusters atop the side structures provide steering control. All controls are located in a raised bridge located well forward on the starboard superstructure. The helmsman's platform is raised to provide 360° vision for the two helmsmen, who have within easy reach all the necessary controls, navigation equipment and instruments. A third seat is provided at this level for another crew member or wave commander. On a lower level in the bridge is an engineer's station with monitoring instrumentation and a radar operator/navigator station. The crew will normally comprise four operating personnel and two deck supervisors.

HULL: Overall structural dimensions of the craft (80 ft length, 43 ft beam and 19 ft height) have been dictated by the well deck dimensions of the US Navy's LSDs (Landing Ships Dock), LPDs (Amphibious Transport Dock).

The main hull is formed by a 4 ft 6 in (1·37 m) deep buoyancy raft with port and starboard side structures. The main deck between the side structures forms the cargo deck, which is 66 ft long by 26 ft 4 in wide (20·11 m by 8·02 m), and provides an unobstructed cargo area of 1,738 sq ft (161·46 m²). A full width ramp is provided at the bow and a narrower ramp, capable of taking the main battle tank, at the stern.

The bottom and deck structures of the hull are separated by longitudinal and transverse bulkheads to form a buoyancy raft with a number of watertight flotation compartments. The craft fuel tanks and bilge system are contained within these compartments.

Plating at the bottom and side of the hull is stiffened by aluminium extrusions, and the main cargo deck is in mechanically fastened hollow truss-type core extrusions. The transverse bulkheads consist of sheet webs of aluminium alloy integrally-stiffened extrusions, with upper and lower bulkhead caps, also of aluminium extrusions.

The basic framing of the side-structures is aluminium back-to-back channels, which coincide with the transverse bulkheads and are spaced apart to straddle the hull bulkheads.

Each sidestructure contains three Avco Lycoming gas-turbines, and their associated air intakes, exhausts, lift fans, transmissions and auxiliary power systems.

SKIRT SYSTEM: Peripheral bag and finger type, with a 5 ft (1·52 m) high cushion compartmented by longitudinal and transverse keels. The upper seal bag attachment hinge line is raised high over the bow ramp area and the vertical diaphragm contains non-return valves similar to those fitted to the SR.N4.

DIMENSIONS:

Length overall	86 ft 9 in	(26·43 m)
stowed	80 ft 0 in	(24·38 m)
Beam overall	47 ft 0 in	(14·32 m)
stowed	43 ft 0 in	(13·10 m)

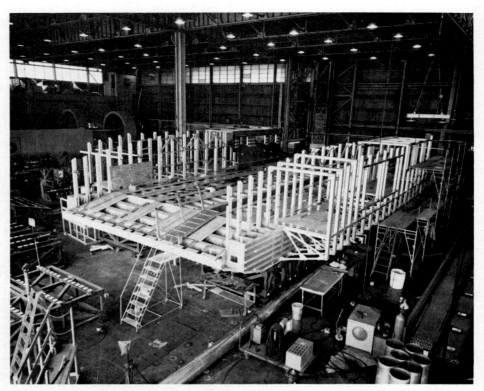

The US Navy's JEFF(B) landing craft is due for completion early in 1976. At the time this photograph was taken, installation of the welded outer trusses and inboard and outboard sidestructures framing was in progress. The main hull (buoyancy raft) had been completed

Powered by two 30 hp JLO 2-cylinder petrol engines, the Bell Model B-23 is a one-sixth scale dynamic model of the JEFF (B) amphibious assault landing craft. Designed for "free-flight" testing, it is radio-controlled and provides data on safety, stability, manoeuvrability and performance

Height	23 ft 6 in	(7·16 m)
Cargo area	1,738 sq ft	(160·71 m²)
Bow ramp width	28 ft 0 in	(5·34 m)
Stern ramp width	14 ft 6 in	(4·41 m)

WEIGHTS:

Normal gross weight	325,000 lb	(147,416 kg)
Normal payload	120,000 lb	(54,431 kg)
Overload payload	150,000 lb	(68,038 kg)

PERFORMANCE:

Speed	50 knots in sea state 2
Range	200 nautical miles
Max gradient continuous	13%

BELL MODEL B-23

This is a one-sixth scale dynamic model of the Bell AALC JEFF(B). Powered by two petrol engines, it is designed for 'free flight' testing under radio control. Data on safety, stability, manoeuvrability and performance is acquired by a lightweight instrumentation system and tape recorder installed aboard the craft.

With cushion inflated, the model is 14 ft 3 in (4·34 m) long, has a beam of 8 ft (2·43 m) and a height of 4 ft (1·21 m). Air cushion depth is 10 in (254·0 mm). The basic weight is 800 lb (362·85 kg), provision being made for the retention of lead ballast to increase the weight to a scale overload condition of 1,750 lb (793·75 kg). This will allow the model to be tested over the entire range of full-scale operating weights. The ballast can be located to allow any desired c.g. or inertia to be obtained.

HULL: The primary structure of the model is fabricated from aluminium honeycomb panels, with secondary structure incorporating fibreglass, styrofoam, and aircraft plywood. The seal system is fabricated in a coated nylon fabric of scale weight and bending stiffness. The model is painted in a bright red and yellow colour scheme. This was selected to provide maximum visibility for the operator and also to obtain the best cine camera coverage for engineering analysis.

LIFT AND PROPULSION: Motive power is provided by two 30 hp JLO two-cylinder, two-cycle petrol engines, one housed in each sidestructure. Each engine drives a scale propeller and a scale fan system through a transmission utilising a centrifugal clutch, tooth belts, and spiral bevel gearboxes. The engines are started electrically, and sufficient fuel is carried for two hours continuous operation.

CONTROLS: The remote control system provides simultaneous proportional control of the primary flight controls and switching of the instrumentation recorder. The ducted propellers are of controllable-pitch, the bow thruster direction and operating mode (forward/reverse) are controlled, the rudders and engine throttles are also included. In all cases, scale travel and scale rate have been maintained. The control system utilises two modified model aeroplane systems with a transmitter layout especially designed for ease of operation. A fail-safe system is arranged to cut the ignition of both engines if radio control is lost for any reason.

The instrumentation and recording system measures the behaviour of the model and the following characteristics: Model air speed (anemometer), cushion pressure in the fore and aft compartments, seal bag pressure, bow vertical acceleration, longitudinal acceleration, c.g. vertical acceleration, rate gyros for pitch, roll, and yaw, bow thruster position, rudder position, starboard propeller pitch, port propeller pitch, starboard side transmission rpm, port side transmission rpm.

The magnetic tape recorder is an environmentally-sealed, lightweight unit, designed originally for torpedo development. It conforms to IRIG standards and data reduction to oscillograph records will be performed at the Slidell Computer Centre.

PERFORMANCE: The model is capable of exploring the entire operational envelope over water, over land, and in surf. A model speed of approximately 20 knots will represent the full-scale design speed of 50 knots. In favourable conditions it is anticipated that model speeds greater than 30 knots will be obtained.

SES-100B TEST CRAFT

The SES-100B is the official designation for the 100-ton class sidehull surface effect ship (SES) test craft which has been built for the U.S. Navy by Bell Aerospace at New Orleans.

It is part of a long-range programme by the U.S. Navy to develop multi-thousand ton, ocean-going ships with speeds of 80 knots or higher.

This programme stems from research undertaken by the U.S Office of Naval Research in 1960, the U.S. Navy Bureau of Ships (now the Naval Ship System Command) and the U.S. Maritime Administration, which in 1961 sponsored the first programme for the development of a 100-ton SES, known as the Columbia.

In 1966, based on the results of these early programmes, a joint office of the U.S. Navy

and Department of Commerce was formed, known as the Joint Surface Effect Ship Programme Office (JSESPO), with the express purpose of determining the feasibility of building and operating large, fast, surface effect ships of 4,000-5,000 tons and capable of 80 knots or higher speed. Design studies conducted by industry for JSESPO (now SESPO, the US Navy having taken over the complete programme in 1971) over the

period 1965-69 covered all aspects of SES design and operation—economic factors, performance characteristics, structural and material parameter and subsystem characteristics—and culminated in the award of two design and construction contracts. Bell Aerospace was awarded a contract to design, build and test a water propeller-driven 100-ton class surface effect ship test craft in January 1969. A similar contract was awarded to

Bell Model B-26, a 7 ft (2·13 m) long radio-controlled model employed initially to provide design data for the SES-100B, and which is now being used to investigate design proposals for Bell's 2,000-ton SES

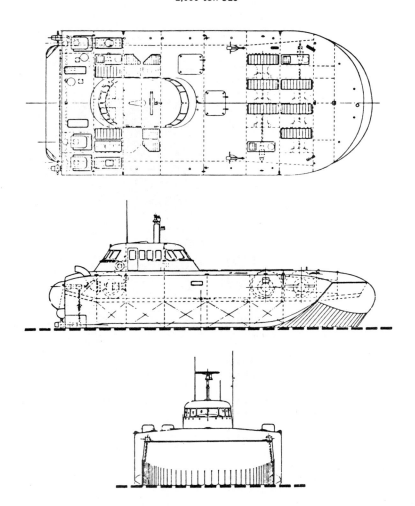

General arrangement of the Bell SES-100B 105-ton test craft

Aerojet-General Corporation for a waterjet-propelled test craft.

Construction of the Bell SES began in August 1970. The vessel was launched on July 22nd 1971 for hovering trials, and builder's trials, with the craft underway, began on February 4th, 1972. A test and evaluation programme encompassing performance trials, stability and seakeeping characteristics, structural load investigations, habitability and operational data, and other pertinent data necessary for the development of high speed surface effect ships, was conducted in the New Orleans area and in the Gulf of Mexico where a variety of sea conditions were experienced.

In January 1974, Bell Aerospace announced that the SES-100B had successfully completed the testing necessary to confirm and expand the technology necessary for the design of a 2,000-ton ocean-going SES. Tests are continuing in the Gulf of Mexico, off Panama City, Florida, in support of the 2KSES development programme. The current programme embraces the evaluation of acoustics, structural loads in higher sea states and higher speeds, seal (skirt) loads and ride control.

In April 1974, the SES-100B achieved a speed in excess of 80 knots, which was improved upon in a subsequent high-speed run in November of that year. Actual speeds in excess of 80 knots are classified. A US Navy crew has operated the SES-100B during the majority of the recent test runs.

Development of SES systems will result in the production of very high speed, multi-thousand ton ships for a variety of missions. Such development would make it possible for the US Navy to have a smaller but more effective fleet which would revolutionise naval warfare.

HULL: The SES-100B is a single, all-welded continuous structure, incorporating two catamaran-style sidehulls and is constructed from high-strength, corrosion-resistant marine aluminium alloy sheet and plate. The hull carries an integral deckhouse welded to the after portion of the weather deck. The deckhouse is so positioned to optimize the ride quality and habitability of the ship's complement of personnel while retaining good visibility from the command station.

The sidehulls, which virtually skim the surface of the water, provide basic stability to the craft and also seal the air cushion and prevent leakage along the port and starboard sides of the ship. The sealing of the air cushion is completed at the bow and stern by flexible fabric seals. The bow seal is of pressurised bag type with convoluted fingers not unlike the proven design previously used on the Bell skimmers. The stern seal is of Bell design and capable of providing the necessary trim to the craft.

The hull was constructed to BAC design under contract by Levingston Shipbuilding Co. of Orange, Texas. Other major subcontractors for the SES-100B were the Buehler Corporation of Indianapolis, Indiana, for the propulsion transmission system; the Philadelphia Gear Corporation of King of Prussia, Pennsylvania, for the supercavitating controllable-pitch, partially-submerged propellers; Astrospace Labs of Huntsville, Alabama, for the lift fans built to BAC design; and EMR Telemetry of Sarasota, Florida, for the Data Acquisition Console. The remaining

Top: Propulsive thrust on the SES-100B is provided by three Pratt & Whitney FT12A-6 marine gas-turbines driving two semi-submerged supercavitating propellers, each mounted directly on the stern of a side hull and positioned so that at high speeds the blades are only partially submerged. Each propeller has six variable-pitch blades

Centre: The SES-100B, 105-ton surface effect ship testcraft seen at speed in Sea State 3 in the Gulf of Mexico, off Panama City

Bottom: The deckhouse is at the aft end of the weatherdeck and accommodates a four-man crew and up to six observers. The engines—three FT12A-6s for propulsion and three ST6-J70s for lift—are located beneath the weatherdeck. Air is drawn through demister screens to minimise seawater and spray ingestion

construction of the craft, including outfitting, was undertaken by Bell Aerospace personnel in New Orleans.

LIFT AND PROPULSION: Power is supplied to the lift system by three United Aircraft of Canada (UACL) ST6J-70 marine gas turbines. The engine-fan systems provide pressurised air to seals and cushion in both normal modes of operation and in the event of system failure. An important feature of the design has been to ensure the safety of ship and crew since the craft is designed to investigate the boundaries of ship operation at high speed in rough seas. The fans, constructed from marine aluminium, are of centrifugal design for ruggedness and stability of operation.

Power is supplied to the two marine propellers by three Pratt & Whitney FT 12A-6 marine gas turbines.

Auxiliary power for engine starting and emergency use is provided by a Solar T-62T-27 high speed turbine producing 100 shp at 8,000 RPM.

All engines are housed in engine rooms beneath the weather deck and take in air through appropriately placed demister screens to minimize sea water and spray ingestion.

The fuel system, which also serves as a ballast system, is integral with the sidehulls.

ACCOMMODATION: The deckhouse houses all controls necessary for the operation of the craft and accommodation for four test crew and six observers. It is capable of sustaining the crew and observers for greater than 24 hour missions in life support functions. Navigation and communication equipment for all-weather operation is included in the crew subsystem and housed in the deckhouse.

SYSTEMS, EMERGENCY: Safety equipment in the form of fire detection and extinguishing equipment, life rafts, warning lights, etc, meet the requirements of the U.S. Coast Guard Rules of the Road, both International and Inland.

The characteristics of the SES-100B are as follows:

DIMENSIONS:

Length overall	77 ft 8½ in
Beam	35 ft 0 in
Height (top of radar)	26 ft 11 in

WEIGHTS:

Normal gross weight	105 tons
Normal payload	10 tons

POWER PLANTS:

Propulsion
  Three (3) P&W FT 12A-6 marine gas turbines
Lift:
  Three (3) UACL ST6J-70 marine gas turbines

PERFORMANCE:
Speed greater than 80 knots on calm water

PERSONNEL:

Crew (Test Mission)	Four
Observers	Six

MATERIALS:
Hull and Appendages
        Marine aluminium and titanium
Seals   Nylon supported elastainer

BELL MODEL B-26

This is a radio-controlled ¼th scale free-flight model with sidehulls and seals hydrodynamically representative of the Bell SES-100B. Two contra-rotating air propellers are used for propulsion. A 14-channel

Above and Below: Technical data derived from the Bell SES-100B test programme is being used by Bell in the design and development of the 2,000-ton 2KSES, high-speed, ocean-going surface effect warship, for the US Navy. It would carry a complete combat system, including surface-to-air and surface-to-surface missiles, and anti-submarine sensors and weapons

tape recorder is installed to record engine speeds, rudder position, cushion and seal pressures, sideslip, pitch, yaw and roll rates, model air speed and accelerations.

The model is 7 ft 3 in (2·20 m) long with a 4 ft 3 in (1·29 m) beam. The basic weight is 480 lb (217·71 kg), with provision for up to 320 lb (145·14 kg) of lead ballast, permitting tests over a wide range of weight and trim conditions. Separate bow, stern and sidehull modules permit variations of seal and sidehull configurations.

HULL: Built into the centre module are four centrifugal lift fans, which are connected through gear belts to an 80 cc, single-cylinder, two-cycle petrol engine. The main structural elements are fabricated in aluminium and edge-grain balsa sandwiched with the bulk of the remaining elements which are built in aircraft plywood, wood and epoxy. All unassigned areas are filled with cast, rigid foam. Bow and stern modules are made of aircraft plywood and wood, and incorporate seal feed air passages. The sidehulls are designed as separate structures. Provision is made for the installation of strain gauges on the attachment linkages,

permitting the measurement of hydrodynamic drag.

The seal system is in a coated nylon fabric of scale weight. The patterns were photo-reductions of the Bell SES-100B seals.

PROPULSION: Power is provided by a 40 hp, two-cylinder, two-cycle JLO petrol engine, driving two propellers through a system of gear belts. The engine is started electrically from a battery aboard a chase boat. The model is released from the chase boat when started and recovered upon shutdown.

CONTROLS: An adapted six-channel model aircraft radio-control unit provides proportional control of the lift and propulsion engine throttles and scale rate control of the rudders, with on/off control of the recorder, event marker and shutdown. A fail-safe shutdown is incorporated to ground the ignition systems of both engines upon command or loss of radio signal.

PERFORMANCE: The model has explored the operational envelope of the SES-100B, at scale speeds, in excess of 70 knots. At the time of going to press it was being employed in the investigation of proposed designs for the Bell 2KSES, the modular construction permitting replacment of the hydrodynamic elements with new configurations of seals and planing surfaces.

BELL 2,000-TON SES

In November 1972 it was announced that Bell Aerospace had been awarded a US$2·9 million contract by US Naval Ship Systems Command to conduct a preliminary design study and define a total programme plan for a 2,000-ton operational prototype surface effect ship. In July 1974, Bell was awarded a $36 million contract to conduct an advanced development programme for the 2KSES.

Plans call for the development of the SES propulsion system, including the transmission and waterjet inlet and pump, the air-cushion containment system of lift fans and large flexible seals, and a system to provide control of the ship's ride characteristics in various sea states.

The vessel would have a complete combat system, including surface-to-air and surface-to-surface missiles, and anti-submarine sensors and weapons.

The accompanying impression shows one of the configurations under consideration—a vessel 250 ft (76·20 m) long, with a beam of 106 ft (32·30 m). More than 200 engineers and designers at Bell New Orleans Operations are involved in the 2KSES advanced development programme. Major subcontractors are: The Autonetics Division, Rockwell International, for a role in combat systems integration; Gibbs & Cox Inc, naval architecture, crew support and auxiliary systems; Hydronautics Inc, hydrodynamic design and studies of propeller propulsion and waterjet inlets, the Aerojet Liquid Rocket Co, and the Rocketdyne Division of Rockwell International for waterjet propulsion, Avondale Shipyards Inc, for outfitting and fabrication, installation and furnishing of the deckhouse and British Hovercraft Corporation for flexible seal design and other engineering tasks.

Power would be supplied by six 20,000 shp General Electric LM-2500 marinised gas-turbines, two for lift and four for driving the vessel's waterjet propulsion system.

Bell has built three $\frac{1}{30}$th-scale models to assist with the 2KSES design and development programme—the SM-2, SM-4 and SM-5.

The SM-2 is a hydrodynamic, towing-tank model with a centrifugal lift fan system, removable sidehulls, and bow and stern modules. It is being used to determine hydrodynamic performance, stability, wave resistance and seakeeping. The SM-2 is also being used in bow and stern seal hydrodynamic development and stability tests.

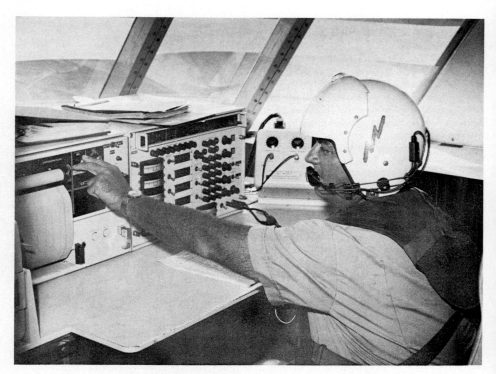

A test engineer at the SES-100B data acquisition console transfers technical data, collected during a test run, from the craft to the initial examination facility ashore for post-mission analysis. The DAS can monitor and record up to 253 separate parameters in 12 different categories during tests. Altogether, 336 strain gauges, accelerometers, vibration and pressure transducers are installed at various points throughout the craft to provide design data

Impression of the projected Bell Vanguard mixed traffic ferry. The basic configuration is that of Jeff (B), but scaled-up to accommodate fifty-four cars on the open central deck and 192 passengers in cabins in the two sidestructures

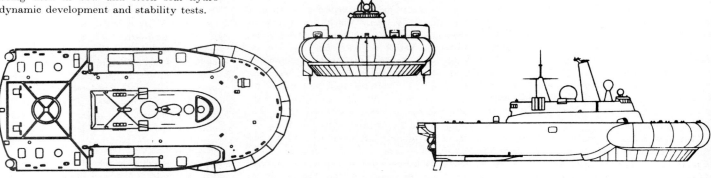

General arrangement of the Bell SES-100B 105-ton test craft

The SM-4, another towing tank model, is hydrodynamically representative of the 2KSES with respect to bow and stern seals, and is used to evaluate seal drag, loads, geometry and performance and assists in overall bow and stern seal development through hydrodynamic seal study.

The SM-5 is a wind tunnel model aerodynamically representative of the 2KSES hull, superstructure, air inlets and exhausts. It is being used by Bell to evaluate aerodynamic loads and moments, air flow distribution patterns, lift system inlet pressures and flows, optimisation of above deck configuration, and for engine exhaust plume investigation.

VANGUARD

This is a projected mixed-traffic ferry based on the Jeff (B) assault landing craft configuration, but with twice the length and beam.

The design requirements call for a craft about 150 ft long by 68 ft wide, capable of carrying fifty-four North American size cars and 192 passengers. The cars would be carried on the open central deck, while the passengers would be accommodated in cabins in the port and starboard sidestructures flanking the deck.

Intended to operate in both coastal areas and coastal waterways, the Vanguard has been suggested as ideal for US and Canadian ferry routes including Portland, Maine—Yarmouth, Nova Scotia, Victoria Island—Vancouver, BC and on Prince Edward Island.

Typical cross-section of a 2,000-ton surface effect ship's centre hull constructed by Bell as part of its weld development programme. Constructed in 5456 aluminium alloy, the structure weighs 25 tons. Fabrication of the ships hull and bulkheads will require over 300,000 linear feet of high strength welding of aluminium plates up to $\frac{3}{4}$ in (19·05 mm) thick. The company has evolved a system which automates more than 60% of the welding in a flat position

Two preliminary design studies prepared by Bell for naval surface effect ships. *Top:* a multi-thousand ton ASW vessel propelled by ducted fans and capable of 100 knots, and *Bottom,* a large amphibious assault craft, designed for the direct to distant beachheads. A combined fanjet and waterjet propulsion system would be employed—deployment of assault forces from the US mainland the waterjets for long-range overwater cruising, and the fanjets for shallow water, surf and overland operations.

BERTELSEN MANUFACTURING COMPANY INC

HEAD OFFICE:
9999 Roosevelt Road, Westchester, Illinois 60153

WORKS:
113 Commercial Street, Neponset, Illinois 61345

and

4819 Cortland Street, Chicago, Illinois 60639

TELEPHONE:
312-681-5606, 309-594-2041

OFFICERS:
William R. Bertelsen, Chairman of the Board, Vice-President and Director of Research

William C. Stein, President and Treasurer

Charles A. Brady, Secretary

Dr William R. Bertelsen, a general practitioner and talented engineer, was one of the first to build and drive an air cushion vehicle.

His interest was largely inspired by the difficulties he faced when trying to visit patients by car over icy roads. Having discovered that a helicopter would be too expensive to be a practical solution, he set to work to develop a vehicle that could be lifted free of the ground by air pumped beneath its base. Dr Bertelsen designed his first Aeromobile air cushion vehicle in 1950, and has since built and tested fourteen full-scale vehicles, ranging from simple plenum craft to ram-wings. One, the 18 ft long Aeromobile 200-2, was a star exhibit at the US Government's Trade Fairs in Tokyo, Turin, Zagreb and New Delhi in 1961. First design to be marketed by the company is the Aeromobile 13, a 4 passenger amphibious communications and light utility ACV. The prototype was built in 1968 and trials are complete. A description of this model will be found in JSS 1972-73 and earlier editions. An Aeromobile system of rapid transit, based on the Aeromobile 13, is described in the section devoted to Tracked Skimmers in this edition.

AEROMOBILE 14

Aeromobile 14 is a lightweight amphibious two or three-seater employing a single gimbal mounted lift fan/propulsion unit of similar design and construction to that introduced by Bertelsen on the Aeromobile 13.

The prototype was completed early in 1969 and trials ended in 1970.

LIFT PROPULSION AND CONTROLS: A single duct-mounted 55 hp (740 cc) JLO twin-cylinder engine driving a 36 in (914 mm) diameter eight-bladed axial-flow fan supplies lift, propulsion and control. The duct is spherical and gimbal-mounted at its centre so that it can be tilted and rotated as required in any direction. The discharge end of the duct faces a fitted aperture in the deck, from which air is fed into the cushion. When the fan shaft is vertical (no tilt), all the discharged air is fed into the cushion. By tilting the gimbal, the operator allows air from the fan to escape across the deck to provide thrust for propulsion and control.

Apart from the propulsion slipstream, there is no loss of lift air since the spherical duct fits closely into the deck aperture, and rotation of the sphere does not increase the air gap. Cushion pressure is 14 lb ft².

A simple mechanical linkage connected to handlebars enables the operator to tilt the fan duct fore-aft, right and left and make

Aeromobile 14 research platform employed by Bertelsen Manufacturing Co for the development of designs using single gimbal-mounted lift/fan/propulsion units.

integrated movements. The only other controls are a throttle and a choke. Fuel is carried in a single 12 gallon (US) tank located in the deck structure at the CG, with a fuelling point in the centre deck. Recommended fuel is regular automotive gasoline mixed with two-cycle oil.

HULL: Moulded fibreglass with foam filling. Design load 1,100 lb gross weight.

SKIRT: Urethane nylon with conical exterior configuration. Depth 1 ft 0 in (304 mm).

ACCOMMODATION: Tandem seating for three, with operator forward with control handlebars.

SYSTEMS: Electrical: 12 volt alternator on engine for starting.

NAVIGATION: Magnetic compass.

DIMENSIONS:
Length overall, power off 13 ft 0 in (3·96 m)
Length overall, skirt inflated
                           13 ft 0 in (3·96 m)
Beam overall, power off   7 ft 0 in (2·13 m)
Beam overall, skirt inflated 7 ft 0 in (2·13 m)
Height overall on landing pads, power off
                            3 ft 0 in (0·914 m)
Height overall, skirt inflated
                            4 ft 0 in (1·21 m)
Draft afloat   4 in (101 mm)
Draft hovering   3 in (76 mm)
Cushion area   60 sq ft (5·57 m²)
Skirt depth   12 in (304 mm)

WEIGHTS:
Normal empty weight   700 lb (317 kg)
Normal all-up weight   1,100 lb (499 kg)
Normal gross weight   1,100 lb (499 kg)
Normal payload   400 lb (181 kg)
Max payload   500 lb (226 kg)

PERFORMANCE:
Max speed over calm water
                           50 mph (80·46 km/h)
Cruising speed, calm water
                           40 mph (64·37 km/h)
Turning circle diameter at 30 knots
                           100 ft (30·4 m)
Max wave capability   3 ft (0·914 m)
Max survival sea state 5 ft waves (1·52 m)
Still air range and endurance at cruising
  speed   2½ hours
Max gradient, static conditions   10%
Vertical obstacle clearance 1 ft (304 mm)
Price: On request.

AEROMOBILE 15

Employing the same lift, propulsion and control system as the Aeromobile 14, the Aeromobile 15 is a light amphibious four-seater powered by a single 125 hp Mercury outboard engine and capable of a speed of 60 knots over calm water.

The prototype is complete and development is continuing.

LIFT AND PROPULSION: A single duct-mounted 125 hp Mercury outboard engine driving a 36 in (914 mm) diameter, sixteen-bladed adjustable-pitch aluminium alloy fan, supplies lift, propulsion and control. The duct is spherical and gimbal-mounted at its centre so that it can be tilted and rotated in any direction. When the fan shaft is vertical, the total airflow is discharged into the cushion. By tilting the gimbal the operator allows air from the fan to escape across the stern to provide thrust for propulsion and control. At the maximum tilt angle of 90° for maximum thrust only 30% of the fan air is delivered to the cushion.

Propulsion and/or control forces, including braking thrust, can be applied throughout 360° from the stern by tilting the duct in the required direction.

The fan duct is controlled from the driver's position by servo system. The driver has a wheel on a control column. Turning the wheel tilts the duct sideways to produce yaw force, and fore-and-aft movement of the column tilts the duct fore-and-aft to produce forward propulsion or braking. Fuel is carried in one 18-gallon tank located on the cabin floor beneath the rear seat at the C of G. The fuelling point is located on the left deck outside the cabin. Fuel is automotive gasoline with two-cycle oil.

HULL: Moulded fibreglass.

SKIRT: Urethane nylon fabric, 1 ft 6 in (45·7 mm) deep.

ACCOMMODATION: Entry to the cabin is through a sliding canopy which moves from the windshield rearwards. Two bench type seats are fitted, one forward for the driver and one passenger, and one aft for two passengers. The cabin may be heated or air-conditioned if required. In emergencies the sliding canopy, windows and windshield may be kicked out.

SYSTEMS: ELECTRICAL: 12 volt alternator and 12 volt storage battery.

COMMUNICATIONS AND NAVIGATION:
A magnetic compass is standard. Radio, radar and other navigation aids optional.

DIMENSIONS, EXTERNAL:

Length overall, power off	18 ft 0 in (5·48 m)
Length overall, skirt inflated	18 ft 8 in (5·68 m)
Beam overall, power off	8 ft 0 in (2·43 m)
Beam overall, skirt inflated	9 ft 10 in (2·99 m)
Height overall, on pads, power off	4 ft 4 in (1·32 m)
Height overall, skirt inflated	5 ft 9 in (1·75 m)
Draft afloat	5½ in (139 mm)
Draft hovering	4 in (101 mm)
Cushion area	90 ft² (8·36 m²)
Skirt depth	1 ft 6 in (457 mm)

DIMENSIONS, INTERNAL:

Cabin:

Length	10 ft 6 in (3·2 m)
Max width	4 ft 2 in (1·27 m)
Max height	4 ft 0 in (1·21 m)
Floor area	40 ft² (3·71 m²)

The sliding canopy opens 3 ft (·914 m) rearward from windshield.

WEIGHTS:

Normal empty weight	1,300 lb (589·64 kg)
Normal all-up weight	2,100 lb (952·50 kg)
Normal gross weight	2,100 lb (952·50 kg)
Normal payload	700 lb (317·50 kg)
Max payload	1,000 lb (453·57 kg)

PERFORMANCE (at normal operating weight, estimated):

Max speed over calm water, max power	60 knots
Max continuous power	50 knots
Cruising speed, calm water	50 knots
Turning circle at 30 knots	500 ft (152·4 m)
Max wave capability	3 ft (914 mm)
Max survival sea state	5 ft (1·52 m) waves
Still air range and endurance at cruising speed	3 hours
Max gradient, static conditions	10%
Vertical obstacle clearance	1 ft 3 in (381 mm)

Aeromobile 15, a 60-knot four-seater powered by a modified 125 hp Mercury outboard. The vehicle is at present being employed as a test-bed for the gimbal-mounted lift/propulsion system. The photographs show the gimbal duct in neutral and in high forward tilt

PRICE AND TERMS: On request.

DEPARTMENT OF THE NAVY, NAVAL SEA SYSTEMS COMMAND (NAVSEA)

HEADQUARTERS:

Washington, DC 20360

PROGRAMME MANAGER, HOVERCRAFT AND HYDROFOILS:

James L. Schuler

OFFICE:

US Naval Sea Systems Command, Advanced Technology Systems Division, Code 032, National Center 3, Room 10E54, Washington, DC 20362

The US Naval Sea System Command (NAVSEA), formerly known as the Bureau of Ships, has the responsibility for the research, design construction and logistic support of all US Navy Ships. The Research Directorate of NAVSEA has been the primary technical sponsor of all US Navy hovercraft and hydrofoil programmes since 1960.

The Programme Manager responsible for the development of both types of vessel is Mr. James L. Schuler. Technical Managers have been appointed for each of the several research and development programmes managed and directed by NAVSEA. Technical Manager of the Amphibious Assault Landing Craft Programme is Mr. Melvin Brown of the Naval Ship Research and Development Centre, Carderock, Maryland. This programme includes the JEFF configuration, which is an ACV landing craft based on the designs prepared by Bell Aerospace and Aerojet-General Corporation. Details will be found under the respective entries for the two companies.

Technical manager for the Advanced Hydrofoil Systems Programme is Mr. Robert Johnston of the NSRDC at Carderock. This programme includes operation and trials of the PCH-1 and AGEH-1, as well as testing the PGH-1. Current emphasis is on the development of larger and faster hydrofoils.

DEPARTMENT OF DEFENCE, ADVANCED RESEARCH PROJECTS AGENCY

HEADQUARTERS:

1400 Wilson Boulevard, Arlington, Virginia 22209

ARPA ARCTIC SEV PROGRAMME

Brian K. Hannula, Programme Manager, Advanced Engineering Office
J. U. Kordenbrock, Technical Manager

In the spring of 1970, the US Defence Department's Advanced Research Projects Agency (ARPA) initiated a programme to develop the technology required to exploit the arctic military potential of the SEV. The ARPA SEV Programme, with technical management being provided by the Naval Research and Development Centre, Carderock, Maryland, was due for completion summer of 1974. By that time it was expected that the technology required to build an all-weather arctic SEV, with a gross weight as high as 600 tons and a cruise speed as great as 80 knots, would have been developed A vehicle with these or lesser specifications is considered adequate to perform most potential arctic SEV missions.

Major programme tasks have included quantitative arctic environment definition, mission analysis and vehicle and sub-system technology development. Primary emphasis during the remainder of the programme will be placed on the completion of preliminary design packages for nominally 150-ton and 500-ton SEVs. These design packages will include a review and specification of requirements, parametric analysis to identify basic vehicle configurations and performance characteristics, trade-off studies to select the most suitable vehicle sub-systems, model test data, layout drawings and cost estimates for detailed vehicle design and manufacture.

DOBSON PRODUCTS CO.

HEAD OFFICE:

2241 South Ritchey, Santa Ana, California 92705

TELEPHONE:

(714) 557-2987

WORKS:

Santa Ana, California

DIRECTOR:

Franklin A. Dobson

Dobson Products Co. was formed by Franklin A. Dobson in 1963 to develop and market small ACVs either in complete, factory built form, or as kits for private use. His first model, the Dobson Air Dart, won the first ACV race in Canberra in 1964. The company's Model F two-seater, has been described and illustrated in JSS 1973-74 and earlier editions.

The first Dobson craft designed for quantity production is the Model H.

DOBSON AIR CAR, MODEL H

This is a simplified and slightly larger machine than the original Model H. It has more efficient lift and thrust systems together with simplified controls and a slightly lower structural weight.

LIFT AND PROPULSION: A single engine is used for both lift and propulsion. The engine powers a 4-bladed fan forward and a 2-bladed, variable-pitch propeller aft on the same shaft.

CONTROLS: Lateral motion of a control stick operates a rudder, while fore-and-aft motion controls the propeller pitch, forward for thrust, aft for braking. The control stick also incorporates a motorcycle type twist-grip throttle.

HULL AND SKIRT: Hinged floats are used for buoyancy and these also support a flexible skirt which gives about an 8 in (203 mm) obstacle clearance. With the floats hinged upwards or removed. the overall width is less than 4 ft (1·21 cm).

DIMENSIONS:

Length	11 ft 0 in (3·35 m)
Width	7 ft 6 in (2·28 m)
Height	4 ft 3 in (1·29 m)
Folded width	3 ft 8 in (1·14 m)
Obstacle clearance	8 in (203 mm)
Cushion area	55 sq ft (5·11 sq m)

WEIGHTS:

Empty weight	230 lb (104·32 kg)
Tools and miscell	10 lb (4·52 kg)
Fuel (6¾ U.S. gal)	40 lb (18·14 kg)
Pilot	160 lb (72·57 kg)
Passenger	160 lb (72·57 kg)
Maximum gross weight	600 lb (272·14 kg)

PERFORMANCE: (at gross weight, 80% power), sea level

Dobson Air Car Model H

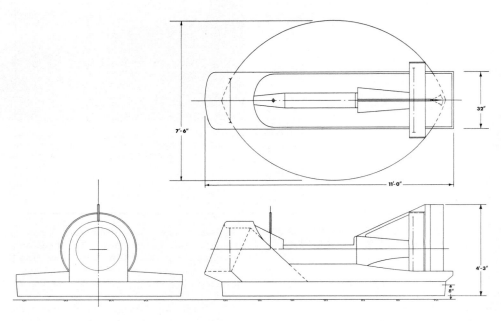

Cushion pressure	10·9 p.s.f.	Maximum speed	35-45 mpg (56-72 km/h)
Daylight clearance	1·5 in (457 mm)	Noise level	95 Db
Obstacle clearance	8 in (203 mm)	Endurance at 80% power	2·5 hours
Static thrust	75 lb (34·01 kg)	Range	100 miles (160·93 km)
Maximum gradient	1:8	Miles per gallon (U.S.)	15 (24·14 km)

E.M.G. ENGINEERING CO.

HEAD OFFICE:

18518 South Broadway, Gardena, California 90248, USA

OFFICER:

Eugene M. Gluhareff, General Manager

Eugene Gluhareff is a former helicopter designer and project engineer at Sikorsky Aircraft Co. Gluhareff Helicopters was formed in 1952 to build and market small one-man helicopters equipped with G8-2 liquid propane pressure-jet engines. In recent years the company has designed two single-seat ACVs, the MEG-1H Yellow

Jacket, powered by two go-cart engines and the MEG-2H Yellow Streak, a similar but larger craft propelled by Gluhareff pressure-jets.

MEG-1H YELLOW JACKET

This single-seat, recreational ACV has a maximum speed of 60 mph (96·50 km/h) over land and 20 mph (32·18 km/h) over water. More than 3,000 sets of plans have been sold since 1971 when the company began marketing plans and component parts.

LIFT AND PROPULSION: Integrated system. Motive power supplied by two 10 hp

Chrysler 820 go-kart engines located side-by-side aft of the open cockpit. Each drives a 2 ft 10 in (0·863 mm) diameter, six-bladed, solid spruce fan at 3,600 rpm. Fan blades are cambered. Fuel is carried in a cylindrical ¾ gal (US) go-kart tank mounted above the hull between the two engines. Propulsion air is expelled through twin thrust ports aft. CONTROLS: At low speeds craft heading is governed by the differential movement of two pedal-operated thrust ports aft or kinesthetic control. By leaning in the required direction the craft can be made to spin, move backwards, forwards or sideways.

Stick-operated aerodynamic rudders become effective at about 20-25 mph (32-40·2 km/h).

HULL: Triangular planform, designed to generate aerodynamic lift at speed. Welded structure, mainly in ⅞ in (22·22 mm) diameter 4130 thinwall steel tubing. Thin aluminium skin sections in 2924-T4.20 gauge are pop-riveted into place. Intake ducts and nose sections are in glass fibre. Cockpit box is in riveted aluminium. A tricycle undercarriage is fitted to assist ground handling.

SKIRT: Fabricated in canvas, with 4130 steel reinforcing tubes at hem.

DIMENSIONS:

Length overall	10 ft 7 in (3·22 m)
Max beam	7 ft (2·13 m)
Skirt depth	6 in (152 mm)

WEIGHTS:

Normal empty weight	165 lb (74·83 kg)
Normal gross weight	331 lb (150·13 kg)

PERFORMANCE:

Max speed, calm water 15-20 mph (24·1-32·8 km/h)
Max speed over land 60 mph (96·56 km/h)
Vertical obstacle clearance 6 in (152 mm)

PRICE:
Construction plans US $15·00 per set. Ready-made components available.

MEG-2H YELLOW STREAK

Similar in basic design to the Yellow Jacket, this developed model employs two fin-mounted G8-2-15 pressure-jet engines, each developing 18 lb st for propulsive thrust.

The Gluhareff MEG-1H Yellow jacket single-seat recreational ACV, powered by two 10 bhp Chrysler 820 go-kart engines. Each drives a six-bladed solid spruce fan. Propulsion air is expelled through twin thrust ports aft

EGLEN HOVERCRAFT INC

HEAD OFFICE:
801 Poplar Street, Terre Haute, Indiana, 47807
Telephone: 812-234 4307

DIRECTORS:
Jan Eglen, President
Alfred Brames, Secretary
O. Keith Owen, Jr, Treasurer
Lewis R. Poole, Controller
Woodrow S. Nasser, Counsel
Melvin McKibben, Asst Secretary
Paul Ferreira, Director
George Kassis, Director
Clarence Fauber, Director

EXECUTIVES:
Jan Eglen, General Manager
Lewis R. Poole, Works Manager
Lionel Saunders, Director of Production and Research
Terry Moore, Assistant Production Manager

MIDDLE EAST REPRESENTATIVE:
Al-Rodhan Trading & Contracting Est.,
PO Box 5020,
Kuwait, Arabian Gulf

Eglen Hovercraft Inc. was chartered in August 1969, to design and manufacture recreational hovercraft and other air cushion devices. The company is at present concentrating on the production of the Hoverbug, an amphibious two-seater with a moulded plastic hull. The company is also producing the new Mk 2 model and four- and six-seat ACVs which incorporate a number of design improvements, including the employment of

Eglen Hovercraft Hoverbug, a plastic-hulled two-seater powered by two Rockwell-JLO engines. Speeds of up to 60 mph (96·56 km/h) have been attained in this craft over water with one person aboard

shock-mountings for both the lift and thrust engines. A new product, the Terrehover hoverplatform, is described in the section devoted to ACV Trailers and Heavy Load Carriers.

HOVERBUG Mk 2

A two-seat recreational ACV, the Hoverbug is powered by two Rockwell JLO engines and has a maximum speed of 30 mph (48·28 km/h) over water and 35 mph (56 km/h) overland. The standard version has an open

cockpit, but a cabin top to form an enclosed cockpit is available as an optional extra.

The craft is available in either fully assembled or kit form.

LIFT AND PROPULSION: A 22 hp Rockwell JLO-295 two-cycle engine, mounted immediately aft of the cockpit, drives a 2ft 0 in (609 mm) diameter, 10-bladed Multiwing fan for lift. Thrust is supplied by a 25 hp Rockwell JLO 395 driving a 3 ft 0 in (914 mm) diameter, Banks-Maxwell 2-bladed propeller. Both lift and thrust engines on the Mk 2 model have shock-absorbing mountings, reducing the vibration transmitted to the hull by about 90%. Similar mountings are also employed to attach the thrust duct to the thrust engine frame, resulting in a longer life expectancy for the duct and the rudders, which are now mounted directly onto the duct. The propeller is of laminated hardwood, tipped in stainless steel. The company is currently investigating the use of a 4-bladed propeller in order to reduce noise generation. Fuel capacity is 5 gallons (22·73 litres), representing about 2 hours running. Quick-release fittings to the fuel system facilitate maintenance.

CONTROLS: Directional control is provided by twin aerodynamic rudders hinged at the rear of the propeller duct and operating in the slipstream. Rudder installation on the Mk 2 has been modified to improve rate of turn. Additional pulleys have been introduced into the steering system for smoother steering. Cockpit controls comprise a steering wheel, two ignition switches, two throttles, two chokes, two emergency "kill" switches and a navigational lights switch.

HULL: High gloss, high impact plastics hull, formed by a thermovacuum moulding process developed by Hoosier Fibreglass Industries, Terre Haute, Indiana. Material used is Cycolacbrand ABS, supplied by the Marbon Division of Borg Warner Corporation. Hull side loading racks can be supplied as an optional extra. Two 6 in (152 mm) deep buoyancy chambers in the base of the hull are filled with foam plastic to provide 150% reserve buoyancy. Removable skids are fitted beneath.

SKIRT: Bag type, 1 ft 0 in (304 mm) deep, fabricated in neoprene-coated nylon. Skirt attachment system facilitates rapid removal and refitting.

ACCOMMODATION: Driver and passenger sit side-by-side in an open cockpit on a 4ft 0 in (1·21 m) wide bench-type seat. Optional extras include a cabin enclosure, windshield wipers and a custom upholstered seat.

SYSTEMS: Electrical : 12 volt, 75 watt system for engine starting instruments and navigation lights.

DIMENSIONS:

Length overall, power on	10 ft 0 in (3·04 m)
Beam overall, power on	6 ft 6 in (1·98 m)
Draft afloat	6 in (152 mm)
Skirt depth	1 ft 0 in (304 mm)
Cabin width	4 ft 0 in (1·21 m)

WEIGHTS:

Normal empty weight	400 lb
Payload	400 lb

PERFORMANCE:

Max recommended speed:

over water	30 mph (48·28 km/h)
over land	35 mph (56·32 km/h)
over ice	40 mph (64·37 km/h)

Wave capability (max)

1 ft 6 in - 2 ft 0 in (457-609 mm)

Max gradient at all up weight   1 : 6

PRICE:

Cost of complete craft, FOB Terre Haute:
US$2,495·00

Cost of standard kit   US$1,800·00

OFFSHORE SURVEY SIX-SEATER

This new Eglen utility hovercraft is designed for a variety of duties including off-shore surveys. Of mixed wood and fibreglass construction, it carries a payload of 1,625 lb (737 kg) and cruises at 35 knots. Construction time is 4-6 months depending on optional equipment or special features

New four-seater, developed from the Eglen Hoverbug, during trials

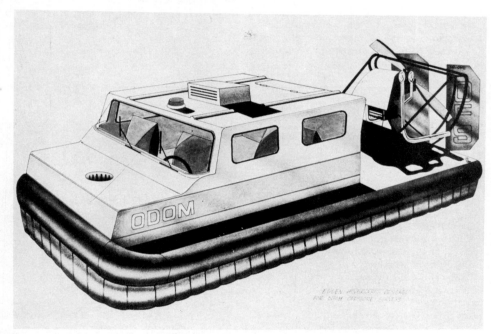

Impression of the new Eglen Hovercraft six-seat offshore survey and utility vehicle

required.

LIFT AND PROPULSION: Lift air is provided by a 90 hp Continental PC-60 aero-engine driving a 24 in (609 mm) diameter Rotafoil fan. Cushion pressure is 17-19 psf. Thrust is supplied by a 100 hp Lycoming air cooled piston engine driving a two-bladed Dobson reversible-pitch propeller.

CONTROLS: Craft heading is controlled by twin aerodynamic rudders hinged to the tubular metal guard aft of the propeller. Reversible and variable-pitch propeller provides braking and reverse thrust.

HULL: Wooden frame covered with fibreglass skin and finished with epoxy marine exterior paint. Cabin superstructure is moulded fibreglass with 30 oz Durasonic ¼ in foam-backed sound proofing. Windows are of the "push out" type, in tinted plastic. Total fuel capacity is 55 gallons.

SKIRT: 14 in (355 mm) deep HDL type.

ACCOMMODATION: Seats provided for driver and five passengers. Optional items include seat belts, heating and air-conditioning and intercom system.

SYSTEMS, ELECTRICAL: 12 volt dc, with auxiliary outlets. Batteries: 2-12 volt, 72 amp hour capacity.

DIMENSIONS:

Length	24 ft (7·31 m)
Beam	10 ft (on cushion) (3·04 m)
Skirt depth	1 ft 2 in (355 mm)
Hover gap	¾ in (19 mm)

WEIGHTS:

Empty weight	2,500 lb (1,179·98 kg)
Payload (incl 400 lb fuel)	1,625 lb
Overload capacity	500 lb (226·79 kg)
Total weight in overload condition	4,625 lb (2,097·85 kg)

TERMS: On request. Domestic orders 50% payment with order, balance upon delivery. Overseas orders. Irrevocable letter of credit for full price placed with American Fletcher National Bank in Indianapolis, Indiana.

GEMCO INC

HEAD OFFICE:
 PO Box 1191, Lynnwood, Washington 98036
TELEPHONE: (206) 743-3669
OFFICERS:
 Gerald W. Crisman, President

A. J. Doug Nunally, Vice President
Edward J. Birney
Michael S. Curtis, Secretary
William D. Crisman, Financial Adviser

Gemco Inc has designed and built a number of light and ultra-light craft, including the first to cross the Mississippi (in 1959).

The company is now concentrating on the development of a new two-seat sports vehicle. the 4/5 seat Eagle, the prototype of which is under construction; two passenger ferries, one for 10-11 passengers the other for thirty, and the Alaskan, a utility vehicle with a payload capacity of 10-12 tons.

HELIBARGE SYSTEMS INC

HEAD OFFICE:
10145 N. North Portland Road
Post Office Box 03159
Portland, Oregon 97203
TELEPHONE:
 Area Code (503) 286-3661
SENIOR EXECUTIVES:
 Glen Widing
 Allan Bigler
 Walter Crowley

Helibarge Systems was incorporated in 1971 to promote the use of "Helibarges" in commercial and military applications. The principle was conceived and developed by Walter A. Crowley and is described in US Patent No. 3,285,535. It combines a helicopter with an air cushion barge, employing the rotor downwash of the helicopter to pressurise the air cushion.

HELIBARGE MODEL HBX-150

The Helibarge is an amphibious ground effect machine designed to transport cargo over water, ice fields, marshland, tundra, deserts and other relatively flat areas. Basically it is a flat-decked, cargo-carrying platform designed to be transported by helicopter, using the downwash air pressure developed by the helicopter rotor as the source of power for lift. Separate engine-driven propellers, in combinations with rudders, would provide propulsion, braking and steering.

Although the HBX-150 is designed specifically for the UH-1H, other Helibarges can be designed for transport by other helicopters, ranging from the Gyrodyne QH-50C drone to the Sikorsky S-64 series.

Some of the advantages claimed for the system include greater payload and daylight/obstacle clearance capabilities, improved operating range and lower first cost.

The overall dimensions of the Helibarge are approximately three times that of the diameter of the helicopter rotor. Thus, the Helibarge Model HBX-150 with UH-1H Helicopter would have a diameter of 150 ft (45·72 m).

LIFT AND PROPULSION: Thrust is supplied by two 1,400 shp T53-L-13 propeller-turbines, each driving a 3-bladed, controllable-pitch propeller. Lift air is supplied by the helicopter rotor downwash which is blown via a collapsible diffuser duct into the plenum. A locking mechanism secures the duct in the open position. Remote actuators may be included in production craft. Louvres or other forms of covering surround the helicopter platform and are retained in the closed position while the helicopter is landing.

HULL: Deck panels are light, buoyant structures of aluminium honeycomb, each 5 ft × 10 ft 6 in (1·52 m × 3·20 m) and mounted on a framework. They will be capable of supporting foot traffic or light cargo. Loads of up to 15 tons can be carried on each of the two load platforms, one each side of the craft. Inflatable landing pads will extend beneath the structure to provide support for concen-

Landing sequence prior to the operation of the Model HBX-150 Helibarge. *Top:* UH-1H helicopter approaches central platform of the Helibarge, which is resting on a solid, level surface. Duct is folded flat and louvres surrounding platform are shut. *Bottom:* Diffuser duct is raised and secured in place, louvres are opened and the vehicle is ready for work

Three 72 ft (21·94 m) diameter Helibarges combined to form a single 600-ton capacity unit for oil industry applications

trated loads and to protect the hard skirt air duct used to supply air to the flexible skirt stiffeners. The helicopter platform is adjustable for height and angle to enable the helicopter rotor shaft to be positioned accurately in relation to the diffuser duct. Slots in the platform align the helicopter skids in the direction of travel and a cargo hook attachment point anchors the helicopter. SKIRT: Made in 32 oz/yd² neoprene-nylon material with inflatable stiffening "fingers" built-in. Skirt depth 7 ft 6 in (2·28 m). Replaceable sections fastened by air-tight zippers. ACCOMMODATION: Control cabin is equipped with two seats, one for driver and one for engineer/navigator. Cabin is fully air-conditioned, heated and ventilated and has stowable sleeping accommodation for three. CONTROLS: Craft direction is controlled by

differential propeller pitch and aerodynamic rudders mounted aft of the propulsion engines. Pitch and roll trim is provided by four ballast tanks.

HBX-150 (UH-1H)
DIMENSIONS: EXTERNAL:

DIAMETER:	150 ft 0 in (45·72 m)

AREA:

Height overall on landing pads, power off	17 ft 0 in (5·18 m)
Height overall, skirt inflated (excluding daylight hover clearance)	23 ft 0 in (7·01 m)
Draft afloat	2 in (50 mm)
Cushion area	17,672 ft² (1,270·15 m²)
Skirt depth	7 ft 6 in (2·27 m)

DIMENSIONS, INTERNAL:

Length	10 ft 0 in (3·04 m)

Max width	20 ft 0 in (6·09 m)
Max height	8 ft 0 in (2·43 m)
Floor area	200 ft² (18·58 m²)

WEIGHTS:

Normal empty weight	50 tons
Normal all-up weight	94 tons
Normal payload (cargo)	30 tons
Max payload (incl fuel)	44 tons

PERFORMANCE:

Max speed over calm water	50 mph (80·46 km/h)
Cruising speed	40 mph;(64·37 km/h)
Water speed in 4 ft waves and 15 knot headwind	35 mph (52·32 km/h)
Still air range and endurance at cruising speed, 10% reserve	520 miles (804·67 km)
Range and endurance in 4 ft waves, 15 knot headwind	350 miles (10 hours at 35 mph)
Max gradient, static conditions	5%
Vertical obstacle clearance	8 ft (2·43 m)

HOVERMARINE CORPORATION

CORPORATE AND MARKETING OFFICES:
Three Gateway Center, Pittsburgh, Pennsylvania 15222
TELEPHONE:
(412) 288-0450
TELEX:
81-2479
MANUFACTURING AND ENGINEERING FACILITY:
805 Marina Road, P.O. Box R, Titusville, Florida 32780
TELEPHONE:
(305) 269-6712
SUBSIDIARY:
Hovermarine Transport, Ltd., Hazel Wharf, Hazel Road, Woolston, Southampton, SO2 7GB
TELEPHONE:
Southampton 446831
TELEX:
(851) 47141
DIRECTORS:
H. Arthur Bellows, Jr, Chairman
The Triangle Corporation, New York, New York
Max W. S. Bishop, US Ambassador (Ret.), Ailey, Georgia
Charles C. Cohen, Partner, Reed Smith Shaw & McClay, Pittsburgh, Pennsylvania
Edward F. Davison, President
Hovermarine Corporation
William A. Zebedee, Chairman
Hovermarine Corporation
OFFICERS:
HOVERMARINE CORPORATION:
William A. Zebedee, Chairman of the Board
Edward F. Davison, President
Robert C. Kintz, Vice-President, Finance
Arnold M. Hall, Vice-President
U.S. MANUFACTURE:
Hovermarine Corporation manufactures HM.2 craft at a 25,000 sq ft production facility in Titusville, Florida. Located on the Indian River adjacent to Cape Canaveral, it has the capacity to manufacture up to 24 HM.2 craft per year. Previously the craft was manufactured only by the company's English subsidiary, Hovermarine Transport Limited.

Prior to manufacture in the US Hovermarine had been prohibited from offering the HM.2 in the U.S., due to legislation which restricts the domestic sale of foreign built craft. The U.S. facility produces craft for

Hovermarine Corporation HM.2 manufacturing facility at Titusville, Florida, on the Indian River, adjacent to Cape Canaveral

An HM.2 operating off the coast of Florida

the North and Central American market and the U.K. facility produces craft for other parts of the world.

In addition to its commercial ACV activities Hovermarine is engaged in surface effect ship research projects for both the U.S. and

British governments. Hovermarine was also a sub-contractor to Lockheed Aircraft Corporation for component design for a 2,000 ton prototype surface effect ship for the U.S. Navy.

HM.2 HOVERFERRY

A rigid sidewall hovercraft, the HM.2 hoverferry carries 60 passengers in an air conditioned cabin fitted with aircraft style seats and has a maximum speed of 35 knots. It is propelled by marine diesel engines and twin underwater propellers.

Craft of this type have accumulated over 60 million passenger miles to date on commuter/tourist routes.

As a waterbus, the HM.2 provides competitive low-cost passenger travel at a cost of operation of 3 to 4 cents per passenger mile for a typical service. Its fuel consumption is 32 gal/hr (0·014 gal/passenger-mile).

DIMENSIONS:

Overall length	51 ft (15·54 m)
Overall beam	20 ft (6·09 m)
Overall height	13 ft 9 in (4·19 m)
Height above waterline—on cushion*	
	11 ft 10½ in (3·62 m)
Height above waterline—off cushion	
	8 ft 10½ in (2·71 m)
Draught on cushion*	2 ft 10½ in (0·87 m)
Draught off cushion	4 ft 10½ in (1·49 m)
Cabin size (length × width)	
	22 ft × 16 ft (6·70 m × 4·88 m)
Cabin height at centre line	
	6 ft 6 in (1·98 m)
Entrance size (height × width)	
	6 ft 3 in × 4 ft (1·90 m × 1·22 m)

*These heights and draughts take account of 2° bow up trim on cushion.

WEIGHTS:

Standard gross weight	43,500 lb (19,732 kg)
Normal pay-load	60 passengers
Freight	11,000 lb (4,990 kg)

PERFORMANCE: (at standard gross weight)

Max speed—calm water, no wind	
	35 knots (65 km/h)
Acceleration—0·35 kt	36·5 secs
Deceleration—from max speed	
(normal)	250 ft (76 m)
(emergency)	150 ft (45 m)
Endurance	4·8 hours

HM.2 GENERAL PURPOSE CRAFT

The HM.2 general purpose craft utilizes the same hull and machinery as the HM.2 hoverferry. The superstructure and deck are designed to meet the needs of various special applications including:

Hydrographic survey craft; crew boat; oil spill recovery craft; air sea rescue; pilot

An HM.2 general purpose craft

cutter and patrol craft.

With a maximum speed of 35 knots and a payload of up to 11,000 lbs. it provides a high work output at low capital and operating cost.

The rigid sidewalls resist sideslipping in cross-winds and when turning. Positive directional control is maintained in all conditions and at all speeds. Relatively little wash is created by the craft on cushion.

Manoeuvrability is good throughout the speed range, permitting the HM.2 to operate safely in congested waterways or coastal areas. The twin rudders, mounted beneath the sidewalls, ensure banked turns. The craft has a turning circle of as little as 850 ft. (260 m) diameter at maximum speed. At low speeds, the widely spaced marine propellers allow the craft to be turned through 360° in its own length.

DIMENSIONS:

Overall length	50 ft 0 in (15·24 m)
Overall beam	19 ft 0 in (5·8 m)
Hull depth (base to deck)	
	6 ft 6 in (1·99 m)
Overall height (to top of cabin)	
	13 ft 4 in (4·10 m)
Draft on-cushion	2 ft 10½ in (0·87 m)
Draft off-cushion	4 ft 10½ in (1·49 m)
Wheelhouse area 14 ft × 14 approx	
	(4·3 m × 4·3 m)
After cabin area	14 ft × 14 ft approx
	(4·3 m × 4·3 m)
Cabin at centre line height·	
	6 ft 6 in (2·00 m)

WEIGHTS:

Total disposable payload including fuel and optional extras	11,000 lbs
Standard gross weight 43,500 lb (19,732 kg)	
Max permissible gross weight	
	44,500 lb (20,200 kg)

PERFORMANCE (at standard gross weight):

Maximum speed—calm water, no wind	
	35 knots (65 km/h)
Acceleration—0·30 knots	36·5 secs
Deceleration—from max speed (normal)	
	250 ft (76 m)
Deceleration—from max speed (emergency)	
	150 ft (45 m)

HOVERSPORT, INC

HEAD OFFICE:
313 Balsam Street, Palm Beach Gardens, Fla. 33403

TELEPHONE:
(305) 622-6568

EXECUTIVES:
Scott D. Thatcher, President
Donaldson A. Dow, Secretary and Treasurer

Hoversport was founded early in 1969 and was chartered in January 1971. Its first commercial design was the HS-1B Stingray, a circular-planform runabout which is sold either fully-assembled or in kit form. This was followed by the HS-1A single-seater and a two-seat model, the HS-11, both available as kits only. Two recent developments are the HS-IV, a 150 hp 4-5 seater with an enclosed cabin, and the HS-TR, a hovertrailer with a 1,500 lb (680·38 kg) payload capacity.

HS-1B STINGRAY

This single-seat recreational runabout for enthusiasts is designed to fit into the average station wagon or on top of a family car.

The craft is available in three different forms:

Basic: a starter or experimental kit for use in schools, or for individuals. Includes fibreglass shell with integral moulded fuel tank, engine, tool kit, etc.

Standard: Complete with all materials required for flight, including neoprene impregnated skirt material.

Amphibian: In addition to the parts supplied with the standard version, this contains a fibreglass and foam flotation system which provides 150% buoyancy in the event of engine failure.

LIFT AND PROPULSION: Integrated system powered by a 15·5 hp JLO L230 2-cycle engine driving a 2 ft 1¾ in (654 mm) diameter laminated wood fan. The primary air flow, used for direct thrust, is directed through a propulsive slot control flap aft of the fan duct. The secondary air flow, for cushion lift passes down into an open plenum. A fibreglass fuel tank, with a capacity of 2 US gallons is moulded into the back rest. Fuel is 20 : 1 petrol oil mixture.

Skirt is of "C" type, fabricated in abrasion resistant neoprene impregnated nylon.

CONTROLS: Craft heading is controlled kinesthetically and by a single aerodynamic rudder aft of the propulsive air slot. The rudder is operated by a single column on which is mounted a twist-grip for controlling forward speed.

HULL: Entire structure, including fuel tank, folding side panels, seats, lift duct, thrust duct and mount support, is fabricated in cloth reinforced fibreglass. Side panels are removable to simplify transport and storage. Craft will fit into the average station wagon or on top of a family car.

DIMENSIONS:

Hull diameter	8 ft 0 in (2·43 m)
Height overall, power off	
	1 ft 10 in (558 mm)
Folded length	8 ft 0 in (2·43 m)
Folded width	3 ft 6 in (1·06 m)
Folded height	1 ft 10 in (0·558 m)
Skirt depth	8 in (0·203 m)

WEIGHTS:

Normal empty weight	150 lb (68·03 kg)
Normal all-up weight	400 lb (181·42 kg)
Normal payload	250 lb (113·39 kg)

PERFORMANCE:

Max speed, calm water	
	20 mph (32·18 km/h)
Max speed over land	33 mph (53·10 km/h)
Max speed over ice	40 mph (64·37 km/h)
Still air range	70 miles (112·65 km)
Gradient from static start	12-15%
Vertical obstacle clearance	
	8 in (203 mm)

PRICE AND TERMS: Basic version, $635·00; Standard, $795·00; Amphibian, $995·00. Terms: 50% with order, balance prior to shipment or COD. HS-1B assembly plans, $5·00.

HOVERSPORT HS-11

This is a twin-engined amphibious craft designed to carry a load of up to 400 lb (181·42 kg) over snow, swampland and water at speeds up to 40 mph (64·37 km/h).

LIFT AND PROPULSION: Cushion lift is supplied by a 15½ hp Rockwell JLO-230 air-cooled two-stroke engine driving a 2 ft 6 in (762 mm) diameter 6-bladed axial fan made in laminated wood. Fan air is delivered to the cushion via a peripheral bag type skirt. A second 15½ hp engine of the same type drives a 2 ft 6 in (762 mm) diameter Banks-Maxwell or Arrowcraft two-bladed propeller for thrust. A 2 US gallon (7·57 l) tank is located internally, forward of the lift engine.

SKIRT: Bag type, 8 in (203 mm) high. Annular slot for air entry to skirt, with slot for air exit and contact holes for laminar flow and ejection of dust.

CONTROLS: A control stick operates two aerodynamic rudders for directional control. Reverse thrust is not available, but the craft can be rotated easily for changes in direction. The control stick is located in front of the right hand seat, ahead of which are the master switches, choke actuators and twin throttles.

ACCOMMODATION: Driver and passenger sit side-by-side in a semi-enclosed cockpit on a bench type seat. A wind screen can be fitted if required.

Hoversport HS-11, two seat light amphibious sports craft

HS-1B recreational ACV

HULL: Wooden structure with waterproof fabric covering.

DIMENSIONS:

Length	13 ft 0 in (3·96 m)
Beam	8 ft 0 in (2·43 m)
Height overall, power on	3 ft 10 in (1·16 m)
Cabin width	2 ft 7 in (0·787 m)

WEIGHTS:

Gross weight	750 lb (340·17 kg)
Payload	400 lb (181 kg)

PERFORMANCE:

Cruising speed over land	
	35 mph (56·32 km/h)
Water speed	8-30 mph (13·48 km/h)

PRICE:
Generally costs between US$400·00 and $750·00 to build. Total materials package, $679·00. Special discounts for schools and quantity purchasers. Plans US$10·50.

LIPPISCH RESEARCH CORPORATION

HEAD OFFICE:
   3450 Cottage Grove Avenue SE, Cedar Rapids, Iowa 52403
TELEPHONE:
   (319) 365-0175
SALES OFFICE:
   Ten Old Post Office Road, Silver Spring, Maryland 20910

TELEPHONE:
   (301) 588-3311
STAFF PERSONNEL:
   Dr Alexander M. Lippisch FRAeS, President
   George G. Lippisch, Vice-President
   Bryce M. Fisher, Treasurer
   Dr Herschel Shosteck, Director of Marketing

Lippisch Research Corporation was founded in 1966 to furnish engineering design and consultancy services to airframe manufacturers and others. In recent years, the Corporation has concentrated on the development of ram-wing and wingless vehicles based on research concepts originated by Dr

The "winged hull" ground effect vehicle concept originated by Dr. Alexander M. Lippisch has received extensive model, wind tunnel and prototype testing. The X-112, *upper left*, the earliest flying prototype, confirmed stability characteristics in and out of ground effect. Tests of the X-113 Am, *upper right*, in the North Sea, more than verified wind tunnel data on efficiency (50% less power required in ground effect). Projected configurations include a two-seat sports and utility craft, *lower left*, and a 6-ton river bus, *lower right*

Alexander M. Lippisch.

Dr Lippisch is renowned as "father" of the delta wing. His designs included the first delta-wing glider, built in 1928 and the first operational rocket-propelled fighter, the Me 163 of World War II.

The need for more reliable and efficient surface transportation for relatively under-developed areas of the world, most of which are either water-bound or water-traced, led Dr Lippisch to investigate air cushion concepts.

He determined that air cushion vehicles employing the dynamic ground effect principle offered greater speed, higher power efficiency, controllability, and flexibility in terms of the kinds of terrain which could be crossed, than aerostatic types. The primary problem, theoretically, lay in the pitch instability of conventional wings when flown at various distances from the surface; i.e., the centre of pressure travels rearward as the surface is approached, causing the nose of a craft to pitch downward.

Dr. Lippisch discovered that a low aspect ratio wing, properly designed, would solve this instability problem. The result of his studies was the "winged hull" concept.

The major research work has been performed under contract with or in cooperation with Rhein-Flugzeugbau GmbH and Dornier Gmbh

DESIGN: The "winged hull" combines the waterborne stability of the catamaran with

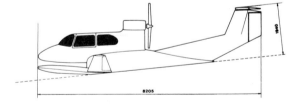
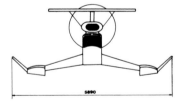
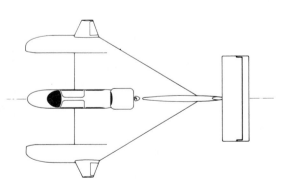

General arrangement of the Lippisch X-113B, a projected two-seat version of the X-113 Am

the airborne stability of a unique, reversed delta wing with negative dihedral along the leading edge. The wing tips, or catamaran-type floats, and the wing's trailing edge are on the same plane. This special shape creates stable ground effect, enabling the craft to maintain a selected height from the

surface automatically. Moreover, it solves the stability problem. The centre of pressure for the wing remains fixed whether the craft is in or out of ground effect.

The small-span, low aspect ratio wing design of the hull lends itself to simple, rugged construction which will withstand strong impacts without sacrificing loaded weight.

POWER PLANT: Conventional aircraft propulsion is employed.

CONTROLS AND PERFORMANCE: Control of the "winged hull" has proved in flight tests to be remarkably simple and safe. Conventional aircraft controls are used.

At low speeds, the craft operates as a planing boat. During take-off from the water, no control pressures are applied: gradual increase in speed develops the required lift and ground effect automatically. The craft is operated at a height above the surface of up to one-half the hull beam (wing span) for optimum performance.

Flight testing has shown craft of this type to be extremely manoeuvrable. They can travel at speed along a river and negotiate turns of only a few hundred feet in radius.

Because of its inherent stability, the "winged hull' is not restricted to flying in ground effect. It can leave ground effect to fly above obstacles such as bridges, for example, or to operate above a fog bank. Prototype vehicles have converted from ground effect to altitude and back again with no difficulty.

It manoeuvres at altitude in much the same way as a slow-flying aircraft; however, it is least efficient when operated out of ground effect during the brief periods it might be required to do so.

Whilst resembling an aircraft in form and control, the "winged hull is designed, of course, for highest efficiency in ground effect. Flight tests, including a series performed over rough water in the North Sea near Bremerhaven, have established that 50% less power is required in ground effect, enabling operations in excess of 50 ton-miles per gallon of fuel at speeds in the 90-180 knot range.

APPLICATIONS: "Winged hull" designs ranging from small, two-seat sports and utility craft propelled by Volkswagen engines to river buses. Coastal transports of several tons' have been initiated. A retractable wheeled undercarriage would permit amphibious operations in areas poorly suited for dock facilities.

No special depth of water is required when the craft is in ground effect; it will operate

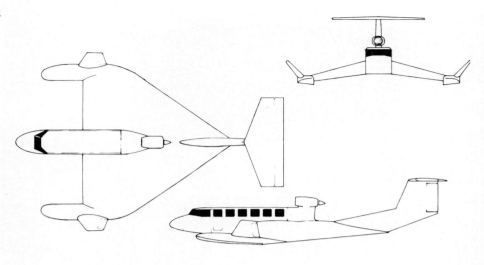

General arrangement of the projected 6-ton river bus

Aero-Skimmer under test. Employing the same basic principles as that of the Aerofoil Boat, but employing water-screw propulsion, craft of this type have reached a speed of 150 knots

equally well over sand banks, beaches, deserts and arctic regions.

Military applications include fast river patrol boats, anti-submarine warfare (ASW) craft, as well as personnel and supply transports.

The Lippisch Research Corporation offers its design services to potential users and will undertake studies for specific applications.

AERO-SKIMMER

In addition to the aerofoil boat, Lippisch Research Corporation is in the process of developing a sea-going vehicle designed for operation in the surface effect region.

Its unique configuration overcomes the speed barriers created by supercavitations induced drag on both ship hulls and hydrofoils. At higher speed, only the propeller blades contact the water. The hull itself lifts clear, being supported entirely by aerodynamic surface effect. The present manned research vehicle is designed for specialised naval purposes and reaches over-water speeds in excess of 150 knots.

LOCKHEED-GEORGIA

HEAD OFFICE:
Hartford, Conn., USA

EXECUTIVES:
R. H. Lange, Manager of Transport Design

Lockheed Georgia's 1·2 million lb Spanloader cargo flying-wing is one of several new projects which, in certain roles will fly in ground effect. The Spanloader, which will have a span of 252 ft (76·81 m) and a length of 208 ft (63·39 m), will be powered by six turbofans, each delivering 52,500 lb thrust.

The standard model is designed to carry a 550,000 lb payload, most of which will be packed in standard 8 × 8 ft × 20 ft (2·4 × 2·4 × 6·09 m) containers, over a distance of 5,000 n. miles. The wing has a thickness of 11 ft (3·35 m) and can accommodate two rows of containers, side-by-side in a cargo compartment which is 300 ft (91·44 m) long. There is an additional 92 ft (28·04 m) long cargo compartment in the fuselage, providing

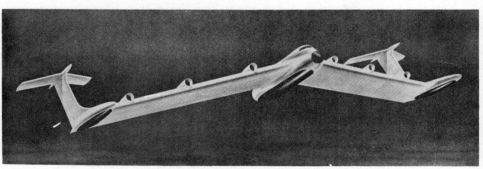

Lockheed-Georgia Spanloader

sufficient space for a total of 38 containers.

A feature of the craft is the use of an air cushion landing system, instead of a conventional landing gear. Two cushions will be located in streamlined containers beneath the wings, and a third will be located beneath the fuselage.

The company states that the low footprint pressure of 2·08 psi will allow the craft to operate from grass or water.

Among possible military applications will be that of long range A & W patrol. By operating in ground effect, it is estimated that the Spanloader would have an endurance of 56 hours, during which time it could cover 11,500 nautical miles at a cruising speed of 200 knots. In this configuration, payload capacity would be 110,000 lb.

MARITIME DYNAMICS

HEAD OFFICE:
PO Box 465, Tacoma, Washington 98401
USA

TELEPHONES:
(206) 7591709
(206) 922-5233

EXECUTIVES:
William C. House, President

Maritime Dynamics is at present undertaking SEV data reduction, performance analysis and model testing for the US Navy. It is also developing a number of new ACV concepts.

POWER BREEZE

HEAD OFFICE:
8139 Matilija, Panorama City, California 91402

TELEPHONE:
(213) 785-0197

EXECUTIVES:
Dan W. Henderson Jr, President/Designer
Power Breeze Air Cushion Vehicle Systems

was founded originally to stimulate public interest in ACVs, and is currently selling plans to home builders for a small, easily assembled amphibious single-seater.

A set of plans costs $5·00 and a ready made skirt costs $35·00.

Total cost of construction in the USA, including ply for the hull, skirt material, metal tubing, propeller and engine is about $400. Weight of the craft is 250 lb (113 kg) and the maximum speed is approximately 25 mph (40·23 km/h).

A number of craft have been built to this design in the United States and Australia.

In addition to selling plans, the company is now engaged in the sales of second-hand ACVs, and specialises in finding craft to meet the individual needs of its clients.

ROHR INDUSTRIES, INC.

CORPORATE HEADQUARTERS:
Foot of H Street, PO Box 878, Chula Vista, California 92012

TELEPHONE:
(714) 426-7111

EXECUTIVES:
Burt F. Raynes, Chairman
Frank E. McCreery, Vice-Chairman
Frederick W. Garry, President
Jerome J. Filiciotto, Group Vice-President, Aerospace and Marine Systems

SURFACE EFFECT SYSTEMS DIVISION:
PO Box 23000, San Diego, California 92123

TELEPHONE:
(714) 560-8008

TWX:
910-335-1599

EXECUTIVES:
Wilfred J. Eggington, Vice-President and General Manager
G. Douglas McGhee, 2KSES Programme Manager
W. A. Pulver, Director, Manufacturing
Lynd J. Esch, Manager, Advanced Programmes
George G. Halvorson, Manager, Test and Evaluation
Howard L. Kubel, Manager, Division Planning
John C. Quady, Manager, Advanced Engineering
Darrell L. Reed, Division Controller

Founded in 1960, Rohr Industries is a growing and diversified designer and builder of ground transportation, marine and aerospace systems, as well as industrial products.

Rohr's main plant occupies 130 acres of land with more than 2 million square feet of covered accommodation. The Chula Vista facility accommodates more than 3,000 items of major production equipment, representing an investment of $31 million. The company has 3,000 employees. Manufacturing facilities include machines, tooling and precision welding equipment that have been utilised extensively in the production of welded aluminium marine structures, including boat hulls and offshore mooring systems for fuel transfer.

Rohr's SES Division joined Litton Industries in 1972 to begin work on preliminary design studies of a US Navy 2,000-ton SES with ocean-going capabilities. While working on the design studies, Rohr continued its R&D programme (begun in 1970) with the US Navy test craft, XR-1.

On completing the preliminary design studies, a contract for the advanced development of the 2,000-ton concept was awarded to Rohr by the US Navy in July 1974.

Current work covers bow and stern seals; materials for seals and structures; lift fans; ride control devices to minimise vertical motions; waterjet pumps and reduction gearing. Testing of proposed features is undertaken aboard the XR-1 and the SES-100A, one of two testcraft built by the Navy to support the 2,000-ton study programme. Following this development programme, the ship system design will be finalised and the Navy will begin construction and test of a prototype.

2KSES (2,200-ton Surface Effect Ship)

Rohr Industries was one of the two successful competitors for the 2,000-ton surface effect ship development programme under the direction of the US Navy Surface Effect Ship Project Office. The development contract was awarded in June 1974. The scope of the contract includes the analysis, testing and

development of the waterjet pumps, cushion seals, lift and motion control system, and hull structures to expand the existing technology base for the design and construction of a large, ocean-going SES.

Additional activities conducted by Rohr include research and development programmes undertaken for the US Navy with the XR-1 and maintenance support of the SES-100A. Rohr's responsibilities in these programmes include design, modification, testing and evaluation of equipment, methods and concepts relating to SES technology, and direct support of US Navy testing programmes.

In the commercial sector, as part of its expanding marine role, Rohr is conducting preliminary studies leading to the development of advanced marine vehicles to meet demands in mass urban transportation and

Rohr's preliminary design for a 2,000 ton ASW SES for the US Navy. At the rear end of the deckhouse superstructure hangar space is provided

the offshore oil industry.

The objectives of the Navy's 2KSES programme are to demonstrate the feasibility of a large, ocean-going SES and to evaluate its potential as a weapon system. At present, the programme is concentrated on the development and testing of the ship's major subsystems and parallel ship design.

LIFT AND PROPULSION: Power for the lift system is provided by two General Electric LM-2500 gas-turbine engines. Lift fans are the centrifugal type, approximately 15 ft 0 in (13 m) in diameter. A total of six fans are installed, three fans on each side of the ship.

Propulsive power is provided by four General Electric LM-2500 gas-turbine engines driving four waterjet pumps through reduction gearing.

CUSHION AIR CONTAINMENT: Cushion air is contained by long rigid sidewalls with flexible seal installations forward and aft. The forward and aft seals are inflated by the cushion air supply and employ a planing surface at the lower extremities to eliminate flagellation damage and minimise hydrodynamic drag. They are fully retractable to facilitate craft operation off-cushion.

CONTROLS: Craft direction is controlled by differential and vectored thrust. Craft motion is controlled by a cushion pressure relief system and variable geometry inlets on the lift fans.

HULL: Longitudinally-framed, aluminium alloy structure, welded throughout. Plating is marine-grade aluminium alloy with extruded stiffeners. Design criteria ensures structural integrity in sea state 9.

ACCOMMODATION: Accommodation is provided for a complement of 125 men. Accommodation standards are to US Navy requirements and include berthing, commissary, recreation and laundry spaces. All living and working spaces are air-conditioned.

SYSTEMS: Electrical: Three Solar Saturn gas-turbine generators of 720 kw capacity each.

COMMUNICATIONS AND NAVIGATION: Communication and navigation system includes a US Navy Junior Participating Tactical Data System and an anti-collision radar.

ARMAMENT: Based on latest available Navy equipment for the selected mission demonstrations.

DIMENSIONS:

Length overall	238 ft 6 in (72·69 m)
Beam overall	108 ft 0 in (32·91 m)
Cushion height	18 ft 0 in (5·48 m)
Cushion area	17,000 sq ft (1,579 m²)

WEIGHTS:

Normal empty weight	1,280 tons
Normal all-up weight	2,200 tons

PERFORMANCE:

Maximum speed	approximately 80 knots

SES-100A

The SES-100A, one of two major testcraft supporting the 2,200-ton SES development, was developed by the Aerojet General Corporation under the sponsorship of the US Navy Surface Effect Ship Project Office.

Following completion of over two years of extensive contractor trials, the custody of the craft was transferred to the US Navy in July 1974. The waterjet propulsion system was modified to incorporate variable-geometry flush inlets, in lieu of the original pod-type ram inlets. This major conversion was

Rohr's preliminary design for a 2,000 ton ASW SES for the US Navy. At the rear end of the deckhouse superstructure hangar space is provided

accomplished, under Navy direction, by Hydronautics Inc. and the Tacoma Boat Company. Subsequently the craft was moved from the Seattle, Washington area to the Navy's Surface Effect Ship Test Facility (SESTF) at the Naval Air Station, Patuxent River, Maryland, where tests have been resumed.

Rohr Industries, under Navy contract, provides craft maintenance, logistics and engineering services, test planning and data handling support to the Navy's SES-100A test programme.

Primary objectives of the current test programme are a thorough evaluation of the propulsion system following the recent installation of variable-area, flush inlets.

LIFT AND PROPULSION: Motive power for the integrated lift/propulsion system is supplied by four 3,500 shp Avco Lycoming gas-turbines. The transmission system couples the gas-turbines to two Aerojet General two-stage axial/centrifugal waterjet pumps and three axial-flow lift fans through

reduction gears. Powerplant airflow is supplied through demisters from inlets located on the topside. The two waterjet pumps (port and starboard units) are installed on rail mounts that permit them to be removed through a port in the transom. The three axial-flow fans are located in compartments between the port and starboard engines. The four gas-turbines can be employed in any combination to drive the lift/propulsion system.

The variable geometry waterjet inlets are illustrated in the accompanying cutaway. To provide cavitation-free operation over a wide range of speeds, the throat area of the inlet diffuser is varied by means of a hydraulically actuated linkage connected to the flexible diffuser roof. At low speeds, and while the craft is passing through the "hump" speed, the diffuser throat is in the open position; it is then progressively closed to maintain the correct water flow rate as the speed increases.

CONTROLS: At low speeds, directional

The SES-100A surface effect ship is undergoing tests at the US Navy's SES test facility at Patuxent River Naval Air Station, Maryland, with the assistance of Rohr personnel

control is provided by waterjet thrust vector and at high speeds by movable skegs, port and starboard. The fuel and fuel-trim subsystem comprises four fuel storage tanks—two in each sidewall; a service tank and bow and stern trim tanks. Trim is adjusted by transferring fuel from tank to tank by means of the fuel transfer pumps.

HULL: The hull, constructed by the Tacoma Boatbuilding Co., Tacoma, Washington, is a welded aluminium structure divided into compartments by transverse and longitudinal bulkheads. The weatherdeck, cargo deck and bridge are in glass-reinforced plastic.

ACCOMMODATION: The bridge, which is air-conditioned and sound-insulated, is located on the centreline forward. It accommodates four crew members and six observers.

SYSTEMS: Electrical. Power generation and distribution system supplies electrical and electronic operational equipment and the data acquisitioned subsystem (DAS). The primary purpose of the DAS is to measure selected testcraft performance parameters and record the resulting data on magnetic tape. The secondary purpose is to provide instantaneous data display.

COMMUNICATIONS: Standard marine radio is carried and radar is included for collision avoidance. A gyro compass is fitted.

HYDRAULIC SYSTEM: 3,000 psig pressure and 100 psig return pressure.

COMPRESSED AIR: Engine bleed air is used for stern seal spring pressurisation. Stored compressed air is used for turbine starting and braking.

DIMENSIONS:

Length overall	81 ft 11 in (24·9 m)
Beam overall	41 ft 11 in (12·7 m)
Length-to-beam ratio	1 : 95
Cushion area	2,467 sq ft (230 m²)
Height on cushion	23 ft 0 in (7·01 m)
Draft displacement condition	10 ft 7½ in (3·22 m)
Freeboard (design load waterline)	8 ft 7½ in (2·62 m)

WEIGHTS:

Light displacement	72·8 short tons
Loaded displacement design	100 short tons

PERFORMANCE:

Designed max speed	80 knots

XR-1 TESTCRAFT

Rohr Industries operates the XR-1 SES research testcraft under US Navy contract. Originally built by the Naval Air Engineering Facility in 1963, the XR-1 was the first USN craft to demonstrate the captured air bubble principle. Early tests of this craft contributed to the formulation of the Navy's SES development and to the decision in 1966 to establish the SES Project Office

In 1970, the XR-1 was equipped with waterjets and assigned to Rohr for further development and evaluation. Since then, the craft has undergone a series of modifications to evaluate new concepts in cushion seals, waterjet inlet systems, lift air distribution, craft structures, and associated developments in instrumentation. It was the first craft of its type to demonstrate flush and variable-geometry waterjet inlets, and to provide operational data on the performance of these concepts under sea state conditions where inlet broaching is induced.

In 1973 further modifications of the craft were undertaken, including the replacement of the earlier rigid, articulated seals with

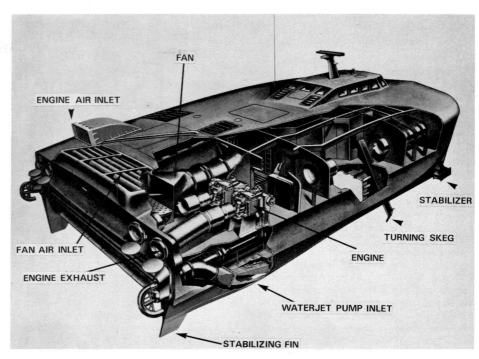

Cutaway drawing of the SES-100A showing one of the two flush-mounted waterjet inlets and the new stabilising fins which replace the original pod-type inlet and fin assembly

flexible, rubberised-fabric seals and the installation of a redesigned lift system to permit investigation of the effects of variations in lift-air distribution. In addition, a structural test programme was undertaken, involving rebuilding of the bow structure and incorporating instrumentation to permit measurement of structural loads due to slamming in heavy seas.

Although much smaller and less sophisticated than the SES-100A or SES-100B, the XR-1 has proven to be a versatile and relatively inexpensive research vehicle for investigating new SES concepts and for verifying scaling techniques for application in the design of larger craft.

Currently, the XR-1 is undergoing further modifications to demonstrate a refined waterjet inlet concept, flexible-planing-type seals, variable-output lift fans, heave attenuation devices and an integrated heave attenuation control system. This latest version of the XR-1 will permit early evaluation of these subsystems and their effects on overall craft performance.

DIMENSIONS:

Overall length	50 ft 0 in (15·0 m)
Overall beam	20 ft 0 in (6·0 m)
Cushion depth	3 ft 5 in (1·0 m)
All-up weight	39,600 lbs (17,961 km)

PROPULSION: Two T53-L-7A Avco-Lycoming gas-turbines; two Pratt & Whitney Seajet 6-1A pumpjets.

LIFT SYSTEM: Three Aerojet Liquid Rocket Co. variable output centrifugal fans; two prs.-heave attenuation valves. Cushion pressure—35,000 cfm at 60 psf.

Maximum speed in calm water—over 40 knots.

ADVANCED PROGRAMMES

Rohr Industries' SES Division also includes substantial advanced development and design capability in the SES, ACV and hydrofoil areas. Current advanced design activity includes development of proprietary technology in propulsion, seals and other high performance ship subsystems as well as competitive participation in military and commercial high-speed ship design and production programmes.

The US Navy's XR-1, a 17-ton waterjet-propelled test-craft which has been assigned to Rohr for development and evaluation

SESLAR AIR CUSHION VEHICLES

HEAD OFFICE:

3059 'A' Street, San Diego, California 92102

DIRECTORS:

Patrick and Linda Seslar

Seslar Air Cushion Vehicles was formed in 1969 to develop small, easily-built ACVs. SACV's latest prototype Scootair Mk. II, is now on permanent display in the San Diego Aerospace Museum, San Diego, California. Scootair Mk II was developed from an earlier design, Scootair Mk I, a 125 lb (56·69 kg) portable craft powered by a 3 hp engine.

SCOOTAIR MK II

Scootair Mk II features simplified and improved construction coupled with the use of an off-the-shelf propulsion unit.

LIFT AND PROPULSION: Power for lift is provided by a 3 hp, cycle engine driving an axial fan, located in the centre of the platform. Thrust is provided by a modified 7 hp air-boat air drive engine bolted to the deck aft of the lift engine and fan.

CONTROLS: Craft heading is controlled by a column which activates a rudder in the thrust unit slipstream. The control column incorporates the thrust engine throttle.

HULL: The platform is built in ¼ in (6·35 mm) marine ply bonded to frame structural

Scootair Mk II

members. Outer deck panels fold upwards for transport reducing the beam to 3 ft 6 in (1·06 m).

DIMENSIONS:

Diameter	9 ft 0 in (2·74 m)
Height (off cushion)	3 ft 0 in (0·914 m)
Height (on cushion)	3 ft 8 in (1·14 m)

WEIGHTS:

Empty	175 lb (79·37 kg)
Payload	220 lb (90·71 kg)

PERFORMANCE:

Speed	30 mph (48·28 km/h)

SURFACE EFFECT SHIPS PROJECT OFFICE

OFFICE:

PO Box 34401, Bethesda, Maryland 20084

CABLE ADDRESS:

SESPO, c/o Naval Ship Research and Development Center, Bethesda, Maryland

EXECUTIVES:

Captain C. J. Boyd, USN, Project Manager

The Surface Effect Ships Project Office, originally sponsored by both the Navy and Commerce Departments, became a wholly Navy sponsored operation on July 1, 1971. In early December 1971, Captain Carl J. Boyd, formerly Commanding Officer, USS Springfield, Sixth Fleet Flagship, was assigned to duties as Deputy Project Manager. Captain Boyd became Project Manager in February 1972.

With the change in sponsorship of the project, there was also a change in programe direction. This change is best described by the following quote from remarks made by Admiral Elmo R. Zumwalt, Jr., former Chief of Naval Operations: "It is my personal conviction that the development of a large SES has the potential for affecting other aspects of naval warfare as profoundly as nuclear power has affected submarine warfare".

The surface effect ship represents a major breakthrough in naval and maritime technology. The U.S. Navy believes the SES principle can be applied in open ocean ships of 2,000 to 10,000 tons. Such ships, capable of sustained speeds of 80-100 knots, would, in the opinion of the Navy, have revolutionary applications in the Navy's missions to control the seas and to project military strength abroad.

The Surface Effect Ship (SES) is a variation of the air cushion vehicle. ACVs employ a cushion of air contained by a flexible skirt around the hull and are normally propelled by air propellers driven by gas-turbine engines. Craft of this type are under

Two 100-ton SES's being employed by the US Navy to provide design data for the 2KSES. The SES-100A, *above*, is propelled by waterjets with flush inlets and has attained speeds in excess of 70 knots, while the SES-100B, *below*, is propelled by partially submerged-supercavitating propellers and has attained speeds in excess of 80 knots. These craft have helped to verify the ability of the SES to operate at predicted speeds, thereby paving the way for the 100-knot Navy

development by the U.S. Navy for use as advanced amphibious landing craft. The SES principle employs rigid sidewalls, integral to the hull structure, with flexible seals fore and aft to contain the air cushion. The rigid sidewalls permit the use of water propulsion, either waterjets or propellers, which is more efficient than airscrews at SES operational speeds. They also provide added stability. The U.S. Navy's SES programme has been orientated to this approach since it is believed that it will be superior to the more conventional air cushion vehicle for ships of ocean-going size.

The SES development programme is aimed at expanding the technology to ships of ocean-going size. Phase I of the programme, 1966 to 1973, was focussed on the design, development, construction, and tests of two 100-ton testcraft embodying different approaches to the critical technological areas of propulsion, sidewalls and seals, lift sytems, and systems of stability and control. The two 100-ton testcraft were completed in 1973 and have since been undergoing extensive testing. Tests to date have demonstrated the validity of the SES concept, and provided verification of the design data base needed for proceeding to larger size ships. Phase II, based on Phase I accomplishments and a major Navy mission analysis, focusses on the design, development, construction and test of one RDT & E funded test ship of about 2,000-ton (2KSES). Construction of this ship will take approximately 3 years and is expected to be completed by mid-1981. At-sea tests of the 2,000-ton ship will entail approximately four months of contractor demonstration, followed by approximately one year of Navy testing, which will include evaluation of the ship's ability to perform in an operational environment. Since the ultimate objective of the SES programme is to introduce this technology on a broader scale in the future, the development programme plan also includes planning and preliminary design studies for a class of SES escort ships of approximately 2,000-3,000 ton size as well as for further development of the SES technology to support design and construction of larger vessels. Plans for both the SES escort and the larger SES will be technology-paced and synchronized with the development and test of the 2,000-ton prototype.

Project Events Background

Conducted tests of XR-1, XR-3 and XR-5 manned model testcraft; converted XR-1 from air propulsion to waterjet propulsion utilising both ram and flush inlets and conducted successful tests to 42 knots, top speed for XR-1; initiated key subsystem development in seal design and materials, partially submerged supervacitating propelers and waterjet propulsion, lift fans, structural design and materials and aerodynamic/hydrodynamic response; designed, constructed and tested two 100-ton testcraft (SES 100A has waterjet propulsion; SES 100B has semi-submerged supercavitating propellers). Both 100-ton testcraft have conducted evaluations throughout the operating envelope, which helped to verify the SES principle. Data was obtained on drag, lift, stability, propulsive efficiency, air cushion/seal performance and riding qualities. Test data obtained conformed to design predictions for the essential characteristics necessary to the design of

Proposals for a 2,000-ton SES by Bell, *above*, and Rohr, *below*. The vessel will be a weaponised test ship, used to demonstrate the all-round capabilities and open ocean performance of surface effect ships in various fleet roles including ASW, surface and anti-air warfare

XR-I, seen in C configuration, weighs 20 tons. Though smaller than the 100-ton test craft, it has proved to be a versatile research vessel for investigating new SES concepts and for verifying scaling techniques which will be applied to larger SESs

larger SES. Conducted Surface Effect Ship Mission Analysis to examine the more important missions for SES; completed sizing which determined the 2,000-ton SES to be the smallest practical size for evaluation of an ocean-going ship, and that such a ship could be developed with acceptable technical risk.

As a result of Defense Systems Acquisition Review Council (DSARC) review in October 1972, SECDEF authorised Navy to award contracts for preliminary design of a 2,000-ton SES, using four competing contractors. A DSARC review in December 1973 led to a decision by SECDEF authorising the Navy to develop and test SES-unique subsystem for two 2,000-ton prototypes and to carry out the necessary concurrent ship design effort for updating the two preliminary designs.

Recent Developments

SES Test Facility—The Surface Effect Ship Test Facility (SESTF) was completed in April 1973 for the U.S. Navy as a test facility for the SES-100A and B and other testcraft as assigned. Other surface effect ships, including the XR-2, XR-5, and the British Wellington class BH-7, have operated from the SESTF.

The Facility, located at the Naval Air Station, Patuxent River, Maryland, consists of a 195-ton capacity syncrolift, a transfer yard with two transfer cars, and a boathouse with support facilities. The boathouse consists of two bays occupying 24,000 square feet. This area can be closed against the weather and is heated and lit, providing an all-weather maintenance and support capability. A warehouse (8,000 square feet), a machine shop (3,000 square feet), and office space (5,000 square feet) complete the Facility. The Facility has access to the telemetering and real-time data reduction facilities of NAS, Patuxent River, allowing it to monitor and to correct test missions, as needed.

The SES-100A is based there and has been undergoing a complete Test and Evaluation programme since March 1975 validating 2,000-ton and larger surface effect ship designs.

Surface Effect Ships attain high speeds: Both the waterjet-propelled SES-100A and its sister ship the SES-100B, which is driven by partially submerged supercavitating propellers, have established new speed records for naval surface vehicles. The SES-100A exceeded 70 knots while the SES-100B exceeded 80 knots. These accomplishments help to verify the ability of SES craft to operate at predicted speeds thereby paving the way for the "100 Knot Navy".

Flush Waterjet Inlet Retrofit: Flush waterjet inlets were designed, built and retrofitted on the SES-100A, a 100-ton waterjet propelled experimental surface effect craft. This craft is currently conducting tests with the new inlets. Flush inlets provide lower drag and are less susceptible to debris ingestion and damage than pod-mounted inlets. The lower drag results in higher craft speed and range.

2,000-ton SES contracts awarded: In July 1974, two contracts, amounting to about $72 million, were awarded to Bell Aerospace Corporation and Rohr Industries to develop SES-critical sub-systems and to conduct parallel ship design effort. The data generated from these contracts will minimise the risk in the design and construction of a large open ocean SES prototype. In late 1974, R & D constraints led to a decision for the development of one SES prototype. By June 1976, when the current sub-system and parallel ship design contracts are due for completion, one contractor is expected to have been selected to design and construct the large SES prototype. However, the decision for the contract design, detail design and construction of the prototype awaits a future DSARC (scheduled for mid-1976).

XR-3, a two-man testcraft operated for SESPO by the Naval Post Graduate School, Monterey, California, is used for preliminary evaluation of performance and control. It also provides junior naval officers with the opportunity to operate an SES

XR-5, a 46 ft, 7,500 lb, free-running, manned craft was designed and built for SESPO in 1973. This craft is used to verify the operating characteristics of the high length-to-beam concept. Power performance, dynamic structural response, seakeeping and dynamic stability characteristics can be evaluated almost simultaneously in varying sea states and heading. It has attained 20 knots in 10 in waves which scaled up to 60 knots in 7 ft seas for an SES of 4,000 tons

SESPO's surface effect ship test facility with the SES-100A in the background. When the 100A docks, the 195-ton sycnrolift raises the craft, together with the transfer car on which it rests, to the deck level. The transfer car and craft are then moved into the boathouse via a rail system

SKIMMERS INCORPORATED

HEAD OFFICE:
PO Box 855, Severna Park, Maryland,
21146

TELEPHONE:
301-647-0526

DIRECTORS:
M. W. Beardsley. President and General
Manager
H. L. Beardsley
W. D. Preston

OVERSEAS REPRESENTATIVE:
United Kingdom: Airhover Ltd, St. Osyth,
Essex

Skimmers Inc was formed in April 1966 to
produce plans and components for use by
homebuilders in constructing the Fan-Jet
Skimmer sport ACV. It is affiliated with the
Beardsley Air Car Co.

FAN-JET SKIMMER

Fan-Jet Skimmer is one of the world's
first practical solo sport ACVs. It was
designed by Col. Melville Beardsley, a
former USAF technical officer, and one of the
pioneers in ACV development in the United
States.

The Fan-Jet Skimmer was designed to be
the simplest and cheapest one-man ACV that
could be devised. More than forty craft
of this type have been built to date. The
company is now developing a two-seat sports
ACV.

HULL: The main structural component
is a tractor inner tube, giving 700 lb of
buoyancy, around which is an aluminium
framework of square tube, and L girders.
The topside bow profile is in plywood. The
structure is decked in vinyl-coated nylon
fabric, which is also used for the self-extending
skirt system.

LIFT AND PROPULSION: Power for the
integrated lift/propulsion system is provided
by a Chrysler 2-cycle 6 hp engine, driving an
18 in axial flow fan. The fan has a marine

plywood hub with 9 sheet metal formed
blades. The primary air flow, used for
direct thrust, is ejected through a propulsive
slot control flap located aft of the fan duct.
The area of the slot can be varied by a hinged-
flap controlled by a lever. This and the
throttle lever and ignition switch are the
only controls. The secondary air flow, for
cushion lift, passes into a rearward plenum
chamber.

CONTROL: The craft is steered by kinesthetic control (body movement) which the
designer feels is the ideal method of control
for a craft of this size.

DIMENSIONS:
Length overall	9 ft 8 in (2·9 m)
Beam overall	6 ft 2 in (1·8 m)
Height overall on landing pads	
	36 in (0·9 m)
Skirt depth	9 in (0·2 m)
Draft afloat	5 in (0·12 m)
Cushion area	44 sq ft (4·0 m²)

WEIGHTS:
Normal all-up weight	250 lb (113 kg)
Normal payload (operating)	150 lb (68 kg)
Maximum payload	180 lb (397 kg) app

PERFORMANCE:
Max speed, calm water	18 mph (29 km/h)
Cruising speed, calm water	
	18 mph (29 km/h)

The Fan-Jet Skimmer

Max wave capability	6 in app (153 mm)
Still air range	35 miles app (56 km)
Max gradient, static conditions	5° app
Vertical obstacle clearance	5 in (127 mm)

For full over-the-hump performance with
an operator weighing more than 175 lb the
installation of two power plants is recommended each identical with the standard
single power unit. With an operator weighing up to 225 lb the speed of the twin is
approx 20% greater than the standard
single engine.

With the overall length of the twin-engine
model increased to 11 ft 2 in, it will carry a
useful load of 350 lb at maximum speeds of
approximately 35 mph over smooth land and
22 mph over calm water.

Price: USA, f.o.b. Severna Park, Maryland:
$1,200·00 for complete vehicle
$595 for kit

Terms of payment   50% down

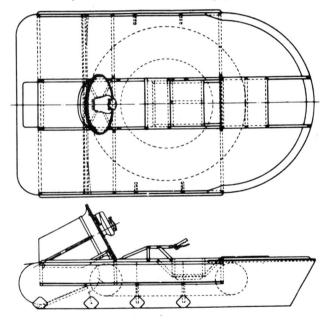

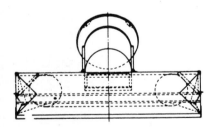

The Fan-Jet Skimmer, designed by Melville Beardsley

UNIVERSAL HOVERCRAFT

HEAD OFFICE:
2611 182nd Place, Redondo Beach, California 90278

TELEPHONE:
374 1904

DIRECTOR:
R. J. Windt

Formed in 1969, this company has designed
and built twenty different sports ACV
prototypes, ranging from an ultra-light single
seater powered by a model aircraft engine,
to a six-seater powered by an engine of 110 hp.
Plans of some of these designs are available
to homebuilders.

The company is currently developing three
different single-engine amphibious craft—an
11 ft two-seater, a 13 ft four-seater and a
16 ft six-seater. Work has also been undertaken on air cushion vehicles propelled by
waterjets, outboard motors and sails.

UH-10

This single-seat amphibious runabout was
one of the company's earliest designs. Construction of the prototype was completed in
November 1969. The vehicle, which is of
wooden construction, attains 30 mph (48·28
km/h) over land and 25 mph (40·23 km/h)
over water.

LIFT AND PROPULSION: Integrated
system employing a single McCulloch 101

2-cycle 116 cc engine, which drives a 1 ft 9 in
(0·53 m) diameter, 12-bladed centrifugal fan
mounted vertically on a shaft inside a transverse duct Air is drawn by the fan from each
end of the duct. Propulsion air is expelled
through an outlet nozzle aft and lift air is
ducted into a plenum below. Maximum
thrust is 32 lb (14·51 kg).

HULL: Frame is built from fir ribs and
stringers and covered with ⅛ in ply.

ACCOMMODATION: Open cockpit with
seat for driver. Craft will carry one person
or a load of up to 170 lb (79·35 kg) over
water, and up to 225 lb (102·05 kg) over land.

CONTROLS: Multiple rudders in the thrust
air outlet provide directional control.

DIMENSIONS:

Length	10 ft 4 in (3·14 m)
Beam	6 ft 0 in (1·82 m)
Height, off cushion	2 ft 6 in (0·76 m)

WEIGHTS:

Weight empty	135 lb (61·23 kg)
Normal loaded weight	310 lb (140·14 kg)
Max loaded weight	360 lb (163·28 kg)

PERFORMANCE:

Max speed:	
Over land	30 mph (48·28 km/h)
Over water	25 mph (40·23 km/h)
Max gradient	10%

PRICE: Complete set of plans for home-building, US$6·00.

UH-11

An ultra-light runabout of wooden construction, the UH-11 seats two and has a top speed of 35 mph (56·32 km/h).

LIFT AND PROPULSION: Integrated system employing a single Chrysler 2-cycle 133 cc engine, which drives a 1 ft 8 in (0·50 m) diameter, 4-bladed fan for lift and a 4 ft 0 in (1·21 m) 2-bladed fan for propulsion. Power is transmitted to the lift fan via a flexible drive and to the propulsion fan through a reduction ratio belt drive.

HULL: Structure built with fir ribs and stringers and covered in ⅛ in (3·17 mm) ply.

ACCOMMODATION: Enclosed cabin with side-by-side seating for driver and passenger.

CONTROLS: Twin aerodynamic rudders, hinged to the rear of the propeller guard, provide directional control.

DIMENSIONS:

Length	11·5 ft (3·48 m)
Width	5·5 ft (1·65 m)
Height (off cushion)	3·5 ft (1·04 m)

WEIGHTS:

Weight empty	150 lb (68 kg)
Normal loaded	350 lb (158·75 kg)
Max loaded	400 lb (181·43 kg)

PERFORMANCE:

Max speed:	
over land	35 mph (56·32 km/h)
over water	30 mph (48·28 km/h)
Max gradient	12%

PRICE: Complete plans US$10.00.

UH-12T

This amphibious two-seater is based on the company's original prototype which was built early in 1969. The new hull is easier to build and provides automatic pitch control. As thrust is increased, the aerofoil-shaped hull generates more lift, offsetting the pitching moment caused by thrust. The height of the centre of thrust has also been reduced.

LIFT AND PROPULSION: Motive power for the lift system is provided by 133 cc Chrysler 2-cycle petrol engine which drives a 2 ft 2 in diameter (0·66 m) 4-bladed fan at 4,500 rpm. About 5% of the cushion air is employed to inflate the bag-type skirt. Thrust is provided by a 25 hp JLO 395 2-cycle engine driving a 3 ft 0 in (0·914 m) diameter 2-bladed ducted propeller.

HULL: Mixed wood and fibreglass construction. Structure comprises fir ribs and stringers covered with ⅛ in plywood. Cockpit floor and other highly stressed areas strengthened with fibreglass.

CONTROLS: Directional control is provided by a single aerodynamic rudder.

ACCOMMODATION: Single bench seat for driver and one passenger. Cockpit canopy

UH-10, an amphibious single-seater powered by single McCulloch 101 2-cycle 116 cc engine

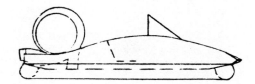
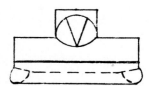

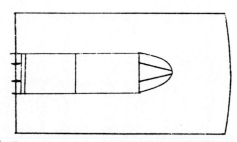

General arrangement of the UH-10 light ACV runabout. Of wooden construction, it attains 30 mph over land and 25 mph over water

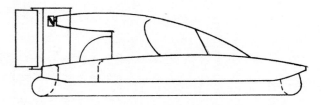
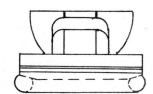

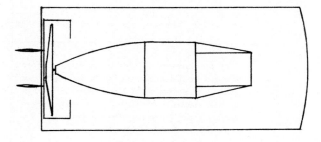

UH-II two-seater powered by a Chrysler 2-cycle, 133 cc engine

can be fitted for use in cold weather.

DIMENSIONS:

Length overall	12 ft 6 in (3·81 m)
Beam overall	6 ft 0 in (1·82 m)

WEIGHTS:

Empty weight	275 lb (124·73 kg)
All-up weight	600 lb (272·14 kg)

PERFORMANCE:

Max speed:	
over land	55 mph (88·51 km/h)
over water	50 mph (80·46 km/h)
Max gradient	26%

PRICE AND TERMS: Plans US$15·00 per set.

UH-14T

A "stretched" version of the UH-12T, this model has a length of 14 ft (4·26 m) and a beam of 6 ft 6 in (1·98 m).

LIFT AND PROPULSION: Systems identical to those of UH-12T, but thrust engines with up to 25% more power may be installed.

SKIRT: 12 in (307 mm) bag skirt.

ACCOMMODATION: Single bench seat forward for driver and passenger; optional rear seat for one adult or two children.

WEIGHTS:

Empty weight	400 lb (181·42 kg)
All-up weight	950 lb (430·893 kg)

PRICE:

Complete set of plans, US$20.00.

UH-17S

Construction of the UH-17S, which has an integrated lift/propulsion system powered by either a Volkswagen or Corvair engine of 50-140 hp, was completed in May 1970. The craft, which seats a driver and up to three passengers, is said to be extremely quiet and control is precise. It is capable of towing water or snow skiers, sleds or ski boards.

LIFT AND PROPULSION: A single 75 hp Corvair automobile engine drives a 3 ft 6 in (1·06 m) diameter fan mounted vertically on a shaft inside a transverse duct. Air is drawn by the fan from each end of the duct. Propulsion air is expelled through outlets at the stern and lift air is ducted into a plenum below. The fan feeds air into the cushion at 240 cfs and provides 150 lb thrust.

ACCOMMODATION: Enclosed cabin seating driver and up to three passengers on two bench-type seats.

DIMENSIONS:

Length	17 ft 10 in (5·43 m)
Beam	7 ft 11 in (2·41 m)

WEIGHTS:

Empty weight	950 lb (430·89 kg)
Normal loaded weight	1,600 lb (725·71 kg)
Max loaded weight	1,900 lb (861·78 kg)

PERFORMANCE:

Max speed:	
over land	42 mph (67·59 km/h)
over water	35-40 mph (65·64 km/h)
Continuous gradient at 1,200 lb	12%

No plans available.

UH-18T

The prototype of this amphibious six-seater was built in 1971 and has accumulated over 400 operating hours, mainly on open seas.

It was the first hovercraft to visit Catalina island, 26 miles (41·84 km) off the coast of California and the first to complete the journey from los Angeles to San Diego (105 miles (168·98 km) across open seas. It has also been employed extensively for water and snow skiing.

The aerofoil shaped hull is similar to that of the UH-12T and UH-14T.

LIFT AND PROPULSION: Lift is provided by a 25 hp JLO 395 2-cycle engine driving a 2 ft 6 in diameter 4-bladed fan at 3,200 rpm. About 5% of the air is employed to inflate the bag skirt. Propulsive thrust is supplied by an 85 hp Corvair automobile engine driving a 5 ft 0 in (1·52 m) diameter 2-bladed propeller at up to 2,800 rpm.

SKIRT: 1 ft 6 in (0·46 m) diameter bag skirt, providing 1 ft 0 in (0·304 m) vertical clearance.

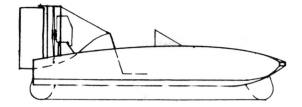
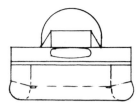
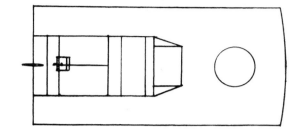

The UH-12T, an amphibious two-seater with a maximum speed of 55 mph (88·51 km/h)

UH-14T, a stretched version of the UH 12T two-seater

Universal Hovercraft UH 18T

HULL: Mixed wood and grp construction. Hull frame is built from fir ribs and stringers and covered with ¼ in ply. Highly stressed areas covered with glass fibre.

ACCOMMODATION: Driver and up to five passengers seated on two 3-place bench seats. Cabin can be enclosed by canopy in cold weather.

CONTROLS: Craft heading is controlled by a single rudder operating in the propeller slipstream and two auxiliary rudders hinged to the rear of twin fins, one each side of the propeller guard. All three rudders are operated by a steering wheel. Separate throttle provided for lift and thrust engines.

DIMENSIONS:
Length	18 ft 3 in (5·56 m)
Beam	8 ft 0 in (2·43 m)
Height, off cushion	6 ft 0 in (1·82 m)
on cushion	7 ft 0 in (2·13 m)

WEIGHTS:
Empty weight	1,000 lb (453·57 kg)
Normal loaded	2,000 lb (907·14 kg)
Max loaded	2,400 lb (1,088 kg)

PERFORMANCE:
Max speed:	
over land	70 mph (112·65 km/h)
over water	60 mph (96·56 km/h)
Max gradient	31%

PRICE:
Complete set of plans for homebuilding. US$ 25·00.

A feature of the UH-17S is the integrated lift/propulsion system powered by a 75 hp Corvair automobile engine

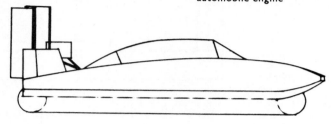

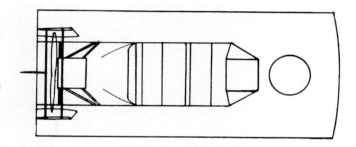
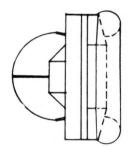

Universal Hovercraft UH-18T, a six seater of mixed wood and grp construction. Propulsive thrust is supplied by an 85 hp Corvair engine driving a 5 ft 0 in (1·52 m) diameter 2-bladed propeller

---

WATER RESEARCH COMPANY

HEAD OFFICE:
  3003 North Central Avenue, Suite 600, Phoenix, Arizona 85012
TELEPHONE:
  (602) 265-7722
EXECUTIVES:
  Richard R. Greer, President
  Dr John H. McMasters, Chief Engineer
  (Members of American Society of Naval Engineers)

The Water Research Company was formed in 1972 to consolidate activities surrounding the patents held or applied for by Richard R. Greer relating to various aspects of water-borne vehicles. The company has subsequently prepared conceptual studies on a class of winged surface effect vessels (WSEV) intended to fill a variety of US Navy and commercial freight applications. The conclusions of this study were published in the Naval Engineers' Journal, April 1974. The company is able to undertake analytical studies on hydrofoil, SES and WIG systems, and can provide contract co-ordinating services for such systems. The company has no immediate plans for acquiring hardware development facilities.

THE UNION OF SOVIET SOCIALIST REPUBLICS

CENTRAL LABORATORY OF LIFESAVING TECHNOLOGY

HEAD OFFICE: Moscow
EXECUTIVES:
  Yury Makarov, Chief Engineer
  A. V. Gremyatskiy, Designer
  Yevgeniy P. Grunin, Designer
  N. L. Ivanov, Designer
  S. Chernyavskiy
  Y. Gorbenko
CONSULTANT:
  V. Shavrov
DIRECTOR OF FLIGHT TRIALS:
  A. Baluyev

The Central Laboratory of Rescue Techniques, a division of OSVOD—the Rescue Organisation for Inland Waters—has designed a small aerodynamic ram-wing machine, capable of 75 mph (120 km/h), which will be used to answer distress calls on the Soviet

One of the first three prototypes of Eska-1 operating out of ground effect at between 60-90 ft (20-30 m). Maximum effective flying height in ground effect is 1 ft-5 ft (0·3-1·5 m). The vehicle, a two-seat aerodynamic ram-wing, is employed as an experimental, high-speed rescue and liaison craft on Russian inland waterways.

lakes, rivers and canals. The vehicle, which is available in several versions, is the Eska—an abbreviation of Ekranolyetny Spasatyelny Kater-Amphibya (Surface-effect Amphibious Lifeboat). It has also been referred to as the Ekranolet and the Nizkolet (skimmer).

Apart from meeting emergency situations on waterways, the craft, which is amphibious, is capable of operating in deserts, tundra, arctic icefields and steppeland. Derivatives are to be employed as support vehicles for geologists, communications engineers and construction groups.

In Russian publications emphasis has been given to the potential value of such craft in opening up the mineral wealth of Siberia, the Soviet Far East, Far North and other virgin territories.

As with the X 113 Am and other machines of this type, the vehicle operates on the principle that by flying in close proximity to the ground, the so-called image flow reduces drag by about 70%. Whereas an average aircraft at normal flight altitude carries about 9 lb (4 kg) per hp of engine output, the wing-in-ground effect machine, on its dynamic air-cushion carries up to 44 lb (20 kg), an improvement of more than 400%. Weight efficiency of the craft (ratio of useful load to all-up weight), is 48·9%.

At angles of attack of 2-8 degrees near the ground, its lift is 40-45% greater than when flying out of ground effect. In addition the supporting surface hinders the vortex flow from the lower wing surface to the upper surface which decreases induction drag.

Control of the Ezka is said to be easy and pilots require no special training. Within ground effect it is no more complicated to control than a car.

The design, which has been strongly influenced by the Lippisch "aerofoil boat" concept, employs an almost identical short span, low aspect ratio reversed delta wing with anhedral on the leading edge, dihedral tips and wing floats. Preliminary details are given below.

ESKA-1

Designed initially as an amphibious high-speed rescue craft for use on Russia's inland waterways, the Eska has been developed into a general utility vehicle with a wide range of applications in underdeveloped areas.

Eska-1 completed its first flight on August 29th 1973, over the Klyazminskoye reservoir, carrying a pilot, passenger and an additional load. It took off at 74·5 mph (120 km/h) after a run of 87-100 yards (80-100 m) and flew for several minutes at between 60-90 ft (20-30 m), before descending to make a low level pass across sandy spits and banks and forcing its way through the thickets and reeds of an islet. After climbing to avoid a launch coming to meet it, it landed and taxied out of the water onto a gently sloping bank.

The youthful design group responsible for the Eska-1 took two years to study world experience of ramwing and aerodynamic ram-wing construction, after which a series of small-scale models were built, followed by the construction and test of five different full-size craft.

Three prototypes similar to Eska-1 had been built by mid-February 1974. Two other models, one with fabric-covered flying surfaces and rear hull, the other a four

Above: The Eska-1 has been strongly influenced by the Lippisch "Aerofoil boat" concept, and employs an anhedral, reversed delta wing, dihedral tips and wing floats.
Below: Close-up, showing details of the forward hull and cockpit which is based on that of a two-seat sports boat. Power is supplied by a 30 hp M-63 motorcycle. Maximum speed with full load, in ground effect is 72-80 mph (122 km/h)

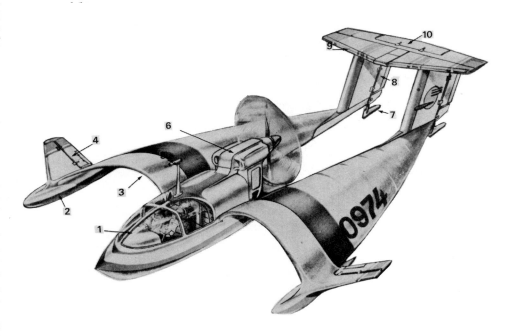

Twin-boom parawing ekranoplan concept. 1. cabin; 2. float; 3. split parawing; 4. aileron; 5. pressure head; 6. powerplant; 7. hydrodynamic rudder; 8. aerodynamic rudder; 10. elevator

seater, were reported under construction in March 1974. Variants with larger cabins and more powerful engines are being developed.

POWER PLANT: Single 30 hp M-63 motorcycle engine, on tripod dorsal mounting aft of cockpit, drives via shafting a two-bladed fixed-pitch propeller.

CONSTRUCTION: Forward hull design based on that of two-seat sports boat. Corrosion resistant aluminium alloy construction employed for first three craft. Heavy fabric covering employed on wings inboard of tips and hull aft of crew compartment on one later model.

CONTROLS: Single aircraft-type control stick, incorporating engine throttle, located in the centre of the cockpit. Conventional foot-operated bar to control rudder.

ACCOMMODATION: Enclosed cabin for two, seated side-by-side. Access is via hinged hood. Initial arrangement is for rescuer/pilot, with one seat available for the person being rescued. Three and four seat models are under development.

DIMENSIONS:

Wing span overall	22 ft 5⅔ in (6·9 m)
Length	24 ft 7 in (7·55 m)
Height	8 ft 2½ in (2·5 m)
Wing area	148·13 sq ft (13·85 m²)
Tail area	32·4 sq ft (3 m²)

WEIGHTS:

All-up weight	992 lb (450 kg)
Empty weight	507 lb (230 kg)
Useful load	485 lb (220 kg)
Weight efficiency	48·9%

PERFORMANCE:

Max speed with full load in ground effect	75·80 mph (122 km/h)
Cruising speed	68·35 mph (110 km/h)
Take-off speed	34·17 mph (55 km/h)
Landing speed	31-34 mph (50-55 km/h)
Take-off run from water	87-109 yards (80-100 m)
Take-off run from snow	54-65 yards (50-60 m)
Landing run on water (without braking parachute)	43·74 yards (40 m)
Most effective flying height in surface effect	1 ft -4 ft 11 in (0·3-1·5 m)
Max altitude, with 50% load, for obstacle clearance	up to 164 ft (50 m)
Range with full fuel supply	186-217 miles (300-350 km)
Wing loading	(32·5 kg/m²)
Power loading	33 lb/hp (15 kg/hp)

Limiting weather conditions—can operate in force 5 winds

PARAWING EKRANOPLANS

The originator of the idea of applying Rogallo-type flexible delta wings to light ekranoplans is Yevgeniy Grunin, one of the designers of the Eska-1. The parawing is well known for its outstanding aerodynamic qualities and stability and is convenient for transport and storage. Grunin, assisted by S. Chernyavskiy and N. Ivanov, fitted a flexible wing to the fuselage of the Czechoslovakian Let L-13J Blanik, a powered version of the well known two-seat, all-metal sailplane. Power is supplied by a 42 hp Jawa M-150 piston-engine driving a 3 ft 7¼ in (1·10 m) diameter Avia V210 propeller on a tripod mounted aft of the cockpit, an

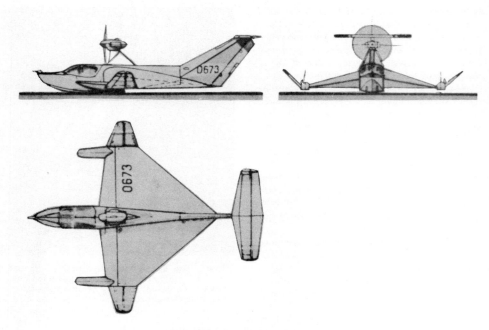

General arrangement of Eska-1

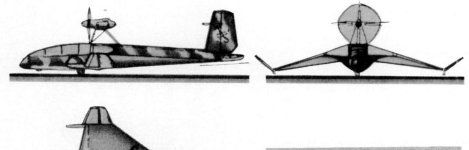

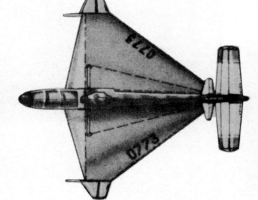

General arrangement of the Shmel, a modified Let L-13J Blanik powered glider fitted with a para-wing

Parawing derivative of the Eska-1

arrangement almost identical to that employed on Eska-1. Profiting from the encouraging results of the flight trials, the team has designed a number of small ekranoplan projects incorporating flexible wings, including a modified version of the An-2V, the floatplane version of the Antanov An-2, single-engine general-purpose biplane, still widely employed throughout the Soviet Union. The nature of the modifications can be seen in the accompanying sketch. Realisation of the project would give the 27-year-old design a completely new lease of life and provide a substantial aid to communications in underdeveloped areas for a relatively low investment.

Project for adapting the Antonov An-2V to a parawing ekranoplan configuration

KHARKOV AVIATION INSTITUTE
ADDRESS: Kharkov

In August 1973, it was reported in Pravda that the Institute of Aviation, Kharkov, had built two amphibious ACVs. At the same time, it was mentioned that ACV research and development was being undertaken at forty national enterprises, in Moscow, Tomsk, Gorki, Gorlovka, Ufa and Volgograd.

KRASNOYE SORMOVO
ADDRESS:
Gorky

This shipyard began work in the ACV field by building a five-passenger air cushion river craft known as the Raduga in 1960-61. Since then it has built the Sormovich, a 30-ton peripheral jet ACV for 50 passengers, the Neva, a plenum-chambered type craft seating 38 and the Gorkovchanin, a 48-seat sidewall craft for shallow, winding rivers.

The latter is now in service on a number of rivers, together with a derivative, the Zarnitsa.

The design of an 80-seat rigid sidewall ferry the Orion, was approved by the Soviet Ministry of Inland Waterways in 1970. Construction of the prototype began in 1972 and trials began in October 1973. The craft, bearing the serial number 01, will provide a service connecting Kalinin with towns and villages on the shores of the river Soz.

Preliminary details of an off-shore derivative, the Rassvet (Dawn) have been announced.

In 1969, prototypes of two new fully skirted hovercraft made their debut, the Breeze, a light utility craft, and the Skate, a 50-seat passenger ferry with an all-up weight of 27 tons and a cruising speed of 57·5 mph. Military versions of the Skate are now in production in addition to the passenger ferry model. Development of the Skate and its naval and army counterparts is believed to have been undertaken in conjunction with the Leningrad Institute of Marine Engineers, also thought to be responsible for the design and construction of the Soviet Union's

Aist, a 220-ton amphibious hovercraft operated by the Soviet Navy.

biggest skirted hovercraft, known in the West as Aist, which is generally similar in shape, size and performance to the SR.N4. The vessel, which is in service with the Soviet Navy as an assault landing craft, is illustrated in this section.

The Sormovo yard is likely to have been responsible for building of the world's largest air cushion vehicle—a wing-in-ground effect machine capable of carrying 800-900 troops at speeds up to 300 knots. In April 1972 it was announced that plans were in hand to build wing-in-ground effect machines

capable of navigating rivers at a speed of about 155 mph (250 km/h). A number of these craft are understood to be in experimental service.

220-TON NAVAL ACV
NATO Code Name: "AIST"

"Aist" the first large Soviet amphibious hovercraft, is undergoing proving trials with the Soviet Navy. Built in Leningrad, it is similar in appearance to the SR.N4 Mk. II Mountbatten though probably heavier by some 20 tons and 15 ft (4·57 m) longer (145 ft compared with 130 ft).

Since delivery to the Soviet Navy, the vessel has been employed mainly as a medium-short range, heavy logistic craft, delivering mechanised infantry and tanks to simulated beach heads. In a TV film commemorating the 30th Anniversary of the ending of the Great Patriotic War (World War II) a number of new weapons and forms of transportation in use by the Soviet armed forces were pesented, among them an Aist and two Gus air-cushion assault landing craft.

While the latter unloaded part of an assault wave of Soviet marine infantry, Aist lowered its bow loading door/ramp to land a new main battle tank. Alternative military uses for amphibious craft of the Aist type would be mine countermeasures, ASW and missile craft and open sea fast patrol.

Details of the lift and propulsion system are not yet available. Motive power is thought to be supplied by six gas-turbines driving four centrifugal lift fans and four identical, pylon-mounted propeller units. Each propeller has variable and reversible pitch, negative pitch being applied for braking and reversing.

Intakes for the four centrifugal lift fans are located in the top of the superstructure, two port and two starboard, forward of the propeller units.

HULL: Built mainly in marine corrosion resistant aluminium alloys. Structure appears to follow standard practice for large amphibious ACVs. The main hull is formed by a buoyancy raft based on a grid of longitudinal and transverse frames which form a number of flotation compartments. Two main longitudinal vertically stiffened bulkheads run the length of the craft, separating the central load deck from the outer or sidestructures, which contain the gas-turbines and their associated air intakes, exhausts, lift fans, transmissions and auxiliary power system.

A full-width ramp is provided at the bow and a second at the stern providing through loading facilities.

The wheelhouse is located above the cabin superstructure. A remotely-operated rapid-fire cannon can be sited either above or ahead of the cabin.

DIMENSIONS:
Length overall	145 ft 0 in (44·19 m)
Beam overall	55 ft 0 in (16·76 m)

WEIGHTS:
All-up weight	220 tons

PERFORMANCE:
Max speed	About 70 knots

BREEZE

This interesting light amphibious ACV has external features which are reminiscent of the Vickers VA-2 and VA-3.

It was developed by an amateur design group led by German Koronatov, a graduate of the Leningrad Shipbuilding Institute.

The design incorporates the cabin and propulsion system of the Kamov KA-30 Aerosled. The craft performed well across ice and water during trials, and in August 1973 it was reported that it had undergone successful tests on the Vuoksa river.

LIFT AND PROPULSION: Thrust is provided by a 260 hp A1-14RS radial piston engine driving an AV-59 three-bladed metal, controllable and reversible pitch propeller. Lift is supplied by two Moskvich 407 auto-

Top: The Breeze light amphibious ACV for ten-passengers. Thrust is supplied by a radial aircraft engine driving a 3-bladed airscrew, and lift by twin Moskvich 407 automotive engines, each driving a set of four centrifugal fans mounted in series on a common shaft. Fan air is drawn through fixed louvres

Bottom: Passengers boarding the Breeze. To facilitate access to the cabin a panel is removed from the lift fan cowl ahead of the engine and a handrail and steps are slotted into position.

motive engines mounted aft on the side-structures, one port and one starboard, each driving a set of four centrifugal fans mounted on a common shaft.

CONTROLS: Directional control over most of the speed range is provided by twin rudders. Low speed control is assisted by puff ports fore and aft.

HULL: Riveted corrosion-resistant aluminium alloy.

SKIRT: Fingered bag type, in rubberised fabric.

ACCOMMODATION: In standard form the craft accommodates a driver and 8 passengers.

DIMENSIONS:
Length overall, power off	approx 30 ft (9·14 m)

WEIGHTS:
All-up weight	4 tons

PERFORMANCE:
Hard structure clearance	1 ft 8 in (50 cm)
Maximum speed, over land and water	62 mph (100 km/h)

CHAYKA-1

News of the existence of the Chakya-1 ACV passenger ferry was given in Moscow for the first time on December 13th, 1974. The vehicle is the first of a series of thirty air cushion vehicles of this type being built at the Sosnovskiy shipbuilding yard in Kirovskaya Oblast for the Black Sea Shipping Line.

The Chakya-1 will operate between resorts in the Crimea and Caucasus.

GORKOVCHANIN

The Gorkovchanin is a waterjet-propelled, 48-seat, rigid sidewall ACV, designed for water-bus services on secondary rivers with a guaranteed depth of 1 ft 8 in (0·5 m). In view of the winding nature of these rivers, the craft operates at the relatively low speed of 19-22 mph (30-35 km/h). No marked reduction of speed is necessary in water up to 1 ft 8 in (50 cm) deep.

The craft has been developed from a ten seat scale model built at the experimental yard of the Institute of Water Transport Engineers at Gorky in 1963, and the pre-production prototype was completed in September 1968. Design was undertaken by a team at the Volgobaltsudoproekt special design office.

Preliminary trials were conducted in September and October 1968, and official trials were completed on the Sura river in May and June 1969. During speed tests over a measured mile with a full complement of passengers aboard, 22·75 mph (36·6 km/h) was attained. The main engine developed 265 hp of which approximately 30 hp was used to drive the centrifugal fan.

The craft has covered the journey from Gorky to Moscow (622 miles (1,016 km)) and back in 31 and 27 running hours respectively at an average speed of approximately 22 mph (35 km/h) and has good manoeuvrability when running both ahead and astern. The craft is in production and large numbers are in service. The type is now being superseded by an improved model, the Zarnitsa.

LIFT AND PROPULSION: Integrated system powered by a 3D6H diesel engine rated at 250 hp continuous. The engine is mounted aft and drives a 3 ft 1¾ in (960 mm) diameter six-bladed centrifugal fan for lift, and a 1 ft 4½ in (410 mm) diameter single stage water-jet rotor for propulsion. Fan air is taken directly from the engine compartment. Skirts of rubberised fabric are fitted fore and aft. The bow skirt of production craft is of segmented type. Cushion pressure is 180 kg/cm².

The waterjet intake duct is located 4 in (100 mm) below the displacement water level to prevent air entry, with a consequent réduction in the navigable draught.

CONTROLS: Vanes located in the waterjet stream provide directional control. Thrust reversal is achieved by the use of waterflow deflectors.

HULL: Similar in appearance to that of the Zarya, the hull is in riveted D16 corrosion resistant aluminium alloy. The hull bottom and sides have transverse frames and the sidewalls and superstructure top longitudinal frames. Thickness of plating on sides and bottom is 1/16 in (1·5 mm) (3/32 in, (2·5 mm) in the bow section); and on the sidewalls 3/64 in (1 mm) (up to 13/64 in (5 mm) in the bow section).

The Gorkovchanin rigid sidewall waterbus

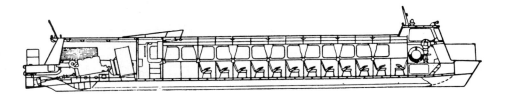

Inboard profile **of the Gorkovchanin sidewall craft, powered by a single 265 hp 2D12AL diesel**

An unidentified Soviet research ACV during trials on the Volga

Deck plates are 3/32 in (1 mm) thick and the top of the superstructure is in 1/64 in (0·8 mm) plating.

Acoustic and thermal insulation includes use of 4 in (100 mm) thick foam polystyrene sheeting.

ACCOMMODATION: Seats are provided for a crew of 2, who are accommodated in a raised wheelhouse, and 28 passengers. Access to the passenger saloon, which is equipped with airliner-type seats, is through a single door located at the bow in the centre of the wheelhouse. The craft runs bow-on to flat sloping banks to embark and disembark passengers.

SYSTEMS: Electrical: One 1·2 kW, 24 volt dc, engine-operated generator and batteries.

COMMUNICATIONS: Car radio in wheelhouse and speakers in passenger saloon.

DIMENSIONS:

Length overall	73 ft 2 in (22·30 m)
Beam overall	13 ft 3½ in (4·05 m)
Hull beam	12 ft 7⅞ in (3·85 m)
Height of hull to top of wheelhouse	10 ft 9⅞ in (3·3 m)
Height of sidewalls	1 ft 5¾ in (0·45 m)

Draught afloat	2 ft 1⅝ in (0·45 m)
Draught cushion borne	1 ft 4⅞ in (0·65 m)

WEIGHTS:
All-up weight with 48 passengers, crew and fuel   14·30 tons

PERFORMANCE:
Normal service speed
    19-22 mph (30-35 km/h)

Distance and time from full ahead to full astern   65·6 yards (60 m) and 14 seconds

NAVAL RESEARCH HOVERCRAFT

A 15-ton experimental ACV has been employed by the Soviet Navy since 1967 to assess the potential of hovercraft for naval applications and investigate controlability and manoeuvrability. Lift is provided by a single 350 hp radial aircraft engine driving a centrifugal fan and propulsion by two pylon-mounted radials of the same type driving controllable-pitch airscrews.

DIMENSIONS:

Length	70 ft 0 in (21·33 m)
Beam	30 ft 0 in (9·14 m)

WEIGHTS:
Displacement.   15 tons

PERFORMANCE:

Max speed   50 knots

LOGISTIC SUPPORT ACV
NATO Code Name: "GUS"

It is thought that twenty or more of these 27-ton logistic support craft are in service with the Soviet army and navy.

The craft is a variant of the Skate, which was designed as a 50-seat amphibious passenger ferry, but which does not appear to have been put into production.

Photographs have appeared in the Soviet press showing Gus in use as an amphibious assault landing craft for the Soviet Marine Infantry.

LIFT AND PROPULSION: Motive power is provided by three 780 hp TVD 10 marine gas-turbines mounted aft. Two drive three bladed variable and reversible-pitch propellers for thrust and the third drives an axial lift fan. Cushion air is drawn through a raised intake aft of the cabin superstructure.

CONTROLS: Craft direction is controlled by differential propeller pitch, twin aerodynamic rudders and forward and aft puff ports. Elevators provide pitch trim at cruising speed.

HULL: Hull and superstructure are in conventional corrosion-resistant marine light alloy. Basic structure comprises a central load-carrying platform which incorporates buoyancy tanks and outer sections to support the side ducts and skirt. The cabin, fuel tanks, lift fan bay engines and tail unit are mounted on the platform.

ACCOMMODATION: Up to fifty troops are accommodated in an air-conditioned cabin. Commander and navigator are seated in a raised wheelhouse.

DIMENSIONS, EXTERNAL:

Length overall, power on 67 ft 7 in (20·6 m)

Beam overall, power on 23 ft 11⅜ in (7·3 m)

WEIGHTS:

Normal operating weight   27 tons

PERFORMANCE:

Cruising speed   57·5 mph (92·5 km/h)

Normal cruising range   230 miles (370 km)

ORION

Design of the Orion, a rigid sidewall ACV with seats for 80 passengers, was approved in Moscow in the autumn of 1970. The prototype, built in Leningrad, began her trials in October 1973, and arrived at her port of registry, Kalinin, in late 1974, bearing the serial number 01.

Series production of vessels of this typw is to be undertaken at the Sosnovska Shipbuilding Yard in Kirovskaya Oblast.

According to Soviet reports most shallow rivers are accesible to the Orion, which is capable of landing and taking on passengers anywhere. The craft has been tested on a tributary of the Volga and its draft, only 11¾ in (30 cm), has proved ideal. It is also ideal for Siberia, in underdeveloped areas where the rivers are the only highways The new craft is said to equal at least the speed of hydrofoils of comparable capacity. It will service a route which will link Kalinin with towns and villages along the shores of the Soz, a secondary river. Cruising speed is 37 mph (60 km/h).

EKRANOPLAN EXPERIMENTAL

A giant Soviet experimental wing-in-ground-effect machine, with a span of 131 ft 3 in (40 m) and a length of nearly 400 ft (122 m), is undergoing tests on the Caspian sea.

This 15-ton research craft has been employed by the Soviet Navy to assess the potential of the skirted air cushion vehicle for naval applications

Above and below: Two variants of the "Gus", a growing number of which are in service with the Soviet Navy as logistics support and amphibious assault landing craft for the marine infantry. Note the raised wave commander's or observer's position above the wheelhouse on the craft below

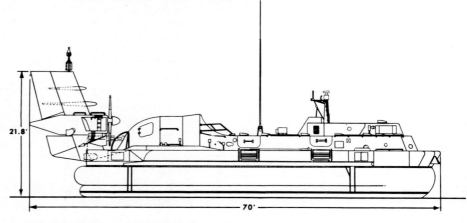

Outboard profile of the Soviet navy version of the 27-ton Gus-class multiduty ACV

Trials began in 1965 and are continuing in the company of proportionally smaller models.

The machine, which operates at heights of 23-43 ft (7-14 m) above the water, has a speed of about 300 knots. Power is supplied by eight marinised gas-turbines mounted above a stub wing forward, and two 'booster' turbines installed at the base of the dihedral tailplane aft. All ten engines are employed at take-off, when thrust has to be 2·5-35 times greater than that required to maintain cruising conditions in flight.

At take-off the thrust from the eight forward engines is deflected downwards to create additional cushion pressure beneath the wing. After take-off the jet exhaust is directed above the upper surface of the wing to create additional lift.

Western WIG specialists, commenting on an artist's impression published in the United States in January 1974, say that the wingl design does not facilitate pitch stability during its transition from ground-effect to free flight and back again. Thus the machine is probably intended to fly only in close proximity to the surface. This means it may not be able to operate safely either in extremely turbulent weather conditions or in areas where it would encounter projections higher than 50 ft (15·24 m) above the surface.

Soviet experts maintain that craft of this type should be able to negotiate sand spits, shallows, marshes, ice, snow, relatively even and gently sloping banks and low obstacles. Low bridges have been mentioned. They are also stated to be sufficiently seaworthy to operate in rough seas. Wide employment of this type of vessel is foreseen, particularly in the Soviet Navy, which has suggested that they will be invaluable in amphibious operations.

Large numbers of troops could be carried to the selected landing zones with little regard to the condition of the sea, tidal currents, underwater obstacles and minefields, none of which would constitute a hazard.

Advantages in the battle zone will include high speed manoeuvring, and a considerable reduction in the time taken to undertake a mission compared with conventional landing craft.

The capacity of the WIG craft, Ekranoplan machines as they are known in the Soviet Union, will enable them to carry the biggest

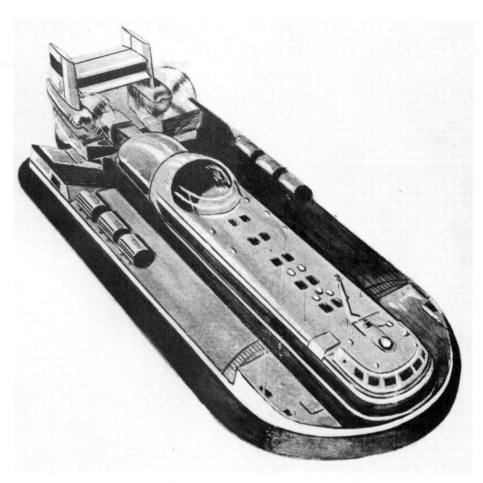

Impression of the Skate 50-seat amphibious hoverferry

items of military equipment. Another application for this type of vehicle, according to its designers, is ASW patrol, where its considerable range and endurance will prove an advantage.

References have been made in Soviet technical publications to vehicles with chords of 30-40 m (98 ft 6 in—131 ft 2 in) and speeds of 400 knots being under consideration. This suggests that research is being aimed at a number of alternative configurations including flying wings and delta wings.

EKRANOPLAN RIVER BUSES

The Ministry of the River Fleet announced in April 1972 that it planned to build craft of the Ekranoplan (WIG) type "which

will travel within several metres of a river surface at speeds of some 155 mph (250 km/h)".

It seems probable that in order to avoid navigation problems in busy river port areas these craft will be of smaller overall dimensions than the 131 ft 3 in (40 m) span machine described earlier. Low aspect ratio wings are likely to be employed and it is possible that these early production craft are of 5-6 tons displacement. A number of these machines were reported to be in experimental service in 1973.

On Moscow television in July, 1973, a programme commemorating Soviet Navy Day traced the progress of high speed water transportation and confirmed that ekranoplanes

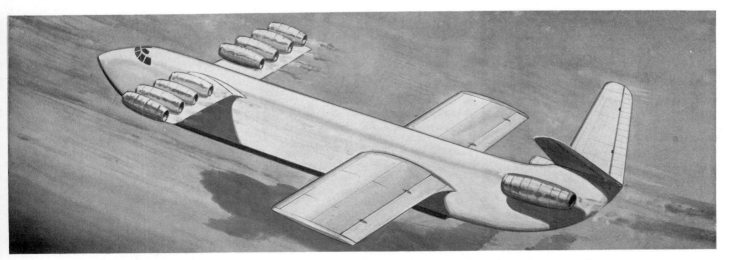

The giant Soviet ten-jet experimental Ekranoplan which is currently undergoing tests on the Caspian Sea

are being developed in the Soviet Union. The craft were described by the commentator as "ground gliders", capable of operating over land, water, snow and ice. A small machine built in Odessa in the early 1960s was shown to viewers, together with a completely new research craft of much larger size.

The craft is of catamaran configuration and carries up to forty passengers in each of the two hulls. The crew and operating controls are accommodated in a central pod carried on the forward wing.

Thrust is provided by six marinised gas-turbines mounted in pairs on the triple fins aft. Length of the craft is about 100 ft.

RADUGA

This experimental amphibious ACV was completed at the Krasnoye Sormovo shipyard in the summer of 1962 and is reported to have attained a speed of 100 km/h (62 mph) during trials.

Built originally as a peripheral jet type, it is now being used to develop control techniques, and provide amphibious experience and data on skirt design.

LIFT AND PROPULSION: The craft is powered by two 220 hp air-cooled radial engines. One, mounted amidships, drives a 5 ft 11 in (1·8 m) 12-bladed lift fan; the second, mounted on a pylon at the stern, drives a two-bladed propeller for propulsion. The fan delivers air to the cushion via a continuous peripheral skirt, the bow and side sections of which are of the fingered bag type.
HULL: Riveted aluminium construction.
ACCOMMODATION: The cabin seats five.
CONTROLS: Directional control is provided by an aerodynamic rudder operating on the propeller slipstream.
DIMENSIONS:

Length	30 ft 10 in (9·40 m)
Beam	13 ft 6 in (4·12 m)

WEIGHTS:

Operating weight	3 tons

PERFORMANCE:

Maximum speed	75 mph (120 km/h)
Endurance	3 hours

RASSVET (DAWN)

A derivative of the Zarnitsa, the Rassvet is designed for local sea routes and appears to be an offshore counterpart to the Orion sidewall ACV which is intended for river services.

Features include shallow draft, good manoevrability and seagoing qualities and simple construction.
LIFT AND PROPULSION: Total output of engines driving the lift fans is 150 hp. Propulsive thrust is thought to be supplied by twin 520 hp diesel engines, driving two waterjets.
ACCOMMODATION: Up to eighty passengers are accommodated in an air-conditioned cab in airliner-type seats. Captain and engineer are accommodated in an elevated wheelhouse, forward.
DIMENSIONS:

Length overall	86 ft 11·7 in (26·51 m)
Beam overall	23 ft 3½ in (7·10 m)
Height	29 ft 8·6 in (9·06 m)
Draft on cushion	2 ft 3·6 in (0·7 m)

WEIGHTS:

Displacement fully loaded	
	44 tons (44·7 tonnes)

PERFORMANCE:

Cruising speed	25 knots
Endurance at cruising speed	6 hours

Impression of a new catamaran-hulled Ekranoplan research craft now under development in the Soviet Union. Designed for high speed long distance passenger services along the main Soviet rivers, it rides on a dynamic air cushion formed between its wings and the supporting surface below. Seats are provided for forty passengers in each of the twin hulls. Top speed is likely to be between 150-200 knots

The Raduga experimental air cushion vehicle

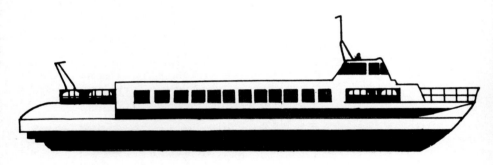

Rassvet (Dawn), a new 80-seat sidewall-type ferry for short sea routes

SORMOVICH

Launched in October 1965, the Sormovich is a 50-passenger ACV designed by Mr Valeri Schoenberg, Chief Constructor of the Krasnoye Sormovo Shipyard, with the assistance of the N. E. Zhukovski Central Institute of Aerodynamics.

In general layout, the craft represents a "scale-up" of the configuration tested with the Raduga.

In 1970 the craft was equipped with a 4 ft deep flexible skirt. Several experimental services have been operated with the craft. It is not yet in production, although orders are expected from the Ministry of the River Fleet.
TESTS: Rigorous acceptance trials included a special programme of runs between Gorky and Gorodets, Gorky and Lyskovo, Gorky and Vasilsursk, and also on the Gorky Reservoir.

These trials confirmed the craft's ability to operate across shoals, sandy spits and dykes, and run on to dry land for cargo handling and repairs.

In the air-cushion mode, her ability to maintain course up- and downwind is satisfactory, and controlled entirely by the rudders. In sidewinds, control is by combined rudder movement and differential propeller pitch. Steering during turns by rudders alone is unsatisfactory, the turning-circle diameter being 2,734-3,280 yds (2,500-3,000 m) with substantial drift. Turning is improved if the manoeuvre is accomplished by varying propeller pitch. The distance from the inception of the manoeuvre to securing a 180 deg. course then drops to 765-1,093 yards (700-1,000 m) and the diameter of the subsequent turning circle falls to 164 yards (150 m.)

Collision avoidance manoeuvres with a floating object employing rudder deflection, showed that avoidance is feasible at a distance of not under 546 yards (500 m). This distance can be reduced, however, if the manoeuvre is accomplished with variable propeller pitch. Successful undertaking of this manoeuvre depends largely on the skill of the operator.

In the air-cushion mode, while accelerating to 37-43 mph (60-70 km/h) and turning through 180 deg in both directions, stability is adequate in any of the load conditions investigated, and passengers may move about freely.

In addition to the basic flight-trial programme, tests were made to check vehicle response to sudden splash-down in case of the emergency shutdown of the main engine while underway. The splash-down tests were conducted at various speeds and drift angles, and showed that the loads imposed are not excessive and that the passengers were not alarmed. In 4 ft (1·2 m) waves the craft operates at reduced speed, but steering control and satisfactory passenger comfort are maintained.

Since late 1970, Sormovich has been in experimental service with the Volga United Steamship Company.

While operating on the Gorky-Cheboksary run in light conditions and with passengers aboard during the 1971 season, various problem areas were identified. In particular, it was found necessary to improve the reliability of the airscrew and fan drive transmission; improve the design of flexible-skirt and select a stronger material from which it can be manufactured; find ways of reducing engine noise and improve its operation and maintenance; render more effective the devices employed to reduce craft drift during high-speed turns; and raise the overall economic efficiency of the craft.

After modification, the vehicle returned to experimental service on the Gorky-Cheboksary-Gorky passenger run in 1972, with flights scheduled for daylight hours only, in winds not over 32-39 f/sec (10-12 m/sec) and at speeds not above 50 mph (80 km/h). The route selected was generally beyond that negotiable by a conventional vessel, with depths not less than 1 ft 8 in (0·5 m).

Two crew training flights and 42 passenger flights were undertaken during this particular service. Some 5,655 people were carried a total of 15,534 miles (25,000 km).

However, experimental operation of the craft during the 1972 season was a financial loss. The economic viability of Sormovich, as in the previous season, was impaired by the craft being withdrawn from service to eliminate main transmission reduction gear defects and attend to various other repair and maintenance jobs.

A passenger survey indicated that noise levels in the rear of the saloon are acceptable, but high exterior noise levels are a nuisance to shore personnel and members of the public in the vicinity.

Experimental operation of the Sormovich has indicated the possibility of its being used on inland waterways.

During the 1972/73 off-season period, measures were being taken to eliminate the shortcomings revealed, replace the reduction gear, improve flexible-skirt nozzle elements, and undertake various other modifications found necessary. There are grounds for believing that these measures will make Sormovich into a viable economic proposition.

Above and below: The Sormovich ACV passenger ferry, powered by a single 2,300 hp Ivchenko AI-20K gas turbine

LIFT AND PROPULSION: All machinery is located aft behind a sound-proof bulkhead to keep down the noise level in the passenger compartments. A single 2,300 hp Ivchenko AI-20K shaft-turbine, at the extreme stern, drives the integrated lift/propulsion system. Its output shaft passes first to a differential gearbox from which shafts extend sideways to the two four-blade ducted variable pitch propellers. A further shaft runs forward from the differential to a bevel gearbox from which a drive-shaft runs vertically upward to the 12-blade variable pitch lift-fan mounted under the intake on the rear of the roof of the vehicle. The gas-turbine operates on diesel fuel. Cushion area is 220 m².

CONTROLS: Each propeller duct contains two hydraulically-actuated rudders, working in the slipstream.

HULL: Light alloy buoyancy type, with air feeding to the cushion through a peripheral slot. There is a fore and aft stability slot on each side parallel to and about 5 ft (1·50 m) inboard of the peripheral slot.

ACCOMMODATION: The crew compartment, forward, contains two seats and is separated from the main cabin by a partition containing a door. The front two rows of seats in the cabin are only four-abreast to facilitate entry through the forward door on each side. The remaining 42 seats are six-abreast, in three-chair units with centre aisle. Aft of the cabin is a wardrobe on the port side, with a buffet opposite on the starboard side. Then comes the main entry lobby, with a passenger door on the port side and service door opposite, followed by a toilet (port) and baggage hold (starboard).

An unusual feature of the Sormovich is that it is fitted with retractable wheels which can be lowered to avoid damage to the hull when the craft operates over uneven ice or rough country. The wheels are carried on lightly-sprung legs, enabling them to ride easily over obstructions.

The craft is equipped for navigation at night.

DIMENSIONS:

Length	96 ft 0 in (29·2 m)
Beam	32 ft 9½ in (10·00 m)
Height to top of hull, on cushion (7 m)	

WEIGHTS:

Normal loaded weight	36·5 m tons

PERFORMANCE:

Max cruising speed	74·56 mph (120 km/h)

ZARNITSA

Evolved from Gorkovchanin, the Zarnitsa is a 48-50 seat waterjet-propelled rigid sidewall ferry designed to operate on shallow rivers, some less than 2ft 3in (0·70m) deep. Series production has begun and at least twenty were scheduled for delivery during 1973.

The prototype was put into trial service on the Vyatka river, in the Kirov region, in the summer of 1972, and the first production models began operating on shallow, secondary rivers later in the year. During 1973-74, Zarnitsas entered service on tributaries of the Kama, Lena and Volga. In March 1974, Zarnitsa-7 was reported to have been delivered to the Kama River Shipping Line which will employ the vessel on the upper shallow reaches of the Vishera and Chusovaya rivers.

LIFT AND PROPULSION, CONTROLS, HULL: Arrangements almost identical to those of the Gorkovchanin.

ACCOMODATION: Seats are provided for two crew members, who are accommodated in the raised wheelhouse, forward, and 48-50 passengers. Access to the passenger saloon is via a single door located at the bow in the centre of the wheelhouse. The craft runs bow-on to flat sloping banks to embark and disembark passengers.

DIMENSIONS:

Length	72 ft 3 in (22·3 m)
Beam	12 ft 8 in (3·85 m)
Skeg depth	1 ft 6 in (0·45 m)

WEIGHTS:

Light displacement	9 metric tons
All-up weight, with 48 passengers, crew and hull	15 m tons

PERFORMANCE:

Service speed	20-22 mph (33-35 km/h)

ZARYA (DAWN)

Experiments with high speed "aeroglisseur" (literally air skimmer) water buses, capable of negotiating the many shallow waterways in the Soviet Union, began in 1961.

The object was to develop a vessel for

Top: Zaryas in series production at the Moscow Shipbuilding and Ship Repair Yard. Zarya-157 was delivered by rail to Khabarovsk in the autumn of 1974. It will operate on a 200 km route in the Amur basin. *Centre:* Stern view of a Zarya in service on one of the shallow tributaries of the Volga. The vessel is powered by an 830 hp M-400 12-cylinder diesel driving a single-stage waterjet. Cruising speed is 27·96 mph (45 km/h). *Bottom:* Compared with earlier variants, this new model of the Zarya is distinguished by its trimaran bow, introduced for improved seakeeping. The new bow design allows the vessel to be routed into major waterways

services on shallow waters, with depths of only 20 in (0·5 m), at speeds of at least 21·5 knots. The prototype Zarya, called the Opytnye-1 (experimental), was put into experimental operations on the river Msta in 1963. During trials the craft attained a speed of 26 mph (42 km/h) and proved to have a turning radius of 44·76 yards (40·70 m). The craft runs bow-on to any flat, sloping bank to embark passengers.

Built with a strong aluminium alloy hull and equipped with a well protected waterjet, the craft is unharmed by floating logs, even when they are encountered at full speed.

Variants include models with a flat load deck in place of the passenger cabin superstructure amidships, and used as light freight vessels.

Zarya was designed by a team at the Central Design Office of the Ministry of the

River Fleet Gorky, working in conjunction with the Leningrad Water Transport Institute. Series production is under way at the Moscow Shipbuilding and Ship Repair Yard of the Ministry of the River Fleet.

The latest model is distinguished by its trimaran bow configuration, which gives improved performance in waves and enables the craft to be routed on major waterways.

LIFT AND PROPULSION : Power is provided by a single M-400 watercooled, supercharged, 12-cylinder V-type diesel with a normal service output of 830 hp at 1,650 rpm and a maximum output of 1,100 hp at 1,800 rpm. It has a variable-speed governor and reversing clutch and drives a single 2 ft 2½ in (0·7 m) diameter waterjet impeller.

The waterjet is of single-stage type, with a semi-submerged jet discharge. The impeller sucks in water through an intake duct which

is covered by a protective grille. The discharged water flows around two steering vanes which provide directional control. Waterjet reversal deflectors are employed to reverse the craft or to reduce the waterjet thrust when variations in speed are necessary.

A localised ram-air cushion, introduced by an upswept nose and contained on either side by shallow skegs, lifts the bow clear of the water as the craft picks up speed. The airflow also provides air/foam lubrication for the remainder of the flat-bottomed hull.

HULL : Hull and superstructure are of all-welded aluminium alloy plate construction, the constituent parts being joined by argon-shielded arc welding. Framing is of mixed type, with transverse framing at the sides and the main longitudinal elements within the hull bottom. The outside shell and bottom plating is $\frac{13}{64}$ in (5 mm) thick, except

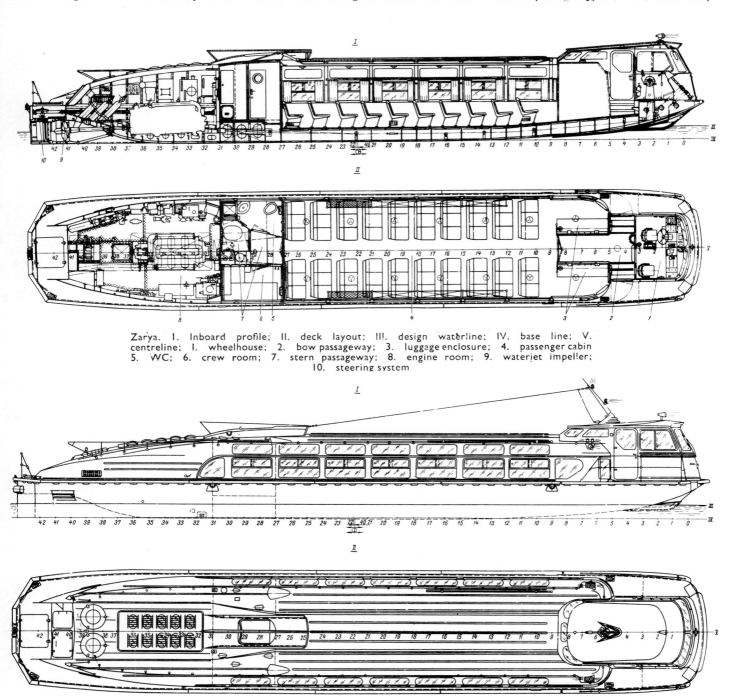

Zarya. I. Inboard profile; II. deck layout; III. design waterline; IV. base line; V. centreline; 1. wheelhouse; 2. bow passageway; 3. luggage enclosure; 4. passenger cabin 5. WC; 6. crew room; 7. stern passageway; 8. engine room; 9. waterjet impeller; 10. steering system

Outboard profile and plan of the 60-seat Zarya, waterjet-propelled river-bus for the base at the bow where it is $\frac{15}{64}$ in (6 mm) thick. The wheelhouse is in moulded glass-reinforced plastic.

ACCOMMODATION: Three transverse bulk-heads divide the hull into four compartments. Behind the forepeak and wheelhouse is the passenger cabin, and aft of this is a compartment housing the crew room, WC and diesel fuel tank. Aft of this is the engine and steering compartment. The raised wheelhouse, located at the bow, gives 360 deg. visibility. Installed in the passenger cabin in the 60-seat version, are twenty rows of seats, three abreast, ten rows each side of a centre aisle. Five additional seats are installed in short range models and 15 standing passengers can be accommodated. Life jackets for passengers are stowed in lockers in the baggage compartment and under seats at the rear of the cabin.

The crew off-duty room contains a sofa, table, wall-mounted cupboard, folding stool and a mirror. The WC contains a wash basin, a bowel, mirror and soap tray.

The wheelhouse has rotating seats for the captain and engineer, two sun visors and there are two windscreen wipers.

Both the passenger cabin and wheelhouse are heated by warm air produced by hot water from the closed circuit main engine cooling system. Warm air is admitted into the passenger cabin and wheelhouse through a perforated chamber at the bulkhead. The engine room is heated by two 1·2 kW electric heaters and the crew room by a 0·6 kW electric heater. Windows of the wheelhouse and the wheelhouse itself are heated by a 330 kW electric heater.

CONTROLS: Irrespective of load, the radius of turn is between 98-164 ft (30-50 m) with the rudder put hard over at an angle of 30 degrees. This can be decreased if necessary by either throttling down the engine or closing the valves of the reversing system. At slow speed the craft is capable of pinwheeling. The time required to stop the vessel is 8-10 seconds, the coasting distance being between 164-196 ft (50-60 m). Manoeuvrability of the craft is such that it is able to navigate small winding rivers with waterways of 39-49 ft (12-15 m) wide with the radii of windings varying between 131-229 ft (40-70 m) without slowing down.

The vessel can easily pull into shore without landing facilities, providing the river bed slope is no steeper than 3 degrees. The time required for pulling in, embarking passengers, then leaving, averages 1·5 minutes. Steps to facilitate access are located at the bow, port and starboard, and lowered by a control in the wheelhouse.

SYSTEMS, ELECTRICAL: Main engine driven 1 kW generator, rated at 27·5 V, charges the storage batteries and meets the demands of 24 V circuits while the vessel is underway. Four lead-acid batteries to supply 24 V for monitoring and alarm circuitry and starting the main engine. Equipment supplied for charging the storage batteries from a shore-based 220 V cource.

FIRE-FIGHTING: Two tanks containing fire-extinguishing compound and hoses for fighting an outbreak in the engine room. System can be brought into operation either from the engine room or from the wheelhouse. Engine room is also provided with two portable carbon dioxide fire extinguishers. Another of the same type is provided in the

The Zarnitsa, a derivative of the Gorkovchanin, is now in series production and at least twenty of this type were scheduled for delivery during 1973

The Skat on display in Moscow

wheelhouse and two foam fire extinguishers are standard equipment in the main cabin.

FUEL: Craft is refuelled through a filling hose and a neck on the port side of the superstructure. Fuel is fed to the main engine from a service tank with a capacity of 4·13 m³, sufficient to enable a vessel to cruise for 8 hours without refuelling. In addition, there is a 400 l storage tank which contains a 2 hour reserve to be used in an emergency. The same tank supplies fuel to a water heater.

COMPRESSED AIR: Starting system for main engines comprising three 45 ll air-cylinders, valves (safety, shut-off, pressure reducing and starting) and piping. Pressure 150-75 kgf/cm². Two cylinders in operation, one standby.

DIMENSIONS:

Length	72 ft 3¼ in (22·1 m)
Beam	12 ft 10¾ in (3·93 m)
Moulded depth	3 ft 11½ in (1·2 m)
Draft	1 ft 5¾ in (0·45 m)

WEIGHTS:

Weight empty	16·68 tonnes
Weight with 60 passengers, and stores for 8 hour trip	24·78 tonnes

PERFORMANCE:

Speed (in channel of 0·8 m depth)
27·96 mph (45 km/h)

Range—suitable for service distances of 93 miles (150 km) and above

Endurance at cruising speed   8 hours

UFA AVIATION INSTITUTE

An experimental circular planform ACV, the Skat, has been designed and built by students of the UFA Aviation Institute. The vehicle was displayed in 1970 in Moscow at the USSR National Economy Achievements Exhibition.

OIIMF (ODESSA ENGINEERING INSTITUTE OF THE MERCHANT FLEET)
OIIMF-2

This is one of a number of experimental wing-in-ground-effect machines built at the institute by a group of students under the direction of Y. Budnitskiy.

The craft is a single-seater with an all-up weight of 926-992 lb (420-450 kg) and a payload of 176-220 lb (80-100 kg). The wings, floats and hull are of semimonocoque construction and built in duralumin.

Power is supplied by two 18 hp aircooled motorcycle engines driving two 3 ft 11 in (1·2 m) diameter two-bladed airscrews.

Special flaps have been designed to improve the starting characteristics of the craft by creating a static air cushion through the utilisation of the airscrew slipstream. The flaps are located between the wings and are secured by special shock absorption cables in the operating position at the moment of starting the craft. As speed increases so the flaps hinge upwards automatically.

Tests indicate that the flaps noticeably decrease the leakage of air from the high pressure area under the aft wing, thus increasing wing lift and unloading the floats.

A vertical tail assembly and flap are provided for steering and stabilisation.

The OIIMF-2 single-seat wing-in-ground effect research craft.

The flap on the aft wing is designed to balance the craft during starting and control it in pitch. The leading wing barely generates any lift at low speeds, therefore a pitching moment, obtained by deflecting the flap upwards, must be created during the initial period of its run in order to balance the craft. As speed increases and the forward wing comes into operation, the centre of pressure shifts forward, which requires a diving moment (deflection of the flap downward) in order to balance the craft.

Static stability in pitch is provided by constant contact of the aft section of the floats with the water surface and the cor-responding stabilising effect of the forward wing.

The vehicle has good manoeuvrability, and the turning diameter, at a speed of 20 mph is approximately 32 ft.

DIMENSIONS:

Length overall	16 ft 5 in (5·0 m)
Hull beam	10 ft 6 in (3·2 m)
Wing span	9 ft 2¼ in (2·8 m)
Chord, forward lower wing	3 ft 4 in (1 m)
Chord, upper wing	9 ft 10 in (3 m)

ACV OPERATORS

THE AMERICAS
NORTH AMERICA AND CANADA

CANADA

CANADIAN COAST GUARD HOVERCRAFT UNIT

HEADQUARTERS:

Canadian Coast Guard, Canadian Marine Transportation Administration, Ministry of Transport, Transport Canada Building, Ottawa, K1A 0N7, Ontario

UNIT ADDRESSES:

Canadian Coast Guard Hovercraft Unit, P.O. Box 68, Vancouver A.M.F., B.C., Canada

TELEPHONE:

604-273-2383

Canadian Hovercraft Unit, Ministry of Transport, P.O. Box 310, Parry Sound, Ontario P2A 2X4, Canada

TELEPHONE:

705 746-2196

Capt. W. J. H. Stuart, Director, Canadian Coast Guard Marine Operations, MoT

ADMINISTRATION:

Mr. H. Buchanan, Regional Director Marine Services (Western)

Mr. John McGrath, OIC, CCG Hovercraft Unit

The Canadian Coast Guard Hovercraft Unit in Vancouver was formed on August 5th 1968, to evaluate the use of hovercraft in search and rescue and other Coast Guard duties.

OPERATIONS:

The normal area of patrol is the Straits of Georgia and Gulf Islands—an area of approximately 500 square miles. The unit is often called upon outside this area on search and rescue missions.

The average patrol distance is 80 n.m.

Since April 1st, 1969, The Unit has carried out well over 400 S.A.R. missions, directly involving some 478 persons. These included marine, aircraft distress and mercy missions.

Other operations included the checking, servicing and repairing of marine navigational aids within the patrol area; aircraft accident inspection; water pollution investigation; carriage of Steamship Inspectors for spot safety checks of tugs; working with police departments; excercises with the Royal Canadian Navy; training and familiarisation of selected Government personnel, and experimental work with other Government agencies.

In January 1974 the Canadian Coast Guard took delivery of a refurbished Voyageur 002, which it is operating from the CCG Base, Parry Sound, Georgian Bay, Lake Huron. The craft is undergoing a one-year trial in the aids to navigation (A to N) and search and rescue (SAR) roles. In early ice-breaking trials passages were cleared in 15 in thick ice. The crew assigned to the craft includes two operators, one of whom serves as first officer, two engineer technicians and three deck-hands. During the winter of 1974-75, the Voyageur proved that it could break ice to a thickness of 20 in. It was also successful in breaking river ice jams of much greater thickness.

EQUIPMENT: One SR.N5, registration CH-CCG, modified to Coast Guard requirements, Equipment includes 2 × 25 man inflatable liferafts, 2 × 100 gal auxiliary fuel tanks (extending endurance to 7 hours at max power), stretchers, first aid kit, fire fighting equipment, towing gear and other S.A.R. equipment.

One Bell Aerospace Voyageur, registration CH-CGA.

AGENCE MARITIME INC

HEAD OFFICE:

276 St James Street, Montreal, Quebec

TELEPHONE:

(514) 842-2791

This organisation, a division of Logistec, is operating Voyageur 004 on a community service route linking the Quebec communities of St. Joseph de la Rive with the St. Lawrence River island, Ile aux Coudres. The operation is being sponsored by the Quebec Ministry of Transport, Marine Branch, and began on May 15th, 1975. Operations are from 8 a.m. to 5 p.m. on weekdays, and trucks, school buses and other vehicles are being carried. The 2 mile journey takes less than 5 minutes with the Voyageur, compared with 25 minutes by conventional ferry.

Trucks, school buses and other vehicles are carried by Voyageur 004 on a scheduled 8 a.m. to 5 p.m. daily service operated by Agence Maritime Inc, between St. Joseph de la Rive and the St. Lawrence River Island, Ile aux Coudres

NORTHERN TRANSPORTATION COMPANY LIMITED

OPERATIONS OFFICE:

9945-108 Street; Edmonton, Alberta T5K 2G9

TELEPHONE:

(403) 423-9201

TELEX:

037-2480

DIRECTORS:

W. M. Gilchrist (President)

L. R. Montpetit (Executive Vice President)

W. B. Hunter (Vice-President, Operations)

P. L. P. Macdonnell

H. Basil Robinson

Murray Watts

J. H. Parker

A. B. Caywood

CH-NTB, a flat-deck version of the SR.N5, is employed by Northern Transportation Company in the MacKenzie Delta and Beaufort Sea areas in support of oil industry activities.

DIRECTOR OF AIR CUSHION VEHICLE OPER-
ATIONS:
Bert W. Mead

Northern Transportation Company Limited (NTCL) is a wholly-owned subsidiary of Eldorado Nuclear Limited and was formed in 1931. It is Canada's largest Western Arctic marine transportation operator—and serves approximately 4,800 miles of water routes throughout the Mackenzie River Basin and the Western Arctic. The fleet includes three ocean-going ships, 28 diesel tugs, 163 all steel dual purpose barges with varied capacities up to 1,500 tons, 4 thruster barges and the fleet has a reported capability of some 560,000 tons of cargo in any one season.

To supplement its Marine, Trucking and Aviation Divisions, NTCL operates two BHC SR.N6 vehicles in the McKenzie Delta and Beaufort Sea area in support of oil industry activities.

One craft, CH-NTA, is a standard passenger version and at the end of the 1974 season had completed in excess of 25,000 miles, all within the Arctic circle. The second machine, CH-NTB, has been modified to enable rapid conversion from passenger to flat-deck configuration.

CH-NTA, a standard passenger version of the SR.N5 belonging to Northern Transportation, has completed 25,000 miles of operation within the Arctic circle.

In flat-deck configuration, a standard payload is approximately 10,000 pounds, plus four passengers. Its passenger capacity when not converted is 26. Both machines have VHF, AM, VHF FM, HFSSB, emergency locators, radio compass and radio telephone. A wide variety of support equipment necessitated by the extreme cold is fitted, including dual cabin heating systems.

ALYESKA PIPELINE SERVICE CO

Operates two 160-ton payload hover transporters, "Yukon Princess 1" and "Yukon Princess 2" across the River Yukon.

These hover-transporters carry a substantial number of heavy vehicles as well as equipment and supplies across the river, 20 hours a day, throughout the year. The trans- porters are winched across the Yukon and can be unloaded and re-loaded in thirty minutes employing the roll-on, roll-off system.

UNITED STATES

BELL AEROSPACE COMPANY

In 1974-5, Bell Aerospace Company continued operational trials of its 100-ton surface effect ship test craft in the Gulf of Mexico and St. Andrew Bay at Panama City, Florida. The craft, designed and constructed for the US Navy's Surface Effect Ship Project Office, underwent initial testing on Louisiana's Lake Pontchartrain, near New Orleans, until June of 1973. Bell established test operations at Panama City in 1973, where the SES-100B will continue to be utilised extensively to provide technical information to support advanced development efforts for the 2,000-ton surface effect ship 2KSES.

UNITED STATES ARMY

In 1972, a Bell SK-5 Model 7255 of the US Army's Cold Region Research Laboratory, Houghton, Michigan, was operated in Alaska for extended tests over varying arctic terrain and waterways. In early 1973, the SK-5 was shipped to the US Army's Weapons Command, St. Louis, Missouri, for continued operations.

SCIENCE APPLICATIONS, INC.

HEAD OFFICE:
1651 Old Meadow Road, McLean, Virginia 22101, USA
TELEPHONE:
(703) 790-5900

Science Applications, Inc. is a high tech- nology research and development company dedicated to the practical introduction of advanced technology to fulfill new and important national and international requirements. In keeping with this concept, Science Applications, Inc. in 1974 developed the concept for and sponsored the utilisation of a 'Voyageur' ACV to provide essential heavy load transportation services in support of oil exploration and geophysical activities in Northern Alaska. The company continues to hold the Jones Act waiver which permits operation of the craft in Alaska until early 1976.

SOUTH AMERICA

BOLIVIA
AMERICAN TRADERS INC.

HEAD OFFICE:
La Paz

American Traders Inc operates a specially furnished version of the sidewall HM.2 Mk III hovercraft on Lake Titicaca, between Tiquina Huatajata in Bolivia and Puno, Peru. Lake Titicaca is at an altitude of over 12,500 ft above sea level. Craft operated: HM.2-324.

BRAZIL
COMPANHIA DE NAVAGACAO BAHIANA

ADDRESS:
Po Box 1406, Av. Franca, Salvador, Bahia.
A Hovermarine HM. 2 sidewall hovercraft operates out of Salvador (Bahia) to the site of a large oil refinery on the opposite side of the bay. During off-peak hours the craft operates sightseeing tours.

Craft operated; HM.2 MkIII 306 "Hover-marine One"
Route(s): Commuter service out of Salvador and routes in Todos os Santos Bay.

SERVICOS DE TRANSPORTES DA BAIXA DA GUANABARA (STBG)

This company operates three HM2 Mk III sidewall hovercraft on a 3 n. mile route bet- ween communities and business areas in the Bay of Guanabara, Rio de Janeiro.
Craft employed:

HM2 321 "Gavea"
HM2 322 "Gragoata"
HM2 323 "Guarativa"

AFRICA

AFRICA:
ZAIRE
SOCIETE MINIERE DE BAKWANGA
Mbujimayi
R. C. Lulubourg 10,424
Craft operated: CC.7 002

NIGERIA
PIPELINE CONTRACTORS INCORPORATED
Craft operated: Sealand SH.2 007 (The operator of this craft is an oil exploration company and the craft will assist in this activities.)

ASIA

BRUNEI:
GOVERNMENT OF BRUNEI
Craft operated: SR.N5 019 (AMBD 110)
Reports suggest that this craft may not be in an operational state.

HONG KONG
HONG KONG AND YAUMATI FERRY CO.
This company, which is believed to be the biggest passenger ferry operator in the world, operates a fleet of four HM.2 Mk III sidewall hovercraft on routes within the Crown Colony of Hong Kong, including the central/Tsun Wan route.
Craft operated: HM.2-326 (HYF-101)
327 (HYF-102)
328 (HYF-103)
329 (HYF-104)

PAKISTAN
The Pakistan Coast Guard authority is understood to have purchased two SH-2 five or six seat craft for patrol and interception duties.
Craft employed: SH.2 009, SH.2 010

THAILAND:
Thai Customs Authority
Klong Toly
Bangkok
Craft operated: MV-PP1 001 "Customs Hovercraft 1"

TOUR ROYALE
Bangkok, Thailand
This company intends operating a fleet of at least three HM.2 hovercraft on routes in

Bangkok and other locations.

INDIA:
City and Industrial Development Corp of Maharashtra Ltd
Nirmal
2nd Floor
Nariman Point
Bombay 40001
Telephone: 294515 (9 lines)
Telegrams: CITWIN
Executive: M. N. Palwankar, Manager, Town Services
Craft operated: HM.2 Mk III 214 "Jalpriya"
Route(s): Between Greater Bombay and New Bombay linking Appollo Bunder and Ferry Wharf with Uran and Elephanta.

AUSTRALASIA

AUSTRALIA
DOLPHIN FERRIES
Sydney
Formed in August 1973, this company operates a single HM2 Mk III craft on regular commuter and tourist services from Circular Quay in Sydney Harbour and began operations in November of that year. Managing director of the firm is Mr Bjarne J. Halvorsen.
Craft employed: HM2 319 "Blue Dolphin".

MUNDOO PASTORAL COMPANY
ADDRESS:
Mundoo Island, South Australia
A Hovergem G-6 agricultural ACV is

employed by this company for carrying personnel, cattle and equipment to various islands in the Mundoo group.

THE NATIONAL PARKS COMMISSION
ADDRESS:
Flinders House,
17 Flinders Street,
Adelaide, S. Australia 5000
The Commission employs a Taylorcraft Skimmer for patrol and supervisory work in the Coorong National Park. The Coorong is a large shallow lake within the park. It is about 90 miles long by ½-1 mile wide and connects with the Murray River and the sea.

Illegal poaching of water fowl is a problem and the Skimair is employed to overcome this. Patrols are undertaken about twice a week and total about 7-8 operating hours. The craft operates at up to 70 miles from base.

NEW ZEALAND:
DEPARTMENT OF CIVIL AVIATION
The New Zealand Department of Civil Aviation is operating one SR.N6 Winchester for crash rescue services at Mangere Airport, Aukland.
Craft operated: SN.N6 014 "Whakatopa"

EUROPE & MEDITERRANEAN

ITALY:
ITAL HOVER SpA
Zaltere 66
Venice
Craft operated: HM.2 Mk III 302 "Mare 3"
Route(s): Venice-Sattomarina-Grado

ITALIAN INTERFORCE UNIT
Ancona
Craft operated: SR.N6 036 (HC 9801)
PORTUGAL:
SOCIEDADE TURISTICA PONTA DO ADOXE SARL
Avenida Casal Ribeiro 46-6·
Lisbon
Craft operated: HM2. Mk III 301 "Torralta" HM.2 Mk III 308 "Soltroia" HM.2 Mk III 316 "Troiamar" HM.2 Mk III 318 "Troiano"
Route(s): Setubal-Troia/Sesimbra
GREECE:
HELLENIC HOVERCRAFT LINES ("HOVERLINES")
Piraeus

MANAGING DIRECTOR:
Mr. A. N. Vomvoyiannis
Craft operated: HM.2 Mk III 304 "Natouro 2" HM.2 Mk III 307 "Natouro 1"
Route(s): Piraeus-Hydra-Spetsai-Porto Heli
NORWAY:
De Bla Omnibusser A/S
Stromsveien 196
Oslo 6
DIRECTOR:
Mr Dahlseide
Craft operated: HM.2 Mk III 317 "Fjordbuss 1"
Route(s): Oslo-Horten, with calls at Drobak, Filtvet and Tofte
BELGIUM:
Ministry of Works
Antwerp
Craft operated:
HM.2 Mk III 315 "Kallo" (Employed as River Scheldt survey craft).
HOVERCROSS LTD
HEAD OFFICE:

St. Helier, Jersey, C.I.
Hovercross Ltd operates between Gorey, Jersey, and Carteret, France, with HM.2-012 on charter from International Hoverservices Ltd, of Southampton. The service began in July 1975 and it is hoped that services will be maintained until September each year. Other C.I. services are also undertaken.
FRANCE:
LANGUEDOC-ROUSILLON REGIONAL DEVELOPMENT BOARD
Montpellier & Perpignan
Craft operated: 2 × N.102 craft
FRENCH NAVY
Toulon
Craft operated: 2 × N.102
GIRONDE PORT AUTHORITY
Bordeaux
Craft operated: N.300 001 and N.300 002
Route(s): Blaye-Lamarque
ISRAEL
ISRAELI NAVY
The Israeli Navy is understood to have

taken delivery of two SH-2 Mk 2 six seater hovercraft for use as support craft. A further two SH.2s of the Mk 5 version, with increased payload capacity are on order.

SOVIET UNION:
MINISTRY OF THE RIVER FLEET

The 50 seat Sormovich ACV has been operating experimental services on the Volga and Oka rivers and a derivative was expected to go into production in 1975. The most widely used commercial ACV at present is the 48-50 seat Zarnitsa sidewall craft. This is being followed into production by the enlarged, 80-seat Orion and the Rassvet (Dawn). The former is intended for services on inland waterways, the latter for local sea routes. Another new ACV passenger ferry is the Chaika, thirty of which are to be built at Sosnovska for the Black Sea Shipping Line.

Well over one hundred Zarya air-lubricated hull craft have been completed and many of these are in service on shallow rivers in the eastern areas of the Soviet Union. Wing-in-ground effect machines are being developed for high-speed ferry services along the main rivers. These are described as being capable of travelling within several metres of river surface at speeds of some 155 mph (250 km/h).

SOVIET NAVY

Several experimental ACVs are being evaluated by the Soviet Navy, and a military version of the Skate is now in limited service with the Soviet naval infantry as a high speed logistics transport. Largest craft in service is the 200-ton "Aist", similar in many respects to the SR.N4 Mountbatten and employed to carry tanks and mechanised infantry.

SOVIET ARMY

A military version of the Skate 50-seat fast ferry is in limited service with the Soviet Army.

UNITED KINGDOM

BRITISH RAIL HOVERCRAFT LIMITED
(Seaspeed Hovercraft)

HEAD OFFICE:
 Royal London House, 22/25 Finsbury Square, London EC2P 2BQ
TELEPHONE:
 01-628-3050
TELEX:
 883339

DOVER ROUTE HEADQUARTERS
 Seaspeed Hoverport, Eastern Docks, Dover
TELEPHONE:
 Dover (0304) 203574
TELEX:
 965079
RESERVATIONS:
 7 Cambridge Terrace, Dover
TELEPHONE:
 01-606 3681
TELEX:
 96158

SOLENT ROUTE HEADQUARTERS
 Marine Court, The Parade, Cowes, I.O.W.
TELEPHONE:
 Cowes (098 382) 2303
TELEX:
 86252

DIRECTORS:
 D. McKenna, CBE, Chairman
 J. M. Lefeaux, Managing Director
 Lord Black of Barrow-in-Furness
 G. R. Hill
 J. Posner

SENIOR EXECUTIVES:
 P. A. Yerbury, Chief Engineer
 A. Tame, Commercial and Planning Manager
 A. H. Thorne, Route Manager, Dover Strait
 R. B. W. Gladstone, Route Manager, Solent

British Rail Hovercraft Ltd, a wholly-owned subsidiary of British Railways Board, was formed in March 1966 and launched its first commercial service in July, 1966, between Southampton and Cowes. The cross-channel service for passengers and cars between specially constructed hovercraft terminals at Dover and Boulogne began in August, 1968 using an SR.N4 'The Princess Margaret'. A year later the service was augmented by the introduction of a sister craft 'The Princess Anne' and in October 1970 a service was initiated between Dover and Calais.

In association with British Rail and French Railways the company operates a through

The Princess Margaret, one of two SR.N4 hovercraft operated by British Rail Hovercraft Ltd on its Seaspeed cross-channel routes, Dover-Boulogne and Dover-Calais.

The Princess Anne, sister craft to the Princess Margaret, arriving in front of the Seaspeed terminal building at Boulogne. In the foreground is one of the fast "Autotrains" which enable the company to operate a through London/Paris service taking about 6 hours.

London/Paris service taking about 6 hours, using special trains operating from a platform alongside the Boulogne hovercraft terminal. At Calais a coach connection with Ostend and Brussels is provided, enabling the through London/Brussels service to be performed by rail/hovercraft/coach in 7 hours.

A further coach service from Calais to Lille was introduced in May 1974, giving a London/Lille journey time of 5½ hours.

Seaspeed's plans for stretching their two SR.N4 Mark 1 craft by 47 ft were shelved in November 1973 because of the economic situation at that time.

However, following H.M. Government's decision in January 1975 to abandon the Channel Tunnel project, Seaspeed have revived their investment plans and a joint British Rail Hovercraft Ltd/British Hovercraft Corporation design for a 55 ft 'stretch' to their two Mk 1 craft is being actively considered. Application for investment authority was being made at the time of going to press.

The stretched craft design will be designated SR.N4 Mk III and it will involve lengthening the craft to 185 ft. This modification will increase the vehicle capacity to a maximum of 55 cars and 420 passengers. The four marine Proteus gas-turbines are to be uprated to 3,800 shp each and each will drive a propeller/fan unit with a 21 ft (6·40 m) diameter propeller. The additional power will ensure that the performance of the current craft would be maintained.

Craft motion will be considerably less than that experienced on the standard SR.N4 and for similar comfort levels the larger craft will be capable of operating in waves up to 2 ft (0·61 m) higher than the present craft.

REPRESENTATION OVERSEAS:

SNCF, Armement Naval, 3 Rue Ambroise Paré 75001, Paris, France

DEPARTMENT OF TRADE AND INDUSTRY (DTI).

CRAFT OPERATED:

CC.7 001 (XW249)

HM.2 Mk III 310 (XW555)

HD.2 001—Held by National Physical Laboratory for R & D purposes.

HOVERLLOYD LIMITED

ADDRESS:

International Hoverport, Sandwich Road, Ramsgate, Kent

TELEPHONE:

Thanet (0843) 54881/54761 499-9481

TELEX:

96323

LONDON OFFICE:

Board of Chief Executive, Sales Administration, 49 Charles Street, London W1X 8AE

TELEPHONE:

01-493 5525

TELEX:

262374

DIRECTORS:

Ingemar Blennow (Swedish) Chairman

James A. Hodgson, Deputy Chairman and Managing Director

James Clement

Hans Pihlo (Swedish)

Hoverlloyd was formed by two shipping companies, Swedish Lloyd and Swedish American Line (now both members of the Brostrom group) to operate a cross-Channel car and passenger ferry service between Ramsgate and Calais. The company operates three BHC SR.N4 Mk. II widened Mountbattens.

The crossing between Ramsgate and Calais takes 40 minutes and there are up to twenty return trips a day in summer and a minimum of four a day in winter. On May 1st, 1969, the company opened coach/hovercraft/coach services between London and Paris. This service takes eight hours and a single fare costs £9·00. There are up to five daily departures during summer and two during winter.

On April 1st 1974, Hoverlloyd opened coach/hovercraft/coach services between London/Kortrijk and Brussels. The service takes seven hours to Brussels and a single fare to either destination costs £8·50. There are two daily services in the summer peak and a daily departure is maintained year-round.

Vehicles loading at Dover

Sea Hawk, one of the two lengthened SR.N6s employed by British Rail Hovercraft Ltd on the Southampton-Cowes route

Hoverlloyd's three SR N4's, operating on the Pegwell Bay (Ramsgate)/Calais route carried 828,000 passengers and 120,000 vehicles across the English Channel in 1974. The craft above converted from a standard SR.N4, carries 280 passengers and 37 vehicles, compared with 254 passengers and 30 vehicles on the standard craft. This increase in capacity was achieved by removing the two inner passenger cabins to increase the car deck area and by widening the outer passenger cabins

Passengers are able to buy tickets from travel agents, or by making a booking direct from Hoverlloyd or at the Hoverport Those travelling with a car pay only for their car, according to its length. The car charge covers the driver and up to four passengers. For vehicles there are three tariffs; 'A', 'B' and 'C'. 'A' tariff is more expensive and is applied in peak hours during summer, in either direction, according to a detailed traffic analysis. 'B' tariff is cheaper and accounts for the balance of the departures listed for the summer. The 'C' tariff applies until May (except over Christmas when tariff 'B' applies) and this represents reductions of up to 30% on normal vehicle fares. The tariffs have been designed to encourage

a balance in the origin of cross-channel traffic, and to spread the daily peaks of traffic.

The company's hoverport covers 12½ acres below the cliffs at the north end of Pegwell Bay, Ramsgate. The site is raised 8 ft above the level of the beach, so that operations are not affected by tides. It consists of a group of long low buildings running parallel to the cliffs. Between the buildings and the cliffs is a car park and the car reception area which is joined to the main Ramsgate-Sandwich road by an access road built up the cliff face.

In front of the building is a large square concrete apron with a semi-circular ramp extending at one end. The SR.N4 makes the most convenient approach, parks on the apron in front of the building while it loads and unloads, then departs from the most suitable point.

These buildings contain the main passenger and car terminal area which includes the inspection halls for customs and immigration, duty free shops, cafe, bar, restaurant, banks and other passenger facilities. Next to this area are the administrative offices.
Craft operated:
"Swift" (SR.N4 002) registration GH 2004
"Sure" (SR.N4 003) registration GH 2005
"Sir Christopher" (SR.N4 005) registration GH 2008

HOVERWORK LIMITED
(Wholly owned subsidiary of Hovertravel Limited)

HEAD OFFICE:
12 Lind Street, Ryde, Isle of Wight
TELEPHONE:
Ryde 5181
TELEX:
86513
CABLE:
Hoverwork Ryde
DIRECTORS:
D. R. Robertson (Chairman)
C. D. J. Bland (Managing Director)
E. W. H. Gifford
A. C. Smith
R. G. Clarke

Hoverwork Limited is a subsidiary of Hovertravel Limited and was formed in 1966. The company provides crew training and charter facilities for all available types of ACVs, thus bridging the gap between the operators and manufacturers.

The company has trained over 45 hovercraft captains and has received some 40 charter contracts, including film sequences and the operation of the SRN6 craft for mineral surveys all over the world. The company operated the hovercraft passenger service during Expo'67 at Montreal and a service at the 1970 Algiers Exposition.

Hoverwork is the largest international operator of hovercraft, having access to Hovertravel's three 38 seater SR.N6s as well as their own five ton SR.N5 GH-2009 flat deck-freighter and a multi-purpose SR.N5 GH-2041. Hoverwork has undertaken operations in areas from the Arctic to the equator. These have included logistics operations in the northern part of Svalbard and in equatorial parts of South America. To date Hoverwork has operated in the following countries: Canada, South America, Mexico, Brunei, Holland, Bahrain, Kuwait, The Trucial States, Saudi Arabia, Algeria, Tunisia, English North Sea, Spitsbergen and Australia.

During 1975, the company conducted operations in Saudi Arabia, the Netherlands, United Kingdom, Australia, Iran and Canada, in conjunction with Northern Transportation Company Ltd.

Typical of the company's activities is the logistic support being provided by SR.N5 GH-2041 during the construction of a trial reservoir on the inter-tidal south eastern foreshore of The Wash.

Shaped like a gigantic doughnut, the reservoir, when completed this September, will form the basis of 'The Wash Feasibility Study'. This study has been commissioned by the Central Water Planning Unit and if successful could lead to the construction of a series of reservoirs around the estuaries

Above and below: Hoverwork's SR.N5 GH-2041, which has been on call 24 hours a day to carry personnel, spares and provisions to the trial reservoir site on the south-eastern foreshore of the Wash

of the rivers Nene and Ouse.

All construction work is being carried out by Van Oord Werkendam, a subsidiary company of Ham Dredging Limited. The consultant engineers for the study are Binney and Partners.

The finished reservoir will consist of some 100,000 tons of Belgian granite and 410,000 cubic metres of sand. All materials are supplied by sea using conventional tugs, barges and floating cranes. Personnel, spares and provisions are brought out to the site by hovercraft which operates over the type of marginal terrain that is ideally suited for ACV operations. Between the site and the base at Gedney Drove End lie 1¼ miles of marsh, mud flats, sand banks all of which are criss-crossed with gulleys and riverlets.

Commenting on his first experience of working with a hovercraft, Jos Van Kyk, Assistant Project Engineer said: "We weren't quite sure just what the capabilities and reliability of the craft were at first, now we would be lost without it".

Crewed by Hoverwork personnel the craft is available 24 hours a day, this usually means a 6.a.m. to 9 p.m. day with the odd night-time emergency.

Work on the feasibility study, which began on 1st March, 1975, is expected to be completed towards the end of September 1975

HOVERTRAVEL LIMITED
HEAD OFFICE:
12 Lind Street, Ryde, Isle of Wight
TELEPHONE:
Ryde 5181 (STD 0983)
TELEX:
86513-Hoverwork
CABLE
Hovertravel, Ryde
TERMINAL OFFICES
Quay Road, Ryde, Isle of Wight (Tel. 3051)
Clarence Pier, Southsea (Tel. 29988)
DIRECTORS:
D. R. Robertson (Chairman)
C. D. J. Bland (Chief Executive and Managing Director)
E. W. H. Gifford
D. E. Webb
SENIOR EXECUTIVES:
G. Palin (Company Secretary)
R. G. Clarke (General Manager)

Hovertravel Limited, formed in 1965, is a £120,000 company whose main activity has been the operation of two SR.N6 Winchester class hovercraft in the Solent, primarily between Ryde and Southsea. The distance is just over four miles and the frequency varies between one return trip per hour in the winter and five return trips per hour in the summer.

Approximately 400,000 passengers are

carried per year, together with fifty tons of freight. The service has gained in popularity and the total number of passengers carried by July 1974 was well over 3 million. The maximum number of passengers carried in one day (using both hovercraft) was over 4,000.

Another craft which had been built at Bembridge, where Hovertravel has extensive workshop facilities, came into service on August 8th 1974. This was the SR.N6 055 GH2035—a 58-seat SR.N6 1S.

The combined fleet operated by Hovertravel and Hoverwork, which during 1975 completed an estimated 6,000 hours of operation, includes:-

1 SR.N6 1S GH2035
3 SR.N6s GH2010, 2012, 2013
1 SR.N6 Flat Deck GH2011
2 SR.N5s with freight decks GH2009 and GH2041

INTERNATIONAL HOVERSERVICES LIMITED

HEAD OFFICE:
138 Rownhams Lane, North Baddesley, Southampton SO5 9LT
TELEPHONE:
0421 23 2588

DIRECTORS:
Captain A. S. Hands MRIN, Chairman and Joint Managing Director
Lieut. Comdr. M. D. Dawson, RN MNI, Secretary and Joint Managing Director
L. R. Colquhoun, DFC, GM, DFM

International Hoverservices Limited was formed in January 1969 to operate hovercraft and the first service between Bournemouth and Swanage was opened in July 1970. Since then the company has operated various scheduled and charter services in the Solent and Poole Bay areas, among which is a daily industrial commuter service for Vosper Thornycroft Limited between Cowes, Isle of Wight and their shipyard in Southampton.

The Company provides staff for overseas operations and provides a consultancy and training service for both prospective and existing operatos.

CRAFT OPERATED:
HM.2 Mark III Nos. 302 305, 312

NAVAL HOVERCRAFT TRIALS UNIT

ADDRESS:
HMS Daedalus, Lee-on-Solent, Hampshire PO13 9NY
TELEPHONE:

Lee-on-Solent 550143 (STD 0705)
COMMANDING OFFICER:
Commander W. R. Hart, AFC, AFRAeS, RN

With the departure of Army and RAF personnel in December 1974 the old Inter-service Hovercraft Unit wound up and became a single service under the control of the Navy.

On January 1st, 1975 the Naval Hover-craft Trials Unit (NHTU) was formed, and on January 17th, 1975, in the presence of Sir Christopher Cockerell and Mr Frank Judd, MP (Navy Minister), the Flag Officer Naval Air Command, Vice Admiral P. M. Austin commissioned the new unit at Lee-on-Solent.

The Navy's interest in hovercraft is mainly in the Mine Countermeasures field.

CRAFT OPERATED:
SR.N5 002 (XT 492)
SR.N6 027 (XV 859)
SR.N6 035 (XV 617)
SR.N6 033 (XV615)
SR.N6 MK V 003 (XT 493) in reserve
*BH7 001 (XW 255)
*Modified to Mk IV version embodying bow door.

Craft operated by the Naval Hovercraft Trials Unit, HMS Daedalus, Lee-on-Solent. *Top left:* The BHC SR.N5. *Top right:* The 60-knot SR.N6 Mk 2. Using radar and optical navigation aids, the craft can be employed for high-speed coastal surveillance in low visibility and at night. *Bottom left:* SR.N6 027, which operated in the Falkland Islands with Naval Party 8902. *Bottom right:* The Royal Navy's 50-ton BH.7 which, in 1972, travelled over 5,000 miles under its own power and operated to within 60 miles of the Arctic circle

MIDDLE EAST

IRAN
IMPERIAL IRANIAN NAVY
Hovercraft base: Khosrowabad

Eight BHC Winchesters are being operated by the Imperial Iranian Navy on logistics

duties and coastal patrol.

Four BH.7 Wellingtons, two Mk 4s and two Mk 5s, are also in service and two more Mk 5s are under construction. The first two

craft, BH.7 Mk 4s, are operated in the logistic support role. The Mk 5 is a multi-role craft and is designed to carry surface-surface, surface-air missiles on its side decks.

IMPERIAL IRANIAN NAVY
Craft operated: SR.N6 040(IIN 01) Mark 4
SR.N6 041(IIN 02) Mark 4
SR.N6 042(IIN 03) Mark 3
SR.N6 043(IIN 04) Mark 3
SR.N6 044(IIN 05) Mark 4
SR.N6 045(IIN 06) Mark 4
SR.N6 046(IIN 07) Mark 4
SR.N6 047(IIN 08) Mark 4
BH.7 002(IIN 101) Mk 4
BH.7 003(IIN 102) Mk 4
BH.7 004(IIN 103) Mk 5
BH.7 005(IIN 104) Mk 5
To be delivered during 1975
BH.7 006(IIN 105) Mk 5
BH.7 007(IIN 106) Mk 5

BH.7 Wellington Mk 5 of the Imperial
Iranian Navy

SAUDI ARABIA
Saudi Arabian Coastal and Frontier Guard
Ministry of the Interior
Airport Road
Riyadh

The Saudi Arabian Coastal and Frontier Guard operates a number of SR.N6 Win-

chesters on patrol, contraband control, search and rescue and liaison duties. The craft are attached to bases at Jeddah and Aziziyah on the east and west coasts.
Craft operated: SR.N6 038
SR.N6 048

SR.N6 049
SR.N6 050
SR.N6 051
SR.N6 052
SR.N6 053
SR.N6 054

JAPAN
Airport Hovercraft Service Co. Ltd.
Started in July 1972, using MV-PP5 09, "Angel No. 1", on a service linking Kajiki and Ibusuki in the Kagoshima Bay. The route currently takes over two hours to accomplish by car but with the hovercraft the 60 km route is achieved in less than an hour. A second craft, MV-PP5 1— 'Angel No. 2'— was added to the service in 1973, "Angel No. 3" was delivered in the summer of 1974 and "Angel No. 5" in June 1975.

Japanese National Railways
Kokutetsu Building, 625 Marunouchi 1-chome, Chiyoda-ku, Tokyo

A service between Uno in Okayama Perfecture and Takamatsu in Kagaw Prefecture was inaugerated in November 1972, using MV-PP5 007, named "Kamome" (Sea Gull).

Meitetsu Kaijo Kankosen K. K.
99-1, Shin-myiazaka-cho, Atsuta-ku, Nagoya City

Began regular services across the Mikawa and Ise Bays between Gamagori and Toba in September 1969 with an intermediate stop at Nishin. The craft employed is MV-PP 5 02 which has been named "Haku-cho".

Nippon Hoverline Co Ltd
Sakal Building Edo-cho 1, Ikutaku, Kobe City, Hyogo Pref.

Began its first service in December 1974, with MV-PP5-11 and 12, named Akatombo (Red Dragonfly) Nos 51 and 52, linking the two cities of Osaka and Tokushima, in Western Japan. The route distance of 98 km is covered in 1 hour 25 mins. Each craft carries 48 passengers as opposed to the standard 52-seat configuration on the PP5.

Oita Hoverferry Co Ltd
1309 Nishi-shinchi, Imatsura, Oita City
Operating three MV-PP5 craft, numbers 04, 05 and 06, named "Hobby 1, 2 and 3"

on a service between Oita Airport, Oita and Beppu cities. Service began in 1971.

Ryuku Kaiun Co Ltd
1-1 Nishihoi—Machi, Naha
Manager: Ryosei Kuwae

Operates MV-PP15s—01, 02 and 03—on route between Naha and Expo '75 Port at Okinawa. This service began on July 20th, 1975 and the three PP15s each take about 40 minutes to complete the 36-mile route.

Yaeyama Kanko Ferry K.K.
No 1 Aza-ohkawa, Ishigaki City, Okinawa

Delivered to her owners in the spring of 1972, MV-PP5 08—"Koryu"—operates a service linking Ishigaki and Iriomote Island, a distance of about 30 km, taking about 20 minutes, compared with the 2 hours taken by the ships used previously. Yaeyama Kanko Ferry Co Ltd is a joint investment of Taketomi City, Ryuku Kaiun and several other local shipping concerns.

ACV TRAILERS

AND

HEAVY LIFT SYSTEMS

AUSTRALIA

TAYLORCRAFT TRANSPORT (DEVELOPMENT) PTY LTD

HEAD OFFICE:
Parafield Airport, South Australia 5106

TELEPHONE:
(08) 258 4944

DIRECTORS:
R. V. Taylor
J. Taylor

Taylorcraft has built an ACV trailer unit for carrying loads of up to 1¼ tons over a wide range of soft or wet surfaces. A smaller version is being built for carrying fruit and vegetables from the point of harvesting to the point of dispatch.

TRAILAIRE I

This air cushion assisted trailer is intended for use in situations where the ground is too soft or wet to allow the use of normal trailers. One or more may be towed by a tractor or single units may be man-handled as required. The skirt and lift unit are removable allowing operation as a normal trailer in good conditions. Lift engine is a Kawasaki KT 300.

Towbar and tow ball are interchangeable to simplify handling in confined spaces.

Operation as conventional trailer:

DIMENSIONS:
Length overall (including towbar)
                        18 ft 0 in (5·49 m)
Width   6 ft 0 in (1·83 m)
Load Space 6 ft × 12 ft (1·83 m × 3·66 m)
                (Wheel arches at centre)
Loading Height   2 ft (0·61 m)
TYRES: 6·40 × 13
WEIGHTS:
Tare   330 lb (150 kg)
Payload (Max)   30 cwt (1,524 kg)
TRACK: 5 ft (1·52 m) centres

Operation as air cushion assisted trailer:

DIMENSIONS:
Length overall   18 ft 6 in (5·54 m)
Width   8 ft (2·24 m)
Load space
  2 each of 6 ft × 4 ft (1·83 m × 1·22 m)
Loading height   2 ft (0·61 m)
WEIGHTS:
Tare   580 lb (263 kg)
Payload (Max)   24 cwt (1,219 kg)
Cushion pressure (Max) 45 lb/sq ft
FUEL:
25 : 1 petrol oil   2·1 gals (10 litres)

TRAILAIRE II

The basic Trailaire unit is an 8 ft × 16 ft (2·43 × 4·87 m) platform capable of lifting 1¼ tons on its deck. At the rear of the platform an enclosed 127 air-cooled engine and fan assembly provides lifting power. At its gross weight the Trailaire loads the surface beneath to only 30 lb sq ft—less than one hundredth of the loading of an equivalent tracked or wheeled vehicle. Drag is very low and the unit may be used over a wide range of soft or wet surfaces, including mud banks and sandbars.

Units may be coupled together to provide load platforms of 24 ft × 8 ft (7·31 m × 2·43 m), 16 ft × 12 ft (4·87 m × 3·65 m) (2½ tons payload) or 16 ft × 24 ft (4·87 m × 7·31 m) (5 tons) or spaced to carry long loads, such as pipes. They can be towed by light vehicles or winched over land. Over water an outboard motor or a water pump unit may be used for propulsion.

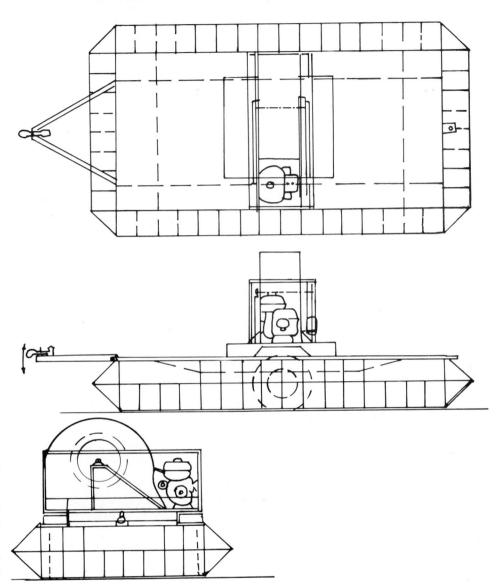

Taylorcraft Trailaire I, intended for use in situations where the ground is too wet to permit the use of conventional trailers. Both skirt and lift systems can be removed to allow operation as a normal wheeled trailer in good conditions

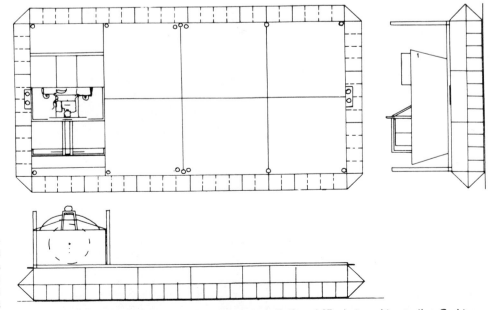

General arrangement of the Trailaire II, an 8 ft × 16 ft (3·43 × 4·87 m) air cushion trailer. Cushion air is generated by an automotive engine driving a 2 ft 3 in (685 mm) diameter centrifugal fan

Space alongside the lift engine allows an operator to ride on the platform clear of the load space. Sockets around the platform edge are provided to accept posts to fence-in the load area.

Ground clearance of the standard unit is 10 in (254 mm) but greater clearance can be provided if required. For amphibious operation buoyancy tanks can be fitted, though the standard unit can be operated over water as long as the engine maintains lift.

DIMENSIONS: (Single Unit)	Hard Structure	Overall on Cushion
Length	16 ft 9 in (5·10 m)	17 ft 8 in (5·38 m)
Width	8 ft 1 in (2·46 m)	9 ft 8 in (2·94 m)
Height of Deck	10 in 254 mm	20 in (0·50 m)
Height of Lift Unit	4 ft 0 in (1·21 m)	4 ft 10 in (1·47 m)
Load Space	12 ft 4 in × 8 ft 0 in (3·75 m × 2·43 m)	
Fence Height (Posts)	4 ft 10 in (1·47 m)	

CANADA

JOHN N. BROCKLESBY TRANSPORT LTD

11175 Parkway Boulevard, Ville d'Anjou, Montreal, Quebec HIJ 1S2

EXECUTIVES:

B Gauthier, Eng, Vice-President

G. E. Simard, General Manager

TELEPHONE: (514) 352-0700

TELEX:

01 2746

Brocklesby, a member of the Canada Steamship Line Group of companies, is licensee for Air Cushion Equipment Ltd's industrial skirt system.

The company has employed the system to move a 500-ton oil tank in Quebec City. The tank, which was 150 ft (45·72 m) in diameter, was raised 14 in (355 mm) on its segmented skirt and moved a distance of one mile (1·60 m) over a variety of surfaces to the tank farm of a storage firm, St Lawrence Stevedoring Co. Ltd.

HOVER-JAK LTD.

HEAD OFFICE:

169 Centre Street East, Richmond Hill, Ontario, Canada L4C 1A5

OFFICERS:

See ACV section.

This company is the Canadian licence holder for the Bertin system of independently fed multiple plenum chambers. The Hover-Jak HJ-15, a 15-ton payload ACV trailer employing this system is currently undergoing trials

HJ-15

The HJ-15, 15-ton capacity air cushion trailer, is of rugged simple construction and can be dismantled easily for transportation by conventional highway truck or cargo plane. The platform folds to a size of 40 ft × 9 ft × 5 ft 6 in (12·97 m × 2·74 m × 1·67 m). Engine and fan assemblies are removable as two separate units.

Lift is provided by two centrifugal fans mounted at the rear and driven by two Deutz B/F 8L413 diesel engines. The HJ-15 is designed for amphibious applications and has a buoyancy at gross weight of 150%.

Propulsion is provided by swamp crawler vehicles, boats, winching or by helicopter.

DIMENSIONS:

Length overall   40 ft (12·2 m)

Hover-Jak HJ-15 15-ton capacity air cushion trailer being towed by a Sikorsky S-55 helicopter

Width	18 ft (5·5 m)	Payload	15 tons
Height, base of hardstructure to top		PERFORMANCE:	
of fan assembly	9 ft (2·75 m)	Towing speed (helicopter at full load	
			20 mph plus (32·18 km/h)
WEIGHTS:		Clearance height	2 ft 5 in (74 cm)
Empty weight	8 tons	Endurance, normal tanks	10 hours

BELL AEROSPACE CANADA

HEAD OFFICE:

Post Office Box 160, Grand Bend, Ontario, Canada

TELEPHONE:

(519) 238-2333

Experiments undertaken with models together with the ACT-100 hoverplatform and the Canadian Coast Guard Voyageur have demonstrated the potential of ACVs as ice-breakers. As a result of these tests, a full-scale platform is now being designed by Bell Aerospace Canada for use in conjunction with the Canadian Coast Guard ship Montcalm.

The platform is 53 ft (13·1 m) wide and 32 ft (9·75 m) long and is designed to provide a variety of weights and cushion pressures. Water pumped into the platform's ballast tanks gives it an operating weight ranging from 170,350-365,000 lb, with cushion pressures from ·7 to 1·5 lb/sq in.

If built, the platform would be used for full-scale evaluation of the concept.

Impression of the proposed ice-breaking platforms which would be attached to the bow of the Canadian Coast Guard ship Montcalm for trials. Tests have shown that ACV platforms provide significant improvements in the capability of an icebreaking ship

FRANCE

SEDAM

HEAD OFFICE:
80 Avenue de la Grande Armée, 75 Paris
17 eme
TELEPHONE:
380-17-69
TELEX:
29-124 Paris

Sedam is developing two amphibious hoverbarges, one of 50 t the other of 100 t capacity, to offload cargo ships in ports which, because of the vast growth of sea transport, have become almost permanently congested.

This congestion is forcing large numbers of vessels to queue up to be unloaded, and sometimes necessitates a wait of 30-100 days. Such delays, because of the high cost of demurrage and insurance, frequently lead to an increase of 50% to 100% in freighting charges.

Sedam is proposing the use of its two Amphibarges to unload the vessels and carry their cargo to warehouses close to the port, but clear of the main areas of congestion. Their amphibious capability would enable them to make the transition from water to land and carry their loads up to the warehouses where conventional fork lift trucks, mobile cranes and other freight handling equipment would be employed for offloading.

The manufacture of components for the Amphibarges could take place in the countries in which they are to be used. This would not only permit the customer to make considerable savings in transport costs. it would also create a source of local employment.

Features of the proposed Amphibarges would include the following:

LIFT AND PROPULSION: Either two diesel engines or two gas-turbines to power the lift system. Gas turbines specified for the 100 t capacity Amphibarge are two 2,250 shp Avco Lycoming TF25As. On this craft each engine will drive two axial-flow fans which will feed air into the multiple skirt system. On both designs lift engines, fans, exhausts, transmissions and auxiliary power systems are installed amidship in side structures ensuring that the load decks are kept completely clear for cargo.

Among the alternative methods of propulsion proposed are small tugs, outboard motors, air propellers, a ship-to-shore cable system and, for on-shore work, tractors or caterpillar tracks. The latter would help to check the effect of wind and sloping terrain.

HULL: Modular raft structure comprising a number of cylindrical buoyancy tanks laid side-to-side longitudinally, Surmounting the buoyancy tanks are supports for the deck, and below it the multiple skirt system and landing pads.

SKIRT SYSTEM: Bertin multiple skirt system with jupes arranged in two rows, one outer, one inner, around the outer periphery of the craft. 100 t Amphibarge has additional line of skirts arranged below hull centreline to form longitudinal keel.

ACCOMMODATION: The operator's position and all the necessary controls are located in the raised bridge above the engine compartment on the starboard side. Crew would normally comprise an operator, engineer and seaman.

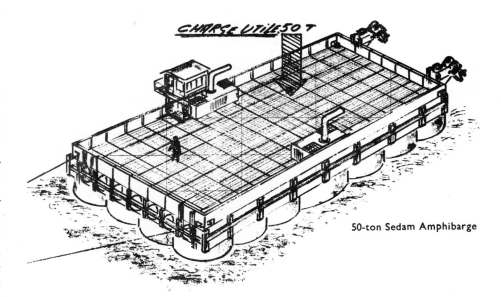

50-ton Sedam Amphibarge

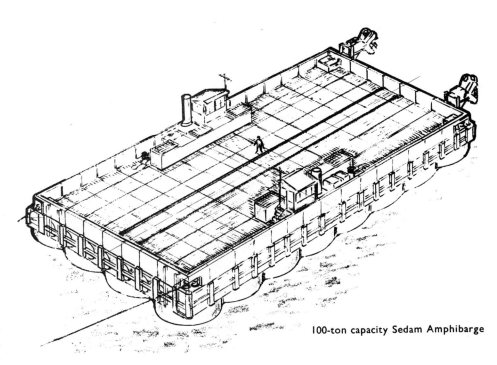

100-ton capacity Sedam Amphibarge

PERFORMANCE:
Operating speed on water   =
                    3·1 to 3·7 mph (5·6 km/h)
On land   depending on type of propulsion

DIMENSIONS:	50 t Craft	100 t Craft
Length	72 ft 2 in (22 m)	104 ft 11 in (32 m)
Beam	39 ft 4½ in (12 m)	55 ft 9¼ in (17 m)
Area	2,842 ft² (264 m²)	5,856 ft² (544 m²)
Skirt depth	3 ft 3 in (1 m)	4 ft 3⅛ in (1·3 m)
WEIGHTS:		
Weight of craft	60 t	120 t
Total weight	110 t	220 t
Payload	50 t	100 t

JAPAN

MITSUI SHIPBUILDING & ENGINEERING CO LTD

HEAD OFFICE:
6-4 Tsukiji 5-chome, Chuo-ku, Tokyo, Japan

Mitsui has designed a 310-ton hoverbarge, designed for use in either deep or shallow waters. A feature of the craft, designated SEP-1, is the provision of jack-up legs, similar to those employed on some offshore oil rigs. This facility enables the craft to be located above test or survey sites in shallow waters or in areas of marsh or tundra.

UNITED KINGDOM

An ACE high-pressure skirt system being employed to lift an 820-tonne concrete caisson.

AIR CUSHION EQUIPMENT LTD

HEAD OFFICE:
360 Shirley Road, Southampton
TELEPHONE:
Southampton 776468
TELEX:
47106
CABLES:
HOVERACE SOTON
WORKS:
35 Randolph Street, Shirley, Southampton
DIRECTORS:
L. A. Hopkins
T. C. A. Horn
W. A. Melhiush
O. J. Coleman
J. M. Horn
P. B. A. Hopkins
B. H. Wright
G. Parkes
A. Latham
P. Stevens
CHIEF DESIGNER: R. Gilbert
CHIEF ENGINEER: G. Parkes
MARKETING MANAGER: A. Latham

Since April 1968, Air Cushion Equipment has been involved in all aspects of air cushion technology, concentrating mainly on the industrial application of hovering devices. Over the last two years considerable development effort has been devoted to the creation of a range of products using water as the cushion fluid in the more specialised field of dense load movement.

A range of skirt and system types have been covered by the Company's association, in either licensing, consultancy, design and or manufacturing contracts, with companies now selling or operating hovering equipment both at home and overseas.
These include:
Vosper Thornycroft Ltd—VTI
Arctic Engineers and Constructors—ACT 100
CEGB—Heavy load transporter

Hovertrailers International Ltd—Hovertrailers, aircraft recovery platforms
Mears Construction Ltd—Oil storage tank moving
Mackley ACE Ltd—Hover platforms, hover dredger, large hover barges
NRDC—Medical applications development
Government Ministries—System development, contracts and hover application surveys
Hovermarine Transport—Skirt manufacture

ACE has studied the application of skirt systems to many unusual devices and is capable of the project management for total contracts, whether it be a normal or special application of either the air or water cushion principle. The Company accepts contracts to cover the field of air cushion technology, including feasibility studies, design and development, test engineering or system manufacture.

LOW PRESSURE AIR SYSTEMS

Design services are offered in the application of the hover principle utilising low-pressure air (2 psi and below) for the movement of heavy and awkward loads over unprepared ground. This embraces air cushion systems engineering and the design and manufacture of skirts.

Out of this design development capability emerged the hovertrailer concept, aircraft recovery equipment, amphibious platforms and barges. The foundations of the technology used by Hovertrailers International Ltd and Mackley Ace Ltd emanated from technology vested in the design and development expertise, backed by the skirt manufacturing facilities available at ACE. The two most significant products using ACE design and manufacturing skills are those of Arctic Engineers and Constructors ACT-100, 264-ton auw transporter and the Mackley Ace Sea Pearl, 750-ton auw transporter.

HIGH PRESSURE AIR SYSTEMS

Under a contract awarded by the UK Department of Trade, high pressure air systems have been investigated up to 11 psi statically and 7·5 psi dynamically culminating in the lifting and movement of an 820-tonne concrete caisson. This development programme has led to a greater understanding of air cushion systems in general for large skirted areas and has led to an improvement of design and manufacturing techniques throughout the pressure range up to 11 psi. For operating on roads and bridges the company has developed for CEGB a segmented skirt system which can be clamped beneath a road trailer and will operate at cushion pressuring up to 5·5 psi.

This system can be adapted to fit most trailers used by the heavy haulage contractors and gives a more uniform load distribution over the length of the vehicle, thus relieving stress or concentrated loads from weak ground or bridge structures.

HIGH PRESSURE WATER SYSTEMS

Market and technical research has shown that to lift and move large and dense loads is technically difficult and expensive. For the past two years the company has been investigating new methods of adapting skirt systems for the dense load movement sector of the market, all the time reducing both the capital and operating costs. The latest product to emerge is known as the ACE Water Skate.

The Water Skate uses water as the cushion fluid and has been tested up to 100 psi. Modular in application the total system can be used in multiples of the required number from a range of sizes starting at 30 tonne and 50 tonne capacities and projected up to 1,000 tonnes. The equipment uses normal contractors' pumps to give water at the required pressure and flow. One pump can feed several modules via a control manifold and console. The manifold can be used to vary the pressures to each module thus eliminating the necessity to present equipment symmetrically about the centre of gravity. The pressure gauges can be calibrated in weight giving the operator the ability to weigh a bulky structure and to identify the centre of gravity to verify practical readings against calculation.

The areas of use for this new product are diverse, but include the movement of oil-rig jacket structures and deck modules, concrete caissons, transformers, ship sections and hulls, plant and machinery and bridge sections.

TANK MOVING

Tank moving, using an air cushion for support, has now become a well established procedure. The method offers many advantages over the older conventional forms of movement such as water flotation, mechanical skidding, cranes or bogies. Route preparation is kept to a minimum and it is seldom necessary to reinforce the tank. A tank move can usually be completed in about seven to ten days, depending on the size of the tank and the distance to be moved. Once the skirt has been assembled to the tank and the tank has been lifted from its foundation, the distance that it can be moved is infinite and only requires the provision of an appropriate means of propulsion and a clearway of adequate width.

With all other methods movement is normally limited to comparatively short distances, or the time for the move becomes very extended.

The skirt system is fitted directly to the tank and is attached to specially designed attachment rails which are tensioned round the tank. No welding is required and hence the system can be used in high fire risk areas. As it is composed of a number of individual segments, the skirt can be attached to any size of tank by using the appropriate number of segments. Special segments are available to accommodate manholes and pipe outlets and others are fitted with hose attachments through which air is fed to the cushion system.

As air is ducted from the fan to the cushion area it percolates through the tank foundation until sufficient pressure is built up to lift the tank. No jacking is required. Once on cushion the tank can be towed or winched to its new location. The air cushion system allows omnidirectional mobility, hence to change direction or rotate the tank about its vertical axis, only requires the application of towing forces in the appropriate direction. Location to dimensional tolerances of ± 2 in can easily be obtained. The towing force required is usually in the order of 1% of the weight of the tank.

Tanks of all types can be moved on air including those with floating, fixed and column supported roofs and welded or rivetted construction. The illustration shows a 700 tonnes floating roof tank being moved in Panillac for Shell France. This is the largest tank moved on air to date and on this occasion an added innovation was used, floating the roof on a second cushion of air during the move. This not only reduces the possibility of damage to the roof, but also

An ACE segmented skirt developed for the Central Electricity Generating Board. By distributing the gross weight beneath the entire underside of a transporter, the bending moments and sheer forces imposed on bridges is reduced so that heavy transformers can be carried across without risk

The ACE Water Skate, designed to move large and dense loads, uses water instead of air as the cushion liquid. This particular module is seen lifting a 200-tonne load

This 700-ton oil storage tank is the largest ever moved by Air Cushion Equipment's hover flotation method. The operation was undertaken at Pauillac for Shell France. While the tank was being moved, the roof was floated on a second cushion of air to reduce both the possibility of damage to the roof and the pressure differential developed across the bottom of the tank

reduces the pressure differential developed across the bottom of the tank.

Tank moving on air cushion is undertaken by licenced contractors as follows:
UK, Western Europe and Arabian Gulf (part) —Mears Construction Ltd

USA—Hover Systems Inc
Canada—Brocklesby Transport Ltd
South Africa—National Process Industries
Pty

Roof of a liquid petroleum gas tank approaching the top. Seen in the photograph is the skirt seal and one of the stub connections on the inner face of the tank onto which the roof rafters are bolted or welded

TANK ROOF LIFT SYSTEM

Air Cushion Equipment Ltd in conjunction with Whessoe has developed an application of the segmented seal which enables large unsupported arched tank roofs to be raised pneumatically after the construction of the tank's sidewalls.

The system allows the free span roof to be constructed at ground level prior to the erection of the tank. On the completion of the tank shell the roof is lifted pneumatically to the top where it is held on a cushion of air while the roof rafters are bolted or welded onto the stub connections already attached to the shell of the tank.

The low air loss and fine control permit movements up and down by increments of $\frac{1}{8}$ in, allowing holes in the rafters and stubs to be aligned.

As a safety precaution in the event of engine failure while the roof is being raised, four special segmented non-return valves are built into the feedlines at the point of air entry into the tank shell. These close automatically when the pressure under the roof exceeds the pressure of the air delivered from the fan.

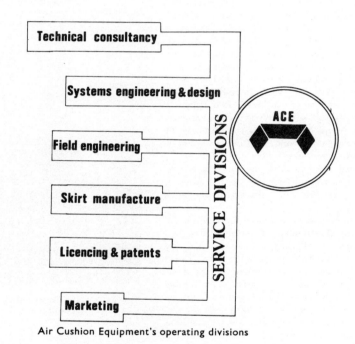

Air Cushion Equipment's operating divisions

BRITISH HOVERCRAFT CORPORATION

HEAD OFFICE:
Osborne, East Cowes, Isle of Wight
DIRECTORS:
See ACV Section

AIR CUSHION HEAVY LOAD TRANSPORTER (AIR CUSHION EQUIPMENT SERIES I)

The development of this equipment was prompted initially by the Central Electricity Generating Board, which is constantly faced with route-planning problems caused by the high weights of laden transporters.

Transformer units now going into service weigh between 155 and 250 tons and 400 ton units are in prospect. On occasion the CEGB has been involved in the heavy expense of strengthening and even rebuilding bridges to accept these loads when no alternative route has been available.

The use of air-cushion equipment, however, provides a practical and economic alternative. By providing an air-cushion under the centre section of an existing transporter it is possible

The CEGB Heavy Load Transporter

to support a high proportion of its gross weight. Distributing the gross load over the whole length of the transporter reduces the bending moments and sheer force imposed on bridges so that these heavy transformers can be transported without risk over existing bridges.

The investigation into and development of this air-cushion transporter has been supported by the CEGB with the co-operation of the Ministry of Transport and the road haulage companies that operate the transporters.

The transporter illustrated has a length of 90 ft (27·4 m) and a maximum width of 16 ft 10 in (5·13 m). The payload is normally supported between two bogies each of which may have up to 48 wheels.

The skirt containing the air cushion is an easily handled unit which is fitted under the load and side beams of the trailer. Any spaces between the load and trailer frame are 'timbered-in' to take the upward thrust.

This type of skirt system can be built to suit any size of transporter and the one illustrated measures 32 ft (9·57 m) × 14 ft (4·26 m). It is constructed largely of nylon/neoprene sheet extending across the underside of the load platform and formed into a bellows around its periphery. To the bottom of the bellows is attached a series of plates, each about 1 ft (0·30 m) long, which make contact with the road surface. Thus, the only escape route for air from the cushion is through the small gap formed between the plates and the ground by the roughness of the surface.

Any general unevenness of the surface, such as the camber of a road or the hump of a bridge, causes the bellows of the 'skirt' to flex so that the plates can remain in contact with the road.

The cushion was designed for a 155-ton lift, when the cushion pressure reaches 5·4 pounds per square inch. At this pressure, when moving over the roughest road surfaces, the volume of air escaping from underneath the shoes is approximately 13,200 cu ft/min (373·5 m³/min) (free air volume flow).

The power to maintain the air cushion is provided by four Rolls-Royce B81SV petrol engines delivering 235 hp (gross) at 4,000 rpm. Each engine drives, through a gearbox, its own centrifugal compressor, with engine, gearbox and compressor mounted together on a steel underbed as a complete working unit. The four units supplying the power are built onto a road vehicle chassis. This vehicle, which also contains stowage space for the folded cushion container, is attached to the rear of the transporter train whenever it is required for a bridge crossing. It is connected to the air cushion through four, 1 ft diameter air ducts, each connected to a power unit. The ducts are connected by sections of flexible hose to allow for relative movement between the vehicles.

The first commercial load carried by the transporter was a 155-ton transformer for delivery to the Central Electricity Board's sub-station at Legacy, near Wrexham, from the A.E.I. Transformer Division Works at Wythenshawe, Manchester. The route involved crossing the Felin Puleston Bridge which, under normal circumstances, was incapable of withstanding the combined weight of the transporter and the transformer. By using the air cushion to relieve the load on the transporter's wheels the stress on the bridge was reduced by about 70 tons.

Had a conventional transporter been used the bridge would have had to be strengthened at a cost equal to about half the cost of developing and equipping the transporter.

Optimum relief is obtained by taking up about one-third of the gross load in the skirt and transferring this proportion from the bogies to a position under the piece being carried. Current requirements are for redistribution of between 85 tons and 125 tons of the gross load in this manner and to date nearly 700 bridges have been crossed using the air cushion with savings in bridge strengthening costs estimated to be in the region of £2 million.

Future movements of larger plants are likely to call for relief up to 200 tons. Recognising this potential requirement and also the fact that the existing equipment has already had a considerable part of its operating life the Board decided in 1973, to order a second set of equipment, designated Series II, which would cover all present and anticipated future requirements whilst allowing the Series I equipment to be held for back up and stand by duties. The latter has become particularly important in view of the substantial increase in air cushion assisted movements during the last 18 months.

Series II equipment incorporates new features and design improvements made in the light of operating experience with the original system; main differences being centred around the air supply units.

Air is supplied by four 200 hp gas turbines running on diesel fuel and each directly coupled to an axial compressor to give an output potential up to 7·3 psi with a 20% increase in air capability. The gas-turbines, supplied by Noel Penny Turbines Ltd. are mounted together on a module on the swan necks of the heavy load trailer. The swan necks also carry the control cabin, fuel tanks, batteries, and battery charger so that no separate air supply vehicle is required. The trailer can now operate as a single unit when the air cushion is in situ. The need for flexible air duct sections is avoided, also the loss of time in connecting or disconnecting flexible sections and replacing the rear tractor by the blower vehicle as is required for Series I equipment.

The Series II equipment has had its initial commissioning trials and is expected to be in full commercial service by the end of 1975. A line diagram, accompanying this entry, indicates the differences in layout between the Series I and Series II equipment.

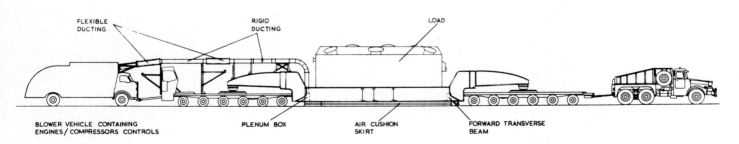

SERIES I ARRANGEMENT

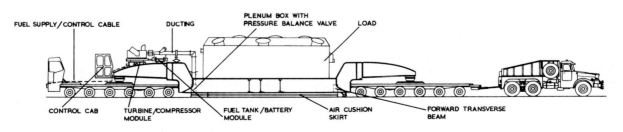

SERIES II ARRANGEMENT

UBM HOVER-SYSTEMS

HEAD OFFICE:
Lower William Street, Northam, South-
ampton SO9 2DN
TELEPHONE:
Southampton 34366
TELEX:
47106 Hovetrail Soton
DIRECTORS:
C. S. Richards
G. P. P. Schwerdt
SENIOR EXECUTIVES:
D. Williamson, Marketing Manager
I. R. Bristow, Technical Manager

UBM hover-systems (formerly Hovertrailers
International Ltd) is a division of UBM
Engineering Limited, a subsidiary of United
Builders Merchants Group Limited. It was
founded to specialise in the development,
construction and marketing of two ranges of
hover equipment—aircraft recovery systems
and non-self-propelled industrial hover-
platforms of various types.

AIRCRAFT RECOVERY SYSTEMS

The hover method of aircraft recovery is
designed to overcome the enormous difficulties
involved in recovering wide-bodied aircraft.
It is capable of the recovery of aircraft up to
the size and weight of the Boeing 747, and is
constructed in modular form so that it can be
transported in a standard Boeing 707 air
freighter. The advantages of the system are
that recovery can be achieved very quickly
regardless of the condition of the ground
surface, and that secondary damage to the
aircraft is reduced to a minimum.

The system was demonstrated at London
Heathrow Airport when a DC-4 was hovered
over a variety of ground surfaces. During
the demonstration it was manoeuvred and
hovered across soft ground at speeds of up to
16 km/h (10 mph). Additionally, the
equipment has been used under airport
operating conditions at Gatwick Airport for
the movement of a Britannia. The aircraft
was hovered over soft ground for nearly a
mile, and at one point was hauled across
a 20 ft (6·09 m) wide drainage ditch on a
bridge constructed of light steel beams and
plywood sheets.

A second method of recovery on hover has
recently been developed which dispenses with
the pneumatic elevators normally used to
support the aircraft. It is designed primarily for small military aircraft of up to 25
tons, and permits the clearance of disabled
machines from a runway or the surrounding
area quicker and easier than by cranes.

INDUSTRIAL HOVER-PLATFORMS

These non-self-propelled platforms are
designed to transport a wide variety of heavy
loads over terrain which is impassable for
conventional wheeled or tracked vehicles
under load. They may be used in widely
varying application fields from civil engineering, pipe or cable laying, forestry work,
geological and mineral surveying, to agricultural, conservation or drainage schemes.
The basic structure is a rigid steel platform
with a strong welded subframe to which a
hover skirt is attached. The lift power is
supplied by a centrifugal fan driven by a
petrol or diesel engine mounted on the
platform. Special wheels fitted to swinging
arms at the rear of the platform give directional control on side slopes and when
reversing. Hover height of the platforms

Bristol Britannia airliner being hovered across a ditch at Gatwick Airport.

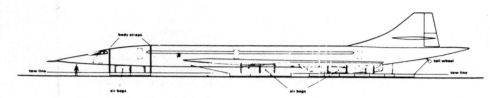

Drawing showing how hover platforms and air bags would be positioned to recover a Concorde airliner

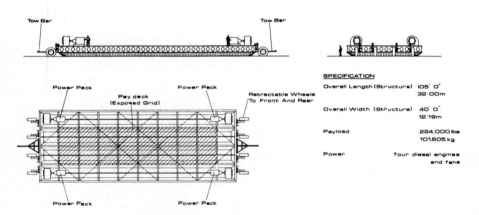

SPECIFICATION	
Overall Length (Structure)	105' 0" 32·00m
Overall Width (Structure)	40' 0" 12·19m
Payload	224,000 lbs 101,605 kg
Power	four diesel engines and fans

A standard 100-ton capacity hover platform

A hover platform loaded with six 12·19 m (40 ft) by 0·68 m (3 ft) diameter pipes crossing soft sand

varies according to design and size. Individual units of up to 100 tons capacity are
available, and awkward loads with high
centres of gravity may be transported by
linking together two platforms of the same
type. Platforms of this type have been sold
in the United Kingdom, Europe, Africa,
Asia, North and South America and Australia.

Both the aircraft recovery systems and
industrial platforms may be either towed or
winched. The ground bearing pressure of
the air cushion system is usually less than
1 psi, and the towing force required is very
low. For operation in extremely marshy
conditions, fully-tracked low ground pressure
tractors are the most suitable towing vehicles.

MACKLEY-ACE LIMITED

HEAD OFFICE:
421/427 Millbrook Road, Southampton
SO1 3HY
TELEPHONE:
0703 781844
TELEX:
477434 Mackace Soton
DIRECTORS:
D. G. W. Turner (Managing)
J. R. Mackley (Chairman)

F. R. Mackley, CEng, FICE
A. Truslar (Secretary)
M. Fripp

Mackley Ace Limited, a wholly owned subsidiary of J. T. Mackley and Company Limited, have specialised in the design and construction of cushion supported platform for use in many facets of Industry. They helped to build the world's first hover dredger, have built a range of modular platforms, built the world's largest hover

transporter, with a 250-ton capacity in the Middle East and have built two 160-ton hover transporters to cross the River Yukon in Alaska. They are now studying greater payload capacities.

They have recently developed a simple self-propulsion system for their hover platforms. The company has also announced a completely new system for laying submarine cables which simplifies the un-reeling of the cable.

Top left: 160-ton payload hover platform employed as a chain ferry to carry vehicles and equipment across the Yukon river. *Bottom left:* Sea Pearl, the world's biggest hover transporter, in operation in the Arabian Gulf. *Top right:* A Mackace 15-ton payload modular platform. *Bottom right:* A Mackace hoverplatform equipped with outboard motors undergoing trials with the British Army

250 TON ACT

Sea Pearl, the world's largest hover transporter, was launched during 1974 and now operates between Abu Dhabi and Das Island in the Arabian Gulf.

It carries pre-fabricated sections of a liquid natural gas plant for a distance of about 110 miles. Sea Pearl is towed by crawler tractors on land and by a work boat at sea. The use of an amphibious hovercraft allows components to be transported from the fabrication site across rocks and sand, to the sea and then across the sea and directly onto site without having to change the mode of transport for each sector of the journey.

LIFT SYSTEM: Cushion lift is supplied by two 890 hp MWM TBD 602 V12 diesels, each

driving a 4 ft 7 in (1·39 m) diameter Alldays Peacock 1,400 BA DIDW centrifugal fan. Each fan delivers 135,000 cu ft (3,823 cu m) of air per minute, giving a cushion pressure of 1 lb sq in (0·7 kg m²).

SKIRT: 4 ft (1·21 m) deep, open segment type, with double segments aft and an anti-spray flap.

BALLAST: A seawater ballast system is fitted to permit the craft to be employed as ship-to-shore transporters.

DECK EQUIPMENT: Two 10 ton hydraulic winches are fitted at the bow for loading plant components, which will either be mounted on rollers or hoverpallets. Twin hydraulic capstans are located amidships for use during mooring, manoeuvring and

anchoring.

ACCOMMODATION: Elevated bridge and quarters for a five-man crew.

PERFORMANCE, FULLY LOADED:
Calm water, towing force of 15 tons 7 knots
In 9 ft (2·74 m) high by 250 ft (76·20 m)
long waves   3 knots

DIMENSIONS:

Length overall	180 ft 0 in (58·46 m)
Beam overall	80 ft 0 in (24·38 m)
Length, load deck	158 ft 0 in (48·16 m)
Beam, load deck	52 ft 0 in (15·85 m)
Height on cushion	32·70 ft (9·94 m)
Height off cushion	28·70 ft (8·72 m)

WEIGHTS:

All-up weight	750 tons
Payload	250 tons

160 TON AIR CUSHION FERRY

Following experiments conducted in November 1974, Mackace was awarded contracts to build two of these cable-drawn hover ferries, which are now operating across the River Yukon in Alaska.   Named the Yukon Princess I and Yukon Princess II, the platforms are used to carry vehicles and equipment across the River Yukon whether frozen solid, breaking up, liquid or just covered with thin ice.   The hover platforms are based on a modular float raft with special Mackley Ace skirt frames attached to the periphery.   The cushion system gives a hover height of 48 inches when fully laden.   In mid-June, 1975 the two craft were carrying up to 2,000 tons of cargo across the Yukon daily.

LIFT SYSTEM: Two 700 hp GM Detroit diesel engines, designed to operate in temperatures of minus 60°F.   The engines each drive an Alldays Peacock 1,100 BA DIDW centrifugal fan.   Each fan delivers 92,000 cu ft (2,605 cu metres) of air per minute, giving a cushion pressure of 1 lb per square inch (0·7 kg per sq metre).

SKIRT: 5 ft deep, segmented skirt with spray skirt.

WINCHING SYSTEM: Two winches are used to tow the craft backwards and forwards across the 5,000 ft (1,500 metres) crossing.

ACCOMMODATION: There is a heated cabin for the crew and an elevated bridge.

DIMENSIONS (Yukon Princess I):

Length overall	127 ft (38·7 m)
Beam overall	84·5 ft (25·7 m)
Length of load deck	98·3 ft (29·9 m)
Beam of load deck	56 ft (17 m)
Height on cushion	25 ft (7·62 m)
Height off cushion	20 ft (6·1 m)

WEIGHTS (Yukon Princess I):

All-up weight	370 t (375·9 tonne)
Payload	160 t (162·6 tonne)

DIMENSIONS (Yukon Princess II):

Length overall	126·5 ft (38·5 m)
Beam overall	81·5 ft (24·8 m)
Length of load deck	97·8 ft (29·8 m)
Beam of load deck	53 ft (16·1 m)
Height on cushion	25 ft (7·62 m)
Height off cushion	20 ft (6·1 m)

WEIGHTS (Yukon Princess II):

All-up weight	412 t (418·6 tonne)
Payload	160 t (162·6 tonne)

HOVERPLATFORMS

Mackley Ace modular hoverplatform designs have ranged in payload capacity from 15 to 95 tons.

Based on the standard Uniflote pontoon, each platform can be expanded or contracted to suit particular requirements.

Specially fabricated skirt frames are cantilevered off the side of the Uniflote pontoons. The neoprene-coated nylon weave is attached beneath these frames to protect it against accidental damage.

Each frame has its own skirt section attached and is quickly replaced if damaged.   The self-contained power packs to power the lift system are also mounted on the skirt frames, leaving the deck area clear.   Contract labour can handle and assemble the platforms on site.   The platforms are normally winched or towed, although it is possible to propel them with suitable outboard motors such as

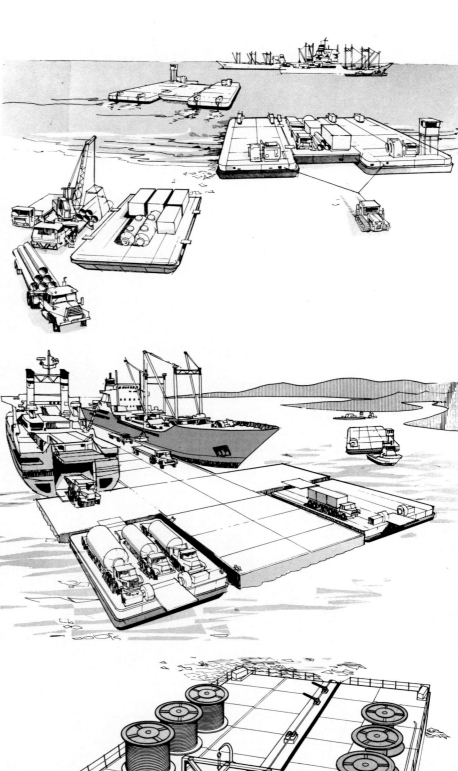

Top-and centre: Two proposed ship-to-shore systems employing Mackace transporters. *Below:* The spin tank system of cable laying, developed by Mackley Ace, employs a cushion of low pressure water and a skirt to support a cable driven on a vertical axis, thereby eliminating problems of overfeed, reel sagging and cable snatch

Harbor-masters. During 1975, specifications for a new range of self-propelled hover platforms should be completed.

SPIN TANK

This was developed in response to a request for a simplified cable laying system. The Mackley Ace Spin Tank system of cable laying employs a cushion of low pressure water and simple skirt to support a cable drum on a vertical axis, thus eliminating problems with cable snatch, reel sagging and over-feed. The system has been tested at Mackley Ace's test facilities.

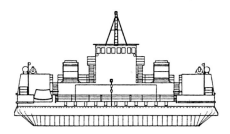

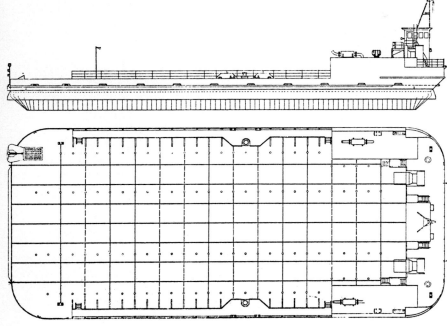

General arrangement of the 250-ton payload capacity Mackley-Ace hover transporter

---

MEARS CONSTRUCTION LIMITED

HEAD OFFICE:
154-158, Sydenham Road, London, SE26 5LA

TELEPHONE:
01-778-7851

TELEX:
947157

EXECUTIVES:

R. W. Bale, BSc, CEng, FICE, Director-in-Charge Air Cushion Division

P. F. Morgan, Manager, Air Cushion Division

Mears Construction Limited holds the franchise for Air Cushion Equipment Ltd's system of tank moving throughout the U.K., Western Europe and part of the Middle East.

The heaviest load moved by the company to date was a 700-ton tank relocated for Shell Française at their refinery near Bordeaux.

The service is available on a four-phase basis, comprising a desk study, and a site survey followed by the shipment of equipment and the moving operation.

The equipment consists of a wrap-around segmented skirt, together with air supply fans, motors and ducting, all of which can be readily shipped to sites anywhere in the above territories.

Site surveys are undertaken by a Mears engineer in conjunction with an appointed local contractor. The local contractor provides non-specialist plant and equipment for the move, Mears provides the lift equipment, and each move is undertaken as a joint venture under the direct control of a Mears engineer.

A 175 ft (53 m) diameter tank, weighing 620 tons, relocated for Esso at their refinery in Antwerp
The technique employed by Mears Construction Ltd is shown in the accompanying diagram

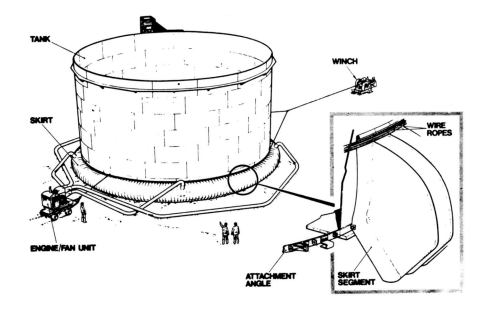

ROBERT TRILLO LIMITED

HEAD OFFICE:

Broadlands, Brockenhurst, Hampshire
SO4 7SX

TELEPHONE:

Brockenhurst 2220

Robert Trillo Limited is UK representative for A/S Seiga Harvester Company Limited, Copenhagen, manufacturer of the Seiga Tortoise multiterrain vehicle. The vehicle is suitable not only as a tug for hovertrailers, but also as a support vehicle for large hover-platforms.

SEIGA TORTOISE

The Seiga Tortoise is an amphibious transporter capable of negotiating swamps, soft earth, mud banks, sand, snow and open water. Special low pressure tyres are fitted to avoid damage to vegetation and enable the vehicle to roll fully-loaded from land to water or vice versa. The vehicle has hydraulic load tilting facility.

POWER PLANT: Motive power is supplied by either a 39 hp Volkswagen VW Type 124 petrol engine or Lombardini Type LDA 673 diesel, air-cooled, 3 cyl engine, delivering 36 hp at 3,000 rpm. Clutch is of dry single plate type. Gear rear-axle assembly is Type VW Type 002 300 041 D, with 4 forward and 1 reverse gear. Gear ratio is 1: 3·80; 2: 2·06; 3: 1·22; 4: 0·82; R: 3·88. A gear-wheel pump, 3 cm³/rev is fitted.

SYSTEMS: Electrical: 12 volt, 36 Ah battery for two headlights 5·1 in (130 mm), Oil pressure control, battery charging control, light switch (and ignition switch), push-button starter, hour-meter, battery.

CONTROLS: The front wheel drive is directly from a differential box by chain-drive. Rear wheels are driven by synchronised hydraulic motor. Pumps driven by heavy duty chains from VW gearbox output shaft. Steering is hydraulically assisted and employs two pistons working on turn-tabled backwheels.

BRAKES: Two foot pedals independently operating hand brakes applied on drums on each output shaft of engine gearbox.

Seiga Tortoise, a multiterrain vehicle which is to be employed as a tug for hovertrailers and as a support vehicle for large hover platforms

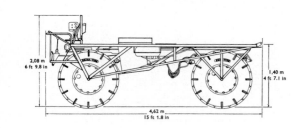
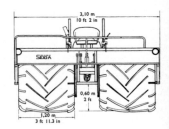
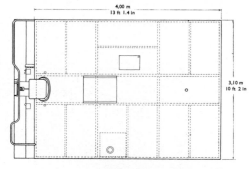

General arrangement of the Seiga Tortoise.

DIMENSIONS:

Length overall	15 ft 1 in (4·62 m)
Width overall	10 ft 2 in (3·10 m)
Height overall	6 ft 9 in (2·08 m)
Deck height	4 ft 7 in (1·40 m)
Deck length	13 ft 1½ in (4·00 m)
Deck width	10 ft 2 in (3·10 m)
Wheel diameter	4 ft 3 in (1·30 m)
Wheel width	3 ft 11 in (1·20 m)
Wheel base	9 ft 4 in (2·85 m)

WEIGHTS:

Empty, Volkswagen 127	3,300 lb (1,500 kg)
Empty, Lombardini 673	3,630 lb (3,630 kg)

PERFORMANCE:

Speed over land

1st gear	2·3 mph (3·6 km/h)
2nd gear	4·3 mph (6·7 km/h)
3rd gear	7·0 mph (11·0 km/h)
4th gear	10·6 mph (17·0 km/h)
Reverse gear	2·5 mph (3·8 km/h)

Speed over water, wheel propulsion only

	2·3 mph (3·6 km/h)
Gradient	30-40°

THE UNITED STATES OF AMERICA

ARCTIC ENGINEERS AND CONSTRUCTORS

HEAD OFFICE:

1770 St. James Place, Suite 512, Houston, Texas 77027

TELEPHONE: (713) 626-9773

CABLES: ARENCO

TELEX: 762587

EXECUTIVES:

R. G. Longaker, General Manager

L. G. Nichols, Technical Manager

M. R. Bade, Director of Administration

ASSOCIATED COMPANIES:

Arctic Systems, Calgary, Alberta, Canada

Arctic Engineers and Constructors, a joint venture of Global Marine Inc of Los Angeles and Raymond International Inc of Houston, was formed to create a single company with the capability and experience to offer a complete construction and drilling service to the petroleum industry in the Arctic.

Prior to the formation of Arctic E&C, engineers of the two parent companies had conducted an extensive environment, design, equipment and engineering study of the problems involved in the search for and production of petroleum in the arctic. The study's objective was to analyse and define the operational problems encountered both onshore and offshore. It included analyses of climate, ice properties and distribution, land and air transport vehicles, drilling and construction, transportable arctic housing, and past and present Arctic drilling operations.

It was concluded that air cushion transporters, used on a year-round basis, would offer substantial economic and technical advantages in arctic drilling, construction, and transportation.

The company's air cushion transporters are designed to transport heavy equipment and as a foundation support for drilling and construction equipment. The transporters are non-self-propelled and of simple robust construction for ease of operation and maintenance. The company designs air cushion transporters to suit specific operations. It owns and operates the transporters under contract to its clients.

Apart from its activities in the development

and exploitation of air cushion transporters, the company has also developed an air-cushion assisted Arctic Marine Pipelay System (AMPS) and a unique ice breaking attachment for conventional ships. By linking a VIBAC craft (Vehicle, Ice Breaking, Air Cushion) to the bow of a conventional ship, the ship's ice passage ability is greatly enhanced.

A further development is the company's Pneumatically Induced Pitching System (PIPS) which significantly improves a vessels icebreaking ability by inducing large amplitude pitching at the natural frequency of a given hull.

The company is licensed by Hovercraft Development Ltd.

ACT-100

Construction of the prototype ACT-100 was completed in April 1971. The craft is essentially an ACV barge designed to transport 100-ton payloads throughout the year across Arctic tundra, muskeg and marsh without unduly disturbing the soil and vegetation. It will also traverse offshore ice and open water.

Five months of testing under arctic winter conditions on the Great Slave Lake at Yellowknife during 1971-72 demonstrated that the craft is able to operate in temperatures of —50 deg F without difficulty. It proved extremely stable and manoeuvrable when travelling over level terrain, slopes, water, and over varying thicknesses of ice. It also showed unusual icebreaking ability in thicknesses up to 660 mm (26 in) and had no difficulty in traversing broken ice.

The Canadian Ministry of Transport employed the ACT-100 under contract to investigate the feasibility of operating air cushion ferries in the Mackenzie River highway system. Initial trials were conducted at Tuktoyaktuk, NWT, in November 1972. The craft was towed 322 km (200 miles) up the Mackenzie for final ferry trials at Arctic Red River in June 1973.

In December 1973 the ACT-100 was employed by Imperial Oil Ltd to transport drill rig supplies and equipment from Langley Island to Adgo Island. Adgo is an expendable artificial island constructed by Imperial in the Beaufort Sea to support an exploratory drilling operation. The ACT-100 carried loads of up to 99·8 tons over ice, broken ice, and water.

LIFT: Cushion air is supplied by two 640 hp Caterpillar D-348 diesel engines driving two 4 ft 6¼ in (1·37 m) diameter Joy 5425 N.O.L. steel centrifugal fans. Air is fed directly into the cushion without ducting. Cushion pressure is 144 psf. Diesel is contained in a single 500 US gal integral tank in the main hull amidships.

CONTROLS: Towing cables to pull vehicle and wheels beneath center of hull. A liquid ballast is provided for trim.

HULL: Box-type hull in A537 low temperature alloy steel. Hull is designed to support a 100-ton payload.

SKIRT: 1·52 m (5 ft) deep fully segmented skirt in rubber-coated nylon.

CREW: Control cabin accommodates one operator and assistant. A third member of the operating crew is the towing vehicle operator.

ACCOMMODATION: A "habitat" unit, with complete camp facilities for 35-40 men and storage facilities, can be mounted on the hull.

The ACT-100 air cushion transporter

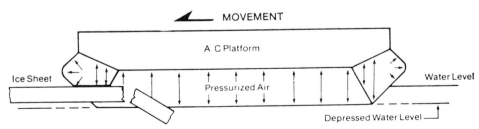

MOVEMENT

A C Platform

Ice Sheet

Pressurized Air

Water Level

Depressed Water Level

Action of the air cushion platform when an ice sheet is encountered. On contact, the skirt rises above the ice, continuing to act as an air seal. The ice sheet then loses its flotation support from below as the water beneath it is depressed by the cushion of pressurised air within the skirt zone. The ice sheet then becomes a cantilevered ledge and on reaching its critical length breaks, and the overhang section falls off into the displaced water below. The arrows in the drawing above show the force vectors within the skirt

SYSTEMS: 110/220 volt, 60 cycle 30 kW generator for lighting, control and pumping.
COMMUNICATIONS: None permanently installed.

DIMENSIONS:
Length overall:

power off	23·71 m (75 ft 3⅜ in)
skirt inflated	24·15 m (79 ft 3 in)

Beam overall:
  power off   13·74 m (57 ft 0⅜ in)
  skirt inflated   18·59 m (61 ft 0 in)
Height overall:
  power off   1·98 m (6 ft 6 in)
  skirt inflated   3·20 m (10 ft 6 in)
Draft afloat   1·04 m (3 ft 5 in)
Cushion area   308·068 m² (3,316 sq ft)
Skirt depth   1·52 m (5 ft 0 in)
CONTROL CABIN:
  Length   2·43 m (8 ft 0 in)
  Max width   2·74 m (9 ft 0 in)
  Max height   2·43 m (8 ft 0 in)
  Floor area   6·89 m² (72 sq ft)
FREIGHT HOLDS: Open deck, with tankage available beneath.
WEIGHTS:
  Normal empty weight   150 US tons
  Normal all-up weight   250 US tons
  Normal payload   100 US tons
  Max payload   130 US tons
PERFORMANCE (at normal operating weright):
  Speed (dependent on tow vehicle)
                             6 mph (9·65 km/h) plus
  Still air range and endurance at cruising speed: 12 hours at average speed of 9·65 km/h (6 mph) = 115·87 km (72 miles)
  Vertical obstacle clearance
                             1·21 m (4 ft 0 in)

ADS

The company's latest vehicle—the ADS (Arctic Drilling System) combines a large air cushion barge with modern offshore drilling equipment and an ice-melting positioning system. It is designed for arctic offshore use.

The system offers two important advantages: (1) the complete drilling system can move between locations at any time during the summer or winter, and (2) the unit can remain over the well bore in ice moving at moderate speeds.

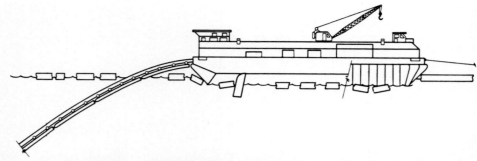

Side view of the Arctic Marine Pipelaying System, which will act as a combined ice-breaker and pipelaying barge. Conventional pipelaying barges are unable to operate in ice covered water. The AMPS will be able to operate in ice, thus greatly extending the limited northern working season

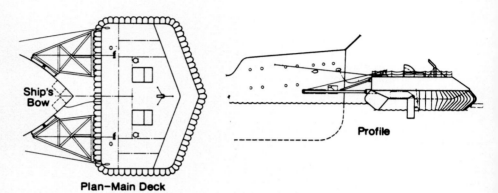

The VIBAC air cushion ice-breaking applicator unit designed for attachment to conventional ships travelling through Arctic waters. The unit was an outcome of experience with the ACT-100 in the Mackenzie River where it continuously broke ice as thick as 27 in (0.685 m)

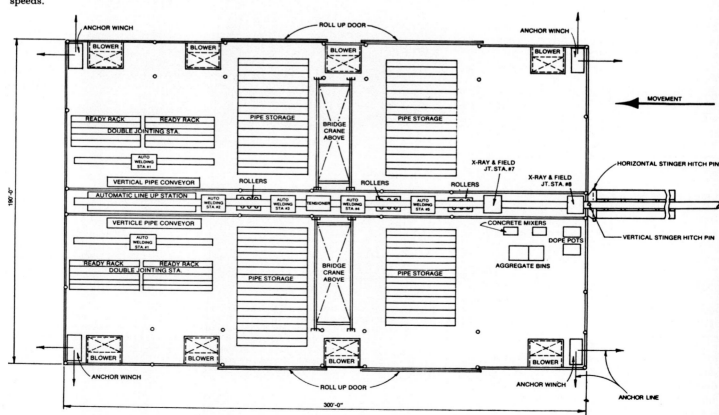

Operating deck of the Arctic Marine Pipelayer System (AMPS) showing the pipe handling equipment located beneath the winterisation covering which will maintain the work area at temperatures well above freezing

The three basic components of the ADS are:
(1) a large 70·4 by 43·7 by 4·5 m (231 by 143·5 by 15 ft) self-contained, shallow-draft aluminium drilling hull.

(2) an air-cushion system capable of lifting the hull—complete with drilling, crew, and drilling expendables—2·59 m (8·5 ft) above the surface.

(3) an external hull heating system capable of melting a ledge of ice moving from any direction at a rate of 4·57 m (15 ft) per day, using waste heat from three 1,300 hp Caterpillar D-399 diesel engines.

LIFT AND PROPULSION: A 4,000 kW common-bus ac power generating system, with silicon-controlled rectifiers, supplies power to the drilling equipment and lift fan drive motors. The system comprises five 800 kw, 1,200 rpm ac generators, driven by five Caterpillar D-399, series B diesel engines, each delivering 1,300 hp at 1,200 rpm. Because the unit will not hover while drilling, the power system will serve a dual purpose. It will be used to drive the drilling equipment when located above a well bore, and the lift fans when moving to a new location.

The fans deliver a maximum pressure of 1·78 psig. For normal rig moves the maximum cushion pressure will be used only in an emergency.

SKIRT: 8 ft 6 in (2·59 m) deep, fully-segmented HDL-type skirt in nylon rubber.

PROPULSION: Moving the ADS during the winter season will be accomplished by onboard mooring winches and logistic support vehicles. The support vehicles will pull out approximately 3,000 ft (914·40 m) of 1¾ in (44·45 mm) wire line for each of two modified National 4204-E winches mounted on the bow of the drilling hull. The support vehicles will act as dead men while the winches are taking up the line and pulling the ADS forward.

The support vehicles will have special design features to lock onto the ice sheet and resist the estimated 150,000 lb (68,038·86 kg) maximum lifting force. Winches on-board, powered by GE 752 dc motors, will provide a winching speed of 4 mph (6·43 km/h). An overall average moving velocity of 1 to 2 mph (1·60-3·21 km/h), providing a 24-48-mile (38·62-77·24 km) rig move in one day is anticipated.

It is expected that icebreaker workboats will permit the ADS to be towed through moderately thick ice during the winter season.

LOGISTIC SUPPORT: Candidate vehicles include ice-breaking workboats; self-propelled, 25-ton Voyageur hovercraft; large payload air-cushion barges; conventional barges frozen-in near the drilling locations; fixed-wing aircraft; tracked vehicles and large rubber-tyred vehicles. The selection will be determined by specific condition, economics, availability and other operator requirements.

HULL HEATING SYSTEM: An external heating system on the hull will permit the vessel to remain over the well bore in ice moving at moderate speed.

A four-point mooring system, with ice anchors attached to the ice sheet, allows tension to be pulled on appropriate anchor lines opposing the direction of motion of the ice sheet. This action forces the hot side of the hull to bear against the encroaching ice face. Sufficient heat transfer to the ice sheet melts the ice at a rate equal to the ice sheet motion.

Impression of the 3,840-ton ADS, designed to carry a complete offshore drilling system

It is anticipated that motion of land-fast ice will be random, and with anchor placement 1,000 ft or more away from the drilling unit, resetting of the anchor spread should not be necessary. However, the ice anchors can be reset.

It is only necessary to melt a ledge of ice equivalent to the draft of the hull and the side or sides exposed to ice motion. If the ice thickness exceeds the hull draft, an auxiliary ice removal system is used below the centre well so that the total projected area of the centre well is open through the ice sheet. Deployment of this system is necessary for riser and guidelines protection and for BOP retrieval when necessary.

This drilling well provides communication between the water below the ice sheet and the "lake" in which the ADS is floating while drilling. This makes the unit buoyant without its weight being transferred to the ice sheet below the barge hull.

The primary hull-heating system uses waste heat recovered from three of the five available D-399 Caterpillar engines during normal drilling operations. Sufficient BTUs are available from this source to melt a volume of sea ice moving toward a corner of the hull at 15 ft per day and exposing the drilling draft area of one side and one end of the hull to ice motion.

A considerable amount of research and development was committed to the ice-melting system. Both model and full scale studies were conducted to learn the mechanism of heat transfer and fluid flow between the hull and ice sheet and to establish heat input requirements for different velocities. These studies confirmed the mathematical model and proved the validity of the concept.

CONTROLS AND SYSTEMS: A central drilling control room is provided for the well-control personnel. Instrumentation will be installed to provide data on mud weight, mud pump pressure and flow rates, casing pressure, pit level, bit weight, rotary torque, rate of penetration and other critical drilling details. All remote BOP and choke line controls will be housed in the centre.

The design also features a large bulk mud, cement storage and handling system. The bulk storage system will accommodate 6,060 cu ft of mud and 3,140 cu ft of cement. A pneumatic bulk-handling system permits rapid material transfer.

ACCOMMODATION: A totally enclosed and heated working environment will help maintain maximum crew efficiency, even during the coldest Arctic weather. Modern crew quarters for 70 men and a large helipad are included.

A preliminary specification for the 3,840-ton ADS is given below.

DIMENSIONS:

Length overall	231 ft 0 in (70·4 m)
Beam overall	143·5 ft (43·7 m)
Depth of hull	15 ft 0 in (4·5 m)

WEIGHTS AND CAPACITIES:

Gross weight	3,840 long tons
Casing	360 long tons
5 in drilling pipe	12,000 ft
Reserve mud	2,357 bbl
Active mud	746 bbl
Bulk mud	6,060 cu ft
Bulk cement	3,140 cu ft
Stacked materials	17,556 cu ft
Drill water	10,695 bbl
Fresh water	746 bbl
Portable water	746 bbl
Fuel oil	3,731 bbl
Lubricating oil	1,500 gal
Total complement	70 persons

Design of the ADS is 95% complete. The unit, with a gross weight of 3,840 long tons, is designed to operate in land-fast ice in water depths from 0-183 m (0 to 600 ft) during the 7-8 month arctic winter season and in water depths of 9·14-183 m (30 to 600 ft) during the open-water summer season. The ADS is designed to operate in nearshore conditions in the Beaufort Sea at the Mackenzie Delta, the Alaskan North Slope, and the inter-island areas of the Canadian Arctic Islands. It could be used in any arctic land-fast ice areas including the continental shelves of Greenland and Siberia.

ARCTIC MARINE PIPELAYER SYSTEM (AMPS)

A combined air cushion pipelaying barge and icebreaker is being designed by Arctic Engineers and Constructors for Arctic operations.

The concept is the result of extensive tests which proved that air cushion platforms are able to carry exceptionally heavy loads over all types of arctic surfaces and break ice over water.

The barge, which will have a gross weight of 6,000 tons, will be capable of laying pipes of up to 48 in (1·21 m) diameter in waters that are either covered in ice up to 7 ft (2·13 m) deep—or ice-free. Typical areas in which craft of this type could be employed are Prudhoe Bay, Mackenzie Delta, the Canadian Archipelago and the continental shelves of Siberia and Greenland.

The barge, known as the Arctic Marine Pipelay System, will operate at an air pressure of 2 psi and the total lifting force will be in excess of 7,000 tons.

LIFT AND PROPULSION: Cushion lift will be provided by diesel engines developing in excess of 8,000 hp and driving eight fans rated at 85,000 cfm. The skirt, fabricated in rubber-coated nylon, will be 8 ft 6 in (2·59 m) deep. During ice-free periods the skirt and cushion lift system would be removed and the craft would be operated as a conventional pipelaying barge.

Propulsion would involve the use of an on-board winch pulling a cable attached to a conventional bottom anchor system in open water and an ice-anchor system while operating over ice. These will provide the forward pull rate which will be governed by the speed needed for welding joints.

Forward speed when travelling without pipelaying in progress would be 1-2 mph (1·60-3·21 km/h).

HULL: Aluminium barge-type construction 300 ft long, 190 ft wide and 15 ft deep (91·44 m × 57·91 m × 4·57 m). A centreline lay system would be employed using a gantry or bridge-type crane handling pipe joints from storage to the double-joint make-up line.

ACCOMMODATION: Entire operating deck will be protected by a winterisation enclosure which will maintain the work area at temperatures well above freezing. Complete crew quarters for a full complement of more than 100 men will be located within the hull structure.

SYSTEMS, PIPE LAYING:

It is estimated that 48 in pipe could be laid at 2,400 ft per 24 hour day using manual welding. This could be increased by 30-40% if automatic welding processes were introduced. Provision would be made to employ double-jointing before setting out, so that the craft would move 80 ft at a time instead of the normal 40 ft.

The use of two ACV barge units in tandem is envisaged, with a connecting gantry bridge, to control the lowering of pipelines in waters with depths below 400 ft.

The ACV system permits pipe-laying when the water depth is less than the barge's floating depth. This means it can be employed over marshland, swamps and inland areas where the terrain is reasonably flat.

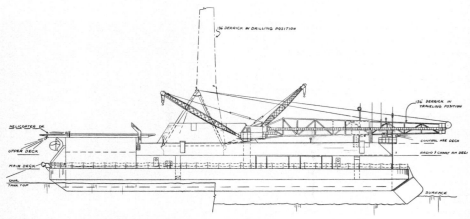

Above: Profile of the 231 ft (70·4 m) long, 3,840-ton air-cushion arctic offshore drilling system (ADS), showing the derrick in travelling and drilling position, the control house and helipad.
Below: A smaller version of the ADS with a length of 154 ft (46·93 m). Height of the derrick in drilling position, would be 136 ft (41·45m) measured above the upper deck

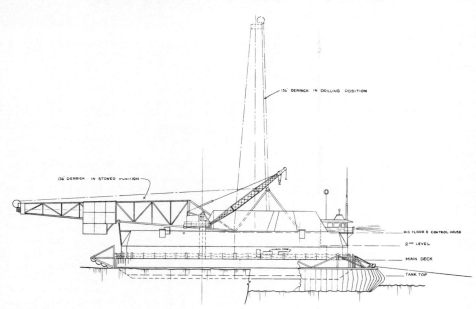

DIMENSIONS:

Length overall	300 ft (91·44 m)
Beam overall	190 ft (57·91 m)
Depth, hull structure	15 ft (4·57 m)
cushion depth	8 ft 6 in (2·59 m)

WEIGHTS:

Hull-to-deck	1,100 tons
Superstructure	250 tons
Power plant	350 tons
Supplies	400 tons
Service and misc. equipment	600 tons
Pipeline equipment	500 tons
Stored pipe, 48 in diameter	2,800 tons
Gross weight	6,000 tons
Safety margin for overload including ice and snow	1,000 tons
Lifting force	7,000 tons

VEHICLE, ICE-BREAKING, AIR-CUSHION (VIBAC)

The icebreaking characteristics of the ACT-100 has led to the development of a new vehicle designed specifically to aid the passage of a conventional ship through ice-bound waters.

The craft, known as the VIBAC system, is attached to the bow of the ship as soon as it enters an ice-field. Close visual observation and films have revealed what happens when air cushion platform approaches an ice sheet, and how the air cushion ice-breaking phenomenon takes place.

On making contact with the ice sheet the skirt rises up over the ice while continuing to maintain its air seal. The ice sheet then penetrates the zone of pressurized air beneath the craft, where the water level with the skirt area is depressed to a lower level than the bottom of the ice layer. The ice has now become a cantilevered ledge without water support beneath. When the cantilevered section reaches its critical length, failure occurs and the overhanging section breaks off and falls in to the depressed water below.

A plough-like deflector attached to the VIBAC unit will thrust the ice aside as the vessel progresses through the ice sheet.

EGLEN HOVERCRAFT INC

HEAD OFFICE:
801 Poplar Street, Terre Haute, Indiana 47807

TELEPHONE:
(812) 234 4307

TERREHOVER

Eglen Hovercraft Inc has designed and built a prototype hover platform, in order to investigate possible agricultural applications.

Particular attention is being given to its use for transporting heavy loads, including fertiliser tanks, over wet and muddy fields which cannot be negotiated by conventional farm equipment.

The prototype Terrehover is built in wood and measures 16 ft (4·87 m) long by 8 ft (2·43 m) wide. Air is put under pressure by two 2 ft (0·60 m) diameter axial-flow fans, driven by two JLO Rockwell L395 two-cycle engines. An H.D.L. type segmented skirt is used and the hoverheight is 9 in (228 mm).

Although designed originally to lift 2,000 lb (907·18 kg) the platform has successfully lifted 4,000 lb (1,814·37 kg), and has applied fertilizer in conditions normally considered too severe for conventional fertilizing equipment. The prototype is towed by another vehicle with low pressure tyres, but the production version will be self-propelled, with the operator housed in a cab mounted on the platform. Two centrifugal fans, powered by a small diesel engine, will be used and the engine will also drive an hydraulic pump which will power a hydrostatic motor for propulsion.

The vehicle will be capable of highway operation, riding on wheels which will be retracted while in the hovering mode.

Negotiations are under way for a joint development programme with an agricultural equipment company.

The prototype Eglen Terrehover, a 16 ft (4·87 m) long hover platform, designed for carrying agricultural equipment over wet and muddy terrain. Production models will be self-propelled, with the operator seated in an enclosed cabin

UNION OF SOVIET SOCIALIST REPUBLICS

ALL-UNION OIL MACHINERY RESEARCH INSTITUTE, WEST SIBERIA (VNII neftmash)

HEAD OFFICE: Tyumen

DIRECTOR:
A. V. Vladimirskii

EXECUTIVE:
V. A. Shibanov, Head of Air Cushion Vehicle Department

Air cushion platforms with load capacities of up to 200 tons have been under development in the West Siberian lowlands since 1965. Some 80% of the gas and petroleum sites in this area are located amidst almost impassable swamps, salt marshes, taiga and stretches of water.

In the Tyumensk area, where deep wells are being drilled, more than 200 tons of support equipment are required at each site in addition to between 130-180 tons of drilling gear. In 1965, a group of ACV engineers and designers headed by V. A. Shibanov left the Urals for Tyumen to apply their efforts to the design of a hoverplatform capable of carrying a complete oil rig across tundra and taiga, and also to the design and construction of an all-terrain vehicle capable of towing the drilling rig, on hover, to the drilling sites.

Small scale models were employed by the group during the development stages, and several attempts were made before a completely satisfactory design was conceived.

The most successful arrangement—the BU-75-VP—is illustrated. It comprises a rectangular, all-metal buoyancy raft (the load carrying member), with side structures to carry a bag-type skirt. A derrick, derived from a standard BU-75 drilling rig, was mounted on the central raft, and the drilling pump, generally delivered to sites separately, was also installed on board. Apart from specialist items of oil drilling gear, the platform is equipped with lift fans and drilling engines which serve a dual purpose by driving the lift fans when the platform is changing location.

Two tractors are normally required to tow the platform in a fully loaded condition.

Transport and routing problems are now greatly simplified as the need to detour virtually impassable lakes, marshes, and snow or water-filled ravines no longer arises. The rig has been employed in oilfields at Shaimskoye, Urai and Samotlor.

Two more multi-ton cargo-carrying ACV

The BU-75-VP oil rig, the first in the world to be mounted on an air-cushion platform

platforms have been completed at the Tyumen Ship Repair yard. One new platform, which was put into service in 1974, has a load capacity of 200 tons.

A more recent design has been undergoing tests at the Strezhevoye workings at Alexandrov field in the Tomsk region. Large ACV rigs with a capacity of several thousand tons are under development.

BU-75-VP
DIMENSIONS:
Length	98·43 ft (30 m)
Width	65·62 ft (20 m)

WEIGHTS:

All-up weight	170 tonnes

PERFORMANCE:
Speed (depending on towing vehicle)
About 6 mph (9·65 km/h)

ACV TRAILERS

Three ACV trailers are being developed by the organisation—a six-ton platform; the PVP-40 with a cargo capacity of 40 tonnes and a larger derivative with a capacity of 6-ton counterpart is powered by a single gas-turbine driving twin axial-flow fans. Discs or wheels fitted to swinging arms at the rear provide directional control when reversing and operating on slopes. "Trains" of ACV trailers can be employed to carry

60 tonnes. The PVP-40 has been undergoing state acceptance trials in Surgut and the Soviet Far North and if put into production will be employed in the construction of oil installations, pipelines, by geological surveys and on drainage and irrigation schemes.

The PVP-40 is powered by a single diesel engine driving two centrifugal fans. Its 60-ton counterpart is powered by a single gas-turbine driving twin axial-flow fans. Discs or wheels fitted to swinging arms at the rear provide directional control when reversing. "Trains" of ACV trailers can be employed to carry heavy loads and a further development is an articulated trailer, several times the length of platforms like the PVP-40, with one tractor forward and another at the rear.

ACV TRACTORS

Towing requirements for the rigs and ACV Trailers built in Tyumen were met at first by conventional GTT amphibious crawler tractors. Since these were unable to cope with very soft terrain, development of a true multi-terrain tractor was undertaken, and this led to the construction of the Tyumen I. This was the first of a completely new ACV type and combined crawler propulsion with air cushion lift. The first model, now relegated to Tyumen's ACV museum, carried a 2-tonne load at speeds up to 25 mph (40 km/h) in off-road conditions. It is described as a broad, squat vehicle on long narrow caterpillor tracks, with a flexible skirt between its crawlers. The second was the MVP-2 which was upgraded soon afterwards to the

PVP-40 air cushion trailer undergoing field tests.   The trailer, which has a load capacity of 40-tons, is designed for carrying heavy, single-piece cargoes and machines, drilling and oil-production equipment in the difficult and marshy terrain of Russia's Northern regions

Rear view of the PVP-40 air-cushion trailer showing the unusual arrangement of varied length segments on the bag skirt

Articulated ACV trailer.

A, Operating arrangement.
B. How turns are negotiated
1, tractor;
2, cargo areas;
3, flexible skirt;
4, second tractor to stabilise trailer motion.

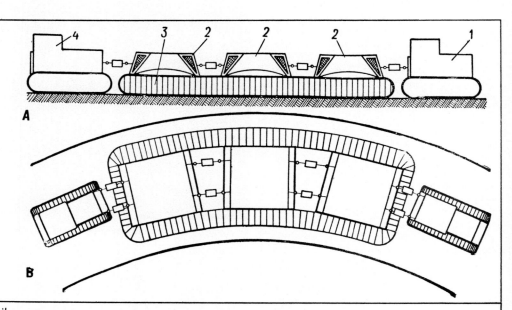

Diagram of a typical Soviet-designed ACV oil rig platform.

1, flexible bag skirt;
2, air cushion;
3, fan;
4, drilling rig engines (employed to drive fans during moves);
5, derrick;
6, drilling rig base;
7, tractor.
h—air gap;
H—hard structure clearance;

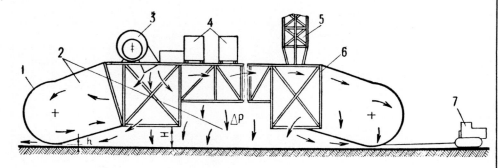

MVP-3 5-tonne capacity model. The MVP-3 uses extremely narrow crawler tracks for propulsion, steering and support on hard surfaces. As with the Bertin Terraplane series of wheel assisted ACVs, the weight transference to the crawler track is variable according to the nature of the terrain being crossed and the gradient. It is said to be capable of 50 mph (80·46 km/h) over swamps with 40 in (1·01 m) high hummocks and cruises at 30 mph (48·28 km/h). At the time of its first demonstration to the Soviet press in July 1974, it had completed 60 miles (96·56 km/h) over Siberian swamps.

Operation of the vehicle appears to be relatively simple. Main controls are an accelerator for the single engine, which has an automatic clutch, and two standard tracked vehicle steering levers which skid-steer through the differential use of the tracks.

The policy at Tyumen is to standardise on composite crawler ACV systems rather than air propeller or endless-screw type propulsion.

A 6 - ton capacity air cushion trailer towed by a five-ton capacity MVP-3 combined ACV/crawler tractor. Both vehicles have been developed by the West Siberian Branch of the All-Union Oil Machinery Research Institute. The first vehicle of this type built in the Soviet Union had completed 621 miles (1,000 km) crossing swamps and other difficult terrain by September 1973

AIR CUSHION LANDING SYSTEMS

FRANCE

BERTIN & CIE

OFFICE AND WORKS:
BP 3, 78370 Plaisir, France
TELEPHONE:
462.25.00
TELEX:
26 619 AVIATOM PLAIS
DIRECTORS:
M. Jean Bertin, President Director General
M. Benjamin Salmon, Director General
M. Michel Perineau, Director General

Bertin & Cie is now developing air cushion landing systems based upon the company's technique of separately-fed multiple plenum chambers.

ATTERROGLISSEUR

The Atterroglisseur is an air cushion drop platform for damping both vertically and horizontally the landing of heavy loads dropped by parachute. The system comprises a platform carrying the load and an air cushion system which includes inflatable balloons fitted on the underside of the platform, a light tray at the base of the balloons, and flexible skirts beneath the tray connected to the balloons.

While in the aircraft, the complete air cushion system is tightly packed beneath the platform and secured in position by a plate. When the platform is dropped, the securing plate detaches itself automatically and both the flexible skirts and the balloons inflate.

On landing the balloons deflate first, thus feeding the skirts continuously. It is only when the balloons are empty that the skirts slowly collapse to bring the platform to a standstill.

AIRCRAFT LANDING SYSTEM

The same basic system but incorporating air generators is being developed as an air cushion landing system for heavy cargo aircraft and wing-in-ground-effect machines, providing them with multi-terrain landing and take-off capability.

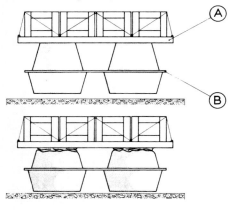

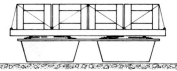

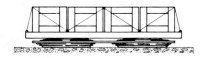

Bertin Atteroglisseur in action. The system is designed to prevent loads dropped by parachute from turning over on hitting the ground. As the loaded platform lands, balloons beneath it cushion the impact as they deflate. Air from the balloons is then fed below into a series of multiple skirts, inflating them and creating an air cushion. This allows the platform to skim the terrain in the dropping zone while the parachutes settle, thus reducing the possibility of the platform and load overturning. When the balloons are finally deflated, the skirts collapse and friction brings the platform to a standstill

Bertin air cushion landing system employed on a giant cargo carrying wing-in-ground-effect machine, providing multi-terrain landing and take-off capability

Four phases during an air drop employing an Atteroglisseur skirted platform: 1. During descent, balloons above the multi-skirt cells are fully inflated; 2. On hitting the ground the balloons are gradually crushed and eject air below to inflate the skirts; 3. Balloons are deflated and collapse; 4. Skirts are flattened and increased friction through surface contact brings the platform to a halt. The platform comprises: A.The load platform with balloons fitted below and B. a light tray, to which the lower ends of the balloons are secured. The multi-cell skirts are hung beneath the tray

THE UNITED STATES OF AMERICA

BELL AEROSPACE

HEAD OFFICE:
  Buffalo, New York 14240
TELEPHONE:
  Area Code 716 297-1000
OFFICERS:
  See ACV Section

The air cushion landing system is designed by Bell to replace wheels, skis, or floats on any size or type of aircraft, with a single system combining the functional capabilities of them all.

This application of the air cushion principle is an outgrowth of work in the field of air cushion vehicles. The system minimises airstrip requirements and enables aircraft to take-off and land on unprepared surfaces, in open fields, on open water, ice, snow, marsh, sand or dirt. Factors contributing to this feasibility are the very low pressure in the bag supporting the aircraft, the elimination of friction because of the air jets, and the increased area of contact during braking.

It has proved to be an ideal gear for crosswind take-off and landing.

The first aircraft to be fitted with ACLS was a Lake LA-4 light amphibian. In November 1970 Bell was awarded a USAF contract to install this equipment on a de Havilland CC-115 Buffalo.

The aircraft, so modified, was redesignated XC-8A and delivered to the USAF in November 1973.

ACLS-EQUIPPED LA-4

Preliminary tests were undertaken with the aid of a specially equipped LA-4 amphibian which performed its first take-off and landing in September 1969, in 25 mph (40·23 km/h) winds on Lake Erie.

The LA-4 ACLS consists primarily of a doughnut-shaped bag inflated to a thickness of approximately 2 ft (·60 m) by an axial fan. The fan, powered by a separate engine, forces air down into the bag. This flow of air escapes through thousands of small jet nozzles on the underside of the bag, providing a cushion of air upon which the aircraft floats. The bag is fabricated from multiple layers of stretch nylon cloth for strength, natural rubber for elasticity and coated with neoprene for environmental stability. When deflated during flight its elasticity ensures that it retracts tightly against the underside of the hull.

At touchdown, six brake skids on the underside of the bag are brought into contact with the landing surface by pneumatic pillows. When fully inflated for maximum braking, these pillows are each slightly larger than a basketball. For parking on land or water a lightweight internal bladder seals the air jets, thus supporting the aircraft at rest, or providing buoyancy to keep it afloat indefinitely.

Above: The De Havilland XC-8A with its ACLS bag inflated
Below: Equipped with ACLS, the XC-8A can operate from a range of surfaces including rough ground, marshland, ice, snow, water and grass. Floats are mounted beneath each wing for operation on and from water. Fibreglass spring skids beneath the floats prevent the machine from rolling excessively while taxiing

DIMENSIONS:
Aircraft

Wing span	38 ft 0 in (11·58 m)
Overall length	24 ft 11 in (7·59 m)
Gross wing area	170 sq ft (15·79 m²)

Air Cushion

Length	16 ft 0 in (4·87 m)
Width	3 ft 10 in (1·16 m)
Area	45 sq ft (4·18 m²)

LOADINGS:

Wing loading	15 lb per sq ft
Air cushion pressure	55 lb per sq ft

WEIGHTS:

Gross operating weight	2,500 lb (1,113·92 kg)
Air cushion system weight	258 lb (117 kg)

POWER PLANTS:
  Propulsion engine rating:

Lycoming Model 0 360 01A	180 bhp

Air Cushion Engine rating:

Modified McCulloch Model 4318F (driving 2-stage axial fan)	90 bhp

PERFORMANCE:

Cruising speed	125 mph (201 km/h)
Stalling speed	54 mph (86·9 km/h)
Take-off run	650 ft (198·12 m)
Landing run	475 ft (144·78 m)

ACLS-EQUIPPED XC-8A BUFFALO

Current activities are being conducted under a joint United States/Canadian programme to adapt the ACLS for military transport aircraft. This would allow such aircraft to operate from a variety of surfaces, including rough fields, soft soils, swamps, water, ice and snow. A contract for the first phase, covering programme definition and air cushion trunk fabrication, was awarded to Bell by the USAF Flight Dynamics Laboratory in November 1970.

It was decided to use a de Havilland Canada XC-8A Buffalo STOL military transport aircraft, loaned by the Canadian Department of National Defence, as the testbed aircraft for this programme.

United Aircraft of Canada Ltd was made responsible for development and flight qualification of the auxiliary power system, and de Havilland Aircraft of Canada Ltd. modified the XC-8A testbed aircraft to take the ACLS installation. The Canadian government funded the work of these two companies.

Taxi tests and an initial take-off on the ACLS were completed in March 1975. The first ACLS landing of the XC-8A took place at Wright-Patterson, Air Force Base, Dayton, Ohio, on Friday April 11th, 1975.

ACLS employs a layer of air instead of wheels as the ground contracting medium. The system's trunk, a large inner-tube like arrangement, encircles the underside of the fuselage, and, on inflation, provides an air duct and seal for the air cushion.

The underside of the rubberised trunk is perforated with hundreds of vent holes through which air is allowed to escape to form the air cushion.

The two ST6F-70 gas-turbine engines that drive the two-stage fan system to supply air to the ACLS trunk were developed by United Aircraft of Canada, Ltd.

Because the ACLS distributes the weight of an aircraft over a considerably larger area than conventional wheeled systems, and itself exerts a ground pressure of less than 3 lb/sq in (0·20 kg/cm²) it permits operations on surfaces with very low bearing strength.

Hamilton Standard Division of United Aircraft Corp. has modified the standard Buffalo propellers to give the pilot direct control of the blade angle. By changing the blade settings differentially, he has more positive directional control while taxiing.

Six skids on the bottom operate when the pilot applies the aircraft brakes. The braking action pushes the skids, of tyre tread-type material, against the ground and stops the aircraft. Stopping distance is comparable to that of conventional wheel and brake landing systems.

The Buffalo will be able to operate from a range of surfaces including grass, unprepared rough ground, snow and water as well as paved surfaces.

Balancer floats have been mounted on struts beneath each wing for operation on and from water. Beneath the floats are fibreglass spring skids to prevent excessive roll and protect the propellers while taxiing over land.

XC-8A BUFFALO
DIMENSIONS:
AIRCRAFT:

Wing span	96 ft 0 in (29·26 m)

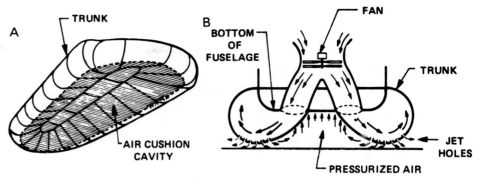

ACLS PRINCIPLE
A. Function of the inflated trunk, left, is to contain the pressurised air in the air cushion cavity. This cushion of air supports the weight of the craft.
B. Air continuously forced through the jet holes pressurises the air cushion cavity, and also provides air bearing lubrication between the trunk and its supporting surface.

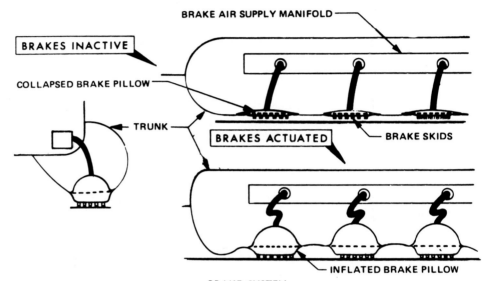

BRAKE SYSTEM
Inflation of the brake pillow of the ACLS-equipped plane brings multiple brake skids into ground contact, drawing the aircraft to a halt

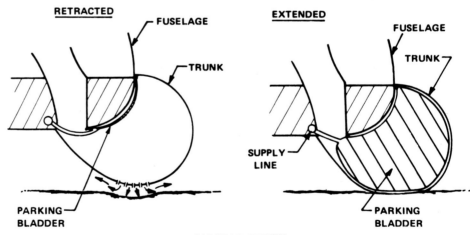

PARKING SYSTEM
A separate bladder within the rubberised air cushion trunk is inflated to support the weight of the aircraft when parked

Overall length	77 ft 4 in (23·57 m)		WEIGHTS:	
Gross wing area	945 sq ft (22·63 m²)		Gross operating weight	
AIR CUSHION:				41,000 lb (18,597 kg)
Length	32 ft 2 in (10·25 m)		Air Cushion system weight	
Width	14 ft 0 in (4·26 m)			2,220 lb (1,006·92 kg)
Area	228 sq ft (21·18 m²)		POWER PLANT:	
			Propulsion engines:	
LOADINGS:			Two General Electric Model CT64-820-1,	
Wing loading	14·8 lb per sq ft		rated at 3,055 eshp	
Air cushion pressure	170 lb per sq ft		Air cushion engines:	

Two United Aircraft of Canada ST6F-70, rated at 800 bhp

PERFORMANCE:
Cruising speed at 10,000 ft   230 knots TAS
Stalling speed, 40 degree flap
   at 39,000 lb   66 knots

Take-off run on level surface	1,130 ft
to 50 feet from level surface	1,640 ft
Landing run	
from 50 feet on level surface	1,130 ft
on level surface	650 ft

ACLS APPLICATION CONTRACTS

Bell has also studied the feasibility of using an ACLS on Space Shuttle vehicles and an Advanced Technology Transport under NASA contract, a high-performance fighter under US Navy contract, and has designed an ACLS for a Remotely Piloted Vehicle—the Australian Jindivik—under a USAF contract.

UNION OF SOVIET SOCIALIST REPUBLICS

BARTINI

Robert Oros di Bartini, a Soviet aircraft designer of Italian birth, has indicated that air cushion landing systems are under development in the Soviet Union, and will possibly replace conventional wheeled undercarriages on aircraft by the end of the century.

His Stal-6, of 1933, was the first in the Soviet Union with a completely retractable undercarriage.

Bartini is former head of the group of designers at the Scientific Research Institute of the Civil Air Fleet.   His Stal-7 was shown at the 15th Paris Aviation Salon and achieved a world speed record in 1939.   He worked with Lavochkin and Myasishchev on fighter development and his later designs include the ER-2 long-range night bomber.   In recent years he has participated in the development of VTOL aircraft.

TRACKED SKIMMERS

BRAZIL

FEI
FACULTY OF INDUSTRIAL ENGINEERING

ADDRESS:

Research Vehicle Department (DEPV), Faculty of Industrial Engineering, São Bernado do Campo, Avenido Oreste Romano 112, São Paulo

TELEPHONE:

443 1155

SENIOR EXECUTIVES:

Baj. Rigoberto Soler Gisbert, Director of Vehicle Research

The Vehicle Research Department of the FEI, founded in 1968, has designed a number of small air cushion vehicles, one of which is about to be put into production.

The Department's first and most ambitious project to date has been the design and construction of the TALAV tracked air cushion vehicle, development of which is being supported by the Ministry for Industry and Commerce through FUNAT—a government fund for sponsoring new technological developments.

The prototype, an all-metal vehicle propelled by twin Marbore VIs, and seating 20 passengers, displays several novel features, including the siting of the main passenger access door at the front. The whole of the front section moves forward telescopically to provide space for entry and exit. This arrangement facilitates the loading of freight when necessary, and should an emergency stop occur when carrying passengers on a narrow elevated guideway, walking out through the front will be far safer than through the sides, say the designers.

It is also stated that passenger handling will be simplified at termini, where the vehicles can be drawn up side-by-side without the need to devote valuable space for platforms.

The main application foreseen for vehicles of this type is that of city centre to suburbs or city centre to airport links.

To enable construction to be undertaken without difficulty in developing areas where manpower is available, the structure is based on easily-handled sub-assemblies and standard panels of aluminium honeycomb.

The design team is at present concentrating on the development of an efficient yet economical approach to the construction of guideways.

LIFT AND PROPULSION: Cushion air is delivered by fans powered by a 70 hp engine. Cushion pressure, 40 lb ft², cushion area

Above and below: Prototype of the FEI, 20-seat TALAV tracked air cushion vehicle. Designed to cruise at 200 mph (321·86 km/h), the vehicle is powered by twin Turbomeca Marbore VI gas-turbines

3,250 ft². Two 900 lb st Turbomeca Marbore VI gas-turbines supply propulsive thrust.

DIMENSIONS, EXTERNAL:

Length	51 ft (15·54 m)
Width	7·4 ft (2·26 m)
Height	9 ft 5 in (2·87 m)

DIMENSIONS, INTERNAL:

Internal height, passenger saloon
7 ft 0 in (2·13 m)

WEIGHTS:

Empty weight	6,500 lb (2,948·35 kg)
Loaded weight	13,000 lb (5,896·70 kg)

PERFORMANCE:

Cruising speed	200 mph (321·86 km/h)

FRANCE

SOCIÉTÉ DE L'AEROTRAIN

HEAD OFFICE:

Tour Anjou, 33, quai National, 92806 Puteaux

TELEPHONE:

776 43 34

TELEX:

61385 Bertrin Puteau

PRESIDENT DIRECTOR GENERAL:

Jean Bertin

DIRECTOR GENERAL:

André Garnault

Jean Berthelot, International Division

Originally named "Société d'Etudes de l'Aerotrain", this company was formed on April 15, 1965 to develop a high speed transportation system based on air cushion support and guidance principles conceived by Bertin & Cie.

The Aerotrain has completed its experi-

mental phase as far as the air cushion technique is concerned. The 01 half-scale prototype, after nearly three years of test runs at speeds up to 215 mph (346 km/h), has successfully attained its phased design requirements, namely the verification of dynamic behaviour, the development of integrated suspension systems, and the accumulation of data for the design and costing of full-scale operational vehicles.

The 02 half-scale prototype has undergone similar tests in order to produce data for vehicles operating at speeds above 200 mph (322 km/h). A speed of 263 mph (322 km/h) was attained by the vehicle in January 1969.

There are three families of Aerotrain systems, Interurban, with a speed of 225 mph (360 km/h); Suburban, with a speed of 113 mph (180 km/h) and the new Tridim system, designed for speeds of up to 50 mph (80 km/h) as the distance between stations generally ranges between several hundred yards and one or two miles. The speeds selected will be based on economic considerations. Suburban systems will cover a variety of routes from city centres to airports and city centres to satellite towns and suburban areas. The size, speed and control system of each vehicle will be decided according to the route.

Current studies are aimed primarily at developing associated techniques including propulsion modes for the various speeds and environments, controls, signals and stations.

A mathematical model has been developed in order to computerise the various parameters for both families of applications. This will enable operating costs to be obtained, in an optimised form, for given traffic requirements.

Two full-scale vehicles, the 80-seat Orleans inter-city Aerotrain and the 40-44 seat suburban Aerotrain have undergone extensive trials. During trials between 1969 and 1971, the 80-seat 1-80 "Orleans" Aerotrain has completed more than 700 hours of operation on its 18 km (11·2 mile) track north of Orleans, carrying more than 10,000 people at a speed of 160 mph (260 km/h). In January 1973, the vehicle was taken to the UTA maintenance facility at Le Bourget airport where it was equipped with a 15,000 lb st JT8D-11 turbofan, permitting its speed to be studied in the 220-250 mph (360-400 km/h) range.

In November 1973, a speed of 250 mph (400 km/h) was attained and by May 1974, 150 hours of operation had been logged in this configuration, during which 2,000 professionally interested passengers had been carried.

All these programmes, completed or under way, represent a financial development effort of roughly $22 million. The French Government, which has extended its support at every stage by means of various loans, subsidies and orders, decided at a Cabinet meeting in July 1971 to build a rapid transit line from the new business centre of Paris, La Défense to the New Town of Cergy-Pontoise, using the Aerotrain air cushion technique and propelled by linear induction motor.

A substantial amount of the land for the track has been acquired and construction will begin in 1975.

In November 1969, the company formed a US subsidiary, Aerotrain Systems Inc, to build and market Aerotrains in the United States and Mexico. The company is jointly held by Rohr Industries Inc, Bertin et Cie and Société de l'Aerotrain. Rohr's interest is 80%. The company's first prototype was completed in December 1972 and will be tested in 1974 on an experimental line built at the US Department of Transport centre at Pueblo, California.

The experimental Aerotrain 01 running at 215 mph over its 4·2 mile long test track, located south-west of Paris, near Gometz-la-Ville.

Turntables are installed at each end of the present Aerotrain test track, but they will not be used normally on operational lines. In service Aerotrains will be able to manoeuvre independently on the flat floor surfaces of stations

In 1971, another subsidiary was formed, Aerotrain Scandinavia AB, in which the Salen Group has a 50% interest. A third company, formed in Brazil with the support of four French banks, is Aerotrain Systems de Transporte.

In December 1973 an agreement was signed between Bertin & Cie, Aerotrain, Spie-Batignolles, Jeumont-Schneider, SGTE MTE and Francorail-MTE, who will co-operate in the promotion and operation of Aerotrain systems and various aspects of production.

EXPERIMENTAL AEROTRAIN AEROTRAIN 01

An experimental, half-scale prototype, this vehicle was operated along a test track 4·2 miles (6·7 km) long. The track has an inverted T cross section, the vertical portion being 1 ft 10 in (55 cm) high and the horizontal base 5 ft 11 in (1·80 m) wide. A turn-table is fitted at each end.

The vehicle is of light alloy construction. The slender body has seats at the front for six people, and an engine compartment at the rear. Lift and guidance are provided by two centrifugal fans, driven by two 50 hp Renault Gordini motor car engines, linked by a shaft. The fans supply air to the guidance and lift cushions at a pressure of about 0·35 lb/sq in (25 gr/cm²), the maximum airflow being 350 cu ft/sec (10 m³/sec). Propulsion is provided by a 260 hp Continental aero-engine, mounted at the top of a 3 ft 11 in (1·20 m) tail pylon and driving a reversible-pitch propeller, which is also used for normal braking. There are brake pads at the rear of the vehicle which grip the vertical track section like a disc brake.

The first test run on the track was made on December 29, 1965. The prototype was intended to evaluate and demonstrate the Aerotrain principle on a small scale, and was developed with the active support of the French Government and French Railways.

Although the vehicle was designed for a maximum speed of 125 mph (200 km/h) tests have been undertaken at higher speeds with the help of booster rockets to supplement the propulsive airscrew. In December 1967, the vehicle reached the top speed of 215 mph (345 km/h) several times with a jet engine assisted by two booster rockets.

DIMENSIONS:

Length overall	32 ft 10 in (10·00 m)
Width overall	6 ft 7 in (2·00 m)
Height overall	12 ft 2 in (3·70 m)
Height to top of body	5 ft 3 in (1·60 m)

WEIGHTS:

Basic weight	5,500 lb (2,500 kg)

PERFORMANCE:

Cruising speed	125 mph (200 km/h)
Top speed	188 mph (303 km/h)

EXPERIMENTAL AEROTRAIN 02

Aerotrain 02 is an experimental half-scale prototype designed for high speed tests on the track at Gometz used by the first prototype.

Due to the track's relatively short length, a more powerful thrust engine, a Pratt & Whitney JT 12, is installed in order to maintain high speeds over a distance of 1·3 miles (2 km) for performance measurements.

During its first series of test runs, the Aerotrain 02 attained 235 mph (378 km/h). A booster rocket was then added, and a series of tests followed, culminating in a record speed of 263 mph (422 km/h) being attained. The average speed recorded over the 2/3 mile track was 255 mph (411 km/h).

The air cushions for lift and guidance are provided by fans driven by a Turbomeca Palouste gas-turbine. At high speed, the dynamic pressure is sufficient to feed the air cushions.

The internal space has been devoted in the main to test instrumentation. Seats are provided only for the pilot and a test engineer.

Aerotrains 01 and 02 were both equipped with propulsion engines which were readily available from the aviation market and capable of giving high speed on a short test track. Operational vehicles use quieter power arrangements.

The Aerotrain 02, a research vehicle built for tests up to and above 250 mph on the No. 1 track at Gometz

The I-80HV Aerotrain with its new turbofan thrust unit

FULL-SCALE AEROTRAIN
I-80 ORLEANS INTERCITY PROJECT

This medium range inter-city vehicle (the Orleans-Paris line will be 70 miles (113 km) long) was designed originally with airscrew propulsion for speeds up to 186·41 mph (300 km/h), but has now been equipped with a silenced turbofan engine which has increased its speed to 250 mph (400 km/h). The vehicle carries 80 passengers in airline comfort in an air-conditioned and sound-proofed cabin.

The lift and guidance air cushions are fed by two axial fans driven by a 400 hp Turbomeca Astazou gas turbine. At high speeds, they will be fed by dynamic intake pressure.

On the original model thrust was supplied by a shrouded propeller, driven independently by two 1,300 hp Turmo 111 gas-turbines.

In January 1973, the vehicle was taken to the UTA maintenance facility at Le Bourget, where it has been fitted with a 15,000 lb thrust Pratt & Whitney JT8D-11 turbofan, which will permit the systematic study of the I-80 and its components at speeds in the 220-250 mph (354-426 km/h) range.

Hydraulically retractable tyred wheels are incorporated to help to achieve silent operation near and in stations, and also to assist in manoeuvring and switching the vehicle on station floors. The vertical rail of the inverted T track is unnecessary at low speeds.

A very low empty-weight-to-payload ratio has been possible because of the lack of concentrated loads inherent in the vehicle. This permits the use of lightweight supporting structures—tracks and stations.

Vehicles will not be coupled, so that very high frequency services can be maintained throughout the day. With headways as low as one minute, simple or articulated vehicles offer a range of capacities which largely cope with the peaks of traffic expected in known intercity lines.

Two articulated cars with seats for up to 160 passengers and luxury models with a wider aisle and reduced seating capacity are being considered in feasibility studies being undertaken for several projected routes.

DIMENSIONS:
Length overall	101 ft 8 in (30·50 m)
Length at track level	92 ft 6 in (27·75 m)
Height at fan jet air intake	
	17 ft 0 in (5·10 m)
Width	10 ft 8 in (3·20 m)

WEIGHTS:
Gross weight	24 metric tons

PERFORMANCE:
Test speed range
220-250 mph (354-426 km/h)

THE GUIDEWAY

The first leg of the future Orleans to Paris line—a track 11·5 miles (18·5 km) long— was completed in July 1969. It includes turntables at both ends and a central platform for manoeuvring and switching.

In mid-1973 the French Government confirmed that the line is to be completed in due course, but did not announce details.

The track has been designed for a service speed of 250 mph (402 km/h). It is mounted on pylons along the entire route. The prefabricated concrete beams, of 67 ft (20 m) span, have a minimum ground clearance of 16 ft (4·90 m). This allows the track to be constructed across roads and cultivated land.

Due to the low stresses produced by the Aerotrain vehicles it has been possible to design a lightweight elevated track structure, which is less expensive than an equivalent ground track. Local ground subsidence, which may occur during the first years after erection, will be countered by adjusting the pylon heads. This will be limited to a simple jacking operation using built-in devices in the pylon structure.

The radii of curves and gradient angles will depend upon the accelerations admissible without causing discomfort to passengers. Banking can be provided if necessary. Banking of 7% is in fact incorporated in three curves in the Orleans track. The radius requirements are therefore the same as for other guided systems of transport for similar speeds. The advantage of the Aerotrain track is that there are no gradient limitations and it can therefore be constructed with a much smaller number of curves.

Aerotrain guideway track beams can be adjusted at the pylon heads in the event of ground subsidence

TESTS

By May 1974, the vehicle had completed more than 850 hours of operation, during which it logged more than 30,000 miles and carried nearly 13,000 passengers.

During the investigation tests, over one hundred technical parameters were systematically measured under various configurations and throughout the entire performance envelope.

Speed, acceleration and braking characteristics have confirmed expectations, and the riding comfort has proven to be highly satisfactory. Under all operating conditions, including propeller reverse braking, negotiating curves and in cross winds of 31 mph (50 km/h), the average accelerations were less than 0·6 m/s² at all times, with values of 0·3 to 0·5 m/s² during normal cruising conditions.

Since the interior noise level in the passenger compartment is between 75 and 78 dBA, it is possible to converse in normal tones. A level 70-72 dBA will be reached on series production vehicles.

External noise, 90-95 dBA at 65 yards (60 m) compares favourably to that of a modern electric train, with a much shorter duration.

During the 850 hours of operation there was no breakdown which caused the vehicle to stop on the guideway, with the exception of a single incident involving hydraulic circuits to the propeller, which were repaired in less than an hour. Only three items, other than the air cushions, have necessitated a major repair since the vehicle was put on the guideway. The air cushions have been completely trouble-free.

The third phase of the test programme consisted of an endurance, or accelerated service test involving 200 hours of running time. Thirty-six operating days were utilised and during the average six hours of continuous operation were completed. The cruising speed established was 154·33 mph (250 km/h). Since this involved acceleration and deceleration between 0 and 154·33 mph (250 km/h) every six minutes, a commercial operation of 1,000-2,000 hours or 200,000-400,000 km in terms of wear on the vehicle was simulated. The rate of air cushion lip wear experienced indicates a useful lip life of 40,000 to 50,000 km and a practically negligible cost factor of ·001 to ·002 francs per passenger/kilometer.

It is to be noted that cultivation has been resumed around and underneath the guideway which, in sharp contrast with the high permanent way maintenance costs experienced by the railways, has required no maintenance whatsoever since it was built.

SIDE VIEW

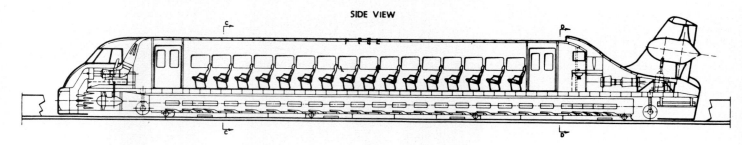

PLAN VIEW

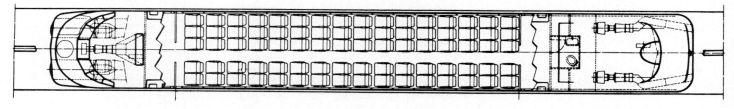

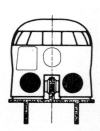

FRONT

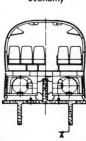

CC
Economy

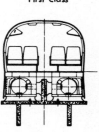

CC
First Class

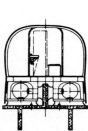

DD

REAR

The Aerotrain I-80—a typical Aerotrain configuration for medium-range inter-city traffic, carrying 80 passengers at a cruising speed of 180 mph and a top speed of 190 mph

The prefabricated concrete beams of the Orleans track have a minimum ground clearance of 16 ft (4·87 m). This allows the track to be constructed across roads and agricultural land without causing obstruction
Photo: P. M. Lambermont

HIGH SPEED 1-80 HV "ORLEANS" AERO-TRAIN

In November 1973, the 1-80 "Orleans" Aerotrain began a series of tests with a new propulsion system. The two Turmo III gas-turbines, which powered a shrouded propeller, were replaced by a 15,000 lb thrust Pratt & Whitney JT8D-II turbofan, fitted with a sound supressor system designed by Bertin & Cie. The ride characteristics remained outstanding at speeds up to 250 mph (426 km/h) in spite of the size of the new propulsion unit which resulted in the vehicle being 4 tons over weight.

The compressors and air feeders remained unchanged.

On March 5th, 1974, the vehicle attained 270 mph (430 km/h), with an average speed (in each direction) of 263 mph (418 km/h) over a distance of 1·86 miles. The sound insulation has been extremely effective, resulting in a noise level 21b lower than the original propulsion system.

SUBURBAN AEROTRAIN
AEROTRAIN S-44

The prototype 40-44 passenger suburban vehicle is equipped with a linear induction motor. The vehicle underwent trials at Gometz between 1969 and 1972, where its 2 mile (3 km) test track runs parallel to that used by the Aerotrain 01 and 02 experimental vehicles. During its test programme the vehicle was operated at speeds up to 105 mph (170 km/h). The S-44 is currently undergoing modification as part of the company's development programme for the new 15 mile (24 km) La Défense—Cergy line.

The power for the two axial lift fans is provided by a 525 hp GM Chevrolet V-8 car engine. Practically silent operation is achieved since there is no noise of rolling wheels. No vibration is communicated to the track structure which can therefore be erected in urban areas without fear of any noise disturbing local communities, even if steel is used for the longer spans of the guideway.

This vehicle is equipped with an electrical linear motor developed by the Société Le Moteur Linéaire (Merlin & Gerin Group). It provides a thrust of 18,000 N at 85 mph

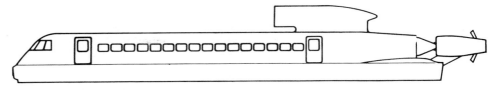

Side view showing the revised configuration of the I-80HV Aerotrain with its new turbofan thrust unit

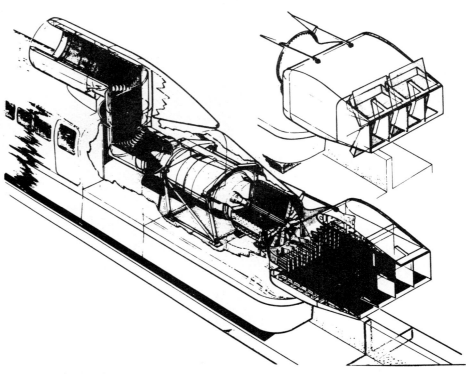

The I-80HV Orleans Aerotrain after being fitted with a 15,000 lb thrust Pratt & Whitney JT8D-11 turbofan, which will permit the behaviour of the vehicle's systems to be studied at speeds of 220-250 mph (354-426 km/h). Considerable attention has been given to sound attenuation. As seen in the cutaway drawing, the air intake has been designed for the maximum effectiveness, and a special high dilution ejection system suppresses the noise of the exhaust gases

(137 km/h) and has been currently operated at speeds above 100 mph (160·93 km/h).

Electric current is collected from the three-phase 1,000 V power line set alongside the track.

Braking performance is particularly efficient. During normal operation braking is obtained either by dephasing the linear motor supply (or in the case of failure of this supply by feeding it with DC current from the battery),

Prototype of the 40-44 seat suburban Aerotrain seen on its I.9 miles (3 km) test track at Gometz

or by a hydraulic braking system equipped with friction pads which grip the vertical portion of the track.

The passenger cabin is divided into four ten-seat compartments, each provided with two doors. An additional half-compartment forward can accommodate four passengers seated on folding seats.

Automatic doors are provided on both sides of each passenger compartment which will help to reduce stopping time. The coupling of several of these vehicles will be possible, but this should only be necessary at peak hours for heavy commuter traffic.

The seating arrangement is optional; each of the various layouts is optimised to provide the maximum possible space for passengers.

DIMENSIONS:
Length	47 ft 0 in (14·4 m)
Beam	9 ft 4 in (2·75 m)
Height	10 ft 2 in (3·10 m)

WEIGHTS:
Loaded weight:
linear motor weight	25,000 lb (11,500 kg)
automotive version	22,000 lb (10,000 kg)

PERFORMANCE:
Cruising speed	113 mph (180 km/h)

A lower speed system is being designed for urban lines with stations only ½ mile apart.

THE GUIDEWAY

In this programme the track is at ground level. The horizontal support is an asphalt carpet and the upright is an aluminium beam which is used for both guiding the vehicle and as an induction rail for the linear motor. A 1·9 mile (3 km) long track has been constructed at the company's base at Gometz.

Operational suburban lines will generally be supported on pylons in order to leave the ground free. The use of an elevated track will reduce the construction time and avoid costly tunnelling on many sections of urban/suburban projects.

PROJECT STUDIES

Société de l'Aérotrain has conducted detailed studies of a dozen projects. The technical and operational characteristics of the vehicles may substantially differ from those of the two prototypes, particularly as regards capacity and cruising speed.

The mathematical model, which has enabled the company to examine technico-economical optimisation procedures, an approach to operations, station design, and baggage handling has produced data based on a number of projected situations. The two major fields which are being investigated are inter-city services and suburban links, mainly between city centres and airports.

Suburban links require, in some cases, a higher capacity than the one provided by the Gometz-type vehicle. Capacity can be increased by widening the vehicles, or coupling them, to provide an hourly capacity of around 10,000 passengers each way.

Projects of an almost urban nature are also being investigated with the Tridim version.

CERGY-PONTOISE—LA DEFENSE SUBURBAN AEROTRAIN

The French government decided in July 1971 to build an Aerotrain rapid transit line from the new business centre of La Défense, just outside Paris, to the new town of Cergy-Pontoise. The line is to be opened in early 1979. Detailed studies are under way and on-site works will begin before the end of 1974.

Artist's impression of the Cergy-Défense suburban Aerotrain

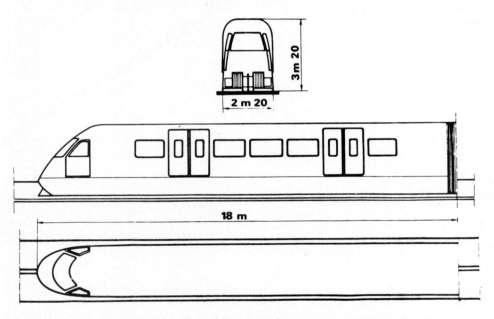

A unit of the suburban Aerotrain. Two of these 80-seat units are coupled to form a vehicle, and on the Cergy-Défense line, two vehicles will be coupled to form each train—providing a total seating capacity per train of 320 passengers

The travel time between Cergy-Pontoise and La Défense will be less than 10 minutes. The line will connect with a new express metro linking La Défense with Etoile, and the Opéra, the journey times being 4 and 7 minutes respectively.

Cergy-Pontoise will have a population of 200,000 by 1975 and between 350,000 and 400,000 by the year 2000. It is to be a satellite town of the capital and is about 30 km west of Paris.

TRACK: The length of the route will be 15 miles (24 km). Later it may be extended to cater for urban developments. A part of it will be laid alongside freeways to be constructed during the next 5 years, necessitating a few additional land acquisitions.

The track will be elevated for most of the distance, providing a clearance of 16 ft (5 m) above ground. Supporting pylons will be 66 to 83 ft (20-25 m) apart. The track itself will be 17 ft 8 in (5·30 m) and will be double. Each side will have an aluminium alloy vertical centre rail providing both guidance for the vehicles and the secondary, or induction element, for the linear motor.

Electric power is supplied by wayside rails carrying 1500v dc.

The horizontal radii of curves are kept above 1,200 m to allow a high cruising speed. The steepest slope is 6% and occurs when climbing a cliff after a crossing of the Seine.

The Aerotrain vehicle to be used on this service will be supported and guided by air cushions, and propelled by a linear induction motor.

The vehicles will each comprise two units, and on the Cergy-Défense line a train will consist of two coupled vehicles.

SUPPORT AND GUIDANCE: Each unit has its own air cushion guidance and support systems, air for which is put under pressure by electrically driven fans.

PROPULSION: Each unit will be equipped with a linear induction motor of variable voltage and frequency which will be regulated by on-board power-control equipment.

BRAKING: Two systems will be employed:

TIME TABLE: The line was expected to be opened at the beginning of 1979. Although the contract for the construction was signed on June 21st, 1974, it was cancelled the following month by a new French government which introduced sweeping cutbacks in public expenditure to counter inflation.

Another line for the first commercial operation is being selected. One possibility is in the Marseilles area, with a section linking the suburbs of the city with Marignane airport and Aix-en-Provence, and extensions to the industrial complexes and new cities under construction around Etang de Berre.

A three-phase powerline alongside the track at ground level provides electric current for the linear motor

Above and below: The Rohr-built Aerotrain, constructed under a US Department of Transportation contract. The vehicle, which is 94 ft long, will carry 60 passengers at speeds up to 150 mph. On May 9th 1975, the vehicle became the first all-electric TACV to attain 100 mph. The speed will be increased up to 150 mph when the Dept. of Transportation's test track is lengthened to its planned 5·7 miles towards the end of 1975

TRIDIM URBAN TRANSPORTATION SYSTEM

The Tridim system has been designed to solve the transportation problem in urban areas or suburbs where the distance between stations ranges from a few kilometres down to several hundred metres.

It is believed that the solution to this problem lies in an overhead transportation system adapted to passenger flows ranging from a few thousand to 10-15,000 per hour and offering appreciable comfort, speed and frequency. To transport 6,000 passengers per hour, trains of 3 vehicles of 50 seats each every 90 seconds will be sufficient. If a larger module is adopted, 20,000 passengers can be carried hourly.

The Tridim system is designed to meet these requirements through the use of an air cushion for suspension and a flexible rack-and-pinion system, rubber-tyred traction-wheels, or linear induction motor for propulsion.

It consists of small-size self-powered air cushion vehicles moving on a lightweight overhead track.

The capacity of each vehicle can be between 4 and 100 seats according to customer requirements. The required capacity can be obtained by varying the width and the length of the vehicles or grouping any number of vehicles to form a train. Since June 1973, a 4-6 seat prototype vehicle has been under test at a research centre of the French National Electricity Company (E.D.F.) located at Les Renardières, near Fontainebleau, on a 1,000 ft (305 m) track which includes a straight section, grades, curves and points.

Characteristics of this vehicle are as follows:

Loaded weight	1·2 tons
Nominal propulsion power	15 kW
Lifting power	4 kW
Max speed	50 km/h
Max slope	20%
Power supply	cc 160V
Number of air cushions	8
Air pressure	900 kg/m²

The Tridim vehicle is built on a modular basis, with additional modules being added as required to provide the desired capacity.

In the case of the type VM 1 (designed for a specific client), the passengers are transported in modules measuring approximately 10 ft by 6 ft and equipped with 9 seats

A 4-seat Tridim urban transport vehicle on its "switchback" test track

placed along the longitudinal walls. There is also room for a minimum of 4 standing passengers, which brings the rush-hour capacity to 13 passengers for each module, i.e. 52 per vehicle, 36 of whom are seated (the vehicle consists of 4 modules).

Propulsion and lift are obtained from electric energy collected from a "third" rail (direct-current power supply).

The vehicle is guided by a low metal rail fixed on the track in line with the vehicle axis. This is the inverted-T track fundamental to the Aerotrain technique. Besides its guidance function, this rail carries the propulsion rack and keeps the vehicle retained on the track, which makes overturning impossible in the event of incident or abnormal operating conditions.

LIFT: The basic advantages of employing the air-cushion principle are:

Suspension of concentrated loads and shocks, hence possibility of a lightweight vehicle structure on the one hand, and of the overhead track on the other; the absence of rolling noise and vibration; vehicle maintenance drastically reduced, and virtually non-existent for the track; and finally low total cost of the transportation system due to the simplicity and the lightweight of the track.

The air cushion system requires a power supply of only 4 to 5 hp per supported metric ton. This is expected to be reduced to the order of 2 hp per metric ton. The air cushion supply is operated by sound-insulated electric fans.

PROPULSION: In the case of the VM 1 the vehicle is propelled by a patented rack-and-pinion system. But alternative methods include rubber-tyred traction wheels acting on the centre guidance rail or linear induction motor, according to requirements. The former consists of a dual rack fixed on the guiding rail and two pinions carried by the vehicles and driven by electric propulsion motors. It allows operation on tracks with steep slopes and maintain acceleration and braking performance in any weather including conditions of snow and ice.

The ability to climb steep slopes enables the stations to be built at street level or at the level of another transportation system for ease of transfer.

OVERHEAD TRACK: The system is intended primarily for an overhead track but it can also be used at ground level or as an underground system. In the case of an overhead track, the viaduct can be made of metal or of reinforced concrete, the choice

Aerotrain Tridim urban transport vehicle

between the two materials being dictated mainly by the line layout.

This consists of pylons supporting beams of 66 ft to 100 ft span carrying the guideway which has a width of about 7 ft 4 in for single track or 15 ft 6 in for dual track in the case of the VM 1 system. The track itself consists mainly of the guiding rail with its rack.

The absence of concentrated loads, either static or dynamic, allows the use of a light viaduct, which leads to less cost.

As an example, with metal construction, a dual track viaduct weighs approximately 1,300 lbs per metre (VM 1).

VM1 SPECIFICATION:

The system can be adapted to client specification.

Capacity of the VM 1 is 52 passengers, 36 of whom are seated.

DIMENSIONS:

Length	53 ft 4 in
Width	6 ft 4 in
Height	8 ft 6 in

WEIGHTS:

Empty weight	13,000 lb
Loaded weight	21,800 lb

PERFORMANCE:

Nominal speed	40/50 mph
Maximum speed	50/65 mph
Average acceleration between 0 and 40 mph	0·12 g
Emergency deceleration	0·2 g
Allowable slope at 40 mph	3%
Maximum allowable slope at reduced speed	15% to 25%
Minimum turning radius	80 ft approx.

MOTOR POWER:

for propulsion	150 kW approx.
for cushion	35 kW

OVERHEAD TRACK:

Span	66 ft to 100 ft for normal span
Height above ground	16 ft on the average

Width of track:

single track	7 ft 4 in
dual track	15 ft 4 in

Electrical power supply by conductor rail

URBA

Compagnie d'Energetique Lineaire mb

HEAD OFFICE:

5 Rue Monge, 92 Vanves, France

OFFICERS:

M. E. Barthalon, ScMMIT, Ecole Polytechnique, President Director General

UK REPRESENTATIVE:

mBm Powercels Ltd,
25 Bedford Row, London WC1

P. Watson, BA MIMarE, Managing Director

The URBA mass transport system, invented in 1966 by M. Maurice Barthalon, aims at providing a means of urban transport which combines absence of noise, vibration and atmospheric pollution with low capital and maintenance costs and a high degree of flexibility of installation and operation. The vehicle, which may operate singly or in trains, is suspended from its track by an air lift system in which the pressure is sub-atmospheric, and propulsion is by electric linear induction motors. The cabin of the vehicle is suspended from a number of Dynavac air bogies which run within an elevated track the section of which is like a flattened, inverted

The URBA 4 prototype seats 6/12 passengers and has a cruising speed of 50 mph (80 km/h)

U, with inward facing flanges on the bottom edges of the sides, on which the air bogies sit when at rest. The Dynavac air bogies house the lift fans which draw air from the space between the track and the top of the bogie, so producing a pressure difference which causes the air bogie to lift off the track flanges.

Special sealing arrangements provide a controlled leak into the lift chamber which decreases as the weight of the vehicle increases, so increasing the pressure difference. The air bogies therefore remain in a stable, floating condition without being in contact with the track.

Lateral guidance is provided by similar but smaller Dynavac cushions between the sides of the bogie and the sides of the track. The air bogies also house the linear induction motors which react with a reactor rail projecting downwards from the centre of the track. This effectively divides the lift chamber into two independent halves, thus providing a degree of roll control. The suspension between the cabin and the air bogie acts as a secondary suspension system (the air cushion being the primary) and provides for articulation of the air bogies so that the vehicle can take curves of small radius.

In order to carry the development of URBA from a vehicle to a fully integrated public transport system, the Société d'Etudes de l'URBA (SETURBA) has been formed by the Caisse des Dépöts et Consignation, the Enterprise Bouygues and the Gazocéan-Technigaz Group.

The registered office of the Society is at 4 Place Raoul Dautry, Paris 15.

SETURBA has accelerated the application of URBA by confirming, technically and economically, the best means of applying this new method of transport and has prepared the constitution of a new company charged with the industrial and commercial development of the URBA system.

A technical and financial appraisal of URBA, undertaken by the SETURBA study group, proved favourable, and this has led to the establishment of Société de l'URBA (S.U.), supported by former associates of SETURBA, finance companies, banks and investors. Capital investment will be between F10-15 million. SETURBA has also launched a marketing programme to communities in France where likely applications are foreseen.

The company states that public funds are being made available in the form of research and development grants, and that the next phase of URBA's development programme is budgeted at F 30 million.

URBA has been specially designed to satisfy the transport needs of medium-size towns of 200,000 to 1,000,000 inhabitants, and the suburbs of large cities.

The prototype URBA 4, and later two URBA 8s coupled together, were demonstrated at Lyon during 1968. The prototype has been in daily use for almost four years at the Ecole Centrale of Lyon, where research and development has been supported by D.G.R.S.T., D.A.T.A.R., A.N.V.A.R. and the Ministry of Transport. To date it has carried 30,000 visitors. The computer analysis of its dynamic behaviour has confirmed its stability, its comfort and its ability to take small radius curves.

Several recent international assessments, including a searching study by Eurofinance, consider URBA as one of the most promising of the new means of transport for the years 1970 to 1990. A certain number of towns in France and abroad, including Rouen, Bordeaux and Montpellier, are already at the stage of serious preliminary studies. Three different lines located in the outskirts of Paris have been studied. A special study has also been undertaken for the new business centre of La Defénse, on the western side of Paris. These bring out the favourable capital and operating costs which should place the price per passenger per kilométre of URBA at a level comparable with that of the bus today.

URBA 8

A prototype urban and suburban monorail URBA 8 is an improved version of the URBA 4, with three linear motors instead of two, and seats for eight passengers. Two URBA 8s were demonstrated at Lyon on December 4th, 1968, on an 87 yard (79 m) track. They operated singly and coupled, with acceleration and deceleration in the range 0·25 to 0·35 g (with 0·5 g deceleration in an emerg-

Impression of a single-track URBA 30 line, with supporting columns located in the centre of a highway

URBA 20, a light urban transport vehicle with a service speed of 45 mph (72 km/h) and seating 20 passengers

ency), and at speeds up to 30 mph (48·28 km/h). It consists of a rectangular-framed cabin seating up to eight passengers and suspended from three Dynavac air bogies running in an experimental 260 ft (80 m) track.

PROPULSION: Propulsion and normal braking is by three Merlin Gerin linear motors of 25 kW, weighing 176 lb (80 kg) and providing a thrust of 220 lb (100 kg) at starting 66 lb (30 kg) at normal service speed. Supply is from 380 volt, 3-phase, 50 cycle mains. The motor is the first to be designed as an industrial unit for vehicle propulsion. An alumin-

ium conductor fin runs down the centre of the track and a set of coils is mounted in each bogie. Conductor rails for current supply to the linear motor and lift fans are in the base of the fin.

CABIN: The cabin is rectangular and measures 14 ft 10 in (4·5 m) long, 5 ft 3 in (1·6 m) wide and 4 ft (1·2 m) high. It is built from 4 cm square section tube and diecast corners of a type normally used for the framework of holiday bungalows.

The floor is of light alloy and the sides are perspex. Suspension between the cabin and the three air bogies is by rubber cord springs and hydraulic automobile shock absorbers.

Tests have demonstrated that the air bogie concept is suitable for sharp curves, can climb steep slopes and provides good acceleration and braking. It cannot be derailed.

URBA 20

An enlarged version of the URBA 4, this model will seat 20 passengers in a cylindrical cabin and have a top speed of 45 mph (72 km/h). More efficient lift fans will be employed on this model which will require a total of 12 kW for lift power. All-up weight

will be 10,470 lb (4,750 kg).

URBA 30

This is the first model designed to go into service as a public transport system and will seat 30 passengers in rows, three abreast. The initial design will have 5 special, lightweight automatic doors on one side. Overall dimensions of the cabin will be: length 29 ft 6 in (9 m), width 6 ft 3 in (1·9 m), height 6 ft 7 in (2 m) overall, loaded weight 5·3 tons. Propulsion will be by linear motors.

Cost of the double overhead track for the URBA 30 will be in the region of £200,000 per mile excluding wayleaves.

FIRST COMMERCIAL LINE

Bids have been submitted by the Société de l'URBA for two projects, the most promising being a line between the centre of a new town to the south of Paris, and the nearby railway station. The line will be about 3·21 km (2 miles) in length and will have gradients of 10%.

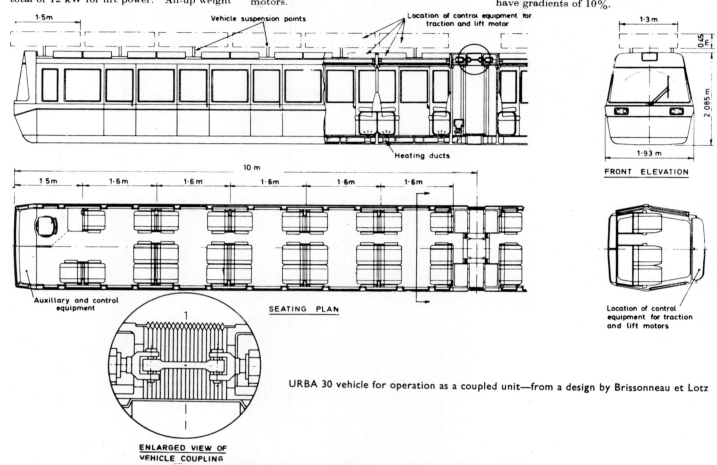

URBA 30 vehicle for operation as a coupled unit—from a design by Brissonneau et Lotz

GERMAN FEDERAL REPUBLIC

TRANSRAPID-EMS
Gesellschaft fur elektromagnetische Schnell-verkehrssysteme (Joint Venture Group Krauss-Maffei and MBB)

HEAD OFFICE:
D-8000 Munich, Steindorfstr. 13
TELEPHONE:
(089) 226694/22 73 40
TELEX:
529463 trmue

In April 1974 it was announced that Krauss-Maffei (KM) and Messerschmitt-Bolkow-Blohm (MBB) are to develop jointly a high-speed transportation system.

As agreed with the Federal Minister of Research and Technology, the corporate managements of both companies have decided to conduct their future development activities for a track-guided high-speed transportation system—started in the late sixties—on a joint basis.

In 1971 both companies presented to the public the world's first large-scale test vehicles supported, guided, and driven by magnetic fields. In the meantime extensive testing performed on test rigs and test tracks at Munchen-Allach and Ottobrunn has demonstrated that contact-free magnetic

Transrapid dynamic magnet test stand

suspension using controlled electromagnets can be achieved and is practical for high-speed ground transportation systems.

Both companies, using different approaches, arrived at very similar research results.

The chief objective of the joint venture group is to develop a uniform high-speed transportation system for Europe for economic long-haul passenger and freight transportation. To achieve this aim, international links, such as co-operation with DAF Netherlands began in 1973, and plans for the formation of an international management corporation for high-speed transportation are under way.

Research work is being financed by the Federal Minister of Research and Technology as well as by funds from the two companies.

During 1974 speeds up to 248 mph (400 km/h) will be attained by the magnetic suspension test vehicles of the joint venture group.

TRACK

The track for a rapid transit system based on the principle of magnetic suspension and guidance would consist of the supporting concrete pylons and beams, the ferromagnetic support and guidance rails, the secondary part of the linear motor, and the power rails.

In order to ensure the safe operation of a rapid transit system on the one hand, and not to endanger the environment by its operation on the other, the track will be supported on pylons spaced approximately 52 ft 6 in (16 m) apart with the elevation (clearance) of the track being at least 14 ft 9 in (4·50 m). This eliminates to a large extent, the need for special structures at intersections with roads, rail tracks, etc.

A fast and reliable switching system for traffic diverging from and merging with the main line is necessary for smooth and safe operation of a rapid transit system. To meet this need, MBB has developed an electromagnetically controlled switching device that has no moving parts situated on the track.

PRINCIPLE OF MAGNETIC LEVITATION

In the selected principle of magnetic attraction, the vehicles are supported and guided by controlled electromagnets along armature rails fastened to the guideway. Sensors continuously measure the air gap between the vehicle magnets and the armature rails (10-20 mm). The data measured is transmitted to the control unit which controls the attractive forces of the magnets and thus keeps the vehicle in a hovering condition.

In addition to the development of the magnetic levitation and guidance system, vehicle development also includes other components, such as linear motor propulsion energy transfer, vehicle frame, braking, emergency gliding and safety systems. The design of cost-saving, elevated guideways and planning of the necessary stationary facilities, such as stations, power supply, etc. are of equal significance for the overall system.

Knowledge and experience gained and substantiated through extensive testing on various test stands formed the basis for the construction of experimental vehicles and test tracks in Ottobrunn, München-Allach and Manching.

TEST STANDS

Static, dynamic and rotating magnet test stands were built for the purpose of defining

Above and below: First full-scale test vehicle to employ magnetic suspension guidance and propulsion, was MBB's basic experimental craft. Weighing 5·6 metric tons and 23 ft (7 m) in length, it has reached 62 mph (100 km/h) on a 766 yard (700 m) track

and optimising magnets for the levitation and guidance system and various control techniques. Support force losses and braking forces on magnets as a result of eddy current effects at high speeds can be measured and power transmission methods tested on rotation test stands. Switching tests with magnetically levitated vehicles are performed on switch test stands. Linear motor test stands are used to determine thrust and lateral forces on single- and double-sided linear motors and to measure temperature, current and voltage.

BASIC VEHICLE

MBB began work on the vehicle and the test track began in July of 1970. On February 4, 1971, the first suspension tests of the experimental vehicle took place in the test laboratory. On April 2, 1971, the first test runs were made on MBB's special test track.

On May 5, 1971, the experimental vehicle was presented to the public for the first time in the presence of the Federal Minister for Educational Science and the Federal Minister for Transportation.

It demonstrated the feasibility of magnetic suspension and guidance with linear motor propulsion, and it provided information on those parameters not covered during simulation of the system and development of the components.

Weighing 5·6 metric tons and with a length of 23 ft, it has an asynchronous linear motor with 200 kW nominal power which is capable of accelerating the vehicle on the 766 yard (700 m) test track to a speed of 62 mph (100 km/h).

Four controlled suspension magnets and two guidance magnets on each side of the vehicle lift it and guide it during operation with a nominal air gap of ½ in (14 mm) between the magnets and the rails.

TRANSRAPID 02 RESEARCH VEHICLE

In October 1971 Krauss-Maffei started operating an experimental 39 ft 4 in (12 m) long vehicle on a 1,093 yard (1,000 m) test track. It reached a maximum speed of 99 mph (160 km/h). A novel power pick-up system ensures troublefree transmission of electric energy at high speeds. A secondary suspension system with pneumatic shock absorbers and vibration dampers constitutes the link between the vehicle superstructure and the hovering chassis.

Guideway and vehicle concepts provide realistic test data. The test results obtained so far have revealed that the system requirements can be fulfilled without difficulty.

TRACK:
Length   1,093 yards (1,000 m)
Radius of curvature   875 yards (800 m)
EXPERIMENTAL VEHICLE:
Length   38 ft 4½ in (11·70 m)

Width	9 ft 6 in (2·90 m)
Height above track surface	
	6 ft 8¾ in (2·05 m)
Number of seats	1 × 7/9
Weight	appr 11 Mp
Payload	appr 2 Mp
Design speed of vehicle	
	appr 220 mph (350 km/h)

PROPULSION BY LINEAR INDUCTION
MOTOR:

Thrust (transient)	appr 3·2 Mp
Present vehicle speed (due to short track length)	appr 100 mph (160 km/h)
Synchronous speed LIM at 50 cps	
	appr 112 mph (180 km/h)

SERVICE BRAKES:

Brake retardation by LIM	appr 2·5 m/sec/²
by jaw brake	appr 8·5 m/sec/²
by friction brake	appr 8·0 m/sec/²

ELECTROMAGNETIC SUPPORT AND
GUIDANCE SYSTEM:

Specific carrying capacity
appr 800 kp/m magnet length (25 mm air gap)

Air gap	½ in 1 in (10·25 mm)

POWER SUPPLY:

Support and guidance system:
Voltage 380 V three-phase current, 50 cp

Output	32 kW

TRANSRAPID 03 RESEARCH VEHICLE

In October 1971, the company started operating a dual-purpose test facility which allows a comprehensive system comparison between magnetic cushion and air cushion techniques using same vehicles on the same track with completely identical operating conditions. Vehicles and track have been designed for a maximum speed of approximately 220 mph (350 km/h). The track length is 0·6 miles (1,000 m) allowing the attainment of a speed of about 100 mph (160·93 km/h), which has already been reached with the magnetic cushion vehicle. This experimental system provides realistic information since it subjects the support, guidance and propulsion system to extreme loads both during straight runs and cornering.

Transrapid 03 is the basic Transrapid 8-ton research vehicle adapted for tests as a tracked air cushion vehicle. The payload of two tons and overall dimensions are identical to those of the vehicle in its earlier configuration. The programme, which is supported by the Federal Ministry of Research and Technology, is enabling the TACV and Maglev concepts to be compared under identical conditions for the first time.

Tests with aircushion support began at the end of 1972 and finished in 1973.

As a TACV, the vehicle is supported and guided by a total of 14 air cushion pads. Six, each with a cushion area of 3 m², support the vehicle on its elevated concrete guideway, and eight, mounted in pairs, each of about 1 m² cushion area, provide lateral guidance along the LIM reaction rail. The air cushion lift system is of plenum type and each pad has a rubber skirt. Cushion air is supplied by a two-stage compressor.

The vehicle is propelled by a French-made LIM system, which accelerates the vehicle to 90 mph (145 km/h) on its 1,093 yard (1,000 m) guideway.

Comparisons covered the following areas: vehicle dynamics; weight; load tolerances; vertical air gap tolerances; specific power requirements for support and guidance;

Krauss-Maffei's Transrapid research vehicle in 02 configuration, with magnetic support, guidance and propulsion systems

Transrapid's 03 research craft permitted a full systems comparison between magnetic and air cushion techniques, using the same vehicle on the same track under completely identical operating conditions

effects on the environment (noise level); reliability; life; reaction to weather influences; maximum speed; aerodynamic drag; investment, operating and maintenance costs.

Result of the comparison: Magnetic levitation technology is superior.

TRACK:

Length	1,093 yards (1,000 m)
Radius of curvature	875 yards (800 m)

EXPERIMENTAL VEHICLE:

Length	38 ft 4½ in (11·7 m)
Width	9 ft 6 in (2·9 m)
Height above track surface	
	6 ft 8¾ in (2·05 m)
Number of seats	10
Weight	appr. 8 mp
Payload	appr. 2 mp
Design speed of vehicle	
	appr. 220 mph (350 km/h)

PROPULSION BY LINEAR INDUCTION
MOTOR:

Thrust (transient)	appr. 3·2 Mp

Present vehicle speed (due to short track
length)   appr. 100 mph (160 km/h)
Synchronous speed LIM at 50 cps
        appr. 112 mph (180 km/h)
SERVICE BRAKES:
  Brake retardation by LIM appr. 2·3 m/sec/²
  by jaw brake   appr. 8·5 m/sec/²
  by friction brake   appr. 8·0 m/sec/²
ELECTROMAGNETIC SUPPORT AND
  GUIDANCE SYSTEM:
  Specific carrying capacity
  appr. 800 kp/m magnet length (25 mm air
    gap)
  Air gap   ½ in 1 in (10·25 mm)
POWER SUPPLY:
  Support and guidance system:
  Voltage 380 V three-phase current, 50 cp
  Output   32 kW
  LIM:
  Voltage 2·6 KV three-phase current, 50 cps
  Output   5 MVA

MAGNET TEST VEHICLE

Operation of the magnet test vehicle started
on the Ottobrunn test track in 1972. This
test vehicle consists of a platform supported
and guided by wheels and accelerated by a
hot water rocket.

The magnet test vehicle was used to test
magnets as well as the air gap between
magnet and rail and acceleration sensors at
different speed levels up to 225 km/h. The
components were tested in conjunction with
an instrumented test rail mounted in the
guideway.

DIMENSIONS:
  Vehicle:

Length	11 ft 9¾ in (3·6 m)
Width	8 ft 2¾ in (2·5 m)
Starting weight	2,866 lb (1,300 kg)
Max speed	139 mph (225 km/h)
Propulsion:	
Type	hot water rocket
Guideway:	
Length	722 yards (660 m)

COMPONENT TEST VEHICLE KOMET

The Komet is an unmanned, magnetically
levitated and guided vehicle with a mounting
rack for components to be tested. This
mounting rack allows the installation of
magnets, linear motors and power pick-ups
of various designs, which can be tested in
combination with equally easily replaceable
instrumented rails at speeds up to 400 km/h.
The test data are transmitted to a fixed
receiving station via a telemetry system.
The Komet is accelerated by means of a
thrust sled equipped with up to six hot-
water rockets in order to achieve the desired
high speeds on only 1,300 meters length of
test track.

TECHNICAL DATA:
  Component Test Vehicle:

Length	8·5 m
Width	2·5 m
Height	1·7 m
Weight (without instrumented components)	8,800 kg
Max speed	400 km/h
Thrust sled:	
Length	5·0 m
Width	2·5 m
Height	1·5 m

The MBB hot-water rocket-driven test carrier on its track at Ottobrunn

The Komet, an unmanned magnetically-guided and levitated component-test vehicle, capable of speeds of up to 248 mph (400 km/h)

Transrapid 04, the world's largest passenger vehicle employing magnetic levitation and a linear induction motor for propulsion

Starting weight	7,500 kg	Test section	300 m
Guideway		Deceleration and safety section	700 m
Track gauge	2·2 m	**TRANSRAPID 04**	
Length	1,300 m	The Transrapid 04 is the largest passenger-	
incl. acceleration section	300 m	carrying magnetically levitated and LIM-	

propelled experimental vehicle in existence to date.

The elevated guideway, with curves of different radii, represents a further development on the way to future applications. Different design principles and materials, such as concrete and steel, were used in order to test various alternatives. For the first time, a LIM reaction rail was mounted horizontally on the guideway beam.

The 2,400 m test track allows the testing of different system components under realistic conditions and at higher speeds. The results of the test programme will be the basis for the definition of future test vehicles and large-scale test facilities.

TECHNICAL DATA:

Vehicle:

Length	15·0 m
Width	3·4 m
Height	2·8 m
Weight	16,500 kg
Max speed	v250 km/h

Propulsion:

Type	asynchronous linear motor
Max thrust	50,000 N

Guideway:

Track gauge	3·2 m
Length	2,400 m
Radii of curvature	800-3,100 m
Span	17-20 m
Max guideway inclination	±11°

PRE-PROTOTYPE TRAIN

Based on the R&D results gained at Krauss-Maffei and MBB, Transrapid-E.M.S, in collaboration with the research and design departments of the parent companies, is currently designing a pre-prototype train. This is to be used for large-scale tests at the "Test Centre for Transportation Technology" planned by the Ministry of Transport and Ministry of Research and Technology in the Donauried Area (Bavaria). This test phase is to ensure the technical serviceability of components and vehicles prior to their final operation in realistic long-duration tests and to provide information on their reliability, safety, maintainability, riding comfort, cost-effectiveness and environmental compatibility

TECHNICAL DATA:

Train (Concept):

Length	90·0 m
Width	3·6 m
Height	4·2 m
Capacity	300 passengers
Max speed	500 km/h

Propulsion:

Type	linear motor

Elevated track employed for the Transrapid 04

Transrapid concept for a 310 mph (500 km/h) pro totype train for 160 passengers. The first section of the vehicle will be tested at the government operated test facility for transport technology, near Augsburg, from 1978 onwards. Vehicles of similar design, with LIM propulsion, will first be applied to link densely populated areas, or to connect them with the big airports

AEG-BBC-SIEMENS

HEAD OFFICE:

D-852 Erlangen, Froebelstr. 19-25

TELEPHONE:

09131-72457

CABLE/TELEX:

6 29 871

DIRECTOR:

Dipl.-Ing. A. Lichtenberg

The Federal German government has funded a joint programme by AEG; Siemens and Brown-Boveri for the design and construction of a repulsive magnetic levitation system which aims at being efficient, economical to operate, comfortable, clean and silent. Self-stabilising lift and guidance forces produced by superconducting magnets provide levitation heights of between 10 and 20 cm. The magnetically suspended vehicles are driven by linear induction motors which can be controlled over their entire speed range with low losses. Tests have recently begun on a special test track at the Siemens Research Centre in Erlangen. The track is laid out in a circle 306 yards (280 m) in diameter to enable individual components of the system to be subjected to endurance tests, using telemetric equipment, in both the rolling and suspended positions. The power supply equipment, the asynchronous linear motor and the magnet bearers, are currently being subjected to detailed tests in the rolling position. Test runs with full magnetic levitation were planned for Autumn 1975.

Testing will later be transferred to a large test track at Donauried, financed by Federal funds.

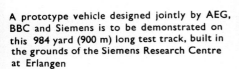

A prototype vehicle designed jointly by AEG, BBC and Siemens is to be demonstrated on this 984 yard (900 m) long test track, built in the grounds of the Siemens Research Centre at Erlangen

ITALY

PALERMO UNIVERSITY

HEAD OFFICE:

Aeronautical Institute, University of Palermo, Viale delle Scienze 90128, Palermo

TELEPHONE:

222748-317172-227439

DIRECTOR:

Professor Ennio Mattioli

The Aeronautical Institute, Palermo University began its tracked ACV research programme in 1967. During 1970-71 the Institute undertook a series of theoretical studies and investigations in the TACV field and began the construction of the I.A.P.3.

The Institute is now engaged in research in the field of magnetic levitation and SLIM (single-face linear-induction motors) propulsion.

I.A.P.3

A half-scale TACV prototype, the I.A.P.3 began its trials in May 1972 along a U-shaped concrete guideway.

The vehicle can be operated from either forward or rear driving positions and the basic design permits the coupling of a number of units to form a train.

Lift is provided partly by air cushion pads and partly by an electro-magnetic system.

Propulsion is by single-faced linear induction motor. An electronically controlled suspension system is fitted at present, but the vehicle can be converted to a magnetic suspension system.

DIMENSIONS:

Length	43 ft 3½ in (13·20 m)
Beam	10 ft 0½ in (3·06 m)

WEIGHT:

Loaded	10 tons

PERFORMANCE:

Designed for speed tests up to	155 mph (250 km/h)

View from the I.A.P.3's cabin, showing the driver's and observer's positions and a section of the U-shaped concrete guideway.   In the centre of the guideway are the SLIM induction plates

The I.A.P.3 half-scale TACV prototype on the guideway at Trapani-Milo airport

THE UNITED STATES OF AMERICA

AEROTRAIN SYSTEMS, INC

A subsidiary of Rohr Industries, Inc

HEAD OFFICE:
Chula Vista, California 92012

TELEPHONE:
(714) 426-7111

DIRECTORS:
B. F. Raynes, Chairman
F. E. McCreery
K. W. Tantlinger
A. K. Openchowski
L. Kaplan
J. Bertin
M. F. Millard
A. Garnault

EXECUTIVES:
K. W. Tantlinger, President
A. K. Openchowski, Vice-President
T. T. Brekka, Treasurer

Aerotrain Systems, Inc (formerly Aeroglide Systems, Inc) is a jointly held subsidiary of Rohr Corporation, Bertin & Cie, and Societe de l'Aerotrain. Rohr's interest in Aerotrain Systems, Inc is 60 per cent. Rohr will manufacture and market in the United States and Mexico, the high speed, guided air cushion transportation systems developed by the two French companies. Research, development and testing will be undertaken by Rohr, at the company's main plant at Chula Vista.

Aerotrain Systems, Inc is currently studying the application of tracked air cushion vehicles of various capacities, speeds, and modes of propulsion for fast passenger services between central metropolitan areas and airports, and also between cities. The former will probably travel at speeds below 200 mph (322 km/h) and the latter will operate at speeds over 200 mph (322 km/h). Either gas-turbines driving propellers or linear induction motors may be used for propulsion, the choice depending on routes and noise restrictions.

Aerotrain Systems has been testing a 94 ft long prototype of the Aerotrain at the US Department of Transportation Test Centre, Pueblo, Colorado, since September, 1974, starting with low-speed trials to check the basic subsystems and components. High speed testing began on April 7th, 1975 and on May 9th, 1975, the vehicle became the first all-electric prototype tracked air cushion

SYSTEMS SPECIFICATION (1)

The following specifications are representative of prototype vehicles and are subject to change based on continuing vehicle development.

	M-60	M-80	M-100
VEHICLE:			
Model number			
Passenger Capacity	60	80	100
DIMENSIONS:			
Overall length	94·0 ft	110·0 ft	124·2 ft
Overall height	10·8 ft	10·8 ft	10·8 ft
Overall width	10·7 ft	10·7 ft	10·7 ft
Interior cabin height	6·8 ft	6·8 ft	6·8 ft
Interior cabin width	9·5 ft	9·5 ft	9·5 ft
WEIGHT:			
Net vehicle weight	46,000 lb	54,000 lb	60,000 lb
Passengers and Baggage	14,000 lb	16,000 lb	20,000 lb
Gross vehicle weight	60,000 lb	70,000 lb	80,000 lb
POWER:			
LIM propulsion	3,415 KW	3,415 KW	3,415 KW
Maximum electrical load	4,100 KW	4,199 KW	4,298 KW
Average electrical load (cruise)	2,800 KW	3,899 KW	2,998 KW
PERFORMANCE:			
Cruising speed	150 mph	150 mph	150 mph
Maximum speed	170 mph	170 mph	170 mph
Acceleration distance to cruising speed	1·75 mi	2·3 mi	2·7 mi
Normal stopping distance	1·5 mi	1·5 mi	1·5 mi
Emergency stopping distance	0·5 mi	0·5 mi	0·5 mi
Allowable grade at cruise speed	5·5%	4·7%	4·2%
GUIDEWAY:			
Elevated roadbed width	135 in	135 in	135 in
Reaction rail height (overall)	33 in	33 in	33 in
Surface waviness		⅛ inch in 25 feet	
Minimum vertical turn	10,000 ft	10,000 ft	10,000 ft
Minimum horizontal turning radius	1,500 ft	500 ft	700 ft
ELECTRIFICATION:			
3 phase ac power supplied from wayside			
Frequency	60 Hz	60 Hz	60 Hz
Voltage	4,160 volt	4,160 volt	1,460 volt
Substation spacing	5·0 mi	4·0 mi	3·3 mi

vehicle to attain a speed of 100 mph (160·934 km/h).

Attainment of this speed was a significant step in Phase III of the Department of Transportation programme to design, build and test a prototype high-speed ground transportation system to complement existing transportation systems at speeds greater than 150 mph (241·40 km/h) for high-density intercity services. The test programme will provide first hand information for transportation planners when confronted with future transportation needs for high-speed

corridor applications for relatively short distances.

The speed of the Aerotrain Systems prototype is at present limited to 100 mph (160·934 km/h) by the length of the existing 3-mile guideway. It will be increased to 150 mph (241·40 km/h) when the guideway is lengthened to the planned 5·7 miles.

AEROTRAIN 150 mph AIRPORT ACCESS SERIES

The Aerotrain vehicle represents the adoption of the tracked air cushion vehicle

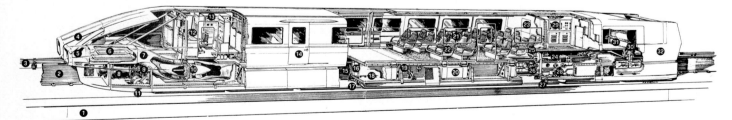

1	PRESTRESSED CONCRETE GUIDEWAY BEAMS	**11**	AUXILIARY DRIVE WHEELS
2	ALUMINIUM REACTION RAIL	**12**	AUTOMATIC TRAIN CONTROL CONSOLE
3	3-PHASE WAYSIDE POWER DISTRIBUTION SYSTEM	**13**	AUXILIARY TRAIN EQUIPMENT
4	FRANGIBLE SAFETY FOREBODY	**14**	FLUSH PASSENGER DOORS
5	SUSPENSION AIR INLET	**15**	GUIDANCE AIR CUSHIONS
6	SOUND SUPPRESSOR	**16**	SUSPENSION AIR DISTRIBUTION DUCTS
7	INLET AIR DUCTING	**17**	LIFT AIR CUSHIONS
8	COMPRESSOR MOTOR	**18**	AIR DISTRIBUTION ORIFICES
9	COMPRESSOR SPEED REDUCTION	**19**	EMERGENCY STOP BY PASS DOORS
10	LIFT COMPRESSOR	**20**	AIR CONDITIONING UNITS
		21	PASSENGER COMPARTMENT

22	AIRCRAFT QUALITY SEATS
23	EMERGENCY EXIT DOORS
24	LINEAR INDUCTION MOTOR
25	LIM SUPPORT SYSTEM
26	LIM GUIDANCE WHEELS
27	AUXILIARY SUPPORT SKIS
28	PROPULSION COOLING DUCTS
29	PROPULSION CONTROL BAY
30	MECHANICAL BRAKE
31	BAGGAGE COMPARTMENT (OPTIONAL)
32	FRANGIBLE SAFETY AFTERBODY

technology developed by Société de l'Aérotrain and Bertin et Cie to the requirements of US applications.

The inverted "tee" guideway and K type air cushion have been fully developed and are available for operational use.

Linear induction propulsion and high speed three phase power collection systems have been demonstrated at the facilities of Société de l'Aérotrain and are available for revenue producing TACV systems.

AEROTRAIN VEHICLE: The Aerotrain vehicle, featuring a 60 to 100 passenger size cabin and lightweight construction, operates on an inverted "tee" shaped guideway by linear induction motor propulsion at speeds up to 150 mph. Electric motor driven compressors supply pressurised air for the lift and guidance air cushion suspensions.

POWER COLLECTION: A power collection unit, mounted on one side of the vehicle, collects 3-phase, 4,160 volt, electrical power from the wayside power distribution rails. Power is collected by sliding contact with the power distribution rails and the collection unit is articulated from the vehicle to accommodate relative motion.

ELECTRICAL PROPULSION: A polyphase linear induction motor provides the thrust required to accelerate, maintain speed, and dynamically brake the vehicle. The LIM primary is mounted in the vehicle afterbody. The LIM secondary is the reaction rail which is mounted on the guideway. Separate motor fans provide both LIM cooling by forced convection and LIM guidance by a set of air bearing units attached to opposite ends of the LIM. A Thryistor variable voltage power control unit is used to limit acceleration onset. A power supply furnishes controlled dc current for dynamic braking. Static power factor correction capacitors compensate for the LIM reactive power.

AIR CUSHION SUSPENSION: The low pressure air cushion suspension system raises the vehicle from the guideway providing relatively friction-free motion. The secondary suspension integrates with the air cushion to damp the effects of dynamic disturbance from guideway irregularities and cross winds. The associated air supply system contains an air inlet with guide vanes, a forward plenum, two compressors, supply ducts, and cushion supply scoops. Two constant speed, 3-phase, induction motors drive the compressor units.

BRAKING: LIM dynamic braking reduces vehicle speed to approximately 50 mph, whereupon a hydraulic system circuit applies frictional braking at the reaction rail for final stopping. In an emergency, the air cushions can be vented to rest the vehicle on skids for additional braking which is controlled to not exceed 0·4 g deceleration. A pneumatic system applied to the hydraulic system frictional brakes provides redundancy.

PASSENGER CABIN: The typical seating arrangement illustrated features 22 inch seat width and 34 inch seat pitch. Each seat contains a seat belt and protective padding. Exposed hard metal surfaces are avoided.

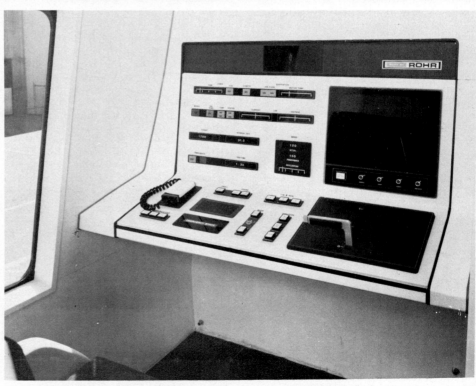

Top: The Rohr-built Aerotrain, a 60-seat operational prototype ordered by the US Department of Transportation. This particular model is propelled by a linear induction motor, and rides on a Bertin air cushion suspension system *Centre:* Interior of the Aerotrain Systems Inc M-60 prototype Automatic air conditioning is provided *Bottom:* The vehicle, designed to operate at 150 mph, is controlled by computer, but has provision for a manual override. The driver monitors the track at the front and rear by a closed circuit television system. Seen in this photograph is the automatic control console

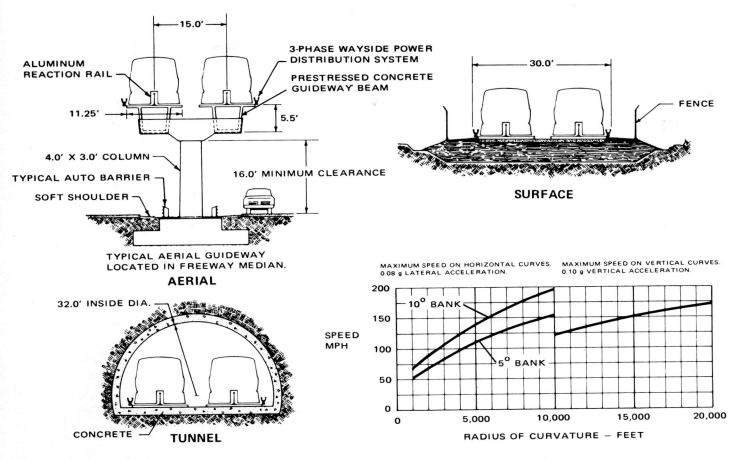

Types of guideway envisaged for the Aerotrain and graphs showing the radius of track curvature and the maximum speed on horizontal and vertical curves

The cabin interior acoustical treatment maintains the noise level below 65 dB (A). The vehicle external acoustical treatment maintains the noise level below 73 dB(A) at 50 feet to the side of the vehicle (measured on the dB(A) scale with a reference of 0·0002 microbars). Multiple air conditioning units modularly mounted in the undercar area maintain the passenger and crew compartment environment at 65° to 75°F.

(1) Automatic Train Control and other Subsystems available to individual application requirements.

AIRESEARCH MANUFACTURING COMPANY A division of the Garrett Corporation

ADDRESS:
2525 West 190th Street, Torrance, California 90509

TELEPHONE:
(213) 323-9500

EXECUTIVES:
John A. Teske, Vice-President and Manager
Dan W. Derbes, Assistant Manager
William L. Bowler, Manager, Ground Transportation Systems

AiResearch Manufacturing Company is a division of the Garrett Corporation, Los Angeles. It is engaged primarily in the design, development and manufacture of sophisticated systems and components for aerospace and ground transportation. Products include environmental controls, electronics, electromechanical and turbomachinery, heat transfer and cryogenics and ground transportation and industrial power systems. Located in the Los Angeles suburb of Torrance, AiResearch employs approximately 4,500 persons. The firm pioneered the concept of air conditioned and pressurised aircraft for high-altitude flight, and today more than 90 per cent of the aircraft built in the free world are equipped with AiResearch systems.

In the field of surface transportation AiResearch has developed and built a linear induction motor research vehicle (LIMRV) for the US Department of Transportation. The LIMRV runs on standard railroad track with a reaction rail mounted in the centre of the track. It is designed for 402·336 km/h (250 mph) and has achieved speeds in excess of 255 mph to date. AiResearch also developed and built the LIM propulsion system for the Grumman-built tracked levitated research vehicle (TLRV) tests of which began in 1974.

Other surface transportation systems under development include a dual power, gas-turbine/electric propulsion system for commuter cars, a flywheel energy storage system for subway and commuter cars, a wayside electric power collection system for high speed vehicles (this system has been tested at 482·80 km/h (300 mph), and the Advanced Concept Train (ACT-1).

LINEAR INDUCTION MOTOR RESEARCH VEHICLE (LIMRV)

Starting in 1966, AiResearch performed a study for the U.S. Department of Transportation, Federal Railroad Administration, aimed at proving the feasibility of using linear induction motors as propulsion systems for high-speed ground transportation vehicles.

Subsequently, AiResearch was elected to build a demonstration LIM and a vehicle to test the propulsion system. The vehicle was completed in December 1969. In January 1970 a year-long slow speed test programme was started in Torrance, California on a one-quarter mile (0·40 km) test track. In May 1971 the vehicle was moved to Pueblo, Colorado, site of the Department of Transportation Test Centre, where high-speed track and 6·2 miles (10·05 km) of reaction rail were installed. The track is standard gauge railroad track.

In September 1971 AiResearch personnel began testing the LIM propulsion system for the Federal Railroad Administration. In incremental steps the vehicle was operated at successively higher speeds. The vehicle and LIM are designed for a top speed of 250 mph (402·33 km/h). A new world speed record for a steel-wheeled vehicle running on steel rails was established in August 1974 during test runs that reached 255 mph (410·38 km/h). The vehicle has been equipped with two gas-turbines so that it can be accelerated to 402·336 km/h (250 mph) in a shorter distance than is possible with LIM propulsion alone. The faster rate of acceleration permits data to be obtained on the LIM propulsion at its top speed and at the same time provide adequate safety margins for braking and stopping within the limits of the track available 9·67 km (6·2 miles).

LIM FOR TRACKED LEVITATED RESEARCH VEHICLE (TLRV)

Under a US Department of Transportation contract, AiResearch has designed and constructed a LIM propulsion system for the second-generation tracked levitated research vehicle built by Grumman Aerospace Corporation.

The LIM propulsion system is designed to produce 10,000 pounds of thrust continuous at 300 mph (8,000 hp) and was installed in the TLRV in 1974.

The LIM propulsion system is supported and guided by its own air cushion system which was designed and fabricated by AiResearch. The vehicle is suspended with a separate air cushion system.

AiResearch has also designed a wayside power collection system for this 300 mph vehicle under a separate Department of Transportation contract. Both DOT contracts are under the auspices of the Federal Railroad Administration. The vehicle is being tested at Pueblo, Colorado.

To propel the TLRV at 300 mph (482·80 km/h) AiResearch has designed the propulsion system to include two identical LIM power modules each to provide one-half of the maximum vehicle thrust requirements, only one of which is installed for the initial test phases. The two LIMs have a combined system rating of 10,000 lb of thrust continuous at 300 mph (8,000 hp). The two LIM modules are mounted in tandem under the TLRV.

Since the TLRV is a research vehicle, the propulsion system was sized primarily to attain high acceleration. Initial acceleration with two power modules is about 6·0 mph/sec and even at 250 mph the acceleration is still about 3·3 mph/sec. With thrust at full acceleration, a speed of 300 mph is reached in about one minute. By way of comparison, the average initial acceleration of conventional trains is only one-sixth that of the LIM-propelled TLRV due to passenger comfort limits.

LINEAR INDUCTION MOTORS

The LIM horseshoe shaped windings in the vehicle straddle and react electromagnetically with an aluminium reaction rail mounted vertically in the centre of the guideway. Thrust and speed of the LIM are controlled by a power conditioning unit which varies the voltage and frequency applied to the LIM.

Input power for propulsion is obtained from a wayside power pickup at 8,250 volts, 3 phase 60 Hz. The wayside power collector was designed and built by AiResearch.

Much of the experience in design, fabrication, and testing of the company's first LIM system has been incorporated in the TLRV LIM. Significant differences include a higher output-to-weight ratio and fully independent suspension for the TLRV LIM. The improvement in specific thrust is achieved principally by direct liquid cooling and the use of high strength-to-weight structural materials such as titanium.

Independent suspension of the LIM is achieved by the use of air cushions for both support and guidance and a first-degree-of-freedom thrust link connection with the vehicle chassis. Only the thrust axis is restrained.

LIM REACTION RAIL

The LIM reaction rail serves a dual purpose in the TLRV propulsion system: (1) it provides the electrical secondary for the LIM

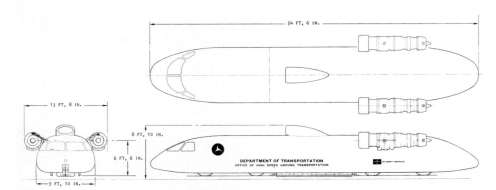

Above: General arrangement of the AiResearch Linear Induction Motor Research Vehicle (LIMVR). **Below:** Twin gas-turbines have been fitted enabling the vehicle to accelerate to 402.336 km/h (250 mph) on the existing 9.67 km (6.2 mile) US Department of Transportation's high speed test track, near Pueblo, California. The vehicle established a new world speed record for a steel-wheeled vehicle running on steel rails in August 1974 when it reached 255 mph (410.38 km/h)

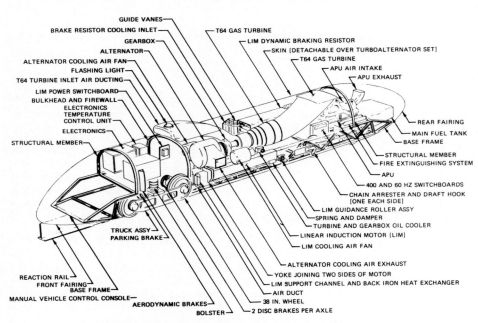

Garrett/AiResearch linear induction motor research vehicle

and functions as a continuous reactive thrust element, and (2) it provides a surface suitable for the vertical air cushions which laterally guide the LIM.

POWER CONDITIONING UNIT (PCU)

The LIM propulsion system power conditioning unit converts 3 phase, fixed voltage, 60 Hz wayside power into 3 phase, variable voltage, variable-frequency output power suitable for operating the LIM at various speed conditions. The PCU is comprised of five main components: a phase delay rectifier, a high voltage inductor, an inverter, a synchronous condenser, and field power supply. Two PCU's are required for the full LIM propulsion system, one for each LIM.

BERTELSEN INC

HEAD OFFICE:
9999 Roosevelt Road,
Westchester,
Illinois 60153
TELEPHONE:
312-681-5606
WORKS:
113 Commercial Street,
Neponset,
Illinois 61345

Dr. William R. Bertelsen, Director of Research, Bertelsen Inc, has proposed the use of a vehicle based on the twin-gimbal Aeromobile 13 for a tracked skimmer system. It is described in US Patent No. 3,845,716 issued on November 5th 1974.

Dr. Bertelsen suggests that the system, based on the use of ACVs in simple, graded earth grooves, would be ideal for mass transportation in developing countries where no large investments have been made in roads, railways or airlines. The fuel can be petroleum in oil-rich areas or hydrogen in the depleted or polluted areas. Whereas in densely populated countries new rights of way will inevitably be elevated or underground, there should be little difficulty in obtaining rights for the guideways in developing countries. In large countries with relatively empty interiors, the low-cost surface groove will be ideal.

Current or abandoned railway rights-of-way can be used for the Bertelsen Aeromobile-Aeroduct system, since rail gradients are acceptable to the Aeromobile. Hills can be climbed by the use of steps on which the vehicle is on the level or slightly inclined uphill most of the time. It climbs simply by lifting its mass in ground effect up each step, each of which would be slightly lower than its skirt height. Relatively low propulsive power is necessary to climb a hill in

Impression of a tracked air cushion vehicle, based on the Bertelsen Aeromobile 13, in its guideway System

this manner and no increase in lift power is necessary.

The Aeromobile vehicles employed for the system would be fully automated. Journey data would be fed into an onboard mini-computer and the vehicles would follow the route through signals emitted at junction points. A tape could guide the car across the country with a sleeping or reading driver. Dr. Bertelsen states that the car would move from low-to-high speed lanes automatically and remain in high-speed lanes until the signals at junctions told it to move down into a slower lane before turning off. This process

would be repeated automatically until the car left the automatic guideway system.

In more developed countries, the bottom of the guideway could be protected by concrete. Tunnels would be built in steel or concrete. Bridges across rivers or canyons would probably take the form of a suspended aluminium tube.

The system is designed to be all-inclusive, providing every type of transport need, from personal transit, "mass" transit, taxis, police, fire and emergency service, mail, freight, parcel, grocery and milk delivery to refuse pickup.

FORD MOTOR COMPANY

North American Automotive Operations
HEAD OFFICE:
20000 Rotunda Drive, Dearborn, Michigan
48121
MAILING ADDRESS:
PO Box 2053, Dearborn, Michigan

Since 1969, Ford has been conducting a research programme aimed at answering a number of questions concerned with magnetic levitation. In 1971, the US Department of Transportation awarded the company a research contract to study the feasibility of magnetic support in greater depth. In particular, the company was asked to look at problems related to system stability and the cryogenics of superconducting magnets.

Ford's first-phase contract is reported to have been $130,000, and a second-phase contract, awarded in 1972, was for $200,000. A third phase, awarded in 1973, was for $75,000. A fourth phase, awarded in 1974, was for approximately $400,000.

The research programme was discontinued in early 1975 following a US Department of Transportation decision to terminate support for magnetically levitated and other high-speed, tracked-levitated vehicle research and concentrate on programmes with greater potential for immediate and near-term improvements in passenger transportation.

Tests being undertaken with a model equipped with permanent magnets over a torating aluminium wheel in Ford's Scientific Laboratory

Conceptually, the simplest levitation scheme is one in which the vehicle contains a large number of permanent magnets, and the track is also made of permanent magnets, arranged in such a way that the magnets in the vehicle are repelled by the magnets in the roadbed. This scheme has serious drawbacks, however, because the weight of the permanent magnets is so large that a clearance of only a fraction of an inch can be achieved. Furthermore the system is unstable and active control devices would be needed.

A much better scheme uses several high-strength electromagnets in the vehicle and no magnets in the track. Instead the track is covered with an aluminium sheet or plate. There is no magnetic levitation when the vehicle is at rest, but when the vehicle moves it generates electrical currents in the aluminum. These in turn produce a magnetic field which pushes up on the electromagnets in the vehicle. The magnetic field gets stronger as the vehicle speeds up, but it levels off at speeds of 50 to 100 mph. Thus the vehicle moves on wheels at low speeds, but lifts off as the speed increases.

Ordinary electromagnets in the vehicle require a lot of electrical power to maintain them. In the past ten years, however, there has been a very great development in superconducting magnets. These magnets must be maintained at cryogenic temperatures, but do not require additional electrical power once they are energised. They require some refrigerator power on a continuous basis, but this is small compared to the amount of electrical power required by a conventional electromagnet.

Detailed calculations and experiments with superconducting magnets situated over a rotating aluminium wheel have shown that

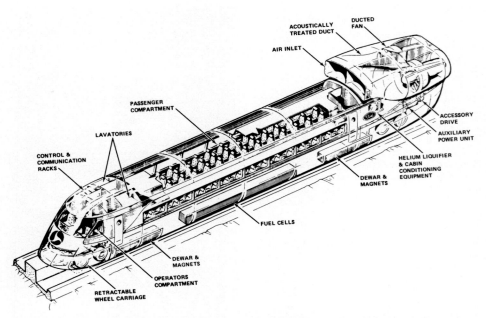

Cutaway of a Ford project for a MAGLEV vehicle propelled by gas-turbine-driven ducted fans

this magnetic levitation concept is a sound one. Lateral guidance can also be provided magnetically. Some active control is needed to help stabilise the system against perturbations, but the control power needed is quite small.

As part of its programme, the company has built superconducting magnets and subjected them to simulated conditions they would encounter when employed operationally. The company has also tested a servo-controlled, attraction magnetic system, and investigated problems likely to arise from the use of superconducting magnets, including shielding of passengers from magnetic fields.

Another area of investigation at Ford, is passenger comfort. A suspension damping system will be necessary to ensure a comfortable ride. The company believes that this can be achieved at speeds up to 482·78 km/h (300 mph) by employing either an active control system or, with passive damping, a secondary suspension system.

The final phase involved a detailed system study of a high-speed, passenger-carrying system using magnetically-levitated vehicles, and a detailed test plan for testing high-speed rocket-propelled, magnetically-levitated model vehicles on a 3,281 ft (1,000 m) long guideway.

GRUMMAN AEROSPACE CORPORATION

HEAD OFFICE AND WORKS:
   South Oyster Bay Road, Bethpage, Long Island, New York 11714
CHAIRMAN OF THE BOARD AND CHIEF EXECUTIVE OFFICER:
   J. G. Gavin, Jr.
PRESIDENT:
   G. M. Skurla
SENIOR VICE-PRESIDENT:
   I. G. Hedrick
DIRECTOR, GROUND TRANSPORTATION:
   R. V. Benito

Grumman has completed the detail design and fabrication of a 300 mph (483 km/h) tracked levitated research vehicle TLRV under contract to the US Department of Transportation.

In 1975 the Department was forced to curtail the programme due to financial constraints. The Grumman Tracked Levitated Research Vehicle is being used by the Department for further development of the AiResearch-designed linear motor propulsion system (LIMPS). No provision has been made for further research on air cushion guidance or levitation systems.

Grumman is supporting the tests by operating and maintaining the vehicle.

GRUMMAN TLRV

The Grumman TLRV is a 51 ft (15·54 m) long air cushion research vehicle designed to

Grumman's 51 ft (14·54 m) research vehicle in its guideway at the Department of Transportation's High Speed Test Centre, Pueblo, Colorado

ride in a U-shaped track at speeds up to 300 mph (483 km/h). The maximum use is made of developed aerospace hardware and the materials and processes used in the construction of the vehicle are conventional.

The craft was designed to investigate aerodynamic performance and stability, dynamic response of both vehicle and guideway members, secondary suspension requirements, air cushion design and the wearability of flexible skirt material.

LIFT AND PROPULSION: Three externally mounted JT15D turbofans are employed as compressors for cushion air. Air from the bypass fans is ducted to four lift pads and four guidance pads. During 1973 the vehicle was operated up to 90 mph (144·84 km/h) using only residual thrust from the

JT15Ds for propulsion and was expected to reach 125 mph (201·16 km/h) in that mode. With the linear motor installed, the vehicle is expected to attain speeds in the region of 300 mph (483 km/h).

SECONDARY SUSPENSION SYSTEMS: The body is connected to the chassis by elements which can be operated in an active or passive mode. The entire body can also be banked with respect to the chassis to substantially eliminate lateral acceleration during turns. The levitation and guidance cushions are connected to the chassis by elements which can also be operated actively or passively.

ACCOMMODATION AND SAFETY FEATURES: The vehicle requires only one operator. Three additional seats are provided, however. One seat is for use by a test instrumentation engineer, and the other two will provide observer accommodation. The cabin is surrounded by a strong primary structure and has a 'bird proof' windshield. Both entrance doors are accessible to all crew members. Fire protection includes detection and suppression systems, foam-filled fuel tanks, fire walls and fuel tanks located remotely from the cabin.

BRAKING SYSTEM: Normal braking is applied by aero-brake, reverse thrust and friction pads. Provision for emergency braking includes a form of arresting system built into the guideway, and a 7 ft (2·13 m) diameter drag chute.

DIMENSIONS:
Length overall	51 ft 0 in (15·54 m)
Width overall	12 ft 0 in (3·65 m)
Height overall	13 ft 2 in (4·01 m)

OPERATING WEIGHT:
Aero propulsion	34,000 lb (15,422 kg)
Linear induction motor	62,000 lb (28,123 kg)

PERFORMANCE:
Max speed	300 mph (483 km/h)
Min acceleration distance, 0-300 mph (0-483 km/h)	1·9 miles app (3·1 km)
Min braking distance	1·5 miles app (2·4 km)

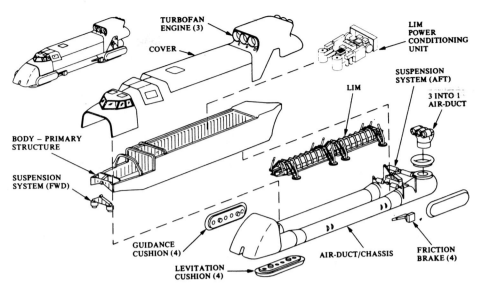

Exploded drawing of the Grumman T L RV , showing the turbofan installation linear induction motor, and body and cover structure

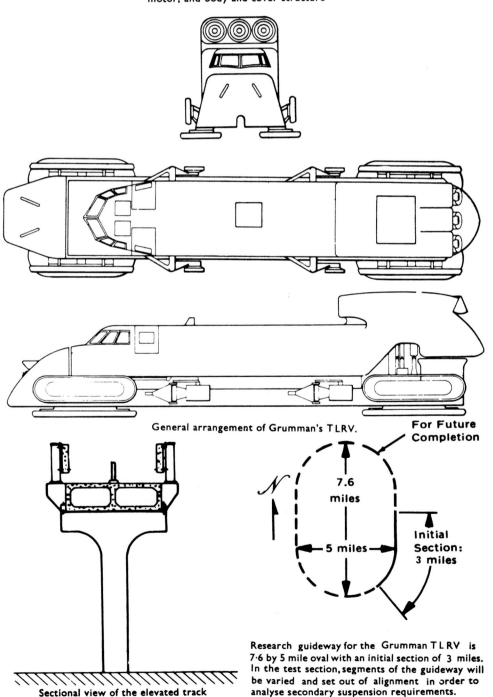

General arrangement of Grumman's T L RV.

Sectional view of the elevated track

Research guideway for the Grumman T L RV is 7·6 by 5 mile oval with an initial section of 3 miles. In the test section, segments of the guideway will be varied and set out of alignment in order to analyse secondary suspension requirements.

AIR CUSHION APPLICATORS, CONVEYORS and PALLETS

AUSTRALIA

SOUTHERN HYDRO-HOVER

HEAD OFFICE:
P.O. Box 23, Walkerville, South Australia 5081
TELEPHONE:
Unley, South Australia 49-7278

OFFICERS:
Trevor de V. Webb, Owner/Manager
E. S. Jones, Works Manager
Southern Hydro-Hover was founded in 1966 by T. W. Webb and T. de V. Webb to build

small ACVs under licence. In 1968/69, work switched to an air-cushion conveyor system, now patented and under development. T. W. Webb died in 1969 and his son T. de V. Webb is continuing work on this project.

TAYLORCRAFT TRANSPORT (DEVELOP-MENT) PTY LTD

HEAD OFFICE:
Parafield Airport, South Australia 5106
TELEPHONE: 584944
DIRECTORS:
R. V. Taylor
J. Taylor

In addition to a series of light air cushion vehicles, Taylorcraft Transport (Development) Pty Ltd has built a small load-carrying platform, the Portair, which is available to order. Larger platforms in the Trailaire series are described in the section devoted to ACV Trailers and Heavy Lift Systems.

PORTAIR

This is a pedestrian operated load-carrying platform for use in soft, wet or sandy locations where the use of wheeled carriers is precluded. It may be used with pallets where the 6 in (152 mm) lift permits easy loading. A payload of up to 600 lb (272 kg) may be carried, depending on the slope of the ground to be traversed.

Lift is provided by a Wisconsin HS-8D engine driving a 20 in (508 mm) diameter centrifugal fan.

A Portaire pedestrian-operated load-carrying platform equipped for spraying

DIMENSIONS:
Length	5 ft (1·52 m)
Width	3 ft 6 in (1·06 m)
Height	2 ft 6 in (0·762 m)

Hard structure clearance   8 in (204 mm)

WEIGHT:
Empty	135 lb (61·23 kg)

FRANCE

SOCIÉTÉ BERTIN & CIE

OFFICE AND WORKS:
BP No. 3, 78370 Plaisir, France
TELEPHONE:
462.25.00
TELEX:
26.619
DIRECTORS:
Jean Bertin, President Director General
Benjamin Salmon, Director General
Michel Perineau, Director General

Air Cushion Handling Division
OFFICER:
M. Croix-Marie
ADDRESS:
Centre d'Essais Aérotrain, Gometz la Ville 91400 Orsay, France
TELEPHONE:
592.03.18
TELEX:
60.090

Research on ground effect and air cushion principle applications has been undertaken by Bertin et Cie since 1956. The company developed the original technique of separately fed plenum chambers surrounded by flexible skirts—see entries for SEDAM (ACVs) and Société de l'Aérotrain (Tracked Skimmers). The same basic technology is being applied extensively to industrial materials handling.

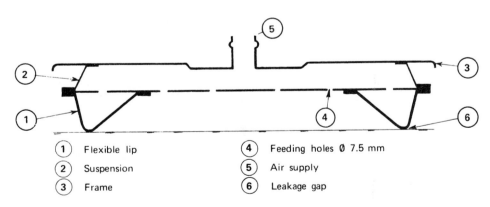

1	Flexible lip	4	Feeding holes Ø 7.5 mm
2	Suspension	5	Air supply
3	Frame	6	Leakage gap

Basic configuration and components of a Bertin circular cushion

In the past, developments in this field have mainly covered special applications. A stage has now been reached where standard equipment can be made available for a large number of handling applications.

Bertin has now made available standard components and, according to the type of problem to be solved, offers clients 'do-it-yourself-kits'', plus advice, technological assistance or full design services.

STANDARD DO-IT-YOURSELF KITS

These are available in the following configurations:

1. Circular Cushions

These form the basis of the handling platforms. Their positioning and number is determined by function, the weight and nature of the loads (height, position of centre of gravity etc.).

Three cushions at least must be employed to ensure stability.

The cushions can be fitted on to a chassis with spring fastenings.

The flexible lips will not suffer wear under normal conditions but are interchangeable in cases of accidental damage.

Circular cushions are produced as standard units in three sizes: ϕ 300, ϕ 450, ϕ 600.

General characteristics are given in the accompanying table.

2. Standard Modules

Standard Modules complete with chassis and a standard circular cushion can be supplied, ready for use. The lift capacity of these modules is comparable to that of the corresponding circular cushion. Chassis can be modified as required.

3. Honeycomb Cushions

Honeycomb cushions are available in three standard sizes. Fully stable, these cushions allow full use of the load bearing surface for lift. In addition they are very thin but can bear very heavy loads when at rest.

These cushions employ inflatable joints to seal off adjacent square cells which are fed separately through vents from a single plenum. The plenum itself is fed from any suitable compressed air source.

STANDARD UNITS FOR SPECIAL APPLICATIONS

For moving and positioning loads in factories and buildings with low ceiling heights air cushion skids have been designed. These metal pads have no flexible seals, and used over a very even surface, they operate without surface contact on an air film a few hundredths of a millimetre deep.

Applications include a 3,000 kg payload platform—for feeding a press mounted on seven skids 200 mm in diameter. This unit can withstand a pressure of 26,000 kg when at rest beneath the press.

MACHINERY HANDLING IN FACTORIES

Major applications of Bertin air cushions to solve machinery and material handling within factories, listed in the past issues of Jane's Surface Skimmers, include:

Air film cushion sheer tables (1966):

Air cushion platforms to install 40,000 lb machinery units within factory buildings (1966):

Air cushion chassis for moving machinery (1968):

Air cushion conveyors adapted to specific loads (1969):

Air film conveyors for the transfer of soft or tacky sheet material (1970):

Loading platform for lorries (1970):

Cast mould press feeding platform on air cushions (1971):

Transfer of 12 ton spinning mills on air cushions (1972):

Permanent air cushion platforms for the transfer of 5 ton diesel engine cooling units from the assembly line to the dispatching area (1972):

Air cushion platforms for precise positioning of metal blanks under a magnetic unstacking unit (1973);

Permanent air cushion platforms fitted under 30 ton profiling machines facilitating the use of alternative machines along a production line (1973).

Standard Bertin circular cushion

Circular Cushions	ϕ 300	ϕ 450	ϕ 600
Overall diameter	0,364 m	0,540 m	0,680 m
Height at rest	0,035 m	0,050 m	0,050 m
Weight	5,5 kg	8,5 kg	14 kg
Lift area	0,07 m²	0.16 m²	0,28 m²
Load capacity	500 kg	1,200 kg	2,500 kg
Air Supply	through connection to a compressed air network from an adapted low pressure compressor		

Honeycomb Cushions Major characteristics:	Type 1	Type 2	Type 3
Length × width (mm)	626 × 329	416 × 768	590 × 590
Height at rest (mm)	22	32	30
Lift area (m²)	0,162	0,250	0,250
Load capacity (kg)	1,000	1,700	3,000

Metal air cushion skids fitted beneath a platform used to feed loads of up to 3,000 kg to a press Off-cushion, beneath the press, the platform withstands pressures of up to 26,000 kg.

Since the Eighth Edition of Janes' Surface Skimmers, new industrial applications of special interest have included:

1. Air cushion platforms for taking heavy industrial components into an X-ray control chamber, through a staggered wall entrance, and positioning the equipment within the X-ray chamber itself. The platform consists of 28 Ø 600 circular cushions and bears 50 ton loads.

2. Air cushion turntables for moving glass plate stands in a glass factory so as to gain space and permit precise positioning of the stand. Twenty Ø 400 cushions are used to lubricate the platform. For 50 ton loads the effort required for rotation does not exceed 120 kg.

3. Air cushion platforms permitting the movement in the least possible space of railway trucks along their assembly line. Two platforms operate within a shallow pit and allow the railway trucks to be rotated at right angles, without the need for a space-consuming turntable.

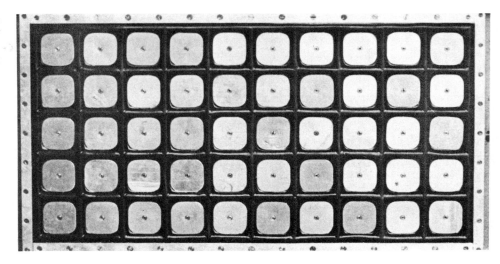

Underside of standard honeycomb cushion showing the inflatable joints which seal off adjacent square cushion cells

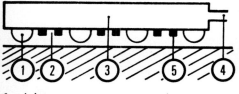

1 joint
2 aperture
3 chamber
4 air supply
5 resting pads

Diagram showing the basic structure of the Bertin honeycomb air cushion pallets

One of four 30-ton profiling units in a metallurgical centre, each of which is fitted with sixteen Bertin circular cushions. Only 88 lb (40 kg) of traction effort is needed to reposition each unit in readiness for production change overs

Standard module, ready assembled, comprising chassis and one circular cushion.

Chassis can be modified as required

ETABLISSEMENTS NEU
HEAD OFFICE:
    Sac Postal No. 28, 59 Lille, France
    Etablissements NEU is a licensee of Jet-
stream Systems Co of Hayward, California.
Details of the conveyor system built by the
company can be found under the entry for
Jetstream Systems Company, USA.

GERMANY

HELMUT FRANK BLECHVERARBEITUNG
HEAD OFFICE:
Laufdorferstrasse, D-6331 Bonbaden, West
Germany
This company manufactures Jetstream
conveyor systems under licence.

ITALY

DEL MONEGO
HEAD OFFICE:
    Piazza della Republica 8, Milan
Del Monego produces Jetstream conveyor
systems under licence.

JAPAN

EBARA MANUFACTURING COMPANY
HEAD OFFICE:
    11 Haneda Asahicho, Ota-Ku, Tokyo
This company produces Jetstream conveyor
systems under licence.

TRINIDAD

COELACANTH GEMCO LTD
HEAD OFFICE:
    1 Richardson Street, Point Fortin, Trinidad,
    West Indies
DIRECTORS:
    Nigel Seale
    Kelvin Corbie
SECRETARY:
    R. Varma

Coelacanth Gemco Ltd., the first company
to specialise in the design and construction
of air cushion vehicles in the West Indies,
has developed a hover conveyor system and
a hover pallet.

The pallet, measuring 3 ft × 4 ft, is capable
of lifting and moving 1,000 lb, while operated
by one man and great potential is seen for
the use of these units within Trinidad
factories.

The hover-conveyor system is designed in
modules of 10 ft and 15 ft, enabling a system
of any length to be devised to suit changing
production line requirements.

Coelacanth Gemco is also working on a
self-contained unit, powered by a 100 hp
diesel engine driving a 36 in eight-blade
axial fan at 2,500 rpm to produce 30,000 cu ft
of air per minute at 6 in w.g. pressure.

This will be used in the movement of oil
company tanks between various locations.
Multiples of this unit will enable tanks of any
size to be moved after attaching the skirt
system.

A Coelacanth hoverpallet employed in a workshop to move air-conditioning equipment. This
particular model lifts loads up to 1,000 lb (453·592 kg). Other models, operating on factory air
supplies of 80 lb sq in, will carry loads of up to 15 tons. The model seen above operates on either
115 or 230 volts ac

UNITED KINGDOM

AIRMATIC ENGINEERING LTD

HEAD OFFICE:
King Street, Sileby, Leicestershire

TELEPHONE:
Sileby 2816 (STD Code 050 981)

EXECUTIVES:

P. Lucas, Marketing Manager

This company is manufacturing and marketing the Pneu-move air bearing system under licence from the National Research Development Corporation of the United Kingdom.

ROTARY AIR TABLES

A range of rotary air tables, of 1-2 tons capacity and 61-84 in (1,550-2,150 mm) in diameter is available for rotating heavy loads. Rotation requires the minimum of physical effort. The equipment is designed for a number of applications, including the following: spray booth, fettling, machine assembly, marking out and inspection.

AIR FLOTATION TABLES

In 1975 the company introduced a range of air flotation tables, based on the principles employed in the Pneu-move air-bearing pad. Large, heavy sheets can be handled by one man and positioned accurately with the finger tips. Built-in pneumatically-operated breaker bars save time in cutting.

Existing tables of any size can be converted to Air Floatation Tables without difficulty. Alternatively, complete tables can be supplied and installed. Standard types of workshop air compressor are suitable, the output depending on the area of the table surface.

PNEU-MOVE

The Pneu-move system has been developed by the National Engineering Laboratory to enable heavy loads to be moved by hand without necessitating an expensive, high precision, operating surface.

Its low friction, small size, and low power requirement suit it for the movement of heavy machinery, particularly where man-handling in confined spaces may be necessary. It is also suitable for use in the production lines of heavy components where it eliminates the need for powered conveyors, allows accurate positioning because of the low friction, and gives secure parking by switching off the air supply.

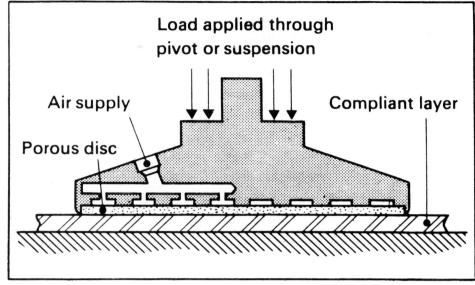

Sectional view of a Pneu-move air bearing pad. The undersides of the pads have porous stainless steel surfaces which ride on the air flow created between the porous surface and a layer of compliant material below, such as neoprene sheet

The system consists of an air bearing, mounted on a ball to allow some pivoting, and a track of a compliant material. It can be operated from a normal workshop air supply of 85 psi.

Applications include:

The installation of machines where suitable lifting facilities do not exist in the hosiery, printing, and carton-making industries.

A production flow line, e.g. final assembly of machine tools.

The movement of heavy raw materials, including steel plate.

The handling of components during manufacture, e.g. large fabrications between operations.

Assembly of mining machinery on site.

The movement of heavy loads without damage to floors, in machine tool showrooms and lecture theatres.

Pneu-move air bearing pads enable heavy loads to be moved quickly by hand, without damaging floors

PNEU-MOVE AIRMATS

Derived from the company's air bearing pads, the Pneu-move air-mats are designed for the movement of heavy moulds, fixtures and work-pieces across machine tables. Air pressure and flow requirements are low and existing workshop air lines can be used. A range of standard sizes is available but other sizes and special designs can be produced by the company, the standard air supply connector is ¼ in (6·35 mm) BSP.

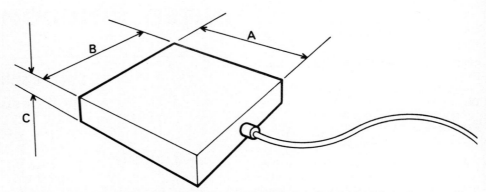

Pneu-Move-Air-Mat. Designed to carry heavy loads over holes and slots on machine tables, the Air-Mat is suitable for moving components in drilling, tapping, milling, rubber and plastics moulding and many other machine operations

The above tables give typical performance for a supply of pressure 6kp/cm². (85 psig) of Pneu-Move Air-Mats when used on an average machine tool table with a continuous surface. For loads less than those shown, lower supply pressures may be used, with correspondingly lower airflow rates. Where holes and slots are to be traversed, or if the table is badly worn, some allowance must be made for increased airflow and reduced maximum load.

Ref.No.	Dimensions in mm (inches)			Max.load kgf (lbf)		Airflow m³ / min(scfm)	
	A	B	C				
AM 1	150(6)	150(6)	25(1)	450	(1000)	0.085	(3)
AM 2	150(6)	300(12)	25(1)	900	(2000)	0.170	(6)
AM 3	200(8)	150(6)	30(1¼)	675	(1500)	0.127	(4.5)
AM 4	200(8)	300(12)	30(1¼)	1350	(3000)	0.255	(9)
AM 5	200(8)	600(24)	30(1¼)	2700	(6000)	0.51	(18)
AM 6	300 (12)	300(12)	40(1½)	1800	(4000)	0.34	(12)
AM 7	300(12)	450(18)	40(1½)	2700	(6000)	0.51	(18)
AM 8	450(18)	450(18)	50(2)	4500	(10000)	0.85	(30)
AM 9	600(24)	600(24)	45(1¾)	7200	(16000)	1.36	(48)

BRITISH HOVERCRAFT CORPORATION

HEAD OFFICE:
East Cowes, Isle of Wight
DIRECTORS:
See ACV section

FLOATLOAD (1 Ton)

The 1-ton Floatload hoverpallet consists of a load-carrying, steel and plywood sandwich platform with four easily removable rubber diaphragm assemblies underneath. Air is supplied through a 1 in BSP connector and control valve.

Designed for moving loads of up to 1 ton on smooth floors, the hoverpallet can also be used in conjunction with standard fork lift trucks, pallets and stillages, which can easily be modified for this purpose. Single man operation of the loaded pallet is easily effected.

Loads may be placed directly on to the platform of the Floataload hoverpallet, but a simple bridge system allowing the units to be slid under the load is more economical.

When this is done the centre of pressure should be approximately under the centre of the load.

Operation is by opening the control valve until the load is airborne. The load can then be pushed, pulled or spun with minimum effort, the valve being closed and Floataload withdrawn when the load reaches the required position.

Floataload will operate satisfactorily over any smooth non-porous surface. Sheet metal, linoleum, vinyl, sealed concrete, plywood,

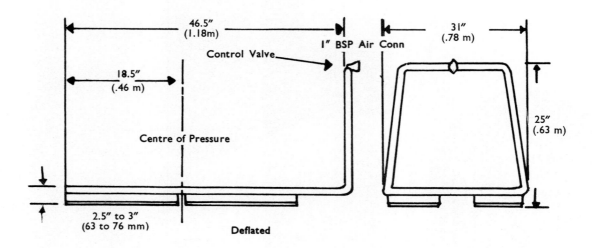

BHC 1-ton Floataload hoverpallet

smooth asphalt, and similar surfaces are all suitable.

DIMENSIONS:

Max length of pallet   3 ft 10 in (1·16 m)

Width of pallet   2 ft 7 in (0·78 m)

AIR PRESSURE:

Working air pressure for 100 lb (45·3 kg) load   3 lb sq in (0·21 kgf/cm²)

Working air pressure for 1,000 lb (453·5 kg) load   6 lb sq in (0·42 kgf/cm²)

¾ in BSP connection, 1 ton load   8 lb sq in (0·56 kgf/m²)

LIGHT HOVERCRAFT COMPANY

HEAD OFFICE:

Felbridge Hotel & Investment Co Ltd, London Road, East Grinstead, Sussex

TELEPHONE:

0342 24424

EXECUTIVES:

Lindsay H. F. Gatward, Proprietor

This company markets a pedestrian controlled hoverpallet which has a payload capacity of 3 cwt (150 kg).

Lift power is provided by an 8 hp Briggs & Stratton petrol engine which drives a plastic/alloy axial fan mounted beneath a close mesh safety guard. Since the power unit is of the lawn mower type, the general noise level is low.

The pallet which is built in glassfibre can be used over a wide range of unprepared surfaces including snow, ice, mud, water, grass, swamp and sand. Ploughed fields with ridges of up to 6 in (152 mm) can be traversed with a reduced payload. The over-water and swamp applications are restricted by the amount the operator is prepared to become immersed, or the degree by which this ability to control the vehicle is impaired. Machines can be winched across areas of deep water. Working under these conditions, however, applications such as wildfowling, reed collection, slurry control and insect spraying in swamp areas are possible.

Two directional wheels are fitted and these can be adjusted or removed according to the degree of directional control or ground contact pressure required.

A clip-on spraying unit, manufactured by E. Allman & Co Ltd, Birdham Road, Chichester, Sussex, has been developed for use in conjunction with the pallet.

Skirt is of HDC segmented type in nylon-coated polyurethane. Depth is 5 in (127 mm).

SPECIFICATIONS:

Length with handle	9 ft 6 in (2·89 m)
Width	4 ft (1·21 m)
Height with handle	3 ft (0·91 m)
Weight (approx)	160 lb (72·57 kg)
Skirt depth	5 in (127 mm)
Fuel capacity	6 pints (3·40 l)
Engine	319 cc (4-cycle)
Endurance (approx)	2 hrs per gallon
Payload	3 cwt (150 kg)
Payload area	28 sq ft (2·6 m²)

Top: Light Hovercraft Co's hoverpallets can be used over a wide variety of unprepared surfaces including agricultural land. A clip-on attachment can be supplied for crop-spraying

Centre: Assembled hoverpallets ready for despatch. The plastic/alloy axial lift fan is mounted beneath a close mesh safety guard

Bottom: One of the applications for which the hoverpallet has proved ideal is that of snow removal. Its payload capacity is 2 cwt (152 kg)

LING SYSTEMS LTD

HEAD OFFICE:
Unit 8, Station Road, Gamlingay, Sandy, Bedford SG193HG, England

This company is the exclusive licensee in the United Kingdom, Eire and the Netherlands for Jetstream conveyor systems.

ROLAIR SYSTEMS (UK) LTD

HEAD OFFICE:
56 Brompton Square, London, SW3 2AG

TELEPHONE:
01 584 8511, 01 584 8010

CABLES:
Projectser London SW3

TELEX:
888941 Chamcom: for Projectser

DIRECTORS:
B. H. Wright, RD, BSc, BCom, CEng, MIEE, Chairman and Managing Director

D. L. Campbell, MC
M. F. Dowding, CBE, MA, CEng, MIMechE
N. F. Haycock, CEng, MIEE
R. H. Lacey, CEng, MIMechE
Lord Macpherson of Drumochter, JP

Rolair Systems (UK) Ltd has an exclusive manufacturing licence from Rolair Systems Inc., Santa Barbara. Since starting in early 1974, it has supplied some 40 installations, including a 1,000-ton oil rig module movement system for Williams Brothers Offshore Ltd., Newcastle; a 150-ton ingot mould transporter for BSC, Sheffield; a 200-ton ship

section transporter for Sunderland Shipbuilders Ltd., a 200-ton generator movement system for Brush Electrical Machines Ltd.; a 300-ton transformer handling installation for Hawker Siddeley Power Transformers Ltd.; a 120-ton ladle transfer car for BSC, Llanwern and a 180-ton rotor handling system for GEC Turbine Generators Ltd. Other smaller systems have been supplied to C.E.G.B., Rolls-Royce, Pilkington Bros. Ltd., BP Chemicals International, Philips (Croydon) Ltd., Crompton Parkinson Ltd. and Westland Helicopters Ltd.

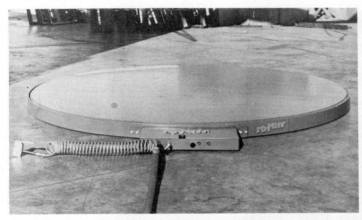

Left: Rolair low profile turntable. The lower picture shows the table with its free-floating load deck removed revealing the air bearings beneath. *Right:* 100-ton Rolair transporter used to carry Hawker Siddeley power transformers. This unit, together with two others of the same type, can be employed either as single or multiple units to lift one, two or three hundred ton loads

UNITED STATES

AERO-GO INC

HEAD OFFICE AND WORKS:
5800 Corson Avenue South, Seattle, Washington 98108

TELEPHONE:
206/763-9380

EXECUTIVES:
Frank M. Cohee, President and General Manager
Kenneth G. Wood, Vice-President, Engineering
William A. Shannon, Vice-President, Sales

EUROPEAN DISTRIBUTORS:
United Kingdom:
Applied Technology Co. Ltd., London (Heathrow) Airport, England
Telephone: SKYport 2811

One of two 70-ton capacity max mobile machine tool bed plate positioning systems built by Aero-Go for Westinghouse Electric Corporation under full load test

Scandinavian Representative:
Aero-Go Scandinavia AB, Box 5, S-73050,
Skultuna, Sweden
Telephone: 021-70-900

Aero-Go was founded in April, 1967 to commercialise air film and air cushion devices developed by the Boeing Company. It holds the exclusive world licence for products and patent rights of Boeing in this field.

The company has developed and is selling the Aero-Caster air film bearing in eight sizes ranging from 12 in to 48 in diameter. These are manufactured in neoprene impregnated nylon material and are thus highly resistant to tearing damage and capable of supporting very large loads. Lifting capacity ranges from 1,000 lb in the 12 in (304 mm) size to 80,000 lb in the 48 in (1·21 m) size. Individual Aero-Casters are employed in combinations to transport heavy loads. Load module systems are available, complete with portable blowers, hose manifolds and air controls.

Aero-Casters are also incorporated in standard pallets designed for a wide range of applications, including loading and unloading trucks, movement of loaded scissor-lift tables, wire and cable reel carriers, paper and fabric rolls and production machinery. The Company builds Aero-Trucks and Aero-Turntables to meet customer requirements.

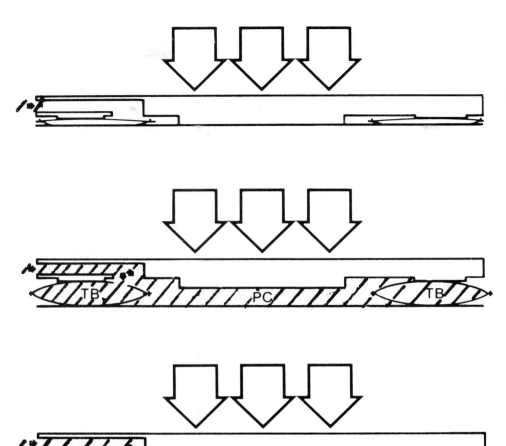

Step one: Aero-Caster "off cushion". The load is solidly supported on the landing pads. Black arrows represent fluid flow. Step two: Fluid enters flexible torus bag (TB) and plenum chamber (PC). Step three: When fluid forced in to the plenum chamber exceeds total load, caster then floats load off the floor

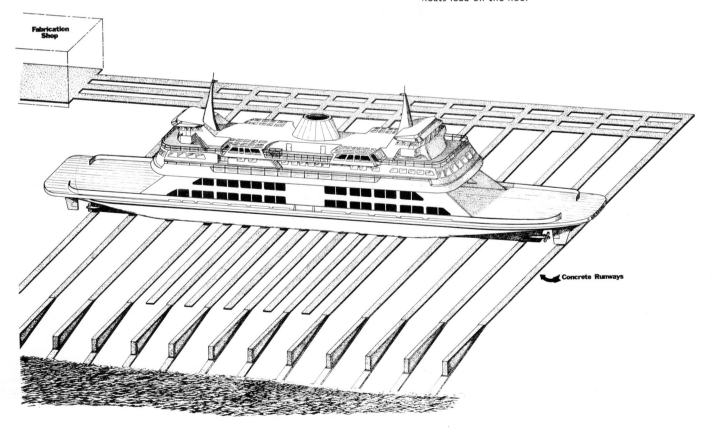

Layout at Vancouver Shipyards, where ship subsections are being lifted and transferred through each assembly stage and finally positioned for side-launching by Aero-Go's water film handling system

AERO-TURNTABLES

Aero-Turntables are available for use in factory production lines or such applications as paint booths and product shipping/receiving points. Multi-ton capacity air film turntables have been installed for lifting and rotating Boeing 747 jumbo jets during pre-flight testing and compass calibration.

In 1971 Aero-Go installed three air turntables for rotation of rapid transit rail cars for the Bay Area Rapid Transit (BART) system in Northern California. The turntables have been constructed to ride on water film should there be an electrical power failure.

In effect, the Aero-Caster is an open-ended piston with a dynamic end-seal that conserves the volume of air required to lift and float loads. The thin air film under this peripheral seal lubricates the bearing and allows it to float freely only ·005 in above the floor surface. As the caster moves across the surface, the flexible seal automatically contours to provide a constant gap and thus maintain a uniform air flow. When the air is shut off, the captured air bubble within the caster escapes, slowly lowering the load gently and safely to the ground. The casters are self pressure-regulating systems that may be operated without separate line regulators.

MAX MOBILE MACHINE TOOL BED PLATE POSITIONING SYSTEM

The max mobile bed-plate transport system can instantly "float" pre-fixed workpieces up to a machine tool and precisely align them within a few thousandths of an inch. They arrive ready set-up and are secured at the machine on flush-to-floor docking points.

The max system combines standards Aero-Caster air film bearings with bed plates and part holding fixtures.

Aero-Casters free the load from the floor to float on a thin layer of nearly-frictionless air. Load movement becomes possible in any direction with 1 lb of force for every 1,000 lb of load weight. The system allows heavy parts to be set-up in a staging area away from the machine. When the machine completes its drilling, boring or milling, the next workpiece is ready to be moved into an exact work position at the tool, which continues to work without waiting for the parts to be set-up.

When floating a total load of 100 tons (machine plus part), the equipment is powered by a 3 hp electric-hydraulic system. Guidance is positively controlled by cam followers and surface engaging wheels.

Rotation around a central, retractable floor-contacting pivot pin system and forward/reverse directional travel are all remotely controlled by one operator from a portable console. Hydraulically-driven wheels propel the equipped in any direction at speeds from 0-20 fpm as desired.

Final precise positioning at the tool is performed by stopping the max over load-bearing floor plates which align with landing pads on the unit's underside. Two tapered index pins are then engaged down into floor sockets. The operator deflates the Aero-Casters and the Max settles to the floor and is docked ready for machining to begin.

SHIPYARD FLUID HANDLING SYSTEM

In the spring of 1975, Vancouver Shipyards in British Columbia began lifting and transferring ship subsections. The first completed vessel, weighing 3,400 tons, was moved into launch position totally through the use of Aero-Go fluid bearings.

The basic water bearing building block and runway system allows shipyards to re-evaluate and expand their production potential. They can consider manufacturing oil drilling platforms, barges, or any of a variety of structures fabricated from steel.

The fluid bearing provides the capacity of lifting, rotating, and omni-directional transportation. Sections "floated" together can be accurately raised, lowered, tilted or warped, achieving exact alignment for efficient field welding.

The Vancouver Shipyard system includes 84 model K48NHDW Aero-Caster water film load modules. Each load-carrying module is approximately 2 in deep and 4 ft square, and weighs approximately 170 lb. The module assembly comprises a 48 in diameter, doughnut-shaped water film bearing, constructed of high-strength, flexible nylon-reinforced materials, joined with a square load-mounting top plate of aluminium extrusion construction.

Each module may receive up to 20 gpm of water, pumped either from a city supply or the sea, to lift a maximum of 40 tons. When inflated, the module raises its load approximately 1½ in. The load is floated on a thin, near frictionless water film between ·005-·007 in thick. On a level plane, the force required to move a 40 ton floating load is 80 lb or only 0·1 % of the weight.

The modules are placed under the vessel's wood cribbing, which is resting on a series of parallel, reinforced concrete runways forming a continuously smooth and non-porous operating surface.

As each ship subsection is prepared to leave the final fabrication ship, the correct quantity of K48NHDW modules are inserted and inflated. Each section is then floated out into the yard under the guidance of small yard tugs or winches. The distance of travel is determined by the overall length of the vessel under construction. Sections are floated together and joined using the omni-directional capability of the bearings, as well as the vertical alignment control created by varying water pressure inputs to various modules. Sections can be accurately raised, lowered, tilted and warped.

The water film transport system permits the construction of several vessels at one time, positioned side-by-side. Or, different types and sizes of vessels can be built in the same area. Modules may be used in different combinations to handle varying section sizes and load eccentricities.

Matching runways reach down to the water's edge. When ready for side-launch at high tide, the modules float the vessel to the ends of the runways and are then removed. A runway trigger mechanism is released, collapsing the runways to meet matching runways embedded in the sea floor, and the vessel slips into the water.

Todd Shipyards, Seattle, was the first shipyard anywhere to use the fluid bearing handling system to move ship modules. The shipyard's first use of the water bearing was in February 1974, moving the "Arctic", a 1,200-ton tug and supply vessel to the launch position.

To lift a full vessel, each bearing is inflated with water to pressures ranging up to 50 lb/sq in. In a few seconds, the ship is vertically raised about 1½ in.

The Arctic was one of six tug and supply vessels built by Todd for Allseas of Panama Ltd. Each vessel measures 228 ft by 44 ft by 19 ft and weighed 1,200 tons when completed. The water film handling system gave the company a competitive edge in meeting a required "six ship delivery within eight months" schedule. Since December 1974, Todd has completed four more similar vessels under a 12-ship contract for Theriot Offshore International Ltd. A ship is being delivered each month until the order is completed. These vessels are being chartered in the North Sea in support of offshore oil-drilling and exploration operations.

As each ship section leaves the final fabrication building, it is rolled out on railway bogies onto a railway track which leads to a 12 in deep concrete-surfaced turntable pit outside. Under these rails are a series of eight Aero-Go model K48NHDW Aero-Caster "water film" load modules. Each module is 48 in square and constructed in aluminium extrusions with a 48 in diameter inflatable Aerocaster water film bearing (48NHDW) made of neoprene-reinforced nylon material beneath. At this point, the sections weigh between 150-250 tons. Each section is rotated 90° on the water film turntable to mate with a matching rail system bed.

When the controls are activated, the water film bearings are inflated with pressurised water in a matter of seconds and the turntable's load "floats" on a thin water film. The friction under the load is so reduced that a ½ in cable strap pulled by a small forklift truck is the only drawbar pull needed to turn each section.

The sections are then rolled off the turntable and continue by rail to the Section Joining Area. Here the water film system is employed to position them for joining and eventually to move the major subassemblies through the final assembly area and eventually to transfer the entire vessel on the side slipways.

The vessel is then moved on a series of up to 29 water film bearing modules which travel over seven, five-foot wide concrete runways. To lift a full vessel each bearing is inflated to approximately 50 psi. In a few seconds, the ship is raised about 1½ inches. This system consumes a total of 480 gallons per minute of water. The thin water film captured between the flexible bottom face of the bearing and the slipway surface is approximately ·005 to ·007 in thick. A four-man team supervises a ship's movement using two powered winches each controlling one line at each end of the ship. The normal travel speed is approximately three feet a minute.

AIRFLOAT CORPORATION

HEAD OFFICE:
1304 North 20th Street, Decatur, Illinois
62521

TELEPHONE:
Area Code 217, 422-8365

GENERAL MANAGER:
David R. Snoeyenbos

OVERSEAS REPRESENTATION:
Airfilm Luftkissenlagertechnik GMBH, 41
Duisburg, Moselstrasse 37, West Germany

H. Englebert NV., Dobbeweg 2-3, Voor-
schoten/Holland

Airfloat Corporation was formed in October,
1967 to develop and apply air bearing
technology, based on a licence granted by
General Motors, and on experience gained
by the principal when working on the G.M.
air bearing development programme.

Airfloat offers a line of air bearing cells,
standard products mounted on air bearings,
and also engineers and fabricates special-
purpose equipment utilising air bearing
technology. A summary of standard products follows:

AIR BEARINGS: A wide variety of types
and sizes range from 6 in (152 mm) diameter
to 43 × 67 in (1·09x1·70 m) racetrack shape
bearings, with capacities from 200 lb to
24,000 lb (90·71 to 10,886 kg) each.

SMALL PLATFORMS: A line of standard
general-purpose air bearing platforms for
loads up to 8,000 lb (3,629 kg). Each
consists of four bearings mounted to a
structural panel, with necessary air controls.

LARGE PLATFORMS: Similar, but for
movements of heavy loads, from 8,000 lb to
120,000 lb (3,629 kg to 54,430 kg). Air
motor powered drive wheels available for
self-propelled operation.

TURNTABLES: 3 ft to 9 ft (·914-2·74 m) in
diameter, up to 40,000 lb (18,143·68 kg)
capacity.

AIR SKIDS: Two-bearing structural platforms. Two or more used together can
move loads of most any size on a film of air,
for almost frictionless handling. They are
frequently used for moving and relocating
machinery in the plant, for die handling, and
for assembly line movement of large machines.

Engineered system applications pursued by
Airfloat include the following:

Equipment for moving very heavy equipment or machinery by use of special very
large air bearings, for loads from 50 tons to
thousands of tons.

High density mobile storage systems, where
rows of storage racks are mounted on air

bearing bases. Groups of rows of racks can
be stored close together with no aisles, and
can be moved aside on air to create an aisle
where needed. Allows savings in floor
space of 40-50%.

A variety of forms of conveyors have been
designed, for flowthrough storage of heavy
palletised loads, assembly line movement of
heavy equipment, shuttle conveyors, etc.

Airfloat air bearings use a continuously
flowing film of air between a flexible diaphragm and floor surface to allow virtually
friction free movement. Thus large loads
can be moved on air bearings with considerably less force than on conventional wheels
or rollers.

Air bearing cells have a flexible diaphragm
which is sealed around the circumference and
attached to the centre of a top plate. Air
supplied to the bearing inflates the diaphragm
and passes through communicating holes in
the diaphragm to the space below. A
continuous air film is formed between the
diaphragm and floor surface as air escapes to
the atmosphere.

The area that is pressurised below the
diaphragm is referred to as the effective
"Support Area"; the "Seal Perimeter" is
the outer boundary of the support area and
the point where the pressurised air escapes
to the atmosphere.

The pressure inside an air bearing depends
upon the load applied to the bearings.
Bearing pressure can be determined for any
given load by dividing the load by the
bearings' support area.

Air bearings operate at maximum efficiency,
on smooth, good quality floor surfaces—
rough or porous floors cause excessive air
consumption. The flexible diaphragm will
conform to gradual floor undulations of ¼ in
to ½ in over an eight foot span without a
noticeable decrease in efficiency. Smooth
surfaces such as terrazo, tile, linoleum, steel
sheet, and sealed concrete allow excellent
performance. Cracks or expansion joints
must be filled or bridged to provide a continuous floor surface. Poor concrete surfaces
that are rough, worn, or pitted can be
improved with readily available patching or
topping materials.

AIRFLOAT CORPORATION
GLASS SHEET TRANSPORTER

ASG Industries, Kingsport, Tennessee, is
employing a specially designed Airfloat
transporter to carry up to 66 ton loads of
glass sheet at a time from in-process storage
to production lines.

The transporter, which uses four air bearing
diaphragms, is operated entirely by remote
control with a "joy stick" on a hand-held
control box connected to the platform by a
12 ft long cable.

Airfloat utility platform, showing four air
bearings, guide wheels and controls

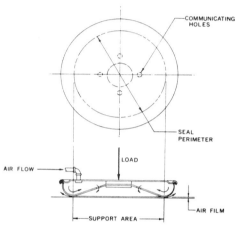

Basic construction of an Airfloat air bearing cell

The operator guides the transporter beneath
the rack, the air bearings are deflated and
the transporter lowered to the floor. The
platform support frame is then raised to the
base of the A-frame rack holding the 11 ft ×
20 ft glass sheets and locked in place. The
air bearing diaphragms on the transporter
are then reinflated and the rack is lifted off
the floor.

The steerable drive wheel is then used to
manoeuvre the rack out of the storage area
and then guide it down an aisle to the
production area.

After a short period of familiarisation,
operators can steer the load down narrow
aisles. By shifting the steering axis, the
transporter can move the rack at right angles
into the bay with only a few inches of clearance
either side.

JETSTREAM SYSTEMS COMPANY

HEAD OFFICE:
3486 Investment Boulevard, Hayward,
California 94545

OFFICERS:
Stanley Lenox, President
Warren P. Landon, Vice-President

Eugene S. Batter, Vice-President, Operations
Stanley E. Hurd, Vice-President, Research
and Development

Jetstream Systems Company holds the
world-wide rights for Jetstream conveyors.
The company is currently producing and

developing Jetstream conveying and processing equipment and Jetsweep storage and
drying systems.

Jetstream uses low-pressure air delivered
to a plenum by a fan or fans and introduced
to the conveyor surface through various
types of orifices along the full length of the
conveyor, to maintain a belt of air flowing

close to the conveyor surface. It conveys granular materials, such as sand, iron pellets, grain, etc; paper and metal trim and scrap; cartons; webs or sheets of paper or metal; and practically any other material within reason.

The air can be heated or cooled to condition the product while it is being conveyed. Extremely good results have been attained, especially in the heating, cooling and drying field. Longer or shorter dwell time can be obtained by using different configurations of the conveyor.

Objects are moved by a succession of angularly disposed openings. The system provides constant controlled power around curves and up inclines including vertical faces. Entry points and spurs, inputs and outputs, can be added easily anywhere along the conveyor.

The objects can be moved upwards along an inclined conveyor and can be discharged into a hopper or other receptacle. The conveyor membrane may be used for moving solid objects by air-jet action and as a support and walkway for workmen while adjusting,

operating or maintaining an associated machine.

POWER SUPPLY: Pressure of air necessary: $\frac{1}{10}$ inch water gauge to $\frac{1}{2}$ psi. Air ducting and centrifugal fans are generally fitted as an integral part of the conveyor.

CONVEYOR SYSTEM: Units are designed to suit product. The length can run to 1,000 ft or more and the width from 1 in to 10 ft or more as necessary.

BLOWER H/P: Power requirements for loadings up to 7 lb sq ft (34·17 kgt/m²) $\frac{1}{500}$ hp/sq ft—$\frac{1}{10}$ hp sq ft

ROLAIR SYSTEMS, INC.
ADDRESS:
  P.O. Box 3036, Santa Barbara, California
TELEPHONE:
  (805) 968 1536
DIRECTORS:
  Henry W. Huthsing, Vice-President
  Terry Baker, Vice-President
  Robert Kieding, Vice-President
  E. Douglas Reddan, President
  Roger Kenyon

Rolair Systems Inc. manufactures a range of equipment making use of compliant air bearings for moving heavy or large loads. The company began operations in March 1968 and now markets air flotation systems, incorporating air bearing caster jacks and pallets.

The basic compliant air bearing device comprises a membrane holding compressed air which conforms to the floor. Controlled escape of this air in a thin layer between membrane and floor forms a frictionless air film which 'floats' the load, enabling it to be moved in any horizontal direction by a force only one-thousandth of the weight of the load. Air pressure is self-regulating according to the bearing size and its load. Typically a 2 ft diameter bearing will lift 4,000 lb; four 2 ft bearings will carry a truck.

Several typical applications are described below.

SHIPYARD PANEL LINE
Rolair has constructed and installed a complete air-film panel handling system for a major US shipyard. Comprising several hundred, pylon-mounted upturned air-bearings, it permits the omnidirectional movement of steel plates measuring 3·65 m by 12·19 m (12 ft by 40 ft) for welding. The plates, which can be positioned with great accuracy, are tack-welded five at a time into 100-ton 'blanket' sections, each measuring 12·19 m by 18·28 m (40 ft by 60 ft). Axis positioning is accomplished through the use of low-horsepower, steerable electric drives.

After all five plates have been tacked together, they are driven by linear casters to an overhead welding station, where they are seam welded on both sides, have channels added, and are then driven to the crane pick-up area.

Above and below: Rolair-designed panel line for a major US shipyard. It enables steel plates, weighing up to 100 tons, to be accurately positioned for welding and then transports them down the line to a crane pick-up area. The plates are used in the construction of giant tankers

OMNI-MOBILE CRANE
Gantry and top-running bridge cranes are available in this line. They can be pushed to the load, lift it and deliver it without the expense of overhead or ground rails. The company has standard designs available of 5-30 tons and will build units of heavier capacities to meet specific requirements.

The Omni-Mobile Crane solves many of the

problems associated with conventional cranes. Its portability allows it to move between bays as well as operating outside the plant, another advantage being that it does not require any changes to the building structure, thus eliminating the need for building permits and civil engineering costs.

The problems associated with compensating

for span are also reduced Normally the span of a bay limits the amount of weight that can be carried on an overhead crane. With the Omni-Mobile crane, the span can be one-half or one-third of the bay's span and the crane is still able to reach any load within the bay. Positioning of loads also becomes easier. As it has frictionless movement in any direction, precise positioning is possible.

Unlike wheeled units, no brakes are necessary to hold the crane in position. By turning off the air, the crane base rests solidly on the floor on specially designed support points.

The Omni-Mobile crane's portability and omnidirectional movement is made possible by the four or more Rolair air bearings located underneath the base of the crane.

The Omni-Mobile crane line includes a gantry type with travelling hook and a travelling bridge type. Optional accessories for both include non-powered, retractable guide wheels for positive control; powered drive wheels for movement of the crane structure; rail guides for floor mounted rail guidance; and remote control units for operation of the air system.

They can be operated using standard shop air, or a separate air compressor.

VARIABLE-PLAN SPORTS STADIUM

Rolair air-bearings will be used to vary the seating configurations of a new 28,000-seat stadium under construction in Honolulu.

The stadium comprises four 7,000-seat sections, and the air-bearings will be employed to rotate each through a 45 degree arc to provide ideal seating patterns for either football or baseball games.

Located under each of the four stadium sections will be twenty-six Rolair transporters, each incorporating four air-bearings. These will be inflated by three main air compressors, each with a capacity of 1,250 cfm. The sections will be moved by a system of lightweight hydraulic jacks. A rail guideline will prevent the sections drifting when 20-knot Pacific tradewinds are blowing. Each stadium section has a fixed pivot point and it is estimated that only 20 minutes will be required to move each one through its 45 degree arc—a total distance of 53·34 m (173 ft).

In baseball configuration the stadium will have an open double "horseshoe" look. For football the four sideline sections will be moved inward to form straight sidelines. In the football position the spectators on the 50 yard line will be only 12·19 m (40 ft) from the sideline, and only 7·62 m (25 ft) away from the goal line.

Ramps connecting the stadium sections extend and retract on air film with each move.

AUTOMATIC MODULAR HOME PRODUCTION LINE

Rolair has designed and installed a fully-automated air-film walking beam conveyor system which moves factory built home modules simultaneously through eighteen assembly stations several times an hour.

The system can handle modules with lengths of up to 60 ft (18·28 m) and widths up to 14 ft (4·26 m).

ASSEMBLY LINE FOR CRAWLER TRACTORS

One of the most advanced air film systems in operation today is in use at the Caterpillar Tractor plant at Gosselies, Belgium, where an automatic assembly line has been installed by Rolair for Model 225 Excavators.

The first line for these vehicles was installed at the company's plant at Aurora, Illinois. Experience with the Aurora plant has led to

Above: A gantry-type Omni-Mobile crane delivering a 4,000 lb (1814.37 kg) load from the production line onto a flatbed truck
Below: An Omni-Mobile crane of the travelling bridge type. Because of its omnidirectional movement, the crane can be moved around obstacles

certain improvements on the Gosselies plant. For example, air tools are used throughout the line, allowing the air-powered transporters to serve as the air supply for the tools. This enables assemblers to connect their tools at the start of the assembly and leave them connected throughout the line.

The assembly operation begins on a 175-ft-long section of track immediately preceding the air pallet area. There, drive assemblies are built on manually-propelled transfer carts.

First, the tractor's two planetary gears are aligned on a stationary fixture. A housing is then lifted into position by an overhead crane. After the housing has been connected to the axles, the unit is lifted onto a transfer cart. Small components are then added to the housing as the cart is moved to the end of the track. The sub-assembly and cart now weighs about 18,000-lb and requires two men to push it. At this point the sub-assembly is lifted by the overhead crane and positioned on one of the air pallets. Now one man can easily move the 9-ton load.

Components are brought to the air pallet line on flat-bed trucks and lifted by crane onto the pallets. Workers climb portable step ladders to perform the necessary

Left: Stadium positioned for football, and *right*, for baseball. Rolair air-bearings are employed to rotate each of the four 7,000-seat sections through a 45-degree arc to provide ideal seating patterns for both games

welding and bolting operations. The same air source that supplies the pallets is used to power air-articulated assembly tools.

Each transporter has a 45 ft hose mounted on a retractable reel. Air hose connectors are installed below the surface every 25 ft along the assembly line. This allows the transporter 90 ft of travel before changing air connectors.

When air is fed into the system, each bearing diaphragm inflates, traps a shallow bubble of air and lifts the load slightly off the floor. Controlled leakage around the edge of the bearings creates a lubricating layer of air between the transporter and floor. Friction is practically eliminated and the transporter can be moved with a minimum of force.

A master clock controls the complete assembly line. Magnetic sensors are located on the bottom of the transporters, and utilising a series of electromagnets embedded every 10 ft along the assembly line floor, the transporter can be directed to move from station to station. The electromagnets are normally energised. When the control clock de-energises a specific electromagnet, the sensor on the transporter opens, providing an air supply to the air bearing, causing the transporter to advance toward the next energised electromagnet. Since each electromagnet is individually controlled, the air transporter can be moved any distance along the line.

At the same time, the air system is activated. Two guide wheels automatically lock onto a V-type floor rail and guide the transporter down the assembly line. As a safety factor, a 25 second delay is provided between air activation and initial machine movement, allowing ample time for assemblers to move from the path of the transporter.

Although the major portion of the line is automatic, some manual movement remains. At the end of the line, where the assembly floor is wide enough for two machines on transporters to operate side-by-side, excavators undergo flushing and computer testing of the hydraulic system. Advancing from the assembly line, the transporter's guide wheels are retracted and two men simply 'float' the 20-ton load into the test area.

In addition to the air film system another innovation for Caterpillar is the use of the team approach. An assembly team matches two assemblers with an inspector, and the three-man team stays with the machine from start to finish. In fact, names of assemblers and inspectors are recorded on metal plates fixed to the finished machine. Better quality has also been achieved through improved methods suggested by the team members, an important benefit of the team-build concept.

With the air film transporter system, Caterpillar feels that the assembly line can be easily altered. It can be lengthened over a weekend simply by laying more concrete. A turn can be added the same way, and if the line has to be shortened, the section no longer required is simply abandoned. A relocation can be effected by simply picking up the whole system and setting it down on a new strip of concrete.

AIRCRAFT GROUND TESTING INSTALLATION

An air flotation system has been installed by Vought to allow quicker positioning of each plane for testing operational equipment. The system uses an air film and replaces hand-operated tripod-type jacks. It has provided not only a saving in time, but a safer environment for testing. Twelve Corsair II light attack aircraft can be closely positioned within a single hangar.

Three air bearings, connected directly to a T-shaped dolly, make up the casters for each of six "sets" of bearings in use in the hangar. Their design is such that they easily handle the 19,000-pound aircraft. On-off air valves for the bearings are operated quickly by a single employee. The bearings have their own stabilizing chamber, eliminating any throttling of incoming air. Inlet air pressure is supplied at 75 psig from standard 1-inch plant lines.

Usually three men hand-manoeuvre the dolly for directional accuracy, although one man can easily push the 9 tons of aircraft supported on the air film. In most cases, the flotation system is used in conjunction with a crane for fine positioning of the craft

during equipping and testing its gears, wheels, and other systems and components.

LOW PROFILE TURNTABLE

In May 1974, Rolair introduced a workshop turntable with load capacities up to 140,000 lb (63,497 kg).

The turntable provides an accurate means of rotating heavy loads in a variety of industrial applications. It has an extremely low profile, projecting only 3-4 in (76-101 mm) above the floor surface, and floats on a thin film of air. Because of its low profile it can be mounted on the surface of existing floors; flush in woodblock floors or in a shallow pit in concrete floors. The necessity for deep pit installation is eliminated.

The system is operated by any standard 90 psi shop air system. The free-floating load deck can be easily removed for installation and inspection.

Turntables are available in sizes up to a 12 ft (3·65 m) diameter table with a 70 ton capacity. Larger capacity tables can be supplied to meet special requirements. A reasonable degree of off-centre loading is possible.

Rotating the Rolair turntable can be done either by hand or by an air-powered drive motor. Hand rotation of even the heaviest loads is possible because of the air film system. One pound (0·45 kg) of force can move a 1,000 lb (453 kg) load.

Optional equipment available for the Rolair turntable includes an air-driven motor which rotates it in either direction at walking speed; an internally-mounted rotational stop that permits a fixed amount of rotation in each direction and a remote control unit.

HEAVY WORKPIECE TOOL BED PLATE

One of the latest additions to Rolair's air film systems is the Omni-Mobile Tool Bed Plate, which combines a system for transporting castings and similar workpieces with flush-to-floor docking points for precise alignment at the machine.

The workpiece is set up apart from the machining operations on a special transporter.

After setting up the particular workpiece, or component, is carried by the transporter to the machine and is precisely positioned on the docking points.

In subsequent operations, as a machining step is completed, the transporter can be rotated. For example, it could be rotated 180° for machining on the opposite face of the workpiece. Or, the transporter can be floated to another machine within the machine tool complex. In this situation, a second transporter with a new workpiece from the setup area can be positioned at the first machine within minutes.

The repeatable, precise positioning possible at various machine tools permits a manufacturer to use a series of less expensive single-function machine tools, rather than the high cost machine tools that incorporate multiple machining operations, and require costly setup times.

The Rolair transporter used in the Omni-Mobile Bed Plate system resembles a standard machine tool bed plate. It has standard 1 in T-slots on 12 in centres (keyslots and other spacings available). Mounted in the slots are key-type fixtures which are used to locate and hold the workpiece.

With the system, the setup workpiece is floated from the setup area onto flush-to-floor docking points adjacent to the machine tool. A built-in, directional air-powered drive system provides propulsion.

Above: The Omni-Mobile Bed Plate transporters permit workpieces to be set up some distance from machine tools, then floated into place and accurately positioned for drilling, welding and other processes

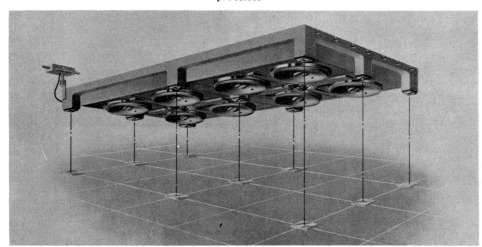

Beneath the transporters are the disc-like air bearings. Precise alignment of each workpiece is assured by machined pads and tapered shot pins on landing struts of the transporter which engage in receptacles in the floor docking points. Positioning within ± .001 in is possible

UNION OF SOVIET SOCIALIST REPUBLICS

LENINGRAD INSTITUTE OF ENGINEERING AND CONSTRUCTION

An air cushion vibrating platform designed to improve the rate of setting and uniformity of concrete has been designed and built by the Leningrad Institute of Engineering and Construction. It oscillates vertically, horizontally and diagonally.

The idea of employing an air cushion in constructing vibrating platforms for the production of prefabricated reinforced concrete was proposed and introduced by technologists in the Byelorussian Ministry of Construction.

Conventional vibrating platforms require considerable quantities of metal in their construction and costly foundations, the weight of which can be 18-20 times the load capacity of the platform. The concentrated dynamic loads frequently lead to the breakdown of the platform's framework, and during operation the vibration and noise cause severe discomfort to plant personnel.

The operating principle of vibrating platforms using air cushions is as follows. Beneath the vibrating platform, which is a framework with a metal bottom, air is fed by a fan to form an air cushion between the foundation and the bottom of the vibrating platform. As a result, the vibrating platform (along with a form filled with mixed concrete) is lifted into the air. The vibrating system is then switched on and the mixture is allowed to set under the influence of vertical oscilla-tions with an amplitude of 0·3-1 mm. To limit power expenditure, the cushion forms a closed system with an elastic apron. The pressure in the air cushion is 600-800 kg/m^2 with a lift of 6-10 tons.

These platforms have a load capacity of 2-3 tons. They do not require special concrete foundations and are mounted on a sandy base 100-150 mm thick. The power consumption of existing mass-produced platforms with load capacities of 4·6 and 8 tons are 14, 20 and 40 kW, respectively, in contrast to 10, 14 and 28 kW for air cushion vibrating platforms. Use is made of the ability of an air cushion to distribute pressure evenly over the en ire reaction surface, and of its outstanding shock absorbing qualities.

NOVOCHERKAASK POLYTECHNIC

The Novocherkaask Polytechnic has developed a series of air pads and platforms capable of supporting loads of up to 12·5 tonnes. The air supply is from a compressor or the factory air supply.

A platform with a load capacity of 40-80 tonnes is in the design stage and a feature is an automatic load relief should the air supply be cut off.

A diagram showing the system evolved at the Polytechnic accompanies this entry. It comprises two or more compressed air pads (1), which are generally rectangular in shape, and two connecting supports for the load or load platform (2). The supports are connected to the air pads by articulated joints (3) and rest on compressed air jacks (4). Air is fed into the pads through a regulator and enters the chamber of the compressed air jack (5). It then passes through the baffle plates (6) which ensure a constant differential in pressure between the cushion air plenums and the compressed air jack chamber. Cushion air enters the plenum (7) and then escapes through the discharge nozzle (8) into the recess (9) between the flexible seals and the supporting surface.

The system has undergone extensive tests and it is thought likely that it will have wide application in Soviet industry, particularly in the movement of machines and material stocks in warehouses.

Students at Novocherkaask Polytechnic with a prototype of their air cushion materials handling platform

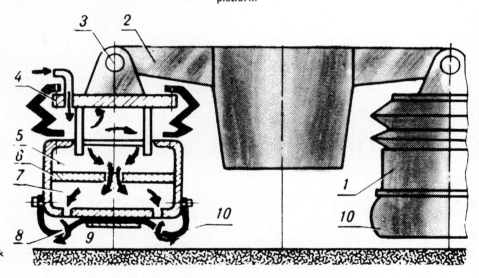

Diagram showing operation of the Novocherkaask Polytechnic air pads and handling platform

HYDROFOILS

CANADA

DE HAVILLAND AIRCRAFT COMPANY OF CANADA, LIMITED

HEAD OFFICE AND WORKS:
Downsview, Ontario, Canada
TELEPHONE:
633-7310 Area Code 416
TELEGRAMS:
Moth Toronto
DIRECTORS:
J. H. Smith, Chairman
B. B. Bundesman, President and Chief Executive Officer
D. B. Annan, Vice-President, Operations
R. M. Barford
D. L. Buchanan, Vice-President, Marketing
J. F. Grandy
W. T. Heaslip, Vice-President, Engineering
F. A. Johnson, Vice-President, Contracts and Programmes Administration
D. N. Kendall
S. B. Kerr, Vice-President, Finance
SENIOR EXECUTIVES:
F. H. Buller, Chief Designer
S. Morita, Hydrofoil Project Manager

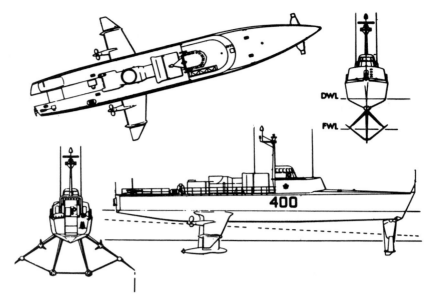

De Havilland FHE-400 ocean-going ASW warship

In early 1961 the Canadian Department of Defense contracted De Havilland Aircraft of Canada Ltd for a feasibility and engineering study based on the NRE ASW hydrofoil report. The company's recommendations were approved in April 1963 and led to the construction of the FHE-400 fast hydrofoil escort warship. The programme had two fundamental objectives: (a) to establish in practice the feasibility of an ocean-going hydrofoil of the proposed size and characteristics (b) to evaluate the prototype as an ASW system.

FHE 400 was commissioned as HMCS Bras d'Or in Halifax and was tested in brief displacement mode trials in September 1968. The foilborne transmission was fitted during the winter of 1968 and the first foilborne trial took place on April 9, 1969. The craft attained a speed of 63 knots during calm water trials in July 1969. Rough water trials during the winter of 1971 culminated in a 2,500 mile "shake down" cruise from Halifax to Bermuda and Norfolk, Va.

Foilborne trials were conducted in 10-15 ft (3·04-4·57 m) waves (sea state 5) at speeds in excess of 40 knots. Hullborne trials were conducted in higher sea states.

While objective (a), to confirm operations feasibility in open ocean conditions, was met, objective (b), ASW system operation, was suspended because of a change in Canadian defence priorities, requiring priority attention to territorial and coastal surveillance. The craft was therefore put into store, although research in this field continued. In May 1974 it was reported that the craft is to be reactivated. In the meantime the company reports that wide interest is being shown in a smaller and similar design—the DHC—MP—(Maritime Patrol) 100—which will have the same seakeeping capability. Possible civil applications include oil-rig resupply, coastguard work and fisheries patrol.

FHE-400

FOILS: The foil system is a canard configuration of the surface piercing type and non-retractable. The steerable bow foil is super-cavitating and designed for good response in a seaway. The subcavitating main foil carries 90% of the static weight and is a combination

of surface-piercing and submerged foils. The centre high speed foil section is protected from ventilation by the struts and the dihedral foils have full-chord fences to inhibit ventilation. Anhedral foils provide reserve lift at take-off and their tips provide roll restoring forces at foilborne speeds. All foil elements are in welded 18% nickel maraging sheet steel and forgings.

The struts are a compromise to provide the optimum fin effect in yaw in conjunction with the steerable bow foil.

HULL: Hull and superstructure are fabricated from ALCAN D54S, and extensive use is made of large extrusions with integral stringers for the plating.

A crew of twenty is carried, comprising eight officers and twelve men. In order to maintain crew alertness at all times, comfortable crew quarters and good messing facilities were considered essential features. Both were intensively studied by the Institute of

Aviation Medicine. The study included the testing of crew bunks on a motion simulator at NCR Ottawa, and the use of a simulator to assess crew efficiency under foilborne conditions.

POWER PLANT: Continuous search for a useful period demands economical operation in any sea state at displacement speeds and the ability to attack at high speeds. For this reason there are two propulsion systems —the foilborne marinised gas-turbine, a 22,000 shp Pratt & Whitney FT4A-2, and a 2,000 bhp Davey-Paxman 16YJCM diesel engine for hullborne power.

The FT4A-2, a marine version of the shaft-turbine engine developed from the JT4 and 5 gas turbine, is enclosed by a protective cowling aft of the bridge.

Shaft power is transmitted to the inboard gearbox directly aft of the engine exhaust elbow and is then transmitted via dual shafts through each of the two inner struts to the outboard gearboxes in the streamlined

During sea trials, the FHE 400 reached a foilborne speed of 62 knots. Capable of all-weather operation, the vessel has a maximum take-off displacement of 235 tons

pods at the intersection of the struts and foils. The dual shafts are combined at the outboard gearboxes into a single drive then taken through an over-running clutch to each of the two 4 ft (1·22 m) diameter fixed-pitch supercavitating propellers.

A governor prevents overspeed if the propellers leave the water in rough seas.

The Paxman Ventura 16YJCM diesel-engine is sited in the engine room, on the ship's centreline. Power is transmitted to the variable pitch hullborne propellers through a dual output gearbox and thence through shafts to gearboxes located in the pods.

The KMW controllable-pitch displacement propellers of 7 ft (2·13 m) diameter are novel, since they are feathered when the craft is foilborne so as to minimise the appendage drag penalty. Slow speed manoeuvring is effected by control of individual propeller pitch settings.

CONTROLS. Diesel power, propeller pitch, main gas turbine speed and individual displacement propeller pitch are all normally controlled by lever from the bridge. Dual wheels are provided to steer the bow foil which acts as the rudder for both foilborne and displacement operation. It is also adjustable to rake enabling the best angle of attack to be selected for foilborne or hull-borne operation. An engineer's console is located in the operation room and starting and stopping of all engines is undertaken from this position. Engine and propeller pitch controls duplicating those on the bridge are provided on the console.

Turns are fully or partially coordinated, depending on speed, by the variable incidence anhedral tips. The tips are also coupled to an auto-pilot and act as stabilisers to supplement the foil system's inherent roll resistance.

SYSTEMS:
AUXILIARY POWER: An auxiliary gas-turbine, a United Aircraft of Canada ST6A-53 rated at 390 hp continuous at 2,100 rpm is used to power electric generators, hydraulic pumps and a salt-water pump. It can also be used to increase the available displacement propulsion power and for emergency propulsion power at reduced speed.

EMERGENCY POWER: The emergency power unit is an AiResearch GTCP-85-291 shaft-coupled turbine rated at 190 hp continuous. In the event of the auxiliary gas turbine becoming unserviceable or being in use for the displacement propulsion, this turbine will power the ship's system. Alternatively bleed air may be drawn from the compressor for main turbine starting.

DIMENSIONS, EXTERNAL:

Length overall, hull	151 ft 0 in	(45·9 m)
Length waterline, hull	147 ft 0 in	(44 m)
Hull beam	21 ft 6 in	(6·5 m)
Width across foils	66 ft 0 in	(20 m)
Draft afloat	23 ft 6 in	(7·16 m)
Freeboard, forward	11 ft 0 in	(3·3 m)

WEIGHTS:

Gross tonnage (normal)	212 tons
Light displacement	165 long tons
Max take-off displacement	235 long tons
Useful load (fuel, crew and military load)	over 70 tons

PERFORMANCE:
Maximum speed, foilborne
50 knots rough water, 60 knots calm water
Cruising speed, hullborne   over 12 knots
Sea state capability
    Sea State 5 significant wave height 10 ft

HMCS Bras D'Or during calm water trials

DHC-MP-100

De Havilland Canada's latest hydrofoil design is the DHC-MP-100, a multi-duty vessel of 104 tons displacement and a maximum speed of 50 knots. Twin gas-turbines power the foilborne propulsion system instead of the single turbine employed in the FHE-400, the foil system has been simplified, and although the craft is smaller than its predecessor the same outstanding sea-keeping performance is maintained.

A worldwide market survey has been undertaken to determine the needs of potential customers outside Canada and reports indicate that considerable interest is being shown in the craft particularly for the following applications: oil rig re-supply, coastguard patrol, search and rescue, customs and excise, gunboat, missilecraft and ASW patrol.

In general the configuration and construction follows that of the FHE-400.

FOILS: Canard, surface-piercing configuration with approximately 90% of the weight carried by the main foil and 10% by the bow foil. The bow foil is of diamond shape and acts as the rudder for both foilborne and hullborne operations. The main foil, of trapeze configuration combines a fully submerged central section with dihedral surfaces outboard.

POWER PLANT, FOILBORNE: Foilborne propulsion is supplied by two 3,100 shp gas-turbines each driving a fixed-pitch super-cavitating three-bladed propeller. Power is transmitted via dual shafts through each of the two inner foil struts to gearboxes at the intersections of the struts and foils.

Among the engines likely to be specified are the Rolls Royce Marine Proteus, the Marine Tyne and the Avco Lycoming TF 40.

POWER PLANT, HULLBORNE: Hullborne propulsion is supplied by two 400 hp diesels driving two two-bladed propellers through outdrive units.

Data for the basic craft and the main variants are given below.

DHC-MP-100 GENERAL PURPOSE

In this configuration, the craft can be equipped for coastguard, search and rescue, fisheries and environmental patrol, customs and excise duties and oil-rig re-supply.

DIMENSIONS, EXTERNAL:

Length	118 ft 1 in	(36 m)
Beam	21 ft 0 in	(6·4 m)
Width across main foil	50 ft 9¾ in	(15·5 m)
Draft hullborne	17 ft 5⅞ in	(5·33 m)
Freeboard, hullborne	8 ft 0 in	(2·44 m)

WEIGHTS:

Crew and supplies	2,930 kg
Roll equipment and fuel	26,800 kg
Total payload	29,730 kg
Basic weight	75,740 kg
Displacement	105,470 kg
	(104 tons)

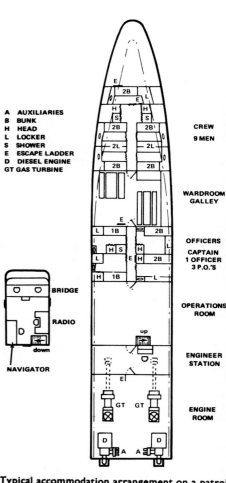

A AUXILIARIES
B BUNK
H HEAD
L LOCKER
S SHOWER
E ESCAPE LADDER
D DIESEL ENGINE
GT GAS TURBINE

CREW
9 MEN

WARDROOM
GALLEY

OFFICERS
CAPTAIN
1 OFFICER
3 P.O.'S

OPERATIONS
ROOM

ENGINEER
STATION

ENGINE
ROOM

BRIDGE
RADIO
NAVIGATOR
up
down

Typical accommodation arrangement on a patrol escort version of the MP-100 hydrofoil

PERFORMANCE:

Maximum speed, est.　50 knots (90 km/h)

Range:

18,000 kg fuel capacity

at 11·5 km/h (10 knots)

　　　　　　　　3,500 km (1,910 nm)

at 74 km/h (40 knots)　1,180 km (642 nm)

27,000 kg fuel capacity

at 18·5 km/h (10 kt)　5,250 km (2,865 nm)

at 74 km/h (40 kt)　1,770 km (963 nm)

GUNBOAT

For coastal patrol, interdiction or for escorting larger ships or convoys, a 57 mm Bofors gun can be fitted. For self-defence a Vulcan gun is mounted on the afterdeck. Other armament installations can be fitted within weight and c of g limits.

Overload fuel will extend the range in displacement condition to a maximum of 4,600 km (2,500 nm). In the maximum overload condition take-off may be restricted to moderate sea states.

The foil system stabilises the vessel and gives it the seakeeping characteristics of a ship of 1,000/1,500 tons, thus improving accuracy of shot and crew performance for a craft of this size.

DIMENSIONS:

As for basic craft

WEIGHTS:

Crew and supplies	2,930 kg
Bofors gun and ammunition	7,140 kg
Vulcan gun system	1,540 kg
Fuel	18,150 kg
Total payload	29,760 kg
Basic weight	75,740 kg
Displacement	105,500 kg
	(104 tons)

PERFORMANCE:

Range at 18·5 km/h	3,500 km (1,910 nm)
Range at 74 km/h	1,180 km (642 nm)

MISSILECRAFT

To complement the gunboat role, the MP-100 may be fitted with missiles like the Harpoon and Exocet. The fire control system is located in the large operations room.

For self-defence a Vulcan gun system is mounted aft between the missile containers. An alternative arrangement is the mounting of the gun on the foredeck and its detection system above the bridge.

DIMENSIONS:

As for basic craft

WEIGHTS:

Crew and supplies	2,930 kg
Missile system	4,530 kg
Vulcan gun system	1,540 kg
Fuel	20,400 kg
Total payload	29,400 kg
Basic weight	75,740 kg
Displacement	105,140 kg
	(103·5 tons)

PERFORMANCE:

Range at 18·5 km/h	3,960 km (2,150 nm)
Range at 74 km/h	1,340 km (723 nm)

ASW PATROL CRAFT

The craft can cruise at convoy speed on its displacement propulsion units while using variable-depth sonar to search for submarines. On making contact it can attack at high speed.

Lightweight VDS gear is installed. This has a low-drag body and cable and can be towed at over 55 km/h (30 kt). The system is of modular construction and can be quickly

A multi-duty hydrofoil of 104 tons displacement, the DHC-MP-100 is available in a variety of configurations, three of which are depicted above:

Top: Equipped as a fast patrol boat or convoy escort, a 57 mm Bofors automatic gun is mounted on the foredeck and for self-defence, a Vulcan gun package is mounted on the afterdeck

Centre: Operated as a missile equipped patrol craft, the MP-100 would carry two launchers aft—Harpoon and Exocet missiles are two choices—and for self-defence, a Vulcan gun pack is mounted aft between the missiles. An alternative arrangement would be to mount the gun on the foredeck and its detection gear above the bridge

Bottom: An ASW version equipped with lightweight VDS gear and torpedoes mounted in multiple tubes. Full sonar and fire-control systems are provided in the operations room

installed or removed. Torpedoes can be mounted in multiple tubes. Sonar and fire-control systems and fitted in the operations room. A Vulcan gun can be mounted on the foredeck with sensors above the bridge.

DIMENSIONS:
As for basic craft

WEIGHTS:

Crew and supplies	2,930 kg
VDS gear	5,080 kg
Torpedoes	3,035 kg
Vulcan gun	1,540 kg
Fire control	4,080 kg
Fuel	15,860 kg

Total payload	32,525 kg
Basic ship	75,740 kg
Displacement	108,265 kg
	(106·8 tons)

PERFORMANCE:

Range at 18·5 km/h	3,150 km (1,710 nm)
Range at 74 km/h	1,040 km (565 nm)

WATER SPYDER MARINE LTD

HEAD OFFICE AND WORKS:
157 Richard Clark Drive, Downsview, Ontario, M3M 1V6

TELEPHONE:
244 5404, Area Code 416

DIRECTORS:
J. F. Lstiburek, President
G. A. Leask, Secretary/Treasurer
A. Lstiburek, Vice-President

SENIOR EXECUTIVES:
L. Civiera, Sales Manager
J. F. Lstiburek, Designer

Water Spyder Marine Ltd is a wholly-owned Canadian company operating under charter issued by the Government of the Province of Ontario. It produces three fibreglass-hulled sports hydrofoils which are available either ready-built or in kit form.

WATER SPYDER 1-A

The Water Spyder 1-A is a single-seat sports hydrofoil powered by long-shaft outboard of 10-25 hp.

FOILS: The foil system comprises a split W-type surface piercing main foil supporting 98% of the load, and an adjustable outrigged trim tab which supports the remaining 2%.

HULL: Two-piece fibreglass reinforced plastic construction, foam-filled for flotation. Standard fittings and regulation running lights.

ACCOMMODATION: Single fibreglass seat.

POWER PLANT: Any suitable outboard engine of 10-25 hp (Mercury, Evinrude or Chrysler) with long shaft.

CONTROLS: Controls include joy-stick and rudder pedals.

DIMENSIONS:
Length overall, hull   6 ft 0 in (1·828 m)
Beam overall, foils retracted
     4 ft 0 in (1·219 m)
Beam overall, foils extended
     7 ft 0 in (2·133 m)

WEIGHTS:
Weight empty   80 lb (36·24 kg)

PERFORMANCE:
Maximum speed   40 mph (64·37 km/h)
Max permissible wave height in foilborne condition   1 ft 6 in (457·2 mm)
Turning radius at cruising speed app
     10 ft (3·04 m)

Cost of standard craft and terms of payment: US$1,000·00. Terms: cash. Delivery 3 weeks app from date of order, f.o.b. Toronto.

WATER SPYDER 2-B

The Water Spyder 2-B is a two-seat sports hydrofoil powered by a long-shaft outboard of 20-35 hp.

FOILS: The foil system comprises a split W-type surface piercing main foil supporting 98% of the load and an adjustable outrigged trim tab which supports the remaining 2%.

HULL: This is a two-piece (deck and hull) moulded fibreglass construction and incorporates buoyancy chambers. Standard fittings include a curved Perspex windshield and regulation running lights, fore and aft.

ACCOMMODATION: The craft seats two in comfortably upholstered seats. Foils and the trim tab assembly are adjustable from inside the cockpit.

POWER PLANT: Any suitable outboard engine of 20-35 hp (Mercury 200L or 350L Chrysler Evinrude) with long-shaft extension.

CONTROLS: Controls include steering wheel with adjustable friction damper and trim tab control.

DIMENSIONS:
Length overall, hull   12 ft 0 in (3·6 m)
Beam overall, foils retracted
     5 ft 4 in (1·6 m)
Beam overall, foils extended
     7 ft 4 in (2·2 m)

WEIGHTS:
Weight empty   220 lb (99·7 kg)

PERFORMANCE:
Max speed   up to 40 mph (64 km/h)
Max permissible wave height in foilborne mode   1 ft 6 in
Turning radius at cruising speed
     10 ft (3 m) app

Cost of standard craft and terms of payment: US$1,600·00. Terms: cash. Delivery: 3 weeks from date of order, f.o.b. Toronto.

WATER SPYDER 6-A

An enlarged version of the Water Spyder 2. Model 6-A is a six-seat family pleasure hydrofoil boat, with a two-piece moulded fibreglass hull.

The seats, located immediately over the main foil, are arranged in two rows of three abreast, one row facing forward, the other aft.

Power is supplied by a long-shaft outboard motor of 60-115 hp.

DIMENSIONS:
Length overall, hull   19 ft 0 in (5·79 m)
Beam overall, foils retracted
     8 ft 3 in (2·5 m)
Beam overall, foils extended
     13 ft 0 in (3·96 m)
Height overall, foils retracted
     4 ft 6 in (1·37 m)
Floor area   30 sq ft (2·78 m²)

WEIGHTS:
Gross tonnage   1 ton app
Weight empty   980 lb (444 kg)

PERFORMANCE:
Max speed   35-40 mph (56-64 km/h)
Cruising speed   32 mph (51 km/h)
Max permissible wave height in foilborne mode   2 ft 6 in (0·76 m)
Turning radius at cruising speed
     20 ft (6·09 m)

Cost of standard craft and terms of payment: US$3,500·00. Terms: cash. Delivery: Three weeks from date of order f.o.b. Toronto.

Water Spyder 6-A is a six-seat hydrofoil. The main foil, trim-tab support and engine fold upward so the craft can be floated on and off a trailer

CHINA (People's Republic of)

HUTANG SHIPYARD
HEAD OFFICE AND YARD:
Shanghai

Hydrofoil torpedo boats of the Hu Chwan (White Swan) Class have been under construction at the Hutang Shipyard, since about 1966. Some 60-70 are in service with the navy of the Chinese People's Republic and another thirty have been lent or leased to the Albanian navy, four to Pakistan and one to Romania.

One of four Hu Chwan-class torpedo/fast attack craft built by the Hutang Shipyard, Shanghai, and supplied to the Pakistan Navy in 1973.

HU CHWAN (WHITE SWAN)
FOILS: The foil system comprises a bow subfoil to facilitate take-off and a main foil of trapeze or shallow vee configuration set back approximately one-third of the hull length from the bow. At high speed in relatively calm conditions the greater part of the hull is raised clear of the water. The main foil and struts retract upwards when the craft is required to cruise in displacement condition.

HULL: High speed V-bottom hull in seawater resistant light alloy.
POWER PLANT: Thought to be two 1,100 hp M-50 watercooled, supercharged 12-cylinder V-type diesels, each driving its own inclined propeller shaft.

ARMAMENT: Two 21 in torpedo tubes, plus four 12·7 in machine guns in two twin mountings.

DIMENSIONS (approximate):
Length overall	70 ft (21·33 m)
Beam overall	16 ft 6 in (5·02 m)
Hull beam	13 ft (3·96 m)

WEIGHTS:
Displacement full load — 45 tons
PERFORMANCE:
Max speed foilborne calm conditions — 55 knots
Range — 500 nm approx

FRANCE

SOCIETE NATIONALE INDUSTRIELLE AEROSPATIALE
HEAD OFFICE:
37 Boulevard de Montmorency, 75781 Paris-Cedex 16, France
TELEPHONE:
224-8400
525-5775
CABLE/TELEX ADDRESS:
Aerospatiale-Paris, AISPA 62059F
WORKS:
Marignane, B.P.13, 13722 Marignane
TELEPHONE:
(91) 89.90.22

In 1966 the Direction des Recherches et Moyens d'Essais (Directorate of Research and Test Facilities) initiated a basic hydrofoil design and research programme with the object of building a prototype hydrofoil ferry with a displacement of 55 tons and a speed of 50 knots.

The companies and organisations co-operating in this programme are: Aerospatiale, project leader: STCAN, the hull test centre; several French government laboratories of the DTCN; SOGREAH, and Constructions Mecaniques de Normandie.

The main headings of the programme are:
Hydrodynamics (foils, struts and hull)
Foil hydroelasticity data and flutter phenomenon
Automatic pilot
Material technology relative to foils, struts and hull

The design and research programme is nearly complete and the results will be processed and refined using a 4-ton submerged foil test craft, the H. 890, designed by Aerospatiale.

The craft, which was launched on June 16th, 1972 is employed in a comprehensive test programme which is under the control of Aerospatiale and DTCN, a French government agency.

In addition to the SA 800 55-ton hydrofoil ferry, preliminary designs have been completed for a missile-carrying 118-ton hydrofoil combat vessel, the H. 851, and a commercial variant, intended for mixed-traffic ferry services. The latest project is a 174 tonne missilecraft with a speed of 54 knots and capable of operating in Force 5 weather at 50 knots. Armament would comprise four Exocet missiles and one rapid-fire automatic cannon.

H.890
This 4·5 seagoing test vehicle is being employed to gather data for foil systems and accelerate the development of autopilot systems for large hydrofoils.

The combination of catamaran hull and pure jet propulsion allows the foils to be arranged in either conventional configuration—two foils forward and one aft—or canard configuration, with one foil forward and two aft.

The vessel was developed and built under

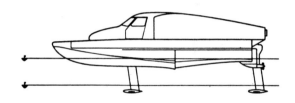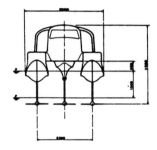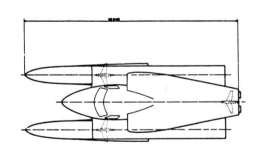

Foil configuration on the H.890 can be changed from canard to conventional (aeroplane) as required

contract to the French government agency DTCN by Aerospatiale's Helicopter Division in conjunction with Constructions Mecaniques de Normandie and SOGREAH of Grenoble. It has been undergoing tests on the Etang de Berre since it was launched on June 16th, 1972. A speed of 50 knots has been reached during trials.

FOILS: Fully submerged system with facilities for changing from conventional (aeroplane) to canard configuration as required. In aeroplane configuration about 70% of the weight is supported by the twin bow foils, which are attached to the port and starboard pontoons, and 30% by the single tail foil, mounted on the central hull section aft.

The stern foil rotates for steering and all three struts are fixed (non-retractable). Lift variation of the three foils is achieved by an autopilot system, developed by Aerospatiale and SFENA, which varies the incidence angles of all three foils. During the first series of tests the foils were tested in conventional configuration. During the second series the canard configuration was adopted.

HULL: Catamaran type, constructed in corrosion-resistant light alloys. Central hull, which incorporates control cabin, engine bay and test instrumentation, is flanked by two stepped pontoons.

ACCOMMODATION: Seating is provided for two—pilot and test observer.

POWER PLANT: Twin 480 daN Turbomeca Marbore VIc gas-turbines, mounted in the central hull structure aft of the cabin, power the craft when foilborne. Hullborne propulsion is supplied by a 20 hp Sachs 370 engine driving via a hydraulic transmission a folding-blade Maucour waterscrew located at the top of the aft foil strut. The waterscrew rotates through ±90° for steering.

DIMENSIONS:

Length overall	34·97 ft (10·66 m)
Length waterline	30·51 ft (9·30 m)
Beam overall	12·80 ft (3·90 m)
Draft afloat	5·64 ft (1·72 m)
Draft foilborne	1·21 ft (0·37 m)

WEIGHTS:

Normal take-off	4·5 m tons

PERFORMANCE:

Cruising speed, foilborne, calm conditions
50 knots
Cruising speed, hullborne, calm conditions
6 knots
Craft is designed to cross waves up to 2·62 ft high without contouring (0·80 m)

The H.890 4-ton submerged foil test vehicle is being employed by the Aerospatiale to develop automatic control systems and gather data for the design of larger vessels. It has attained 50 knots during high speed runs on the Etang de Berre

SA 800

The SA 800 is a design study for a mixed-traffic hydrofoil powered by two Turmo 111C turbines driving a waterjet propulsion unit. Conventional marine light alloy construction is employed and the craft will have incidence-controlled, fully-submerged foils operated by a sonic/electronic sensing system.

A number of variants of the basic design are being studied for alternative applications, including prospecting, marine research, coastal surveillance and naval patrol. Trials conducted with dynamic models have been successful and are continuing. Preliminary design studies are now complete.

FOILS: The foil system is fully submerged and of "aeroplane" configuration. All three foil struts retract hydraulically completely clear of the water. An SNIAS sonic autopilot system controls the incidence angle of the two bow foils and adjustable control flaps on the rear foils.

HULL: The hull is of conventional marine corrosion-resistant aluminium alloys. Features include a deep vee bow, designed to minimise structural loading due to wave impact, and a flat W section aft for good directional control when hullborne.

POWER PLANT: Foilborne propulsion is supplied by two 1,300 shp Turboméca Turmo 111C gas-turbines driving a SOGREAH waterjet propulsion unit mounted at the base of the aft foil strut.

Output from the transmission shafts of the two turbines, which are mounted end-to-end, intakes outwards, athwart the stern, passes first to a main bevel drive

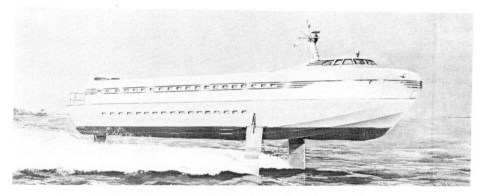

Artist's impression of the SNIA SA-800 waterjet propelled hydrofoil ferry

gearbox, then to a drive shaft which extends downwards through the aft foil strut to a waterjet pump gearbox located in a nacelle beneath the aft foil. Air for the turbines is introduced through intakes at the top of the cabin aft. Filters are fitted to the intakes to prevent the ingestion of water or salt spray into the gas-turbine. There is a separate hullborne propulsion system, with a 400 hp diesel driving twin water propellers beneath the transom.

ACCOMMODATION: The elevated wheelhouse forward of the passenger compartment seats the captain and engineer. All instrumentation is located so that it can be easily monitored. Navigation and collision avoidance radar is fitted. Accommodation is on two decks, each arranged with three seats abreast on either side of a central aisle. As a passenger ferry the craft will seat 200—116 on the upper deck and 84 on the lower; and in mixed traffic configuration

it will carry 8-10 cars on the upper deck with the lower deck seating capacity remaining at 84. Cars are loaded via rear door/ramps. Baggage holds are provided forward of both upper and lower saloons.

DIMENSIONS:

Length overall	88 ft 0 in (26·88 m)
Max beam, deck	18 ft 0 in (5·40 m)

WEIGHTS:

Displacement, fully loaded
55 tons (56 m tons)
Payload (200 passengers with luggage or 84 passengers with luggage and 8-10 cars)
40,300 lb (18,300 kg)

PERFORMANCE:

Max speed, calm conditions	55 knots
Cruising speed	50 knots
Cruising speed, Sea State 5	48 knots
Range, at 50 knots, calm sea	250 nm
at 48 knots, Sea State 5	200 nm

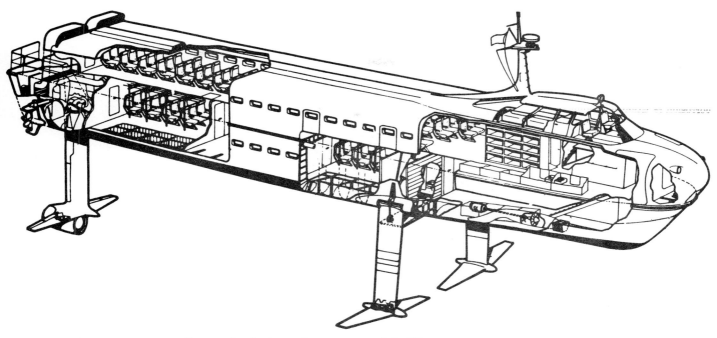

Cutaway showing internal arrangements of the 200-seat passenger ferry

Craft is designed to platform over 10 ft (3 m) high waves, crest to trough, and contour 13 ft (4 m) high waves.

H.851

The H.851 is a preliminary design for a missile-equipped combat hydrofoil capable of all-weather operation. Initially it will have a displacement of 118 tons (120 m. tons) and cruise at 45 knots, but later models, with increased power, are expected to attain nearly 60 knots. Development is being undertaken in conjunction with the French Navy. A civil version employing the same foil system and basic hull is projected.

FOILS: Fully submerged canard arrangement with about 80% of the weight supported by the twin aft foils and 20% by the bow foil. The bow foil strut, which rotates for steering, retracts forwards and upwards ahead of the stem, and the two aft struts rotate rearwards and upwards. The strut locking system is designed to dampen shocks resulting from encounters with floating wreckage. Struts and foils have NACA Series 16 profiles.

Lift variation is achieved by an Aerospatiale autopilot system which varies the incidence angles of all three foils. Trailing-edge flaps on the foils augment lift during take-off.

HULL: Constructed in marine corrosion-resistant aluminium alloys.

ACCOMMODATION: Berthing, galley and toilet arrangements for crew of 21.

POWER PLANT: Foilborne propulsion is supplied by a single 5,200 kW SNECMA THS 2000 gas-turbine driving two SOGREAH water pumps, one at the base of each foil strut, via mechanical right-angle drives. Hullborne propulsion is provided by a single 770 kW diesel engine driving a single variable-pitch propeller.

ARMAMENT: Four Exocet MM 38 missiles and one 40 mm Bofors rapid-firing cannon.

DIMENSIONS:
Length overall   114·83 ft (35 m)
Beam overall   49·21 ft (15 m)
Draft hullborne   5·90 ft (1·80 m)
Draft foilborne, foils lowered
                               27·23 ft (8·30 m)
WEIGHTS:
Displacement, full load
                               115 tons (117 m. tons)

Impression of the Aerospatiale H.851 missile-equipped combat hydrofoil, being developed in conjunction with the French Navy

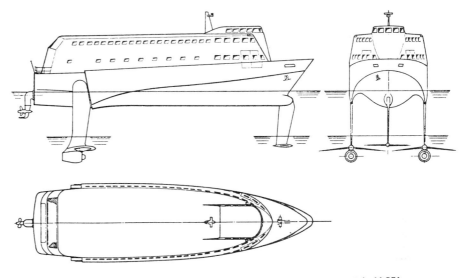

Commercial mixed-traffic variant of the Aerospatiale H.851

PERFORMANCE:

Max speed calm conditions	48 knots
Cruising speed, calm conditions	45 knots
Cruising speed, sea state 5	45 knots
Range and endurance :	
at 45 knots, calm conditions	1,300 nm or 29 hrs
at 45 knots, sea state 5	1,165 nm or 26 hrs
hullborne at 13 knots	2,130 nm or 163 hrs

H.851 CAR/PASSENGER FERRY

A direct derivative of the H.851 fast patrol vessel, this 65-ton mixed-traffic vessel utilises the same basic hull, foils and propulsion system, but has a completely redesigned interior and superstructure. Up to 200 passengers and 15 cars can be carried over short-medium route lengths at a normal service speed of 45 knots.

POWERPLANT: Arrangements similar to those of the H.851. Either one or two engines can be installed for hullborne propulsion, depending on the route(s) operated and the payload requirements. Hullborne power on models projected so far will be provided by either a single 1,100 kW Turbomeca Turmo 111 or a single 600 kW Hispano Suiza diesel. The engine room, at the aft end of the lower deck, is thoroughly soundproofed.

ACCOMMODATION: Up to 200 passengers are accommodated in a large single saloon on the upper deck. The bridge, which is on a separate level above and forward of the upper deck, is reached by a companionway from the passenger saloon. Four WC/washbasin units are provided. Access to the saloon is via two doors, one port, one starboard, at the forward end of the superstructure on the main deck. Eleven cars are carried on the main deck, and four on the lower deck, access to which is provided by two vehicle lifts.

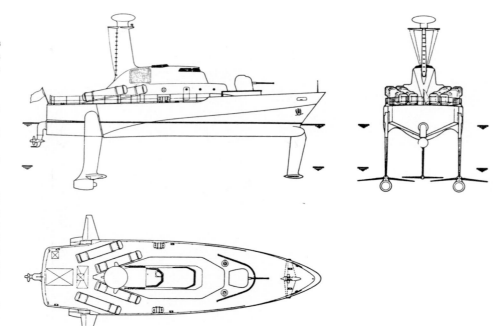

The H.851, 48-knot naval hydrofoil powered by a single SNECMA THS 2,000 gas-turbine driving two SOGREAH water pumps

A bar and a small promenade deck are located at the forward end of the main deck. The vessel will normally carry a crew of eight.

DIMENSIONS:

Length overall	114·83 ft (35 m)
Width across foils	49·21 ft (15 m)
Draft hullborne	5·90 ft (1·8 m)
Draft hullborne, foils lowered	27·23 ft (8·3 m)

WEIGHTS:

Displacement, fully loaded	115 tons (117 m. ton)
Useful load (Divided as required between fuel and payload)	50·2 tons (51 m. tons)

The version to which these figures apply carries 11·8 tons (12 m. tons) of fuel and 38·4 tons (39 m. tons) of payload.

PERFORMANCE:

Max speed, calm sea	48 knots
Normal service speed, calm sea	45 knots
Normal speed, sea state 5	45 knots
Range with 11·8 tons (12 m. tons) of fuel:	
Foilborne at 45 knots, calm sea	550 nm
Foilborne at 45 knots, sea state 5	485 nm
Hullborne at 13 knots (Turmo 111 gas turbine)	520 nm
Hullborne at 11·5 knots (diesel engine)	920 nm

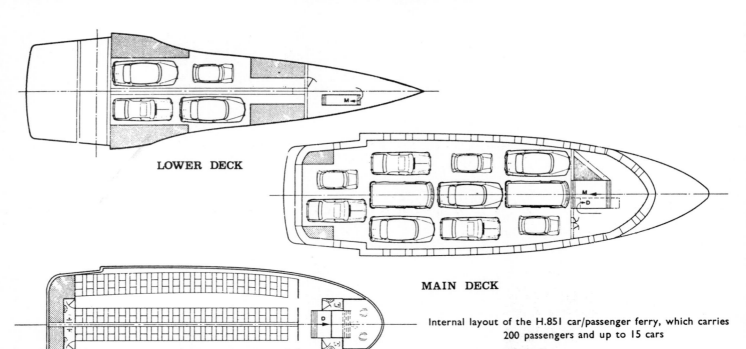

LOWER DECK

MAIN DECK

UPPER DECK

Internal layout of the H.851 car/passenger ferry, which carries 200 passengers and up to 15 cars

HONG KONG

SUPRAMAR PACIFIC SHIPBUILDING CO LTD

HEAD OFFICE:

32 Ko Fai Road, Yau Tong Bay, Kowloon, Hong Kong

TELEPHONE:

3-485211

TELEX:

75042 TFOK HX

YARD:

32 Ko Fai Road, Yau Tong Bay, Kowloon, Hong Kong

TELEPHONE:

3-478 326

OFFICERS AND EXECUTIVES:

Timothy Fok, Director

Charles Choy, Project Manager

Vincent Schweizer, (Supramar Ltd,

Lucerne) Resident Engineer

This company is a licensee of Supramar Ltd, Lucerne. Under the current agreement between the two companies, Supramar Pacific Shipbuilding Co Ltd is permitted to build craft of the following designs—PT 20, PT 20B, PT 50, PTS 75 Mk III and PT 150.

Under construction in the Kowloon yard at present are two PTS 75 Mk IIIs.

ITALY

CNR-ALINAVI FINCANTIERI GROUP

HEAD OFFICE AND WORKS:

Via Cyre 11, Genoa

TELEPHONE:

59951

TELEX:

27168 Cant. GE.

DIRECTORS:

Ginhio Baskinas (CNR), Chairman

Roy Gustafason (Boeing)

Com. te Pietro Notarbartolo (Fincantieri)

MANAGEMENT:

Ing. Francesco Cao, General Manager

Ing. Fabrizio Antonucci, Chief Engineer

This company was formed in 1964 to develop, manufacture and market military advanced marine systems. It is owned jointly by Cantieri Navali Riuniti SpA, (90%), and the Boeing Company (10%).

Under the terms of a Boeing-Alinavi licensing agreement, Alinavi has access to Boeing technology in the field of military fully-submerged foil hydrofoil craft.

In October 1970, the company was awarded a contract by the Italian Navy for the design and construction of the P 420 Sparviero class hydrofoil missilecraft. The craft is an improved version of the Boeing PGH-2 Tucumcari. The first vessel, given the design name Swordfish, was delivered to the Italian navy in July 1974.

SWORDFISH

The Swordfish missile-launching hydrofoil gunboat displaces a maximum of 64 metric tons and is designed for both offensive and defensive missions. Its combination of speed, firepower, and all-weather capability is unique in a ship of this class.

The vessel has fully-submerged foils arranged in canard configuration and an automatic control system. A gas turbine powered waterjet system provides foilborne propulsion and a diesel-driven propeller outdrive provides hullborne propulsion. A typical crew comprises two officers and eight enlisted men.

FOILS: Fully-submerged canard arrangement, with approximately one-third of the dynamic lift provided by the bow foil and two-thirds by the two aft foils. The aft foils retract sideways and the bow hydrofoil retracts forwards into a recess in the bow. Bowdoors preserve the hull lines when the forward hydrofoil is either fully extended or retracted. Foils and struts are built in corrosion-resistant stainless steel.

Anhedral is incorporated in the aft foils to enhance the directional stability of the craft at shallow foil depths. In addition, the anhedral assures positive roll control by eliminating tip broaching during rough

Turning radius of the Swordfish at 40 knots is less than 137 yards (125 m).

Swordfish hullborne with foils retracted. Continuous speed, hullborne, is 8 knots

water manoeuvres.

CONTROLS: Automatic system incorporating two aircraft-type gyros, one to sense pitch and roll and the other to sense yaw, plus three accelerometers to sense vertical movements (heave) of the craft. An ultrasonic height sensor is used to detect and maintain flying height above the water's surface. Informa-

tion from the sensors is sent to a hermetically-sealed solid-state computer, which calculates movements of the control surfaces necessary to maintain boat stability, and/or pre-selected flying height, and sends appropriate commands to the servo-mechanisms that control flap movement.

Foilborne steering: Helm commanded

automatic control system controls hydraulic servo-actuated hydrofoil flaps and steerable forward hydrofoil strut to produce coordinated (banked) turns in design sea conditions.

Hullborne steering: Helm commanded steerable outdrive unit. Helm-driven potentiometer sends signals to a servo-valve controlling steering hydraulic motor. Manual emergency hullborne steering is provided on the aft deck.

HULL: Both hull and superstructure are built entirely in corrosion-resistant aluminium, the hull being welded and the superstructure riveted and welded.

BERTHING: Two fixed berths in the compartment under the bridge, plus eight folding berths in the forward crew space. One toilet and one sink. A folding table with benches in the forward crew space.

POWERPLANT, FOILBORNE: Power for the waterjet is supplied by one Rolls-Royce Proteus 15M/553 gas-turbine. At the customer's option the craft may be fitted with the "sprint" model of this gas-turbine, which incorporates water injection. The "sprint" model ("wet") develops 5,000 shp maximum versus the 4,500 shp of the normal ("dry") Proteus. Adoption of the "sprint" model permits take-off at higher displacements and therefore, more fuel and/or military payload to be carried. It also provides better craft performance in very high sea states, particularly in conditions of high ambient temperatures. The respective performance characteristics of the Swordfish equipped with 'dry' and 'wet' models of the Proteus are shown in the accompanying performance table.

Engine output is transferred to a single double-volute, double-suction, two impeller centrifugal pump, rated at 28,000 US gpm at 1,560 rpm and absorbing app 4,700 shp (4,766 CV). Water is taken in through inlets on the nose of each aft foil at the foil/strut intersection and passes up through the hollow interiors of the struts to the hull, where it is ducted to the pump. From the pump, the water is discharged through twin, fixed-area nozzles located beneath the hull under the pump.

POWERPLANT, HULLBORNE: A General Motors 6V-53 diesel engine, rated at 160 shp (162 CV) at 2,600 rpm, powers a Schottel-Werft SRP-100 steerable propeller outdrive unit, which is mounted on the centreline of the transom. The unit is retractable and rotates through 360°. Propeller is fixed-pitch. Power is delivered to the outdrive at about 1,700 rpm.

FUEL: Fuel oil is NATO 76, carried in three tanks located amidships and integral with the hull, side keelson and platform deck. Total capacity is about 3,850 gallons (14,550 litres).

Fuel oil system: Two primary 208 volt 400 Hz 7 gpm (26·5 l/min) submerged pumps and two standby 28 volt d.c. 7 gpm (26·5 l/min) external pumps. The d.c. pump is started automatically by a pressure switch in the fuel supply line if a.c. pump power is lost.

Craft may be refuelled through main deck connection at dock or at sea. The fuel tanks are equipped with fuel level indicators and vents.

AUXILIARY SYSTEMS: HYDRAULICS: Two independent systems: foilborne and ship service. Systems pressure, 3.000 psi. Systems fluid, MIL-H-5606.

First of the Italian Navy's missile equipped hydrofoil gunboats during foilborne firing tests of its 76 mm Oto Melara cannon. Given the design name Swordfish, the craft is the first of the P420 Sparviero Class.

Foilborne system: normal and standby 21·8 gpm pumps serve hydraulic control system.

Ship service system: normal and standby 32·5 gpm pumps serve other uses including hydrofoil retracting and locking, bowdoor, hullborne outdrive retraction and steering, foilborne turbine starting, foilborne turbine exhaust door, cannon loading, and the fixed saltwater fire pump.

ELECTRICAL: Turbine generator sets: At customer's option, either two or three identical sets, one installed in forward machinery space, the other(s) in the aft machinery space.

Each set consists of a Solar T-62 T-32 gas turbine engine capable of developing a maximum output of 150 shp (152 CV) under standard conditions and driving: a General Electric 208 volt 400 Hz 3-phase alternator rated at 75 KVA; a 30 volt d.c. starter-generator with 200 amp generating capacity; and one hydraulic pump for ship service and hullborne steering.

Starting battery sets: One 24 volt, 34 amp-hr capacity starting battery is provided for the hullborne diesel engine and for each solar turbogenerator set.

Emergency battery set: Two additional 24 volt batteries in parallel provide 68 amp-hr capacity to power in emergency conditions, radios, intercommunications system and navigation lights.

Shore power: Craft requires up to 30 KVA of 200 volt 3-phase 4 wire 400 Hz power.

Intercommunication system: The system consists of one station in each space and three external stations allowing complete craft machinery and weapons coordination.

Every station is a control unit and has a reversible loudspeaker with press-to-talk switch.

Main station is equipped with radio operation access control.

Emergency announcements can be made to all stations simultaneously.

Selective communications are available between any two or more stations.

Electrical alarm, safety and warning system: Systems installed to indicate conditions of smoke or fire in the two machinery rooms or flooding in any compartment. Systems

indicate normal or malfunction conditions of machinery, auxiliary systems, hydrofoil craft automatic control system and hydrofoil extension/retraction position control mechanism.

A portable battery-powered electronic megaphone with provision for connection to an external power supply is stowed on the craft.

NAVIGATION AND COMMUNICATIONS: Navigation light system: All lights are small boat type. Lights are: 2 white masthead signalling lights, one white, one green and one red side navigation light: white stern and bow anchor lights, and 2 red and 1 white man overboard, breakdown and task lights on main mast.

Navigation horn: One electrically operated horn mounted on forward top of deckhouse.

Signal searchlight: One portable incandescent signal searchlight mounted on the deckhouse canopy.

Depth sounder: Transducer on the hull bottom 6 inches (0·152 metres) above the keel and a recorder at the navigation station measure and record water depth from echo soundings. Recorder may be set for sounding depths of 0-20, 20-45, 40-65, 0-60, 50-110, 100-160 fathoms (0-38·6, 38·6-86·9, 77·2-125·4, 0-115·8, 96·5-212, 193-309 metres). Recorder contains electronic circuits and a two-speed mechanism with a stylus which burns a black mark on moving chart paper. A white line mode of recorder operation eliminates false traces below the true bottom line on the chart and allows detection of small objects close to the bottom and an indication of hard or soft composition of the sea bottom.

Navigation set: The shipboard navigation system (ShipNav) automatically performs, independently of all external aids, precise dead reckoning navigation for both foilborne and hullborne operations. It continuously computes and displays the craft's current position, true heading, true course, and true speed. Actual position is displayed digitally on counters in latitude and longitude coordinates and pictorially on standard charts having local coordinate information. Indicators display true heading, course, and speed.

Speed log: Hull rodmeter, foil rodmeter, rodmeter selector switch and calibration unit, transmitter and remote indicator set measures craft hullborne or foilborne speed, computes the distance travelled and displays both at the navigation station and helm..

IFF system: The system consists of an IFF/ATC transponder (APX 72) and an IFF interrogator coupled to the radar.

Navigation and search radar: SMA Model 3RM7-250B radar performs navigation and search operations with master indicator, rayplot with variable range marker (VRN) bearing control unit and remote indicator.

Set operates in "X" band and is tunable from 9,345 MHz to 9,405 MHz. Set has two different transmitters and it is possible to select the proper one by a RF switch unit. Peak power output is 7 kW for navigation purposes and 250 kW for search purposes.

Performance includes a minimum range less than 200 yards (182 metres), range discrimination better than 11 yards (10·00 metres), azimuth discrimination less than 1·2 degrees and maximum range of 40 nautical miles.

HF-SSB radio system AN/ARC-102: The AN/ARC-102 uses the Collins 618T/3 HF single-sideband transceiver for long range voice, CW, data or compatible AM communication in the 2,000 through 29,999 MHz frequency range. It is automatically tuned in 28,000 1-kHz channel increments by means of an operator's remote control unit. The operating frequency is indicated directly in a digital-type presentation. Nominal transmit power is 400 watts pep. in SSB or 125 watts in compatible AM. The system is tuned through the antenna coupler Collins 490T-1 to a helical monopole antenna.

UHF radio system AN/ARC-109: Two identical units are provided. The AN/ARC-109 transceiver has two separate receivers: a main tunable receiver and a guard receiver. Common circuit design is maintained in the two receivers. Each receiver uses carrier-to-noise ratio squelch system. Receiver selectivity is ±22 kHz at —6 db and ±45 kHz at —60 db.

The 20-channel present memory in the frequency control utilises a magnetic core storage system with solid-state drivers and interrogators

DAMAGE CONTROL: Bilge pumps: Pumps are mounted in the bilge of each water-tight compartment and controlled from engineer's station.

Freon flooding systems: Two 53 pound (24 kg) freon FE1301 (CBR F₃) storage cylinders are provided in the engineer's compartment. One 5 pound (2·27 kg) freon cylinder is piped to Proteus turbine shroud. Systems manually controlled by engineer.

Portable fire extinguishers: A 2 pound (1 kg) dry chemical extinguisher is mounted in each of the seven manned compartments.

VENTILATION AND CONDITIONING: Unit air conditioners (6 units) are distributed throughout the manned spaces to provide heating and cooling.

ARMAMENT: A typical military payload consists of:

One dual purpose 76 mm automatic OTO Melara gun and ammunition
Two fixed missile launchers and two ship-to-ship missiles, e.g., Sea Killers, OTOMAT or Exocet
Gunfire and missile launch control system(s)
Other military electronics, e.g. ECM

PARAMETER	Without water injection		With water injection	
	15°C/59°F	22°C/80°F	15°C/59°F	22°C/80°F
Displacement (metric tons)	62·5	60·0	64	64
Military payload (metric tons)	11·7	11·7	14	14
Fuel (metric tons)	9·4	6·9	9·4	9·4
Max foilborne intermittent speed in calm sea (knots)	50	48	50	48
Max foilborne continuous speed in calm sea (knots)	45	43	45	43
Max foilborne continuous speed in Sea State 4 (knots)	41	39	41	39
Hullborne continuous speed (knots)	8	8	8	8
Foilborne range at max continuous speed (n.m.)	400	300	400	400
Hullborne range (n.m.)	1,050	920	1,150	1,050
Turning radius at 40 knots	less than 125 metres			
Foilborne stability: max vertical acceleration	·25 g (rms) in Sea State 4			
Hullborne stability with foils up*	stable in 50 knot wind			
Hullborne stability with foils down*	stable in 70 knot wind			
Endurance	5 days			

The Swordfish, the first missile-launching hydrofoil vessel to be built for the Italian Navy.

A variety of other payloads may be accommodated according to customer needs.

DIMENSIONS:
Length overall   75 ft 4 in (22·95 m)
Length overall, foils retracted
                                        80 ft 7 in (24·6 m)
Width across foils   35 ft 4 in (10·8 m)
Deck beam, max   23 ft 0 in (7·0 m)
WEIGHTS:
Max displacement   64·0 metric tons
PERFORMANCE:
Exact craft performance characteristics depend upon the choice of foilborne gas turbine by the customer and operating conditions which, in turn, can affect the quantity of fuel carried. Performance figures shown below, therefore, are representative:

Foilborne intermittent speed in calm water
                                                     50 knots
Foilborne continuous speed in calm water
                                                     45 knots
Foilborne continuous speed in Sea State 4
                                                  38-40 knots
Hullborne continuous speed, foils down
                                                     7·6 knots
Foilborne range at maximum continuous speed   up to 400 nm
Hullborne range, up to   1,150 nm
Turning radius at maximum foilborne continuous speed less than 410 ft (125 m)
Endurance   5 days

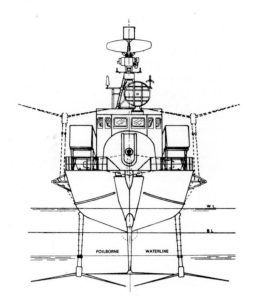

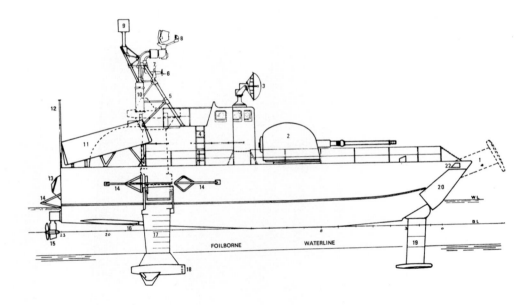

1	Forward hydrofoil retracted	5	Main mast	9	Antenna
2	OTO Melara 76 mm cannon	6	Anemometer	10	Antenna
3	Fire control radar	7	Antenna	11	Surface-to-surface missile launchers (P/S)
4	Vertical ladder	8	Navigation and search radar	12	Ensign staff
				13	Turbine exhaust: foilborne propulsion

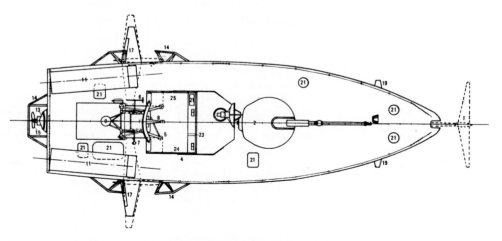

14	Guards	18	Water inlet (P/S): foilborne propulsion	22	Height sensors: automatic control system (P/S)
15	Propeller outdrive: hullborne propulsion	19	Forward hydrofoil extended	23	Optical putter-on
16	Waterjet nozzle (P/S)	20	Bow doors (P/S)	24	Starboard gyrocompass readout
17	Aft hydrofoil extended (P/S)	21	Watertight hatches	25	Port gyrocompass readout

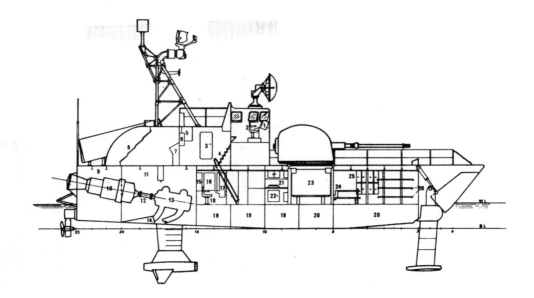

1	Helm/main control console	7	Air intake forward machinery room	15	Main electrical switchboard
2	Helm station (starboard)	8	Demister panels for combustion air	16	Main electrical power distribution panel
	Conning station (port)	9	Aft machinery room	17	Engineer's console
3	Combat Operations Centre (C.O.C.) door	10	Gas turbine engine: foilborne propulsion	18	Engineer's station
4	Companionway ladders	11	Forward machinery room	19	Fuel oil tanks (3)
5	C.O.C. electric power distribution panel	12	Pump drive coupling	20	Void
6	Combat Operations Centre electronics (speed log, radios, etc)	13	Waterjet pump	21	Electric hot plate
		14	Waterjet nozzle (P/S)	22	Refrigerator

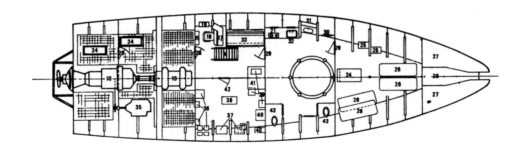

23	Cannon revolving feeding magazine	30	Galley stores locker	37	Fire control radar components
24	Folding mess table with benches (2)	31	Lavatory	38	Fire control radar computer
25	Crew lockers (8)	32	Sink	39	Gyrocompass and Stable element
26	Crew berths (8)	33	Officers' stateroom	40	Electronic equipment
27	Rope locker (P/S)	34	Turbine generator set	41	Automatic control system
28	Forward hydrofoil retraction well	35	Diesel engine: hullborne propulsion	42	Electronic equipment bay (unmanned)
29	Watertight doors	36	Search and navigation radar electronics	43	Water closet

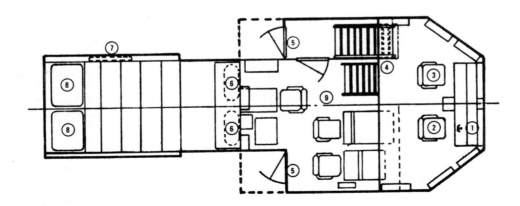

1	Helm/main control console	4	Companionway ladders	7	Exhaust duct
2	Helm station	5	Watertight doors (P/S)	8	Machinery combustion air inlets
3	Conning station	6	Air-inlet planums: forward machinery room (P/S)	9	Combat operations center

CANTIERE NAVALTECNICA S.P.A.

HEAD OFFICE:
Via S. Raineri, 22 Messina

TELEPHONE:
44801 (PBX)

TELEX:
98030 Rodrikez

OFFICERS AND EXECUTIVES:
Cav Del Lavoro Carlo Rodriquez, President
Dott. Ing. Leopoldo Rodriquez, Managing
Director

SENIOR EXECUTIVES:
Dott. Ing. Giovanni Falzea, Yard Director
Cantiere Navaltecnica S.p.A., formerly
known as Leopoldo Rodriquez Shipyard, was
the first in the world to produce hydrofoils in
series, and is now the biggest hydrofoil
builder outside the Soviet Union. On the
initiative of the company's president, Carlo
Rodriquez, the Aliscafi Shipping Company
was established in Sicily to operate the world's
first scheduled seagoing hydrofoil service in
August 1956 between Sicily and the Italian
mainland.

The service was operated by the first
Rodriquez-built Supramar PT 20, Freccia
del Sole. Cutting down the port-to-port
time from Messina to Reggio di Calabria to
one-quarter of that of conventional ferry
boats, and completing 22 daily crossings, the
craft soon proved its commercial viability.
With a seating capacity of 75 passengers the
PT 20 has carried between 800-900 passengers
a day and has conveyed a record number of
some 31,000 in a single month.

The prototype PT 20, a 27-ton craft for 75
passengers, was built by Rodriquez in 1955
and the first PT 50, a 63-ton craft for 140
passengers, was completed by the yard in
1958.

By the end of July 1975, the company will
have built and delivered more than 120
hydrofoils. The new RHS models, the only
craft now built by the company, are fitted
on request with a Hamilton Standard electronic stability augmentation system.

At the time of going to press, the company
had under construction three RHS 70s, one
RHS 140 and one RHS 160. Additionally,
the company has on order two RHS 70s, one
RHS 140 and one RHS 160. Construction
of the company's first RHS 200 is expected
to be under way by the end of 1975.

Apart from these standard designs, the company offers a number of variants, including
the RHS 70/M, 110/M and 140/M fast patrol
craft, the Mafius 300 and 600 fast strike
craft and the RHS Hydroil series of mixed
passenger/freight hydrofoils, based on the
RHS 70, 140 and 160, but adapted for servicing offshore drilling platforms.

RHS 70

This is a 32-ton coastal passenger ferry
with seats for 71 passengers. Power is
supplied by a single 1,350 hp MTU diesel
and the cruising speed is 32·4 knots.

FOILS: Surface-piercing type in partly
hollow welded steel. During operation the
angle of the bow foil can be adjusted within
narrow limits from the steering position by
means of a hydraulic ram operating on a foil
support across the hull.

HULL: V-bottom hull of riveted light metal
alloy construction. Watertight compartments are provided below the passenger
decks and in other parts of the hull.

Shearwater 3, a 71-seat Rodriquez RHS 70 hydrofoil passenger ferry operated by Red Funnel
Steamers Co on the route Southampton-Cowes

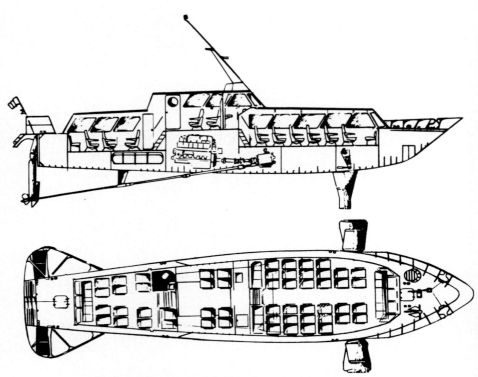

General arrangement of the RHS 70 hydrofoil passenger ferry

POWER PLANT: A single MTU MB 12V493
Ty 71 diesel, developing 1,350 hp at 1,500
rpm, drives a 3-bladed bronze aluminium
propeller through a Zahnradfabrik W 800
H 20 gearbox.

ACCOMMODATION: Forty-four passengers
are accommodated in the forward cabin,
nineteen in the rear compartment and eight
aft of the pilot's position, above the engine
room, in the elevated wheelhouse. A W/C
washbasin unit is provided in the aft passenger compartments. Emergency exits are
provided in each passenger compartment.

SYSTEMS, ELECTRICAL: 24 volt generat-
or driven by the main engine; batteries with a
capacity of 350 Ah.

HYDRAULICS: 120 kg/cm³ pressure hydraulic system for rudder and bow foil incidence control.

DIMENSIONS:

Length overall	72 ft 2 in (22 m)
Width across foils	24 ft 3 in (7·40 m)
Draft hullborne	8 ft 10 in (2·70 m)
Draft foilborne	3 ft 9 in (1·15 m)

WEIGHTS:

Displacement fully loaded	31·5 tons
Useful load	6 tons

PERFORMANCE:

Cruising speed, half loaded	32·4 knots
Max speed, half loaded	36·5 knots

RHS 110

A 54-ton hydrofoil ferry, the RHS 110 is
designed to carry a maximum of 110 passengers over routes of up to 300 miles (485·7 km)
at a cruising speed of 37 knots.

FOILS: Surface-piercing type, in partly
hollow, welded steel . Hydraulically operated

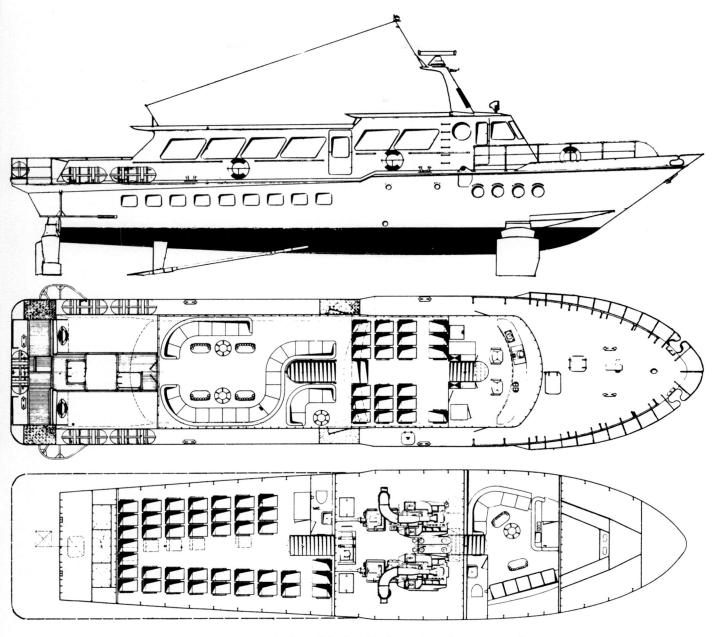

Outboard profile and deck plans of the RHS 110 54-ton hydrofoil passenger ferry

flaps, attached to the trailing edges of the bow and rear foils, are adjusted automatically by a Hamilton Standard stability augmentation system for the damping of heave, pitch and roll-motions. The rear foil is rigidly attached to the transom, its incidence angle being determined during tests.

HULL: Vee-bottom of high-tensile riveted light metal alloy construction, using Peraluman plates and Anticorrodal profiles. The upper deck plates are in 0·137 in (3·5 mm) thick Peraluman. Removable deck sections permit the lifting out and replacement of the main engines. The superstructure which has a removable roof is in 0·078 in (2 mm) thick Peraluman plates, with L and C profile sections. Watertight compartments are provided below the passenger decks and other parts of the hull.

POWERPLANT: Power is supplied by two 12-cylinder supercharged MTU MB 12V493 Ty 71 diesels, each with a maximum output of 1,350 hp at 1,500 rpm. Engine output is transferred to two 3-bladed bronze-aluminium propellers through Zahnradfabrik W 800 H20 gearboxes. Each propeller shaft is 3·5 in (90 mm) in diameter and

RHS 110, a 110-seat passenger ferry equipped with a Hamilton Standard stability augmentation system

supported at three points by seawater lubricated rubber bearings. Steel fuel tanks with a total capacity of 792 gallons (3,600 litres) are located aft of the engine room.

ACCOMMODATION: The wheelhouse/observation deck saloon seats 58, and the lower aft saloon seats 39. Additional passengers

are accommodated in the lower forward saloon, which contains a bar.

In the wheelhouse, the pilot's position is on the port side, together with the radar screen. A second seat is provided for the chief engineer. Passenger seats are of lightweight aircraft type, floors are covered with woollen carpets and the walls and ceilings are clad in vinyl. Two toilets are provided, one in each of the lower saloons.

SYSTEMS:

ELECTRICAL: Engine driven generators supply 220 volts, 50HZ, three-phase ac. Two groups of batteries for 24 volt dc circuit.

HYDRAULICS: Steering, variation of the foil flaps and the anchor windlass operation are all accomplished hydraulically from the wheelhouse. Plant comprises two Bosch pumps installed on the main engines and conveying oil from a 13 gallon (60 litre) tank under pressure to the control cylinders of the rudder, foil flaps and anchor windlass.

FIREFIGHTING: Fixed CO_2 plant for the main engine room, portable CO_2 and foam fire extinguishers of 7 lb (3 kg) and 2 gallon (10 litres) capacity in the saloons, and one water fire fighting plant.

DIMENSIONS, EXTERNAL:

Length overall	84 ft 0 in (25·60 m)
Width across foils	30 ft 2¼ in (9·20 m)
Deck beam, max	19 ft 2 in (5·95 m)
Draft afloat	10 ft 9⅞ in (3·30 m)
Draft foilborne	4 ft 1 in (1·25 m)

WEIGHTS:

Displacement, fully loaded	54 tons

PERFORMANCE:

Max speed	40 knots
Cruising speed	37 knots
Range	300 miles (485·7 km)

RHS 140

This 65-ton hydrofoil passenger ferry seats 125-140 passengers and has a cruising speed of 32·5 knots.

FOILS: Surface-piercing V foils of hollow

Condor 4, an RHS 140 operated by Condor Ltd, the Channel Islands hydrofoil ferry company, between Guernsey, Jersey and St Malo

welded steel construction. Lift of the bow foil can be modified by hydraulically-operated trailing edge flaps.

HULL: Riveted light metal alloy design framed on longitudinal and transverse formers.

ACCOMMODATION: 125-140 passengers seated in three saloons. The belvedere saloon, on the main deck above the engine room, can be equipped with a bar, W/C washbasin units can be installed in the forward and aft saloons.

POWER PLANT: Power is provided by two MTU 12V493 Ty 71 12-cylinder supercharged engines, each developing 1,350 hp at 1,500 rpm. Engine output is transmitted to two 3-bladed 700 mm diameter bronze propellers through Zahnradfabrik gearboxes.

SYSTEMS, ELECTRICAL: Two engine-driven generators supply 24 volt d.c. Two battery sets each with 350 Ah capacity.

HYDRAULICS: Steering and variation of foil flap incidence is accomplished hydraulically from the wheelhouse. Plant comprises

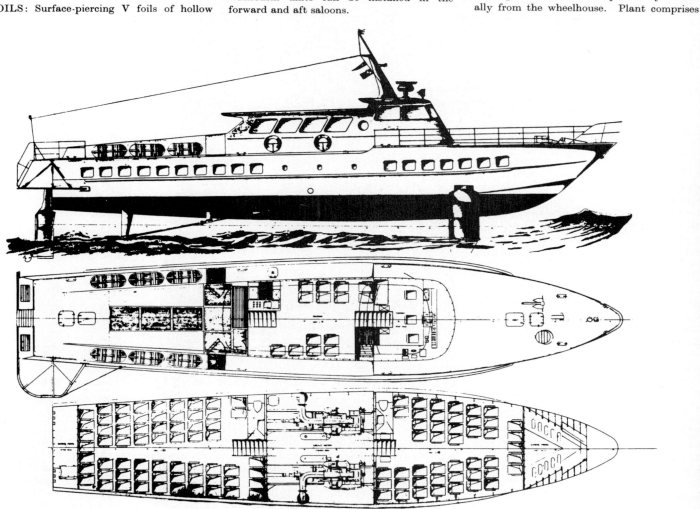

RHS 140, 125-140-seat passenger ferry

two Bosch pumps installed on the main engines and conveying oil from a 15·4 gal (70 litre) tank under pressure to the control cylinders of the rudder and foil flaps.

FIREFIGHTING: Fixed CO_2 plant for the engine room; portable CO_2 and foam fire extinguishers in the saloons. Water intake connected to bilge pump for fire hose connection in emergency.

DIMENSIONS:

Length overall	94 ft 1½ in (28·70 m)
Width across foils	35 ft 2¼ in (10·72 m)
Draft hullborne	11 ft 5¾ in (3·50 m)
Draft foilborne	4 ft 11 in (1·50 m)

WEIGHTS:

Displacement, fully loaded	65 tons
Carrying capacity, including 3 tons bunker, and 5 tons fresh water, lubricating oil and hydraulic system oil	12·5 tons

PERFORMANCE:

Max speed, half load	36 knots
Cruising speed	32·5 knots
Range at cruising speed 900 miles (550 kms)	

RHS 160

One of the latest additions to the Navaltecnica range is the RHS 160, an 82-ton passenger ferry with seats for 160-200 passengers and a cruising speed of 36 knots.

FOILS: Surface-piercing W foils of hollow welded steel construction. Craft in this series feature a bow rudder for improved manoeuvrability in congested waters. The bow rudder works simultaneously with the aft rudders. Hydraulically-operated flaps, attached to the trailing edges of the bow and rear foils, are adjusted automatically by a Hamilton Standard electronic stability augmentation system, for the damping of heave, pitch and roll motions in heavy seas.

HULL: Riveted light metal alloy longitudinal structure, welded in parts using inert gas. The hull shape of the RHS 160 is similar to the RHS 140 series. In the manufacture of the hull, plates of aluminium and magnesium alloy of 4·4% are used whilst angle bars are of a high-resistant aluminium, magnesium and silicon alloy.

ACCOMMODATION: 160-200 passengers seated in three saloons. Fifty-seven passengers are accommodated in the forward cabin, fifty-seven in the rear compartment and forty-six in the belvedere. Forward and aft saloons and belvedere have a toilet, each provided with W/C washbasin units and the usual toilet accessories.

POWER PLANT: Power is provided by two supercharged MTU MB 12V 652 TB 71 4-stroke diesel engines each with a maximum output of 1,950 hp at 1,460 rpm under normal operating conditions. Engine starting is accomplished by compressed air starters. Engine output is transmitted to two 3-bladed bronze propellers through two Zahnradfabrik 900 HS 15 gearboxes.

SYSTEMS, ELECTRICAL: Two 35 KVA generating sets, 220 v, 60 cps, 3-phase. Three insulated cables for ventilation, air-conditioning and power. Two insulated cables for lighting, sockets and other appliances, 24 v d.c. for emergency lighting, auxiliary engine starting and servocontrol. A battery for radio telephone supply is installed on the upper deck. Provision for battery recharge from a.c. line foreseen.

HYDRAULICS: Steering is accomplished hydraulically from the wheelhouse. Plant comprises a Bosch pump installed on the main engines and conveying oil from a 10 gallon (45 litre) tank under pressure to the control cylinders of the rudder and anchor

windlass, whilst a second hydraulic pump, which is also installed on the main engines, conveys oil under pressure to the flap control cylinders.

FIREFIGHTING: Fixed CO_2 plant of four CO_2 bottles of about 20 kg each for the engine room and fuel tank space; portable extinguishers in various parts of the craft. Water intake connected to fire pump for fire connection in emergency.

DIMENSIONS:

Length overall	101 ft 6 in (30·95 m)
Width across foils	41 ft 4 in (12·60 m)
Draft afloat	12 ft 6 in (3·70 m)
Draft foilborne	4 ft 6 in (1·35 m)

WEIGHTS:

Displacement, fully loaded	82 tons
Pay load, passengers and luggage	13·5 tons

PERFORMANCE:

Speed, max	39·0 knots
Speed, cruising	36·0 knots
Cruising, range	300 miles

RHS 200

Construction of this 122 ton, 200-262 seat fast ferry is expected to start in 1975. Power will be provided by two supercharged MTU MB 16V 652 TB 71 4-stroke diesel engines. The designed cruising speed is 37·5 knots

FOILS: Surface-piercing vee foils of hollow welded construction. Hydraulically-operated flaps are fitted to the trailing edge of the bow foil to balance out longitudinal load shifting, assist take-off and adjust the flying height. The craft can also be equipped with the Hamilton Standard electronic stability augmentation system, which employs sensors and servomechanisms to automatically position flaps on the bow and stern

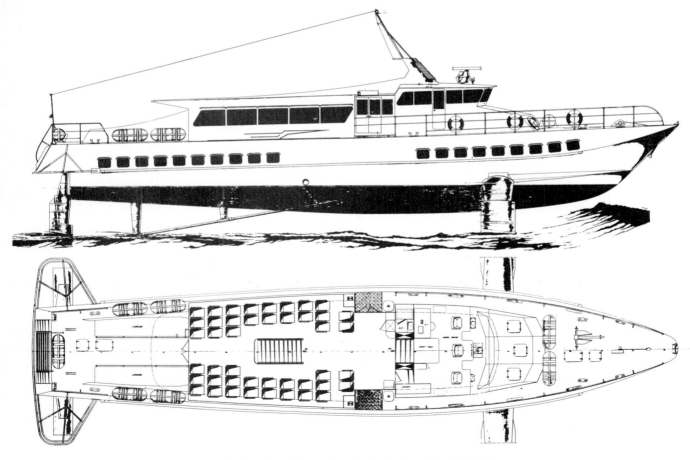

Outboard profiles and main deck plan of the RHS 160

foils for the damping of heave, pitch and roll
motions in heavy seas.

HULL: Vee-bottom hull of high tensile
riveted light metal alloy construction,
employing Peraluman plates and Anticorrodal frames. The rake of the stem is in
galvanised steel.

ACCOMMODATION: Seats can be provided
for up to 262 passengers, according to the
route served. There are three main passenger saloons and a bar. The standard seating
arrangement allows for 60 in the main deck
saloon, 75 in the aft lower saloon and 51 in the
bow passenger saloon. Seating is normally
four abreast in two lines with a central aisle.
The bar, at the forward end of the wheelhouse
belvedere superstructure, has either an 8-
place sofa or 19 chairs.

The wheelhouse, which is raised to provide
a 360° view, is reached from the main deck
belvedere saloon by a short companionway.
Controls and instrumentation are attached to
a panel on the forward bulkhead which
extends the width of the wheelhouse. In the
centre is the steering control and gyrocompass, on the starboard side are controls
for the two engines, gearboxes and controllable-pitch propellers, and on the port side
is the radar. Seats are provided for the
captain, chief engineer and first mate. At
the aft of the wheelhouse is a radio-telephone
and a chart table.

POWER PLANT: Motive power is supplied
by two supercharged MTU MB 16V 652
TB 71 4-stroke diesel engines, each with a
maximum output of 2,415 hp at 1,485 rpm
under normal operating conditions. Engine
output is transferred to two supercavitating,
controllable-pitch propellers.

SYSTEMS, ELECTRICAL: Two generating
sets. One 220 volt, 3-phase a.c., for all
consumer services, the second for charging 24
volt battery sets and operating fire-fighting
and hydraulic pumps. Power distribution

Above and below: The new Rodriquez RHS 160, an 82-ton passenger with seats for 160-180 passengers and a cruising speed of 36 knots

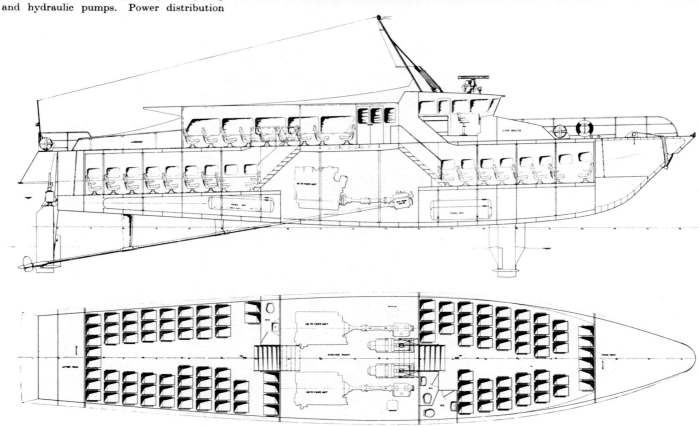

Inboard profile and lower deck plan of the RHS 160

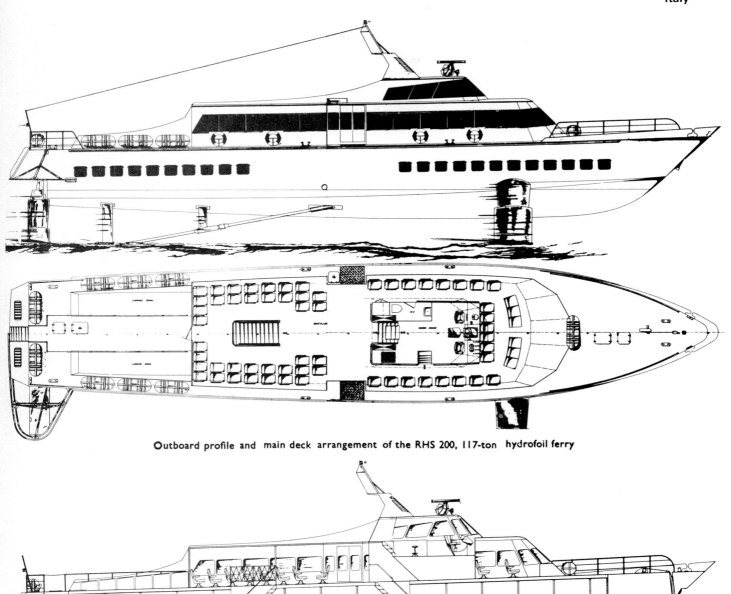

Outboard profile and main deck arrangement of the RHS 200, 117-ton hydrofoil ferry

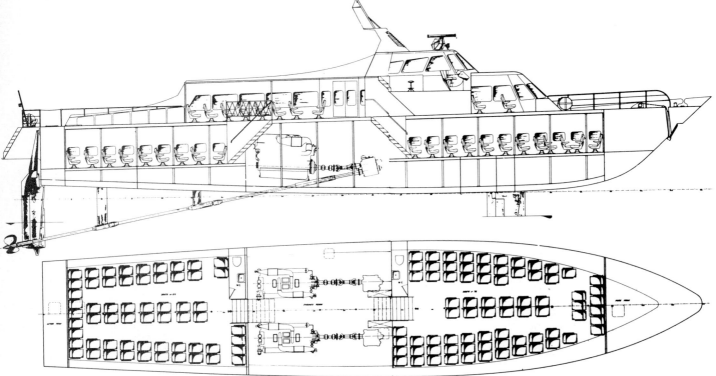

Inboard profile and lower deck arrangement of the RHS 200

panel in wheelhouse for navigation light circuits, cabin lighting, radar, RDF, gyro compass and emergency circuits.

FIREFIGHTING: Fixed CO_2 self-contained automatic systems for power plant and fuel tank spaces, plus portable extinguishers for cabins and holds.

DIMENSIONS:

Length overall   116 ft 5⅝ in (35·50 m)

Width across foils   46 ft 6⅞ in (14·20 m)
Draft afloat   14 ft 2½ in (4·32 m)
Draft foilborne   5 ft 3¾ in (1·62 m)

WEIGHTS:

Displacement fully loaded   122 tons

PERFORMANCE:

Cruising speed   37·5 knots
Maximum speed   41 knots
Cruising range   275 n. miles

RHS ALIYACHT

A luxury hydrofoil yacht of light alloy construction, the RHS Aliyacht is derived from the RHS 110 passenger ferry. It is powered by two 1,350 hp MTU MB 12V493 Ty 71 diesel engines and has a cruising speed of 38 knots.

The craft is equipped with the Hamilton Standard electronic stability augmentation system, which is designed to provide a smoother ride in heavy seas. The system uses sensors and servomechanisms to automatically position foil flaps for the maximum damping of heave, pitch and roll motions.

FOILS: Bow and rear foils are of surface-piercing type, and constructed in partly hollow, welded steel. Two hydraulically-operated flaps, attached to the trailing edges of the bow foil, are adjusted automatically by the stabilisation system for the damping of heave, pitch and roll motions. The rear foil is rigidly attached to the transom, its incidence angle being determined during tests.

HULL: The vee-bottom hull is of high-tensile riveted light metal alloy construction, using Peraluman (aluminium and magnesium alloy) plates and Anticorrodal (aluminium, magnesium and silicon alloy) profiles. The rake of the stem is in 0·137 in (3·5 mm) thick galvanised steel. The superstructure is constructed in 0·078 in (2·0 mm) Peraluman plate, and the roof is detachable to facilitate the removal and replacement of the main engines.

ACCOMMODATION: Main deck accommodation comprises the wheelhouse and radio cabin, a comfortably furnished saloon and a galley. The saloon can be fitted with two four-seat sofas, armchair, tea-table, a meal table with four chairs, and a bar. Below deck, from aft peak forward, is a large cabin for the owner, with its own bathroom and small private drawing room; two double cabins for guests with adjacent WC/wash-basin/shower units, and beyond the engines, a cabin for the captain and engineer, and two

single cabins for guests.

The wheelhouse is reached via a companion-way from the saloon and is connected by a door with the upper deck. The pilot's position, controls and instruments are on the port side, together with the radar screen.

POWER PLANT: Power is supplied by two supercharged 12-cylinder MTU MB 12V 439 Ty 71 diesels, each rated at 1,350 hp at 1,500 rpm. Engine output is transferred to two 3-bladed bronze aluminium-propellers through Zahnradfabrik BW 800 H20 gearboxes.

SYSTEMS: Two 10 kW, 220 volt, three-phase ONAN generating sets, coupled to batteries, provide 24 volts dc for engine starting, instrument, lighting radio etc.

DIMENSIONS, EXTERNAL:

Length overall	78 ft 9 in (24·50 m)
Beam overall	20 ft 0 in (6·10 m)
Hull beam	19 ft 2¼ in (5·85 m)
Draft afloat	9 ft 8⅛ in (2·95 m)
Draft foilborne	4 ft 1¼ in (1·25 m)

WEIGHTS:

Displacement, loaded	52 tons

PERFORMANCE:

Max speed	41 knots
Cruising speed	38 knots
Range	400 miles (644 km)

RHS HYDROILS

These are derivatives of RHS passenger-carrying hydrofoils, and are designed to ferry personnel, materials and equipment between offshore oil rigs and shore bases. Vessels in the series feature an open cargo deck aft of the bridge superstructure instead of an aft passenger saloon. The three main types

are the RHS 70, the RHS 140, and the RHS 160 Hydroil.

RHS 70 HYDROIL

The first of the new series of RHS 70 Hydroil offshore drilling platform supply vessels has been built for ENI Oil Corporation, which is employing the craft in the Adriatic. A mixed passenger/cargo version of the RHS 70 passenger ferry, this variant has an open cargo deck aft of the bridge superstructure in place of the Caribe's main passenger cabin. Dimensions of the cargo deck are: length, 24 ft 7 in (7·50 m); width, 11 ft 6 in (3·50 m) and height, 3 ft 5 in (1·05 m).

FOILS: Bow and rear foils are of surface-piercing vee configuration, with about 66% of the weight supported by the bow foil and 34% by the rear foil. Each foil, together with its struts and horizontal supporting tube, forms a rigid framework which facilitates the exchange of the foil structure. The foils are of hollow-ribbed construction and fabricated from medium Asera steel. The forward foil can be tilted within narrow limits by means of a hydraulic ram acting on the foil strut supporting tube. The angle of attack can therefore be adjusted during operation to assist take-off and counteract the effect of large variations in loading.

HULL: The hull is of riveted light metal alloy (Peraluman) and framed on a combination of longitudinal and transverse formers. Watertight compartments are provided in the bow and stern, and a double-bottom runs from immediately aft of the engine room, beneath the full length of the cargo deck, to

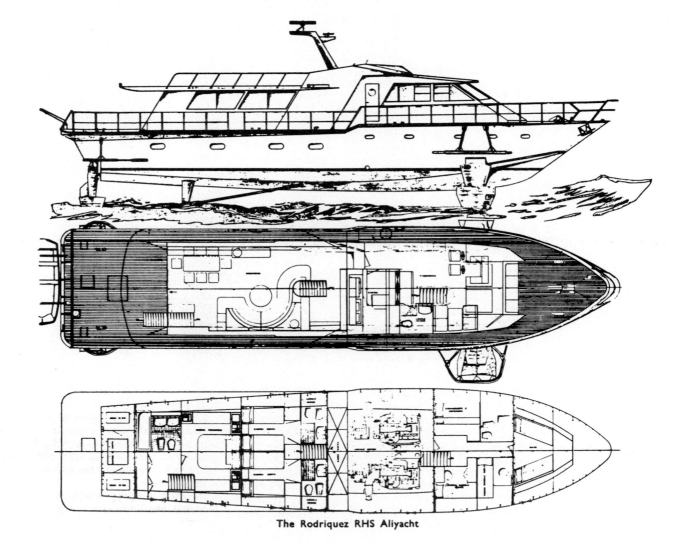

The Rodriquez RHS Aliyacht

The Rodriquez RHS Aliyacht, powered by two MTU diesels each rated at 1,350 hp. Cruising speed is 38 knots and the range 400 miles

Porto Corsini, first of the RHS 70 Hydrofoil 33-ton off-shore drilling platform supply vessels. The craft has been built for ENI, the Italian oil company and is seen operating from one of the company's drilling platforms. Loads of up to 3 tons can be carried on the open cargo deck aft of the bridge structure. Cruising speed with normal payload is 32 knots

the after peak. Contained within the double-bottom are six cylindrical aluminium fuel tanks with a total capacity of 495 gallons (2,250 litres). Access to the fore and aft compartments is via removable deck hatches. The deck is of 0·196 in (5 mm) Peraluman, suitably reinforced to withstand heavily concentrated loads. Two 4·9 in (125 mm) diameter scuppers are provided aft for rapid drainage. Heavy rubber fenders are provided at the bow and stern.

POWER PLANT: Power is supplied by a 12-cylinder supercharged MTU 12V493 Ty 71 with a maximum output of 1,350 hp at 1,500 rpm. Engine output is transferred to a 3-bladed 27·5 in (700 mm) bronze-aluminium propeller through a Zahnradfabrik BW 800 H20 gearbox. The propeller shaft is 3·5 in (90 mm) in diameter, and supported at three points by seawater lubricated rubber bearings. In an emergency, hullborne propulsion is provided by a 105 hp Mercedes OM 352 diesel with a Mercruiser Z-drive. The engine is installed in the aft peak and propels the craft at about 5 knots.

ACCOMMODATION: The craft has a crew of two, and seats up to 12 passengers in a comfortably appointed saloon, immediately aft of the wheelhouse. Passengers have a choice of six armchairs and two three-place settees, one of which converts into a bed

for transporting sick or injured personnel. All seats are equipped with safety belts. Aft of the saloon is a fully equipped galley, with refrigerator, a gas cooker with two gas rings, cupboards, plate rack and sink unit. Two folding wooden tables permit up to eight passengers to take meals at one sitting. A toilet/washbasin unit is provided opposite the galley on the port side. The engine room, wheelhouse and passenger saloon are fully heated and ventilated. A full range of safety equipment is carried including inflatable rafts and lifebelts for each passenger and crew member.

SYSTEMS: Electrical: 220 volt 50 Hz three-phase a.c., 24 volt d.c.; provision for 220 volt 50 Hz three phase shore supply. The d.c. supply is from a 24 volt generator driven by the main engine and feeding a 235 Ah battery. AC supply is derived from a 4-stroke Onan diesel generator set, located in the engine room.

HYDRAULICS. One Bosch Hy/ZFR 1/16 AR 101 for steering and bow foil incidence control.

COMMUNICATIONS AND NAVIGATION: Radio: VHF radio-telephone to customers' requirements.
Radar: Decca, Raytheon etc., to customers' requirements.

DIMENSIONS:

Length overall, hull	68 ft 9 in (20·95 m)
Hull beam	16 ft 7 in (5·06 m)
Width over foils	24 ft 3 in (7·40 m)
Draft afloat	8 ft 10 in (2·70 m)
Draft foilborne	3 ft 9 in (1·14 m)

WEIGHTS:

Max take-off displacement	33·12 tons
Max load on open cargo deck	3 tons

PERFORMANCE (with normal payload)

Cruising speed	32 knots
Range	300 miles (480 km)

RHS 140 HYDROIL

The second in the Navaltecnica Hydroil range is a mixed passenger/cargo version of the 65-ton RHS 140. As with the smaller RHS 70 Hydroil, the main passenger saloon is replaced by a large open cargo deck for loads up to 6 tons. The deck is 31 ft 2 in (9·5 m) long, 15 ft 9 in (4·8 m) wide and 6 ft 4 in (1·9 m) high.

The craft will carry a crew of two and up to 14 passengers. Power will be supplied by two 12-cylinder supercharged MTU 12V493 Ty 71, with a maximum output of 1,350 hp.

DIMENSIONS:

Length overall, hull	93 ft 6 in (28·50 m)
Hull beam	20 ft 0 in (6·10 m)
Width over foils	35 ft 2 in (10·72 m)
Draft hullborne	11ft 6 in (3·50 m)
Draft foilborne	4 ft 11 in (1·50 m)

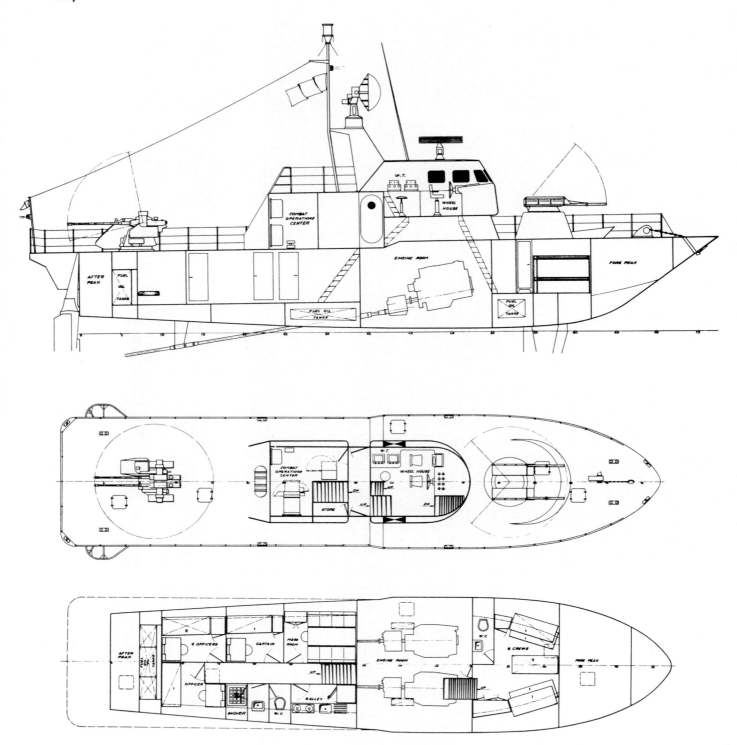

General arrangement of the fast patrol variant of the RHS 110

WEIGHTS:

Normal take-off displacement   64 tons

PERFORMANCE:

Cruising speed   32-34 knots

Range at cruising speed 300 miles (480 km)

RHS 160 HYDROIL

Latest addition to Navaltecnica's range of offshore oil rig support vessels, the RHS 160 features an open cargo deck aft of the bridge superstructure and additional fuel and water tanks in the place of the lower aft passenger saloons. The vessel carries a crew of 5 and forty-two passengers, plus 10 tons of cargo, at a cruising speed of 35 knots.

FOILS: Surface-piercing W foils of hollow,

welded steel construction. Craft in this series feature bow and aft rudders, both of which operate simultaneously. Hydraulically-operated flaps, attached to the trailing edges of the bow and rear foils are adjusted automatically by a Hamilton Standard electronic stability augmentation system, for the damping of heave, pitch and roll motions in heavy seas.

HULL: Vee-bottom hull of high tensile riveted light metal alloy construction. In the manufacture of the hull, plates of aluminium and magnesium alloy of 4·4% are used, whilst angle bars are of a high resistant aluminium, magnesium and silicon alloy. Inert gas welding (Argon) is used for strengthening beams, web frames, keelsons and

stringers. Steel and rubber fenders are fitted aft and in the sides of the main deck to protect the foils from damage when docking.

ACCOMMODATION: Passengers are accommodated in a forward saloon, seating 37, and the upper belvedere saloon, seating five. The seats, designed for maximum comfort, have arms and each is provided with an ash tray and magazine holder. The toilet, finished in Formica or similar laminate, is provided with a WC, basin and normal accessories.

Crew members are accommodated in two cabins forward, that on the starboard being provided with two berths and a locker, while the port cabin has three berths and lockers. The wheelhouse is located well forward and has seats for the master in the centre, chief

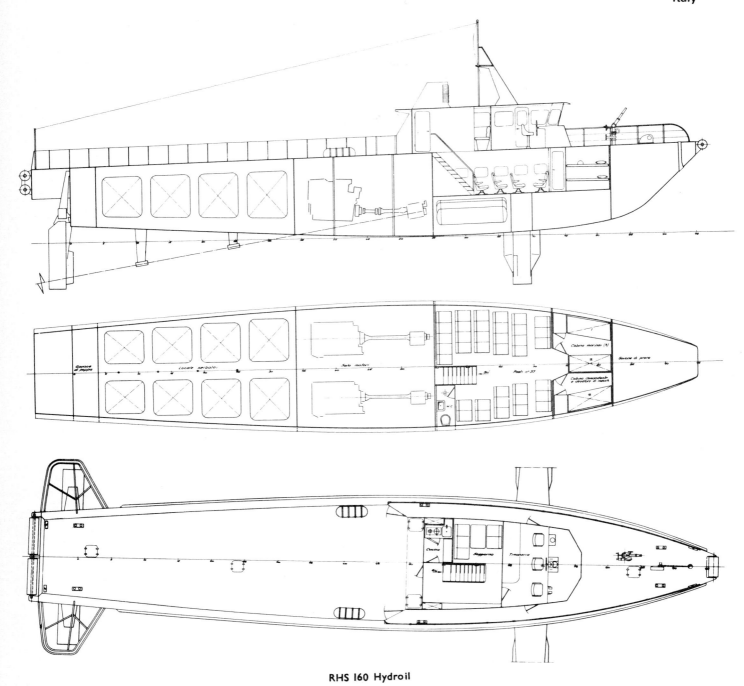

RHS 160 Hydroil

engineer on the starboard side and radar operator on the port side. All steering and other controls are located in the wheelhouse, including a circuit control panel for the navigation lights, craft lighting, radar, gyrocompass and various other electrical consumer and emergency circuits.

POWER PLANT: Power is provided by two supercharged MTU MB 12V TB 71 4-stroke diesel engines, each with a maximum output of 1,950 hp at 1,460 rpm. Engine starting is accomplished by compressed air starters. Output is transmitted to two 3-bladed bronze propellers through two Zahnradfabrik 900 HS 15 gearboxes.

SYSTEMS: ELECTRICAL: Two 35 KVA generating sets, 220 volts, 50 Hz, 3-phase for ventilation and air-conditioning; 220 volts, 50 Hz, single-phase, for lighting and other appliances; 24 volts dc for auxiliary lighting, engine starting and servocontrol.

HYDRAULICS: Steering is accomplished hydraulically from the wheelhouse. Plant comprises a Bosch pump installed on one of the main engines and conveying oil under pressure from a 10 gallon (45 litre) tank to the control cylinders of the rudder and anchor windlass, whilst a second hydraulic pump, which is installed on the other main engine, conveys oil under pressure to the flap control cylinders.

The two systems are interchangeable and equipped with safety valves, manometers and micronic filters.

FIREFIGHTING: Fixed CO_2 plant for engine room and fuel tank space; portable appliances include two 6 kg powder extinguishers and one 5 kg CO_2 extinguisher in the engine room; two 10 l water extinguishers in the passengers saloons and one 6 kg powder extinguisher in the wheelhouse.

Two water extinguishing systems are provided, one driven by the main engine and the other by a motor driven pump. The system can supply a monitor on the upper deck at the bow and two fire hose water outlets located amidships on the upper deck. A dual-purpose water/foam nozzle can be supplied on request.

DIMENSIONS:

Length overall	103 ft 0 in (31·30 m)
Moulded beam	20 ft 4⅛ in (6·20 m)
Width across foils	41 ft 4 in (12·60 m)
Draft hullborne	12 ft 6 in (3·70 m)
Draft foilborne	4 ft 6 in (1·35 m)

WEIGHTS:

Displacement, fully loaded	85 tons

PERFORMANCE:

Cruising speed	35 knots
Cruising range	200 miles

RHS SEARCH AND RESCUE CRAFT

This new variant of the well-known RHS 140 is a multi-purpose rescue craft equipped for a full range of S & R duties, including fire-fighting and wreck marking. It has a top speed of 36 knots and can operate in heavy seas at a considerable distance from its shore base. A Merryweather dual-purpose water/foam monitor is located on the foredeck and a Zodiac inflatable liferaft is carried on the upper deck aft.

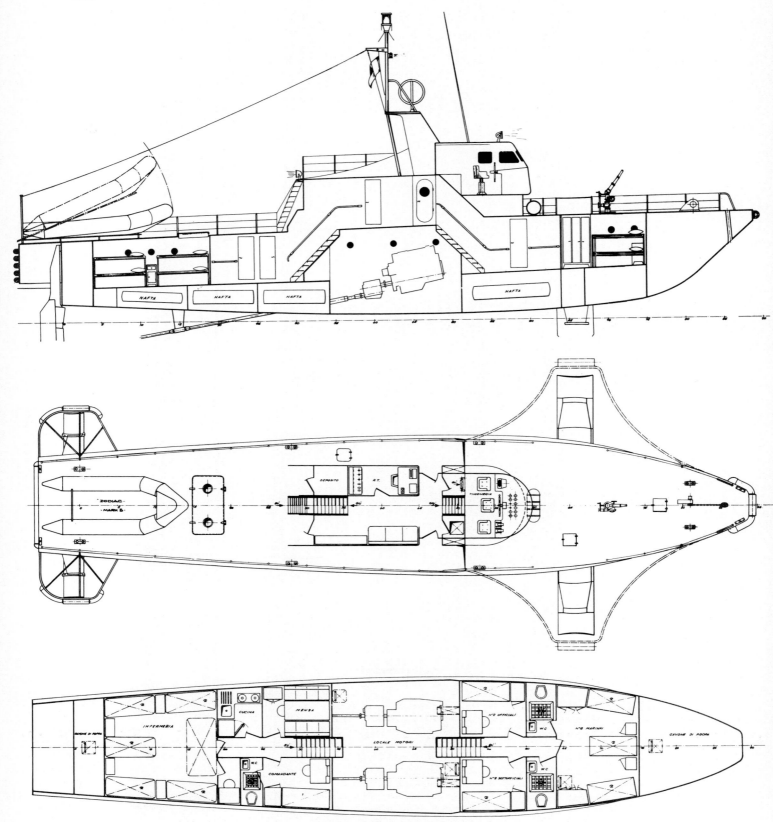

RHS 140 Search and Rescue craft

A sick bay is provided and can be fitted out to accommodate 30-40 survivors.

A feature of the design is the filling of the double bottom with expanded polystyrene to provide sufficient buoyancy to make it unsinkable, even with the watertight compartments flooded.

FOILS: Surface-piercing V foils of hollow, welded steel construction. Foil lift is varied by flaps operated by an electronic/hydraulic system developed by Cantiere Navaltecnica in conjunction with Hamilton Standard. Under calm sea conditions, the flaps can be operated manually.

HULL: Riveted light metal alloy design framed on longitudinal and transverse formers. Areas of the attachment points of the bow and rear foils are reinforced with steel. Steel is also used for the rake of the stem, the stern tube for the propeller shaft and the propeller shaft attachment.

ACCOMMODATION: Berths, lockers and living accommodation provided for a crew of eleven, comprising the captain, two officers, two petty officers and six seamen. Seats are provided in the wheelhouse for an operating crew of three. A "flying bridge" with a duplicated set of instruments and controls, provides improved visibility during search operations. A 10-berth sick bay, complete with a small office for the doctor is provided aft. A large roof hatch is provided in the sick bay through which stretcher casualties can be lowered. If required, the sick bay can be fitted out to accommodate 30-40 survivors.

POWER PLANT: Power is provided by two MTU 12V 493 Ty 71 12-cylinder supercharged diesel engines, each developing 1,350 hp at

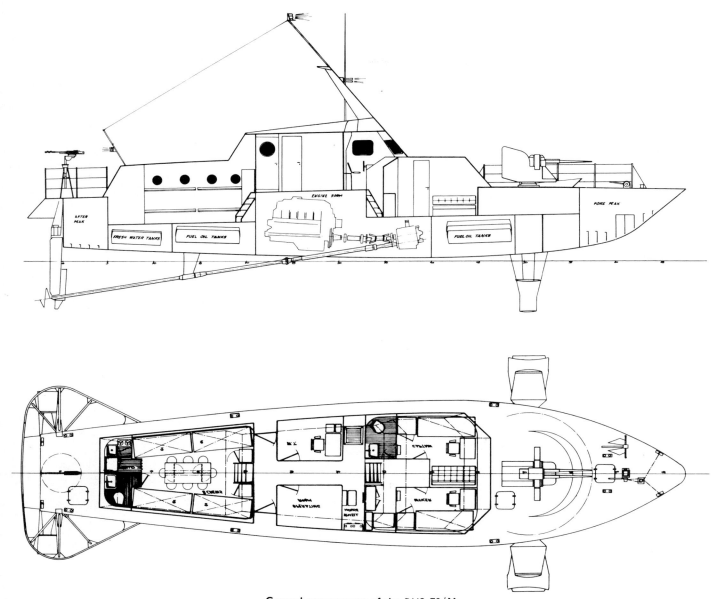

General arrangement of the RHS 70/M

1,500 rpm. Engine output is transmitted to two 3-bladed, 700 mm diameter bronze propellers through Zahnradfabrik gearboxes.

SYSTEMS, ELECTRICAL: Two engine-driven generators of 24 volts d.c. supply essential services and emergency lights. An a.c. system, powered by a generator set, supplies lighting and all other on board consumers. Two battery sets are provided for starting the main engines and generators.

HYDRAULICS: Steering and variation of foil flap incidence is accomplished hydraulically from the wheelhouse. Plant comprises two Bosch pumps installed on the main engines and conveying oil from a tank under pressure to the control cylinders of the rudder and foil flaps.

AIR CONDITIONING: Provided on request.

FIREFIGHTING: Fixed CO_2 plant for the engine room and fuel oil bays; portable CO_2 and foam fire extinguishers at various parts of the craft. One Merryweather dual purpose foam/water monitor.

DIMENSIONS:

Length overall	94 ft 1½ in (28·70 m)
Width across foils	35 ft 2½ in (10·72 m)
Draft hullborne	11 ft 5¾ in (3·50 m)
Draft foilborne	4 ft 11 in (1·50 m)

WEIGHTS:

Displacement, fully loaded

62 tons (63 tonnes)

PERFORMANCE:

Maximum speed	36 knots
Cruising speed	32·5 knots
Endurance at cruising speed	18 hours, 600 miles
Endurance at low speed	50 hours, 600 miles
Cruising range	600 miles (1,110 km)

RHS/M PATROL CRAFT

Derived from RHS passenger vessels, the RHS/M series craft are designed for coast guard and anti-contraband patrol. Suitably armed, they can undertake various naval duties, ranging from patrol to minelaying. The armament shown in the accompanying drawings can be augmented or substituted by sea-to-air and sea-to-sea missiles according to requirements.

RHS 70/M

The RHS 70/M is similar in design and performance to the two PAT 20 patrol hydrofoils built by Rodriquez for the Philipine Navy.

FOILS: Bow and rear foils are of surfacing piercing V configuration and identical to those of the standard PT 20. About 59% of the total weight is borne by the bow foil and 41% by the rear foil. The foils are of hollow ribbed construction and made from medium Asera steel.

Total foil area is 112 sq ft (10·4 m²). The angle of incidence of the forward foil can be varied during flight by means of a hydraulic ram acting on the foil strut supporting tube.

HULL: The hull is of riveted light alloy construction with Peraluman (aluminium and magnesium alloy) plates and Anticorrodal (aluminium, magnesium and silicon alloy) profiles.

ACCOMMODATION: The crew comprises a captain, two officers and eight NCO's and ratings. The pilot's position is on the left of the wheelhouse, with the principal instrumentation; and the radar operator sits on the right with the auxiliary instrumentation. The pilot is provided with an intercom system connecting him with the officer's cabin, engine room and crew cabin. The internal space has been divided as follows:

(a) The forward or bow room, subdivided into two cabins, one for the captain, the other for two officers, and including a WC with washstand and a storeroom with a refrigerator.

(b) The stern room, with eight berths for the NCOs and ratings, a WC with washstand and a galley equipped with a gas stove and an electric refrigerator.

(c) The deck room, aft of the wheelhouse, with tilting sofa and table for R/T equipment.

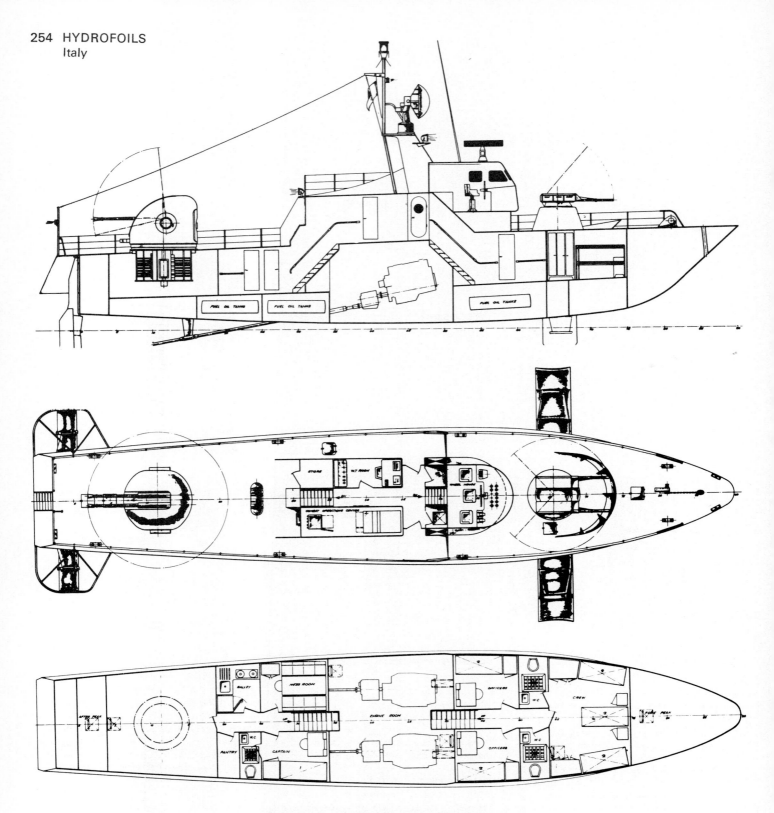

General arrangement of the Rodriquez RHS 140/M

Air conditioning is installed in the captain's and officer's quarters.

POWER PLANT: Power is supplied by a supercharged 12-cylinder MTU 12V493 Ty 71 with a max continuous output of 1,350 hp at 1,500 rpm. Engine output is transferred to a 3-bladed bronze aluminium propeller through a Zahnradfabrik BW 800/S reversible gear. Fuel (total capacity 2,800 kg) is carried in ten cylindrical aluminium tanks located in the double bottom beneath the bow room and the stern room. Dynamic and reserve oil tanks in the engine room give a total oil capacity of 120 kg. An auxiliary engine can be fitted in the stern for emergency operation.

ARMAMENT AND SEARCH EQUIPMENT: Single 12·7 machine-gun mounted above well position in bow, and two searchlights.

SYSTEMS:

ELECTRICAL: 220v, 10 kW, diesel generator with batteries. Supplies instruments, radio and radar and external and internal lights, navigation lights and searchlights.

HYDRAULICS: 120 kg/cm² pressure hydraulic system for steering and varying forward foil incidence angle.

APU: Onan engine for air conditioning when requested.

DIMENSIONS:

Length overall, hull	68 ft 6 in	(20·89 m)
Hull beam	15 ft 8¾ in	(4·79 m)
Beam overall	24 ft 4 in	(7·4 m)
Draft afloat	9 ft 1 in	(2·76 m)
Draft foilborne	4 ft 0 in	(1·20 m)
Height overall:		
hullborne	21 ft 0 in	(6·44 m)
foilborne	26 ft 3 in	(8·00 m)

WEIGHTS:

Net tonnage	28 tons
Light displacement	26 tons
Max take-off displacement	32·5 tons
Useful load	7·6 tons
Max useful load	8·1 tons

PERFORMANCE:

Max speed foilborne	38 knots
Max speed hullborne	13 knots
Cruising speed foilborne	34 knots
Cruising speed hullborne	12 knots
Max permissible sea state foilborne mode	Force 4
Designed range at cruising speed	540 miles (869 km)
Number of seconds and distances to take-off	20 secs, 328 ft (100 m)
Number of seconds and distances to stop	

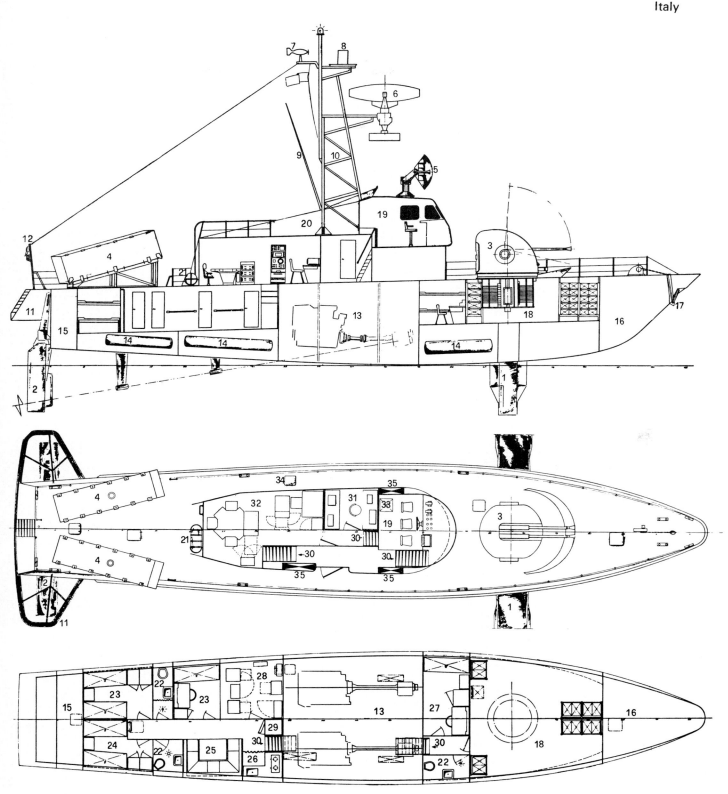

Inboard profile and deck plan of the Mafius 300

craft   12 secs, 164 ft (50 m)
Fuel consumption at cruising speed 145 kg/h
Fuel consumption at max speed   180 kg/h

RHS 110/M

This is the fast patrol boat version of the RHS 110 passenger ferry. Modifications include a revised cabin superstructure with an upper bridge; the installation of two rapid firing cannon, and provision of fuel tanks of additional capacity increasing the operating range to 560 miles (347·96 km).

FOILS, HULL, POWERPLANT: Arrangements similar to those of the RHS 110.

ACCOMMODATION: Berths provided for eight officers and non-commissioned officer

and eight ratings.

DIMENSIONS:

Length overall	83 ft 2 in (25·40 m)
Beam overall	27 ft 6¼ in (8·40 m)
Height of hull structure	9 ft 4 in (2·85 m)
Draft foilborne	4 ft 1 in (2·15 m)
Draft hullborne, fully loaded	
	9 ft 10 in (3·00 m)

WEIGHTS:

Displacement, empty	36 tons
Displacement, loaded	50 tons

PERFORMANCE:

Max speed	41 knots
Cruising speed	38 knot
Cruising range	560 miles (896 km)

RHS 140/M

Derived from the RHS 140 passenger ferry this fast patrol variant is armed with two rapid firing cannon and has a maximum speed of 37 knots. Above the wheelhouse is an open bridge with duplicate steering, engine controls and instrumentation.

FOILS, HULL, POWERPLANT: Arrangements similar to those of the RHS 140.

ACCOMMODATION: Berths, living accommodation for eight commissioned and non-commissioned officers and sixteen ratings.

DIMENSIONS:

Length overall	95 ft 2 in (29 m)
Width across foils	31 ft 6 in (9·60 m)
Height of hull structure	11 ft 8¼ in (3·56 m)

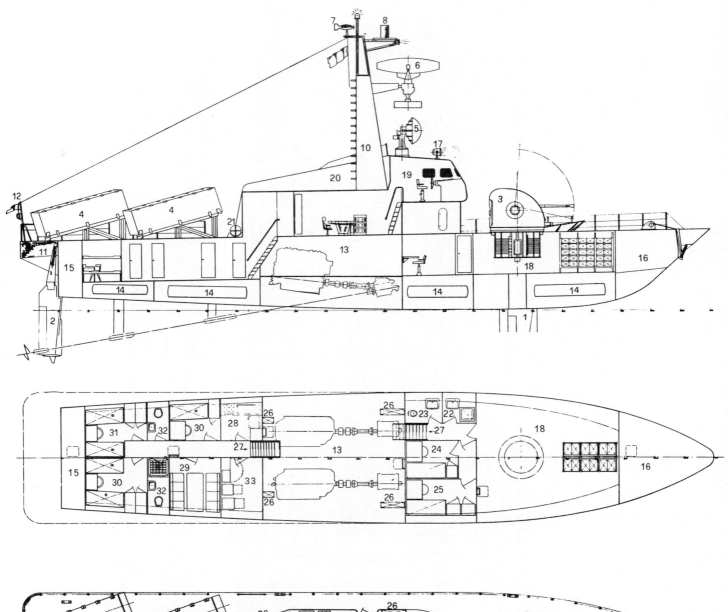

Inboard profile and deck plan of the Mafius 600

WEIGHTS:

Displacement loaded	64 tons
Displacement empty	50 tons

PERFORMANCE:

Max speed foilborne	37 knots
Cruising speed	34 knots
Minimum foilborne speed	23·3 knots
Range	736 miles (1,127 km)

MAFIUS 300 AND 600 FAST STRIKE CRAFT

The 85-ton Mafius 300 and 118-ton Mafius 600 are two hydrofoil missilecraft designed to augment the existing range of Navaltecnica fast patrol boats.

Though differing in size, the two craft are almost identical in terms of overall design, construction and internal arrangements. Both are equipped with the S.A.S. stability augmentation system, which stabilises the vessels in bad weather, and the Breda-Bofors twin 40 mm/L 70 or similar rapid-fire cannon. In addition the Mafius 300 will carry two Otomat or similar missile launchers and the Mafius 600 will carry four.

Power for the Mafius 300 is provided by two 1,950 hp MTU 12V 652 TB 11 diesels, while the Mafius 600 has two MTU 16V 652 TB 71 diesels each rated at 2,600 hp. Maximum speed of both craft is in excess of 38 knots.

Dimensions, weights and performance figures are given at the end of the summary. The following characteristics apply to both designs.

HULL AND SUPERSTRUCTURE: Vee-bottom hull of high tensile riveted light metal alloy construction. Argon gas welding employed on strengthened beams, web frames, keelsons and stringers. Basic hull structure is longitudinal; forepeak and after peak are transverse type structures. Steel is employed for the stern, fore and aft foil attachment points, propeller struts and foils. Cadmium plated rivets are used for jointing steel and light alloy components. Side plating ranges in thickness from 3·5 to 5 mm; the upper deck varies from 3 to 4 mm and plating on the stem and stern platforms is 2 mm thick.

The superstructure is built on transverse frames with stanchions and beams every 300 mm.

FOILS: Surface-piercing W foils of hollow welded steel. Craft in this series have a bow rudder for improved manoeuvrability. The bow rudder works simultaneously with the aft rudders to provide fully co-ordinated turns. Hydraulically operated flaps, attached to the trailing edges of the bow and rear foils are adjusted automatically by an SAS electronic stability augmentation system for the damping of heave, pitch and roll motions in heavy seas.

ACCOMMODATION: Berths, living and working accommdoation and full WC/washroom facilities for total complement of twelve, including commissioned and non-commissioned officers and ratings. The wheelhouse, all living spaces and fire control room are air-conditioned. Ventilation system provided for the engine room.

PROPULSION:

Mafius 300

Two MTU 12V 652 TB 71 4-stroke diesels, each delivering 1,950 hp at 1,460 rpm.

Mafius 600

Two MTU 16V 652 TB 71 4-stroke diesels, each delivering 2,600 hp at 1,460 rpm.

On both designs engine output is transferred via a short intermediate shaft, universal joint and Zahnradfabrik 900 HS 15 gearboxes to two hollow, stainless steel propeller shafts operating two, 3-bladed bronze-aluminium propellers. The drive shafts are supported by brackets and on the aft foils by rubber bearings lubricated by the water coolant system.

Stainless steel controllable-pitch propellers are available as an alternative to the fixed-pitch bronze-aluminium type.

FUEL OIL: Diesel fuel oil is carried in fibreglass-reinforced, welded aluminium tanks located in the double bottom. All tanks are connected to a service tank from which oil is delivered to the injection pumps. Each engine has two suction and two engine pumps. Before reaching the injection pumps, fuel is fed through two filters in parallel, with replaceable filter elements, and water drain cocks. Injection excess fuel is piped back to the service tank.

Tanks are refuelled through necks on the main deck, each equipped with air vents and fuel level calibrated in kgs and gallons.

SYSTEMS: Two systems are installed, each pressurised by a gear pump installed on one of the main engines. The first is used for the steering system and anchor winch, the second supplies the cylinder operating the lift control flaps and the bow rudder. The two systems are interchangeable and equipped with safety valves, manometers and micronic filters. Hydraulic pressure is also used for operating the weapons systems.

DRAINAGE AND FIRE CONTROL: Bilge pumps, operated by the main engines, can empty water from any compartment. Drain valves can be operated from both the engine room or from the deck. One pump can also supply water for fire hoses located on the amidship and aft sections of the vessels, port and starboard.

CO_2 system installed for fuel bays and engine room. Portable dry chemical and foam extinguishers also fitted.

ELECTRICAL: Two systems, dc and ac, 24 volt dc system operates navigation lights, radio and starts auxiliary engines. AC system, for all the other requirements, comprises two diesel generating sets delivering 70 kva, 220 volts, 3-phase 50 Hz. Meters for monitoring voltage, amperage, frequency and power of ac systems are on main switchboard, located in engine room, from which isolated or parallel operation of the two alternators is controlled. Also on board are circuit breaker and switches for the transformer when the craft is connected to shore power, and distributing panels for the power and lighting system.

SAFETY: The presence of smoke, fire and high temperatures in various parts of the craft, as well as the malfunctioning of machinery, auxiliary systems and hydraulics automatically sets off an electric alarm.

NAVIGATION AND COMMUNICATIONS: The craft are equipped with all navigation lights as well as an electrically operated horn and signal lights. Communications and navigation systems (radio, Decca Navigator and Flight Log etc) are fitted to the customers' requirements and are therefore considered optional equipment.

MAFIUS 300:

DIMENSIONS:

Length overall	101·54 ft (30·95 m)
Length, waterline	86·12 ft (26·25 m)
Beam, moulded	20·34 ft (6·20 m)
Beam across foils	41·34 ft (12·50 m)
Draft hullborne	12·14 ft (3·70 m)
Draft foilborne	4·59 ft (1·40 m)

WEIGHTS:

Displacement	83·66 tons (85 tonnes)
Military payload	14·76 tons (15 tonnes)
Liquids, fuel oil and water	
	11·52 tons (11·7 tonnes)

PERFORMANCE:

Maximum speed	
	in excess of 37 knots (68·5 km/h)
Cruising speed	36 knots (66·5 km/h)
Cruising range	500 nm (925 km)

MAFIUS 600:

DIMENSIONS:

Length overall	114·83 ft (35·00 m)
Length, waterline	98·75 ft (30·10 m)
Beam, moulded	22·97 ft (7·00 m)
Beam across foils	47·24 ft (14·40 m)
Draft hullborne	14·93 ft (4·55 m)
Draft foilborne	7·05 ft (2·15 m)

WEIGHTS:

Displacement	116·14 tons (116 tonnes)
Military payload	18·21 tons (18·5 tonnes)
Liquids—oil, fuel, water	
	16·04 tons (16·3 tonnes)

PERFORMANCE:

Maximum speed	38 knots (70·5 km/h)
Cruising speed	37 knots (68·5 km/h)
Cruising range	500 miles (925 km)

SEAFLIGHT SpA Cantiere Navale

HEAD OFFICE:
Villagio Torrefaro Messina 98019

TELEPHONE:
811.200, 812.579

DIRECTOR AND SENIOR EXECUTIVES:
Professor Felice Siracusano, President and Director
Ing. Gregorio Alberto Costa, Director
Dott Ing Giuseppe Zuffo, Director
Dott Ing Emanuele Midolo, Technical Manager

The Seaflight series of hydrofoils use a variable-incidence foil system introduced by Giuseppe Giuffrida who formed this company in 1961. The company is backed by a group of Messina industrialists and currently employs a staff of about sixty.

Construction of the company's yard on the beach at Torre Faro, began in 1962, and the Seaflight P 46 prototype, the C 44, was launched in January 1965. The company has since built eight 30 seat P 46s and six H 57s, the latter being a larger and more powerful development of the P 46, seating 60 passengers. The first of the company's 60-ton L 90 hydrofoils is now in service with Societe Sarda per Navigazione Veloce. The company is at present conducting studies aimed at the further development of the Seaflight variable incidence foil system and the design of a gas-turbine powered waterjet propulsion system for commercial hydrofoils.

Descriptions of the P 46 and military variants of this craft and the H 57 appeared in JSS 1972-73 and earlier editions.

SEAFLIGHT L 90

The L 90, latest passenger ferry hydrofoil in the Seaflight series, seats 118-123 passengers and cruises at 35 knots. The prototype was built under the supervision of Registro Italiano Navale.

FOILS: The foil system is of aeroplane configuration with surface-piercing bow and rear foils. Approximately 60% of the load is supported by the bow foil and 40% by the rear foil.

The bow foil, of W type, is attached to a supporting tube inside the hull by a central and two lateral struts. The foil pivots around the axis of the supporting tube between positions of maximum and minimum incidence. The lift and drag generated by the foil tends to rotate it backwards, particularly during take-off and in rough seas, but this movement is opposed by a spring attached to an arm on the foil assembly shaft. The system is designed to produce the same amount of lift, whether the speed varies or the foil's submerged surface varies in a wave crest or cavity.

Foils, struts and the supporting tube are fabricated in steel. Four shear points are provided, two inside the hull at the attachment points of the support tube arm and the automatic incidence control system, and two externally, at the point of attachment of the two subfoils to the central strut. In the event of damage, the affected foils and their supporting structure can be quickly and easily repaired.

The rear foil combines a horizontal submerged centre section with inclined surface-piercing areas. It is attached to the hull by two struts and the two rudder supports and the angle of incidence is fixed.

HULL: Riveted light alloy construction is employed throughout. The structure is of the transverse type with frames spaced 1 ft 0 in (300 mm) apart. Full-length longitudinal members reinforce the hull bottom and the decks and run from stem to stern. All plates and sections are specially treated by the company for added protection against corrosion. Braking load of the plates is 30-35 kg/sq mm. The hull is designed for two compartment sub-division and will remain afloat with any two adjacent compartments flooded.

ACCOMMODATION: The standard version accommodates a crew of 3-4 and 118-123 passengers, who are seated in three large saloons. Entry is through one of two side doors, one port, one starboard, in the central saloon, which provides access via a companionway to the aft saloon, the forward saloon and the wheelhouses. There are two WC washbasin units in the aft saloon and one in the forward saloon.

The pilot's position, instruments and controls are on the starboard side of the wheelhouse and there is a crew member's observation position on the port side. Access to the engine room is from the wheelhouse via a watertight hatch.

POWER PLANT: Power is supplied by two supercharged 12 cylinder Mercedes-Maybach MB 820 Dc diesels, each with a maximum continuous output of 1,100 shp at 1,400 rpm. Engine output is transferred to two high tensile bronze propellers through Zahnradfabrik BW 800/s reversible gears.

SYSTEMS:

ELECTRICAL: Two engine driven generators coupled to two battery sets provide 24 volts dc for engine starting, instruments, lighting, radio, etc. Separate diesel ac generating plant can be installed if required.

COMMUNICATIONS AND NAVIGATION: Ship-shore vhf and radar to customer's requirements.

DIMENSIONS, EXTERNAL:

Length overall	89 ft 4 in (27·24 m)
Length waterline, hull	74 ft 6 in (22·70 m)
Draft afloat	10 ft 1 in (3·07 m)
Draft foilborne	4 ft 1¼ in (1·25 m)
Hull beam	19 ft 9¾ in (6·04 m)
Width across foils	32 ft 9¾ in (10·00 m)
Freeboard	5 ft 5 in (1·35 m)
Height overall	26 ft 3 in (8·00 m)

Seaflight's L.90 prototype undergoing trials in April 1973. The vessel is now in service with Societe Sarda per Navigazione Veloce on the route Civitavecchia—Olbia

DIMENSIONS, INTERNAL:

Aft passenger saloon compartment, including WC:

Length	28 ft 6½ in (8·70 m)
Max width	15 ft 5 in (4·70 m)
Max height	5 ft 6 in (1·95 m)
Floor area	398 sq ft (37 m²)
Volume	2,472 cu ft (70 m³)
Max take-off displacement	59·5 tons
Deadweight (incl fuel, water, passengers, crew)	14 tons
Payload	10 tons

PERFORMANCE

Cruising speed foilborne 32·4-35 knots

Max wave height in foilborne mode	5 ft 3 in (1·60 m)
Range at cruising speed	270 nautical miles (500 km)
Turning radius at crusing speed	328 yards (300 m)
Take-off distance	218 yards (200 m)

Take-off time	30 seconds
Stopping distance	87 yards (80 m)
Stopping time	10 seconds
Fuel consumption at cruising speed	300 kg/h

Main deck saloon, excluding wheelhouse:

Length	16 ft 8¾ in (5·10 m)
Max width	15 ft 9 in (4·80 m)
Height	6 ft 5 in (195 m)
Turning radius at cruising speed	392 ft (120 m)
Take-off distance	427 ft (130 m)
Max-height	6 ft 5 in (1·95 m)
Floor area	258 cu ft (24 m³)
Volume	1,589 cu ft (45 m³)

Wheelhouse

Length	6 ft 2¾ in (1·90 m)
Width	9 ft 10 in (3·00 m)
Height	6 ft 2¾ in (1·90 m)
Area	64 sq ft (6 m²)
Volume	423 cu ft (12 m³)

WEIGHTS:

Light displacement	45 tons

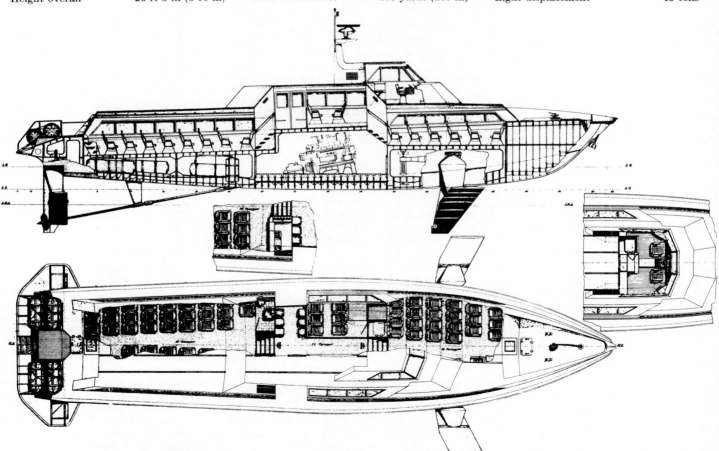

Inboard profile and plan views of the Seaflight L90 passenger ferry hydrofoil. Power is supplied by two 1,100 hp MB 820 DC diesels

JAPAN

HITACHI SHIPBUILDING & ENGINEERING CO LTD

HEAD OFFICE:
47 Edobori 1-chome, Nishi-ku, Osaka, Japan
TELEPHONE:
Osaka 443-8051
CABLES:
Shipyard, Osaka
TELEX:
J 63376
WORKS:
Mizue-cho 4-1, Kawasaki-ku, Kawasaki
City, Japan
TELEPHONE:
Kawasaki 288-1111
DIRECTORS AND EXECUTIVES:
Takao Nagata, President
Nobuo Inoue, Executive Vice-President,
General Manager of Shipbuilding Division
(Sales Director)
Giichi Miyashita, Manager of Kanagawa
Shipyard

Hitachi, the Supramar licencee in Japan, has been building PT 3, PT 20 and PT 50 hydrofoils since 1961. The majority of these have been built for fast passenger ferry services across the Japanese Inland Sea, cutting across deep bays which road vehicles might take two-to-three hours to drive round, and out to offshore islands. Other PT 20s and 50s have been exported to Hong Kong and Australia for ferry services.

Specifications of the PT 3, PT 20 and PT 50 will be found under Supramar (Switzerland). The Hitachi-built craft are identical apart from minor items.

In the spring of 1974, the company completed the first PT 50 Mk II to be built at its Kawasaki yard. The vessel Hikari 2, is powered by two licence-built MTU MB 820Db diesels, seats 123 passengers and cruises at 33 knots. It was delivered to its owner, Setonaikai Kisen Co. Ltd, of Hiroshima City in March 1975.

By the end of March 1975, Hitachi had built a total of twenty-three PT 50s and fourteen PT 20s. Two more PT 50s are under construction.

A special military hydrofoil, based on the Schertel-Sachsenburg foil system, and designated PT 32, has been designed by the company and two are in service with the Philippine Navy.

First PT 50 Mk II to be completed is the Hikari 2, built by Hitachi Shipbuilding & Engineering Co at its Kawasaki yard for Setonaikai Kisen Co Ltd. The vessel, which carries 123 passengers and a crew of seven, is employed on the route Hiroshima-Imabari

Hankyu Lines of Kobe City operates this 131-seat Hitachi PT 50 between Kobe and Naruto

---

POLAND

GDANSK SHIP RESEARCH INSTITUTE

ADDRESS:
Technical University, Gdansk
TELEPHONE:
41-47-12
DIRECTORS:
Prof. Dr. Lech Kobylinski

Research on problems connected with hydrofoil design and construction has been conducted by the Department of Theoretical Naval Architecture at Gdansk Technical University since 1956.

Experience with various dynamic test models led to the construction of the K-3 four-seat runabout which, powered by an FSC Lublin converted auto-engine, has a top speed of 27 knots (50 km/h).

In 1961 the Department was invited by the Central Board of Inland Navigation and United Inland Shipping and River Shipyards Gdansk, to design a hydrofoil passenger ferry for service in the Firth of Szczecin. Designated ZRYW-1 the craft seats 76 passengers and cruises at 35 knots. It was completed in 1965. A second craft, the W-2, intended for passenger services in the Baltic, is under development.

During 1966 the Ship Research Institute designed two hydrofoil sports craft, the WS-4 Amor and the WS-6 Eros. The prototypes were completed in 1967 and both types were put into series production during 1972.

In 1971, a catamaran-hulled research hydrofoil, the Badacz II, was built for the Ship Hydrodynamics Division of the Institute. The vessel is employed to tow models of ACVs and hydrofoils in coastal waters and provide data and performance measurements. It is also being employed to test new propulsion systems.

The largest hydrofoil craft to be designed by the Institute is a 300-ton passenger/car ferry.

Details of the ZRYW-1, Amor, Eros and Badacz II can be found in JSS 1974-75 and earlier editions.

SINGAPORE

VOSPER THORNYCROFT PRIVATE LTD, SUPRAMAR LING HYDROFOIL DIVISION

HEAD OFFICE:
GPO Box 95, Singapore 1
TELEPHONE:
467144
TELEX:
RS 21219
WORKS:
200 Tanjong Rhu, Singapore 15
DIRECTORS:
John Rix, Chairman
R. Du Cane, Managing Director
R. G. Bennett
G. E. Maynard
Prof. Yeoh Ghim Seng,

A. A. C. Griffith
S. N. Houghton
EXECUTIVES:
Poul Bakmand, Hydrofoil Sales

Vosper Thornycroft Private Limited, the Singapore subsidiary of the British warship design and construction specialists, is the sole builder in South East Asia of the Supramar range of hydrofoils. The parent company in the UK has an agreement with Supramar AG of Lucerne, Switzerland and the prototype PTS 75 Mk III has been built at the Portchester shipyard for Far East Hydrofoils, Hong Kong. The agreement in Singapore is between Vosper Thornycroft Private Ltd and Supramar-Ling Private

Limited, a company established after the signing of a licence agreement between Supramar and Mr Charles Tow Siang Ling, a Singapore businessman.

The Supramar-Ling Division of Vosper Thornycroft Private is building PT 20s and PT 50s and marketing them jointly with Supramar-Ling Private. This is Vosper Thornycroft's first joint venture with a Singapore company and the first time any Singapore shipyard has built hydrofoils.

The vessels under construction are mainly for export. They will be used for high-speed passenger transport, logistic support and patrol duties. Details of the designs are given in this section under Supramar AG, Switzerland.

SWITZERLAND

SUPRAMAR AG
HEAD OFFICE:
Denkmalstrasse 2, 6006 Lucerne
TELEPHONE:
041-36 96 36
TELEX: 78228
MARKETING DEPARTMENT:
Supramar Trade Ltd., Denkmalstrasse 2, 6006 Lucerne

MANAGEMENT:
Hussain Najadi, Chairman and Managing Director
Ing Volker Jost, Technical Director and Assistant Managing Director
Baron Hanns von Schertel, Technical Director
DESIGN:
Dipl Ing Ernst Jaksch, Chief

Section Heads:
Dipl Ing Ernst Jaksch, Foil Design
Ing Volker Jost, Hull
Dipl Ing Georg Chvojka, Machinery
Dipl Ing Otto Muench, Controls
RESEARCH AND DEVELOPMENT:
Baron Hanns von Schertel, Head of Development
Section Heads:
Dipl Ing Georg Chvojka, Analysis and EDP

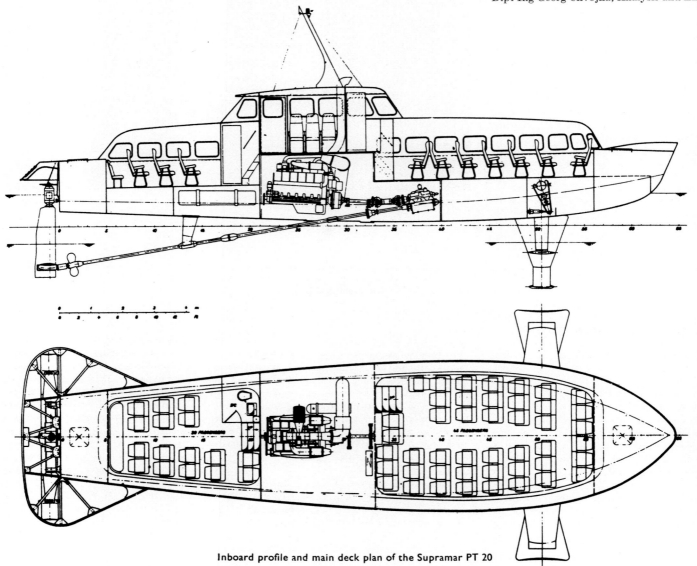

Inboard profile and main deck plan of the Supramar PT 20

Dipl Ing Eugen Schatté, Propulsion and Tests

Dr Ing Hermann de Witt, Hydrodynamics

Supramar was founded in Switzerland in 1952 to develop on a commercial basis the hydrofoil system introduced by the Schertel-Sachsenberg Hydrofoil Syndicate and its licensee, the Gebruder Sachsenberg Shipyard.

The co-operation between the companies started in 1937 and led to the development of the VS6, a 17 ton hydrofoil, which in 1941 attained 47·5 knots, and the VS8 an 80-ton supply hydrofoil completed in 1943 which attained 41 knots. The inherently stable, rigid V-foil system used on these and subsequent Supramar vessels, stems from experimental work undertaken by Baron Hanns von Schertel between 1927-1937.

In May 1953, a Supramar PT 10, 32-passenger hydrofoil began the world's first regular passenger hydrofoil service on Lake Maggiore, between Switzerland and Italy. In August 1956, the first Rodriquez-built Supramar PT 20 opened a service across the Straits of Messina and became the first hydrofoil to be licenced by a marine classification authority for carrying passengers at sea.

Established originally as a research and design office, Supramar has recently been reorganised and will produce hydrofoils of its own design at shipyards independently of the arrangements with its licencees.

The Marketing Department provides, in addition to its normal marketing functions, consultancy service covering financing, leasing and operating.

Supramar employs a staff of over 20, mainly highly qualified scientists and engineers specialising in hydrodynamics, marine engineering, foil design, propulsion and shipyard production. In addition to building its own hydrofoils it licenses other shipyards to produce its hydrofoil designs.

Supramar hydrofoils being built by these companies are referred to elsewhere in this section under the respective company headings.

The latest Supramar design is the PTS 75 Mk III, a development of the PT 50 with increased engine power and full air stabilisation. The prototype was constructed by Vosper Thornycroft at the company's Portchester yard and delivered to Hong Kong in late 1974. The company has also completed designs for a modernised PT 50 which is available as the PT 50 Mk 11. A new version of the PT 150 D, the PTS 150 Mk 111, is being introduced with improved air stabilisation and a higher cruising speed. Supramar is now concentrating on the development of second generation hydrofoils with improved performance and greater passenger comfort.

The company is also developing a fully submerged foil system with air stabilisation. First craft to use this system is the Supramar ST 3A, a 4·9 ton experimental boat built under a US Navy contract. During tests in the Mediterranean it demonstrated promising stability and seakeeping qualities and reached a speed of 54·5 knots. Supramar has completed the design of a patrol boat hydrofoil which meets the tactical requirements of the NATO navies. The vessel, the MT 250G, has an operational displacement of 250 tons and a maximum intermittent speed of 60 knots.

PT 20 Mk 11

The PT 20 Mk 11, a 27-ton boat for 72 passengers, is considered by Supramar to be the smallest size hydrofoil suitable for passenger-carrying coastal services. The first of this very successful series was built by the Rodriquez shipyard at Messina in 1955 and since then nearly 70 PT 20s of various types have been built in Sicily, Japan, Holland and Norway. The design has been approved by almost every classification society. Fast patrol boat variants are also available.

FOILS: Foils are of standard Schertel-Sachsenberg, surface-piercing type, with 58% of the load supported by the bow foil and the remaining 42% by the rear foil. Submerged foil area in foilborne condition is 5·50 m². Together with the struts and a horizontal guide, each foil forms a uniform framework which facilitates the exchange of the foil elements. The medium steel foils are of partly hollow, welded construction. The angle of incidence of the bow foil can be adjusted within narrow limits from the steering stand by means of a hydraulic ram operating on a foil support across the hull. To counteract the effects of large variations in passenger load and to ensure optimum behaviour in sea waves the angle of attack can be adjusted during operation.

HULL: The hull has a V-bottom with an externally added step riveted into place. Frames, bulkheads, foundations, superstructure and all internal construction is in corrosion-proof light alloy. Platings are of AlMg 5 and the frames, bars and other members are made in AlMgSi. Watertight compartments are provided below the passenger decks and in other parts of the hull.

POWER PLANT: Power is supplied by a supercharged, 12-cylinder MTU 12V 493 TY 70 diesel with an exhaust turbo-compressor. Maximum continuous output is 1,100 hp at 1,400 rpm. A BW 800/HS 20 reversible gear, developed by Zahnradfabrik Friedrichshafen AG, is placed between the engine and the drive shaft.

ACCOMMODATION: The boat is controlled entirely from the bridge which is located above the engine room. Forty-six passengers are accommodated in the forward cabin, twenty in the rear compartment and six aft of the pilot's stand in the elevated wheelhouse. There is an emergency exit in each passenger compartment, and the craft is equipped with an inflatable life raft and life belts for each person. A crew of four is carried.

SYSTEMS:

ELECTRICAL: 24 volt generator driven by the main engine; batteries with a capacity of approx 250 Ah.

HYDRAULICS: 120 kg/cm² pressure hydraulic system for rudder and bow foil incidence control.

COMMUNICATIONS AND NAVIGATION: VHF ship-shore radio is supplied as standard equipment. Radar is optional.

DIMENSIONS, EXTERNAL:

Length overall, hull	68·07 ft (20·75 m)
Length over deck	67·50 ft (19·95 m)
Hull beam, max	16·37 ft (4·99 m)
Width across foils	26·39 ft (8·07 m)
Draft hullborne	10·10 ft (3·08 m)
Draft foilborne	4·59 ft (1·40 m)

DIMENSIONS, INTERNAL:

Aft cabin (inc toilet)	145 sq ft (13·5 m²)
Volume	954 cu ft (27·0 m³)
Forward cabin	280 sq ft (26·0 m²)
Volume	1,766 cu ft (50·0 m³)
Main deck level (inc wheelhouse)	129 sq ft (12·0 m²)
Volume	847 cu ft (24·0 m³)

WEIGHTS:

Gross tonnage	approx 56 tons
Max take-off displacement	32 tons
Light displacement	25 tons
Deadweight (inc fuel, oil, water, passengers, baggage and crew)	7 tons
Payload	5·4 tons

PERFORMANCE (with normal payload):

Cruising speed, foilborne	34 knots (63 km/h)
Max permissible wave height in foilborne mode	4·25 ft (1·29 m)
Designed range at cruising speed	216 nautical miles (400 km)
Turning radius	427 ft approx (130 m)
Take-off distance	493 ft approx (150 m)

A Supramar PT 20 built by Hitachi Shipbuilding & Engineering Co Ltd

Take-off time	25 sec
Stopping distance	230 ft (70 m)
Fuel consumption at cruising speed 150 kg/h	

SEA TEST: Prototype tests were undertaken in the Mediterranean in every kind of sea condition, and further tests have taken place off Japan. Acceleration measurements have shown maximum values below 0·5g when accelerometer had been fitted above the bow foil. Maximum lateral acceleration was 0·32g. Measurements were made in wave heights of approx 1·2 to 1·5 m. These are the maximum measurements obtained and subsequent tests have seldom equalled these figures.

PT 20B Mk 11

In this model of the PT 20, the engine room and bridge are arranged in the foreship. This improves the pilot's vision in waters likely to have an influx of driftwood and provides a large main passenger cabin with seats for 55 and an upper deck cabin with seating for 16 passengers.

The layout of this craft has been based on experience gained with the Supramar PT 27 which was designed for servicing the offshore drilling platforms on Lake Maracaibo. This design has been slightly modified to meet the requirements of passenger services.

FOILS: The foil design is similar to that of the PT 20 Mk 11. About 66% of the total weight is borne by the bow foil and 34% by the rear foil. Submerged foil area in foil-borne condition is 6·2 m². The forward foil can be tilted within narrow limits by means of a hydraulic ram acting on the foil strut supporting tube. The angle of attack can therefore be adjusted during operation to assist take-off and to counteract the effect of large variations in passenger loads.

A Supramar PT 20B

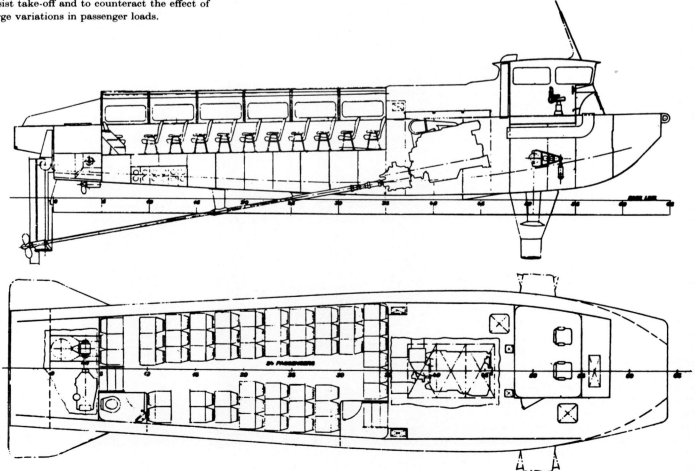

Inboard profile and passenger deck plan of the Supramar PTL 28 utility craft and supply vessel

HULL: This is of riveted light metal alloy design and framed on a combination of longitudinal and transverse formers. Watertight compartments are provided below the passenger decks and in other parts of the hull, and some are filled with foam-type plastic.

POWER PLANT: Power is supplied by a supercharged 12 cyl MTU 12V 493 TY 70 diesel with a max continuous output of 1,100 hp at 1,400 rpm. Average time between major overhauls is approx 10,000 hours. Engine output is transferred to a 3-bladed 700 mm diameter bronze subcavitating propeller through a BW 800/H 20 reversible gear made by Zahnradfabrik. The propeller shaft is supported at three points by seawater lubricated rubber bearings.

ACCOMMODATION: The PT 20B Mk 11 has a crew of 4 and seats 71 passengers. The main passenger compartment seats 55, and the small cabin behind the pilot's stand seats a further 16. Access to the main compartment is through either of two doors, located port and starboard, to the rear of the wheelhouse. An emergency exit is provided at the rear of the main passenger compartment.

The PT 20B Mk 2 can also be delivered with fully integrated air conditioning equipment. The total passenger capacity will then be reduced to 69.

A full range of safety equipment is carried, including inflatable rafts and lifebelts for each passenger and crew member.

SYSTEMS:

ELECTRICAL: 24 volt generator driven by the main engine, batteries with a capacity of approx 250 Ah.

HYDRAULICS: 120 kg/cm² pressure hydraulic system for operating rudder and bow foil angle of incidence control.

COMMUNICATIONS AND NAVIGATION: A vhf ship-shore radio is supplied as standard equipment. Radar is an optional extra.

DIMENSIONS, EXTERNAL:

Length overall, hull	68·40 ft (24·16 m)
Length over deck	63·98 ft (19·15 m)
Hull beam, max	16·93 ft (5·16 m)
Width over foils	28·22 ft (8·60 m)
Draft hullborne	9·84 ft (3·00 m)
Draft foilborne	4·27 ft (1·30 m)

DIMENSIONS, INTERNAL:

Main passenger compartment (inc toilet):

Length	30 ft 7 in (9·3 m)
Width	12 ft 6 in (3·8 m)
Height	6 ft 7 in (2·0 m)
Floor area	237 sq ft (22·1 m²)
Volume	1,553 cu ft (44·0 m²)

WEIGHT:

Gross tonnage	50 tons, app
Max take-off displacement	32·5 tons
Light displacement	25·4 tons
Deadweight (inc fuel, oil, water, passengers, luggage, crew)	7·5 tons
Payload	5·8 tons

PERFORMANCE (with normal payload):

Cruising speed	34 knots (63 km/h)
Max permissible wave height in foilborne mode	4·25 ft (1·29 m)
Turning radius	426 ft (app 130 m)
Take-off distance	492 ft (app 150 m)
Take-off time	app 30 sec
Stopping distance	231 ft (app 70 m)
Stopping time	app 10 sec
Fuel consumption at cruising speed 150 kg/h	

PTL 28

The PTL 28 is derived from the PT 27 utility and oil rig supply vessel, three of which have been in service for more than ten years with the Shell Oil Company on Maracaibo Lake, Venezuela.

Features of the new craft include facilities for loading across the bow as well as the stern, twin rudders for improved manoeuvrability, and a variety of structural and mechanical modifications to simplify and reduce maintenance. The Schottel drive now has only two bevel gears, the hull is of welded construction, and the foil and propeller mounting arrangements have been redesigned to facilitate servicing. All components of a non-essential nature have been omitted.

Normally seats are provided for 54, but the number of passengers can be increased if the range is reduced. The weather deck above the engine room is available for cargo; heavy loads are compensated by a reduction in passenger capacity. A cargo compartment can be made available at the rear of the passenger cabin (up to frame 17), a typical load being 4,023 lb (1,825 kg) of cargo combined with 33 passengers.

FOILS: Schertel-Sachsenburg surface-piercing system similar to that of the PT 20 Mk 11. Bow foil of hollow welded stainless steel. Foil, vertical struts, inclined fins and horizontal supporting tube form a framed structure which can easily be detached when necessary. The complete assembly divides into two to facilitate transport. Once the angle of incidence is adjusted no further alteration is necessary.

The rear foil is similar to the bow foil in type and construction. The complete system is mounted on its bearings at the transom by four bolts.

HULL: Constructed in seawater-resistant light metal alloy, the V-bottomed hull is of hard chine type and framed longitudinally. All joints are welded. Hoist fittings are provided to facilitate maintenance.

POWER PLANT: Power is supplied by a 12-cylinder MTU 12V493 TY70 diesel, rated at 1,000 hp at 1,400 rpm continuous and 1,350 hp at 1,500 rpm maximum.

Engine output is transferred to a 3-bladed bronze propeller through a Zahnradfabrik BW 800 H20 reverse gearbox. Hullborne propulsion is provided by a 150 hp diesel engine directly coupled to a Schottel Z-drive unit which can be rotated through 360°. During take-off and when foilborne, the lower bevel gear and hullborne propeller are retracted hydraulically into a recess in the hull bottom.

ACCOMMODATION: The PTL 28 has a crew of three and seats 54 passengers in a single saloon aft of the engine room. The bridge is located forward and provides a 360° view. The captain's seat, together with the operating controls and instrumentation, is located on the hull centreline.

DIMENSIONS, EXTERNAL:

Length overall	68·08 ft (20·75 m)
Length over deck	66·93 ft (20·40 m)
Beam over deck	16·73 ft (5·10 m)
Width over foils	26·25 ft (8·00 m)
Draft hullborne	9·68 ft (2·95 m)
Draft foilborne	4·92 ft (1·50 m)

A Supramar PTL 28 employed by Shell for servicing offshore oil platforms on Lake Maracaibo, Venezuela

WEIGHTS:
Displacement fully loaded

27·56 tons (28·00 t)

Disposable load   5·51 tons (5·60 t)

Light displacement   22·05 tons (22·40 t)

PERFORMANCE:

Speed max   39·00 knots (72·00 km/h)

Speed cruising   35·00 knots (65·00 km/h)

Range   140 nm approx (260 km)

PT 50 Mk II

The successful and profitable operation of the PT 20 led to the development of the PT 50, a 63-ton hydrofoil passenger ferry designed for offshore and inter-island services. The prototype was completed early in 1958, and more than thirty are now operating regular passenger services in areas ranging from the Baltic and Mediterranean to the Japanese Inland Sea.

The craft has been approved by almost every Classification Society including Registro Italiano Navale, Germanischer Lloyd, Det Norske Veritas, American Bureau of Shipping and the Japanese Ministry of Transport. The requirements of the SOLAS 1960 convention for international traffic can be met by the type if required.

FOILS: Both rear and forward foils are rigidly attached to the hull but the lift of the forward foil can be modified by hydraulically operated flaps, which are fitted to assist take-off and turning, and for making slight course corrections and adjustment of the flying height. The foils are of hollow construction using fine grain and MSt 52-3 steel throughout. Foils in stainless steel construction are optional.

The bow foil comprises the following elements:

Two fins, forming connecting links between the foil and the supporting structure which is riveted to the hull.

The hydrofoil which (according to its foil section characteristics) generates the lift and, with the stern foil, provides transverse stability in foilborne conditions.

Two struts, which transmit the main lift loads to the supporting structure.

The rear foil system comprises the following elements: the hydrofoil, which generates the lift, two side struts, and the single rudder which transmits the lift to the supporting structure.

For improved passenger comfort the PT 50 Mk 11 can be provided with a roll stabiliser on the bow foil. The system, including the motion sensing device, has been developed by Supramar.

HULL: Of hard chine construction, the hull is of partly riveted, partly welded light metal alloy design and framed on longitudinal and transverse formers. Steel is used only for highly stressed parts such as the foil fittings, and the shaft brackets and exits.

ACCOMMODATION: The PT 50 Mk II is available in three interior configurations:

1. For 111 passengers including bar and catering facilities.

2. Standard version, with seats for 122 passengers.

3. Commuter version, seating 136 passengers.

The crew varies from 6-8 members, depending mainly on local regulations.

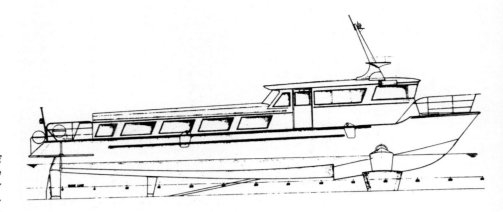

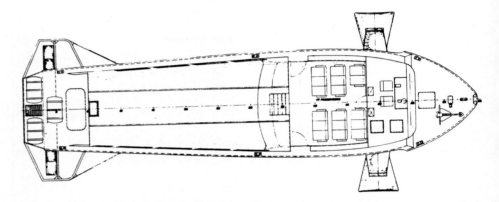

Supramar PT 20B Mk II. *Above:* Outboard profile and plan. *Below:* Inboard profile and passenger deck

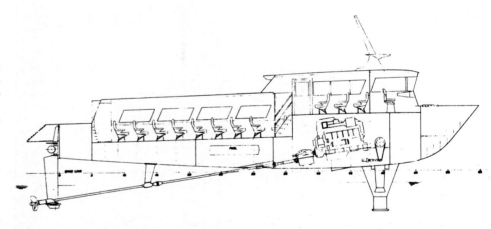

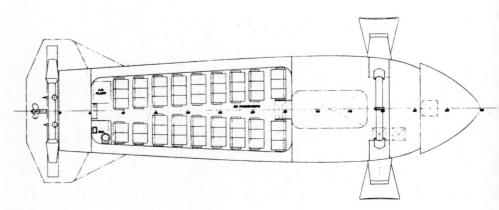

Passenger seats are of lightweight aircraft type and the centre aisle between the seat rows has a clear width of 30 in (0·76 m). Ceilings are covered with lightweight plastic material and the walls, including web frames, are clad in luxury plywood or artificial wood. Toilets are provided in the rear and forward passenger spaces. Floors in the passenger compartments are provided with thick carpets. Each passenger compartment has an emergency exit. Inflatable life rafts and lifebelts are provided for 110% of the passenger and crew capacity.

POWER PLANT: The craft is powered by two MTU 12V 331 TC 71 turbocharged diesels, each developing 1,100 hp at 2,140 rpm continuous. Engine output is transmitted to two 3-bladed 700 mm diameter bronze propellers through two inclined stainless steel propeller shafts, each supported at four points by seawater lubricated runner bearings. Reverse and reduction gear with built-in thrust is manufactured by Zahnradfabrik Friedrichshafen, Germany. The reverse clutches are solenoid-operated from the bridge.

Eight cylindrical fuel tanks with a total capacity of 3,650 litres are located in the aft peak and below the tank deck. Oil capacity is 320 litres.

SYSTEMS, ELECTRICAL: Engine driven generator; 24 volt battery set.

HYDRAULICS: 120 kg/cm² pressure hydraulic system for operating twin rudders and front foil flaps.

AIR CONDITIONING: Air conditioning can be provided as optional equipment.

COMMUNICATIONS AND NAVIGATION: Standard equipment includes UHF and VHF radio telephone. Radar and Decca Navigator is optional.

DIMENSIONS, EXTERNAL:

Length overall	91·00 ft (27·75 m)
Length over deck	86·60 ft (26·40 m)
Hull beam max	19·15 ft (5·84 m)
Beam over deck	17·91 ft (5·46 m)
Width over foils	35·40 ft (10·80 m)
Draft hullborne	11·66 ft (3·55 m)
Draft foilborne	5·08 ft (1·55 m)

DIMENSIONS, INTERNAL:

Aft passenger compartment (inc toilet):

Length	29 ft 7 in (9·0 m)
Width	16 ft 0 in (4·9 m)
Height	6 ft 7 in (2·0 m)
Floor area	474 sq ft (44·1 m²)
Volume	3,108 cu ft (88·0 m³)

Forward passenger compartment (inc toilet):

Length	23 ft 3½ in (7·1 m)
Width	17 ft 9 in (5·4 m)
Height	6 ft 7 in (2·0 m)
Floor area	412 sq ft (37·3 m²)
Volume	2,703 cu ft (67·6 m³)

Main deck foyer:

Length	12 ft 9½ in (3·9 m)
Width	13 ft 1½ in (4·0 m)
Height	6 ft 7 in (2·0 m)
Floor area	161 sq ft (15·0 m²)
Volume	2,030 cu ft (57·6 m³)

WEIGHTS:

Max take-off displacement	63·3 tons
Light displacement	49·3 tons
Deadweight (inc fuel, oil, water, passengers, baggage and crew)	14·0 tons
Payload	9·5 tons

PERFORMANCE (with normal payload):

Max speed foilborne 36·5 knots (67·5 km/h)

Balsa, a Hitachi-built PT 50 operated between Hong Kong and Macao by Far East Hydrofoil Co Ltd

Two Hitachi-built PT 50s operating in support of EXPO '75 at Okinawa, Japan

Cruising speed foilborne	34·0 knots (63 km/h)
Range	325 nm (600 km)
Turning radius	1,542 ft (470 m)
Take-off distance	819 ft (250 m)
Take-off time	35 sec
Stopping distance	264 ft (80 m)
Time to stop craft	10 sec
Fuel consumption at cruising speed	710 lb/h (300 kg/h)

PTS 75 Mk III

The Supramar PTS 75 Mk III is an advanced derivative of the PT 50. It seats up to 160 passengers and is designed for higher speed, improved seaworthiness and greater riding comfort. By increasing the specific PT 50 engine power of 43 hp/t to 50 hp/t a top speed of about 38 knots is obtained with the vessel fully loaded, and sufficient power is provided for operation in tropical waters.

An improved Schertel-Supramar air stabilisation system is fitted, and this, combined with a new W-foil configuration, considerably reduces rolling, pitching and vertical accelerations. The vessel can operate foilborne in waves up to 6 ft (1·82 m)

in height with full power.

The prototype was completed at the Vosper Thornycroft, Paulsgrove, Portsmouth yard in May 1974, and two further craft of this type are being constructed by Supramar's licencee in Hong Kong—Supramar Pacific Shipbuilding Co Ltd.

FOILS: The foil configuration is surface piercing and incorporates the Schertel-Supramar air stabilisation system. The bow foil assembly forms a rigid framework which facilitates the exchange of the foil structure. The foil is of hollow steel construction. It has three supporting struts, one on the centre line and one on either side. These are bolted to welded steel suspension points on the keel and chine respectively. Hydraulically operated flaps are fitted to the trailing edges to assist take-off, facilitate course corrections and provide automatic stabilisation when low frequency disturbances are encountered.

The rear foil is of surface-piercing Schertel-Supramar type and attached to the transom. Method of construction is the same as that employed for the bow foil. The complete assembly—foil, rudder sternpost, rudder, and two inclined struts—forms a rigid frame unit which is attached or detached as necessary. The aftermost propeller bearings are attached to the foil, the propellers being sited aft of the foil.

HULL: Hard chine type, constructed in partly riveted, partly welded corrosion resistant light metal alloy. A longitudinal frame system is employed, with transverse frames 900 mm apart. Steel is used only for highly stressed parts such as the foil fittings and shaft exits. A new hull construction method is being employed for this design. The hull is built in the inverted position and turned upright after the plating is completed.

ACCOMMODATION: Depending on operating requirements, between 130 and 160 passengers can be accommodated in three saloons. In the standard version airliner type seats are provided for 135 passengers, 19 in the upper aft saloon, 61 in the lower aft saloon and 55 in the lower forward saloon.

Ceilings are covered with lightweight plastic material, walls including web frames, are clad in luxury ply or artificial wood, and the floors are provided with thick carpets.

Three toilets are installed on the upper deck, within easy reach of all three saloons.

Passengers board the craft through wide side doors on the upper deck opening to a central foyer from which companionways lead to the lower passenger saloons. A promenade deck is available aft of the upper saloon and can be reached by passengers from the lower saloons via the foyer. Sufficient space for luggage is provided in the foyer. The upper aft saloon can be modified into a small dining room, if required, reducing the passenger capacity by 19.

All passenger saloons have emergency exits. A lifebelt is stowed beneath each seat and most of the inflatable life rafts are stowed aft and on the forward main deck.

POWER PLANT: Power is supplied by two 12 cylinder, MTU MB12 V652 SB70 supercharged diesels, each with a normal continuous output of 1,650 hp at 1,380 rpm, and 1,950 hp at 1,460 rpm maximum. Under tropical conditions normal continuous rating is 1,590 hp at 1,380 rpm and 1,810 hp at 1,460 rpm maximum. Engine output is transferred to two 3 ft 1⅜ in (950 mm) dia-

meter 3-bladed bronze propellers through a Zahnradfabrik BW 900 HS 15 reversible gearbox, which is hydraulically operated and remotely controlled from the wheelhouse. The propeller shafts are in stainless steel and supported at four points by seawater lubricated rubber bearings. Fuel is carried in integral tanks beneath the lower deck in the bottom compartments.

SYSTEMS, ELECTRICAL: Two 37 KVA water-cooled 60 c/s diesel-driven 380 V generators installed in the engine room. An emergency generator of similar capacity is provided at main deck level.

HYDRAULICS: 120 kg/cm² pressure hydraulic system for operating all hydraulic driven consumers.

AIR CONDITIONING: An air conditioning system is provided. Capacity is sufficient for adequate temperature and humidity conditions in all passenger saloons and on the bridge when operating the craft in tropical conditions.

COMMUNICATIONS AND NAVIGATION: UHF radio, VHF radio-telephone and magnetic compass are standard. Radar, Decca Navigator and gyro compass to

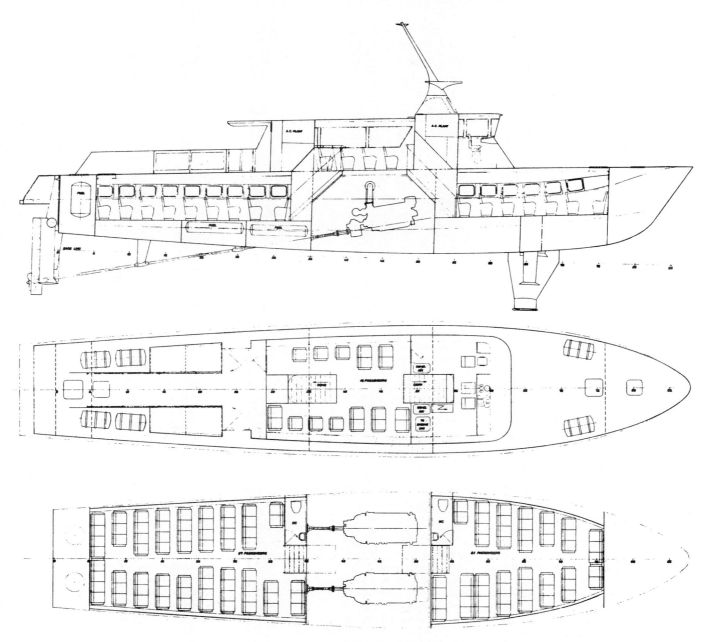

Inboard profile and main deck view of the Supramar PT 50 Mk II

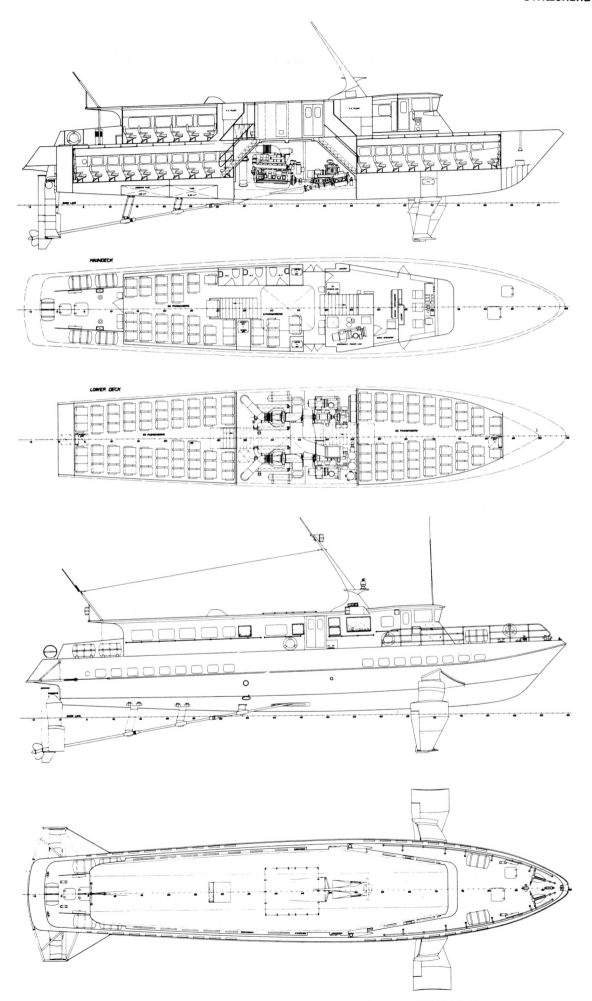

Inboard and outboard profiles and deck views of the new Supramar PTS 75 Mk III

customer's requirements.

DIMENSIONS, EXTERNAL:

Length overall, hull	98·5 ft	(30·0 m)
Length overall, deck	96·0 ft	(29·2 m)
Hull beam max	19·1 ft	(5·8 m)
Width across foils	38·1 ft	(11·6 m)
Draft afloat	13·1 ft	(4·0 m)
Draft foilborne	6·7 ft	(1·96 m)

DIMENSIONS, INTERNAL (Standard version)

Aft lower saloon:

Length	9·0 m
Width	4·6 m
Height	2·15 m
Floor area	42·0 m²
Volume	92·0 m³

Forward lower saloon:

Length	8·1 m
Width	4·7 m
Height	2·15 m
Floor area	37·0 m²
Volume	82·0 m³

Upper aft saloon:

Length	4·5 m
Width	4·2 m
Height	2·1 m
Floor area	18·0 m²
Volume	38·0 m³

Foyer:

Length	5·1 m
Width	4·2 m
Height	2·1 m
Floor area	20 m²
Volume	42 m³

WEIGHTS:

Max take-off displacement	85·0 tons
Light displacement	68·5 tons
Disposable load	16·5 tons

(incl fuel, oil, water, passengers luggage and crew)

PERFORMANCE (with normal payload):

Cruising speed	36·0 knots	(66·5 km/h)
Max speed	39·0 knots	(72·5 km/h)
Range	180 nm	
Turning radius approx	2,350 ft	(700 m)
Take-off distance approx	1,600 ft	(500 m)
Take-off time approx	50 sec	
Stopping distance approx	330 ft	(100 m)
Time to stop the craft approx	20 sec	
Fuel consumption at cruising speed	approx 600 kg/h	

First of the new Supramar PTS 75 Mk III series during trials on the Solent in May 1974. The vessel was built by Vosper Thornycroft Ltd at the company's Portchester shipyard for Far East Hydrofoil Co. Ltd. of Hong Kong

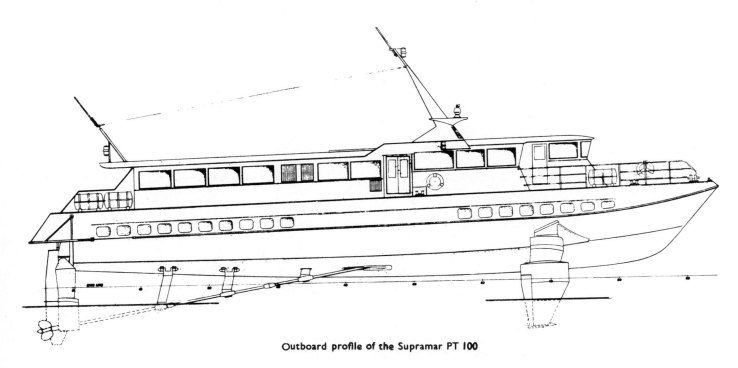

Outboard profile of the Supramar PT 100

SUPRAMAR PT 100

A variant of the PTS 75 Mk III is the PT 100, designed especially for short-haul commuter routes and accommodating 200 passengers.

Main dimensions and characteristics are identical to those of the PTS 75 Mk 111. The layout is shown in the accompanying general arrangement drawing.

SUPRAMAR PTS 150 Mk III

The Supramar PTS 150 Mk III carries 250 passengers and is the world's largest seagoing hydrofoil. The vessels fulfil SOLAS requirements, and have been built under the supervision of Det Norske Veritas, which has granted the class designation IA2-Hydrofoil-K.

FOILS: The foil configuration is a combined surface piercing and submerged system. The bow foil, which provides the necessary static transverse stability, is of the Schertel-Sachsenburg surface-piercing V design and carries 6% of the load. The rear foil, which bears about 40% is of the submerged, Schertel-Subramar air-stabilised type. In foilborne conditions the boat is inherently stable.

Hydraulically-actuated flaps are fitted at the trailing edges of the bow foil to assist take-off and adjust the flying height.

The rear foil is fully submerged.

Air stabilisation is fitted to the rear foil which gives the necessary transverse and longitudinal stability and improves passenger comfort under heavy sea conditions. Separate port and starboard systems are installed to stabilise rolling and pitching.

The system feeds air from the free atmosphere through air exits to the foil upper surface (the low pressure region) decreasing the lift. The amount to lift is varied by the quantity of air admitted, this being controlled by a valve actuated by signals from a damped pendulum and a rate gyro. The stabilising moment is produced by decreasing the available air volume for the more submerged side and increasing that of the less submerged one.

The rear foil includes the lift-generating sections, rudders and the rear suspension structure which serves as a connecting element with the hull. Struts for the aftermost propeller bearings are also attached to the rear foil, the propellers being sited beneath the foil. The complete assembly is a framed structure which can easily be detached from the transom. The angle of attack of the rear foil can be controlled hydraulically both during take-off and when foilborne.

The surface piercing bow foil is provided with air exits on the upper surface (the low pressure region) in order to vary lift and control pitch and heave motions by the quantity of air admitted. This is released by a valve which is actuated by amplified signals taken from a vertical accelerometer and a rate sensor.

Front and rear foil are of hollow construction and by the extensive use of welding, the number of connecting parts requiring screws, bolts or similar means of attachment is reduced to a minimum.

HULL: Partly riveted and partly welded construction and a system of longitudinal and transverse frames has been adopted. It has fairly high deadrise and hard chine sections for performance as a planing hull and for structural impacts in a seaway while foilborne. A step is provided to facilitate take-off. While the main or structure deck is continuous from bow to stern, the lower deck is interrupted by the engine room, sited amidships. The superstructure, which is also longitudinally and transversely framed, is not included in the load bearing structure. Several expansion

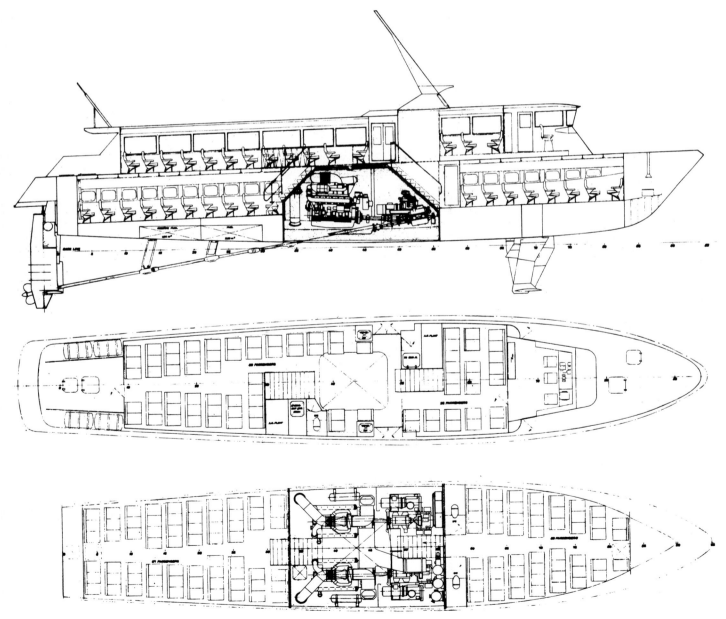

Inboard profile and deck plans of the Supramar PT 100, a short-haul commuter version of the PTS 75 Mk III, accommodating 200 passengers

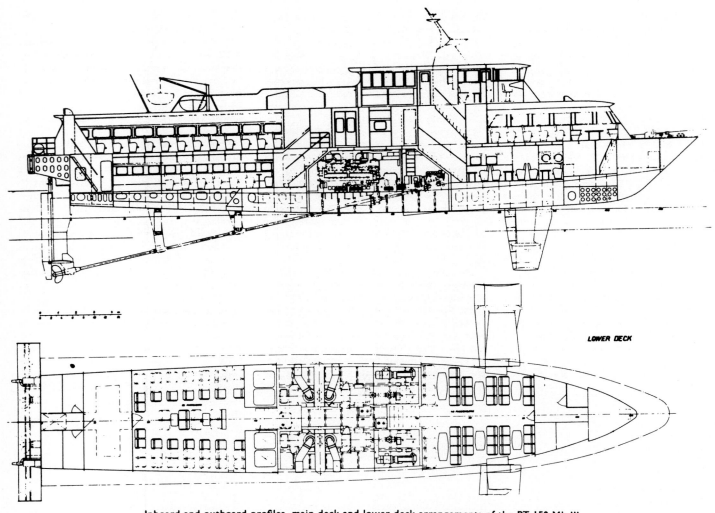

LOWER DECK

Inboard and outboard profiles, main deck and lower deck arrangements of the PT 150 Mk III

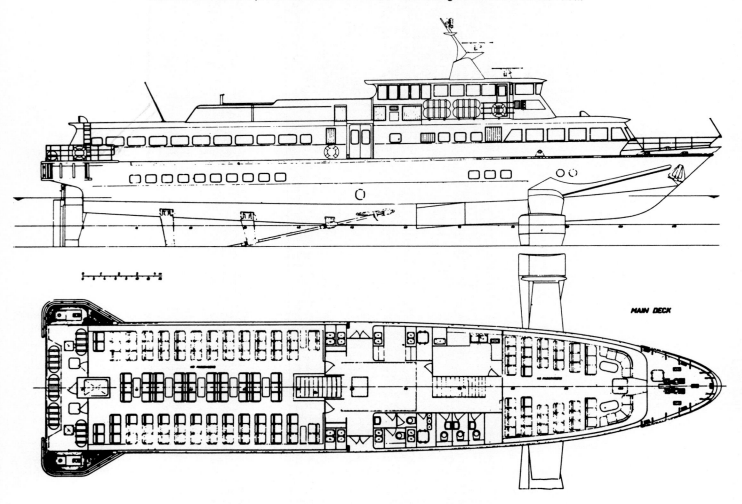

MAIN DECK

joints have therefore been provided.

ACCOMMODATION: The PTS 150 Mk 111 carries 250 passengers in four saloons, two on the main deck and two on the lower deck. The forward compartment main deck, seats 48, and the aft compartment 110. On the lower deck the forward compartment seats 40 and the aft compartment 52.

Passengers board the craft through double doors to the single centralised foyer, from which doors and companion ladders lead to the respective passenger saloons on the upper and lower decks.

Provision is made for all passengers to be served in their seats with cold meals and drinks as in an airliner.

Passenger seats are of lightweight aircraft type. Floors and ceilings are covered with lightweight plastic materials and the walls are clad in luxury plywood. Each passenger saloon has fitted carpets. Each room has an independent ventilation unit. Six toilets are provided.

The bridge, which is on a separate level above the main deck, slightly forward of midships, is reached by a companion ladder at the aft of the forward passenger compartment. All passenger saloons have emergency exits.

The craft carries 12 inflatable RFD liferafts (for 110% of the classified number of passengers and crew) which are stowed along both sides of the superstructure deck, and on the aft maindeck. Lifebelts are arranged beneath the seats.

POWER PLANT: Power is supplied by two 20-cylinder MTU MD 20V 538 TB8 supercharged and intercooled diesels each rated at 3,400 hp continuous. To improve torque characteristics during take-off two engine-mounted Maybach torque converters are provided.

Reverse and reduction gears are of the lightweight Zahnradfabrik BW 1500HS22 hydraulically-operated type, and incorporate the propeller thrust bearings. They have three shafts and two gear trains, one of which has an idler. The output shafts rotate either in the same direction as the input shaft or the opposite direction, depending upon the gear through which power is directed. Selection is by pneumo-hydraulic double-plate clutches on the input shafts. A mechanical lock-up is provided so that the gear can transmit full torque in the event of clutch slip while in service. This takes the form of a dog clutch which is effective in one direction, and can only be engaged in the "stop" condition. The gearboxes each have integral oil pumps for lubrication and clutch operation.

The angle between the engine crankshaft and the parallel shaft of the gearbox is accommodated by a cardan shaft with universal joints. The converter gear main shaft bearings, as well as those on the reverse gear primary shaft, are proportioned in such a way as to resist the forces and couples imposed by the cardan shaft universal joints. As a protection against accidents the cardan shaft is installed within a substantial removable tunnel.

SYSTEMS, ELECTRICAL: The total electrical system is supplied by three diesel generators with an output of 65 KVA each, one of them being an emergency generator installed on the upper deck.

In the event of an electrical failure the emergency generator is switched on auto-

Interior of the PT 150 DC showing *above* the forward saloon on the upper deck and *below* the aft saloon on the upper deck

matically. The engines are started by fresh air and are fresh-water cooled. The following systems are supplied by the electrical plant. For power and permanently installed heating and cooling equipment: 380 V rotary current, 50 cps. For light, pockets and instrumentation: 220 V ac, 50 cps. For remote control and monitoring 24 V ac.

HYDRAULICS: Steering, variation of the front foil flap angle and the angle of attack of the rear foil are all operated hydraulically. Each system has its own circuit which is monitored by a pressure controlled pilot lamp.

CONTROL: Starting, manoeuvring and operation of the craft is controlled from the bridge, but in cases of emergency the main engines may be controlled from the engine room.

The two main engines are each controlled by an operating lever designed for single-handed control. Propeller reversal is also by means of these levers, the reverse gear

being actuated by pneumatic remote control between bridge and main engines.

To start the boat both operating levers must be put in the "full ahead" position simultaneously. The engine mounted torque converter gear is actuated automatically. Foilborne speed can be regulated by fine adjusting of the operating levers. No other control devices are necessary for the main engines.

Levers for variation of the front foil flap angle and the angle of attack of the rear foil are actuated only before and after starting. During foilborne operation these can be used for trim compensation. All instrumentation and monitoring equipment is installed on the bridge.

AIR CONDITIONING: The vessel is equipped with air conditioning and heating plant which guarantees a room temperature of between 20 and 25°C, dependent upon the relative humidity. Air rate is 25 m²/h, person.

COMMUNICATION AND NAVIGATION:
Standard navigation equipment includes a
gyro master compass with transformers,
rectifiers and one multiple steering repeater
positioned ahead of the helmsman, Loran or
Decca Navigator and radar.

Communications equipment includes radio
telephone equipment for normal and emergency use.

DIMENSIONS, EXTERNAL:

Length overall, hull	124·2 ft (37·9 m)
Length overall, deck	121·8 ft (37·10 m)
Hull beam, max	24·6 ft (7·50 m)
Deck beam, max	24·2 ft (7·40 m)
Width across foils	52·45 ft (16·0 m)
Draft afloat	18 ft (5·5 m)
Draft foilborne	8·5 ft (2·6 m)

WEIGHTS:

Displacement, fully loaded	165 tons
Disposable load (payload plus consumable stores)	23 tons
Passenger capacity	250

PERFORMANCE:

Cruising speed at 6,880 hp 36·5 knots
(67·5 km/h)

Range 250 nm (400 km)

Max permissible wave height in foilborne
mode at full power (head seas) for passenger acceptability 10 ft (3·0 m)

ST 3A FULLY SUBMERGED FOIL RESEARCH CRAFT

In 1965 the US Navy awarded Supramar a
contract for the construction and testing of a
5-ton research craft with fully submerged air
stabilised foils. The object of the tests was
the investigation of the effectiveness and
reliability of the Schertel-Supramar air
stabilisation system under a variety of wave
conditions.

FOIL SYSTEM: The craft is fitted with two
fully submerged bow foils and one fully
submerged rear foil. The load distribution
is 62% on the bow foils and 38% on rear foil.
The centre of the front foils is 3 ft 11 in
(1·20 m) from the craft centre line. Normal
submergence depth for the bow foils is 1 ft
8 in (0·50 m) and for the rear foil 1 ft 2 in
(0·35 m). Foil outlines are tapered. The
foils are in solid stainless steel "Remanit"
2604 Mo S (standard German designation:
X4 Cv Ni Mo Nb 25 7).

The front foils are connected by 5 ft 3 in
(1·6 m) long struts to a supporting tube to
which they are flanged. The tube pivots to
enable the angle of attack to be adjusted.

The struts are of welded stainless steel
plate and have solid leading edges. At their
top is a casing which accommodates the
devices for transmitting signals from the
sensors to the air valves which are located in
the foil centres. On the outer faces of the
front foil struts are small auxiliary fins which
give added stability during the transition
from displacement condition to the onset of
air stabilisation. The rudder flap is attached
to the end of the rear foil strut.

AIR FEED SYSTEM: Lift variation is
achieved without movable foil parts. Each
foil has two air ducts with outlets on the
suction side. Air is drawn through these
apertures from the free atmosphere via the
foil suspension tube and the hollow struts.
Air valves, controlled by sensors, govern the
quantity of air admitted to the respective
ducts. Lift is normally only influenced by
the air emitting from the rearward row of
outlets. No power is required for a change in

A Westermoen-built PT 150DC operated between Malmo and Copenhagen

Supramar ST 3A

lift. The forward row, which is fed by
overpressure, is automatically engaged for
attaining very low or negative lift. For this
purpose, a comparatively small quantity of
air is drained off from the last stage of the
turbine compressor, reduced by a valve to
about 1 atm, and then accumulated in a
reservoir before it is led to the control valve.
The slight power loss in the turbine is
compensated by a drag reduction of the foil
which takes place in the pressure fed condition.

CONTROLS: The signals of a depth sensor,
a rate gyro and damped pendulum are added
and amplified. The pneumatic follow-up
amplifier draws its propulsion power from
the subpressure which is produced at a
suction opening at the strut near the foil.
The amplifier output is connected with the
air valve. The depth sensor probes the
submergence depth digitally by means of
suction orifices at the front struts. No
motor-driven power source is required for
the control system which, as well as the air

feed system for lift variation of the foils, is
designed for simplicity and reliability.

HULL: The hull, which is of hard chine
construction, is basically that of a standard
Supramar ST 3, modified to accommodate a
new foil system, gas-turbine and test equipment. To facilitate take-off, a step is
provided at frame 24 (see inboard profile)
and a ram wedge is fastened to the stern
bottom.

The hull clearance (tip of step to water
surface) of only 1 ft 2¼ in (0·36 m) was due to
the requirement that an existing ST 3 hull,
with an inclined propeller shaft, should be
used for the tests.

Hull, transverse framing and superstructure are of riveted light metal alloy. The
main engine, ducting for fresh air, exhaust
pipe and most of the auxiliary units are
positioned between frames 0–16½.

Above the Vee-drive, between frames 16½
and 20, there is an observation platform which
lies 8 in (200 mm) lower than the turbine
casing. From this platform the outer section

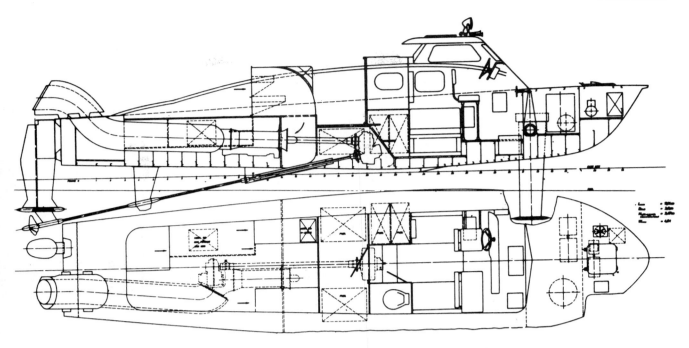

Inboard profile and deck plan of the ST 3A foil research craft

of the front foils can be observed. A short staircase at frame 20 leads to the wheelhouse which extends to forward bulkhead 31. At the front of the wheelhouse are two seats for pilot and observer, controls and the steering wheel which is hydraulically connected with the rudder flap. In the rear section two benches are arranged in longitudinal direction. The stabilisation control device is located direct behind bulkhead 31 so that it can be easily watched by the observer. The sequence and control system for the gas-turbine is arranged on the port side, between frames 20 and 23.

POWER PLANT: The craft is powered by a 1,000 hp GE 7LM100 PG 102 gas-turbine. Engine output is transferred to a 1 ft 3 in (0·38 m) diameter S-C bronze propeller through a reduction gear, a Vee-drive and an inclined stainless steel shaft. A 35 hp Mercury outboard is installed on the port side of the transom to provide auxiliary propulsion. To feed the stabilisation gyros a 6 hp gasoline engine is installed in the forepeak and coupled to a 3-phase ac generator.

DIMENSIONS:

Length overall (hull)	33 ft 10 in (10·32 m)
Breadth over foils	11 ft 10 in (3·6 m)
Breadth over hull	8 ft 10 in (2·7 m)
Draft hullborne	5 ft 1 in (1·55 m)
Draft foilborne (front foil)	1 ft 7½ in (0·50 m)
Hull clearance	1 ft 2½ in (0·36 m)

WEIGHTS:

Displacement	4·9 tons

PERFORMANCE:

Max measured test speed	54·5 knots (101 km/h)
Max speed (design)	56 knots (104 km/h)
Take-off time	14·5 sec
Stopping distance (50 kt to 5 kt)	390 ft (120 m)
Turning radius at 40 kt	750 ft (230 m)

SEA TEST: Sea trials along the Mediterranean coast revealed that the craft, despite a small hull clearance, is capable of taking waves 3-4 ft (0·9-1·2 m) high, and with a minimum length of about 100-120 ft (30·4-36·4 m), at 45 kt in all courses from head to beam seas, partially contouring. In waves

The ST 3A showing the fully-submerged air-stabilized foils. Two small dihedral fins are attached to the outer sides of the struts of the two bow foils to provide additional stability during the transition from hullborne to foilborne mode

over 4 ft (1·2 m) the hull periodically touches wave crests, which is accompanied by a marked speed reduction (very high froude number) during water contacting. In a following sea, and in all courses up to about 60° to a following sea, foilborne operation was limited to 2½ ft (0·76 m) waves due to the control system, which at that time had no heave sensor. A further improvement will be achieved when the lower foil side feeding, which is still under development, materialises. The smooth run in waves can be seen in the accompanying table of mean vertical acceleration over the bow foil. At a wave height of 3 ft (0·91 m) (1/10 of boat length), vertical accelerations of only 0·08 g have been measured, which compares very favourably with the sea test results of other craft with fully submerged foils.

SUPRAMAR MT 250G

This is a design concept for a 250 t patrol boat hydrofoil which meets the tactical requirements established by the West German and other NATO navies. It conforms to the fast patrol boat standards of the West German Navy and has a max intermittent speed of 60 knots.

Main dimensions of the vessel are similar to those of the Swedish Spica class, Vosper Tenacity, Israeli Sa'ar class and the West German Type 148. It is designed for all-weather operation in the western Baltic, the Skagerrak and other areas with similar operational conditions.

Foilborne propulsion is supplied by gas-turbine powered waterjets. The foil system is of fully-submerged type employing the Schertel-Supramar air stabilisation system.

FOILS: Canard system with a single fully submerged bow foil and two fully submerged rear foils. The foils are of welded hollow shell construction in stainless steel. All three are retracted hydraulically. The design avoids the use of hinged doors or panels to raise the bow foil.

CONTROLS: The lift forces generated by the foils are varied by air drawn from the free atmosphere and fed through air exits to the foil upper surface. The airflow decreases lift and the flow is deflected away from the foil section with an effect similar to that of a deflected flap.

The stabilisation system smooths the vessel's foilborne flight by controlling the lift of the foils. It consists of four units: the sensors, a computer (for automatic flight control), a command unit and the actuators.

The sensors measure the boat's attitude relative to the water surface and the horizon. The flight sensor is responsible for the maintenance of the correct height of the craft above the surface. It is a digital system with detectors positioned along the strut of the front foil. The main advantage of this system over analog sensors (sonic height sensors or capacitive sensors) is its higher reliability. Should one detector fail, the mean height of flight is changed and the range of the sensor decreases slightly but the vessel continues to operate in the foilborne mode. Special sensors have been developed for pitch and roll angles, using the minimum number of moving parts. The application of these sensors to hydrofoils is possible because ships have narrow limits of pitch and roll angles and the frequency range to be dealt with is limited. The sensors need a run-up time of only about twenty seconds. The sensors for vertical and lateral acceleration are of conventional strain-gauge type.

The computer, used for automatic flight control, computes the appropriate command signals to the actuators from the signals received from the sensors. It is an electronic, all-transistorised unit comprising a number of sealed watertight modules.

The command unit is located on the bridge, and from here the vessel can be trimmed in pitch, height and roll to the required attitude. The desired response of the stabilization system to the waves (platforming or contouring) can be selected on a sea state selector switch, whilst the indicator display gives an overall view of the whole stabilisation system.

The actuators (electro-hydraulic servo actuators) control the air valves which regulate air flow to the apertures on the foils.

HULL: Welded seawater-resistant aluminium construction with longitudinal foaming system and integral tanks for fuel oil.

INTERNAL LAYOUT/ACCOMMODATION

Accommodation and operations rooms are located almost entirely below deck leaving a relatively large free deck area. Crew would normally comprise twenty-two officers and ratings with three in reserve. Operating and control rooms are all fully air-conditioned. Minelaying equipment conforming to NATO standards can be installed as an alternative to missile launchers. Stand-by-space is available for a substantial number of Mk 55 mines. There are three officers' cabins and two crew rooms, two toilets with wash basins, one pantry, store

rooms, operating and control rooms for shp and machinery. The control and operations rooms have direct access to the bridge and the radio room. The engine has two subdivisions and contains two separate generator sets.

POWER PLANT: Foilborne propulsion is supplied by a marinised gas-turbine driving waterjets. Hullborne propulsion is supplied by a diesel engine driving a propeller.

ARMAMENT: Four MM38 Exocet missiles, 1, 76 mm OTO-Melara gun with 250 rounds, 2, 20 mm Rheinmetall cannon with 4,000 rounds.

FIRE CONTROL SYSTEM: Thomson-CSF Vega-Pollux or Hollandse Signaal.

DIMENSIONS:
Length overall	127 ft 11 in	(39·0 m)
Max beam across deck	26 ft 3 in	(8·0 m)
Draft, foilborne	8 ft 2 in	(2·5 m)
Draft, hullborne		
Foils extended	22 ft 3 in	(6·8 m)
Foils retracted	5 ft 10 in	(1·8 m)

WEIGHTS:
Operational displacement	250 t

Impression of the Supramar MT 250 G, 250 ton missile-equipped hydrofoil patrol boat. Gas-turbine-driven waterjets will propel the craft. Maximum intermittent speed will be 60 knots

A Westermoen-built PT 150

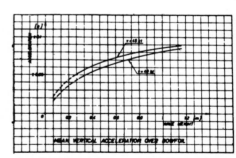
Graph snowing mean vertical accelerations over the ST 3A's bow foil in a seaway

PERFORMANCE:
Max intermittent speed foilborne	60 knots
Max intermittent speed hullborne	25 knots
Max continuous speed foilborne	53 knots
Max continuous speed hullborne	20 knots
Range at maximum speed	400 nm
Sea endurance	3 days

SUPRAMAR 500-SEAT PASSENGER FERRY

In August 1972, Supramar revealed that it is undertaking studies for the design of a 500-seat passenger ferry.

UNITED KINGDOM

AIRAVIA LTD

HEAD OFFICE:
20 North Road,
Shanklin,
Isle of Wight

TELEPHONE:
098-386-3643
098-386-2850

LONDON OFFICE:
The Tower Hotel
St. Katharine's Way
London, E1 9LD

Airavia Ltd is the first company outside the Soviet Union to specialise in the sales, servicing, maintenance and operation of Soviet hydrofoils. Founded in January 1968, it is the appointed sales and marketing representative for passenger vessels of Sormovo design in the United Kingdom, British Commonwealth, Western Europe and other Western countries.

The company has sold Volga hydrofoils in Western Europe and the USA, and through its operating subsidiary, Speed Hydrofoils Ltd, has operated these high speed runabouts as in-shore pleasure craft in the United Kingdom and Mediterranean.

In April 1974 the company took delivery of two 58 seat Raketa Ts (tropicalised model) which underwent modification to meet British Department of Trade and company operating requirements. After modification and trials the vessels were each issued with British Civil Passenger Operating Certificates and licenced to carry up to 100 passengers on approved routes. The first of the Airavia-modified craft was then shipped to Manila where it is in service with Bataan Manila Ferry Services. The second is operating on the River Thames with Speed Hydrofoils Ltd. In 1975, Airavia took delivery of a third Raketa, a non-tropicalised model, which was also put into service on the River Thames after DOT modifications. The vessel, a Raketa M, was fitted with sliding embarkation doors at the bow to facilitate passenger handling.

Airavia is currently negotiating sales of Russian-built hydrofoils to operating companies based principally in the United Kingdom, Western Europe, Mediterranean, Pacific, Africa and South America.

In addition to outright sales of these and other Soviet-built hydrofoil craft, the company also leases vessels on wet or dry charters and provides technical and marketing consultancy, servicing, and crew training support for new services.

RAKETA TA

This is the standard tropicalised Raketa 58-seat passenger ferry adapted to meet British Department of Trade operating requirements and licensed to carry up to 100 passengers on approved routes. Power is supplied by an M-401A supercharged diesel giving a service speed of 35 knots.

The crew comprises a captain, mate/engineer, deckhand and a hostess.

FOILS: The foil system comprises one bow foil, one aft foil and a pair of planing subfoils located immediately aft of the bow foil. Foils, subfoils and struts are all in welded stainless steel. The bow foil, which incorporates sweepback, and the straight aft foil are both supported by three vertical struts.

Top: Raketa Thames, an Airavia-modified Raketa M operated on the Thames by Speed Hydrofoils Ltd. Sliding embarkation doors give direct access to the passenger saloon. *Centre:* Interior of the Raketa's wheelhouse. A hydraulic remote control system is installed for the operation of the main and auxiliary engines, reverse gear and fuel supply. *Bottom:* Passenger access on the Raketa TA is via either a platform to the upper deck or through detachable "gates" on the promenade deck

The base of the centre strut aft forms the end bearing for the inclined propeller shaft.

HULL: The hull is framed on longitudinal and transverse formers, with all the main elements—plates, bulkheads, partitions, platforms and decks—in riveted duralumin. The stern is in interwelded steel strips. Below the freeboard deck the hull is divided into six watertight compartments employing web-framing.

ACCOMMODATION: The passenger saloon seats 58 in aircraft-type reclining seats. Six Norris Warming air-conditioning units and two electric fan heaters are installed in the saloon and one in the wheelhouse. Cool air is distributed through the saloon by eight electric fans mounted on the ceiling, four each side. One fan is installed in the wheelhouse. A ram-air intake provides ventilation when the craft is under way.

At the aft of the saloon is a bar, on either side of which are doors leading to the promenade deck. At the forward end of the saloon is a door leading to the forecastle. Aft of the bar is the engine room, storerooms, two toilets and a companionway leading up to the wheelhouse.

Features of the TA. model include the substitution of three fixed windows on either side of the saloon, by three hinged to open fully outwards to allow passenger escape in an emergency. Hand holds for standing passengers in the backs of the aisle seats in the saloon are provided. Additional handrails are fitted in the side gangways and at the foot of the companionway leading to the upper deck. In the interest of child safety a net is fitted across the promenade deck, aft.

Passenger access is via either a platform to the upper deck or through detachable "gates" combined with upward hinging roof panels. on the promenade deck, port and starboard.

Since life jackets are not required under British regulations for a Class 5 Passenger Certificate, life rafts have been substituted. Five 20-place Salter buoyant rafts are stowed in open trays above the passenger saloon superstructure ahead of the wheelhouse.

Four lifebelts are carried, two on the lower deck, and two on the upper deck.

A British made CO_2 firefighting system is installed, with controls in the wheelhouse. Freestanding fire extinguishers are all of British design and manufacture.

POWER PLANT: The main engine is an M-401A, watercooled, supercharged 12-cylinder V-type diesel, with a normal cruising output of 1,100 hp. This drives, via a reverse gear and inclined steel shaft, a 3-bladed cast bronze propeller. Fuel (low sulphur content diesel) is carried in two steel tanks with a total capacity of 190 Imp gallons. Copper or stainless steel fuel lines are employed throughout.

A compressed air system, comprising a propeller-shaft-driven air compressor and two 40 l compressed air bottles is provided for main engine starting, emergency stopping, operating the foghorn and scavenging the water intake.

The diesel generator unit comprises a Perkins P3.152 diesel engine employed in conjunction with a Stamford C20 alternator. In addition to the fire suppression system in the engine room, the walls are covered in Rocksil asbestos matting which will contain a fire outbreak for 15 minutes, allowing passengers ample time to escape from the vessel in an emergency.

CONTROLS: The wheelhouse is equipped with a hydraulic remote control system for the main engine and auxiliary engines, reverse gear and fuel supply. The balanced rudder, in aluminium-magnesium alloy, is controlled hydraulically by turning the wheel. A hand tiller is employed in an emergency. Employment of exhaust gas as a side thruster to assist mooring is permitted at 850 rpm.

SYSTEMS, ELECTRICAL:

A 3 kw generator, rated at 27·5V and coupled to the main engine is the main power source while the vessel is under way. A 50 cycle, 230V, 1,500 rpm 3-phase alternator supplies ac power. Four 12 volt acid storage batteries, each with a 132 ah capacity and connected in series to give 24 volts, supply power during short stops.

HYDRAULICS: The system for controlling the main engine, reverse gear and fuel supply consists of control levers located in the wheelhouse and on the main engine, power cylinders located on the main engine, a filter tank, pipelines and fittings.

HEATING AND VENTILATION: Passenger saloon and wheelhouse are provided with natural ventilation using ram inflow when the boat is in motion. Norris Warming air-conditioning is fitted for hot weather.

NAVIGATION:

LIGHTS: A rotating yellow light, range 5 miles and flashing 60 times a minute is carried on the masthead and operated at all times when the vessel is under way. In addition a masthead light, range 5 miles, and port, starboard and stern lights are fitted for night operation.

AUDIO NAVAIDS: A foghorn is mounted above the wheelhouse and an 8-in bell is carried in the bow.

RADIO: Marconi vhf radio is carried for ship-ship and ship-shore communication.

RADAR: Decca radar is fitted for night operation.

INTERCOM: A public address system is installed and intercom speakers link the wheelhouse with the saloon, promenade deck, engine room and forecastle.

DIMENSIONS:

Length overall	88 ft 5 in (29·96 m)
Beam amidship	16 ft 5 in (5·0 m)
Freeboard	2 ft 7½ in (0·8 m)
Height overall (excl mast)	14 ft 8 in (4·46 m)
Draft hullborne	5 ft 11 in (1·8 m)
Draft foilborne	3 ft 7¼ in (1·1 m)

WEIGHTS:

Displacement, fully loaded	27·09 tonnes
light	20·31 tonnes

PERFORMANCE:

Service speed	35 knots
Max speed	38 knots
Max wave height foilborne	2 ft 8 in (0·8 m)
hullborne	4 ft 11 in (1·5 m)
Turning diameter hullborne	3-4 boat lengths
foilborne	15-16 boat lengths

NEW HYDROFIN LTD

HEAD OFFICE:
Burfield Flat, Bosham Lane, Bosham, Sussex

MANAGING DIRECTOR:
Christopher Hook

Christopher Hook's early Hydrofins demonstrated for the first time the stability and excellent seakeeping qualities of incidence-controlled, submerged foil craft, and marked a turning point in hydrofoil design.

Nearly seventy Hydrofins of various types have been built since 1949 in Norway, the USA, Poland and Israel. The company's latest design is the 22 ft Channel Skipper, a four-seat fibreglass-hulled runabout.

CHANNEL SKIPPER

Developed from the earlier K2 Hydrofin, the K2D Channel Skipper is a four-seat sports hydrofoil fitted with mechanical wave sensors to control the incidence angle of the fully submerged main foils.

FOILS: The fully submerged foil system is of "aeroplane" configuration with 65% of the weight carried on the two main foils and the remainder on the aft foil. All three foils have swept back leading and trailing edges. A high-riding crash preventer plane is mounted ahead of and beneath the bow. The plane is also used as a platform for mounting a lightweight pitch sensor which is hinged to the rear. The sensor rides on the waves and continuously transmits their shape through a connecting linkage to vary the incidence angle of the main foils as necessary to maintain them at the required depth. A filter system ensures that the craft ignores small waves and that the hull is flown over the crests of waves exceeding the height of the keel over the water.

Two additional sensors, trailing from port and starboard beams immediately aft of the main struts, provide roll control. The pilot has overriding control through a control column, operated in the same manner as that of an aircraft.

All three foils and the crash plane arm are retractable. The crash plane arm retracts into a hull slot: the two main foils swing forward above the displacement waterline and the rear foil strut assembly retracts upwards into the hull at the same time raising the propeller and drive shaft.

POWER PLANT: Motive power is provided by a single 80 hp Ford diesel engine, driving a 3-bladed propeller through a Z-drive.

DIMENSIONS:

Length overall	22 ft 0 in (6·71 m)
Length waterline, hull	18 ft 0 in (5·48 m)
Hull beam	6 ft 7 in (2·00 m)
Length overall, foils extended	19 ft 7 in (5·96 m)
Max beam, foils retracted	10 ft 9 in (3·27 m)
Max beam, foils extended	13 ft 5 in (4·09 m)
Draft afloat, foils retracted	1 ft 7 in (0·48 m)
Draft afloat, foils extended	5 ft 3 in (1·60 m)
Freeboard	2 ft 6 in (0·78 m)

WEIGHTS:

Gross tonnage	1·8 tons

Net tonnage   1·2 tons
Light displacement   1·2 tons
Useful load (fuel, water, passengers, bag-
age and crew)   1,300 lb (598 kg)
PERFORMANCE:
Cruising speed, foilborne 32 knots (51 km/h)
Cruising speed, hullborne
                        8-12 knots (14-21 km/h)
Sea state capability   Unlimited in seas
    corresponding to Barnaby's "average
    rough sea" providing they conform as
    regards proportions
Turning radius at cruising speed
    150 ft (45·7 m) fully banked on turns.

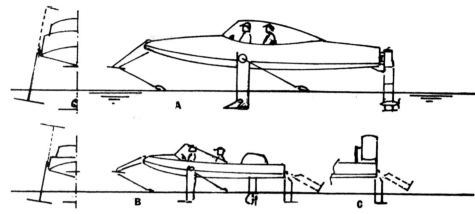

A, New Hydrofin Channel Skipper; B, Hydrofin conversion kit employing a standard long-shaft
outboard; C. Hydrofin craft propelled by a ducted fan

UNITED STATES OF AMERICA

Pegasus, first of the Boeing/NATO PHM (Patrol Hydrofoil Missile) class vessels, became foilborne
for the first time on February 25th, 1975. Since then it has been undergoing weapons tests and
operational evaluation. Main armament comprises eight AGM-84A Harpoon anti-ship missiles
and one rapid-fire 76 mm cannon. The PHM class will be employed in the counter-missile ship
and other roles by the navies of the United States, Federal German Republic and Italy. Top
speed is stated to be in excess of 50 knots

BOEING AEROSPACE COMPANY
Naval Systems Division
HEAD OFFICE:
PO Box, 3999 Seattle, Washington 98124
TELEPHONE:
Area 206, 237-2710
EXECUTIVE:
Darrell A. Cole, Vice-President and General
    Manager, Naval Systems Division
The Boeing Advanced Marine Systems
Organisation, now part of the company's
Naval Systems Division, was formed in 1959
to conduct research, development, design,
manufacture and the testing of high perform-
ance marine vehicle systems. Boeing's entry
into the hydrofoil field was announced in
June 1960, when the company was awarded
a $2 million contract for the construction of

the US Navy's 120-ton PCH-1 High Point, a
canard design which was the outcome of
experiments with a similar arrangement in
the US Navy test craft Sea Legs.
    Boeing has also built a jet-driven hydro-
plane, the HTS, for testing foil models at
full-scale velocity; the Fresh-1, a manned
craft for testing superventilating or supercavitating foils at speeds between 60-100
knots and a water-jet test vehicle, Little
Squirt. Descriptions of Fresh-1 and Little
Squirt appear in JSS 1970-71 and earlier
editions. The company also completed a
highly successful waterjet propelled gunboat,
the PGH-2 Tucumcari, for the US Navy's
Ship Systems Command. Its operational
trials included several months of combat
evaluation in Vietnam as part of the US

Navy's coastal surveillance force. Data
provided by the vessel assisted the design and
development of the NATO/PHM, which is a
'scaled up' Tucumcari, and the Jetfoil
passenger ferry.
    High Point was modified by Boeing during
1972 to incorporate a new automatic control
system, new struts and foils, a new diesel for
hullborne propulsion and a steerable forward
strut to provide improved manoeuvrability.
The craft was returned to the US Navy in a
new configuration, identified as Mod-1, in
March 1973. In its revised form it is
employed as a testbed for hydrofoil weapons
compatability.
    On April 4th 1975, the PCH was operated
by the US Coast Guard for one month as part
of a continuing research and development

programme to evaluate high-speed water craft for the US Coast Guard use. Operating in Puget Sound and around San Francisco, the craft was employed on fisheries patrol, marine environmental protection and search and rescue missions.

On January 19th 1973, the keel was laid for the first 110-ton 250-seat Jetfoil passenger ferry. The hull was assembled in a former 727 assembly building at Renton, Washington, and the first craft was launched on March 29th, 1974 on Lake Washington, which is adjacent to the plant. The first five Jetfoils are now in operation and another five are under construction.

The company is at present examining the possibility of exporting the Jetfoil on a modular basis, with the customer purchasing a basic hull, which would contain all the essential systems, and installing his own superstructure.

In April 1973, US Naval Ship Systems Command awarded the company a $42,602,384 contract for the design and development of the 235 metric ton NATO PHM missile-equipped patrol boat, under the terms of which Boeing is to build lead craft for the US Navy for evaluation. The first PHM, Pegasus, was launched on November 9th 1974. Delivery of the first craft to the US Navy was due to take place in late 1975. Participating in the NATO PHM programme with the US Navy are Italy and the Federal Republic of Germany. Early on in the programme participating countries are expected to purchase Boeing-built PHMs for their own navies. The contract calls tentatively for twenty-three craft to follow the lead vessel. Design studies are now being completed on bigger and faster hydrofoil including the 1,300-1,500 ton Destroyer Escort Hydrofoil (DEH), a vessel capable of open ocean missions and of crossing the Atlantic without refuelling.

PCH-1 HIGH POINT

General design of the PCH-1 High Point was specified by the US Navy's Bureau of Ships, with responsibility for detail design and construction assigned to Boeing. The ship was accepted by the US Navy in August 1963 and based at the Puget Sound Naval Shipyard at Bremerton, Washington. Since then it has been undergoing a wide range of tests to evaluate the performance of an inshore hydrofoil ASW system.

High Point had a major modification and overhaul by Boeing in 1972 and was returned to the US Navy in March 1973. The new configuration is identified as Mod-1. In its revised form it is employed as a weapons test-bed to evaluate PHM missile ship equipment and weapons and ASW devices. Two RGM-84A-1 Harpoon blast test vehicles were successfully launched from the deck of the vessel while foilborne at 40 knots off British Columbia on the US-Canadian Nanoose range during December 1973-January 1974.

Both firings were conducted in normal sea conditions and moderate winds, the first being made while foilborne with the vessel straight and level, and the second while turning foilborne at 5 deg/sec. The dynamic stability of the craft was measured throughout the tests and the gas-turbine was monitored to establish any possible harmful effects caused by the blast of the Aerojet-General 300 lb solid-propellant booster employed in the launch. The success of the test confirmed

Above: The PCH-1 High Point launching a McDonnell Douglas RGM-84A-1 Harpoon anti-ship missile during tests on the Joint US-Canadian Range, Nanoose, Canada, in January 1974. *Below:* PCH-1 bearing the insignia of the US Coast Guard, which operated the vessel during the month of April 1975 as part of a continuing research and development programme to evaluate high-speed water craft for S & R missions, fisheries patrol and marine environmental protection

the suitability of the launch canister design for use on the PHM and other hydrofoils.

During April 1975, the PCH-1 was employed by the US Coast Guard in Puget Sound and off San Francisco. It undertook a number of duties, from fisheries patrol to search and rescue missions, as part of a programme to evaluate high-speed water craft for possible use by the US Coast Guard.

FOILS: Submerged fixed incidence canard foil system, with 68 per cent of the foil area located aft, and trailing-edge flaps on all foils for lift control, is a scaled-up version of that employed on Sea Legs. The foil struts retract vertically into the hull. Foils are of built-up construction in HY-80 weldable steel, and struts are in HY-130 steel.

HULL: Hull and superstructure are of all-welded, corrosion resistant 5456 aluminium. Integral plate stiffener extrusions are extensively used for decks and portions of the sides not having excessive curvature.

ACCOMMODATION: A crew of 18 is carried to provide a three-section watch: on duty at any given time are one officer of the deck/helmsman, one lookout on bridge, one radar operator and one navigator required in combat information centre, and two engineers on watch in main control. The wheelhouse seats two operators—OOD on port and the helmsman on the starboard side. In addition there are seats for two observers. Crew accommodation is ventilated and heated only. Entry is via four watertight doors in the deckhouse and two watertight hatches on main deck.

POWER PLANT: Foilborne propulsion is provided by two Proteus Model 1273 gas-turbines, each rated at 4,250 hp max and 3,800 hp continuous. The turbines are located aft and take air through the two towers housing the retracted foil struts. The exhaust is discharged directly aft through the transom. Each gas-turbine is coupled to a pair of contra-rotating, subcavitating five-bladed propellers, 34 in. in diameter, through two right-angle gearboxes one at the top of each aft strut and the others in each of the underwater nacelles.

Hullborne propulsion is supplied by a single GM 12-V-71 (N75) rated at 525 hp for continuous operation. The engine is coupled to a 43 in (1,092 mm) diameter propeller through a retractable outdrive unit, which is steerable through 360 degrees and rotates about the axis of the horizontal shaft for retraction.

CONTROLS: Altitude and foilborne stability are controlled by an automatic control system, the heart of which is a computer. This governs motion of the trailing-edge flaps and the steerable forward strut in response to inputs from ultrasonic height sensors, position and rate gyros, accelerometers, feedback on control surface positions and helm commands. The system is active and all control surfaces are continuously moving in response to computer commands. On the bow foil, which is of single inverted tee (T) configuration, lift is varied by two trailing-edge flaps driven by a single actuator. The aft foil, of shallow M configuration, has two ailerons and two trailing-edge flaps. Each flap and its corresponding aileron are driven by a single hydraulic actuator.

Pitch is controlled by the flaps on the forward and aft foils. The gains in the control system were selected to provide automatic trim. Roll is controlled by differential operation of the flaps on the aft foil system. A roll to steer system causes the vessel to perform banked turns. Hullborne steering is accomplished by rotation of the hullborne propulsion unit about a vertical axis. This unit can also be rotated upward 87° about a longitudinal axis to eliminate its drag during foilborne operation.

The attitude control is entirely automatic except for steering. The take-off procedure on the PCH-1 is simply to set the desired flying height, then advance the throttles. At a gross weight of 117 tons take-off occurs at 24 knots with 3,750 total horsepower delivered to the transmission system, the speed stabilizing at 40 knots at that power setting. Minimum foilborne speed is 24 knots. At a cruising speed of 44 knots 4,400 hp is required, with propellers turning at 1,350 rpm.

SYSTEMS: ELECTRICAL: 100 kw (450 volts, 60 cycles 30).

HYDRAULICS: 3,000 psi ship's service for hullborne steering, strut and foil extension/retraction, engineering auxiliaries, and separate 3,000 psi system for foilborne control surfaces.

ELECTRONICS: Raytheon Pathfinder 1605, radar, UHF and HF radio transceivers.

ARMAMENT: Two fixed twin-tube Mk 32 torpedo tubes mounted on main deck at waist of ship.

DIMENSIONS:

Length overall, hull	115 ft 9 in (35·28 m)
Length waterline, hull	110 ft 5 in (33·65 m)
Hull beam	30 ft (9·14 m)
Beam overall with foilguards	38·42 ft (11·71 m)
Draught afloat	8·58 ft (2·62 m)
Freeboard	8·75 ft (2·67 m)

WEIGHTS:

Light displacement	99·6 long tons

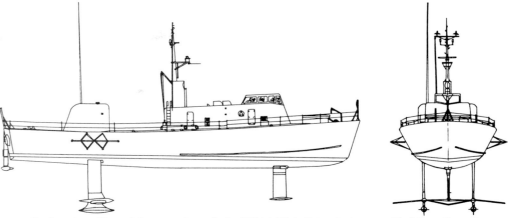

Outboard profile and bow-on view of the PCH-1 High Point in its new Mod-1 configuration. Note the shallow M aft foil, which has two ailerons and two trailing edge flaps. Output of each of the two Proteus 1273 gas-turbines has been uprated to 4,000 shp

Normal take-off displacement	127·2 long tons
Useful load (fuel, water, etc)	27·6 tons

PERFORMANCE:

Max speed foilborne	50 knots
Cruising speed foilborne	30-40 knots
Max speed hullborne	25 knots
Cruising speed hullborne	8 knots

PGH-2 TUCUMCARI

A 58-ton waterjet-propelled hydrofoil gunboat, the PGH-2 was ordered from Boeing by the US Navy's Ship Systems Command in 1966, under a $4 million, fixed price PGH (Patrol Gunboat Hydrofoil) programme. The craft was designed, constructed and tested in 23 months and delivered on schedule to the US Navy on March 7, 1968.

The craft operated with both the US Navy Pacific Fleet Amphibious Command, San Diego, and the Atlantic Amphibious Forces, Norfolk, Virginia. Its operational trials included several months of combat evaluation in Vietnam as part of the US Navy's 24-hour coastal surveillance force in Operation Market time.

In 1971 the craft was deployed to Europe for operation with the US Sixth Fleet in the Mediterranean following a series of demonstrations for officials of NATO navies.

In November 1972, Tucumcari ran aground in the Caribbean, seven miles east of Puerto Rico, while conducting nightime operations with amphibious forces. No crewmen were killed or seriously injured. Due to damages sustained while removing the craft from the coral reef, the craft was struck from the list of active US Navy vessels and sent to the US Naval Research and Development Center where it has been employed for structural evaluation and fire containment tests. A full technical description of the vessel appeared in JSS 1974-75 and earlier editions.

BOEING NATO/PHM

The NATO Hydrofoil Fast Patrol Ship Guided Missile (NATO/PHM) originated in mid-1969 when C-IN-C South presented to NATO a requirement for a large number of fast patrol boats to combat the threat posed by missile-armed fast patrol boats in the Mediterranean.

Bow view of the PHM-1 Pegasus, showing the bow foil fully retracted. Hullborne steering is performed with the aid of a bow thruster seen behind the cab of the tug vehicle. The bridge is manned by the officer of the deck, officer in charge and a helmsman. Immediately beneath the bridge is a combined combat information centre and fire control centre. The remainder of the deck superstructure is occupied by the communications room, a bay for unmanned electronics and quarters for the officer in charge

The concept of a common fast patrol boat was studied, and in September 1970 it was decided that the submerged foil craft of 140-tons proposed by the US Navy was the vessel most suited to NATO mission requirements. In October 1971, the United States indicated that it would proceed at its own expense with the design of the vessel and share the results of the studies with those nations wishing to purchase PHMs. It also offered to conduct all aspects of design and development, contracting and management in co-operation with governments entering into project membership. Costs would be reimbursed only by those nations engaged in the project.

Letters of intent, acknowledging design and cost scheduled obligations, were provided by Italy and the Federal Republic of Germany in April and May 1972, respectively. Although only three governments have decided to participate actively, future project membership is not restricted. Interested observers include Canada, Denmark, the Netherlands, France and the United Kingdom. Greece and Turkey have also considered participation.

In November 1971, the US Navy awarded Boeing a $5·6 million contract for the preliminary design of a 230-ton craft and the purchase of mechanical and electronic components for at least two of the vessels. Seventeen months later, Boeing was awarded a $42,607,384 contract for the design and development of the PHM for NATO navies. Under the terms of the contract the first craft, the Pegasus, was built for the US Navy.

This was launched on November 9th 1974, and made its first foilborne flight on February 25th 1975. Testing is reported to be progressing satisfactorily. Pegasus achieved its classified designed speed, completed the Navy-conducted phase of testing its weapons, and then began operational evaluation in the San Diego area in the summer of 1975. The outcome of the tests is expected to lead to a US Navy production decision by late 1975 or early 1976, followed by a number of overseas procurement orders. Delivery of the vessel to the US Navy is scheduled for late 1975. The contract calls, tentatively, for 23 craft to follow and these are expected to become operational with the US Navy over the next seven years. It is the first US Navy vessel designed and built on the metric system.

On May 3rd 1974, Boeing announced the receipt of a $3,809,235 cost plus fixed fee contract from US Naval Sea Systems Command for the preliminary design of a Patrol Hydrofoil Missile ship for the Federal Republic of Germany. The company stated that the design will be essentially the same as that of the lead vessel. Germany is planning to procure ten craft. The Italian Navy has announced its intention of purchasing four.

Co-operative production will be founded upon a production data package, which will be available after the trials and operation of the first vessel. A competitive procurement from a United States shipbuilder will be available to prospective NATO purchasers, in addition to which each participating nation will receive a complete production data package should they wish to build PHM in their own shipyards. However, it is envisaged that lead ship acquisition will be under a US production contract, on a commercial

Top: A Boeing three-axis automatic control system regulates the height of the PHM's hull above the waves. The canard foil system raises the craft 12 ft or more above the hullborne water line. At a speed of 45 knots, the automatic control system is expected to keep accelerations to below 0.1G for more than 95% of the time in the Mediterranean and for about 90% of the time in the Baltic
Centre: PHM-1 Pegasus during the launching ceremony on November 9th, 1974. Note how the forward 'T' foil/strut assembly retracts into a slot in the bow. As on the earlier Tucumcari, doors preserve the lines of the hull when the strut is either fully extended or retracted
Bottom: Close-up of the stern, showing the shallow 'M' main foil and its control flaps, and one of the two hydraulic actuators employed for retracting and extending the rear foil assembly. Also visible are the foilborne and hullborne waterjet discharge nozzles together with the reverse gates on the latter

basis between Boeing and individual NATO shipbuilders or governments.

The PHM has sufficient design flexibility to allow for individual variations by any country. These variations will be primarily in the weapons systems installed, and the participating nations, current and future, can acquire the standard PHM carrying whatever combat equipment is determined necessary to meet national requirements.

The standard PHM is approximately 131·2 ft (40·0 m) long, has a beam of 28·2 ft (8·6 m) and a full load displacement of about 231 tons (235 tonnes). Foilborne range is in excess of 500 nautical miles at speeds in excess of 40 knots in 8-12 ft seas. The hull form and size, the major structural bulkheads and decks, foils and struts, waterjets, pumps, controls and main propulsion machinery are identical. The auxiliary equipment and arrangements, deckhouse and crew accommodation are also of standard design, but variations in the latter are possible to suit the manning requirements of individual countries.

The PHM is designed on similar lines to the 64-ton Tucumcari, a development of which is being built by Advanced Marine Systems— Alinavi SpA for the Italian Navy. The primary peacetime missions of the craft are to patrol straits and exits through restricted waters, support task force operations and shadow potentially hostile forces. Employment will, in general, depend on national defence requirements and each country's responsibility within NATO. The mission of the PHMs employed by the US Navy will be to conduct surveillance, screening and special operations, with the following contingent tasks: patrol and blockade in coastal areas, island waters and inland sea areas; to augment screening of local convoys against surface attack; to provide fast transport for lightly equipped troops, to augment screening ships during arrival and departure of convoys or amphibious task forces.

FOILS: Fully-submerged canard arrangement with approximately 32% of the dynamic lift provided by the bow foil and 68% by the aft foil. The aft foil retracts rearwards and the bow foil retracts forward into a recess in the bow. Bow doors preserve the hull lines when the forward foil is either fully extended or retracted. The foils and struts are in 17-4 PH stainless high strength steel. Both forward and aft foils are welded assemblies consisting of spars, ribs, and skin. Flaps are fitted to the trailing edges to provide control and lift augmentation at take-off and during flight. The bow foil system incorporates a strut that rotates to provide directional control and reliable turning rates in heavy seas.

The shallow 'M' or inverted double pi configuration of the aft foil is designed for improved hydroelastic and turning characteristics. The primary strut structure consists of spars, ribs and skin welded into watertight assemblies. The struts are designed as beam columns, and rigidly attached to the foil support structure at the hull.

The struts are attached to the hull with pivot pins that allow the foils to rotate clear of the water. Hydraulic actuators are used for retraction and extension, mechanical stops and position locks being employed to secure the foils in either position.

CONTROLS, FOILBORNE: The helm, throttle and an automatic control system (ACS) provide continuous dynamic control during take-off, foilborne operation and landing. Once take-off is complete, the ACS requires no attention on the part of the crew. It controls the craft by sensing craft attitude, motion rates and acceleration, then comparing them electronically with desired values. Any deviations are processed by analog control computer which generates electrical commands causing hydraulic actuators to reposition the control surfaces, thus minimising detected errors. The foilborne control surfaces are trailing edge flaps on each of the foils, plus the rotating bow foil strut which

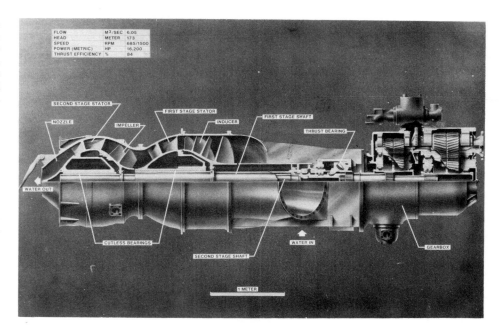

FLOW	M³/SEC	6.05
HEAD	METER	173
SPEED	RPM	685/1500
POWER (METRIC)	HP	16,200
THRUST EFFICIENCY	%	84

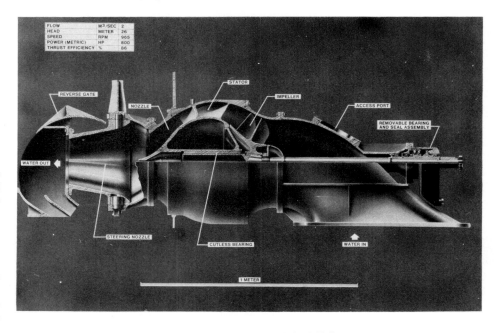

FLOW	M³/SEC	2
HEAD	METER	26
SPEED	RPM	965
POWER (METRIC)	HP	800
THRUST EFFICIENCY	%	86

Sectional drawings of the PHM's foilborne waterjet system, *above,* and hullborne propulsion system, *below,* The twin waterjet pumps of the hullborne system, powered by two Mercedes-Benz 800 hp diesels, propel the craft during long-range cruising and slow speed manoeuvring. Both the waterjet propulsion systems were developed and manufactured by Aerojet Liquid Rocket Company, Sacramento, California

acts as the foilborne rudder.

Manual controls and displays for both hullborne and foilborne conditions are concentrated at the helm station and include the wheel, a foil-depth selector, a foil-depth indicator, a ship-heading indicator and a heading holding switch.

CONTROLS, HULLBORNE: Steering control in the hullborne mode is provided by stern rudders which rotate electrohydraulically in response to the wheel. An automatic heading control, similar to that employed for foilborne operation is incorporated, together with the necessary heading reference provided by the gyrocompass.

POWER PLANT, FOILBORNE: The foilborne propulsion system comprises a single 18,000 shp, two-stage, two-speed waterjet, driven through two sets of reduction gears by a single General Electric LM 2500 marine gas-turbine, developed from the GE TF39, which powers the USAF's C-5 transport and

the DC-10 Trijet.

Both the foilborne and hullborne propulsion systems were designed by Aerojet Liquid Rocket Company, Sacramento, California, under a Boeing contract.

The single foilborne propulsion pump is capable of handling 90,000 gpm and the two hullborne pumps will each operate at approximately 30,000 gpm.

Engine installation and removal for overhaul is accomplished through hatches located in the main deck between the deckhouse and exhaust outlet.

The vessel is capable of operation on JP-5 or diesel fuel.

POWER PLANT, HULLBORNE: Twin waterjet pumps powered by two 800 hp Mercedes-Benz 8V331TC80 diesels propel the vessel when hullborne. The hullborne system provides long-range cruising and slow speed manoeuvring, while the gas turbine is available when required for high-speed foilborne operation.

HULL: Hull and deckhouses are all-welded structures in AL 5465 alloy.

ACCOMMODATION: Crew will average 21 officers and men, but will vary according to the armament carried. Accommodation on the US Navy version is provided for four officers—the CO has a separate cabin—three chief petty officers and fourteen enlisted men. The superstructure accommodates the bridge, which contains steering and engine control consoles and is elevated to provide a 360 degree view. A short ladder from the bridge leads down to the command and surveillance deckhouse that accommodates the fire control, radar, communications and navigation equipment. The size of the deckhouse provides flexibility in accommodating various national equipment requirements. The space aft of the superstructure and forward of the foilborne engine exhaust is used to erect rigging for replenishment and refuelling.

Below the main deck, about one third of the PHM's length is devoted to crew accommodation, the forward third is occupied by the primary gun, automatic loader mechanism, ammunition storage and forward foil, and the after third is occupied by the unmanned machinery spaces.

All manned spaces are equipped with a recirculating air conditioning system to give a maximum air temperature of 27 deg C at 55% relative humidity in summer, and a minimum inside temperature of 18 deg C in winter. The officer staterooms, crew quarters and lounge/messing area are fully air-conditioned, the temperature being controlled by individual thermostats in the spaces concerned.

SYSTEMS, ELECTRICAL: Ship's service electric plant comprises two 200 kw generator sets providing 450 volt 3-phase, 400 Hz AC power. One is capable of handling entire electrical load, the second is provided as a standby. Through the use of static power conversion equipment, limited 3-phase, 60HZ AC power and 28 volt DC is available for equipment requirements. In port, the craft can utilise shore power, or use its own auxiliary power unit for this purpose as well as battery charging and emergency use of navigation and radio equipment.

HYDRAULICS: 3,000 psi to actuate the hullborne and foilborne controls, foil retraction and hullborne engine starting. Dual hydraulic supply is provided to each service with sub-system isolation fore and aft in the event of major damage.

FIRE EXTINGUISHING: Dry chemical equipment throughout craft, and a fixed total flooding-type Freon 1301 system.

WEAPONS/FIRE CONTROL: Either WM-28 radar and weapons control system or American model, the Mk 92. Both systems embody a combined fire control and search antenna system, mounted on a single stabilised platform and enclosed in a fibreglass radome. The Italian Argo system can also be installed.

GUNS: Standard primary gun is the Oto Melara 76 mm gun, which is unmanned and automatically controlled by the fire control system. The craft can also be delivered with secondary guns. If specified two Mk 20 Rh 202 20 mm AA cannon can be provided, one each, port and starboard, adjacent to the fire control antenna structure.

MISSILES: The prototype carries Harpoon missiles with eight launchers, but Exocet, Otomat, Tero or any smaller missile system can be installed. Space is provided aft to accommodate the four launchers, port and starboard, in parallel pairs. The launchers are deck-fixed in elevation and azimuth.

Armament of the standard US Navy version will be eight McDonnell Douglas AGM-84A Harpoon anti-ship missiles in lightweight container launchers; one Mk 75 Mod 1 76 mm cannon and one Mk 92 Mod 1 GFCS.

Western Germany's PHMs will be armed with Aerospatiale Exocet missiles and the Italian vessels will carry Oto Melara Otomats.

The following details apply to the model under construction for the US Navy.

DIMENSIONS:
Length overall,
  foils extended 131·2 ft (40·0 m)
  foils retracted 147 ft 6 in (45 m)
Beam maximum, deck 28·2 ft (8·6 m)
Max width across foils 47 ft 6 in (14·5 m)
Draft:
  hullborne, foils retracted 9ft 5 in (2·9 m)
  hullborne foils extended 23·2 ft (7·1 m)
  foilborne, normal 8·9 ft (2·7 m)
WEIGHTS:
Displacement, full load including margins
  235 metric tons
PERFORMANCE:
Max speed foilborne in excess of 50 knots
Cruising speed foilborne,
  sea state 0-5 in excess of 40 knots
  hullborne in excess of 10 knots
Sea state:
  can negotiate 8·13 ft seas at speeds in excess of 40 knots
Foilborne range in excess of 600 n miles
hullborne range in excess of 1,800 n miles

BOEING JETFOIL 929-100
This is a 110-ton waterjet-propelled commercial hydrofoil for services in relatively rough waters. It employs a fully-submerged, automatically-controlled canard foil arrangement and is powered by two 3,710 hp Allison

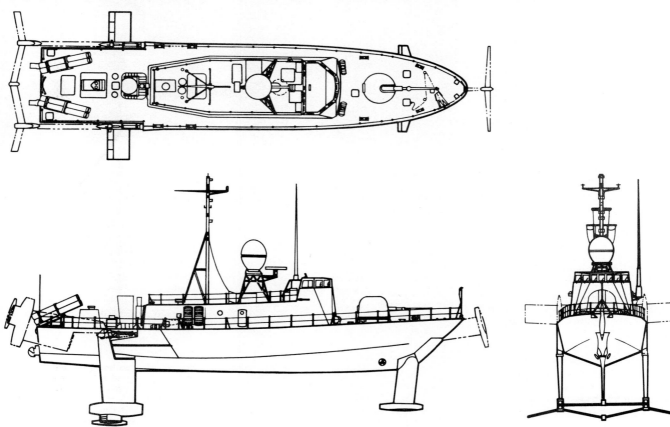

General arrangement of the NATO PHM

501-K20A gas-turbines. Normal foilborne cruising speed is 42 knots.

Typical interior arrangements include a commuter configuration with up to 284 seat and a tourist layout for 190 tourists plus baggage.

The company is also evaluating various utility models with open load decks suitable for search and rescue duties, offshore oil-rig support and firefighting. Two utility derivatives for offshore rig crew and priority/emergency cargo support are showing great potential. They are 50 and 100 seat crew/supply boat versions with considerable cargo capacity for supporting rigs within 50-250 nautical miles from shore.

At the time of going to press five Jetfoils had been delivered or were on order: two for Far East Hydrofoil Co, Hong Kong and three for Pacific Sea Transportation Ltd, Hawaii.

Keel-laying of the first Jetfoil took place at the company's Renton, Washington, plant on January 19th 1973, and the craft was launched on March 29th, 1974. After testing on Puget Sound and in the Pacific, the craft was delivered to Pacific Sea Transportation Ltd for inter-island services in Hawaii. High speed foilborne test began in Puget Sound in mid-July and it was reported that the vessel attained a speed of 48 knots during its runs.

During a rigorous testing programme to prove the boat's design and construction, Jetfoil One operated for 470 hours, including 237 hours foilborne. The latter phase of testing was conducted in the rough waters of the straits of Juan de Fuca and the Pacific Ocean, where it encountered wave swells as high as 30 ft, winds gusting up to 60 knots and wave chop averaging six feet high. At the time of going to press, the vessel was being refurbished prior to delivery to Hawaii in the late summer of 1975 as the third craft for Pacific Sea Transportation's SeaFlite service.

The first operational Jetfoil service was successfully initiated on April 25th by Far East Hydrofoil Co, of Hong Kong, with Jetfoil 002, Madeira. Prior to this, the Jetfoil received its ABS classification, was certificated by the Hong Kong Marine Department and passed US Coast Guard certification trials, although a USCG certificate was not completed since the craft would not be operating in US waters.

The first US service was due to begin in Hawaii on June 15th, with the first of three Jetfoils, 003 Kamehameha, starting inter-island runs. By the end of the summer all five Jetfoils will be in operation. Boeing has another five Jetfoils under construction with long lead items ordered on boats 11-25. An active world-wide marketing programme is underway to sell these high-speed craft, which are currently priced at $7 million.

FOILS: Fully submerged canard arrangement with a single inverted tee strut/foil forward and a three-strut, full-span foil aft. The forward foil assembly is rotated hydraulically through 7 degrees in either direction for steering. All foils have trailing-edge flaps for controlling pitch, roll and yaw and for take-off and landing. Hydraulically-driven foil flap actuators control the variation in flap positions through linkages between actuators and flap hinge points. Foils and struts retract hydraulically above the waterline, the bow foil forward, and the rear foil aft. All structural components of the foil/strut

Top: Jetfoil 002 Madeira during a test run on Puget Sound prior to being shipped to Far East Hydrofoil Co, Hong Kong for its Hong Kong-Macao service. A second Jetfoil has been ordered by the company. Seats are provided on this particular model for 284 passengers. Cruising speed 45 knots (51.8 mph; 83.3 km/h)

Centre: Jetfoil 003 Kamehameha, first of three Jetfoils on order for Pacific Sea Transportation Ltd, Honolulu, was due to start an inter-island service in Hawaii on June 15th, 1975. Note the lower aft promenade deck on this tourist version which carries 190 passengers and their luggage

Bottom: Passenger accommodation is fully air-conditioned and arranged on two decks. This photograph was taken in the upper passenger saloon of Jetfoil 002 Madeira

system are in 15·5 PH corrosion resistant all-welded steel construction.

CONTROL: The craft is controlled by a three-axis automatic system while it is foilborne and during take-off and landing. The system senses the motion and position of the craft by gyros, accelerometers and height sensors, signals from which are combined in the control computer with manual commands from the helm. The resulting computer outputs provide control-surface deflections through electro-hydraulic servo actuators. Lift control is provided by full-span trailing edge flaps on each foil. Forward and aft flaps operate differentially to provide pitch variation and height control. Aft flaps operate differentially to provide roll control for changes of direction.

The vessel banks inwardly into all turns, to ensure maximum passenger comfort. The ACS introduces the correct amount of bank and steering to coordinate the turn in full. Turn rates of up to 6 degrees per second are attained within 5 seconds of providing a heading change command at the helm.

Three basic controls only are required for foilborne operation. The throttle is employed to set the speed, the height command lever to set the required foil depth, and the helm to set the required heading. If a constant course is required, a "heading hold" circuit accomplishes this automatically.

For take-off, the foil depth is set, the two throttles advanced, and the hull clears the water in about 60 seconds. Acceleration continues, until the craft automatically stabilises at the command depth and the speed dictated by the throttle setting. The throttle setting is reduced for landing, the craft settling as the speed drops. The speed normally diminishes from 45 knots (cruising speed) to 15 knots in about 30 seconds. In emergencies more rapid landings can be made by the use of the height command lever to provide hull contact within 2 seconds.

HULL: Hull and deckhouse in marine aluminium. Aircraft assembly techniques used, including high-speed mechanised welding processes.

POWERPLANT: Power for the waterjet propulsion system is supplied by two Allison 501-K20A free-power gas-turbines, each rated at 3,300 shp at 80 deg F (27 deg C) at sea level. Each is connected to a Rocketdyne Powerjet 20 axial-flow pump through a gearbox drive train. The two turbine/pump systems are located in their own bays, port and starboard, separated by the slot in the hull into which the central water strut retracts for hullborne operation. The system propels the craft in both foilborne and hullborne modes. When foilborne, water enters through the inlet located at the forward lower end of the aft centre foil strut. At the top of the duct, the water is split into two paths and enters into each of the two axial flow pumps. It is then discharged at high pressure through nozzles in the hull bottom.

The water path is the same during hullborne operations with the foils extended. When the foils are retracted, the water enters through a flush inlet located in the keel. Reversing and steering for hullborne operation only are accomplished by reverse-flow buckets located immediately aft of the water exit nozzles. A bow thruster is provided for positive steering control at low forward speeds.

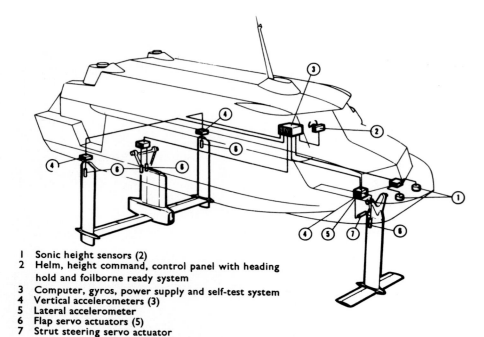

1 Sonic height sensors (2)
2 Helm, height command, control panel with heading hold and foilborne ready system
3 Computer, gyros, power supply and self-test system
4 Vertical accelerometers (3)
5 Lateral accelerometer
6 Flap servo actuators (5)
7 Strut steering servo actuator

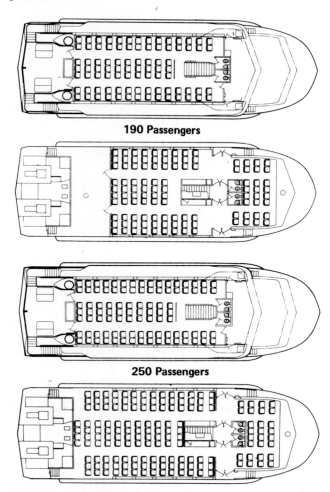

190 Passengers

250 Passengers

Typical interior arrangements on the 929-100 Jetfoil include a commuter configuration with 250 seats, a tourist layout for 190 tourists plus baggage and a mixed-traffic version for 190 passengers plus up to four compact cars. Seats are track mounted to facilitate spacing changes, removal or replacement. Food and beverage service units can be installed

A 4,000 gallon (15,140 litre) integral fuel tank supplies the propulsion turbine and diesel engines. Recommended fuel is Diesel No. 2. The tank is fitted with a 2 in (5 cm) diameter fill pipe and fittings compatible with dockside refuelling equipment. Coalescent-type water separating fuel filters and remote-controlled motor-operated fuel shut-off valves are provided for fire protection.

ACCOMMODATION: Passenger accommo- dation is fully air-conditioned and arranged on two decks, which are connected by a wide, enclosed stairway. The cabins have 3 ft 0 in (91·4 cm) wide aisles and 6 ft 9 in (2·06 m) headroom. In the commuter configuration 56 cu ft (1·58 cu metres) per passenger is provided and 66 cu ft (1·87 cu meters) in the tourist configuration. Floors are carpeted and 2 ft 0 in (61 cm) seats are provided. Lighting is indirect and adjustable from the

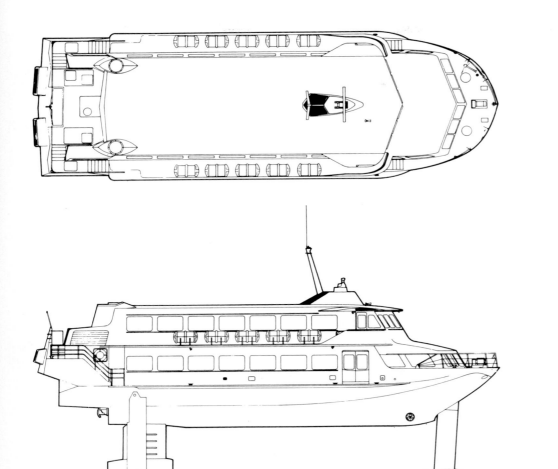

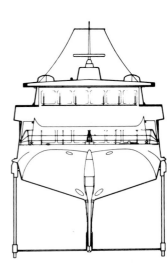

General arrangement of the Boeing Jetfoil

wheelhouse. Interior noise is near conversation level (below 68 db SIL). Passengers are entertained and informed by a public announcement system. Each deck level has two WC/washbasin units. Drinking water dispensers are located on each passenger deck.

Quality of the ride in the craft is comparable with that of a Boeing 727 airliner. The vertical acceleration at the c of g is designed to be no more than 0·04 g, with lateral acceleration less than that of the vertical. Angles of pitch and roll will be less than 1 deg RMS. Passenger discomfort in an emergency landing is prevented by a 'structural fuse', which limits deceleration to less than 0·4 g longitudinally and 0·8 g vertically so that a passenger would not be thrown from his seat in the event of the craft striking a major item of floating debris at full speed. The 'structural fuse', when actuated, causes the foil and strut to rotate backwards, protecting the system from sustaining significant damage. The fuses can be reset while under way in some cases, depending on the degree of impact.

Crew comprises a captain and first officer plus cabin attendants.

SYSTEMS: ELECTRICAL: 60-cycle, 440 volt a.c. electrical system, supplied by two diesel-driven generators rated at 62·5 KVA each. Either is capable of supplying all vital electrical power. 90 KVA capacity shore connection facilities provided, and equipment can accept 50-cycle power. Transformer rectifier units for battery charging provide 28 volts dc from the ac system.

HYDRAULICS: 3,000 psi (210·9 kg/cm²) system to actuate control surfaces. Each pump connected to a separate system to provide split system redundancy in the event of a turbine, pump, distribution system or actuator malfunctioning.

EMERGENCY: Craft meets all applicable safety regulations of the US Coast Guard and SOLAS. Hull provides two-compartment sub-division and a high degree of stability. Life rafts and life jackets are provided.

NAVIGATION: Equipment includes radar. A low-light-level television system covering potential collision zone is available as an optional extra.

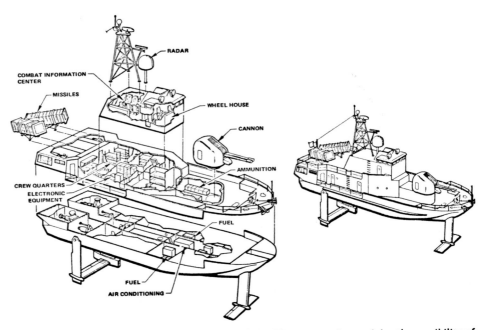

Projected 114-ton fast patrol boat version of the Jetfoil. The company is examining the possibility of exporting the Jetfoil on a modular basis with the customer purchasing a basic hull, which will contain the power plant and all the necessary systems, and installing his own superstructure

DIMENSIONS:
Length overall, foils extended
90 ft (27·4 m)
Length overall, foils retracted
99 ft 0 in (30·1 m)
Beam overall, maximum 31 ft (9·5 m)
Draught afloat, foils retracted 4·8 ft (1·5 m)
foils extended 16·3 ft (5·0 m)
WEIGHTS:
Displacement 110 long tons
PERFORMANCE:
Maximum speed 50 knots
Normal service speed 42 knots
Turning radius at 45 knots
less than 1,000 ft (304·80 m)
Normal endurance at cruising speed 4 hours
Maximum endurance 8 hours
Maximum wave height foilborne
12 ft 0 in (3·65 m)

MODULAR JETFOIL

In November 1974 Boeing announced that consideration was being given to the export of Jetfoils on a modular basis. One approach would be to supply operators, both commercial and military, with the basic Jetfoil hull, complete with foils, powerplant and control system, and the operator would arrange to install his own superstructure.

This would give them access to craft embodying the latest developments in hydrofoil technology and permit them to add superstructure tailored to their own particular needs. Variants would range from passenger ferries and utility craft for offshore marine operations, to coastguard patrol vessels and missile gunboats.

The modular concept is expected to appeal in particular to lesser developed countries, since by completing the craft locally, a useful saving in hard currency could be realised. A substantial amount of the superstructure could be riveted together by fairly low-skilled labour. The cost per hull unit, once production is established, is expected to be about $6 million.

Maintenance requirements are expected to be reasonably low. The Allison 501-K20A gas-turbines have a life of 18,000 hours, and the Boeing autopilot, the most sensitive part of the system, has a life expectancy of 3-4 years under normal operating conditions, allowing 3,000 hours in service each year.

Allison is willing to negotiate contract rates for servicing the gas-turbines at a fixed-rate per operating hour.

Boeing states that modifications could be made to the design to allow the installation of alternative engines, such as the Rolls Royce Tyne or Proteus, should countries like the United Kingdom prefer them.

Weapons suitable for the military models include the Oto Melara 76 mm rapid-fire cannon and the Emerson 30 mm cannon, the Argo control system and the Otomat, Exocet, Penguin and Gabriel anti-ship missiles.

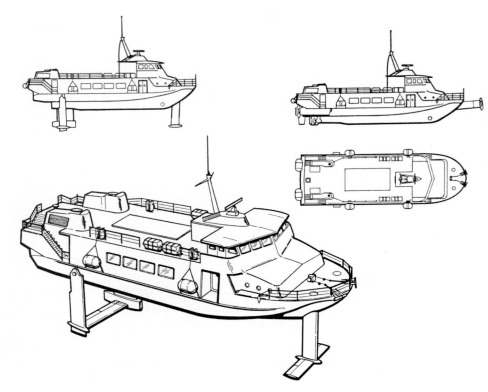

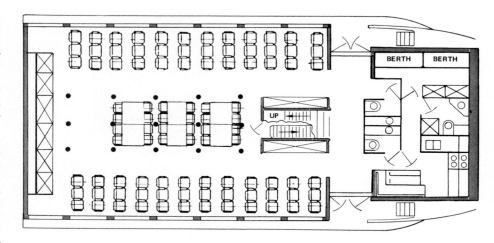

Above and below: Outboard profiles and main deck view of the offshore oil rig support model of the Boeing Jetfoil

Another Boeing concept is the regional final assembly centre, a number of which would be established around the world in order to supply customers with complete vessels made up from imported hulls and superstructures. At the same time the arrangement would meet the growing demand in lesser developed areas for greater participation in industrial programmes.

The centres, which would not be owned or operated by Boeing, would simply be involved with their importation, assembly and marketing. Likely areas for the establishment of these centres include the Caribbean, Greece, Iran, Japan, Taiwan, Indonesia and Scandinavia.

DAK HYDROFOILS

HEAD OFFICE:
P.O. Box, 71 Sausalito, California 94965

PROPRIETOR AND CHIEF DESIGNER:
David A. Keiper

Dak Hydrofoils is currently developing and developing simple low-cost hydrofoil conversion kits for outboard powerboats. These are based on those available from the company for existing racing catamarans.

The arrangement employs identical lateral foils, positioned in a similar location, plus a fully-submerged stern foil. Lighter craft will have a simple foil beneath the outboard engine. Heavier craft, of up to 1,500 lb (680·38 kg) loaded weight have a retractable 6 in (152 mm) chord foil, supported by twin struts.

The propeller is lowered by a combination of engine shaft extension or extensions, and/or lowering the engine by means of parallel bars.

DEPARTMENT OF THE NAVY, NAVAL SEA SYSTEMS COMMAND (NAVSEA)

HEADQUARTERS:

Washington DC 20360

PROGRAMME MANAGER, HOVERCRAFT AND HYDROFOILS:

James L. Schuler

OFFICE ADDRESS:

US Naval Sea Systems Command, Advanced Technology Systems Division (Code 0322), National Center 3, Room 10E54, Washington DC 20362

The Research Directorate of US Naval Sea Systems Command (NAVSEA), has been the primary technical sponsor of all US Navy hydrofoil and hovercraft programmes since 1960.

The programme manager responsible for the development of both types of vessel is Mr. James L. Schuler. Technical managers have been appointed for each of the several research and development programmes managed and directed by NAVSEA. Technical Manager of the US Navy Hydrofoil Research and Development Programme is Mr Robert Johnston, and the Technical Manager of the US Navy Amphibious Assault Landing Craft Advanced Development Programme is Mr Melvin Brown, both of the Naval Ship Research and Development Centre, Carderock, Maryland (NSRDC/C).

This programme includes tests and trials of the PCH-1 High Point, and the AGEH-1

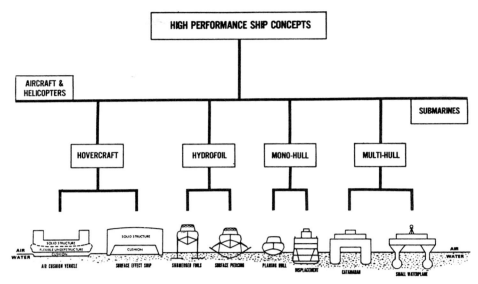

High performance ship concepts under development by US Naval Sea Systems Command

Plainview, as well as the design, construction, test, trials and evaluation of larger and faster hydrofoils.

Other US Navy hydrofoils include the PGH-1 and PHM, as well as the FRESH-1 test craft. The PHM is a Patrol Hydrofoil,

Guided Missile being developed by NAVSEA PMS 303 under the direction of Capt. Edw. W. Molzan, USN. This is a NATO project. sponsored jointly by the US Navy, the Federal Republic of Germany and the Italian Navy.

DYNAFOIL INC.

HEAD OFFICE:

881 West 16th Street, Newport Beach, California 92663

TELEPHONE:

(714) 646-9231

DIRECTORS:

Dr. Paul J. Coleman, Chairman

David J. Cline, President

James M. Dale, Secretary/Treasurer

EXECUTIVES:

King Evers, Marketing & Sales Manager

Dynafoil, Inc. was formed in December 1971 to develop the Dynafoil sport craft. The development of this vehicle began in late 1970 with the construction of IRMA 1. the foil configuration of which has been the foundation for all subsequent work. Patents for the foil configuration have been applied for in all the main consumer countries, and have been granted in the USA.

DYNAFOIL MARK I

This fibre glass-hulled sports hydrofoil is a marine counterpart to the motorcycle and snowmobile. The bow foil is mounted at the base of a handlebar-equipped steering head and the handling characteristics are similar to those of a motor cycle. Production began in June 1975.

FOILS: Canard configuration with a fully submerged main foil located aft and bearing 60% of the load and small incidence-controlled twin-delta foil forward. The angle of incidence is controlled mechanically by a curved planing control foil to achieve a constant flying height. The aft foil has anhedral to prevent tip breeching and ventilation and is set above the propeller. The foils are in cast aluminium while the struts

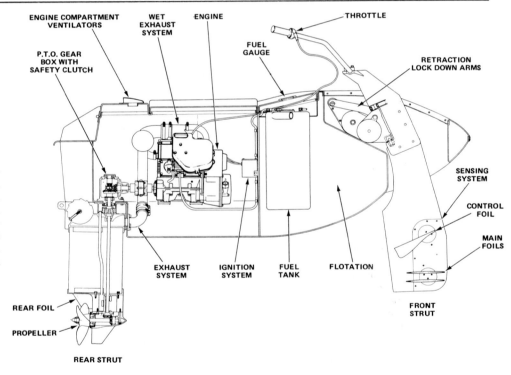

Inboard profile of the Dynafoil Mark I showing the power plant and transmission arrangements

are of fibreglass. Both foils retract fully, the bow foil rotating upwards and rearwards, the aft foil rearwards and upwards against the transom.

CONTROLS: Steering is accomplished by turning the front foil strut. All turns enter a fully co-ordinated bank.

HULL: Two-stage deep V hull, comprises two fibreglass mouldings bonded together at the beltline. After bonding, all voids not employed for functional components are filled with 2 lb density polyurethane foam providing 600 lb of buoyancy.

ACCOMMODATION: Open cockpit with a motor cycle pillion-style seat for two.

POWER PLANT: The Mark I is available with a choice of two engines—either a 340 cc, 30 hp, or a high performance 440 cc, 40 hp, 2-cylinder, 2-stroke Xenoah engine. Power is delivered to the outdrive through a 90° gearbox mounted inboard. The overall gear ratio is 1·75:1. Final drive is through a bevel gear at the base of the rear strut. The propeller is of 3-bladed subcavitating design in cast aluminium. A single 5 gallon (US) (18·92 l) fuel tank is located amidships, with a refuelling neck on the outside hull at the bow.

DIMENSIONS:

Length overall, hull	7 ft 0 in	(2·13 m)
Length overall,		
foils retracted	8 ft 0 in	(2·43 m)
foils extended	7 ft 0 in	(2·13 m)
Hull beam	3 ft 6 in	(1·06 m)
Beam overall,		
foils retracted	3 ft 6 in	(1·06 m)
foils extended	3 ft 6 in	(1·06 m)
Draft afloat,		
foils retracted	1 ft 0 in	(304 mm)
foils extended	3 in	(76 mm)
Draft foilborne	1 ft 6 in	(457 mm)
Freeboard	1 ft 2 in	(355 mm)
Height overall, foils retracted		
	3 ft 6 in	(1·06 m)

WEIGHTS:

Light displacement	350 lbs	(158·75 kg)
Normal take-off displacement		
	550 lbs	(272·14 kg)
Max take-off displacement		
	800 lbs	(362·85 kg)

PERFORMANCE:

Max speed foilborne	40 mph	(64·36 km/h)
Max speed hullborne	5 mph	(8·04 km/h)
Cruising speed,		
foilborne	30 mph	(48·28 km/h)
hullborne	5 mph	(8·04 km/h)
Designed endurance and range at cruising		
speed, approx	65 miles	(104·60 km)
Turning radius at cruising speed		
	15 ft	(4·57 m)
Fuel consumption at max speed		
	4 gph	(15·14 lph)
at cruising speed	2 gph	(7·57 lph)

SEA TEST: Craft has been tested in 3-4 foot chop and 8-10 foot swells.

Above and below: The Dynafoil Mark I two-seat sports hydrofoil. Note the twin delta configuration of the forward foil, the incidence of which is controlled by the curved planing foil located above

EDO CORPORATION, GOVERNMENT PRODUCTS DIVISION

HEAD OFFICE:
13-10 111th Street, College Point, New York 11356

EXECUTIVES:
L. M. Swanson, Director, Air MCM Applications

Edo Corporation has developed a foil-equipped catamaran MCM system which speeds the process of magnetic and acoustic mine clearance and reduces the hazards of mine sweeping operations. The system, the Edo Mark 105, is designed to be towed by the US Navy's RH-53D Sea Stallion and other heavy-lift helicopters of similar size and performance. The first unit formed to operate Mk 105 Airborne Minesweeping Gear was HM-12 helicopter mine countermeasures Squadron, which operated off North Vietnam to clear mines from the entrance to the port of Haiphong and undertook the aerial sweeping of the Suez Canal during the spring of 1974. The operation—code named Nimbus Star—was said to have been a complete success.

If required the equipment can be towed behind a BHC BH.7 amphibious hovercraft or other suitable ACV. Tests with this arrangement have been undertaken in the UK and USA.

Advantages claimed for the system include the following: lower acquisition and maintenance costs; fewer operating personnel required; low equipment vulnerability and bigger areas cleared within a given time.

Normally the helicopter/seasled combination is conveyed to the affected area aboard an amphibious assault craft. The helicopter

The Edo Mark 105, probably the most sophistitated of all mine countermeasures systems, has been under development for some years. It comprises
a helicopter and a towed hydrofoil sea sled, on which is mounted a turbogenerator that energises magnetic sweep cables, thus simulating the
magnetic field of a ship

lifts-off with the sled at the end of a line,
lowers it into the water, extends its foils,
and sets off to sweep the minefield.

The towline, which is 450 ft (137·16 m) long,
also serves as an electric cable for carrying
control signals to the sled, and as a fuel
transfer line in the case of extended operations.

A portable winch in the helicopter is used to
handle the craft, the sweep cables and the
towing cable during launching and retrieval.
The system can be operated from either ships
or shore bases equipped with crane facilities
and small boats for handling the sweep cables
which stream out behind the seasled.

MARK 105 AIRBORNE MINESWEEPING GEAR

The Mk 105 is a helicopter-towed, magnetic
minesweeping system mounted on a 27 ft 6 in
(8·38 m) long catamaran seasled. Foils are
fitted to permit high speed operation and
provide improved seakeeping performance.
Aboard the craft is a turbogenerator which
provides energy for the magnetic sweep
cables and powers a hydraulic pump for foil
retraction.

FOILS: Surface-piercing tandem configuration with two inverted V foils forward and
two aft, balancing the loading between them.
High-riding pitch control subfoils of similar
configuration are located ahead of the two
bow foils. Bow and stern foils are rotated
for retraction and extension by a self-contained hydraulic system.

HULL: Catamaran hull comprising two
tubular pontoons of light metal alloy construction, connected by an aerofoil section
platform on which is mounted a gas-turbine
powered electric generator set and the
retrieval rig structure to which handling lines
are attached. The two ends of the towing
bridle are attached to the inward faces of the
twin pontoon hulls forward of the platform.
Wheels are attached to the underside of the
pontoons to facilitate deck handling. Fuel
for the turbogenerator set is carried in two
centrally located tanks, one in each pontoon.

TOWING: The 450 ft (137·16 m) long towing
cable terminates in an electrical connector
and fuel fitting. As well as providing the
towing links between the platform and the
helicopter, all electrical commands and

supplementary fuel pass through the cable.
The cable consists of an electrical core
containing the individual conductors, around
which is a double layer of steel wire. Surrounding this is a hose, and fuel flows through
the annular space between the inner diameter
of the hose and the steel wire reinforcement.

SYSTEMS: A gas turbine generator set,
mounted within a nacelle on the platform
provides energy for the generation of the
magnetic field. The complete power pack
comprises a gas turbine driven AC generator,
a rectifier, a controller containing the water-
borne electronics and batteries to power the
electronics system.

MAGNETIC SWEEP CABLE: This is
attached to the after end of the sweep boom
located on the underside of the port pontoon.

It comprises an upper electrode attached to
the end of a trailing cable and a lower
electrode fitted to the boom fin. The potential between the electrodes, employing the
water as a conductor, produces a magnetic
field which simulates that of a ship.

CONTROL PROGRAMMER: Located in the
helicopter this is the only manned station
employed in the system. It contains the
airborne electronics and all the controls and
instrumentation necessary.

The console contains the fuel transfer
control panel, turbine indicators, hydrofoil
and sweep boom actuators and the generator
controls and indicators.

HYDRAULICS: Gas-turbine operated pump
for extending and retracting the foils and
sweep boom. Manual pump for emergency
operation.

DIMENSIONS:

Length overall	27 ft 6 in
Beam, catamaran structure only	11 ft 7 in
across foils	21 ft 0 in
Height, foils extended:	
to top of retrieval rig	17 ft 3 in
to top of nacelle	13 ft 6 in
foils retracted, to base of wheels	11 ft 6 in

WEIGHTS:

Empty weight	5,522 lb
Gross weight	6,432 lb

PERFORMANCE:

Towing speeds and sea state capability not available

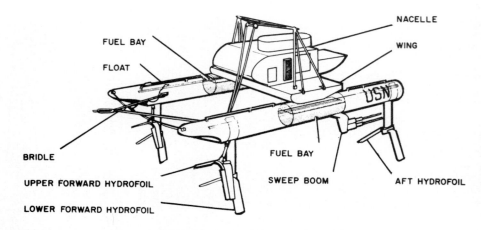

This drawing shows the surface-piercing tandem foil system of the Edo Mark 105 and the high-riding pitch- control-subfoils

GRUMMAN AEROSPACE CORPORATION

HEAD OFFICE:
Bethpage, New York 11714
TELEPHONE:
516-575-2417
CABLE/TELEX:
GRUMAIRBETHPAGENY- 961430
DIRECTORS:
J. G. Gavin, Jr, Chairman
G. M. Skurla, President
SENIOR EXECUTIVES:
I. G. Hedrick, Senior Vice-President
Advanced Systems Technology
T. Kane, Director Marketing

Grumman entered the hydrofoil field in 1956 when it acquired Dynamic Developments Inc, producer of the experimental XCH-4, built for the Office of Naval Research in 1955. Powered by two aircraft engines with air propellers, this eight-ton vessel established a world's speed record for hydrofoil craft, by exceeding 78 knots (145 km/h). In 1958 Grumman designed and built the XCH-6 Sea Wings, also for the Office of Naval Research. Sea Wings was the first hydrofoil to employ both supercavitating foils and a supercavitating propeller and attained speeds in excess of 60 knots.

In 1960, Grumman was awarded a contract by the Maritime Administration for the design and construction of the HS Denison, an 80-ton open ocean research vessel which was launched in June 1962. This craft (described in the 1967-68 edition) was operated at speeds above 60 knots, demonstrating good foilborne manoeuvrability and seakeeping ability in rough water.

Grumman also completed the guidance design for the 328-ton, 212 ft (64·6 m) AG (EH) Plainview for the US Navy. The foils for this craft were the forerunners of those used on the Dolphin and the more recent PGH-1 Flagstaff.

The primary purpose of the Plainview is to establish the possibility of operating large submerged foil craft in high sea states, and explore many possible mission assignments including ASW, hydrographic data collection, surveillance, search and rescue and escort duties.

In December 1972 it was equipped with a single missile container and launched three NATO-configured Sea Sparrow missiles during rough water trials off the coast of Washington. The craft is currently undergoing overhaul. From early 1975 onwards it will be employed as an analysis tool in

Grumman's PGH-I Flagstaff hydrofoil patrol gunboat equipped with a 40 mm rapid-firing cannon

Powered by a 3,550 hp Rolls-Royce Tyne gas turbine, the Flagstaff cruises at more than 40 knots

support of future large hydrofoil development for the US Navy.

Two Dolphin class hydrofoils were built for Grumman by Blohm & Voss, Hamburg but development of this class has now discontinued. The company is now concentrating on the development of military hydrofoils for use by the United States and foreign navies. Flagstaff is currently in service with the US Navy and between April and June 1971 was employed on 152 mm (6 in) gun-firing trials for the Navy Electronics Laboratory at San Diego, California.

A series of underwater explosion tests have been conducted with the Flagstaff in an experiment aimed at obtaining data on the shock responses of hydrofoil craft. The Flagstaff was the first and so far the only hydrofoil to undergo such tests.

In early 1974, the company announced plans for the production of an 83·5 ton derivative, the Flagstaff Mk II, were underway. Power is supplied by either a Rolls-Royce RM-2B or Allison 501K20 gas-turbine and the maximum foilborne speed is 50 knots.

In March 1975, a second developed version of the PG(H)-1 was announced—the Flagstaff Mark III. With an overall length of 83 ft (25·30 m), 10 ft (3·04 m) longer than the Mark II, this model is designed primarily for high endurance operations calling for long range and low payloads. In April this was followed by the announcement of another new design—the Dolphin III. An enlarged model of the Dolphin I (see JANE'S SURFACE SKIMMERS 1970-71 and earlier editions) it is intended as a high-speed utility and crew boat for servicing offshore oil rigs.

PG(H)-1 FLAGSTAFF

The 67·5 ton PG(H)-1 Flagstaff hydrofoil gunboat was launched on January 9th, 1968. It underwent preliminary trials in July 1968, and was delivered and placed in service at West Palm Beach in September 1968.

Since then the craft has operated from the US Naval Base, Coronado, California. For five-and-a-half-months it underwent operational trials in South Vietnam. Between 1st September 1969 and 19th February 1970, Flagstaff was employed on various missions in Phase II of "Opeval" and "Market Time", operating from Da Nang.

Between November and December 1970 the craft was modified to mount a 152 mm M551 gun from a Sheridan light tank on its foredeck. The gun fires conventional 6 in shells or Shillelagh missiles and has a laser range-finder giving instant accurate ranging. It is capable of hitting a target at a range of up to 4 miles (6·43 km).

The craft is currently in use by the US Navy to evaluate fleet equipment and for the study and development of fleet hydrofoil tactics.

FOILS: Fully submerged system of conventional configuration, split forward, and a single foil aft. About 70% of the weight is supported by the twin forward foils and 30% by the aft foil. Foil section is sub cavitating, 16-series. All three foils are incidence-controlled and operated by an Airesearch hydropilot. The stern foil strut rotates ±3° for steering and all three retract completely clear of the water. Foils (by Potvin Kellering) are forged 6061-T652 aluminium and struts (by Blohm & Voss) are in HYSO 4130 and HY80 steel. Foil area is 100 sq ft (9·29 m²).

HULL: The hull structure is of combined welded and riveted corrosion resistant 5456 aluminium. The pilot house roof is of fibreglass sandwich. All frames and bulkheads are welded assemblies and transverse framing is used throughout.

PROPULSION: The main engine is a 3,550 hp Rolls-Royce Tyne Mk 621/10 gas turbine, flat rated to 90°F. Power is transmitted through a mechanical right angle drive to a KaMeWa 45 in (1·14 m) diameter, 3-bladed supercavitating, controllable-pitch propeller. Nominal rpm at cruising speed 1,000. Hullborne power is supplied by two 202 hp GM 6V diesels driving twin Buehler 1 ft 4½ in (419 mm) diameter waterjets, equipped with ±35° steering and reversing nozzles.

SYSTEMS, ELECTRICAL: Ship's service generator sets: twin GM 4-53N diesels with Delco 120 volt, 50kW, 62·5 kVA, 3-phase Delta, 60-cycle at 1,800 rpm. Emergency

Flagstaff from the forward starboard quarter, showing the test installation of a 152 mm M551 howitzer gun turret

power (generators inoperable): 2 sets batteries 200 Ah, 24 volts, for autopilot, gyroscope and navigation lights, all automatically switched.
RADIO: VHF and HF transceivers.
RADAR AND NAVIGATION: Decca TM626 at navigator's station and repeater at commander's station. Bendix ADF-162A automatic direction finder, Raytheon 726 depth sounder, Arma Mk 26 gyrocompass, Chesapeake EM-log speed log, Bendix prototype DRAI and DRT navigation system.
FIREFIGHTING AND DAMAGE CONTROL: Diesel-driven 50 gpm bilge pump, plus 50 gpm diesel-driven deck service pump, portable electric 250 gpm pumps and hand pump. Deck SW connection for fighting fires in other craft. Walter Kidd. Central CF BR fire extinguishing system in two 251 lb cylinders. Four portable 2½ lb Ansul Foray Combo Pacs.
ARMAMENT. Main battery (until Nov 1970): single 40 mm Mk 3 Mod 0 rapid firing cannon. Machine guns: two twin mounts 50 cal Mk 56 Mod 0. Mortar: One 81 mm Mk 2 Mod 0. Small arms: M16 rifles (11), ·38 Cal pistols, 12 ga shotguns. New main gun battery as from December 1970: 152 mm M551 howitzer, firing conventional 6 in shells or Shillelagh

missiles. Laser range finder. Main gun battery has now been removed.
DIMENSIONS:
Length overall hull 73 ft 0 in (22·2 m)
Length overall, foils extended
86 ft 6 in (23·36 m)
Length overall, foils retracted
89 ft 0 in (27·1 m)
Hull beam 21 ft 5 in (6·5 m)
Extreme beam, foils retracted tip-to-tip
37 ft 1 in (11·28 m)
Draft, foils extended, static
13 ft 11 in (4·26 m)
Nominal draft foilborne 5 ft 8 in (1·72 m)
WEIGHTS:
Displacement, fully loaded, as delivered
67·5 long tons
1971, with 152 mm howitzer 72 long tons
PERFORMANCE:
Cruising speed, foilborne
In excess of 40 knots
Cruising speed, hullborne
In excess of 7 knots

FLAGSTAFF MK II

In March 1974, Grumman announced that plans were underway for a developed version of the PG(H)-1, known as the Flagstaff Mk II. Intended primarily for military applications,

The Flagstaff Mk.II can be equipped for a variety of military roles, including missile craft, ASW, search and rescue and fast transport. In the impression above, the craft is armed with Gabriel ship-to-ship missiles

the new model is designed as a high-speed
patrol gunboat or missile craft, but it can be
equipped for a number of alternative roles
including anti-submarine warfare, search and
rescue and fast military transport.

The chief differences between this craft and
its predecessor lie in the installation of a gas
turbine of greater power output—either a
3,800 hp Rolls Royce Tyne RM2B or a
3,950 hp Allison 501-K20A, the introduction
of an improved mechanical right-angle drive,
improved hydropilot system, and the provision of larger foils and longer struts.
The fully loaded displacement is increased
from 67·5 to 83·5 long tons. Max payload,
including fuel, is 65,457 lbs.

FOILS: Fully submerged system of conventional configuration, comprising twin
inverted T foils forward and a single inverted
T foil aft. Approximately 70% of the load is
supported by the two forward foils and 30%
by the aft foil. All three foils are incidence
controlled and operated by a hydro-pilot
system employing electrohydraulic actuators.
The stern foil power strut, together with the
propeller, rotates ±3° for steering and all
three foil/strut units retract completely clear
of the water for hullborne manoeuvring.
The foils are in 7075-T73 aluminium and the
struts are in HY-130 steel. Break joints are
incorporated on the two forward struts, so
that should either of them strike large items
of debris each would break clean at the point
of its connection to its yoke. A shear bolt
releases the aft strut permitting it to rotate
rearwards and upwards above the transom.

HULL: Hull is in welded 5086-H 111 and
H 117 marine aluminium. The deckhouse
and skin are in 1 ft 11⅛ in (587 mm) wide-
ribbed and integrally stiffened extrusions,
each 25 ft (7·62 m) long.

ACCOMMODATION: Crew will vary according to the nature of the missions for which
the craft is employed and the type of armament carried. Minimum crew requirement
is three, maximum is fourteen. The forward
superstructure accommodates the bridge,
which contains steering and engine control
consoles and is elevated to give a 360° view.
The helmsman and CO are seated on a raised
deck and the chief engineer and navigator are
accommodated on the main deck. All crew
accommodation is air conditioned. Entry
to the deckhouse is via two 2 ft 2 in × 5ft 0 in
(660 mm × 1·52 m) watertight doors, one
port, one starboard. An emergency exit is
located aft, behind the pilothouse on the
weather deck. Escape hatches are provided
in the living spaces.

POWER PLANT, FOILBORNE: Foilborne
propulsion is supplied by either a 4,489 hp
Rolls-Royce RM 2B Tyne or a 4,250 hp
Allison 501-K20A gas-turbine. Power is
transmitted to the propeller through a
Grumman Z-drive—a horizontal shaft leading
to a bevel gear over the stern in the aft foil
strut, then via a vertical shaft and a second
bevel gear to a horizontal propeller shaft.
Reduction is 13:1. A 3 ft 9 in (1·14 m)
diameter KaMeWa, 3-bladed controllable-
pitch, supercavitating propeller is fitted.
Fuel—total capacity is 5,179 US gallons—
is carried in four tanks located forward of
CG, in vicinity of main foils. Oil capacity
is 130 US gallons. Fuelling points are
located amidships, on deck aft of deckhouse.
Fuel recommended is JP5 or Diesel No. 2.

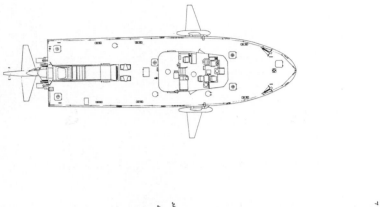

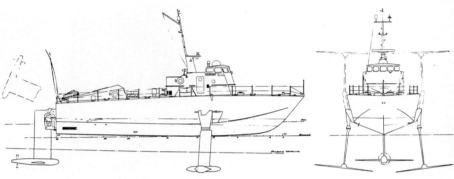

General arrangement of the Grumman Flagstaff Mk.II, 84-ton high-speed patrol gunboat or missile
craft

POWER PLANTS, HULLBORNE: Hullborne propulsion is supplied by two 220 hp
GM 6V-53N diesels, driving two Jacuzzi
14YJ marine waterjets, equipped with
steering and reversing nozzles.

SYSTEMS:

ELECTRICAL: Diesel generator set. Two
GM 4-53N diesel engines driving Delco
generators rated for 50 kw 440 volt 3-phase
service.

HYDRAULICS: 3,000 psi for foil control and
ship service systems.

ELECTRONICS: Decca Model TM 626 radar
with display at navigator's station and
repeater at CO's station.

COMMUNICATIONS: HF system AN/ARC-
94 Collins 618T-2B. VHF system: AN/
ARC-51A.

ARMAMENT:

MISSILES: Standard, Standard ARM, Harpoon, Sea Killer, Sea Sparrow, Exocet MM 38,
Gabriel or Penguin surface-to-surface missiles.

GUNS: Choice of the following systems for
surface engagement, shore bombardment,
AA defence or missile interception: 76/62
Oto Melara, 35 mm Twin Oerlikon, 30 mm
Twin Hispano Suiza, 20 mm Twin Emerson,
20 mm Vulcan, 40 mm Bofors, 30 mm
Emerson GE or 20 mm Phalanx.

ASW: Variety of ASW towed or dunked
sonars available for use in conjunction with
appropriate weapons.

DIMENSIONS, EXTERNAL:

Length overall, hull	73 ft 0 in (22·25 m)
Length waterline, hull	66 ft 8 in (20·34 m)
Length overall, foils retracted	

Length overall, foils extended	91 ft 0 in (27·74 m)
Hull beam	86 ft 10 in (26·45 m)
	21 ft 5 in (6·53 m)
Beam overall foils retracted	39 ft 3 in (11·963 m)
Beam overall, foils extended	40 ft 9 in (12·420 m)
Draft afloat, foils retracted	5 ft 1½ in (1·562 m)
Draft afloat, foils extended	16 ft 0 in (4·87 m)
Draft foilborne	7 ft 8 in (2·33 m)
Freeboard, maximum	7 ft 1¾ in (2·18 m)
Height overall to top of mast	38 ft 1½ in (11·62 m)

DIMENSIONS, INTERNAL:

Cabin length	14 ft 4 in (4·36 m)
Max width	12 ft 0 in (3·65 m)
Max height	9 ft 0 in (2·74 m)
Floor area	160 sq ft (14·86 sq m)
Volume	1,280 cu ft (36·24 cu m)

WEIGHTS:

Light displacement	52·28 long tons
Normal take-off displacement	83·5 long tons
Normal payload	29,957 lbs (9,505·916 kg)
Useful load, including fuel	65,457 lbs (29,690·78 kg)

PERFORMANCE:

Max speed, foilborne	52 knots
Most economical cruising speed	42 knots
Max speed, hullborne (gas-turbine power plant)	20 knots
Cruising speed, hullborne (diesel displacement engines)	9 knots

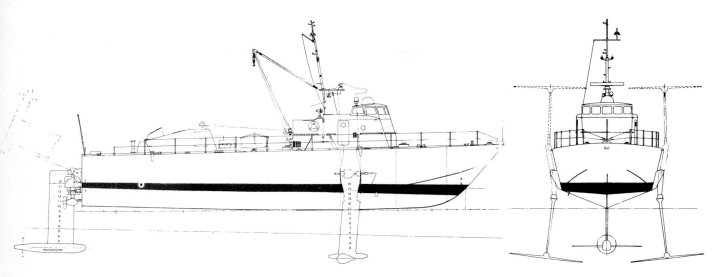

Outboard profile and bow-on view of the 83 ft (25·29 m) long Flagstaff Mark III, a 90-ton military
hydrofoil designed for high endurance operations including search and rescue

Max. permissible sea state in foilborne
mode   4-5
Designed endurance and range at cruising
                        approx 940 nautical miles
Number of seconds to take-off
                                 approx 25 sec
Number of seconds and distance to stop
    craft   3 to 4 seconds, 200 ft (60·96 m)
Fuel consumption at cruising speed
                  1,590 lb/hour (721 kgs/hour)
Fuel consumption at max. speed
                  1,900 lb/hour (860 kgs/hour)
DETAILS OF SEA TEST (based on PG(H)-1)
Location   West Palm Beach, Florida
Sea states   2,3, 4 and 5
Location of accelerometer, forward and
amidships
Heave 0·2± g in 8 ft (2·43 m) high waves
Average 0·05± rms g in 4 ft 6 in (1·37 m)
    high waves

FLAGSTAFF Mk. III

In March 1975 Grumman announced that
plans were underway for a second developed
version of the PG(H)-1—the Flagstaff
Mk.III. The new model is intended primarily for high endurance operations, calling
for long-range and low payloads. These
would include patrol, surveillance and search
and rescue duties.

The chief difference between this craft and
the Flagstaff Mk II are as follows:

An increase of 10 ft (3·04 m) in the overall
length, bringing it to 83 ft 0 in (25·30 m);

Fuel load raised from 15,890 lb (7,207
kg) to 51,390 lb (23,310 kg);

Replacement of the waterjets (for hullborne
propulsion) by propellers on retractable
outdrives;

Installation of more powerful diesel engines,
raising the hullborne speed to 11·5 knots;

Reduction in the useful load of 4,067 lb
to 61,390 lb, due to the longer hull structure.

Design range of the vessel at its most
economical cruising speed of 42 knots is
1,350 nautical miles.

FOILS: Fully submerged system of conventional configuration, comprising twin inverted
T foils forward and a single inverted T foil
aft. Approximately 70% of the load is
carried by the two forward foils and 30% by
the aft foil. All three foils have tapered
planform and the total foil area is 160·5 ft²
(14·91 m²). Foil loading is 1,223·6 lb sq ft
forward and 1,048 lb/sq ft aft. The incidence

angle of the forward foils is variable in
flight from +9° to —4°, while that of the
rear foil is variable from +10° to —2°.
Incidence angles of all three foils are controllable and operated by a hydropilot system
employing electrohydraulic actuators.

The foils are contour machined in 7075-
T73 solid aluminium forgings, and the struts
are of welded construction in HY-130 steel.
The stern foil power strut, together with the
propeller, rotates 3° to port and starboard
for steering, and all three foil/strut units are
retracted hydraulically completely clear of
the water for hullborne manoeuvring. The
forward foils retract sideways through an
angle of 177°, while the rear foil retracts aft
through an angle of 111°. Break joints are
incorporated on the two forward struts.
In the event of ½g impact or more, shear bolts
will separate strut and foil from yoke.
Struts and foils are designed to clear the hull
after separation to prevent hull damage.
A shear bolt releases the aft strut permitting
it to rotate rearwards and upwards above
the transom. The hydraulic retraction cylinders and transmission shaft disconnect
automatically on strut retraction.
HULL: The hull is in welded 5086-H111 and
H117 marine aluminium. The deckhouse
and skin are in 1 ft 11½ in (587 mm) wide
ribbed and integrally stiffened extrusions
each 25 ft (7·62 m) long.

ACCOMMODATION: Crew will vary according to the nature of the missions for
which the craft is employed and the type of
equipment and armament carried. Minimum crew requirement is three, maximum is
fourteen. The forward superstructure accommodates the bridge, which contains
steering and engineering control consoles
and is elevated to give a 360° view. The
helmsman and commanding officer are seated
on a raised deck and the chief engineer and
navigator are accommodated on the main
deck. All crew accommodation is air-
conditioned. Entry to the deckhouse is
via two 2 ft 2 in × 5 ft 0 in (0·660 m × 1·52 m)
watertight doors, one port, one starboard.
An emergency exit is located aft behind the
pilothouse on the weatherdeck. Escape
hatches are provided in the living spaces.
POWER PLANT, FOILBORNE: Motive
power for the foilborne propulsion system is
supplied by either a 4,480 hp Rolls-Royce

RM 2B Tyne or a 4,250 hp Allison 50LK20
A gas-turbine. Power is transmitted to the
propeller via a Grumman Z-drive with a
reduction ratio of 13:1. A 3 ft 9 in (1·14 m)
diameter KaMeWa controllable-pitch, supercavitating propeller is fitted. Fuel is carried
in six integral tanks located amidships,
with a total capacity of 8,770 US gallons.
Recommended fuel is JP-5 or Diesel 1 or 2.
Refuelling points are located amidships on
the weatherdeck, aft of the deckhouse.
Oil capacity is 130 US gallons.
POWER PLANT, HULLBORNE: Motive
power for the hullborne propulsion system is
provided by two Detroit 6-7LN diesels, each
developing 257 hp at 2,300 rpm. Power
is transmitted via two Model OD-8500 precision V-drive retractable outdrives to two
2 ft 2 in (0·660 m) diameter three-bladed
propellers.
SYSTEMS:
AIR-CONDITIONING: 5-ton packaged
water chiller.
ELECTRICAL: Diesel generator set. Two
GM 4-53N diesel engines driving Delco
generators rated for 50 kW, 440 volt, 62·5
KVA, 3-phase, 60Hz at 1,800 rpm.

HYDRAULICS: 3,000 psi pressure for foil
strut retraction, incidence control, foilborne
steering and miscellaneous hydraulic motors.
ELECTRONICS:
STANDARD: Decca radar Model TM626 with
display at navigator's station and repeater
at CO's station. OPTIONAL: Radio HF,
AN/ARC-94 Collins Model 618T2B. UHF
ANARC-51A.
DIMENSIONS:
Length overall, hull   83 ft 0 in (25·30 m)
Length waterline, hull
                          75 ft 0 in (22·80 m)
Length overall, foils retracted
                         101 ft 0 in (30·79 m)
Length overall, foils extended
                          96 ft 10 in (29·54 m)
Hull beam   21 ft 5 in (6·53 m)
Beam overall, foils retracted
                          39 ft 3 in (11·96 m)
Beam overall, foils extended
                          40 ft 9 in (12·41 m)
Draft afloat, foils retracted
                           4 ft 9 in (1·44 m)
Draft afloat, foils extended
                          16 ft 0 in (4·88 m)
Draft foilborne   3 ft 0 in (0·914 m)

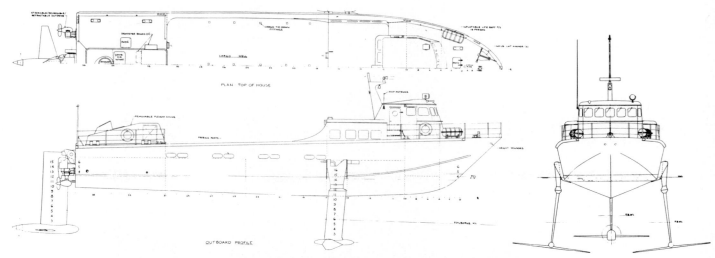

General arrangement of the Grumman Dolphin Mk.III, a 52-knot utility and crew boat for servicing off-shore oil rigs

Freeboard	8 ft 0 in (2·43 m)
Height overall, foilborne cruising	45 ft 0 in (13·71 m)
Height overall, hullborne	33 ft 10 in (10·32 m)

DIMENSIONS, INTERNAL:

Cabin length	14 ft 4 in (4·36 m)
Max. width	12 ft 0 in (3·65 m)
Max. height	9 ft 0 in (2·74 m)
Floor area	160 sq ft (14·86 sq. m)
Volume	1,280 cu ft (36·24 cu. m)

WEIGHTS (LONG TONS):

Light displacement	54·09 tons (54·97 t)
Normal take-off displacement	83·5 tons (84·84 t)
Max. take-off displacement	90·0 tons (91·47 t)
Normal deadweight	29·41 tons (29·87 t)
Maximum deadweight	35·91 tons (36·50 t)
Normal payload	4·46 tons (4·53 t)
Maximum payload	25·71 tons (26·13 t)

PERFORMANCE (with normal payload):

Max. speed, foilborne	52 knots
Cruising speed, foilborne	48 knots
Most economical speed foilborne	42 knots
Max. speed, hullborne	11·5 knots
Cruising speed, hullborne	8·0 knots

Max. sea state and wave height in foilborne mode

Sea State 4-5: wave height 16 ft (4·87m)

Designed range at cruising speed, approx
1,290 n.mi at 48 knots

at most economical speed
1,350 n.mi at 42 knots

Turning radius at cruising speed
750 ft (228 m)

Number of seconds and distance to take-off
30 sec, 1,150 ft (350 m)

Number of seconds and distance to stop
craft   3-4 seconds, 200 ft (60·9 m)

Fuel consumption at max. speed
52 knots = 2,200 lb/hr

Fuel consumption at cruising speed
48 knots = 1,910 lb/hr

Fuel consumption at most economical
foilborne speed 42 knots = 1,590 lb/hr

DETAILS OF SEA TEST (based on PG(H)-1):

Location: West Palm Beach, Florida

Sea State(s): 2, 3, 4 and 5

Location of accelerometers: forward and amidships

Heave: 0·2 ± RMS G in 8 ft (2·43 m)
high waves

0·05 ± RMS G in 4 ft 6 in (1·37 m)
high waves

DOLPHIN MARK III

In April 1975, plans were announced for a second developed version of the Dolphin I, known as the Dolphin III. The new craft, which has an 18 ft by 28 ft (5·47 × 8·51 m) cargo well aft of the deckhouse, is intended primarily as a high speed utility and crew boat for servicing offshore oil rigs.

Among the main differences between the Dolphin III and its predecessor are the following:

An increase of 24·5 tons in the full load displacement, raising it from 59 long tons to 83·5 tons;

An increase of 10 ft (3·04 m) in the overall length, bringing it to 83 ft (25·30 m);

Provision of improved transmission and hydropilot systems;

Installation of a more powerful gas-turbine for foilborne operation;

The rearrangement of the passenger cabin and deck to carry passengers and cargo.

Designed range of the vessel at its most economical cruising speed of 42 knots is 610 nautical miles.

FOILS: Fully submerged system of conventional configuration, comprising twin inverted T foils forward and a single inverted T foil aft. Approximately 70% of the load is carried by the two forward foils and 30% by the aft foil. All three foils have tapered planform and the total foil area is 160·5 ft² (14·91 m²). Foil loading is 1,223·6 lb/sq ft forward and 1,048·8 lb/sq ft aft. Incidence angle of the forward foils is variable in flight from +9° to —4°, while that of the rear foil is variable from +10° to —2°. Incidence angles of all three foils are controlled and operated by a hydropilot system employing electrohydraulic actuators. The foils are contour-machined in 7075-T73 solid aluminium forgings, and the struts are of welded construction in HY-130 steel. The stern foil power strut, together with the propeller, rotates 3° to port and starboard for steering, and all three foil/strut units are retracted hydraulically completely clear of the water for hullborne manoeuvring. The forward foils retract sideways through an angle of 177°, while the rear foil retracts aft through an angle of 111°. Break joints are incorporated on the two forward struts. In the event of ½g impact or more, shear bolts will separate strut and foil from yoke. Struts and foils are also designed to clear the hull after separation to prevent hull damage.

A shear bolt releases the aft strut permitting it to rotate rearwards and upwards above the transom. The hydraulic retraction cylinders and transmission shaft disconnect automatically upon strut retraction.

HULL: The hull is welded 5086-H111 and H117 marine aluminium. The deckhouse and skin are fabricated in 1 ft 11⅛ in (587 mm) wide ribbed and integrally-stiffened extrusions, each 25 ft (7·62 m) long.

ACCOMMODATION: Normal crew requirements are for a captain, engineer, oiler and deckhand. Seating is provided in the wheelhouse for the captain (starboard) engineer (port) and oiler (folding seat). The number of seated passengers accommodated in the cabin aft of the pilothouse can vary from 24 to 48 depending on customer requirements. Air-conditioning is provided in both crew and passenger accommodation. Entry to the pilothouse is via a 2 ft 2 in × 5 ft 0 in (0·660 m × 1·15 m) door. An emergency exit is provided in the passenger cabin, opening onto the cargo well aft. Emergency equipment includes two inflatable 15-person liferafts.

POWER PLANT, FOILBORNE: Motive power for the foilborne propulsion system is provided by either a 4,480 hp Rolls-Royce RM 2B Tyne, or a 4,250 hp Allison 501K20A gas-turbine. Power is transmitted to a 3 ft 9 in (1·14 m) diameter KaMeWa controllable-pitch, supercavitating propeller via a Grumman Z-drive with a reduction ratio of 13:1. Fuel is carried in four integral fuel tanks, with a total capacity of 5,179 US gallons, located in the vicinity of the main foils. Normal fuel load is 3,328 US gal—23,298 lb. Recommended fuel is JP-5 or Diesel 1 or 2. Refuelling points are located on the well deck, aft of the cabin. Oil capacity is 130 US gallons.

POWER PLANT, HULLBORNE: Motive power for the hullborne system is provided by two Detroit 6-71N diesels, each delivering 257 hp at 2,300 rpm. Power is transmitted via two Model OD-8500 precision V-drive retractable outdrives to two 2 ft 2 in diameter, three-bladed propellers.

SYSTEMS:

AIR-CONDITIONING: 5-ton packaged water chiller.

ELECTRICAL: Diesel generator set. Two GM 3-53N diesel engines driving Delco generators rated for 40 kW, 440 volt, 3-phase 60Hz at 1,800 rpm.

HYDRAULICS: 3,000 psi pressure for foil strut retraction, foil incidence control, foilborne steering and miscellaneous hydraulic motors.

ELECTRONICS:
Standard: Raytheon 4100 series or equivalent
Optional: HF radio, AN/ARC 94, Collins 618T2B; UHF radio, AN/ARC-51A

DIMENSIONS, EXTERNAL:
Length overall, hull   83 ft 0 in (25·30 m)
Length waterline, hull 75 ft 0 in (22·86 m)
Length overall, foils retracted
     101 ft 0 in (30·79 m)
Length overall, foil extended
     96 ft 10 in (29·54 m)
Hull beam   21 ft 5 in (6·53 m)
Beam overall, foils retracted
     39 ft 3 in (11·96 m)
Beam overall, foils extended
     40 ft 9 in (12·41 m)
Draft afloat, foils retracted
     4 ft 9 in (1·44 m)
Draft afloat, foils extended
     16 ft 0 in (4·88 m)
Draft foilborne   3 ft 0 in (0·914 m)
Freeboard   8 ft 0 in (2·43 m)
Height overall, foilborne cruising
     45 ft 0 in (13·71 m)
Height overall, hullborne
     33 ft 10½ in (10·32 m)

DIMENSIONS, INTERNAL:
Cabin length   15 ft 3 in (4·63 m)
Max. width   19 ft 6 in (5·90 m)
Max. height   7 ft 6 in (2·28 m)
Floor area   208 ft² (19·32 sq. m)
Volume   1,855 ft³ (51·94 cu. m)
Freight hold:
   Cargo well amidships
   18 ft 0 in × 28 ft 0 in (5·47 m × 8·51 m)

WEIGHTS: (long tons)
Light displacement   46·01 tons (46·77 t)
Normal take-off displacement
     83·50 tons (84·84 t)
Max. take-off displacement
     90·0 tons (91·47 t)
Normal deadweight   37·49 tons (38·07 t)
Max. deadweight   43·99 tons (44·70 t)
Normal payload   26·23 tons (26·66 t)
Max. payload   34·93 tons (35·50 t)

PERFORMANCE:
Max. speed, foilborne   52 knots
Max. speed hullborne   11·5 knot
Cruising speed, foilborne   48 knots
Most economical speed   42 knots
Cruising speed, hullborne   8·0 knots
Max. permissible sea state and wave height in foilborne mode
   Sea states 4-5, wave height 16 ft (4·87 m)
Designed range at cruising speed of 48 knots
     585 n. miles
Designed range at most economical cruising speed of 42 knots   610 n. miles
Turning radius at cruising speed
     750 ft (228 m)
Number of seconds and distance to take-off (theoretical, approx)
     30 seconds, 1,150 ft (350 m)
Number of seconds and distance to stop craft (theoretical, app)
     3-4 seconds, 200 ft (60·9 m)
Fuel consumption at max. speed
     52 knots — 2,200 lb/hr
Fuel consumption at cruising speed
     48 knots — 1,910 lb/hr
   at most economical speed
     42 knots — 1,590 lb/hr
Details of Sea Test (Based on Dolphin 1)

Locations: Kiel, Hamburg West Germany, to Las Palmas, Canary Islands
Sea States 2, 3, 4 and 5
Location of accelerometer: forward and amidships
   Heave 0·2 ± RMS G in 8 ft (2·43 m) high waves
   Heave 0·05 ± G in 4 ft 6 in (1·37 m) high waves

AG(EH)-1 PLAINVIEW

The 320 ton AG (EH)—the designation means auxiliary general experimental hydrofoil—was built by the Lockheed Shipbuilding & Construction Company, Seattle, Washington. It is being used by the US Navy's Hydrofoil Systems Testing Unit, Bremerton, Washington to investigate the performance of a large seagoing hydrofoil under operational conditions. The guidance design and preparations of contract specifications were undertaken by Grumman under the direction of the Bureau of Ships.

A contract for detailed design and construction was awarded to Lockheed Ship building and Construction Company in June 1963 and the hull was launched in June 1965. The craft successfully completed her maiden flight on March 21st, 1968 at Puget Sound and was officially delivered to the US Navy on March 1st 1969. It was given the US Navy classification "In Service, Special" in March 1969 and US Navy research and development trials are continuing.

FOILS: The foil system is fully submerged and automatically controlled by a Hamilton Standard autopilot system similar to that used in High Point. The foil arrangement is of conventional type with 90% of the weight carried on the two main foils and the remainder on the aft foil. The three foils, which have considerable sweep and taper, are geometrically similar with an aspect ratio of 3. The swept back leading edges help to delay cavitation and facilitate the shedding of seaweed and other neutrally buoyant debris. They also reduce impact loads associated with water entry after foil broaching. The main foils have some dihedral while the tail foil is flat.

Total foil area is 509 sq ft, and foil loading is 1,460 lb ft² max. Foils are constructed in welded HY80 steel.

The main foils are extended, retracted and locked in each terminal position by means of a hydraulically-operated activating arm, connected to the upper part of the strut. The two foils are synchronised to be raised and lowered together in the transverse plane.

AGEH-1 Plainview, 328-ton US Navy ocean-going hydrofoil warship research vessel, moored in Puget Sound with foils retracted. Two 4-bladed propellers at the end of the pods on the main foils struts propel the vessel when foilborne

Maximum foilborne speed of the Plainview, which is powered by two 14,500 hp GE LM1500s, is in excess of 50 knots. It is designed to operate in sea state 5 conditions and has undergone trials in 8-10 ft (2·43-3·04 m) waves off Victoria BC

The aft foil operates in a similar manner, but can be raised and lowered independently.

Foil lift variation is by change in the ncidence angle; each can move through +11 deg to —4 deg. The single aft foil controls pitch angle.

The aft foil strut rotates for use as a rudder. Steering can be flat (rudder only) or fully coordinated, using differential main foil angles for banked turns, with the aft strut trailing.

HULL: The hull is almost completely fabricated in 5456 aluminium alloy. All deck, side and bottom plating is made from integrally stiffened, aluminium extruded planks. The hull is predominantly welded construction with the exception of the pilot house and certain longitudinal hull seams that act as crack stoppers.

The hull shape is designed to minimise the structural loadings due to wave impact and the bow shape has been developed for this specific purpose. Bottom deadrise is carried to the transom with the same objective.

ACCOMMODATION: Crew of twenty-five, comprising four officers and twenty-one enlisted men. The pilothouse, CIC compartment, living, messing and berthing spaces are air-conditioned. Sanitary and washroom areas, galley, displacement and main engine room are all mechanically ventilated. In the wheelhouse, the pilot's position is on the left, with the principal instrumentation; the co-pilot is on the right, and the observer between and slightly aft. Entry to the deckhouse is via three standard US Navy quick-acting aluminium doors—one aft port and one forward starboard on the main deck, and one aft on the lower deck. Emergency equipment includes 7-man liferafts, seven life rings, four aircraft markers, one kapok heaving line and emergency scuttles port and starboard.

POWER PLANT: Foilborne propulsion is supplied by two General Electric LM 1500s (marine version of the J-97), each of 14,500 hp continuous rating, connected by shafting and gearing to two 4-bladed, 5 ft 0 in (1·52 m) diameter supercavitating titanium propellers at the end of the propulsion pods on the main foils. The hydrodynamic design of the propellers was undertaken by Hydronautics Inc and they were built by Hamilton Standard. The blades are bolted to the hubs and each blade is replaceable. The air inlet for the main turbines is introduced at the top of the deckhouse. Because of the need to prevent ingestion of water or saltspray into the gas turbines, there are lowered deflectors over the inlet opening, followed by a bank of sheet metal spray separators. There is a dam for solid water separation

In the interests of weight economy, the Plainview's hull is built largely from specially extruded aluminium planks, each 40 ft (12·19 m) in length and 2 ft 1 in (0·635 m) in width. Struts and foils are built in HY-80 and HY-100 steel alloys. The bow shape is designed to minimise structural loadings due to wave impact

and four right angle turns before the air reaches the engine bellmouths.

The hullborne powerplants are two General Motors V12-71 diesels each rated at 500 hp. Each diesel drives aft through a shaft to a right angle gear drive resembling a large outboard motor, mounted on the side of the hull. Each of these right angle drives is retractable about a horizontal axis and steerable about a vertical axis through 360 deg. rotation. A 4 ft 5 in (1·34 m) diameter five-bladed subcavitating propeller is mounted at the end of each right angle drive.

Auxiliary power is supplied by two GMC V8-71 engines driving two 100 kW generators.

SYSTEMS:

AIR CONDITIONING: The pilothouse, CIC compartment, living, messing and berthing spaces are air-conditioned during the cooling season by a 15 ton capacity Trane type compressor system. Sanitary and washroom areas, galley, displacement engine room, main engine room, windlass room and the engineers control booth are all mechanically ventilated.

HYDRAULICS: 3,000 psi operates foils, steering, extension, retraction and locking of struts and anchor windlass and starts propulsion diesels.

ELECTRONICS: Raytheon Pathfinder radar with AN/SPA-25 repeater, AN/WRC-1B Bendix radio, AN/URC-58 radio RF Comm Inc, two AN/ARC-52X Collins radios.

ARMAMENT: Six Mk 32 torpedo tubes in two tri-mounts, port and starboard, aft of the deckhouse. One Mk 44 torpedo stowed

in each tube. Single missile cannister fitted in late 1972 for demonstration launching of three NATO-configured Sea Sparrow missiles.

DIMENSIONS, EXTERNAL:

Length overall, hull	212 ft 0 in (64·61 m)
Length waterline, hull	205 ft 1¾ in (62·48 m)
Length overall, foils retracted	223 ft 8 in (68·17 m)
Length overall, foils extended	219 ft ½ in (66·75 m)
Hull beam	40 ft 5 in (12·31 m)
Beam overall, foils retracted	82 ft 8 in (25·19 m)
Beam overall, foils extended	70 ft 0 in (21·59 m)
Draft afloat, foils retracted	6 ft 3 in (1·90 m)
Freeboard, fwd	15 ft 6 in (4·72 m)
aft	7 ft 6½ in (2·29 m)
Height to top of mast	54 ft 9½ in (16·69 m)

WEIGHTS:

Light displacement	265 tons
Normal take-off	290 tons
Max take-off	328 tons

PERFORMANCE:

Max speed foilborne	in excess of 50 knots
Cruising speed foilborne	42 knots
Max speed hullborne	13·4 knots
Cruising speed hullborne	12 knots
Max permissible sea state and wave height in foilborne mode	
(Design sea state) Beaufort 5 Sea state 5	

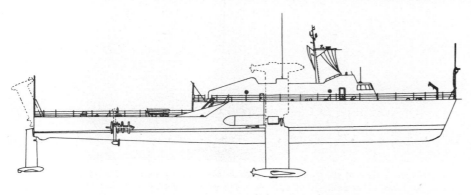
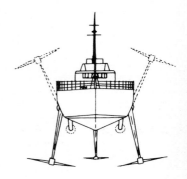

General arrangement of the AGEH-I Plainview

HYDROFOILS INCORPORATED

HEAD OFFICE:
   PO Box 115, Red Bank, N.J. 07701, USA
TELEPHONE:
   (201) 842-1260
OFFICERS:
   Kenneth E. Cook, President

Hydrofoils Incorporated has designed a fibreglass-hulled two-seater, the Mirage, for amateur powerboat racing. The company, in conjunction with the Amateur Power Boat Association, is examining the possibility of establishing a new racing class which could lead to the inception of a water counterpart to multi-turn Grand Prix road racing.

Performance of the Mirage is said to compare favourably with that of other high performance craft. At the time of going to press, production quantities, top speed and the retail price were in the process of being settled. Preliminary details are given below.

MIRAGE

This novel recreational craft is intended as a water-borne equivalent to a two-seater sports car. One major objective has been to produce a craft capable of tight, high-speed turns, thus permitting boats of this type to race on relatively small courses. The prototype is fitted with a 350 cu in Chevrolet automobile engine, but a wide range of alternative petrol engines can be fitted.

FOILS: Surface piercing canard configuration. About 65% of the load is borne by the inverted vee foil aft and the remainder on the small conventional vee foil at the bow. Circular stabiliser foils are attached to the inverted vee main foil at calm water line level to limit the degree of foil immersion, maintaining the hull at a negative angle of attack to prevent it somersaulting at high speed. Foils are of supercavitating design and fabricated in high strength aluminium. Small rudder surfaces are attached at right angles to main foil. Various sizes available. Rudder design is a compromise between maximum steering capability and optimum fin effect to limit yaw, roll and drift in high-speed turns. The aft foils hinge upwards for towing, reducing the overall beam to conform with state trailer laws.

HULL: Planing type hull. Moulded fibreglass structure with aluminium frames and marine ply stringers.

ACCOMMODATION: Open cockpit with twin upholstered bucket seats for driver and one passenger.

POWER PLANT: Single 350 cu in Chevrolet automobile engine installed aft of the cockpit. Output is transferred via a Casalle vee-drive to a Stellings chrome-plated high-performance 2-bladed propeller. Drive is air, water and oil-cooled and provides forward and neutral quick-change. Gear ratios available, 1·03:1/1·37:1. Total fuel capacity is 15 gallons.

CONTROLS: Craft heading is controlled by twin rudders operated from the cockpit by a steering wheel. There is also a foot-operated throttle and a gear shift lever. The boat is equipped with an automatic bilge pump.

SYSTEMS, ELECTRICAL: 12 volts d.c. starter, alternator and voltage regulator.

DIMENSIONS:

Length overall, hull	16 ft 6 in (5·02 m)
Beam overall	13 ft 0 in (3·96 m)
Beam overall, hull	8 ft 0 in (2·43 m)
Draft, hullborne	3 ft 0 in (0·91 m)
Draft, foilborne	1 ft 6 in (457 mm)

Top: The two-seat Mirage racing hydrofoil during tests
Centre: Hull of the Mirage is in moulded glassfibre with an aluminium frame
Bottom: Note the novel canard foil arrangement incorporating an inverted vee main foil with a conventional vee foil forward. Circular "plates" on the main foils are stabilisers which limit the degree of immersion of the main foil thereby maintaining the hull at a negative angle of attack, preventing the craft from somersaulting at high speed

WEIGHTS:
   Displacement   1,800 lb (816·42 kg)

PERFORMANCE:
   Details not available at time of going to press.

UNION OF SOVIET SOCIALIST REPUBLICS

KRASNOYE SOROMOVO SHIPYARD

HEAD OFFICE AND WORKS:
Gorki

OFFICERS:
M. Yuriev, Shipyard Director
Dr Rostilav Yergenievich Alexeyev, Head
of the Central Design Bureau for Hydro-
foil Vessels
Ivan Yerlykin, Chief Hydrofoil Designer

OVERSEAS REPRESENTATIVES:
Achille Onorato, Naples, Italy
United Kingdom, British Commonwealth
and Scandinavian countries:
Airavia Ltd,
20 North Road, Shanklin Isle of Wight,
See separate entry under United Kingdom

Krasnoye Soromovo is one of the oldest
established shipyards in the Soviet Union.
In addition to building displacement craft of
many kinds for the Soviet River Fleet, the
yard constructs the world's widest range of
passenger hydrofoils, many of which are
equipped with the Alexeyev shallow draft
submerged foil system. Dr Alexeyev started
work at the end of 1945 on the design of his
foil system which had to be suitable for
operation on smooth, but open and shallow
rivers and canals. He succeeded in making
use of the immersion depth effect, or surface
effect, for stabilising the foil immersion in
calm waters by the use of small lift coefficients.

The system comprises two main horizontal
lifting surfaces, one forward and one aft, with
little or no dihedral, each carrying approximately half the weight of the vessel. A
submerged foil loses lift gradually as it
approaches the surface from a submergence
of about one chord. This effect prevents the
submerged foils from rising completely to the
surface. Means therefore had to be provided
to assist take-off and prevent the vessel from
sinking back to the displacement condition.
The answer lay in the provision of planing
sub-foils of small aspect ratio in the vicinity
of the forward struts arranged so that when
they are touching the water surface the
main foils are submerged approximately to a
depth of one chord.

The approach embodies characteristics of
the Grunberg principle of inherent angle of
attack variation comprising a "wing" and
a stabiliser system. When the Alexeyev
foils drop below the shallow draught zone,
the craft converts momentarily to the
Grunberg mode of operation duplicating
ts configuration. The otherwise inactive
sub-foils, coming into contact with the water
surface become the Grunberg stabilisers,
causing the foils to climb up into the shallow
draught zone where they resume normal
operation in the Alexeyev mode.

The foils have good riding characteristics
on inland waters and in sheltered waters.

The system was first tested on a small
launch powered by a 77 bhp converted car
engine. Three more small craft were built
to prove the idea, then work began on the
Yard's first multi-seat passenger craft, the
Raketa, the first of which was launched in
June 1957.

The yard also co-operates with the Leningrad Water Transport Institute in the
development of seagoing craft with fully
submerged V-type and trapeze-type surface

Voskhod 2-01 during a test operation on the Gorky-Kineshma route. Features of this 34-knot Raketa replacement are a stern engine room, vee-drive, variable-pitch propeller and embarkation areas fore and aft. The craft can operate foilborne in waves up to 4 ft 7 in (1·4 m) high

piercing foils, similar in configuration to those
of the Schertel-Sachsenburg system. Craft
employing V or trapeze are generally described as being of the Strela-type, Strela being the
first operational Soviet design to use V foils.
Seating 92-passengers, the vessel is powered
by two M-50 diesels and, visually speaking,
is a cross between the PT 20 and the PT 50,
though smaller than the latter. A military
derivative, the Pchela (Bee) is currently
employed by the Soviet frontier police for
coastal patrol in the Baltic, Black Sea,
Caspian and other sea areas.

The first hydrofoil vessels to enter service
with the Soviet Navy were the 75-ton P8-
class, wooden-hulled torpedo boats which
were equipped with bow foils and gas-turbine
boost. These now appear to have been
retired.

Included in this entry are two of the first
photographs to be published of the new
hydrofoil fast patrol boat, based on the Osa

missile-firing FPB hull and given the NATO
code name Turya. Like the earlier P8-
class and the highly successful Chinese Hu
Chwan-class, the new craft has a bow foil
only. Powered by three 4,330 hp diesels
it has a top speed of about 45 knots under
calm conditions. Further military hydrofoil designs are under development.

Amongst new Soviet passenger hydrofoils
being developed are the gas-turbine powered,
89-105 seat Typhoon passenger ferry, the
first Soviet vessel designed for production to
have a fully submerged foil system; the
Voskhod, a 71-seat Raketa replacement, the
250-seat, 45-50 knot, Cyclone and the
350 passenger, 400-ton Luch (Ray). In
June 1973, it was announced that a new
seagoing hydrofoil mixed-traffic ferry had
been designed at Gorky. The craft will carry
200 passengers and 40 vehicles at a speed of
43 mph (70 km/h). The Typhoon, which was
built in Leningrad has been undergoing

operational trials carrying fare-paying passengers between Leningrad and Talinna, a journey time of 4½ hours. Further development of the seagoing Kometa-M is underway, including the fitting of air stabilisation on the stern foil and struts, increased passenger accommodation and the re-location of the engine room aft to reduce noise in the passenger saloon.

Substantial numbers of Soviet hydrofoils—Kometas, Raketas and Volgas—are being exported. Countries in which they are being operated include Yugoslavia, Italy, Iran, France, East Germany, Morocco, Spain, Western Germany, Poland, Romania, the United Kingdom and the Philippines.

Voskhod-2

Designers of the Voskhod, which is destined to replace craft of the 17-year-old Raketa series, have drawn on engineering experience gained with the Raketa, and also the more sophisticated Meteor and Kometa.

Among the basic requirements were that the Raketa's general characteristics should be preserved; foilborne operation should be possible in 1 m (3 ft 3 in) high waves, with a 3% safety factor; accommodation should be acceptable from health and safety viewpoints; noise levels should be significantly reduced, and that the maximum use should be made of standard mechanical, electrical and other components and fittings proven on the Raketa.

In fact, the end product bears little resemblance to its predecessor. In the visual sense, the Voskhod is more akin to a scaled-down Kometa with its engine room aft, replacing the rear passenger saloon.

Among the many design improvements to attract operators in the Soviet bloc countries and elsewhere are the following:

1. Employment of a vee-drive transmission, giving greater mean calm water clearance height aft, thereby reducing hydrodynamic drag under certain load conditions.

2. Provision of alternative embarkation points to facilitate passenger handling; Bow embarkation platforms are incorporated for loading from low level pontoons, and a stern embarkation area, above the engine room, for loading from high landing stages.

3. Raising the number of seated passengers from 64 to 71 for more profitable operation on medium distance services.

4. Generous additional soundproofing, including cowlings on the engine and reduction gear, and the provision of sound absorbing material in the engine room on the deckhead, sides and forward bulkhead.

5. Provision for the future replacement of the M 401A diesel by a 2,000 shp M 415 diesel.

6. Fitting of a variable-pitch, six-bladed propeller for improved handling and operating characteristics.

In June 1974, Voskhod 2-01 was put into service on the route Gorky-Kineshma, across the vast Gorky reservoir which cannot be navigated by the Raketa because of its limited seaworthiness. It continued in service until the end of the 1974 navigation season. During this time it was demonstrated that its operating and technical performance was significantly superior to that of the Raketa.

Experience accumulated during this experimental service indicated the need for a number of minor modifications which will be incorporated in the first series of production craft.

At the time of its inception, it was announced that the Voskhod would be available in a number of versions to suit a variety of local navigation and traffic requirements. Voskhod-3 will be powered by a gas-turbine.

The vessel is designed for high-speed passenger ferry services during daylight hours on rivers, reservoirs, lakes and sheltered waters. It meets the requirements of Soviet River Register Class 'O' with thr following wave restrictions (3% safety margin): foilborne, 4 ft 7 in (1·4 m); hullborne, 6 ft 7 in (2 m).

The passenger saloons are heated and provided with natural and induced ventilation. Full air-conditioning can be installed in craft required for service in tropical conditions. The crew comprises a captain, engineer, deckhand and barman.

FOILS: Fixed foil system, comprising one bow foil, one aft foil, plus an amidship foil to facilitate take-off. Bow and amidship foils appear to be of shallow vee configuration

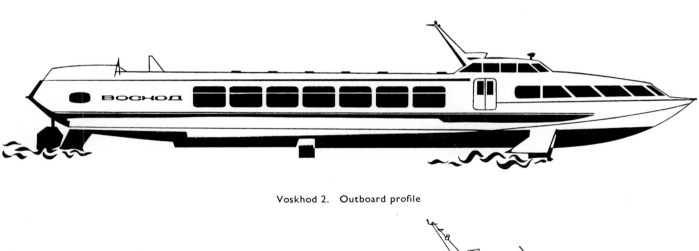

Voskhod 2. Outboard profile

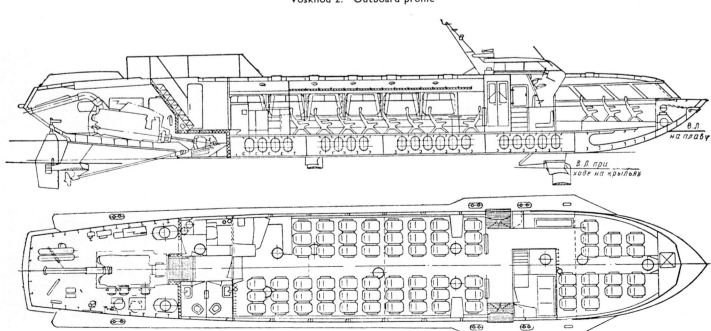

Voskhod 2. Inboard profile and deck plan

and each has four vertical struts. The fully submerged stern foil has two side struts and is supported in the centre by the end bracket of the propeller shaft. The surface and lower parts of the foil struts and stabiliser are in Cr18Ni9Ti stainless steel, while the upper parts of the struts and stabiliser and also the amidship foil are in AMg-61 plate alloy.

HULL: Similar in shape to that of the Kometa and earlier models of the Sormovo hydrofoils series, with a wedge-shaped bow, raked stem and spoon-shaped stern. A single step is provided to facilitate take-off. In fabricating the basic structure, which is largely in AMg-61 aluminium magnesium alloy, extensive use has been made of arc and spot welding. The hull is framed on longitudinal and transverse formers. Below the deck it is divided into eight watertight compartments by transverse bulkheads. It will remain afloat with any one compartment, or the machinery space flooded. Access to the forepeak, which houses the anchor capstan, is via the forward passenger saloon, and then through a rectangular hatch on the forecastle. Aft of the main passenger saloon is an area split into three compartments by two longitudinal bulkheads. The lower central space contains the reduction gear and vee-drive, the starboard compartment contains the sanitary tank and the port compartment forms part of the double-bottom. Entrance to the engine compartment is via a door on the port side of the main deck. An emergency exit is provided on the starboard aft.

POWER PLANT: Power is supplied by a single M-401A water-cooled, supercharged 12-cylinder V-type diesel, delivering a normal service output of 830 hp at 1,450 rpm and a maximum output of 930 hp at 1,550 rpm. The engine is sited aft, with its shaft inclined at 9°. Output is transferred via a flexible coupling to a single, 6-bladed variable-pitch propeller via an R-21 vee-drive gearbox.

CONTROLS: Single semi-balanced rudder in AMg plate provides directional control. Operation of the engine, rudder, reverse gear and fuel supply is effected hydraulically from the wheelhouse.

ACCOMMODATION: Voskhod 2 carries a four-man operating crew, comprising captain, engineer, motorman and barman. Embarkation platforms sited immediately below the wheelhouse provide access for both passengers and crew.

The captain and engineer are accommodated in a raised wheelhouse located between the forward and main saloon. Main engine controls are located in both the wheelhouse and the engine room.

Passengers are accommodated in two saloons, a forward compartment seating 17 and a main saloon seating 54. The main saloon has three exits, two forward, leading to the embarkation platforms and one aft leading to the stern embarkation area. Between the two saloons, on the starboard side, is a crew rest cabin. The saloons are fitted with upholstered seats, racks for small handluggage and pegs for coats. Spacing between seats is 900 mm and the central aisle is 800 mm wide.

At the rear of the main saloon is a small buffet and bar, and aft of the main saloon, at the foot of the rear embarkation steps are two WC/washbasin units.

SYSTEMS; ELECTRICAL: Power supply is 24-27 volts dc. A 3kW generator is attached to the engine and supplies 27·5 volts while the craft is operating. Four 12 volt storage batteries, each of 180 amp/hr capacity and connected in series-parallel to form a single bank, supply power during short stops. An auxiliary circuit can be connected to shore systems for 220 volt, single-phase, 50 c/s AC supply.

FIREFIGHTING: Four carbon dioxide and four foam fire extinguishers for the passenger saloons and wheelhouse. Remote-controlled system employing "3·5" compound in the engine room.

HEATING AND VENTILATION: Heating in the saloons is provided by pipes circulating water from the internal cooling circuit of the engine. Ventilation is both natural, using the dynamic pressure of the approaching air flow, and induced, by means of electric fans.

During the spring and autumn, the temperature of the ventilating air can be heated up to a temperature of 21°C.

DRINKING WATER: Hot and cold water supplies. An electric boiler supplies hot water for washbasins and the small kitchen behind the snackbar. Drinking water tank has capacity of 138 l.

BILGE WATER: System designed for bilge water removal by shore-based facilities or service vessels.

ANCHOR: Matrosov system, weighing 77 lb (35 kg), attached to an anchor cable ⅓ in (8·4 mm) in diameter and 262 ft (80 m) long, and operated by hand winch in the forepeak.

DIMENSIONS:

Length overall	86 ft 7½ in (26·4 m)
Hull length	86 ft 3½ in (26·3 m)
Beam overall	18 ft 0½ in (5·5 m)
Hull height (excl. wheelhouse)	10 ft 6 in (3·2 m)
Draft hullborne	6 ft 6¾ in (2 m)
Draft foilborne	3 ft 7¼ in (1·1 m)

DIMENSIONS, INTERNAL:

Deck area	1,130 sq ft (105 m²)
Deck area per passenger	15·35 sq ft (1·48 m²)

WEIGHTS:

Displacement, fully loaded	27·5 tonnes
Passengers per displacement tonne	2·55

Payload, passengers and buffet/bar equipment	5·9 tonnes
Payload/displacement ratio	21·2%

PERFORMANCE:

Max. speed, calm water, wind not in excess of force 3
at 1,550 rpm (930 hp)
39·76 mph (64 km/h)
at 1,450 rpm (830 hp)
37·28 mph (60 km/h)

Turning circle diameter	
hullborne	348 ft (106 m)
foilborne	1,246 ft (380 m)
Range, based on normal fuel supply of 1,400 kg	310·68 miles (500 km)
Max. wave height, with 3% safety margin	
hullborne	6 ft 7 in (2 m)
foilborne	4 ft 7 in (1·4 m)

TURYA

Latest hydrofoil to enter service with the Soviet Navy is a diesel-powered torpedo-boat with a displacement of about 165 tons. The vessel, which is based on the well-proven Osa missile-firing FPB hull, is equipped with a fixed, surface-piercing vee or trapeze foil set back approximately one-third of the hull length from the bow. At 20-23 knots in relatively calm conditions, the foil system generates sufficient lift to raise the greater part of the hull clear of the water, providing a "sprint" speed of 40-45 knots.

In addition to improving the maximum speed, the foils reduce the vessel's wave impact response, thus enhancing its performance as a weapon platform.

The installation of a pocket-size, variable-depth sonar on the transom suggests that the primary duty of Turya is anti-submarine patrol. The main armament appears to comprise four 21 in single AS torpedo tubes similar to those mounted on the Shershen class, a forward 25 mm twin mount and a twin 57 mm AA mount aft.

A substantial production programme is under way, involving more than one yard in the West and one in the Soviet Far East.

FOILS: Single main foil of trapeze or vee configuration set back one-third of hull length from bow. Raises greater part of hull bottom clear of the water in calm conditions at speed of 20 knots depending on sea conditions and loading. Similar systems

Turya hydrofoil patrol craft

employed earlier on Soviet P.8 class, now retired, and on the highly successful Chinese Hu Chwan class.

HULL: Standard Osa hull, welded steel construction.

POWER PLANT: Believed to be three high-performance diesels, each developing 4,300 hp and driving variable-pitch propellers through inclined shafts.

SYSTEMS, RADAR: Pot Drum and Drum Tilt.

DIMENSIONS:

Length	123 ft 1 in (37·5 m)
Beam	27 ft 10⅝ in (8·5 m)
Draft	5 ft 10⅞ in (1·8 m)

WEIGHTS:

Max. loaded displacement	190 tons
Normal displacement	165 tons

PERFORMANCE:

Max. speed foilborne	40-45 knots

TYPHOON

The Typhoon, a gas-turbine powered fast ferry for 98-105 passengers, is the first production craft with automatically controlled fully-submerged foils to be built in the Soviet Union.

The prototype, constructed in Leningrad, was launched after preliminary fitting out on December 12th, 1969. It is designed to operate at a service speed of 40-42 knots under calm conditions and 38 knots in sea state 4. The craft is at present undergoing trials. Phase 1 of the test programme covered the foil system, the gas-turbine power plant, hull design and mechanical and other systems and during Phase 2, which was undertaken during 1972 and 1973, the vessel was put into passenger service to permit technical assessments to be made under commercial operating conditions.

It is stated that in waves of up to 2 m (6 ft 6 in) high, not more than 10% of the 40-42 knot service speed is lost. Under these conditions, the Typhoon can complete the journey from Leningrad to Tallina, the Estonian capital, in 4½ hours.

Ten new inventions have found application in the design and the prototype has been awarded a certificate by the State Inventions and Discoveries Committee.

FOILS: Fully submerged system of conventional configuration with 77% of the weight borne by the bow foil and 23% by the stern foil. The bow foil is supported by four vertical struts which are tapered from top to bottom. The two outboard struts are supported by auxiliary fins which provide additional stability during the transition from displacement to foilborne mode. Twin rudders are fitted at the trailing edges of the aft foil struts. The foils are built in OCr17Ni7Al high strength stainless steel. A sonic/electronic autopilot system controls four flaps on the bow foil and two on the stern foil. The total weight of the autopilot system, including all electronic components, assemblies, drive mechanisms and cables is less than 1,320 lb (600 kg). The system stabilises the craft from take-off to touchdown in heave and all three axes—pitch, roll and yaw. It is programmed to govern the angle of trim, the c of g position in relation to speed and see that the craft makes coordinated banked turns according to speed and sea state.

Turya hydrofoil patrol craft

Overriding manual control can be introduced if necessary.

Two independent electro hydraulic-drive systems are installed to actuate the flaps. Each has two pumps, one connected to the reduction gear of the main engine, the other to its turbo-compressor. Fluid reaches the actuating mechanisms under a pressure of 150 kg/cm². Should one of the mains leading to the actuating mechanisms become unserviceable the second is connected. The failure of one bow or one stern flap in conditions up to sea state 4 does not reduce the stability of the vessel.

HULL: Similar in shape to that of the Kometa and earlier models in the Sormovo hydrofoil series, with a wedge-shaped bow, raked stem and spoon-shaped stern. There are two steps beneath the hull to facilitate take-off. The hull is of riveted construction and built in high strength aluminium magnesium alloy V-48TL. Longitudinal and transverse framing is employed with a spacing of 19·68 in (500 mm) in the hull and 39·37 in (1,000 mm) in the superstructure. By locating the wheelhouse aft of amidships, it has been possible to reduce the length of the control system cables while preserving good all-round vision.

Beneath the passenger saloon superstructure the hull is divided by transverse bulkheads into nine watertight compartments in which are accommodated the fuel tanks, diesel generators, gas turbines and diesel for hullborne propulsion. A watertight door is installed in the bulkhead separating the diesel generator and gas-turbine compartment. The craft is designed to remain afloat should any two adjacent compartments become flooded.

POWER PLANT: Foilborne power is supplied by two 1,750 hp Ivchenko AI-23C-1 marine gas-turbines, each driving a single 2·23 ft (0·68 m) diameter three-bladed propeller at 2,200 rpm cruising. The gas-turbines are started by starter generators from batteries and exhaust gases are expelled through an extension aft of the transom to prevent the craft from becoming covered with smoke or fumes.

Power from the main engines is transmitted to each propeller via a K-1700 Z-drive column, which is bolted to the transom. The drive shaft of each turbine is connected to the shaft of the upper reduction gear of the Z-drive. Power is transmitted via two sets of bevel gears and two vertical shafts to a nacelle which is divided into three compartments. The central compartment contains the lower reduction gear which transmits power from the two vertical shafts to the propeller shaft.

The stern foil is welded to the casing of the nacelle's bow compartment which contains the stern foil flap actuating mechanism.

Hullborne propulsion is supplied by a 165 hp 6ChSP13/14 low-speed diesel driving two four-bladed propellers through KP-150 right-angle drives, which rotate for steering and retract upwards when the craft is foilborne. The columns are steered either from the central control console in the wheelhouse or from a portable control panel which can be operated from any part of the vessel.

ACCOMMODATION: The vessel carries an operating crew of four—captain, engineer, radio operator/electrician and a seaman. Passengers are accommodated in an air-conditioned saloon equipped with 98-105 airliner-type seats. Glass doors lead from the saloon into the vestibule and onto the promenade deck. From the vestibule there is an entrance to the baggage compartment, wheelhouse and WC/wash basin units. The panels along the sides of the saloon are covered in non-inflammable laminated plastic and above with Pavinol imitation leather glued onto plywood. The deckhead is covered with Pavinol on a wooden frame. A special vibration-absorbing covering has been applied to the bulkhead facing the turbine compartment. The vessel carries a total of 4 crew members.

Rafts type PSN-10 are stored in containers along the sides of the vessel. These can be launched onto the water either by manual

The Typhoon, first gas-turbine powered passenger craft with fully-submerged foils to be built in the Soviet Union. Designed to operate at 36-45 knots, it seats 98-105 passengers. *Top Left:* The basic similarity of the Typhoon's spoon shaped hull to that of the Kometa-M and other Sormovo designs is apparent. *Top Right:* Typhoon during take off. Glass doors lead from the saloon into the vesitbule and onto the promenade deck visible in this photo. *Bottom Left:* View aft from the air-conditioned passenger saloon which can be equipped with 98-105 airliner-type seats. From the vestibule at the far end there are entrances to the baggage compartment, wheelhouse and W/C washbasin units. *Bottom Right:* Captain B. V. Gromov, centre, at the helm, who has been responsible for handling the Typhoon during her trials programme with his engineer, G. V. Shikhurin.

or automatic control from the wheelhouse. Lifebelts and lifejackets are carried aboard the vessel.

SYSTEMS: Electrical: Two 22 kW generators and eight batteries type 6STK-180. Main electrical equipment operates on 400H2. AC current. Shore supply is effected through a transformer.

NAVIGATION. Gyro course indicator, magnetic compass, hydraulic log and anti-collision radar.

COMMUNICATION: Ship-ship, ship-shore transceiver operating on R/T and W/T, also emergency radio.

DIMENSIONS:

Length overall	103 ft 2¼ in (31·4 m)
Width across foils	32 ft 9¾ in (10·0 m)
Hull beam	18 ft 4½ in (5·6 m)
Hull draught, displacement mode	4 ft 3¼ in (1·3 m)
Draft, hullborne, including foils	13 ft 5⅜ in (4·1 m)
Mean draft foilborne	3 ft 7 in-4 ft 3 in (1·1-1·3 m)
Distance of bow foil below hull base line	9 ft 2 in (2·8 m)

WEIGHTS:

Normal loaded displacement	65 tons

PERFORMANCE:

Max speed	45 knots
Service speed	40-42 knots
Hullborne speed	5 knots
Max permissible sea state	

Designed to maintain a cruising speed of 38 knots in sea state 4

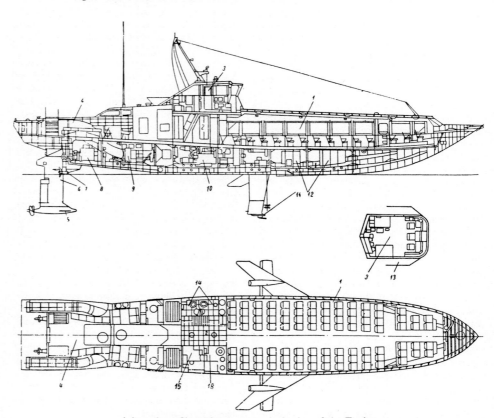

Inboard profile and passenger deck plan of the Typhoon:
1, passenger saloon; 2, vestibule; 3, wheelhouse; 4, promenade deck; 5, stern foil; 6, Z-drive foilborne transmission; 7, Z-drive hullborne transmission; 8, 165 hp diesel, 9, A1-23C-1; gas-turbines 10, diesel generators; 11, bow foil; 12, fuel tanks; 13, bridge; 14, lavatories; 15, bar; 16, baggage compartment

SEA TESTS

In sea state 4, vertical acceleration measured in the bows was reported to be at all times less than 0·5g in January 1975. At the same time it was stated that angles of pitch and roll are around 0·75 degrees. In sea state 4, one bow flap and one stern flap out of action have not adversely affected stability.

BUREVESTNIK

First Soviet gas-turbine hydrofoil to be designed for series production, the Burevestnik has two 2,700 hp marinised aircraft gas turbines driving two two-stage waterjets The prototype was launched in April 1964 and it was intended to build two models; one for medium-range, non-stop inter-city services, seats 130 passengers, the other, for suburban services, seats 150.

There is a four-man crew, comprising captain, engineer, motorman and a seaman.

After extensive trials and modifications, the prototype Burevestnik began operating on the Gorky-Kuibyshev route (about 435 miles (700 km) on April 26, 1968. At the time of going to press with this edition, it was understood that the vessel is still under development and has not yet entered production.

FOILS: There are two main foils and a midship stabiliser foil, all built in titanium alloy. Each is square-tipped and slightly wedge-shaped in planform. The foils are secured to the hull by struts and brackets. Each foil strut is welded to the upper surface of the foils, then bolted to the brackets. Upper and lower ends of the struts are connected by flanges. As with other craft employing the Alexeyev system, the foil incidence can be adjusted when necessary by the insertion of wedges between the flanges and the foils when the craft is in dock.

HULL: Hull and superstructure are built in aluminium-magnesium alloy. The hull is of all-welded construction and framed on longditudinal and transverse formers.

ACCOMMODATION: The prototype has two air-conditioned saloons with airliner-style seating for a total of 150 passengers. The well glazed forward saloon seats 38, and the aft saloon 112. The saloons are decorated with pastel shade panels and sound-proofed with glass fibre insulation. The engine room is at the stern and separated from the saloon by a sound-proof double bulkhead.

POWER PLANT: Motive power is supplied by two 2,700 shp Ivchenko marinised gas turbines, adapted from those of the IL-18 airliner. These operate on either kerosene or light diesel fuel and have a consumption of 300 gallons per hour. Sufficient fuel can be carried to operate non-stop over a range of 270 nautical miles (500 Km). The shaft of each of the two double suction centrifugal pumps for the waterjets is connected with the shaft of one of the turbines by means of a flexible coupling, via a reduction gear.

Auxiliary power is supplied by two 100 hp turbo-generators, used for starting the main engines and generating the electrical supply when the craft is operating.

CONTROLS: Four rudders adjacent to the waterjet streams provide directional control. Reversing is achieved by applying deflectors to reverse the waterflow. The waterjets themselves are fixed and cannot be rotated.

Burevestnik prototype during trials on the Volga

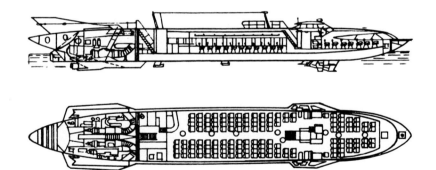

Inboard profile and deck view of the waterjet-propelled Burevestnik, powered by two 2,700 hp Ivchenko AI-20 gas turbines

Operation of the turbines, waterjets, rudders and deflectors is all effected from the wheelhouse by electro-hydraulic control.

SYSTEMS ELECTRICAL: Two 12 kw 28.5 volt generators mounted on each of the main engines supply power when the craft is operating. Two 14 kw 28.5 volt generators driven by the auxiliary turbines supply power when the craft is at rest or when the 12 kw generators are inoperative. Eight acid storage batteries are connected in series to give 24 volts supply power during short stops.

HYDRAULICS: 170 kg/cm² pressure hydraulic system for operating rudders, hydro-reversal unit and anchor.

COMMUNICATIONS: A radio transmitter/receiver with r/t and w/t facilities is installed in the wheelhouse for ship-shore and inter-ship communications on SW and MW bands. A public announcement system is fitted in the passenger saloons and a two-way crew communications system is installed in the wheelhouse, engine room, anchor, gear compartment and mooring stations.

DIMENSIONS:

Overall length	142 ft 0 in (43·3 m)
Hull beam	19 ft 8¼ in (6·0 m)
Width across foils	24 ft 3¼ in (7·4 m)
Draft afloat	6 ft 7 in (2·0 m)
Draft foilborne	1 ft 4 in (0·4 m)

WEIGHTS:

Light displacement	41 tons
Full load displacement (max)	67 tons

PERFORMANCE:

Max fuel load	11·5 tons
Cruising speed	50 knots (93 km/h)
Range	310 miles (500 km)
Max wave height at reduced speed	
	3 ft 3 in-4 ft (1 to 1·2 m)
Max wave height at full speed	2ft (0·6 m)
Speed astern	4-6 mph (6·9 km/h)
Stop to full speed and distance	
	95-100 seconds, 1,203 yds (1,100 m)
Stopping time from full speed and distance	
	25 seconds, 394 yds (360 m)

BYELORUS

This craft was developed from the Raketa via the Chaika for fast passenger services on winding rivers less than 3 ft (1 m) deep and too shallow for vessels of the standard type.

In 1965 it was put into series production at the river shipyard at Gomel, in Byelorussia.
FOILS: The shallow draught submerged foil system consists of one bow foil and one rear foil.

HULL: Hull and superstructure are built in aluminium magnesium alloy. The hull is of all-welded construction and the superstructure is both riveted and welded.

ACCOMMODATION: The craft seats 40 passengers in aircraft-type seats, although the prototype seated only 30.

POWER PLANT: Power is supplied by an M-50 F-3 or M-400 diesel rated at 950 hp maximum and with a normal service output of 600 hp. The wheelhouse is fitted with an electro hydraulic remote control system for the engine and fuel supply.

DIMENSIONS:

Length overall	60 ft 6 in (18·55 m)
Hull beam	15 ft 2 in (4·64 m)
Height overall	13 ft 11 in (4·23 m)
Draft foilborne	1 ft 0 in (0·3 m)
Draft hullborne	2 ft 11 in (0·9 m)

WEIGHTS:

Light displacement	9·6 tons
Take-off displacement	14·5 tons

PERFORMANCE:

Cruising speed	34 knots (60 km/h)

CHAIKA

An experimental 30-passenger craft, Chaika is used as a test bed for the development of diesel-operated waterjet systems. It was designed initially as a 30 passenger waterbus for shallow rivers but was found to be unsuitable for negotiating sharp river bends at high speed. However, craft of this type are reported as being in limited service on the Danube.

In June 1971 it was announced that the craft had been employed in the development of superventilated V and trapeze foils for a speed range exceeding 50-80 knots.
HULL: Hull and superstructure are built in aluminium magnesium alloy.
POWER PLANT: An M-50 diesel, developing 1,200 hp drives a two-stage waterjet.
CONTROLS: Rudders adjacent to the water stream govern the flow of the ejected water for directional control.

DIMENSIONS:

Length overall	86 ft 3 in (26·3 m)
Hull beam	12 ft 6 in (3·8 m)
Draught afloat	3 ft 10 in (1·2 m)
Draught foilborne	1 ft 0 in (0·3 m)

Byelorus, a 30-45 seat hydrofoil for fast ferry services on shallow waters, seen on the Irtysh river. Powered by a 735 hp M-50 diesel driving a waterjet, the craft cruises at 34 knots (60 km/h)

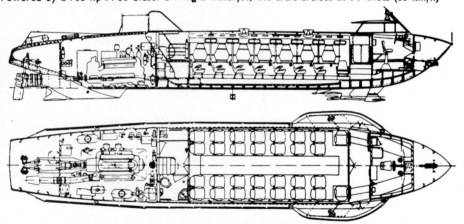

Profile and deck plan of the waterjet-propelled Byelorus, a 40-seat ferry for fast passenger services on winding rivers less than 3 ft 3 in deep

Chaika, an experimental 30-passenger craft powered by a diesel-driven waterjet, is being employed in the development of superventilated V- and trapeze-foil systems for craft with speeds in excess of 80 knots

WEIGHT:

Displacement loaded	14·3 tons

PERFORMANCE:

Cruising speed, foilborne	
	46·5 knots (86 km/h)

CYCLONE

The Cyclone, a project for a 250-seat hydrofoil ferry, was announced in February 1969. Although reports have appeared to the contrary, it was understood in August 1975 that an order for the construction of the prototype is still awaited.

It is believed that the vessel will be powered by two 4,500 hp D25B gas-turbines driving waterjets and have surface-piercing foils of trapeze configuration, similar to those of the Kometa. A stability augmentation system will be fitted. Cruising speed will be 42 knots and the vessel will be capable of operating in heavy seas. It is stated that it will be the fastest of the Soviet Union's commercial hydrofoils.

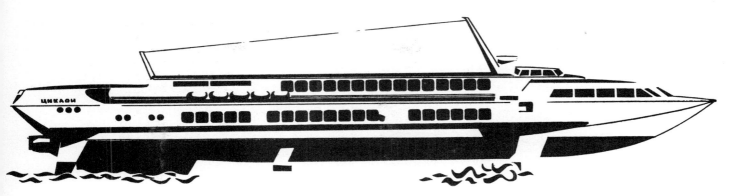

Outboard profile of the 140-ton Cyclone, a project for a waterjet-propelled 250-seat hydrofoil ferry with accommodation on two decks. Design cruising speed is 42 knots

NEW MIXED-TRAFFIC FERRY

In June 1973 it was announced that a new seagoing hydrofoil designed at the Sormovo shipyard will carry 200 passengers and 40 vehicles at a speed of 43·49 mph (70 km/h). It will be able to operate foilborne in waves up to 6ft 7in (2m) high. Although designed primarily for routes on the open sea, the vessel is also likely to be employed on inland waterways.

KOMETA

Derived from the earlier Meteor, the Kometa is the first seagoing hydrofoil to be built in the Soviet Union. The prototype, seating 100 passengers, made its maiden voyage on the Black Sea in the summer of 1961, after which it was employed on various passenger routes on an experimental basis. Operating experience accumulated on these services led to the introduction of various modifications before the craft was put into series production.

Kometas are built mainly at Gorki, but in addition a number are being assembled at Poti, one of the Black Sea yards, from prefabricated sections sent from Gorki.

Kometa operators outside the Soviet Union include Inex-Nautical Touring, Split, Yugoslavia; Empresa Nacional de Cabotage, Cuba; Archille Onorato, Naples, Italy; Vedettes Armoricaines of Brest, France, Transportes Touristiques Intercontinentaux, Morocco and Moroso Hydrofoil Lines, Puerto Rico. Other vessels of this type have been supplied to Iran, Romania, Poland, Bulgaria and Eastern Germany.

One Kometa M was delivered to Airavia Ltd in the United Kingdom in the spring of 1975. At the time of going to press the craft was being modified to meet British Passenger Certificate requirements.

Export orders have mainly been for the Kometa-M, which was introduced in 1968. Two distinguishing features of this model are the employment of new diesel engines, with increased operating hours between overhauls, and a completely revised surface-piercing foil system, with a trapeze bow foil instead of the former Alexeyev shallow draft submerged type.

A fully tropicalised and air-conditioned version is now in production and this is designated Kometa MT.

The present standard production Kometa M seats 113-116. Because of the additional weight of the Kometa-MT's air-conditioning system and other refinements, the seating capacity is reduced in the interest of passenger comfort to 102.

Top: Kometa M demonstration craft operated by Sudoimport. Note the surface-piercing bow foil, with pitch stability sub-foil above Sponsons are attached to the hull fore and aft to protect the foils while mooring. The forward pair are employed as embarkation platforms. *Centre:* One of nine Kometa Ms being operated by Onorato, the Italian Shipping Line. The stabiliser foil amidships facilitates take-off. *Bottom:* A Kometa M of Inex, the Yugoslavian operator. The vessel, which has a service speed of 32 knots, operates a coastal service on the Adriatic between Krila, Zadar and Split

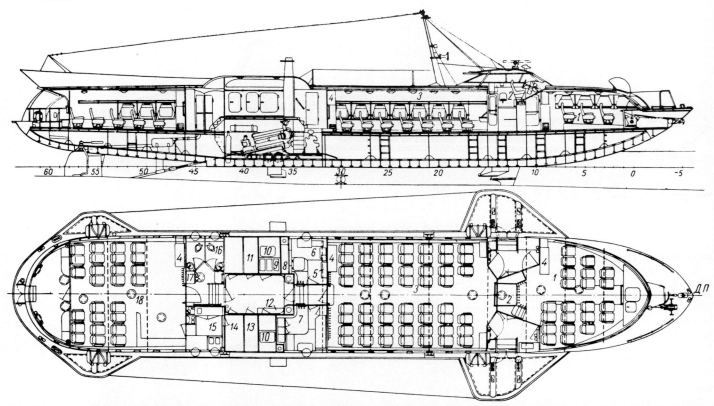

Internal arrangement of the current production Kometa-M, designed for tropical operation. I, 22-seat forward passenger saloon; 2, wheelhouse; 3, 54-seat main passenger saloon; 6 ,control position; 7, duty cabin; 8, liquid fire extinguisher bay; 9, battery room; 10, engine room; 11, boiler room; 12, installation point for portable radio; 13, store; 14, provision store; 15, bar; 16, WC/washbasin units; 17, boatswain's store; 18, 26-seat aft passenger saloon

The standard craft has proved to be exceptionally robust and has a good all-round performance. On one charter, a Kometa M covered 3,300 miles (5,310 km) by sea and river in 127 hours. It can operate foilborne in waves up to 5 ft 7 in (1·7 m) high and travel hullborne in waves up to 11 ft 10 in (3·6 m).

In June 1974 it was announced that, starting in 1975, production of the Kometa would be significantly increased. One of the features of the latest models is the relocation of the engine room aft to reduce the noise in the passenger saloons and the employment of a vee-drive instead of the existing inclined shaft. The arrangement is expected to be similar to that on the Voskhod 2. The revised deck configuration allows more seats to be fitted.

Employment of a surface-piercing trapeze-type bow foil provides the Kometa-M with improved seakeeping capability in waves. The foil system comprises a bow foil, aft foil, and two auxiliaries, one (termed "stabiliser") located above the bow foil for pitch stability, the other sited amidship near the longitudinal centre of gravity to assist take-off. The foils are connected to the hull by struts and brackets. Middle and side struts of the bow foil are of the split type. The lower and upper components of each strut are connected by flanges and bolts. The upper sections are connected to the hull by the same means.

The bow and stern foils are of hollow welded stainless steel construction. The midship and pitch stability foils and the upper components of the foil struts are in aluminium-magnesium alloy.

HULL: Similar in shape to that of the earlier Meteor, the hull has a wedge-shaped bow, raked stem and a spoon-shaped stern. Hull and superstructure are built in A1Mg-61 and A1M-6g alloys. Hull and superstructure

are of all-welded construction using contact and argon arc welding. The hull is framed on longitudinal and transverse formers, the spacing throughout the length of the hull is 500 mm and in the superstructure 1,000 mm.

Below the freeboard deck, the hull is divided by watertight bulkheads into thirteen compartments, which include the engine room, fuel compartments, and those containing the firefighting system, tiller gear and fuel transfer pump.

ACCOMMODATION: The current production model Kometa MT seats 102 passengers. It carries a four-man operating crew, comprising captain, engineer, motorman and a seaman, plus one barman. Embarkation platforms sited immediately below the wheelhouse provide access for both passengers and crew.

The captain and engineer are accommodated in a raised wheelhouse located between the forward and main saloons, and equipped with two seats, a folding stool, chart table, sun shield and a locker for signal flags. The wheelhouse also contains a radar display and radio communications equipment.

Main engine controls are installed in both the wheelhouse and engine room.

Passengers are accommodated in three compartments, a forward saloon seating 22, and central and aft saloons seating 54 and 26 respectively. The central saloon has three exits, two forward, leading to the embarkation platforms and one aft, leading to the promenade deck. This is located in the space above the engine room and is partially covered with a removable metallic awning.

To the starboard side is a crew s off-duty cabin, hydraulic system pump room, bar store and bar, and to the port are two toilets, boiler room, battery room and fire extinguishing equipment.

The aft saloon has two exits, one forward leading to the promenade deck, the other aft, leading to the weather deck, which is used for embarking and disembarking when the vessel is moored by the stern.

Floors of the passenger saloons, crew's cabins, bar and wheelhouse are covered in coloured linoleum and the deckhead in the passenger saloons, as well as bulkheads and the sides above the lower edge of the windows, are finished in light coloured pavinol. Panels of the saloons beneath the windows are covered with plastic.

Passenger saloons are fitted with upholstered chairs, racks for small hand luggage and pegs for clothing. The middle and aft saloons have niches for hand luggage and the former is fitted with cradles for babies. The bar is fully equipped with glass washers, an ice safe, an automatic Freon compressor, electric stove, etc.

SAFETY EQUIPMENT: A full range of lifesaving equipment is carried including inflatable life rafts, each for 25 persons, 138 life jackets, and 6 circular lifebelts, two with life lines and two with luminous buoys. Life rafts are located two on the forward sponsons and two on the aft sponsons. When thrown into the water the liferafts inflate automatically. Life jackets are stowed under the seats in all saloons, and the circular life belts are stowed on the embarkation and promenade platforms. Kometas for export are provided with life jackets on the basis of 25 persons per raft.

FIRE FIGHTING EQUIPMENT: An independent fluid firefighting system is provided for the engine room and fuel bay. An automatic light and sound system signals a fire outbreak. The fire fighting system is put into operation manually from the control deck above the engine room door. Boat spaces are equipped with hand-operated foam and CO_2 fire extinguishers, felt cloths and

fire axes.

POWER PLANT: Power is supplied by two M-401A water-cooled, supercharged 12-cylinder V-type diesels, each with a normal service output of 900 hp at 1,550 rpm and a maximum output of 1,000 hp at 1,600 rpm. Guaranteed service life of each engine before first overhaul is 2,500 hours. Each engine drives via a reverse gear its own inclined shaft and the twin propellers are contra-rotating. The shafts are of steel and are parallel to the craft.

The propellers are of three-bladed design and made of brass.

Main engine controls and gauges are installed in both the wheelhouse and the engine room. A diesel-generator-compressor-pump unit is provided for charging starter air bottles; supplying electric power when at rest; warming the main engines in cold weather and pumping warm air beneath the deck to dry the bilges.

Diesel oil tanks with a total capacity of 6,612 lb (3,000 kg) for the main engines and the auxiliary unit are located in the afterpeak. Two lubricating oil service tanks and one storage tank located at the fore bulkhead of the engine room have a total capacity of 551 lb (250 kg). Diesel and lubricating oil capacity is sufficient to ensure a range of 230 miles (370 km).

CONTROLS: The wheelhouse is equipped with an electro hydraulic remote control system for the engine reverse gear and fuel supply, fuel monitoring equipment, including electric speed counters, pressure gauges, lubricating and fuel oil gauges. The boat is equipped with a single, solid aluminium magnesium alloy balanced rudder, which is controlled through an hydraulic steering system or a hand-operated hydraulic drive. In an emergency, the rudder may be operated by a hand tiller. Maximum rudder angle is 35 degrees in hullborne conditions and 5-6 degrees foilborne. In the event of the steering gear failing the craft can be manoeuvred by differential use of the main engines, the rudder being locked on the centre line. The vessel can be pinwheeled in hullborne condition by setting one engine slow ahead, the other slow astern and turning the rudder hard over.

SYSTEMS:

ELECTRICAL: Power supply is 24 volts dc. A 1kW dc generator is attached to each of the two engines and these supply power while the craft is operating. A 5·6 kW generator is included in the auxiliary unit and supplies power when the craft is at rest. It can also be used when under way for supplying the heating plant or when the 1·0 kW generators are inoperative. Four 12 volt acid storage batteries, each of 180 amp/hr capacity and connected in series to provide 24 volts, supply power during short stops.

HYDRAULICS: The hydraulic system for controlling the main engines and reverse gear consists of control cylinders located in the wheelhouse, power cylinders located on the engines, a filler tank, pipe lines and fittings.

ANCHORS: The craft is equipped with two Matrosov anchors—a main anchor weighing 165 lb (75 kg) and a spare anchor weighing 110 lb (50 kg). The main anchor is raised by means of an electric winch located in the forepeak. The cable of the spare anchor can be heaved in manually and is wound over a drum fitted with a hand brake.

The Meteor is powered by two 12-cylinder M-50 diesels, each with a normal service output of 908 hp. Ahead of the central fin is a removable metallic awning above the promenade deck

COMMUNICATIONS: A radio transmitter/receiver with r/t and w/t facilities is installed in the wheelhouse for ship-shore and inter-ship communications on SW and MW bands. A portable emergency radio and automatic distress signal transmitter are also installed in the wheelhouse. A broadcast system is fitted in the passenger saloons and a two-way crew communications system is installed in the wheelhouse, engine room, anchor gear compartment and mooring stations.

NAVIGATION: The following navigation aids are standard: a gyro compass, magnetic compass (reserve) and log.

KOMETA-M

DIMENSIONS:

Length overall	115 ft 2 in (35·1 m)
Beam	31 ft 6 in (9·6 m)
Height, foilborne from waterline to tip of mast	28 ft 7 in (8·7 m)
Draft, hullborne	11 ft 9¾ in (3·6 m)
Draft, foilborne	5 ft 6⅞ in (1·7 m)

POWER PLANT:

Two 1,100 hp water cooled supercharged 12-cylinder diesels

PERFORMANCE:

Cruising speed	34-35 knots (60-63 km/h)
Fuel consumption gr/bhp/hr	180
Oil consumption gr/bhp/hr	5·0

KOMETA MT

DIMENSIONS:

Length overall	115 ft 2 in (35·1 m)
Beam	36 ft 1 in (11·0 m)
Height, foilborne, waterline to tip of mast	30 ft 2¼ in (9·2 m)
Draft, hullborne	11 ft 9¾ in (3·6 m)
Draft, foilborne	5 ft 6⅞ in (1·7 m)

POWER PLANT:

Two 1,000 hp water-cooled, supercharged 12-cylinder diesels

WEIGHTS:

Light displacement (max.)	46·2 tonnes
Fully loaded displacement (max.)	60·5 tonnes

PERFORMANCE:

Maximum speed	34 knots
Service speed	32 knots (58 km/h)
Fuel consumption, gr/bhp/hr	182
Oil consumption, gr/bhp/hr	58
Range	240 km

Development of the Kometa is continuing. Current research is aimed at the introduction of a stability augmentation system employing either control flaps on the bow foil or air stabilisation on the stern foil and struts; the reduction of labour involved in construction; the introduction of design improvements through the use of grp and sandwich construction; noise reduction in the saloons and the extension of the cruising range.

METEOR

Dr Alexeyev's Meteor made its maiden voyage from Gorki to Moscow in the summer of 1960, bringing high performance and unprecedented comfort to the river boat scene, and setting the pattern for a family of later designs.

The craft is intended for use in daylight hours on local and medium-range routes of up to 373 miles (600 km) in length. It meets the requirements of Class O, experimental type, on the Register of River Shipping in the USSR.

Accommodation is provided for a crew of five and 116 passengers. Cruising speed at the full load displacement of 54·3 tonnes across calm water and in winds of up to Beaufort force 3 is about 35 knots (65 km/h).

FOILS: The foil arrangement comprises a bow foil and a stern foil, with the struts of the bow system carrying two additional planing subfoils. The foils are attached to the struts, which are of split type, by flanges and bolts. The foils are in stainless steel, and the subfoils in aluminium magnesium alloy. The foil incidence can be adjusted when necessary by the insertion of wedges between the flanges and the foils when the vessel is in dock.

HULL: With the exception of the small exposed areas fore and aft, the Meteor's hull and superstructure are built as an integral unit. The hull is framed on longitudinal and transverse formers and both hull and superstructure are of riveted duralumin construction with welded steel members. Below the main deck the hull is sub-divided longitudinally into eight compartments by seven bulkheads. Access to the compartments is via hatches in the main deck. The craft will remain afloat in the event of any two adjacent compartment forward of amidship flooding or any one compartment aft of amidship. Frame spacing in the hull is about 500 mm while that in the superstructure is 1,000 mm.

POWER PLANT: Power is supplied by two M-50 12-cylinder, four-stroke, supercharged, water-cooled diesels with reversing clutches. Each engine has a normal service output of 1,000 hp at 1,700 rpm and a maximum output of 1,100 hp at 1,800 rpm. Specific consumption at rated output g/bhp/hr is not more than 193, and oil, not more than 6. Guaranteed overhaul life is 1,000 hours. Each engine drives its own inclined propeller shaft through a reverse clutch. Propeller shafts are in steel and the propellers, which are 5-bladed, are in brass. The drives are contra-rotating.

Refuelling is effected via filler necks on each side of the hull. Fuel is carried in six tanks located in the engine room. Total fuel capacity is 3,200 kg. Lubricating oil, total capacity 370 l, is carried in two service tanks and a storage tank located on the forward bulkhead in the engine room. Fuel and lubricating oil is sufficient for a cruising range, foilborne, of not less than 373 miles (600 km).

AUXILIARY UNIT: 12 hp diesel for generating electrical power when the craft is at its moorings, warming the main engines in cold weather and operating drainage pump.

CONTROLS: Control of the engines, reverse gear and fuel supply is effected remotely from the wheelhouse with the aid of a hydraulic system comprising transmitter cylinders in the wheelhouse, and actuators on the engine. The engines can also be controlled from the engine room.

Craft heading is controlled by two balanced rudders, the blades of which are in solid aluminium magnesium alloy. The rudders are operated hydraulically from the wheelhouse, the rudder angle being checked by an electric indicator in the wheelhouse. In an emergency, with the craft in hullborne conditions, the rudder is put over with the aid of a detachable hand filler fitted to the rudder stock.

At low speed the craft is capable of turning in its own length by pinwheeling—employing both engines with equal power in opposite directions—one ahead, the other astern.

Minimum diameter of the turning circle is approx 273 yds (250 m) with the engines running at low speed (700-750 rpm) and with the rudder put through an angle of 35

degrees. Turning circle diameter when operating foilborne with the rudder at an angle of 10 degrees is approximately 820 yds (750 m).

The vessel takes-off for foilborne flight in 120-140 seconds, i.e. within a distance of 25-28 lengths of her hull.

Landing run, with engines reversed, ranges from 1·5 to 2 hull lengths, while the braking distance without reversing the engines is within 3-4 lengths of the hull.

ACCOMMODATION: Passengers are accommodated in three compartments, a forward saloon seating 26, and central and aft saloons seating 42 and 44 passengers respectively. The central saloon has three exits, two forward leading to the embarkation platforms and one aft leading to the promenade deck above the engine room. On the port side of central saloon, aft, is a small buffet/bar. Beneath the wheelhouse is a duty crew room and a luggage compartment which opens into the forward saloon.

The aft saloon has two exits, one leading to the promenade deck above the engine room and one to the weather deck aft. Forward and aft on both sides of the craft are sponsons to protect the foil systems during mooring. The forward pair are used as embarkation and disembarkation platforms.

SYSTEMS, ELECTRICAL: 24-28·5 volts dc from the vessel's power supply or 220 volts ac, 50 cycle, from shore-to-ship supply sources.

RADIO: Ship-to-shore radio telephone operating on any of ten pre-selected fixed frequencies. Also passenger announcement system and crew intercom.

NAVIGATION: Magnetic compass.

Meteor. General Arrangement.
A. inboard profile; B. main deck plan. I. waterline hullborne; II. hull base line; III. waterline foilborne; IV. longitudinal centreline. 1. wheelhouse; 2. anchor compartment ; 3 forward passenger saloon, 26 seats; 4. luggage compartment; 5. embarkation companionway; 6. crew duty room; 7. midship passenger saloon, 42 seats; 8. bar; 9. refrigeration unit; 10. engine room; 11. pantry; 12. boatswain's store; 13. calorifies; 14. fire fighting equipment; 15. promenade deck; 16. WCs; 17. tank; 18. aft passenger saloon, 44 seats; 19. tiller gear; 20. four-seat passenger cabin;, 21. storage batteries; 22. hydraulic units; 23. main switchboard

COMPRESSED AIR: System comprises two air storage bottles, each of 40 l capacity, used for starting the main engines, operating emergency stop mechanism, closing feed cocks of the fuel tanks, recharging the hydraulic system accumulator and the ship's siren.

FIREFIGHTING: Remote system for fighting outbreak in engine room, with automatic light and sound indicator operating in wheelhouse. Hand-operated foam and CO_2 extinguishers provided in passenger saloons and wheelhouse.

DIMENSIONS:

Length overall	112 ft 2¼ in (34·5 m)
Beam overall	31 ft 2 in (9·5 m)
Height foilborne above water surface	22 ft 3¾ in (6·8 m)
Draught afloat	7 ft 10½ in (2·4 m)
foilborne	3 ft 11¼ in (1·2 m)

WEIGHTS:

Light displacement	37·2 tonnes
Fully loaded	54·3 tonnes

PERFORMANCE:

Cruising speed, calm water	35 knots (65 km/h)

Limiting sea states:

Foilborne	Beaufort Force 3
Hullborne	Beaufort Force 4

MIR

First Soviet passenger craft to use a surface-piercing foil system was the MIR (Peace), built in the autumn of 1961. Described as the first Soviet seagoing hydrofoil it is in many respects similar to the Supramar PT 50. The hull is of welded aluminium construction and the foils are in high tensile stainless steel. It can undertake voyages in up to State 4 seas and has a maximum speed of 47 knots (87 km/h). Power is supplied by twin M-50 diesels driving twin screws. The engines are electro hydraulically controlled from the wheelhouse, which has an auto-pilot system for emergencies.

MOLNIA

This popular six-seat hydrofoil sports runabout was derived from Alexeyev's original test craft. Many hundreds are available for hire on Russian lakes and rivers and in slightly modified form the type is now being exported to countries including the United Kingdom and the USA. The craft is navigable in protected off-shore water up to 2 miles from the land and has particular appeal for water-taxi and joy-ride operators.

FOILS: The hydrofoil assembly comprises two forward foils, one aft foil and planing sub-foils.

POWER PLANT: Powered by a 77 bhp CAZ652 Volga car engine, it has a top speed of about 32 knots (60 km/h) and a range of about 100 nautical miles (180 km).

HULL: Built in sheet and extruded light alloy, the hull is divided into three compartments by metal bulkheads. The forepeak is used for stores, the midship compartment is the open cockpit, and the compartment houses the engine and gearbox. The cockpit is fitted with a steering wheel, throttle, reverse gear lever and an instrument panel adapted from that of the Volga car. Individual life jackets for each passenger are incorporated into the seat cushions.

DIMENSIONS:

Length overall	27 ft 11 in (8·50 m)
Hull beam	6 ft 5 in (1·95 m)
Draught afloat	2 ft 10 in (0·85 m)
Draught foilborne	1 ft 10 in (0·55 m)

Molnia, a popular six-seat runabout powered by a 77 bhp CAZ652 Volga car engine. Maximum speed is 32 knots (60 km/h).

WEIGHTS:

Displacement:

loaded	1·8 tons
empty	1·25 tons

PERFORMANCE:

Max speed at 1·8 tons displacement	32 knots (60 km/h)
Fuel capacity	17 gall (80 litres)
Range	97 nautical miles (180 km)

NEVKA

This light passenger ferry and sightseeing craft is in series production at a Leningrad shipyard and the first units have been supplied to Yalta for coastal services on the Black Sea. The standard version seats a driver and 14 passengers.

It is understood that an export model is to be available in 1976.

The prototype, illustrated in the accompanying photograph, has an aluminium hull, but production models are in glass-fibre reinforced plastics.

The craft, which is designed to operate in waves up to 3 ft (1 m) high, is the first small hydrofoil in the Soviet Union to employ surface-piercing foils, and also the first to employ a diesel in conjunction with a Z-drive.

In December a 1971 waterjet-propelled variant made its first cruise along the Crimean coast. The 16-mile trip from Yalta to Alushta was made in half an hour.

Nevka prototype during trials. This light passenger ferry and sightseeing craft is now in series production at a Leningrad shipyard. Power is provided by a 235 hp diesel driving a 3-bladed propeller via a Z-drive

Model of a projected luxury cabin cruiser version of the Nevka

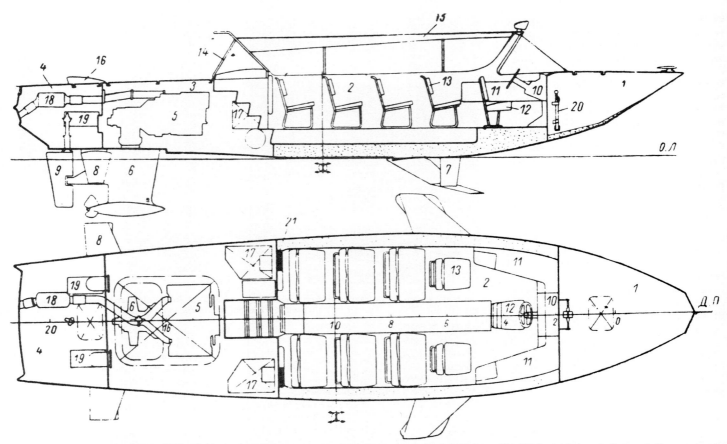

Internal arrangements of the standard Nevka, seating a driver and 14 passengers. (a) inboard profile; (b) deck plan.   1. forepeak; 2. passenger cabin; 3, engine bay; 4, afterpeak; 5, 235 hp 3D20 four-cycle six-cylinder diesel; 6, DK-300 Z-drive; 7, bow foil; 8, rear foil; 9, rudder; 10, control panel; 11, lockers; 12, driver's seat; 13, passenger seat; 14, guard rail; 15, detachable awning; 16, engine air intakes; 17, fuel tank; 18, silencer; 19, storage batteries; 20, anchor; 21. lifebelt

FOILS: Bow and stern foils are of fixed V surface-piercing configuration and made of solid aluminium magnesium alloy.

HULL: Glass fibre reinforced plastic structure assembled in four basic sections. The outer hull is assembled with the transom, the deck with the rib of the windscreen, the cabin/cockpit with the engine air intakes and afterpeak, and the inner hull with the companionway at the aft of the cabin.

The hull contours are designed to facilitate easy transition from hull to foilborne mode and minimise structural loadings due to wave impact. Two transverse steps are incorporated.

ACCOMMODATION: The craft can be supplied with an open cockpit and folding canopy, as a cabin cruiser with a solid top or as a sightseeing craft with a transparent cabin roof. As a cabin cruiser, the craft is equipped with bunks, a galley and toilet. The driver's stand can be located either at the forward end of the cabin or in a raised position amidships.

POWER PLANT: Power is supplied by a single 3D20 four-cycle, six-cylinder diesel, developing 235 hp at 2,200 rpm. The engine, located aft, drives a three-bladed propeller via a DK-300 Z-drive.

Two Pchela fast patrol boats. The craft which is based on the Strela hydrofoil ferry, is operated by the KGB frontier guard. Note the surface-piercing trapeze foils which incorporate pitch stability elements

CONTROLS: Craft heading is controlled by a single balanced rudder in solid aluminium alloy mounted aft of the rear foil main strut and operated by a steering wheel via a mechanical linkage. Other controls include a footpedal to control engine speed, and a reverse lever.

SYSTEMS, ELECTRICAL: Power is 24 volts d.c. A 1kW engine-mounted generator supplies power while the craft is operating. Two 12 volt acid storage batteries, each of 180 amp/hr capacity and connected in series to give 24 volts, supply power during stops.

FIRE FIGHTING: An independent fluid firefighting system of aircraft type is installed in the engine bay and is operated remotely from the driving seat.

DIMENSIONS:

Length overall	35 ft 11 in (10·9 m)
Hull beam	8 ft 11 in (2·7 m)
Beam overall	13 ft 2 in (4·0 m)
Draft, hullborne	5 ft 3 in (1·7 m)
Draft, foilborne	2 ft 9 in (0·9 m)

WEIGHTS:

Max take-off displacement	6 tons
Displacement unloaded	4·1 tons

PERFORMANCE:

Cruising speed	30 knots
Normal cruising range	37 miles
Diameter of turn at max speed	357 ft (109 m)
Take-off time	app 30 secs
Max permissible wave height in foilborne mode	3 ft 3 in (1·0 m)

PCHELA (BEE)

This military derivative of the Strela is in service with the KGB for frontier patrol duties in the Baltic, Black Sea, Caspian and various other sea areas. The craft is equipped with a full range of search and navigation radar and is reported to have a speed of about 35 knots. Twenty-five were built between 1965-1972. The craft carry depth charges and two twin machine gun mounts.

RAKETA

The prototype Raketa was launched in 1957 and was the first multi-seat passenger hydrofoil to employ the Alexeyev shallow draught submerged foil system. Several hundred are now in service on all the major rivers of the USSR.

In January 1973 it was announced that more than three hundred Raketas were being operated on rivers and lakes in the Soviet Union, including sixty-six in service with the Volga United River Shipping Agency.

Variants include the standard non-tropicalised Raketa M seating 64 passengers; the current export model, the 58-seat Raketa T, which is both tropicalised and air-conditioned, and finally the Raketa TA, modified in London by Airavia Ltd, and licensed by the UK Department of Trade to carry up to 100 passengers (58 seated) on high density commuter and tourist routes on sheltered waters. Details of this model are given in the United Kingdom section.

Reports suggest that production of the Raketa has now stopped and that yards previously involved in their fabrication and assembly will be building Voskhod and other designs in future.

Top: Raketa M operated on the Rhine by the Köln-Dusseldorfer Shipping Company between Cologne and Koblenz. Centre: The bow foil and planing stabiliser foils. Bottom: Aft foil assembly comprising the foil, three supporting struts and bearing for the inclined propeller shaft

The description that follows applies to the Raketa T, the standard export variant, powered by an M-401A diesel and with a cruising speed of about 32 knots (58 km/h).

The vessel is designed for high-speed passenger ferry services during daylight hours on rivers, reservoirs and sheltered waters in tropical climates. It meets the requirements of the Soviet River Register Class 'O' with operation restricted to 2 ft 7 in (0·8 m) waves when foilborne and up to 4 ft 11 in (1·5 m) when hullborne.

The passenger saloon is provided with natural and induced ventilation and seats 58. The crew comprises a captain, engineer, deckhand and barman.

FOILS: The foil system comprises one bow foil, one aft foil and two dart-like planing sub-foils, the tips of which are attached to the trailing edges of the outer bow foil struts. Foils, sub-foils and struts are in welded stainless steel. The bow foil, which incorporates sweepback, and the straight aft foil, are both supported by three vertical struts.

The base of the centre strut aft provides the end bearing for the propeller which is located beneath the foil.

HULL: The hull is framed on longitudinal and transverse formers and all the main elements—plating, deck, partitions, bulkheads, platforms and wheelhouse—are in riveted duralumin. The stem is fabricated in interwelded steel strips. Below the freeboard deck the hull is divided into six watertight compartments employing web framing.

ACCOMMODATION: The passenger saloon seats 58 in aircraft-type, adjustable seats. At the aft end of the saloon is a bar. The saloon has one exit on each side leading to the promenade deck and one forward, leading to the forecastle. Aft of the saloon is the engine room, promenade deck with additional seats, two toilets, a storeroom and a companionway leading up to the wheelhouse.

The craft carries a full range of life-saving and firefighting equipment. There are 62 life jackets stowed in the passenger saloon and four for the crew in the wheelhouse and under the embarkation companionway. Two lifebelts are provided on the embarkation platform and two on the promenade deck. Firefighting equipment includes four foam and four CO_2 fire extinguishers, two fire axes, two fire buckets and two felt cloths.

POWER PLANT: Power is supplied by a single M-401A water-cooled, supercharged 12-cylinder V-type diesel, with a normal service output of 900 hp. The engine drives via a reverse gear and inclined stainless steel propeller shaft a three-bladed cast bronze propeller. The fuel system comprises two fuel tanks with a total capacity of 1,400 kg, a fuel priming unit, and a hand fuel booster pump. A compressed air system, comprising a propeller shaft-driven air compressor and two 40-litre compressed air bottles is provided for main engine starting, emergency stopping, operating the foghorn and scavenging the water intake.

The diesel generator unit comprises a Perkins P3.152 diesel engine employed in conjunction with a Stamford C20 alternator.

CONTROLS: The wheelhouse is equipped with a hydraulic remote control system for the engine, reverse gear and fuel supply. The balanced rudder, made in aluminium-magnesium alloy, is controlled hydraulically by turning the wheel. A hand tiller is employed in an emergency. Employment of gas exhaust as a side-thruster to assist mooring is permitted at 850 rpm.

SYSTEMS, Electrical: A 3kW generator, rated at 27·5 V and coupled to the main engine is the main source of power while the vessel is under way. A 50 cycle, 230 V, 1,500 rpm three-phase alternator supplies ac power. Four 12 volt acid storage batteries, each with a 132 ah capacity and connected in series to give 24 volts, supply power during short stops.

HYDRAULICS: The hydraulic system for controlling the main engine, reverse gear and fuel supply, consists of control levers located in the wheelhouse and on the main engine,

The 100 ton Sputnik, first of the Soviet Union's large hydrofoil passenger ferries

The prototype Strela during trials off the Yalta coast

power cylinders located on the engine, a filler tank, pipelines and fittings.

HEATING AND VENTILATION: Passenger saloon and wheelhouse are provided with natural ventilation, using ram inflow when the boat is in motion. Norris warming air-conditioning if fitted for use in hot weather. One conditioner is installed in the wheelhouse and eight are installed in the passenger saloon and bar. The cooled air is distributed throughout the saloon by electric fans installed on the ceiling. One is provided in the wheelhouse. A radio-telephone with a range of about 19 miles (30 km) is installed for ship-to-shore and ship-to-ship communication. The vessel also has a public address system and intercom speakers linking the engine room, wheelhouse and forecastle.

DIMENSIONS:

Length overall	88 ft 5 in (26·96 m)
Beam amidships	16 ft 5 in (5·0 m)
Freeboard	2 ft 7½ in (0·8 m)
Height overall (excl mast)	14 ft 8 in (4·46 m)
Draft, hullborne	5 ft 11 in (1·8 m)
foilborne	3 ft 7¼ in (1·1 m)

WEIGHTS:

Displacement, fully loaded	27·09 tonnes
light	20·31 tonnes

PERFORMANCE:

Service speed, about	32 knots (58 km/h)
Max wave height, foilborne	2 ft 8 in (0·8 m)
Max wave height, hullborne	4 ft 11 in (1·5 m)
Turning diameter, hullborne	3-4 boat lengths
Turning diameter, foilborne	15-16 boat lengths

RAKETA FIRE TENDER

The Raketa fire tender has been designed to tackle fires on river ships and vessels in coastal areas.

The adaptation of an existing fast craft for this purpose had the advantages of reducing development time and building costs.

FOILS: Identical arrangement to that of the standard Raketa.

HULL: Riveted D16 duralumin construction. Two monitors are mounted on the weather deck, one at the bow and one amidships. Water for the two monitors is supplied by an 8HDH rotary pump driven by a 590 hp M609 12-cylinder diesel controlled from the wheelhouse.

Outlets and valves are provided on the two monitor stands for the attachment of one 5·9 in (150 mm) fire-fighting hose to each, or two four-way forks, to which four 3·03 in (77 mm) hoses can be joined. Spray hoses are laid along the sides of the weather deck, one port and one starboard, each with four spray nozzles.

The vessel carries a 220 gal (1,000 l) foam tank and mixer for extinguishing highly inflammable and combustible liquids. Foam can be delivered either by the two monitors or fire hoses.

A special waterjet propulsion system is provided to offset the thrust of the hoses and monitors when working and keep the craft stationary. The vessel is equipped with VHF and UHF radio and a ship's broadcast system for control of the 6-man firefighting crew.

Start-up of the firefighting systems when empty takes 70 seconds and 10 seconds when full.

SPUTNIK

The 100-ton Sputnik was the first of the Soviet Union's large hydrofoils. On its maiden voyage in November 1961, the prototype carried 300 passengers between Gorki and Moscow in 14 hours. Although a heavy autumn storm was encountered en route the craft was able to continue under way at a cruising speed of 40 knots through several large reservoirs with waves running as high as 8 ft.

FOILS: The foil system comprises a bow and rear foil with the outer struts of the bow assembly carrying two additional planing subfoils.

HULL: The hull is welded in AlMg-61 aluminium magnesium alloy. Adoption of an all-welded unit construction facilitated prefabrication of sections at the Sormovo shipyard and elsewhere, the parts being sent to other yards in the USSR for assembly. One yard used for assembling Sputniks is at Batumi, on the Caspian Sea.

POWER PLANT: Power is supplied by four 850 hp M-50 water cooled, supercharged V-type diesels, each driving its own propeller shaft and controlled electro hydraulically from the forward wheelhouse.

ACCOMMODATION: Passengers are accommodated in three saloons, a well-glazed fore compartment seating 68, and central and aft compartments each seating 96. On short, high frequency services, the seating is increased to 108 in the latter compartments by the substitution of padded benches instead of adjustable aircraft-type seats. Two separate off-duty cabins are provided for the 5-man crew. The cabins are attractively finished in

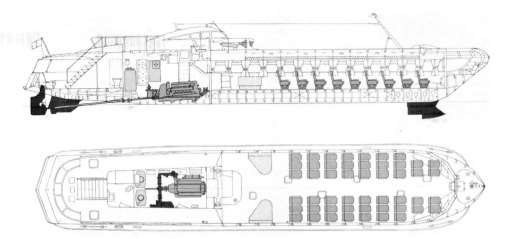

Inboard profile and plan view of the standard 50-seat Raketa. On short-range commuter services, additional passengers are seated around the promenade deck aft, and others are permitted to stand. The high density traffic version accommodates up to 100 passengers

pastel shades and fully insulated against heat and sound. Full fire fighting and other emergency provisions are made and in addition to lifebelts for all passengers and members of the crew, two inflatable rubber boats are carried.

DIMENSIONS:

Length overall	157 ft 2 in (47·9 m)
Beam overall	29 ft 6 in (9·0 m)
Draught afloat	4 ft 3 in (1·3 m)
Draught foilborne	2 ft 10 in (0·9 m)

WEIGHTS:

Displacement full load	110 tons

PERFORMANCE:

Cruising speed	41 knots (75 km/h)

STRELA

Developed from the Mir and intended for services across the Black Sea, the prototype Strela (Arrow) completed its acceptance trials towards the end of 1961. The craft, which was designed and built in Leningrad, was first put into regular passenger service between Odessa and Batumi, and later between Yalta and Sebastapol. More recently a Strela 3 has been operating a service between Leningrad and Tallinn. It covers the distance in four hours, ninety minutes faster than the express train service connecting the two ports.

Two 970 hp 12-cylinder V-type M-50 F3 diesels driving twin screws give the Strela a cruising speed of 40 knots (75 km/h). The craft has a trapeze type surface piercing bow foils with a horizontal centre section between the main struts, and can operate in State 4 seas.

It carries 82-94 passengers in airliner type seats.

DIMENSIONS:

Length overall	96 ft 1 in (29·3 m)
Beam overall	26 ft 4 in (8·3 m)
Draft afloat	7 ft 7 in (2·25 m)
Draft foilborne	3 ft 11 in (1·2 m)

WEIGHTS:

Displacement, full load	46 tons

PERFORMANCE:

Cruising speed	40 knots
Sea state capability	4 ft (1·22 m) waves
Range of operation	740 km
Time to reach service speed from stop	130 seconds
Distance from full speed to stop	234 m
Full speed ahead, to full speed astern	117 m

VIKHR (WHIRLWIND)

Seagoing version of the 100-ton Sputnik, Vikhr employs the same hull and is one of the most powerful passenger hydrofoils operating today. Described as a "coastal liner", it is designed to operate during hours of daylight on inshore services on the Black Sea up to 31 miles (50 km) from the coast. The craft was launched in 1962 and is

The Vikhr employs the same hull as the Sputnik and is designed for regular year round services on the Black Sea

currently in service on the Odessa-Herson route.

FOILS: Compared with the Sputnik, innovations include more sharply swept back foils, a form of stability augmentation, and an amidship foil, in addition to those fore and aft, to increase seaworthiness and stability. The bow and rear foils and their struts are in stainless steel, foil and stabiliser are made in aluminium magnesium alloy.

HULL: Similar to the Sputnik. Two steps are aligned with the flare of the sides. Hull ands superstructure are of welded AIMg·61 aluminium magnesium alloy.

ACCOMMODATION: There are three passenger saloons, seating a total of 268 passengers. The forward saloon seats 78, the central saloon seats 96, and the aft 94. At the rear of the central cabin is a large buffet and bar, beneath which is the engine room. From the bar double doors lead to the off-duty quarters for the seven-man crew.

In high seas, passengers board from the stern, across the promenade deck. In normal conditions, embarkation takes place through a wide passageway across the vessel between the fore and middle saloons. Seats are arranged in rows of four abreast across each cabin with two aisles, each 3 ft 4 in (1 m) wide, between, to ease access to the seats.

POWER PLANT: Power is supplied by four 1,200 hp -M50-F3 diesel engines, with DGKP (diesel generator, compressor pump)

auxiliary engines. Each engine drives a 3-bladed propeller via a reverse gear and its own inclined stainless steel shaft. The central shafts are inclined at 12° 20′ and the side shafts at 13° 13′.

An overriding control valve is fitted to the control systems of the main engines, so that the fuel gauges of all four can be controlled simultaneously. This makes it possible to maintain a uniform load on the engines, immediately the craft becomes foilborne, thus increasing the life of the engines. The craft can operate satisfactorily with one engine out.

CONTROLS: The wheelhouse is equipped with an electro hydraulic remote control system for the engines, reverse gear, fuel supply etc. Twin balanced rudders are hydraulically operated by two separate systems—main and emergency.

SYSTEMS, ELECTRICAL: Power supply is 24 volts dc. A 1kw dc generator is attached to each of the engines and these supply power when operating. Two KG-5·6, 5·6kW generators are included in the auxiliary unit and supply power when at rest. They can also be used when under way for supplying the heating plant or when the 1kW generators are inoperative. Four 12 volt acid storage batteries, each of 180 amp/hr capacity and connected in series to provide 24 volts, supply power during stops.

COMMUNICATIONS: A radio transmitter/receiver is installed in the wheelhouse for ship-shore and inter-ship communication

on r/t, also a receiver. A ship's broadcast system is also installed with speakers in the passenger saloons.

NAVIGATION: Equipment includes radar, and a radio direction finding unit, both with displays in the wheelhouse.

DIMENSIONS:
Length overall	156 ft 0 in (47·54 m)
Beam	29 ft 6 in (9·0 m)
Height to hull to awning deck	
	18 ft 2 in (5·54 m)
Draft afloat	13 ft 6 in (4·1 m)
Draft foilborne	4 ft 11 in (1·5 m)

WEIGHTS:
Displacements, full load	117·5 tons

PERFORMANCE:
Max speed	43 knots (78 km/h)
Cruising speed	35·8 knots (66 km/h)
Cruising range	240 miles (386 km)
Max wave height in foilborne condition	
	4 ft 11 in (1·5 m)
Distance from full speed to full stop	
	328 yards (300 m)
Distance from full speed ahead to full speed astern	245 yards (224 m)
Time to reach service speed from stop.	
	190 seconds

VOLGA 70

Export version of the Molnia sports hydrofoil, the Volga incorporates various design refinements including a completely redesigned bow foil.

A new model powered by a 90 hp Volvo Penta diesel engine and designated Volga

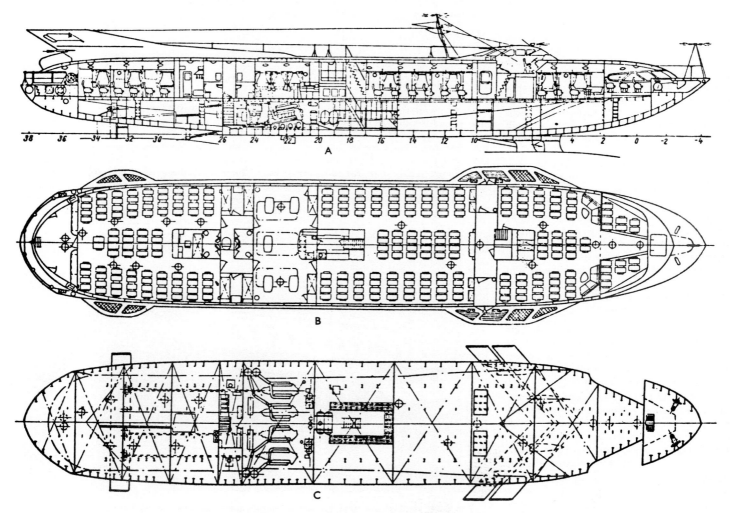

Internal arrangement of the Vikhr. a. profile; b. main deck plan; c. holds

Volga 70 six-seat water taxi and runabout powered by a 106 hp Volvo Penta diesel engine. Cruising speed is 28 knots.

70 was introduced at the end of 1972. The cruising speed is four km/h slower than that of the earlier model, but engine maintenance is easier and the acquisition of spares is simplified in many parts of the world. The new model has been purchased by companies and individuals in the USA, West Germany, Sweden, The Netherlands and Singapore.

FOILS: the foil system consists of a bow foil with stabilizing sub-foil and a rear foil assembly. The foils are of stainless steel.

HULL: Built in sheet and extruded light alloy, the hull is divided into three compartments by metal bulkheads. The forepeak is used for stores, the midship compartment is the open cockpit and the aft compartment houses the engine and gearbox.

ACCOMMODATION: Seats are provided for six—a driver and five passengers. The controls, instruments, magnetic compass and radio receiver are grouped on a panel ahead of the driver's seat. A full range of safety equipment is provided, including life jackets for six, life line, fire extinguisher and distress flares. A folding awning can be supplied.

POWER PLANT: Power is supplied by a 106 hp Volvo Penta AQD32A/270D diesel with a steerable outboard drive, which drives a 3 bladed, stainless steel propeller. Fuel capacity is 26·4 gal (120 l), sufficient for a range of 150 miles.

SYSTEMS
ELECTRICAL: 12 volt dc. Starting, instrument and navigation lights and siren,

are provided by an engine-mounted generator and an acid storage battery.

VOLGA-70

DIMENSIONS:

Length overall	28 ft 1 in (8·55 m)
Beam	6 ft 10⅝ in (2·10 m)
Height above water when foilborne	
	3 ft 2⅝ in (0·98 m)
Draft hullborne	3 ft 0 in (0·92 m)
Draft foilborne	1 ft 8½ in (0·52 m)

WEIGHTS:

Loaded displacement	4,255 lb (1,930 kg)
Light displacement	2,977 lb (1,350 kg)

PERFORMANCE:

Max speed	30 knots
Cruising speed	28 knots
Range	150 miles

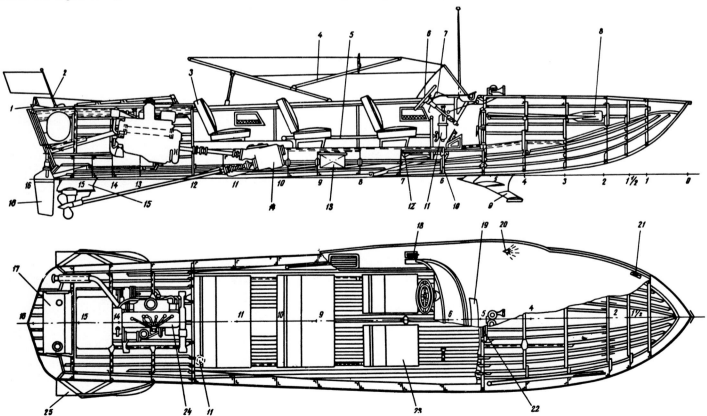

Inboard profile and plan of the Volga

I stern light; 2 flag pole; 3 bench seat; 4 awning; 5 dog hook; 6 steering column; 7 instrument panel; 8 oar; 9 bow foil assembly; 10 anchor line; 11 fire extinguisher OY-2; 12 anchor; 13 storage battery; 14 reduction and reverse gear; 15 rear foil assembly; 16 steering and rudder gear; 17 fuel tank; 18 cleat; 19 air intake; 20 side running light; 21 fairlead; 22 cover of first bulkhead hatch; 23 seat; 24 M652-Y six-cylinder automotive engine; 25 foilguard

SAILING SKIMMERS

POLAND

INSTYTUT LOTNICTWA
(AVIATION INSTITUTE)
ADDRESS:
02256 Warszawa, Al Krakowska 110/114
TELEPHONE:
46-09-93
TELEX:
81-537

Dr. Jerzy Wolf is employing an ultra-light wing, constructed by the Aviation Institute while undertaking research on agricultural aircraft, as a sail for an experimental "skimmer" sailing craft.

The wing raises the hull above the water surface and also acts as a sail.

The object of Dr. Wolf's experiments is to develop a sailing vessel which offers a higher speed that that attained by current sailing hydrofoils.

The wing, which has inherent directional and lateral stability, is hinged to the mast top, slightly ahead of the centre of pressure, and pulls the craft obliquely in a similar way to a kite of high lift/drag ratio. The angles of attack and roll are controlled by lines or push-pull rods connected to a control cross-bar. Craft heading is controlled by a conventional water rudder.

ZAGLOSLIZG (Sailing Skimmer) Z-70

The Z-70, built in 1970, employs a modified Cadet class sailing dinghy hull equipped with an adapted centreboard and rudder. This particular hull design was selected because of its low weight, high rigidity and low construction cost.

The wing, built originally to aid research into an agricultural aircraft project, has been adapted by the addition of a vertical stabiliser. It is covered in Dacron material and has a sail area of 140 sq ft (13·0 m²). The all-up weight is 33 lb (15 kg) and breaking load 1,188 lb (540 kg).

The complete craft has an empty weight of app. 176 lb (80 kg). According to the designer, over-rigging the craft has proved a great help, since it facilitates the transition from hull-borne to sailborne state. Support is also provided by the centreboard and rudder plate. It is stated that very little trim is required in heel.

ZAGLOSLIZG (Sailing Skimmer) Z-71

Designed in 1971, this is equipped with a specially built lightweight strut-and-cable sail wing, differing slightly from the earlier design. It features a trimming device and simplified control.

The craft can be towed in the air behind a motor boat, like a conventional kite-glider.

DIMENSIONS:

Length overall, hull	10 ft 6 in (3·20 m)
Beam	4 ft 3 in (1·30 m)
Draft, centreboard lowered	3 ft 11 in (1·20 m)
Sail wing span	23 ft 0 in (7·0 m)
Max chord sail wing	11 ft 6 in (3·50 m)
Sail wing area	150 sq ft (14 m²)
Aspect ratio	3·5 : 1
Stabiliser area	22 sq ft (2 m²)
Mast height	9 ft 6 in (2·90 m)

WEIGHTS:

Empty weight	154 lb (70 kg)
Gross weight	330 lb (150 kg)
Sail wing	26 lb (12 kg)

PERFORMANCE:

Lift/drag ratio of sail wing	about 6 : 1

Tests with various arrangements of the Z-73s sailwing continued during 1974. *Above:* Equipped with a fixed canard stabiliser. *Below:* a conventional configuration employing a horizontal stabiliser. Foot-operated steering has been installed for the water rudder

Max angle of wing setting	60 deg
Horizontal lift/drag ratio for 45 deg heel	4·2 : 1
Lift/drag ratio of centreboard and rudder plate	10·2 : 1
Max craft/speed wind velocity ratio	3 : 1
Optimum angle of apparent wind	19 deg
Optimum heading angle	109 deg
Wind velocity for take-off	18 fps (5·5 m/s)
Minimum speed for take-off	24 mph (40 km/h)
Optimum airborne speed	34 mph (55 km/h)

Z 73

Developed from the Z-70 and Z-71, the Z-73 employs a modified Cadet class dinghy hull, equipped with a high aspect ratio centre-board and rudder.

During 1974, several further modifications were made to the sailwing, including the addition of a bow stabiliser to assess the advantages of a canard configuration, and a horizontal stabiliser surface to assess the value of a conventional configuration.

The mast was moved aft of the cockpit, and foot-operated rudder bar steering was installed.

Based on the test results, a further development model—the Z-75—is being built, the wing of which will also be used as an ultra-light, tailless hang-glider.

The wing, covered in nylon, incorporates a light vertical stabiliser, and has inherent directional and lateral stability.

Altitude control is based on a combination of incidence and heel angle control. Excessive altitude results in increased drift and a loss of speed and lift. This leads to a restoration of normal trim, with the hull riding at a predetermined height above the water level. The restoring forces are described as being similar to those of a vee-foil sailing hydrofoil.

DIMENSIONS:

Length overall, hull	10 ft 6 in (3·20 m)
Beam	4 ft 3 in (1·30 m)
Draft, centreboard lowered	3 ft 11 in (1·20 m)
Sailwing span	21 ft 4 in (6·5 m)
Aspect ratio	4·7:1
Stabiliser area	13 sq ft (1·2 m²)

WEIGHTS:

Empty weight	150 lbs (68 kg)
Gross weight	330 lb (150 kg)
Sailwing	22 lb (10 kg)

PERFORMANCE: (Design)

Lift/drag ratio, sailwing	app 8:1
Max angle of wing setting	60 deg
Horizontal lift/drag ratio for 45 deg heel	3·5:1
Lift/drag ratio of centre board and rudder	2·1:1
Wind velocity for take-off	21 fps (6·5 m/s)
Minimum speed for take-off	27 mph (45 km/h)
Optimum airborne speed	36 mph (60 km/h)

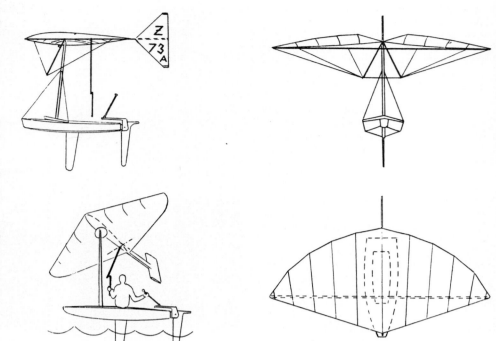

General arrangement of the Z-73A, incorporating a sketch showing the control arrangements

UNITED KINGDOM

NEW HYDROFIN LTD

HEAD OFFICE:

Burfield Flat, Bosham Lane, Bosham, Sussex.

EXECUTIVES:

Christopher Hook, Managing Director

Christopher Hook was responsible for the conception, design and development of the fully-submerged hydrofoil, which he demonstrated in the USA in 1951 with his Red Bug prototype and later with his Miami-built conversion sets. He became a partner of the late Herr G. Sachsenburg, the pioneer hydrofoil builder, and has completed hydrofoil design and consultancy contracts in the US, Israel, Holland, France, Norway and Italy, as well as with Strathclyde University.

He is currently developing a self-tending sail rig for sailing hydrofoil craft comprising sails that tilt to windward and have roller reefing.

The TS 14 retains all the good points of Miss Bosham, the first fully-reefing, rotating rig with sail tilting and transverse stability on a very narrow hull by incidence-controlled hydrofoil. Whereas on Miss Bosham roller reefing was used on sails with an aspect ratio of only 1½, the new reefing method of TS 14 is much simpler and the AR is 3½. The sails (now 4 in number) are of sleeve form, retained at the leech, but free to slide round the large diameter tube mast to accommodate the change in the two cambers as the wind changes sides. To reef, the leech cable is un-hooked at the bottom end plate and the whole sail treated like a curtain. A special line (not shown) pulls the leech cable forward at the top of the mast. Thus one, two, three or four sails may be set and the rig is greatly simplified.

Another important improvement is the

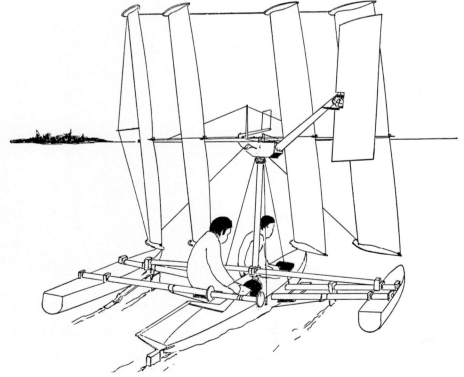

New Hydrofin TS 14

addition of the "seeker", seen as a small rectangular blade directly over the central mast. Its function is to detect small changes in apparent wind direction and apply more air rudder deflection sooner than would result from a fixed air rudder. Too much mechanical advantage to the seeker will produce hunting but the correct amount results in a perfectly steady sail setting, while any turbulence shed by the sails, and picked up by the air rudder, is at once corrected by advance information from the seeker.

Obviously the seeker cannot be given sole control of the air rudder since the pilot must select his course, which may be ahead or astern. To do this he is provided with a line, three turns of which are seen near his right hand. The end discs permit control from either side and the spring-loaded line passes up the centre of the mast to differential levers from which the resultant of pilot and seeker information is transmitted to the air rudder. For instance, if the pilot centres his line, and the seeker is also aligned to the boom, all sails will remain luffed irrespective of the hull attitude to the wind. Whether the boat moves forwards or backwards depends on which way the pilot moves his control line. Sailing, and even tacking backwards is quite easy as is the hove-to position with the hull broadside to the wind to get maximum drift resistance from lee-board(s) and foil strut.

In a gust, putting the helm down makes no difference to the pressure on the sails and it is the air rudder which must be moved by the control line. Similarly, air rudder setting depends on speed. The sail tilting facility is not useful in light airs or in tracking, but even in these positions it permits the sails to be upright despite some heeling. There is thus never a downward component of wind force tending to increase hull displacement as in a heeling yacht. In strong winds a light boat can obtain quite a large air lift from a well tilted sail system. To obtain this effect the masts are attached to the cross-spar (that rotates wth the boom) by forward pointing bolts and the sail cloth must have a "button-hole" in way of these to permit it to slide as described. It will be seen that the mast rigging is a closed frame, ending at the tilting winch in the boom near the central masthead. In small craft this winch is turned by hand but in large craft this will be done by electric winch. Since there is about as much sail area below the bolt axis as there is above, it follows that

wind forces are balanced out, thus greatly reducing the need for bracing wires. If we examine the wind forces in each sail we find about half taken by the mast and transmitted to the rigging described, one quarter taken by the spar connecting all the leeches to the boom and one quarter turned into torques at the ends of the masts. Hence the need for a fairly large diameter tube which, aerodynamically, produces a very gentle stall. Transmission of the torque to the bolt is avoided by a smaller inside tube from bolt to leech and the end plates are supported by gussets (not shown). These will, in practice, prevent the concave camber at the ends. We have not shown this on the drawing because it is only the curve as drawn which demonstrates the general sail camber.

Unlike previous rotating rigs, the roller bearing is at the mast-head thus allowing a fixed mast to be well stayed to the hull. The tubular side float spars are triangulated forward and held by metal strips passing into the hull aft. A drag force brace must be added (not shown) to take float drag. Since the tube system is easily dismantled this very wide craft presents no transport problems and side floats can be proportionately of less displacement and resistance. There is no valid reason why this facility should not be maintained into large sizes.

With increasing sizes the balanced sail too will be much easier to engineer than the same area would be in the classical Bermuda form and enormously easier than the proposed square-rigger with unsupported masts. Inertial forces in a heavy sea will need watching. The long air rudder boom is ultra-light but a spring-loaded joint could be inserted at some stage while the cross spar joint to the main boom will require to be progressively thickened. Tapered masts would tend to reduce inertial problems.

Unorthodox high speed sailing has been

demonstrated at the expense of considerable added complexity of control and the smallest changes of course speed or wind demand constant and considerable control power inputs due to an inherently unstable set of forces.

Twiddle Sail may employ one or two hydrofoils for transverse stability depending on whether the danger of lost downwards lift, due to surfacing, is an acceptable risk or not. In a racing craft it will be acceptable since the speed run may be made with a leeward foil. Hydrofoil incidence control must be automatic by sensor, and with some form of damping of which viscous is best. There is also a need for a pilot adjustment between the sensor and the foil. All this is well understood. The foil may be totally retracted as may be the lee-board shown on the starboard side tube spar.

APPLICATIONS: The uses of such a boat are varied and new ones are being suggested constantly, particularly for the Third World and in steady wind areas with warm climates. Sport, inter-island transport, sight seeing cruises, medical work, fishing fleet service, oil wells, ocean bed exploration and, later on, ocean cruises are some of the proposals. Where delays due to calms could cost money some auxiliary power can be installed on deck. Fuel for same may be stowed in the side floats. In the main, however, this is purely a wind-powered vessel. Building is starting mainly as Technical College projects and for small craft.

Key parts can be supplied in moulded grp such as: two sizes of floats (assembled finished or unjoined sides nested for easy transport), grp hydrofoil with carbon fibres, cross spar, boom and extension are available as well as detailed designs of all parts. (Metric). Special sheet for large R/C model TS 14 or fully flying type. Prices on request.

UNITED STATES OF AMERICA

DAK HYDROFOILS
HEAD OFFICE:
PO Box 71, Sausalito, California 94965
PROPRIETOR AND CHIEF DESIGNER:
David A. Keiper

Design of the Williwaw, the world's first seagoing sailing hydrofoil, began in 1963. Construction of the craft, which is based on a specially designed trimaran hull, began in May 1966 and tests started in November 1967.

After nearly three years of trials along the California coast, Williwaw, manned by David Keiper and one other crew member, successfully completed a 16-day passage between Sausalito, California and Kahului Harbour, Maui, Hawaii, in September 1970—the first ocean crossing by a hydrofoil sailboat.

Heavy seas and strong winds were encountered on the first two days of the voyage, during which the craft made 200 miles per day. At times the craft attained 25 knots, but light winds in mid-ocean prevented the craft from making the passage in record time.

The craft entered chartered sailing yacht service in March 1971, operating from Hanelei Hawaii and before returning to Sausalito, California, completed about 2,000 miles of inter-island sailing around Hawaii, mainly in open sea conditions.

Various modifications to the craft were undertaken during 1974-75, and in the summer of 1975 a second series of sea trials was due to begin in the South Pacific.

Dak Hydrofoils is currently developing simple low-cost hydrofoil conversion kits for existing racing catamarans with lengths ranging from 12-20 ft (3-65-6-90 m). These were test marketed between 1972-1974. Economic conditions permitting, Dak Hydrofoils hopes to begin the full-scale marketing of ready-to-install foil sets for a variety of multihulls in 1976.

The design of 16, 31 and 38 ft (4-87, 9-44 and 11-58 m) hydrofoil trimarans is continuing, and complete boats will be built to order. A modified conversion kit introduced in 1974 is also suitable for outboard powerboats.

WILLIWAW
A prototype sailing hydrofoil, Williwaw has a specially designed trimaran hull attached to which are four foils—a deep V-foil at the bow, a ladder foil at the stern, and one laterally outboard of each of the port and starboard pontoons. The stern foil pivots and serves as a rudder when hullborne.

The craft accommodates 2-3 passengers, together with cruising supplies, and attains 15-17 knots in steady 11-12 knot winds.

It is able to remain fully foilborne for unlimited distances in moderate seas as long

as there is adequate wind power.

Various modifications and improvements were made to the craft during 1974-75. These included the addition of streamlined fairings at the four main intersections of the lifting surfaces and struts on the main foil; the installation of a retractable leeboard for improved windward performance in light airs, and the facing of various aluminium foil fittings with stainless steel to prevent wear and tear around the shear/fastening bolts.

FOILS: The bow foil, of surface-piercing V configuration, is mounted between the pontoon bows and that of the main hull. Foils, supporting struts and sub-foil elements, are of welded aluminium, with a protective coating of vinyl. Foil section is NACA 16-510 with 6 in (152-4 mm) chord throughout the system. The foils have fairly high aspect ratio. Foil loading during a normal take-off is: bow foil 40%, stern foil 20% and leeward lateral foil 40%, depending on sail heeling forces. Dihedral of the bow foil is 30-50 degrees.

The lateral foils, which are not as deep as the bow and stern foils, are of 4-rung ladder type, and have 35 degrees dihedral. The stern foil is of 3-rung ladder configuration with zero dihedral at rest, but craft heel gives it 10-15 degrees dihedral. Under most conditions the rungs are fully submerged.

The entire stern foil pivots for steering action. Shear bolts protect bow and stern foils from damage if debris is struck.

Foil retraction arrangements are as follows:

After the removal of shear bolts the bow foil swings forward and upwards through 90 degrees; the lateral foils swing outwards and over, and are laid flat on the deck through a second pivot axis, and the stern foil swings aft and over through 180 degrees. Retraction of the bow and lateral foils is achieved through the use of a simple block and tackle.

CONTROL: A tiller-operated, combined stern foil and rudder, controls direction in foilborne mode; paired struts, also tiller operated, provide rudder control when hullborne.

HULL: Lightweight, but robust trimaran hull with small wing deck to avoid aerodynamic lift. Marine ply structure sheathed with glass fibre. Built-in attachment points for foils. Mast supported by main frame.

ACCOMMODATION: The craft is designed for 2-3 people, with cruising supplies, but has flown with nine aboard. The deep cockpit accommodates the helmsman and one crew member. The cockpit, which provides adequate shelter from the strong winds developed by high-speed sailing, forms the entrance to main and stern cabins. The main cabin seats four comfortably. There are two berths in the main cabin and one in the stern cabin. The main cabin also includes a galley, shelving and a marine head. There is generous stowage space in the pontoon hulls.

SAIL AND POWERPLANT: Sail power alone on prototype, but a small outboard auxiliary engine can be fitted if required. Total sail area is 380 ft² (35·30 m²).

SYSTEMS: Electronics: Radio direction finder normally carried.

DIMENSIONS:

Length overall, hull	31 ft 4 in (9·54 m)
Length waterline, hull	28 ft 0 in (8·53 m)
Length overall, foils retracted	33 ft 0 in (10·05 m)
Length overall, foils extended	32 ft 0 in (9·75 m)

Hull beam:

Main hull at WL	3 ft 0 in (0·91 m)
Hull overall, foils retracted	16 ft 4 in (4·97 m)
Beam, overall, foils extended	25 ft 0 in (7·62 m)
Draft afloat, foils retracted	1 ft 4 in (0·40 m)
Draft afloat, foils extended	4 ft 0 in (1·21 m)
Draft foilborne	1 ft 6 in-2 ft 6 in (0·45 m-0·76 m)
Freeboard	2 ft (0·61 m)
Pontoon deck	1 ft 6 in-3 ft 6 in (457-762 mm)
Main hull deck	2 ft 6 in-3 ft 6 in (762 mm-1·06 m)
Height overall to masthead	39 ft 0 in (11·88 m)

DIMENSIONS, INTERNAL:

Cabin (Wheelhouse, galley, toilet included)

Length	28 ft 0 in (8·53 m)
Max width	16 ft 0 in (4·87 m)
Max height	5 ft 4 in (1·62 m)
Volume	480 cu ft (13·78 cu m)

WEIGHTS:

Light displacement	2,200 lb (997·88 kg)
Normal take-off displacement	3,000 lb (1,360 kg)

Above: Williwaw sailing in Hawaiian waters at a speed of 20 knots, shortly after her historic transocean crossing from California. Sail twist at top is caused by the Williwaw's speed, attesting to the low drag of the foils. *Below:* Williwaw anchored in home waters at Sausalito, California, after 7,000 miles of voyaging in the Pacific

Max take-off displacement	3,600 lb (1,632 kg)
Normal payload	800 lb (362·8 kg)
Max payload	1,400 lb (635 kg)

PERFORMANCE (in steady wind and calm water, with normal payload):

Take-off speed

Normally 12 knots. Craft is able to take-off with a 12-knot beam wind and accelerate to 18-20 knots

Max speed foilborne	30 knots
Cruising speed foilborne	12-25 knots

Max permissible sea state and wave height in foilborne mode:

Sea state almost unlimited at 12 knot average speed with wind aft of beam. Foils well behaved in all conditions met so far. Sails reefed down in heavy conditions to maintain comfort and ease of handling. Craft shows no tendency to pound.

Turning radius at cruising speed

150 ft (45·72 m)

Number of seconds and distance to take-off:
5 secs in strong wind, two boat lengths

Number of seconds to stop craft

8 seconds, turning dead into wind

SEA TESTS: Craft tested in strong winds with steep breaking seas 15-20 ft (4·57-0·69 m) high off California coast. It has completed a return voyage from the California coast to Hawaii and sailed 2,000 miles (3,218 km) during inter-island charters in Hawaii.

Speed is significantly more than wind speed in conditions of steady wind and calm water. The craft can match wind speed in moderate seas, but not in heavy seas. In heavy seas, broad reaching or beam, it has averaged 15 knots for hours at a time, winds gusting to Force 5 and 6. Speeds may climb to 30 knots or drop to 5 knots, depending upon local wind and waves. Acceleration and decelerations are gradual and not objectionable. The ride is far smoother than that of displacement multihulls.

PACIFIC EXPRESS

Successor to the Williwaw, the Pacific Express is a second generation hydrofoil cruising trimaran. It is wider than its predecessor, has fully buoyant hulls, is equipped with a more efficient hydrofoil system, and has a slightly greater load carrying capacity.

The craft is designed to operate in a wide variety of conditions, from heavy storm seas to light airs, In heavy seas. with foils set, it is exceptionally stable and capable of high speeds. The comfort level is stated to be five times that of a catamaran of similar size and the craft tends to self-steer for 90% of the time, with helm tied.

In light airs and calms, with foils retracted the craft makes the most of the available wind.

FOILS: Configuration similar to that of Williwaw. Foils have a 5 in (127 mm) chord and are fabricated in heavily anodized aluminium. Bolts, washers, etc., are in stainless steel. Bow and lateral foils are fixed while sailing. The tiller-operated combined stern foil and rudder, controls direction when foilborne. All four foils retract manually after the removal of shear bolts.

HULL: Monocoque, marine plywood hull with flush deck sheathed in epoxy-glassfibre.

SAIL: Sloop rig with working sail area of 380 sq ft (25·29 sq m).

ACCOMMODATION: Four berths, settee, galley, shelves and marine head.

DIMENSIONS:

Hull length	31 ft 4 in (9·55 m)
Beam	19 ft 6 in (5·94 m)
Draft	1 ft 5 in (0·43 m)
Draft, foils extended	4 ft 0 in (1·21 m)

Hobie-16 Dak-foil conversion with foils retracted

WEIGHTS:
Normal loaded displacement
2,400 lb (1,088·5 kg)
Light displacement 3,500 lb (1,586·5 kg)
PERFORMANCE:
Maximum speed, foilborne about 30 knots

SPEED FREAK
This is a special racing craft which will

make the maximum possible ratio of boat speed to true wind speed on one tack. although capable of sailing on both tacks. The design is based on a proa hull, which will incorporate special aerodynamic features. Standard 2 in (50 mm) Dak Hydrofoil foil extrusions will be used. Overall length will be 16-20 ft (4·87-6·09 m).

DONALD NIGG

ADDRESS:
7924 Fontana, Prairie Village, Kansas, USA 66208
TELEPHONE:
913-642-2002

Development of the Flying Fish began in 1963 at Lake Quivira, an inland lake in Kansas. Donald Nigg believed that if the pitchpole moment and vertical stability problems could be solved, the front-steering three-point suspension system typical of the modern ice-yacht offered several advantages. Previous craft had often used three-point suspension, but all appear to have used rear steering. To develop this new approach, Exocoetus, an experimental platform was built. It was evolved through three distinct versions during 1964-67 and established the basic feasibility.

Interest in the experiments resulted in numerous requests for plans, but although the craft was ideal as a development platform, it was not a design suitable for home construction. In response to these requests the Flying Fish was developed.

To keep the costs to a minimum, the craft is designed to carry a sail area of 100-150 sq ft. It was anticipated that most of those interested in building a sailing hydrofoil would be small boat sailors, owning a boat carrying a mainsail of this size. The design thus allows the builder to share the sail and rigging with an existing dinghy.

A true development class of sailing hydrofoil has been slow to emerge, but the Flying Fish may mark the beginning of such a class. The amateur Yacht Research Society, Hythe, Kent, United Kingdom, is promoting the design as a development class.

Sets of plans for the Flying Fish have been supplied to potential builders in many countries.

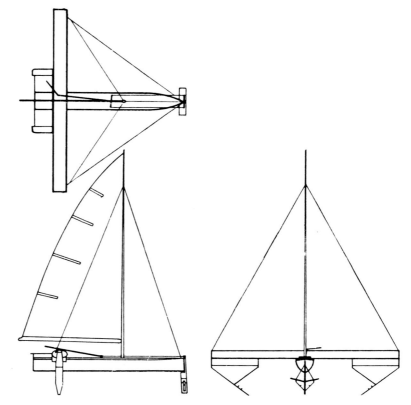

The Nigg Flying Fish

FLYING FISH
First of a development class of sailing hydrofoils, the Flying Fish has been specially developed for home builders. Built mainly in wood and with a length overall of 16 ft 6 in (5·02 m), it has a maximum foilborne speed of more than 30 knots.

The estimated cost of constructing a craft

of this type, less sail and rigging (the 125 sq ft mainsail and rigging from a Y-Flyer were used for the prototype illustrated), is US $250,000.

FOILS: The foil configuration is surface piercing and non-retractable with 16% of the weight supported by the vee bow foil and the remaining 84% by the outrigged main foils.

The latter are also of the vee type, with cantilevered extensions at the apex. Total foil area is 1·42 m² (15·3 sq ft) and the foil loading is 300 lb sq ft max at 30 knots. The front foil and its supporting strut are built in aluminium and oak, and the main foil is in oak only.

STEERING: A basic feature of the design is the use of front rather than rear steering. Directional control is provided by the movement of the hinged bow foil.

HULL: This is an all-wooden structure built in fir plywood, ¼ in thick and sealed. Torque load is carried by the skin, and bending loads are carried by the skin and the internal beam structure.

The crossbeam provides stability when in dock and in a displacement condition at low speeds. At 2-3 knots the horizontal safety foils at the top of the vee of the rear foils provide interim foil stabilisation up to the take-off speed of 5 knots and prevent dragging an end of the crossbeam in the water. At foilborne speeds the safety foils preclude the possibility of an end of the crossbeam being driven into the water by sudden heeling.

RIG: A cat rig of 9·2-13·9 m² (100-150 sq ft) area is recommended.

DIMENSIONS:

Length overall, hull (plus boom overhand at rear, dependent on sail plan)
        5·02 m (16 ft 6 in)
Length waterline, hull 4·87 m (16 ft 0 in)
Beam 6·09 m (20 ft 0 in)
Draft afloat (fixed foils) 1·06 m (3 ft 6 in)

Topping 20 knots on a close reach in a light wind

Draft foilborne
    12-30 in over operating speed range
Height, approx   7·3 m (24 ft 0 in)

PERFORMANCE:

Max speed foilborne
Over 30 knots, design cruise range
        optimised for 20-30 knots
Max speed hullborne 5 knots
Min wind for take-off 10 knots
Number of seconds and distance to take-off (theor. app)

3 secs with 15·2 m (50 ft) run in favourable wind
Number of seconds and distance to stop craft (theor. app)
Can land from 20 knots in 45·6 m (150 ft) in about 6 seconds

SEA TEST: The craft has been tested in 10-25 knot winds, on both sheltered inland lakes and on ocean bays, with a max chop of about 18 inches. Speeds up to approx 30 knots have been attained.

HYDROFOIL OPERATORS

HYDROFOIL OPERATORS

NORTH AMERICA
USA
DEPARTMENT OF THE NAVY,
NAVAL SEA SYSTEMS COMMAND (NAVSEA)

The Boeing/NATO PHM, Patrol Hydrofoil, Guided Missile, is a NATO project, sponsored jointly by the US Navy, the Federal Republic of Germany and the Italian Navy. It is being developed by NAVSEA PMS 303.

The first craft, the Pegasus, began operational evaluation in the San Diego area in the summer of 1975. The outcome of these tests is expected to lead to a US Navy production decision by late 1975 or early 1976, followed by a number of overseas procurement orders.

Sea World
1720 South Shores Road, Mission Bay, San Diego, California
TELEPHONE: 224-3535

This company operates three 28-seat Atlantic Hydrofoils Inc. Sea Worlds (Sprague Engineering Co) on ten minute sightseeing tours around Mission Bay. The craft were the first built on the West Coast to be licensed for commercial use by the US Coast Guard.

US Navy Pacific Fleet Amphibious Command
Type(s): Flagstaff, PGH-1
Base: San Diego

US Naval Ship Research and Development Center
Type(s): High Point, PCH-1; Plainview AGEH-1
Purpose: US Navy hydrofoil development programme.

SOUTH AMERICA
ARGENTINA
Alimar SA
Type(s): PT 50, 3 (Rodriquez)
Route: Buenos Aires-Colonia-Montevideo
BOLIVIA
Crillon Tours Ltd
ADDRESS: PO Box 4785 Av Comacho 1223 Ed, Krsul, La Paz
Type(s): Albatross, 2 (Honold), modified by Helmut Kock
Route: Lake Titicaca
CUBA
Type(s): Kometa M, 1 (Sormovo)
Route(s): Batabano—Nueva Gerona
VENEZUELA
Compania Shell
Type(s): PT 20, 4 (Werf Gusto)
Route: Offshore oil drilling operations on Lake Maracaibo
Naveca SA
Type(s): PT 20, 4 (Rodriquez)
Route: Maracaibo-Cabimas

WEST INDIES
US VIRGIN ISLANDS
Moroso Hydrofoil Wings Inc.
HEAD OFFICE: 737 Canal Street, Building 23, Stamford, Conn 06902
TELEPHONE: (203) 325-4371
Route(s): St Thomas, US Virgin Islands to Puerto Rico
Type(s): Kometa M, 1 (Sormovo)

ASIA AND PACIFIC
CHINA
Navy of the Chinese People's Republic
Type(s): Hu Chwan Class, 60 plus (Shanghai)
Operational areas: Coastal waters

HAWAII
Pacific Sea Transportation Ltd.
Seaflite Services
HEAD OFFICE: 233 Keawe Street, Honolulu, Hawaii
Type(s): Jetfoil, 3 (Boeing)
Route(s): Daily services between Honolulu and Kauai, Maui and Hawaii island.
INDONESIA
Sundaharya Corp, Djakarta
Type(s): PT 20 (Rodriquez)
Route: Indonesia Coast

Madeira, the first of the company's two Boeing Jetfoils. It averages 45 knots and carries 278 passengers.

JAPAN
Boyo Kisen Co. Ltd.
Type(s): PT 50, 1 (Hitachi)
Route(s): Yanai—Matsuyama
Type(s): PT 20, 1, "Shibuki No 2" (Hitachi)
Route(s): Yanai—Matsuyama
Isizaki Kisen Co. Ltd.
Fukae, Ohaki-cho, Saeki-gun,
Hiroshima-ken, Japan
Type(s): PT 50, "Kosei" (Hitachi)
Route(s): Hiroshima-Kure-Matsuyama
Type(s): PT 50, 1 (Hitachi)
Route(s): Hiroshima-Kure-Matsuyama
Type(s): PT 20 "Kinsei", 1 (Hitachi)
Route(s): Onomichi-Matsuyama
Type(s): PT 20 "Tsobasamaru", 1 (Hitachi)
Route(s): Hiroshima-Kure-Matsuyama
Kansai Steamship Co Ltd..
Soze-che, Kita-ku, Osaka
Type(s): PT 50, 1 "Haya Kaze" (Hitachi)
Route(s): Osaka-Koke-Shodoshima-Takamatsu
Type(s): PT 20, 2, "Hayate" Nos 1 and 2 (Hitachi)
Route(s): "Hayate No 1", Himeji-Syodoshima-Takamatsu "Hayate No 2", Koke-Sumoto
Meitetsu Kaijo Kankosen Co.
99-1 Shin-miyazaka-cho, Atsuta-ku, Nagoya City
Type(s): PT 50, 1 "Osyo" (Hitachi)
Route(s): Nagoya-Toba-Gamagori-Nishiura-Irako
Type(s): PT 20, 2 "Taihomaru" and "Hayabusamaru" (Hitachi)
Route(s): Nagoya-Toba-Irako-Gamagori-Shinojima and Kowa-Shinojima-Irako-Toba-Nishiura
Nichimen Co. Ltd.
(Kinkowan Ferry Co. Ltd.)
Type(s): PT 50, 1 "Otori No 3" (Hitachi)
Route(s): Kajiki-Kagoshima-Ibusuki
Nissho-Iwai Co. Ltd.
(Hankyu Lines Co. Ltd.)
Type(s): PT 50, 2 "Zuiho" and "Houo" (Hitachi)
Route(s): Koke-Tokushima
Hankyu Lines Co. Ltd.
Type(s): PT 20, 2, "Amatsu" and "Kasugano"
Route(s): Kobe-Naruto
Setonaikai Kisen Co. Ltd.
Ujina Kaigani-chome, Hiroshima
Type(s): PT 50, 3 "Wakashio", "Otori No 1" and "Otori No 2" (Hitachi)
Route(s): Onomichi-Setoda-Imabari and Hiroshima-Kure-Matsuyama
Type(s): PT 50, 1, "Kondoru" (Hitachi)
Route(s): Hiroshima-Kure-Matsuyama
Type(s): PT 50, 1. (Hitachi)

Route(s): Ónomichi-Setoda-Imbari
Type(s): PT 50, 4 "Hibiki No 1", "No 2" and "No 3" and "Shibuki
No 1" (Hitachi)
Route(s): Onomichi-Setoda-Omishima-Imbari and ("Shibuki No 1")
Yanai-Matsuyama

HONG KONG
Shun Tak Co
Type(s): PT 20, 1 (Rodriquez)
Route: Hong-Kong Macao
Hong Kong Macao Hydrofoil Co
PT 50, 4 (Rodriquez); RHS 140, 5 (Navaltecnica)
Far East Hydrofoil Co. Ltd.
HEAD OFFICE:
36th Floor, Connaught Centre, Connaught Road, Hong Kong
TELEPHONE:
H-243176
TELEX:
74200
CABLES:
Setedam, Hong Kong
DIRECTORS:
Stanley Ho, Managing Director
EXECUTIVES:
K. B. Allport, Group Manager
D. Hay, Technical Manager
Route: Hong Kong-Macao, distance 36 nm by the Southern Route.
Services half-hourly, sunrise to sunset, i.e. 15,400 trips per annum.
Approximate total number of passengers carried per year-1,405,000.
Craft: PT 50, 4, Guia, Penha, Taipa, Balsa (Hitachi Zosen); RHS
110, 4, Cerco, Praia, Barca, Cacilhas (Navaltecnica); RHS 160, 1,
Lilau; (Navaltecnica); PTS 75 Mk 111, 1, Rosa (Vosper Thorny-
croft); Jetfoil, 2, Madeira, Santa Maria, (Boeing).

CEYLON
Royal Ceylon Navy
Type(s): Waterman, 1 (International Aquavion)
Communications and patrol
KOREA
Hans Ryeo Developments Co. Ltd.
Type(s): PT 20, 1 (Rodriquez)
PHILIPPINES
Bataan Manila Ferry Services
Manila
Type(s): Raketa TA (Sormovo/Airavia)

Tourist Hotel and Travel Corporation
Type(s): PT 20, 2 (Rodriquez)
Route: Manila-Corregidor

Philippine Navy
Type(s): PT 20, 2 (Rodriquez); PT 32, 2 "Bontoc", "Baler",
(Hitachi)
Coastal Patrol

AUSTRALASIA
AUSTRALIA
Port Jackson Hydrofoils Pty.
Limited
HEAD OFFICE:
No. 2 Jetty, Circular Quay, Sydney,
N.S.W. 2000
TELEPHONE:
27.9251
CABLES:
"Manlyferries"
TERMINAL OFFICES:
No. 2 Jetty, Circular Quay 27.9251
Manly Wharf, Manly 97.3028
DIRECTORS:
J. C. Needham, Managing Director
Neil M. Barrell, Director
SENIOR EXECUTIVES:
T. S. Morrison, Secretary
G. E. Marshall, Traffic Manager
W. B. McCubbray, Superintending Engineer
OPERATIONS: Routes served and frequency. Sydney to Manly,
7 miles, every 20 minutes between 7 a.m. and 7 p.m.
Approximate number of passengers carried during year: One
million.
CRAFT IN SERVICE:
PT 20, 1 (Hitachi), 72 passengers, built 1965.

Two of the twelve hydrofoils currently operated by Far East Hydrofoil
Co Ltd on its half-hourly service to Macau. The company carries upwards
of 1,405,000 passengers per year over the 36 nm route, and completes
about 15,400 runs. *Top:* Lilau, a 160-seat Navaltecnica RHS 160
which completes the journey at a speed of about 36 knots. *Bottom:*
Barca, RHS 110, which operates at a service speed of 35 knots

PT 50 (Rodriquez), 140 passengers, built in 1966.
PT 20, 1 (Hitachi) "Manly", 72 passengers, built 1965.
PT 50 (Rodriquez), "Fairlight", 140 passengers, built 1966
PT 50 (Rodriquez), "Dee Why", 140 passengers, built 1968
RHS 140 (Navaltecnica), "Curl Curl" built in 1971.

Tires Pty Ltd TD
HEAD OFFICE:
Corner Junction, Road and Gray Terrace, Rosewater, Outer
Harbour, South Australia
Type(s) Aquavion Waterman, 1.
Route: Port Adelaide to Outer Harbour. Hourly service. Also
educational and scenic tours of Port River, Adelaide.

NEW ZEALAND
Kerridge Odeon Corporation
Type(s): PT 20, 1 (Rodriquez)
Route: Auckland-Waiheke Island
EUROPE, MEDITERRANEAN AND NEAR EAST
ALBANIA
Albanian Navy
Type(s): Hu Chwan (White Swan) Class, 30 (Shanghai)
Operating areas: Coastal waters
BULGARIA
Bulgarian Shipping Line
Type(s): Kometa, 4
Route: Bourgas-Nesetow-Varna
Bulgarian River Fleet
Type(s): Meteor, 2; Raketa, 2
Route: Danube, between Rousse and Silistra
CHANNEL ISLANDS
Condor Ltd
Type(s): PT 50, 1 (Rodriquez) RHS 140, 2 (Navaltecnic)
Route: Guernsey-Jersey-St. Malo
DENMARK
Dampskipsselskapet Oresund
Type(s): PT 50, 2 (1 Rodriquez, 1 Westermoen); RHS 140, 1
(Navaltecnic)
Route: Copenhagen-Malmö

EGYPT
Ministry of Commerce, Cairo
Type(s): PT 20, 3 (Rodriquez)
Route: Abu Simbel-Asswan
Nile Sightseeing Service
Type(s): Kometa, 1 (Sormovo)
Route: Sightseeing tour, based on Cairo.
FINLAND
Paijanteen Kantosiipi Oy
Type(s): Raketa, 1 (Krasnoye Sormovo)
Route: Lahti-Jyvaskyla, across Lake Paijane
FRANCE
Vedettes Armoricaines
Ier Eperon,
56 rue d'Aiguillon, 29N Brest.
Type(s): Kometa, 1, (Sormovo)
GERMANY
Water Police
Type(s): PT 4, 3 (German Shipyard)
Route: Patrol service on the Rhine
Köln Düsseldorfer Shipping Co
Type(s): Raketa, 1 "Rhine Arrow" (Sormovo)
Routes: Cologne—Koblenz
GREECE
Hellenic Hydrofoil Lines
Type(s): Kometa 2 (Sormovo), plus one Kometa on order
Route(s): Brindisi—Corfu; Otranto—Corfu (Igoumenitsa)
 80 mile run takes 2½ hours. Fare Drs 600 (£8·80) single
HUNGARY
Hungarian Navigation Company
Type(s): Raketa, 2 Chaika, 2, Meteors, 2 plus (Krasnoye-Sormovo)
Route: Budapest-Vienna
IRAN
Type(s): Kometas (Sormovo)
Service(s): Persian Gulf
ITALY
Aliscafi SNAV, SpA
Type(s): PT 20, 7; PT 50, 8 (Rodriquez) and RHS 110, 1 (Naval-
Route: Messina-Reggio-Isole-Lipari   tecnica)
Onorato
Aliscafi del Tirreno
Naples
Type(s): PT 50, 2 (Westermoen) PT 20, 1 (Rodriquez) Kometa and
 Kometa M, 8 (Sormovo)
Route(s): Naples Bay, Naples-Capri, Naples-Capri-Ischia
SAS, Trapani
Type(s): PT 50, 1; PT 20, 3 (Rodriquez)
Route: Trapani-Egadi Islands
Adriatica SpA di Navigazione
Venezia
Type(s): PT 50, 1 (Rodriquez), RHS 160, 1 (Navaltecnica)
Route: Tremoli-Isoledi Tremiti
Ministry of Transport, Milan
Type(s): PT 20, 2, (Rodriquez); RHS 70, 3 (Navaltecnica)
Route: Lake Garda
Compagnia di Navigazione
Type(s): PT 20, 2 (Rodriquez); RHS 70, 1 (Navaltecnica)
Route: Lake Maggiore
Compagnia di Navigazione
Type(s): PT 20, 2 (Rodriquez); RHS 70, 1 (Navaltecnica)
Route: Lake Como
G. & R. Salvatori, Naples
Type(s): PT 50, 2 (Westermoen)
Route: Naples-Capri
Sar Nav
(Societa Sarda per Navigazione Veloce)
HEAD OFFICE:
 Via Lombardia 38, Olbia
Type(s): Seaflight L90 "Squalo Bianco", 1
Route(s): Civitavecchia-Olbia (Italian Pennisula-Sardinia)
Societa Sirena, Palermo
Type(s): PT 50, 1 (Rodriquez)
Route: Palermo-Ustica
Societa Tosco Sarda di Nav Porto Ferraio
Type(s): PT 20, 3, PT 20 Caribe, 1 (Rodriquez)
Route: Piombino-R, Matina-P. Azzutto
AGIP, Milan
Type(s): PT 20, 1, PT 50, 1 (Rodriquez)

NORWAY
De bla Omnibusser A/S
Type(s): PT 20, 2 (Westermoen)
Route: Oslofjord
Stavangerske Dampskibsselskab
Type(s): PT 50, 2; PT 20, 1, (Rodriquez); RHS 140, 1,
 (Navaltecnica)
Route: Stavanger-Haugesund-Bergen
Hardanger Sunnhordelandske Dampskibsselskap
Box 268, 5001, Bergen
Type(s): PT 20, 1 (Westermoen); RHS 140, 1 (Navaltecnica)
Route: Bergen-Tittelsness
Fosen Trafikklag A/S
Skaneskaia 6, Trondheim
Type(s): PT 20 Nisen (Westermoen)
Services: Trondheim area
Joh. Presthus Rederi
Bergen
Type(s): PT 150, 3 (Westermoen)
Route: Copenhagen-Malmö
MOROCCO
Transports Touristiques Intercontinentaux, Tangier
Type(s): Kometa, 2 (Sormovo design)
Routes: Tangier-Algericas, Tangier-Marbella
POLAND
Central Board of Inland Navigation
Type(s): ZRYW-1
Route: Szczecin-Swinoujscie
Type(s): Kometa 3 (Sormovo)
Route: unknown
ROMANIA
Romanian Navy
Type(s): Hu Chwan, 1
Operating area: Coastal waters
SWEDEN
Svenska Rederiaktiebolaget Oresund
Type(s): PT 50, 2 (Rodriquez), RHS 140, 1 (Navaltecnica)
Route: Copenhagen-Malmo
SWITZERLAND
Societe de Nav, sur le Lac Leman
Type(s): PT 20, 1 (Rodriquez)
Route: Lake Geneva
UNITED KINGDOM
Red Funnel Steamers Ltd
Type(s): Seaflight H 57, 1, RHS 70, 2 (Navaltecnica)
Route: Southampton-Cowes
Speed Hydrofoils Ltd
Tower Hotel,
St Katherines Way,
London, E1

Types: Raketa TA, 1, Raketa M, 1 (Sormovo/Airavia modified)
 Service: Scheduled service, Greenwich, Tower, Westminster.
Also offered on charter. Projected future fleet to include Voskhods
and Kometas.

YUGOSLAVIA
INEX-Nauticki Turizam
Obala Lazareta 3, Split
PP/POB 199,
TELEPHONE: 47-651. 45-758
TELEX: 11227
DIRECTOR: B. Tomic
Type(s): Replacement fleet, understood to comprise two Raketa
Ts and three Kometa MTs
Route(s): Adriatic coastal services; tourist and passenger services
between Italy and Yugoslavia
INEX Nautical Tourism
Kolarceva 8,
Beograd
Telex: 11 240
Globtours
Obala,
Portoroz.

USSR
Ministry of the River Fleet

The Soviet Ministry of the River Fleet operates hydrofoil passenger ferries on practically all the major rivers, lakes, canals and reservoirs from Central Russia to Siberia and the Far East.

In 1958, when hydrofoils were first introduced to the rivers of the USSR, they carried ten thousand passengers. By 1968 the number of passengers carried had grown to three million. During the 1969-70 navigation season there were 80 hydrofoil services on the Volga alone, operated by vessels of the Raketa, Meteor, Sputnik and Burevestnik series. There are now more than 150 hydrofoil passenger services in the Soviet Union and it was stated that in 1972 the 200 craft operating these services carried about 20 million passengers.

In addition to craft on inland waterways employing the Alexeyev shallow draft submerged foil system, Strela-type craft, with surface-piercing foils, operate in the Gulf of Finland, and supported by Kometas and Vikhrs, provide year-round services between ports on the Black Sea.

Three new hydrofoil passenger ferry designs are under development—the Cyclone, a gas-turbine powered craft with seats for 250 and capable of 40 knots, the Typhoon, a gas-turbine powered 90-seat vessel with fully submerged, autostabilised foils and the Voskhod (Sunrise), a Raketa replacement. The Voskhod will provide greater comfort and improved facilities for passengers and crew and air-conditioning will be installed. As with the Raketa, a family of variants will be available to suit a wide variety of operating and traffic conditions. Fastest of the series will be the Voskhod 3, powered by a gas-turbine and capable of 43 knots.

The Raketa has given excellent service and has extremely low operating costs. The cost of carrying passengers on the craft is stated to be lower than that of either displacement-type passenger ferries or automobiles. Similar low-cost operation is demonstrated by the 260-passenger Sputnik on the Moscow-Astrakhan route. It has been found that the cost of operating a Sputnik on this service is only 8% of that of the latest displacement-type passenger ferry of the United Volga Steamship Line. Time saving is one of the most important considerations. In many cases, hydrofoils take passengers to their destinations faster than trains. For example, a Raketa service covers the 516 miles (800 km) from Gorky to Kazan in 12 hours, while trains take 20 hours for the same journey. Price of the ticket is the same, however, whether the journey is undertaken by hydrofoil or rail.

The Meteor service from Moscow to Sormovo takes 13 hours 40 minutes to cover 559 miles (900 km). A conventional passenger ship requires about three days to cover this distance.

Soviet Frontier Police

Some twenty-five Pchela patrol hydrofoils, derived from the Strela passenger ferry, are in service with the Soviet Frontier Police in the Baltic, Caspian and the Black Sea areas.

Soviet Navy

The first sightings of a new hydrofoil fast patrol boat known by the NATO code name Turya, were made in the Baltic in the Spring of 1973. It appears that this new vessel, which is equipped for ASW work, is based on the hull of the Osa missile craft. The design employs a fixed surface-piercing bow foil only. Powered by three 4,330 hp diesels it has a top speed of about 45 knots under calm conditions. Production is in hand at three Soviet naval shipyards.

POWER PLANTS AND
PROPULSION SYSTEMS

CANADA

KOHLER OF CANADA LTD

HEAD OFFICE:
6390 Northwest Drive, Malton, Ontario
TELEPHONE:
416 677-4733
TELEX: 02-29366
EXECUTIVES:
D. W. F. Seston, Director of Marketing and Sales

Several Canadian light air cushion vehicle designs are equipped with Kohler two-cycle engines.

Model:	K-295-1	K-295-2 K-295-2AX	K-340-2 K-340-2AX	K-399-2 K-399-2AX	K-440-2 K-440-2AX
Bore:	2,953 in (75 mm)	2,264 in (57·5 mm)	2,441 in (62 mm)	2,559 in (65 mm)	2,667 in (68 mm)
Stroke:	2,618 in (66·5 mm)	2,205 in (56 mm)	2,205 in (56 mm)	2,362 in (60 mm)	2,362 in (60 mm)
Displacement:	17·93 cu in (294 cc)	17·69 cu in (290 cc)	20·62 cu in (338 cc)	24·28 cu in (398 cc)	26·60 cu in (436 cc)

UNITED AIRCRAFT OF CANADA LTD
(Subsidiary of United Aircraft Corporation)

HEAD OFFICE & WORKS:
P.O. Box 10, Longueuil, Quebec
EXECUTIVES:
T. E. Stephenson, President
R. H. Guthrie, Vice-President, Industrial & Marine Division
E. L. Smith, Vice-President, Operations
E. H. Schweitzer, Vice-President, Product Support
K. H. Sullivan, Vice-President, Marketing
V. W. Tryon, Vice-President, Finance
E. A. Clifford, Engineering Manager, Industrial and Marine Division
P. Henry, PR Manager

In addition to its compact range of low-power aircraft turbines (eg the PT6A turbo-prop, PT6B, PT6T and T400 turboshafts, and JT15D turbofan), UACL also manufactures a marine derivative of the PT6, the ST6 series of turboshafts. These engines are rated at 550 shp and upwards, and are installed in a number of ACV and hydrofoil vessels. These include the FHE-400 ASW hydrofoil where ST6 engines drive the generators and hydraulic pumps for the ship's services and foil control, and also provide emergency propulsion power for hullborne operation. The US prototype Surface Effect Ship SES-100B is equipped with three ST6J-70s to power its eight lift fans, and two ST-60 series engines power the Canadian research hydrofoil Proteus. Two ST6T-75 Twin-Pac turbines power the Bell Aerospace Canada Voyageur hovercraft and a single ST6T-75 provides power in that company's Viking craft. A series of larger Voyageurs will be powered by ST6T-76 engines.

Including aero-engine installations, over 7,000 of this series of gas-turbines have been delivered. Between them they have accumulated running experience in excess of 12 million hours.

UACL ST6 MARINE GAS-TURBINE

UACL ST6 marine gas-turbines are manufactured by United Aircraft of Canada. Details of the engine specifications are given below:
TYPE: A simple cycle free turbine engine with a single spool gas generator and a multi-stage compressor driven by a single stage turbine. Burner section has an annular combustion chamber with downstream injection. The single stage-free turbine is connected to the output shaft via a reduction gearbox.

The UACL ST6T-75 Twin Pac TM is a dual engine with the two engines mounted side-by-side and coupled to a twinning reduction gear.

United Aircraft ST6 gas-turbine

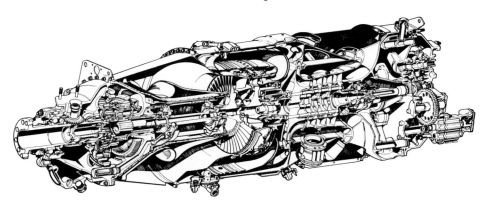

Cutaway of the ST6-70. The model illustrated, the ST6J-70, differs from the ST6K-70 only in the main reduction gearbox

AIR INTAKE: Annular air intake at rear of engine with intake screen.
COMPRESSOR: Three axial-flow stages, plus single centrifugal stage. Single-sided centrifugal compressor with 26 vanes, made from titanium forging. Axial rotor of disc-drum type with stainless steel stator and rotor blades. Stator vanes are brazed to casing. The rotor blades are dove tailed to discs. Discs through-bolted with centrifugal compressor, to shaft. Fabricated one-piece stainless steel casing and radial diffuser.
COMBUSTION CHAMBER: Annular reverse-flow type of stainless steel construction, with 14 Simplex burners. Two glow or spark plug igniters.
GAS GENERATOR: Single-stage axial. Rotor blades mounted by fir tree roots.
POWER TURBINE: Single or dual-stage axial. Rotor blades mounted by fir tree roots.

BEARINGS: Gas generator and power turbine supported by one ball bearing and one roller bearing each.
SHAFT DRIVE: Single, or two-stage planetary reduction gear or direct drive-depending on engine model. Torque measuring system incorporated with reduction gearing.
FUEL GRADE: Aviation turbine fuels, Diesel Nos. 1 and 2 and Navy Diesel.
JET PIPE: Single port exhaust discharging vertically upwards or at 60° port or starboard of vertical. Alternatively twin ports discharging horizontally on some models.
ACCESSORY DRIVES: Mounting pads on accessory case including for starter or starter-generator and tacho-generator. Also tacho-generator drive on power section.
LUBRICATION SYSTEM: One pressure and four scavenge gear type pumps driven by gas generator rotor. Integral oil tank.
OIL SPECIFICATIONS: Type 2 synthetic

lube oil PWA-521 MIL-L-23699.

DIMENSIONS:

Diameter		Approx 19 in
Width ST6T-75, ST6T-76		44·4 in
ST6T-75		31·6 in
ST6J-70		62 in
ST6K-70		60 in
ST6J-77		62 in
ST6L-77		52·2 in
ST6K-77		60 in
ST6L-80		59·4 in
ST6T-75		66·4 in

Weight (Dry):

ST6J-70	350 lb
ST6K-70	317 lb
ST6J-77	319 lb
ST6L-77	306 lb
ST6K-77	350 lb
ST6L-80	360 lb
ST6T-75	730 lb

PERFORMANCE RATINGS:

Maximum (1)

ST6J-70	620 shp at 2,200 rpm
ST6K-70	620 shp at 6,230 rpm
ST6J-77	690 shp at 2,200 rpm
ST6L-77	811 shp at 33,000 rpm
ST6K-77	690 shp at 6,230 rpm
ST6L-80	1,065 shp at 30,000 rpm
ST6T-75	1,700 shp at 6,600 rpm
ST6T-76	1,800 shp at 6,600 rpm

Intermittent (2)

ST6J-70	580 shp
ST6K-70	580 shp
ST6J-77	620 shp
ST6L-77	—
ST6K-77	620 shp
ST6L-80	955 shp
ST6T-75	1,500 shp
ST6T-76	1,600 shp

Normal (2)

ST6J-70	510 shp
ST6K-70	510 shp
ST6J-77	550 shp
ST6L-77	654 shp
ST6K-77	550 shp
ST6L-80	840 shp
ST6T-75	1,300 shp
ST6T-76	1,400 shp

(1)   at 72°F and sea level
(2)   at 59°F and sea level (ISA conditions)

FUEL CONSUMPTION:

At maximum rating:

ST6J-70	0·64 lb/shp/hr
ST6K-70	0·64 lb/shp/hr
ST6J-77	0·62 lb/shp/hr
ST6L-77	0·589 lb/ shp/hr
ST6K-77	0·62 lb/shp/hr
ST6L-80	0·58 lb/shp/hr
ST6T-75	0·62 lb/shp/hr
ST6T-76	0·617 lb/shp/hr

At intermittent rating:

ST6J-70	0·65 lb/shp/hr
ST6K-70	0·65 lb/shp/hr
ST6J-77	0·64 lb/shp/hr
ST6L-77	—
ST6K-77	0·64 lb/shp/hr
ST6L-80	0·60 lb/shp/hr
ST6T-75	0·63 lb/shp/hr
ST6T-76	0·623 lb/shp/hr

At normal rating:

ST6J-70	0·67 lb/shp/hr
ST6K-70	0·67 lb/shp/hr
ST6J-77	0·66 lb/shp/hr
ST6L-77	0·62 lb/shp/hr
ST6K-77	0·66 lb/shp/hr
ST6L-80	0·62 lb/shp/hr
ST6T-75	0·65 lb/shp/hr
ST6T-76	0·64 lb/shp/hr

OIL CONSUMPTION:

All models, less than 0·2 lb/hr.

CLUB FRANCAIS DES AEROGLISSEURS

HEAD OFFICE:

41 and 43 Rue Aristide Briand
95130 Meung sur Loire

Club Francais des Aeroglisseurs is marketing a special propulsion unit for high performance lightweight air cushion vehicles. The unit, given the name "Diagloo", comprises an adapted 600 cc Citroen air-cooled, automotive engine, driving a 4 ft 7$\frac{1}{8}$ in (1·40 m) diameter, two-bladed Merville propeller via a reduction and reverse gearbox. Engine output is 32·5 bhp (33 cv) at 6,000 rpm.

The unit weighs 220 lb (100 kg) and is supplied complete with an aerodynamically profiled hood. Series production has begun. The price is approximately F 5,000.

The Diagloo propulsion unit for light sports ACVs

SOCIÉTÉ TURBOMÉCA

HEAD OFFICE AND WORKS:
Bordes (Pyrénées Atlantiques)

PARIS OFFICE:
1 Rue Beaujon, Paris 8c

PRESIDENT AND DIRECTOR GENERAL:
J. R. Szydolowski

The Société Turboméca was formed in 1938 by MM. Szydlowski and Planiol to develop blowers, compressors and turbines for aeronautical use.

In 1947 the company began development of gas-turbines of low power for driving aircraft auxiliaries and for aircraft propulsion. Since then it has evolved over 68 different types of powerplants, of which 22 have gone into production and 10 have been manufactured under licence in five foreign countries.

Many of Turboméca's production series aircraft turbines have been adapted to

Turbomeca Turmo 1,300 shp IIIc free-turbine turboshaft, two of which will power the projected Aerospatiale SA 800 mixed-traffic hydrofoil ferry

industrial and marine duties including installation in French air cushion vehicles of various types. General descriptions follow of the main Turboméca turbine engines at present in production or under development. Reference is also made to air cushion vehicle and hydrofoil installations.

TURBOMÉCA ARTOUSTE

The Artouste is a single-shaft turboshaft engine which has been manufactured in quantity in two versions, the 400 shp Artouste IIC and the 563 shp Artouste IIIB. The 590 shp Artouste IIID has also been developed. More than 1,500 of the earlier Artouste II were built to power the Sud-Aviation Alouette II helicopter. The Artouste II has a single-stage centrifugal compressor, annular reverse-flow combustor and two-stage axial turbine. In the second generation Artouste III in which the pressure ratio is increased from 3·88 : 1 to 5·2 : 1, a single-axial stage compressor has been added ahead of the centrifugal impeller. The turbine also has an additional stage.

A single Artouste drives the two propulsion airscrews on the Naviplane BC 8.

The following description refers to the Artouste IIIB.

TYPE: Single-shaft axial-plus-centrifugal turboshaft.

COMPRESSOR: Single-stage axial plus single-stage centrifugal compressor. Two diffusers, one radial and the other axial, aft of compressor. Pressure ratio at 33,500 rpm at S/L 5·2 : 1, Air mass flow 9·5 lb/sec (4·3 kg/sec) at 33,500 rpm at S/L.

COMBUSTION CHAMBER: Annular type, with rotary atomiser fuel injection. Torch igniters.

TURBINE: Three-stage axial type. Blades integral with discs. Row of nozzle guide vanes before each stage.

JET PIPE: Fixed type.

STARTING: Automatic with 4,000 watt starter-generator. Two Turboméca igniter plugs.

DIMENSIONS:
Length	71·46 in (1,815 mm)
Height	24·68 in (627 mm)
Width	20·47 in (520 mm)

WEIGHT (Dry):
Equipped	401 lb (182 kg)

PERFORMANCE RATING:
563 shp at 33,500 rpm

FUEL CONSUMPTION:
At T-O and max continuous rating
0·71 lb (322 gr) ehp/rh

TURBOMÉCA TURMO

The Turmo is a free-turbine engine available in both turboshaft and turboprop versions spanning the 1,200 to 2,000 shp power bracket. First generation Turmo IIIC and E series have a single-stage axial plus single-stage centrifugal compressor, annular reverse-flow combustor, two-stage axial compressor-turbine, and mechanically-separate single-, or two-stage power turbine. Second-generation Turmo X engines have an additional axial compressor stage and other refinements. By December 1974 more than 1,400 Turmo engines had been built.

Main versions of the Turmo at present in production or under development include:
Turmo IIIC7: Derived from the Turmo III B, this model (with two-stage power turbine) has a 1,610 shp at max contingency rating and powers early Sud-Aviation SA 321

Turbomeca Turmo XII free-turbine, developed from the Turmo IIIF installed in the turbotrains of SCNF

The 889 shp Turbomeca Turmastazou XIV free-turbine turboshaft

Super-Frelon three-engined military helicopters. Two will power the projected Aerospatiale 46-ton patrol boat hydrofoil under development for the French navy.

The Turmo IIIF also powers the Turbotrains of SNCF.

Turmo IVC; Based on the Turmo IIIC₃, this is a special version with a single-stage power turbine and powers the Sud-Aviation SA 330 Puma twin-engined military helicopter. The engine has a maximum contingency rating of 1,555 shp.

Turmo IIIC₇ This model (which reverts to the standard two-stage power turbine) is in the same series as the Turmo IIIC and E and has a maximum emergency rating of 1,610 shp. It is installed in Sud Aviation SA 321 F and J Super-Frelon civil three engined helicopters.

Turmo IIIC₂; Embodies new materials for the gas generator turbine, and offers an emergency rating of 1,610 shp.

Turmo IIIE₃: Two each rated at 1,282 shp, power the Bertin/Société de l'Aerotrain Orléans 250-80 tracked air-cushion vehicle. Both engines drive a ducted seven-bladed 7 ft 7 in (2·30 m) diameter Ratier-Figeac FH-201 hydraulically operated reversible-pitch propeller for propulsion. The Turmo IIIE is rated at 1,580 shp.

Turmo IIIF: This model has been in

production since 1970 to power the production version of the SNCF Turbotrain operating on the Paris-Caen-Cherbourg, Lyon-Nantes, Lyon-Strasbourg, Lyon-Bordeaux and Bordeaux-Toulouse runs.

In the United States it is employed in the AMTRAK locomotives on the Chicago-St Louis run.

Turmo IIIN₈: Rated at 1,250 shp, this version powers the twin-engined SEDAM Naviplane N300 marine air-cushion vehicle. The engines are cross-coupled to drive two three-bladed 11 ft 10 in (3·60 m) diameter Ratier-Figeac FH 195-196 hydraulically-operated variable-pitch propellers for propulsion and two eleven-bladed 6 ft 3 in (1·85 m) diameter Ratier-Figeac FD 155 hydraulically-operated variable-pitch axial fans for lift.

Turmo XII: Developed from the Turmo IIIC this second-generation model has a two-stage axial compressor ahead of the centrifugal stage. With a maximum continuous rating of 1,610 shp, the Turmo XII is planned for a new SNCF Turbotrain.

Two Turmo IIIC series engines with a combined installed power of 2,564 shp, are to power the projected Sud-Aviation SA800 second-generation hydrofoil.

The following details apply to the Turmo-IIIC₇:

MARK	PERFORMANCES I.S.A. CONDITIONS								COMPRESSOR CHARACTERISTICS (at take-off rating)					TURBINE		Power off-take/propeller RPM (tr/mn)	OVERALL DIMENSIONS (mm)			Bare engine weight (kg)	Equipped engine weight (kg)
	Shaft power at max. contingency rating (ch)	Shaft power at take-off (ch)	Shaft power at max. continuous (ch)	Poussée Residual thrust (kg)	Total equivalent power (ch) Take-off	Max. contin.	S.F.C. at take-off related to (g/ch.h) Shaft power	Total equiv. power	Number of stages Axial	Centrif.	Débit Air mass flow (kg/s)	Pressure ratio	RPM (tr/mn)	Number of stages Gas generator	Free turbine		Length	Width	Height		
TURBOSHAFT ENGINES																					
ARTOUSTE III D	—	598(1)	550	40	634	586	334	315	1	1	4,3	5,2	33 500	3	—	5.864	1815	522	665	130	†178
ASTAZOU II A	—	530	480	35	562	510	288	261	1	1	2,5	6	43 500	3	—	5.922	1427	516	560	115	142
ASTAZOU III	—	598	530	30	625	559	281	269	1	1	2,5	6	43 500	3	—	6.179	1433	483	508	115	147
ASTAZOU XIV H	—	598(1)	598(1)	57	651	651	284	260	2	1	3,33	7,5	43 000	3	—	6.334	1470	500	565		160
ASTAZOU XVIII A	—	885(2)	816				255		2	1	3,35	7,5	43 000	3	—	5.830	1419	533	711		170
TURMO III C7	1 632	1570	1292				287		1	1	6,2	5,90	33 600	2	2		1975	693	718		325
TURMO IV C	1 580	1517	1280				287		1	1	6,15	5,85	33 450	2	1	22 840	2184	637	719		227
ARRIEL	690	650	600				260		1	1	2,4	8	51 800	2	1	6 000	1217	480	626		128
« 1800 ch »	1 935	1800	1650				214		3	1				2	2		2000	570	570		
TURBOPROP ENGINES																					
ASTAZOU XVI D	—	925	796	64	981	852	249	235	2	1	3,33	8,05	43 089	3	—	1 783	1556	581	581		200(3)
ASTAZOU XVI G	—	978	890	64	1 035	946	248	235	2	1	3,33	8	43 000	3	—	1 970	1556	645	645		228
ASTAZOU XX	—	1400	1234	72	1 464	1296	210	201	3	1			42 000	3	—		1677	580	580		
BASTAN VII	—	1060(4)	1060	100	1 150	1150	278	256	2	1	5,85	6,8	32 000	3	—	1 517	1911	736	802		370

MARK	PERFORMANCES I.S.A. CONDITIONS							COMPRESSOR CHARACTERISTICS (at take-off rating)					TURBINE		OVERALL DIMENSIONS (mm)			Bare engine weight (kg)	Equipped engine weight (kg)
	Thrust at take-off (kg)	Thrust at max. continuous (kg)	Ducted fan Dilution	LP compressor pressure ratio	S.F.C. (kg/kg.h) Take-off	Max. continuous		Number of stages Axial	Centrif.	Air mass flow (kg/s)	Pressure ratio	RPM (tr/mn)	Number of stages		Length	Width	Height		
TURBOJET ENGINES																			
ARBIZON III	—	380	330			1,12	1,11	1	1	6	5,5	33 000	1	—	1361	410	410		115
MARBORE II	—	400	400			1,15	1,15		1	8	3,85	22 600	1	—	1566	567	684	140	159
MARBORE VI	—	480	480			1,11	1,11		1	9,6	3,72	21,500	1	—	1416	594	631	140	159
AUBISQUE I A	—	742	625	2	1,5	0,618	0,60	1-1	1	22,2	6,9	33 000	1	—	2288	650	750		292
ADOUR (5)	—	2340(6)	1746	0,79	2,44			2-5		42,7	10,8		1-1	—	2895	795	1137		748
LARZAC 04 (7)	—	1345	1250	1,13		0,703	0,675	2-4		21,7	10,65		1-1	—	1343	600	760		290
ASTAFAN III	—	790(8)	715	7,7	1,32	0,365	0,359	1-2	1	31		43 000	3	—	2030	665	665	210	
ASTAFAN IV	—	1150(9)	1020	7	1,34	0,31	0,305	1-3	1	39		42 000	3	—	2218	780	780	220	

(1) Up to +55° C, or 4,000 m *(4) Up to +40° C, or 3,650 m* *(7) In cooperation with SNECMA*
(2) Up to +35° C *(5) In cooperation with ROLLS-ROYCE* *(8) 850 kg with water injection*
(3) Without starter generator *(6) 3,382 kg reheat lit* *(9) 1,230 kg with water injection* *February 1975*

Table of Turbomeca's current range of gas-turbine engines

TYPE: Free-turbine axial-plus-centrifugal turboshaft.
AIR MASS FLOW: 13·7 lb (6·2 kg)/sec.
DIMENSIONS:
Length 77·8 in (1,976 mm)
Width 27·3 in (693 mm)
Height 28·2 in (717 mm)
WEIGHT DRY:
With standard equipment 715 lb (325 kg)
PERFORMANCE RATINGS:
T-O 1,550 shp
Max continuous 1,292 shp
FUEL CONSUMPTION:
At T-O rating 0·60 lb (273 gr)/shp/hr
At max continuous rating 0·64 lb (291 gr)/shp/hr

TURBOMÉCA MARBORE

The Marbore single-shaft turbojet has been built in greater numbers than any other Turboméca engine. By December 1974 over 9,000 880 lb (400 kg) thrust Marbore IIs and 1,058 lb (480 kg) thrust Marbore VIs had been manufactured by Turboméca and its licensees for trainer aircraft and target drone applications. Of this total, 5,229 Marbore engines were manufactured by Turboméca. In both these versions the engine comprises a single-stage centrifugal compressor, annular reverse-flow combustor and single-stage axial turbine.

Two Marbores will power the SA 890 hydrofoil test platform currently under development by Aérospatiale for the French Ministry of National Defence.

A Marbore II powers the lift system of the SEDAM Naviplane BC8 marine ACV. The exhaust gases are ducted along channels designed to entrain additional air to augment the efflux.

The following details relate to the Marbore VI:
DIMENSIONS:
Length with exhaust cone but without tail-pipe 55·74 in (1,416 mm)
Width 23·35 in (593 mm)
Height 24·82 in (631 mm)
WEIGHT (Dry):
Equipped 309 lb (140 kg)
PERFORMANCE RATINGS:
T-O 1,058 lb (480 kg) at 21,500 rpm
Cruising 925 lb (420 kg) at 20,500 rpm
SPECIFIC FUEL CONSUMPTION:
At T-O rating 1·09
At cruising rating 1·07

TURBOMÉCA ASTAZOU

The Astazou is another of the later generation Turboméca engines, incorporating the experience gained with earlier series and making use of new design techniques. It has an extremely small gas-producer section and has been developed both as a turboshaft and as a turboprop driving a variable-pitch propeller.

The compressor consists of one, or two, axial stages followed by a centrifugal stage, with an annular combustion chamber and three-stage turbine. Accessories are mounted on the rear of the main intake casing. Pressure ratio is 6:1 and air mass flow 5·5 lb/sec (2·5 kg/sec) for the two-stage compressor engines, and 8 : 1 and 7·4 lb/sec (3·4 kg/sec) for the three-stage compressor engines respectively. In the turboshaft version, the rpm of the output shaft is 5,922.

Well over 700 Astazou engines of various types have been built. The following are the main Astazou variants:

Astazou II. This is a 535 hp turboprop (with two-stage compressor) which powers a version of the Naviplane N 102.

Astazou IIA. A 523 shp turboshaft (two-stage compressor) version powering the Sud-Aviation SA 318C Alouette II Astazou helicopter. A 450 shp Astazou provides power for the integrated lift and propulsion system of the SEDAM Naviplane N 102 marine ACV. The engine drives a 5 ft 7 in (1·70 m) diameter axial lift fan and two three-bladed variable-pitch propellers for propulsion.

Astazou IIIN. Rated at 592 hp, is the definitive (two-stage compressor).

Astazou XIV (alias AZ14). Current major production turboprop version (with three-stage compressor) rated at 852 shp. The engine is the standard power plant for the

Naviplane N 102.

Astazou XVI (alias AZ16). First Turbomeca production engine to embody the company's new air-cooled turbine. Rated at 913 shp for Jetstream aircraft.

Astazou XVIII. An uprated version of the Astazou XVI with take-off power of 1,554 ehp and sfc of 0·512 lb (232 gr)/ehp/hr.

Astazou XX. This later version has an additional axial compressor stage, and is rated at take-off at 1,445 ehp for an sfc of 0·45 lb (204 gr)/ehp/hr.

The following details refer to the Astazou IIIN:

DIMENSIONS:
Length	40·7 in (1,433 mm)
Basic diameter	18·1 in (460 mm)

WEIGHT, DRY:
Equipped engine	325 lb (147·5 kg)

PERFORMANCE RATINGS:
T-O	592 shp at 43,500 rpm
Max continuous	523 shp at 43,500 rpm

FUEL CONSUMPTION:
At T-O rating	0·627 lb (284 gr)/shp/hr
At max continuous rating	0·644 lb (292 gr)/shp/hr

TURBOMÉCA BASTAN

A compact single-shaft turboprop in the 1,000 to 2,000 shp power bracket, the Bastan has its main application in the Nord 262. The 1,065 ehp Bastan VIC powering the original 262 series aircraft, comprises a single-stage axial compressor plus single-stage centrifugal compressor, annular reverse-flow combustor and three-stage axial turbine, and is equipped with water-methanol injection. The higher rated Bastan VII is capable of maintaining its 1,135 ehp T-O power up to an ambient temperature of 40°C. This version is entering production to power the new 262C and incorporates an additional axial compressor stage.

The following details refer to the Bastan VII:

DIMENSIONS:
Length	75·2 in (1,911 mm)
Height	31·6 in (802 mm)
Width	21·7 in (550 mm)

WEIGHT, DRY:
Basic engine	639 lb (290 kg)

PERFORMANCE RATINGS:
T-O and max continuous	1,135 ehp

FUEL CONSUMPTION:
At T-O and max continuous ratings	0·572 lb (259 gr)/shp/hr

TURBOMÉCA TURMASTAZOU

This is a new free-turbine direct-drive turboshaft comprising the Astazou XIV single-shaft gas generator section provided with a mechanically-independent power turbine. The Astazou turbine has two stages in place of its normal three, and the power turbine has two stages also. Development is underway of the 889 shp Turmastazou XIV with a view to its use in twin-engined helicopters. The engine has also been proposed for the Bertin/Société de l'Aérotrain Orléans tracked ACV.

Turmastazou XVI. This version introduces the Turboméca air-cooled turbine, and gives a take-off rating of 1,015 shp for an sfc of 0·51 lb (231 gr)/shp/hr.

The following details refer to the Turmastazou XIV:

DIMENSIONS:
Length	54·0 in (1,371 mm)
Height	21·8 in (553 mm)
Width	17·3 in (440 mm

WEIGHT, DRY:
Equipped engine	approximately 341 lb (155 kg)

PERFORMANCE RATINGS:
T-O	889 shp
Max continuous	792 shp

GERMANY

MTU
Motoren-und Turbinen-Union Friedrichshafen GmbH

HEAD OFFICE:
799 Friedrichshafen, Postfach 289

TELEPHONE:
(07541) 2071

TELEX:
MTUFH 0734-360

TELEGRAMME:
MOTORUNION

DIRECTORS:
Rolf Breuning, Executive President
Hugo B. Saemann, Executive President
Dr. Hans Dinger
Dr. Karl A. Müller
Werner Niefer
Dr. Ernst Zimmermann

The MTU-group of companies, formed in 1969 by the M.A.N. AG and the Daimler-Benz AG, consists of MTU-München GmbH and MTU-Friedrichshafen GmbH.

MTU-Friedrichshafen comprises the two plants of the previous Maybach Mercedes-Benz Motorenbau GmbH at Friedrichshafen and is owned 84 by MTU-München GmbH. MTU-München, in turn is owned equally by M.A.N. and Daimler-Benz.

MTU-Friedrichshafen is today the development and production centre for high-speed diesel engines of Maybach, M.A.N. and Mercedes-Benz origin and as such embodies the experience of these companies in diesel engine technology. In addition to diesel engines, MTU-Friedrichshafen is responsible for sales and application of industrial and marine gas-turbines.

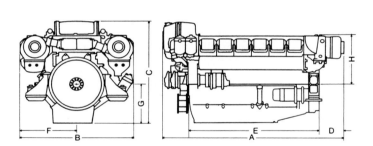

Engine type	A	B	C	D	E	F	G	H
6V331 TC 71-81	1585	1309	1385	218	1023	588	475	717
8V331 TC 71-81	1864	1309	1385	269	1251	598	475	717
12V331 TC 71-81	2429	1403	1352	318	1707	684	442	717

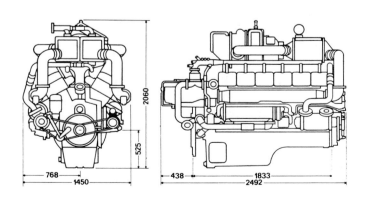

For application in hydrofoils MTU-Friedrichshafen offers the following engines:

331 engine family
12 V 493
652 engine family
538 engine family

The areas of responsibility of the two MTU companies are as follows:

MTU-München:

Development, production and support of light-weight, advanced-technology gas-turbines mainly for aircraft applications.

MTU Friedrichshafen:

Development, production and application of high-performance diesel engines.

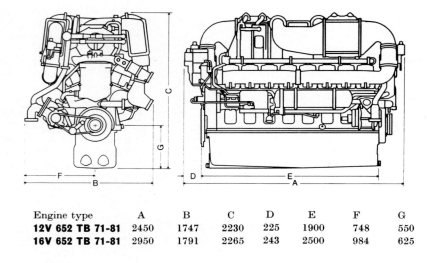

Engine type	A	B	C	D	E	F	G
12V 652 TB 71-81	2450	1747	2230	225	1900	748	550
16V 652 TB 71-81	2950	1791	2265	243	2500	984	625

The following table defines power ranges in connection with application characteristics and reference conditions.

Output characteristics of operational engines usually depend on the special demands of the hydrofoil, from the operating profile to the application, and therefore will be specified for each system.

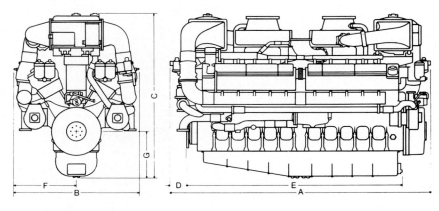

Engine type	A	B	C	D	E	F	G
12V 538 TB 81	2545	1620	2220	220	1785	810	725
16V 538 TB 81-82	3220	1620	2361	459	2252	810	595
20V 538 TB 81	3600	1620	2340	250	2960	810	657

MTU diesel engines for main propulsion of vessels, application groups 1C and 1D:						
Engine model	Continuous output			Intermittent output			Engine weight (dry)
	rpm	kW	hp	rpm	kW	hp	kg
Application group 1C							
6 V 331 TC 71	2055	470	560	2120	450	610	1580
8 V 331 TC 71	2055	550	750	2120	600	815	1920
12 V 331 TC 71	2055	820	1120	2120	900	1220	2910
12 V 493 TY 70	1400	810	1100	1500	1000	1360	3250*
12 V 652 TB 71	1380	1220	1660	1460	1440	1960	4850*
16 V 652 TB 71	1380	1620	2205	1460	1920	2610	6235*
				1000 hours per year			
Application group 1D							
6 V 331 TC 81	2260	450	610	2340	500	680	1580
8 V 331 TC 81	2260	600	815	2340	660	900	1920
12 V 331 TC 81	2260	900	1220	2340	1000	1360	2980
12 V 538 TB 81	1710	1440	1960	1760	1570	2135	5400
16 V 538 TB 81	1710	1920	2610	1760	2100	2860	6950
16 V 538 TB 82	1710	2140	2910	1760	2340	3180	6950
20 V 538 TB 81	1710	2400	3265	1760	2620	3565	9200

*Weight of engine with light alloy housing

—Continuous output A DIN 6270
—Intermittent output Pu DIN 6270 (2 hours within 12 operating hours)
Reference conditions:
 Intake air temperature 20°C (45°C with 331 TC, 32°C with 538 TB 81)
 Seawater temperature 20°C no influence on 331 TC, 27°C with 538 TB 81)
 Barometric pressure 1·0 bar

MTU Marine Gas Turbines built under General Electric licence					
Type	Design	max. output		output speed	weight
		kW	HP	rpm	kg
LM 300*	Single shaft gas generator with free power turbine	**2 500**	3 400	13 600	355
LM 1 500*		**12 800**	17 400	5 500	4 200
LM 2 500*		**20 000**	27 200	3 600	4 500

In co-operation with General Electric Co.
Reference conditions
Intake air temperature 15°C

Atmospheric pressure 1,013 bar
29·92 inches mercury absolute
Relative humidity 0%

RHEIN-FLUGZEUGBAU

HEAD OFFICE:
D-4050 Mönchengladbach 1, Flugplatz,
PB 408

TELEPHONE:
(02161) 66 20 31

TELEX:
08 525 06

DIRECTORS:
Dipl.-Volksw. W. Kutscher
Dipl. Ing. A. Schneider

RFB has developed a fan thrust pod module for wing-in-ground-effect machines, gliders, air cushion vehicles and air-propelled boats.

By combining rotary engines of the Wankel type with a ducted fan, the company has produced an extremely compact power unit which can be mounted on either a fuselage or a wing in much the same way as gas-turbine pods. The air cooling system permits prolonged ground running when necessary with full throttle.

The system has been fitted to the X-113 Am. Aerofoil Boat.

RFB Fan Pod Type SG 85

SG 85:

Length	3 ft 11½ in (1,200 mm)
Height, incl. 2,000 mm connection	3 ft 3⅜ in (1,000 mm)
Width max	2 ft 5½ in (750 mm)
Weight	58 kg
Inside shroud diameter 2 ft 1⅜ in (650 mm)	
Power	50 hp
Static thrust at 5,400 rpm	95 kg
Noise level with full throttle at 1,000 ft altitude	57 dbA

Rotor:
3-blades-rotor in fibre-reinforced plastic with errosive protection.
Shroud: PUR-foam plastic.
Engine cowling: glass-fibre reinforced plastic.
Engine: Rotary engine 2 % KM914/2V-85 ("Wankel" system) with electric starter 12 v., generator, exhaust-gas system and complete assembly sets ready for installation.

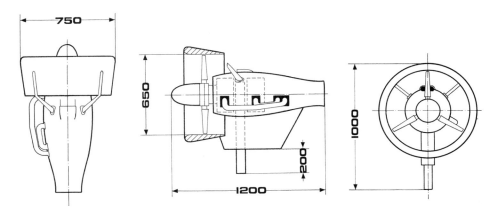

RFB Fan Pod, incorporating a Wankel rotary engine

Connection: Metal-construction as pylon having a connection-part.
Fuel: Mixture 1:30

Fuel consumption:
full throttle   5,500 rpm: 3·3 gph (15 l/h)
crusing speed 5,000 rpm: 2·5 gph (11·5 l/h)

VOLKSWAGEN (GB) LIMITED
(Incorporating Audi NSU (GB) Limited)

REGISTERED OFFICE:
Volkswagen House, Brighton Road, Purley, Surrey CR2 2UQ

TELEPHONE:
01-668 4100

TELEGRAMS:
Veemoto Croydon

TELEX:
263226

WANKEL ROTARY PISTON ENGINE

Relatively high power from a compact, vibration-free, lightweight engine are features which have attracted many lightweight ACV owners to the Wankel rotary design. The description below applies to Type KKM 612.

WANKEL KKM 612

TYPE: Twin-rotor rotary piston engine, water-cooled.
CHAMBER VOLUME: 2 × 497·5 cc
COMPRESSION: 9:1.
OUTPUT: 115 DIN HP/85 KW, 128 SAE HP.
TORQUE: 16 mkp/157 Nm at 4,000 rpm.
CARBURETTOR: Solex twin choke downdraught carburettors with automatic choke.
FUEL PUMP: Diaphragm with filter and electric delivery pump.

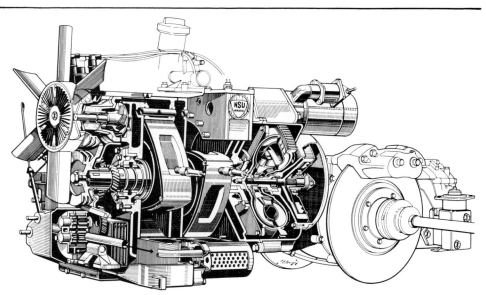

The Wankel KKM 612 115 hp twin-rotor water-cooled piston engine.

PRESSURE-FED CIRCULATORY LUBRICATING SYSTEM: One pump with micro full-flow filter and two gear pairs, one for lubrication of engine bearings and one for oil pressure in the torque converter.

TRANSMISSION: Torque converter.

ELECTRICAL EQUIPMENT: Thyristorised high voltage condenser ignition.

Voltage	12 volt
Starter	12 volt 2 HP
Battery	12 volt 66 Ah
Alternator	14 volt/770 watt (charges even at idling speeds)

TYPE 122

The air-cooled petrol engines powering over 20 million Volkswagen cars and vehicles are also produced as industrial power units in which role they have been proved reliable and economical in millions of hours running. There are three versions available, the Type 122 developed from the 1,192 cc Volkswagen car engine; the 1,584 cc Type 126A developed from the 1,500 cc van engine; and the 1,795 cc Type 127 developed from the 1,700 car engine.

TYPE: Air-cooled four-cylinder, horizontally-opposed four-stroke petrol engine available with or without governor.

CYLINDERS: Four separate cylinders of special grey cast iron, with integral cooling fins. Cast alumimiun heads, one for each two cylinders, with shrunk-in sintered steel valve seats and bronze valve guides. Bore 3·032 in (77 mm). Stroke 2·520 in (64 mm). Cubic capacity 72·74 cu in (1,192 cc). Compression ratio 7:1.

CRANKCASE: Two-part magnesium pressure casting with enclosed oil sump and flange for mounting the engine on machine or pedestal.
CRANKSHAFT: Forged, with hardened journals, mounted in three aluminium bearings and one three-layer, steel-backed bearing (No. 2).
CONNECTING RODS: Forged steel, I-section shank. Three-layer, steel-backed, lead-bronze big-end bearing shells with white metal running surfaces.
PISTONS: Aluminium with steel inserts, two compression rings and one scraper ring.
CAMSHAFT: Grey cast iron, with three steel-backed, shell-type bearings in crankcase, driven by helical gears.
VALVES: One inlet and one exhaust valve per cylinder. Exhaust valves have special armoured seating surfaces. 'Rotocap' valve rotating devices can be fitted on request.

COOLING: Radial fan, driven by belt from crankshaft. Protective grille on fan intake.
LUBRICATION: Forced feed gear-type pump. Full flow, flat tube oil cooler in fan airstream. Oil capacity 4·4 pints (2·5 litres).

CARBURETTOR: Downdraft Solex 26 VFIS on engine with governor. Downdraft Solex 28 PCI with accelerator pump, on engine without governor. Both have choke for cold starting.

IGNITION: With magneto; high tension, partly-supressed Scintilla-Vertex magneto with built-in automatic short-circuit switch as adjustable speed limiter. With coil ignition: 12 volt and centrifugal spark advance distributor.

PLUGS: Bosch W145 T1.
FUEL: Normal commercial petrol of 86 octane rating minimum.
STARTING: Hand cranking lever or electric starter.

Volkswagen Type 127 industrial engine

GOVERNOR: Centrifugal type, operating on carburettor throttle, driven by toothed belt.

EXHAUST SYSTEM: Cylindrical muffler located transversely at bottom of engine, with exhaust pipes from cylinders and damper pipe with short tail pipe.
MOUNTING: By four bolts in the crankcase flange.
COUPLING: Engine is connected to driven shaft by a clutch or flexible fixed-coupling.
PEDESTALS AND TRANSMISSIONS: Suitable flange pedestals, with or without couplings or clutches, can be supplied as well as gearboxes with direct drives or drives of various ratios for clockwise or anti-clockwise rotation.
DIMENSIONS:
Width   29·4 in (748 mm)
Height   26·2 in (665·5 mm)
Length.   29·2 in (740·5 mm)
WEIGHT, Dry:
With standard equipment, approx
                  205 lb (93·5 kg)
PERFORMANCE RATINGS:
Continuous rating
        34 bhp DIN at 3,600 output rpm
FUEL CONSUMPTION:
At 20 bhp at 2,000 output rpm
             0·534 lb (242 gr)/bhp/hr
At 30 bhp at 3,600 output rpm
             0·590 lb (268 gr)/bhp/hr

OIL CONSUMPTION:
Approx 20 to 35 cc/hr at 3,000 output rpm

TYPE 126A

TYPE: Air-cooled four-cylinder, horizon-

tally-opposed four-stroke petrol engine available with or without governor. Construction generally similar to Type 122 with following exceptions:
CYLINDERS: Bore 3·543 in (85·5 mm). Stroke 2·717 in (69·0 mm). Cubic capacity 96·50 cu in (1,584 cc). Compression ratio 7·7 : 1.

CARBURETTOR: Downdraft Solex 26 or 28 VFIS on engine with governor. Downdraft Solex 32 PCI on engine without governor.

DIMENSIONS:
Width   29·9 in (760·0 mm)
Height   26·5 in (675·5 mm)
Length   28·5 in (723·0 mm)
WEIGHT, Dry:
With standard equipment, approx
                  220 lb (100 kg)
PERFORMANCE RATINGS:
Continuous rating
        44 bhp DIN at 3,600 output rpm
FUEL: 90 octane minimum

FUEL CONSUMPTION:
At 28 bhp at 2,000 output rpm
             0·496 lb (225 gr)/bhp/hr
At 44 bhp at 3,600 output rpm
             0·562 lb (255 gr)/bhp/hr
OIL CONSUMPTION:
Approx 25 to 40 cc/hr at 3,000 output rpm

TYPE 127

TYPE: Air-cooled, four-cylinder, horizontally-opposed four-stroke petrol engine of low profile design.

CYLINDERS: Bore 3·740 in (93 mm). Stroke 2·165 in (66 mm). Cubic capacity 109·53 cu in (1,795 cc). Compression ratio 7·3 : 1.

COOLING: Radial fan on crankshaft.

CARBURETTOR: Solex 32 PCI downdraft or tewo Solex 34PDSIT downdraft.

IGNITION: 12 volt battery.

DIMENSIONS:
Width	3·780 in (960 mm)
Height (without air cleaner)	2·189 in (556 mm)
Length	3·264 in (829 mm)

WEIGHT, Dry:
With standard equipment 273 lb (124 kg)

PERFORMANCE RATINGS:
Maximum continuous ratings at 4,000 rpm

Single carburettor	62 bhp DIN
Twin carburettor	68 bhp DIN

FUEL: 90 octane minimum.

FUEL CONSUMPTION:
At 3,000 output rpm
0·506 lb (230 gr)/bhp/hr
At 4,000 output rpm
0·561 lb (255 gr)/bhp/hr

ITALY

C.R.M. FABRICA MOTORI MARINI

HEAD OFFICE:
20121 Milano, via Manzoni, 12

TELEPHONE:
708. 326/327

CABLES:
Cremme

DIRECTORS:
Ing F. Mariani
Ing. B. Piccoletti
Ing. S. Rastelli
Mr. S. Sussi
Minoja p.i. Vittorio

CRM has specialised in building lightweight diesel engines for more than twenty years. The company's engines are used in large numbers of motor torpedo boats, coastal patrol craft and privately-owned motor yachts. More recently, the engines have also been installed in hydrofoils.

During the 1960s the company undertook the development and manufacture of a family of 18, 12 and 9-cylinder diesel engines of lightweight high-speed design, providing a power coverage of 300 bhp to 1,350 bhp. These comprise the 18-cylinder CRM 18D₂ and 18 D/S-2 of 1,050 to 1,350 bhp with mechanically-driven supercharging and turbo-driven supercharging respectively and its cylinders arranged in an unusual W arrangement of three banks of six cylinders each; the 12-cylinder CRM 12 D/S-2 of 900 bhp with two banks of six cylinders and first in the new series to introduce turbo-charging; and the 715 bhp CRM 9 D/S-2 with a W arrangement of three banks of three cylinders and offering the option of turbo-charging or natural aspiration.

Details of these engines are given below.

CRM 18

First in CRM's new series of lightweight high-speed diesels, the CRM 18 is an 18-cylinder unit with its cylinders arranged in a W form comprising three banks of six cylinders. Maximum power is 1,050 bhp at 1,900 rpm with mechanically driven supercharging and 1,350 bhp, at 2,075 rpm, with exhaust gas turbo-charging. One 1,050 bhp 18D/2 engine powers the Finnish Tehi 70-passenger Raketa-type hydrofoil.

The following description relates to the mechanically supercharged CRM 18 D/2 and turbo-supercharged CRM 18 D/S.

TYPE: 18-cylinder in-line W type, four-stroke, water-cooled mechanically-supercharged (CRM 18 D/2) or turbo-supercharged (CRM 18 D/S) diesel engine.

CYLINDERS: Bore: 5·91 in (150 mm). Stroke 7·09 in (180 mm). Swept volume 194·166 cu in (3·18 litres) per cylinder. Total swept volume 3,495 cu in (57·3 litres). Compression ratio 16·25 : 1. Separate pressed-steel cylinder frame side members are surrounded by gas-welded sheet metal

CRM 18 D/S - 2   marine diesel rated at 1,350 bhp at 2,075 rpm

water cooling jacket treated and pressure-coated internally to prevent corrosion. Cylinders are closed at top by a steel plate integral with side wall to complete combustion chamber. Lower half of cylinder is ringed by a drilled flange for bolting to crankcase. Cylinder top also houses a spherical-shaped pre-combustion chamber as well as inlet and exhaust valve seats. Pre-combustion chamber is in high-strength, heat and corrosion resistant steel. A single cast light alloy head, carrying valve guides, pre-combustion chambers and camshaft bearings bridges each bank of cylinders. Head is attached to cylinder bank by multiple studs.

PISTONS: Light alloy forgings with four rings, top ring being chrome-plated and bottom ring acting as oil scarper. Piston crowns shaped to withstand high temperatures especially in vicinity of pre-combustion chamber outlet ports.

CONNECTING RODS: Comprise main and secondary articulated rods, all rods being completely machined I-section steel forgings. Big end of each main rod is bolted to ribbed cap by six studs. Big-end bearings are white metal lined steel shells. Each secondary rod anchored at its lower end to a pivot pin inserted in two lugs protruding from big-end of main connecting rod. Both ends of all secondary rods, and small ends of main rods have bronze bushes.

CRANKSHAFTS: One-piece hollow shaft in nitrided alloy steel, with six throws equi-spaced at 120°. Seven main bearings with white metal lined steel shells. Twelve balancing counterweights.

CRANKCASE: Cast light alloy crankcase bolted to bed plate by studs and tie bolts. Multiple integral reinforced ribs to provide robust structure. Both sides of each casting braced by seven cross ribs incorporating crankshaft bearing supports. Protruding sides of crankcase ribbed throughout length.

VALVE GEAR: Hollow sodium-cooled valves of each bank of cylinders actuated by twin camshafts and six cams on each shaft. Two inlet and two outlet valves per cylinder and one rocker for each pair of valves. End of stem and facing of exhaust valves fitted with Stellite inserts. Valve cooling water forced through passage formed by specially-shaped plate welded to top of cylinder.

FUEL INJECTION: Pumps fitted with variable speed control and pilot injection nozzle.

PRESSURE CHARGER: Two mechanically-driven centrifugal compressors on CRM 18 D/2, or two exhaust gas turbo-driven compressors on CRM 18/0/S-2.

ACCESSORIES: Standard accessories include oil and fresh water heat exchangers; fresh water tank; oil and fresh water thermostats; oil filters, fresh water, salt water and fuel hand pumps; fresh water and oil temperature gauges; engine, reverse gear and reduction gear oil gauges; pre-lubrication, electric pump and engine rpm counter. Optional accessories include engine oil and water pre-heater, and warning and pressure switches.

COOLING SYSTEM: Fresh water.

FUEL: Fuel oil having specific gravity of 0·830 to 0·840.

LUBRICATION SYSTEM: Pressure type

with gear pump.

OIL: Mineral oil to SAE 40 HD.

OIL COOLING: By salt water circulating through heat exchanger.

STARTING: 24 volt 15 hp electric motor and 85 amp, 24 volt alternator for battery charge, or compressed air.

MOUNTING: At any transverse or longitudinal angle tilt to 20°.

REVERSE GEAR: Bevel crown gear wheels with hydraulically-controlled hand brake.

REDUCTION GEAR: Optional fitting with spur gears giving reduction ratios of 0·561 : 1, 0·730 : 1 and 0·846 : 1. Overdrive ratio 1·18 : 1.

PROPELLER THRUST BEARING: Incorporated in reduction gear or in overdrive. Axial thrust 6,620 lb (3,003 kg) at 1,176 rpm

DIMENSIONS:

Height	51·33 in (1,304 mm)
Width	53·15 in (1,350 mm)
Length	116·5 in (2,960 mm)

WEIGHTS, Dry:

Engine	3,690 lb (1,665 kg)
Reverse gear, generator and starter	900 lb (410 kg)
Reduction gear or overdrive, with propeller thrust bearing	330 lb (150 kg)
Total	4,920 lb (2,225 kg)

PERFORMANCE RATINGS:

CRM 18 D/S:

Maximum power　　1,350 bhp at 2,075 rpm

Intermittent service

　　　　　1,250 bhp at 2,020 rpm

Continuous service　1,040 bhp at 1,900 rpm

FUEL CONSUMPTION:

CRM 18 D/S-2 at continuous service rating

　　　　　0·37 lb (0·170 kg)/bhp hr

OIL CONSUMPTION:

CRM 18 D/S-2 at continuous service rating

　　　　　0·007 lb (0·003 kg)/hr

CRM 12 D/S-2

Second in the new CRM series of lightweight diesels is the 900 bhp 12-cylinder 12 D/S-2 with two banks of six cylinders set at 60° to form a V assembly. The bore and stroke are the same as in the CRM 18 series, and many of the components are interchangeable, including the crankshaft, bedplate, cylinders and pistons. The crankcase and connecting rod-assemblies are necessarily of modified design; the secondary rod is anchored at its lower end to a pivot pin inserted on two lugs protruding from the big-end of the main connecting rod. The fuel injection pump is modified to single block housing all 12 pumping elements located between the cylinder banks.

A major innovation first developed on

CRM 9 D/S - 2 marine diesel rated at 715 bhp at 1,950 rpm

the 12 D/S (and later provided for the other engines in the series) was the introduction of an exhaust gas driven turbo-charger. This involved a complete revision of the combustion system and all components comprising the cylinder heads. Conversion to turbo-charging avoided the mechanical power loss expended in driving the blower, and enabled a greater volume of air to be forced into the cylinders. The effect on specific fuel consumption was a reduction to around 0·35 lb to 0·37 lb (160 to 170 gr)/bhp/hr in conjunction with exhaust temperatures not exceeding 530°C (986°F) at maximum rpm. Two Holset turbo-chargers are fitted.

TYPE: 12-cylinder in-line V type, four-stroke water-cooled, turbo-supercharged diesel engines.

DIMENSIONS:

Height	47·4 in (1,204 mm)
Width	47·64 in (1,210 mm)
Length	99·60 in (2,530 mm)

WEIGHTS, Dry:

Engine	2,735 lb (1,240 kg)
Reverse gear, generator and starter	900 lb (410 kg)
Reduction gear or overdrive, with propeller thrust bearing	330 lb (150 kg)
Total	3,965 lb (1,800 kg)

PERFORMANCE RATINGS:

Max power　　　900 bhp at 2,035 rpm

Continuous service　850 bhp at 2,000 rpm

Intermittent service　750 bhp at 1,900 rpm

FUEL CONSUMPTION:

At continuous service rating

　　　　　0·40 lb (0·18 kg)/bhp/hr

CRM 9

Third in development and smallest in the new CRM lightweight series of diesels is the nine-cylinder three-bank engine of similar configuration to the CRM 18 units. Both a naturally-aspirated version, the 415 bhp CRM 9, D/A, and a turbo-supercharged version, the 715 bhp CRM 9 D/S-2, are available.

TYPE: Nine-cylinder in-line W type, four-stroke, water-cooled, naturally-aspirated (CRM 9 D/A) or turbo-supercharged (CRM 9 D/S-2 diesel engine).

WEIGHTS, Dry:

Engine, CRM 9 D/S-2	2,447 lb (1,110 kg)
Reverse and reduction gear, with propeller thrust bearing, generator and starter	1,356 lb (615 kg)
Total	3,803 lb (1,725 kg)

PERFORMANCE RATINGS:

CRM 9 D/S-2, max power

　　　　　715 bhp at 1,950 rpm

Continuous service　550 bhp at 1,800 rpm

Intermittent service　660 bhp at 1,900 rpm

FUEL CONSUMPTION:

CRM 9 D/S-2 at continuous service rating

　　　　　0·385 lb (0·176 kg)/bhp/hr

FIAT/AIFO

Applicazioni Industriali Fiat OM

HEAD OFFICE: Via Carducci 29, Milan

TELEPHONE: 877-066/8

AIFO Carraro V12SS, 700 hp 12-cylinder diesel engines are installed in the H 57 60-passenger hydrofoil ferries built by Seaflight, Messina.

CARRARO V12SS

TYPE: Pre-chamber injection, vee-form 12-cylinder, turbocharged and inter-cooled four-stroke diesel engine.

OUTPUT: Basic engine, 700 bhp; maximum shaft output 650 hp at 1,500 rpm.

BORE AND STROKE: 142 × 180 mm.

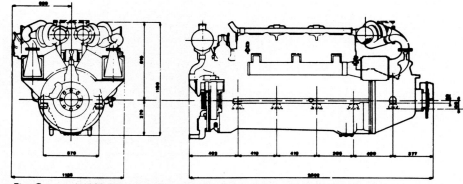

Fiat-Carraro V12SS 700 hp marine diesel. Two of these 12-cylinder water-cooled and supercharged engines power the Seaflight H57 hydrofoil passenger ferry

FUEL INJECTION: Bosch type pumps and centrifugal governor; fuel feeding pumps; fuel cartridge filters.

ENGINE COOLING: By fresh water into closed circuit with thermostatic control valve.

OIL COOLING: By salt water circulating through a heat exchanger.

STARTING: 6 hp starter motor and 600 watt generator for battery charging.

LUBRICATION: By gear pump.

REVERSE GEAR: Hydraulically operated, with brake on transmission.

REDUCTION GEAR: Standard ratios, 1·5 : 1 and 2 : 1.

DRY WEIGHT: 4,120 lb (2,200 kg).

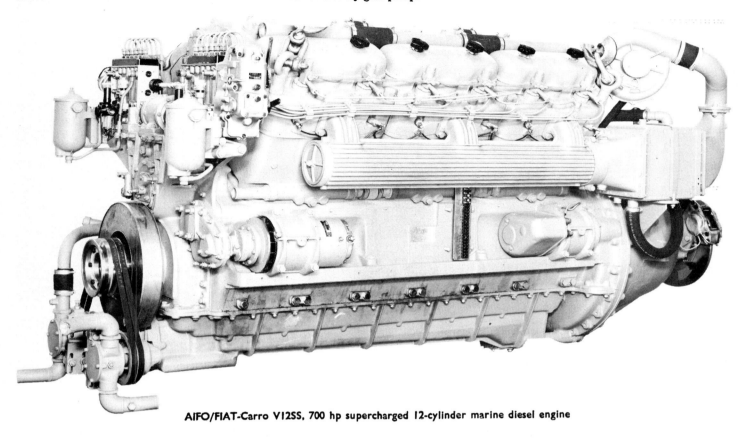

AIFO/FIAT-Carro V12SS, 700 hp supercharged 12-cylinder marine diesel engine

UNITED KINGDOM

CATERPILLAR TRACTOR
Caterpillar Tractor Co Ltd
55 St. James's Street,
London SW1A 1LA
England
TELEPHONE:
01-493 1882

Caterpillar is the UK subsidiary of the Caterpillar Tractor Co, a leading US manufacturer of diesels who has supplied engines worldwide, equivalent to hundreds of millions of diesel horsepower. Engines are sold for marine, electrical power and industrial applications, and are supported by more than 900 Caterpillar dealer facilities for parts and service: more than 14,000 dealer servicemen provide a 24-hour service to diesel operators. The engines are designed to give a high degree of component interchangeability, equal on V-models to 90 per cent of all parts.

Specific applications include Hovertrailer International standard, pipe, logging and high pressure trailers with lifting capacities up to 100 tons, powered by Caterpillar Model 3145, 3160, 3304, D343, D346 and D348 engines. Mackley Ace offshore hover platforms with lifting capacities of 30 tons and over, are powered by Model D334, D346 and D348 engines which are also used in Air Cushion Equipment bulk storage tank removal systems.

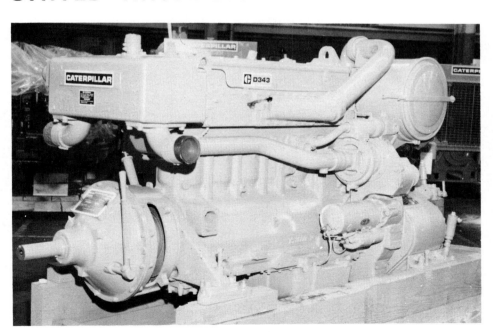

Caterpillar Model D343 marine diesel engine

MODEL 3304NA, 3304T AND 3306T
TYPE: Six-cylinder in-line four-stroke water-cooled, turbo-supercharged diesel engines. Counterclockwise rotation viewed from rear.

CYLINDERS: Bore 4·75 in (121 mm). Stroke 6·0 in (152 mm). Total swept volume 3304NA and 3304T 425 cu in (6·9 litres), and 3306T 638 cu in (10·5 litres).

COMPRESSION RATIO: 17·5 : 1. Molybdenum alloy cast iron cylinder liners water-cooled over full length, and specifically designed to give operating life equal to engine. Cylinder head assemblies cast in molybdenum and nickel alloyed grey iron, with intake manifold cast integrally with head to improve air flow and minimise maintenance. Water 'directors' located in the head force coolant against surfaces near combustion heat to eliminate hot spots.

PISTONS: Copper and nickel alloyed aluminium pistons elliptically ground and tapered from base to crown. Integrally cast iron ring band provides long-life wearing surface for top two of three piston rings. Intermediate ring is of twist design to seal efficiently and improve oil control. All rings are thick chrome plated. Gudgeon pins hardened to Rockwell 50C and ground to a 'fit' tolerance of only 0·0003 in (0·00076 cm). Retained by 'C' ring circlips.

CONNECTING RODS: Forged, hardened and shot-peened for high strength. Steel-backed aluminium bearings.

CRANKSHAFT: Steel forging, induction hardened, stress relieved and shot peened. Journals super-finished to within one micron of final smoothness.

CRANKCASE: Five or seven steel-backed aluminium bearings, with heavily ribbed bearing supports cast integrally with high tensile block.

VALVE GEAR: Valve rotators rotate 3° on each lift-off to give better valve seating and longer life. Exhaust valves faced with cobalt and tungsten alloy to retain hardness at operating temperatures. Exhaust seats have nickel based alloy replaceable inserts. Stainless steel intake valve heads and intake inserts contribute to efficient operation.

FUEL INJECTION: Precombustion chamber fuel system mixes fuel and air to atomize fuel for clean burning, and each chamber has an electric glow plug for reliable cold-weather starts. Capsule-type fuel injection valve with single large-diameter self-cleaning orifice. 'No-adjustment' fuel system with automatic fuel-air ratio control. Separate pump for each cylinder located on side of engine. Easily replaced spin-on filters with plastic-impregnated cellulose filter.

TURBO-SUPERCHARGER: Single-stage centrifugal air compressor driven by single-stage centripetal turbine energised by exhaust gases.

ACCESSORIES: Include fuel priming pump, 24-volt alternator, gear-driven jacket and auxiliary water pumps, speed governor, oil cooler, tachometer drive.

COOLING SYSTEM: Jacket water pump minimum flow 63 gal/min (3·98 litre/sec). Normal sea water pump flow 65 gal/min (4·10 litre/sec) (for six cylinders).

LUBRICATION SYSTEM: Fully-pressurised system with gear-type pump and full-flow heavy duty filter system. Continuous oil spray lubricates piston gudgeon pins. Turbo-supercharger and engine bearings receive immediate lubrication on starts through bypass valve.

OIL COOLING: Tube-bundle type jacket water heat exchanger.

STARTING: Air motor mounted on starboard side of engine. Normal starting air pressure 90-100 lb/sq in. Or, 24-volt electric starter.

GEAR: Reverse and reduction gear hydraulically operated, full power for both clockwise

Caterpillar Model D346 marine diesel engine

and counter-clockwise propeller rotation. Gear ratio 2 : 1, 2·95 : 1, 3·83 : 1, 4·5 : 1.

DIMENSIONS with gear:
3304NA, 3304T:

Height	41·3 in (1,049 mm)
Width	36·0 in (914 mm)
Length	57·0 in (1,447 mm)

3306T:

Height	47·8 in (1,214 mm)
Width	37·2 in (945 mm)
Length	75·8 in (1,925 mm)

WEIGHTS, Dry with gear:

3304NA, 3304T	2,220 lb (1,007 kg)
3306T	2,675 lb (1,210 kg)

PERFORMANCE RATINGS:
3304NA:

Maximum (flywheel)	115 hp
Continuous (shaft)	82 hp

3304T:

Maximum (flywheel)	200 hp
Continuous (shaft)	121 hp

3306T:

Maximum (flywheel)	300 hp
Continuous (shaft)	184 hp
Normal working range	1,500-2,200 rpm

FUEL CONSUMPTIONS:
At continuous (shaft) rating:

3304NA	5·25 gal/hr (19·9 litre/hr)
3304T	7·80 gal/hr (29·5 litre/hr)
3306T	11·10 gal/hr (41·9 litre/hr)

MODELS D343T AND TA, D346, D348 AND D349

(Basic features of these models are in general similar to the D330 and D333 series, with following main differences).

TYPE: Eight, twelve and sixteen cylinder 60°V in-line (except for six-cylinder straight in-line D343), four-stroke, water-cooled, turbo-supercharger-aftercooled diesel engines. Counterclockwise rotation viewed from rear.

CYLINDERS: Bore 5·4 in (137 mm). Stroke 6·5 in (165 mm). Total swept

volume D343 893 cu in (14·6 litre), D346 1,191 cu in (19·5 litre), D348 1,786 cu in (29·3 litre), and D349 2,382 cu in (39·1 litre). Compression ratio, 16·5 : 1, except for D343 16·8 : 1. One-piece nickel-chrome alloyed grey iron cast cylinder block, precision bored and milled. Conventional studs on V models are complemented by extra length studs extending into bearing saddle area.

TURBO-SUPERCHARGER AND AFTER-COOLER: Turbo-charger similar to 3304 and 3306 models with addition of water-cooled aftercooler interposed between compressor air delivery and cylinder manifold. System doubles rate of airflow to engine and lowers exhaust temperatures.

ACCESSORIES: Hydro-mechanical governor gear-driven fuel priming and transfer pumps, gear-driven jacket-water pump.

COOLING SYSTEM: Jacket water pump minimum flow 350 gal/min (22·10 litre/sec) except for D343 160 gal/min (10·10 litre/sec).

GEAR: Ratio, D343 2·1 : 1, 2·5 : 1, 3 : 1, 3·5 : 1, 4·5 : 1 and 6 : 1, D346 2·19 : 1, 3·03 : 1, 4·09 : 1 and 5·17 : 1; D348 2·07 : 1, 2·92 : 1, 3·86 : 1, 5·17 : 1 and 5·28 : 1, D349 2 : 1, 2·94 : 1, 3·54 : 1, 4·67 : 1 and 5·88 : 1. All ratios at 1,800 engine continuous rpm.

DIMENSIONS with gear:
D343TA:

Height	55·65 in (1,413 mm)
Width	41·46 in (1,053 mm)
Length	84·52 in (2,147 mm)

D346:

Height	73·12 in (1,851 mm)
Width	60·12 in (1,527 mm)
Length	102·99 in (2,616 mm)

D348:

Height	77·20 in (1,960 mm)
Width	60·12 in (1,527 mm)
Length	118·73 in (3,015 mm)

D349:

Height	77·20 in (1,960 mm)

Width	60·12 in (1,527 mm)
Length	156·05 in (3,964 mm)

WEIGHTS, Dry with gear:

D343TA	6,040 lb (2,742 kg)
D346	9,320 lb (4,230 kg)
D348	11,335 lb (5,146 kg)
D349	14,855 lb (6,744 kg)

PERFORMANCE RATINGS (flywheel):

D343T:

Maximum, at 2,000 rpm	395 hp
Continuous, at 1,800 rpm	245 hp

D343TA:

Maximum, at 2,000 rpm	550 hp
Continuous, at 1,800 rpm	365 hp

D346:

Maximum, at 2,000 rpm	735 hp
Continuous, at 1,800 rpm	480 hp

D348:

Maximum, at 2,000 rpm	1,100 hp
Continuous, at 1,800 rpm	725 hp

D349:

Maximum, at 2,000 rpm	1,470 hp
Continuous, at 1,800 rpm	970 hp

FUEL CONSUMPTION:

D343T, D343TA:

	19·4 gal/hr (74 litre/hr) at 365 hp
D346:	25·8 gal/hr (95 litre/hr) at 480 hp
D348:	38 gal/hr (144 litre/hr) at 725 hp
D349:	51·6 gal/hr (190 litre/hr) at 970 hp

MODEL 3160

TYPE: Eight cylinder 90°V in-line, four-stroke, water-cooled, normally aspirated diesel engine.

CYLINDERS: Bore 4·5 in (114 mm). Stroke 5·0 in (127 mm). Total swept volume 636 cu in (10·4 litres). Compression ratio 16·5 : 1. Cast heads with integral air inlet manifold in alloyed grey iron. Intake and exhaust valve seats staggered to reduce thermal stress concentrations. Crescent-shaped bevel adjacent to each intake valve seat imparts swirl to incoming air to improve combustion. Bores honed to within 0·00005 in (0·0127 mm) tolerance between top and bottom.

PISTONS: Aluminium alloy pistons tapered and elliptically ground for correct shape under operating load and heat. One compression and one scraper ring with integrally cast nickel-iron insert for compression ring to minimise ring groove wear. Compression ring coated with molybdenum for extra life and less friction, and twisted for seal efficiency and oil control. Fully floating large 1·5 in (38 mm) diameter gudgeon pins, ground to 0·00003 in (0·00762 mm), and hardened on inner and outer surfaces.

CONNECTING RODS: Forged H-section rods, ground to precise balance. Steel-backed aluminium alloy bearings.

CRANKSHAFT: Forged, fixture-quenched, through hardened. 90°V design of engine results in balanced power strokes forces for smooth running.

CRANKCASE: Cast nickel-chrome alloyed grey iron block featuring deep skirt design extending 4 in (101·6 mm) below centre-line of crankshaft for added strength and rigidity. Main bearing caps fit into machined recesses in block rib structure, with securing cap-screws positioned at 30° angles to obviate need for cross-bolting. Five main bearings with large wipe area, supported by ribbed block, recess-fitted bearing blocks. Steel-backed aluminium alloy bearings.

VALVE GEAR: Special heat resistant alloy steel intake and exhaust valves for corrosion resistance. Exhaust valves seat on replaceable hardened steel inserts for long life. Dual valve springs with different resonant frequencies to minimise float and prevent damage if one spring fails.

FUEL INJECTION: Fuel fed from low-pressure diaphragm transfer pump to fuel manifold. Separate pump plunger for each cylinder driven by fuel systems' own camshaft. Four orifices 0·012 in (0·305 mm) wide, spray fuel in cone-shaped pattern against shaped piston crown.

ACCESSORIES: 12-volt charging alternator, hydro-mechanical speed governor, fuel, jacket water and sea or fresh water pumps, 12-volt starter motor.

COOLING SYSTEM: Jacket water pump flow at continuous power rating 60 gal/min (3·79 litre/sec).

LUBRICATION SYSTEM: Gear-driven six-lobe pump passes oil through multi-plate oil cooler, then through two spin-on filters to oil gallery supplying all bearings surfaces with immediate lubrication.

STARTING: 12-volt electric.

GEAR: Reverse and reduction gear, with ratios 1·50 : 1, 1·97 : 1, 2·50 : 1, 2·96 : 1.

DIMENSIONS with gear:

Height	35·75 in (908 mm)
Width	34·3 in (860 mm)
Length	46·3 in (1,590 mm)

WEIGHT, Dry with gear: 1,610 lb (730 kg)

PERFORMANCE RATING (shaft):

Continuous, at 2,400 rpm	146 hp

FUEL CONSUMPTION:

At 75 per cent shaft hp

5·9 gal/hr (22·3 litre/hr)

RUSTON PAXMAN DIESELS LIMITED (a management company of GEC Diesels Limited)

HEAD OFFICE & WORKS:

Vulcan Works, Newton-le-Willows, Lancashire, WA12 8RU

Paxman Works also at:

Hythe Hill, Colchester, CO1 2HW, Lincoln.

LONDON OFFICE (GEC Diesels Ltd):

105-109 The Strand, London WC2R 0BG

Manufactured at the Colchester Works of Ruston Paxman Diesels are three of the world's most advanced diesel designs; the vee-form 'Ventura', built in 6, 8, 12, and 16-cylinder sizes covering 450 to 2,400 bhp, the RP200 built in 8, 12 and 16-cylinder sizes covering 1,000-3,300 bhp, and the Napier 'Deltic'—an 18-cylinder engine of unique triangular configuration—in powers from 1,500 to 4,000 shaft horsepower. These engines, with their compact overall dimensions and low unit weight, are particularly suitable for the propulsion of high-speed craft including hydrofoils and hovercraft.

The 'Ventura' is being incorporated in several current designs for hydrofoils and rigid sidewall ACVs.

VENTURA (YJ) AND VALENTA (RP200) DIESELS

TYPE: YJ engines: Direct injection 60°, vee-form 6, 8, 12 and 16-cylinder, turbocharged or turbo-charged and aftercooled four stroke diesel engine. RP200 engine: Direct injection, vee-form 8, 12 and 16-cylinder, turbocharged and water-cooled, four-stroke engine.

Paxman 12-cylinder Valenta marine diesel developing 2,475 bhp at 1,600 rpm

OUTPUT: YJ engines: 450-2,400 bhp, 1,000-1,600 rev/min. RP200 engines: 1,000-3,300 bhp, 1,000-1,600 rev/min.

BORE AND STROKE: 7·75 × 8·5 in (197 × 216 mm).

SWEPT VOLUME (per cylinder): 401 cu in (6·57 litres).

HOUSING: Fabricated high quality steel plate.

CRANKSHAFT AND MAIN BEARINGS: Fully nitrated shaft carried in aluminium tin pre-finished steel-backed main bearings. Engine fully balanced against primary and secondary forces.

CONNECTING RODS: Fork and blade type with steel-backed, aluminium tin lined large end (forked rod) and steel-backed, lead bronze lined, lead tin flashed bearings (blade rod).

PISTONS: Conventional aluminium alloy, oil cooled with Alfin bonded insert for top ring. Three compression and one oil control rings. (YJ): Three compression and one oil control ring (RP200).

CYLINDER HEAD: High grade casting carrying four valve direct injection system.

LINERS: Wet type seamless steel tube, chrome plated bore and water side surface, honeychromed for surface oil retention.

FUEL INJECTION: External Monobloc pumps located below air manifolds. (YJ): single unit pumps (RP 200). Pump plungers and camshaft lubricated from main engine pressure system. Feed and injection pump driven from engine drive end gear train; a fuel reservoir and air bleed system fitted. Injectors of the multi-hole type spray fuel into the toroidal cavity in the top of piston. Injectors retained by clamp and are external to head cover (YJ); sleeved connection inside cover (RP 200).

GOVERNOR: Standard hydraulic 'Regulateurs Europa' unit with self-contained lubricating oil system; mechanical, electrical or pneumatic controls. Alternative makes available.

PRESSURE CHARGING AND INTERCOOLING: Napier water-cooled exhaust-gas-driven turboblowers mounted above engine. Air to water intercooler of Serck manufacture for after-cooled versions (YJ and RP 200).

LUBRICATION: Pressure lubrication to all bearing surfaces; separate pressure and cooling pumps. (YJ): single pump system (RP 200). Oil coolers mounted externally and integral with engine (fresh water cooled (YJ); sea water cooled (RP 200). Full flow single or duplex oil filter can be supplied. Centrifugal filters fitted as standard (YJ).

FRESH WATER COOLING: Single pump at free end, shaft-driven from drive end gear train. Thermostatic control valve mounted above pump, giving quick warm-up and even temperature control of water and oil circuits (YJ); oil thermostat (RP 200).

EXHAUST: Single outlet from turboblower(s). Dry type manifolds (YJ); water-cooled manifolds (RP 200).

STARTING: Air, electric or hydraulic starting.

FUEL: Gas oil to BS.2869/1970 Class A1 and A2 or equivalent, and certain gas turbine fuels. Other classes of fuel subject to specification being made available.

LUBRICATING OIL: Oils certified to MIL-L-2104B (with a TBN of not less than 9).

OPTIONAL EXTRA EQUIPMENT: Gearboxes, starting control systems, and all

Deltic charge-air cooled, turbo-charged diesel engine with integral reverse reduction gear, developing 4,000 shp

associated engine ancillary equipment necessary for marine applications.

NAPIER DELTIC DIESEL

TYPE: 18-cylinder, opposed piston, liquid cooled, two stroke, compression ignition. Three banks of six cylinders in triangular configuration.

OUTPUT: Covers horsepower range of 1.500-4,000 shaft hp. Charge-cooled engine rating up to 3,000 shaft hp continuous at 1,800 rev/min. Half hour sprint rating up to 4,000 shaft hp at 2,100 rev/min. Weight/power ratio 3·94 lb/shp.

BORE AND STROKE: Bore—5·125 in (130·17 mm). Stroke—7·25 in × 2 (opposed piston) (184·15 mm × 2).

SWEPT VOLUME (total): 5,284 in³ (88·3 litres).

COMBUSTION SYSTEM: Direct injection.

PISTONS: Two piece—body and gudgeon pin housing. Gudgeon pin housing with fully floating gudgeon pin shrunk into body and secured with taper seated circlip. Body-skirt and gudgeon pin housing in light alloy, piston crown in 'Hidurel' material. Oil cooled. Three gas, two oil control and one scraper ring.

CONNECTING RODS: Fork and blade type with steel backed, lead bronze, lead flashed, indium infused thin-wall bearings. Manufactured from drop forgings, machined and polished all over.

CRANKSHAFTS: Three crankshafts machined from forgings and fully nitrided. Each shaft fitted with viscous type torsional vibration damper. Each crankpin carries one inlet and one exhaust piston, thus, the loading on all crankpins is identical and reciprocating forces are balanced within the engine.

CRANKCASES AND CYLINDER BLOCKS

Three crankcases and three cylinder blocks arranged in the form of an inverted equilateral triangle all of light alloy construction. Crankcases substantially webbed and carrying each crankshaft in seven, thin-wall, steelbacked, lead bronze, lead flashed indium infused main bearings. Cylinder blocks each carry six 'wet' type liners, have integrally cast air inlet manifolds and mount the injection pumps camshaft casings.

CYLINDER LINERS: 18 'wet' type liners machined from hollow steel forgings, bores chrome plated with honeychrome process applied, finished by lapping. Coolant side flash tin plated. In areas of liquid contact with exhaust coolant-area, flash chrome plated.

TURBOCHARGER: Geared-in type, single stage, axial flow turbine and single-sided centrifugal compressor mounted on common shaft. Light alloy main castings. Charge-cooled engines have charge-air coolers (one for each cylinder block) incorporated within the overall dimensions of the turbocharger unit.

PHASING GEAR: To combine the output from the three crankshafts. A light alloy gear casing containing an output gear train linked to the crankshafts by quill-shafts and passing the torque to a common output gear. All gears hardened and ground and carried in roller bearings. Gear train also provides drives for auxiliary pumps and engine governor.

FUEL SYSTEM: Pressurised system from engine driven circulating pump supplying 18 'jerk' type fuel injection pumps one per cylinder mounted in banks of six on camshaft casings secured to each cylinder block. Each pump supplies a single injector per cylinder.

LUBRICATION: Dry sump system with engine driven pressure and scavenge pumps. Twin pressure oil filters engine mounted.

COOLING: Closed circuit system with engine driven circulating pump. Engine mounted circulating pumps for sea-water system for cooling coolant heat exchanger and oil cooler, also for charge-air coolers.

STARTING: Air starting to six cylinders of one bank.

MOUNTING: Four point by resilient mounting units.

REVERSE GEAR: Marine reverse reduction gearbox incorporating a hydraulic friction clutch can be supplied as an integral unit.

ROLLS-ROYCE (1971) LIMITED (INDUSTRIAL & MARINE DIVISION)

HEAD OFFICE:
PO Box 72, Ansty, Coventry CV7 9JR, Warwickshire
TELEPHONE:
Coventry 613211 (STD 0203)
TELEGRAMS:
Roycov, Coventry
TELEX:
31637
DIRECTORS:
R. H. Robins (Managing Director)

In April 1967 Rolls-Royce Limited formed a new division merging the former industrial and marine gas-turbine activities of Rolls-Royce and Bristol Siddeley. The new division was known as the Industrial & Marine Gas-Turbine Division of Rolls-Royce.

In May 1971 the present company, Rolls-Royce (1971) Limited, was formed combining all the gas-turbine interests of the former Rolls-Royce company. The four divisions involved are the Industrial & Marine Division, the Derby Engine Division, the Bristol Engine Division and the Small Engine Division.

It offers a wider range of industrial and marine gas-turbines based on aero-engine gas generators than any other manufacturer in the world. It has available for adaptation a large selection of the gas-turbines being developed and manufactured by the Rolls-Royce Derby Engine Division, the Bristol Engine, and Small Engine Divisions. Marinised gas-turbines at present being produced and developed by the Company include the Gnome, Proteus, Tyne, Olympus and Spey.

Over 1,550 of these marine and industrial engines are in service or have been ordered for operation around the world and the total value of the export orders received up to mid-1974 was approximately £85 million. 21 navies have selected the company's marine gas-turbines to power naval craft, following the initial orders from the Royal Navy in the late 1950s.

HYDROFOILS: The Boeing PCH High Point is powered by two Proteus gas-turbines while single Proteus turbines power the Boeing PGH-2 Tucumcari and Alinvani Swordfish. A Tyne powers the Grumman designed PG(H)-1 Flagstaff and the Super Flagstaff. Rolls-Royce marine gas-turbines can also be specified as alternative power-plants for the modular version of the Boeing Jetfoil.

HOVERCRAFT: The Gnome powers the BHC SR.N3, SR.N5 and SR.N6. The Proteus powers the SR.N4, the BH.7 and the new Vosper Thornycroft VT2.

MARINE GNOME

TYPE: Gas-turbine, free-turbine turboshaft.
AIR INTAKE: Annular. 15°C.
COMBUSTION CHAMBER: Annular.
FUEL GRADE:
D.E.R.D. 2494 Avtur/50 Kerosene.
D.E.R.D. 2482 Avtur/40 Kerosene.
Diesel fuel BSS 2869 Class A
DEF 1402 or NATO F75
TURBINE: Two-stage axial-flow generator turbine and a single-stage axial-flow free power turbine.
BEARINGS: Compressor rotor has a roller bearing at the front and a ball bearing at the rear. Gas generator turbine is supported at the front by the compressor rear bearings, and at the rear by a roller bearing.
Single stage power turbine is supported by

Rolls-Royce Marine Tyne RM2D rated at 5,800 bhp

a roller bearing behind the turbine disc and by a ball bearing towards the rear of the turbine shaft.
JET PIPE: Exhaust duct to suit installation.
ACCESSORY DRIVES: Accessory gearbox provides a drive for:—The fuel pump, the hydro-mechanical governor in the flow control unit, the centrifugal fuel filter, the dual tachometer and the engine oil pump.
LUBRICATION SYSTEM: Dry sump.
OIL SPECIFICATION: D.E.R.D. 2487.
MOUNTING: Front: three pads on the front frame casing, one on top, one on each side. Rear without reduction gearbox, mounting point is the rear flange of the exhaust duct centre-body. With reduction gearbox mounting points are provided by two machined faces on the reduction gearbox.
STARTING: Electric.
DIMENSIONS:

Length	72·8 in (1,667 mm)
Width	18·2 in (462 mm)
Height	20·75 in (527 mm)

PERFORMANCE RATINGS:

Max	1,050 bhp
Cont	900 bhp

Ratings are at maximum power-turbine speed, 19,500 rpm. A reduction gearbox is available giving an output speed of 6,650 rpm.
SPECIFIC FUEL CONSUMPTION:

Max	0·625 lb (283 gr) bhp/hr
Cont	0·650 lb (295 gr) bhp/hr

OIL CONSUMPTION:

	1·2 pints (0·67 litre)/hr
Power Turbine	1·5 pints (0·84 litres)/hr

MARINE OLYMPUS

Gas generator and single stage power turbine.
TYPE: Gas-turbine, two-shaft turbojet.
AIR INTAKE: Annular 15°C.
COMBUSTION CHAMBER: Eight.
FUEL GRADE: Diesel fuel B.S.S. 2869 Class A. DEF 2402 or NATO F. 75.
TURBINE (ENGINE): Two stage, each stage driving its own respective compressor—5 stage low pressure or 7 stage high pressure.
TURBINE (POWER): Single stage axial flow.
BEARINGS: Compressor rotor forward end supported by a roller bearing and rear end by a duplex ball bearing.
The power turbine rotor assembly and mainshaft are supported as a cantilever in two white metal bearings housed in a pedestal.
JET PIPE: Exhaust duct to suit installation.
ACCESSORY DRIVES: Power turbine. Accessories are mounted on the main gearbox which is a separate unit transmitting the turbine's power output to the propeller shaft. These include pressure and scavenge oil pumps. Speed signal generator, iso-speedic switch and rev/min indicator are driven by the pedestal-mounted accessory gearbox.

LUBRICATION SYSTEM: The gas generator has its own integral lubrication system which is supplied with oil from a 27 gal tank. Components in the system are:—A pressure pump, main scavenge pump, four auxiliary scavenge pumps and an oil cooler.
Power Turbine. Bearings are lubricated and cooled by a pressure oil system.
OIL SPECIFICATION: Gas generator.
D. Eng R. D. 2487. Power turbine. O.E.P. 69.
MOUNTING: The mounting structure depends on the customer's requirements for a particular application.
STARTING: Air or electric.
DIMENSIONS:

Gas Generator:	
Length	11 ft 9 in (3·6 m)
Width	4 ft 3 in (1·29 m)
Weight	6,500 lb (2·94 kg)
Power Turbine:	
Length	12 ft 9 in (3·9 m)
Width	8 ft 0 in (2·4 m)
Height	9 ft 9 in (3 m)
Complete Unit:	
Length	22 ft 3 in (6·8 m)
Width	8 ft 0 in (2·4 m)
Height	9 ft 9 in (3 m)
Weight	21 tons

PERFORMANCE RATING:
Max
28,000 bhp at max power-turbine speed of 5,660 rpm.
SPECIFIC FUEL CONSUMPTION:

Max	0·47 lb (226 gr) bhp/hr

OIL CONSUMPTION:

Gas Generator:	
Max	1·5 pints (0·84 litres)/hr
Power turbine	1·5 pints (0·84 litres)/hr

MARINE PROTEUS

TYPE: Gas-turbine, free-turbine turboprop.
AIR INTAKE: Radial between the compressor and turbine sections of the engine. 15°C.
COMBUSTION CHAMBERS: Eight, positioned around the compressor casing.
FUEL GRADE: DEF 2402—Distillate diesel fuel.
TURBINE: Four stages coupled in mechanically independent pairs. The first coupled pair drive the compressor, the second pair form the free power turbine, which drives the output shaft.
BEARINGS: HP end of compressor rotor is carried by roller bearing, the rear end by a duplex ball bearing. Compressor turbine rotor shaft is located by a ball thrust bearing, as is the power turbine rotor.
JET PIPE: Exhaust duct to suit installation.
ACCESSORY DRIVES: All accessories are driven by the compressor or power turbine systems. Compressor driven accessories are: compressor tachometer generator, fuel pump and centrifugal oil separator for the breather. The power turbine tachometer generator and

governor are driven by the power turbine. The main oil pressure pump and also the main and auxiliary scavenge pumps, are driven by both the compressor and power turbines through a differential gear.

LUBRICATION SYSTEM: The engine is lubricated by a single gear type pump connected by a differential drive to both the compressor and power turbine systems.

OIL SPECIFICATION: OEP 71. D.E.R.D. 2479/1 or D.E.R.D. 2487 (OX 38).

MOUNTING: Three attachment points comprise two main trunnions one on each side of the engine close to the diffuser casing and a steady bearing located beneath the engine immediately aft of the air intake. Engines are supplied with integrally-mounted reduction gears giving maximum output shaft speeds of 5,240, 1,500 or 1,000 rpm depending on the gearbox selected.

DIMENSIONS:

Length	113 in (2,870 mm)
Diameter	42 in (1,067 mm)
Weight (dry)	3,118 lb (1,414 kg)

PERFORMANCE RATINGS:

Max	4,500 bhp
95 per cent power	4,250 bhp
80 per cent power	3,600 bhp

SPECIFIC FUEL CONSUMPTION:

At max rating	0.565 lb (253 gr)/bhp/hr

OIL CONSUMPTION:

Average	0.5 pints (0.28 litres)/hr

MARINE TYNE RM2D

Gas generator and two stage power turbine.

TYPE: Gas-turbine, two-shaft turboprpo.

AIR INTAKE: Annular. 15°C.

COMBUSTION CHAMBER: Cannular containing ten flame tubes.

FUEL GRADE: Diesel fuel Grade A. DEF 2402B AVCAT.

TURBINE (ENGINE): Two stage, each stage driving its own respective compressor— six stage low pressure and nine stage high pressure.

TURBINE (POWER): Two-stage, axial flow free turbine.

BEARINGS: Compressor rotor forward end supported by a roller bearing and at the rear end by a thrust ball location bearing.

The power turbine front stubshaft is supported on a roller bearing and the rear on a thrust bearing.

JET PIPE: Exhaust duct to suit installation.

ACCESSORY DRIVES: Engine and power turbines accessories are mounted on the external wheelcase of the engine and the primary gearbox accessories gearcase.

LUBRICATION SYSTEM: The gas generator lubricating oil system comprises fuel pump, scavenge pumps, filters, and magnetic plugs. The primary gearbox is also fed from the gas generator lubricating oil system.

OIL SPECIFICATION: DERD 2487

MOUNTING: The forward engine mounting comprises two cantilever frames constructed of tubular members, one each side of the engine. The frames are joined by a diagonal strut across the uppermost members.

The reduction gearbox is supported in a similar way by three tubular steel supports, one either side and one beneath the gearbox. The ends of the engine and gearbox supports

are attached to the central main engine support frame by means of spherical bearings. The centre of the unit is supported through a dogged ring into the main central frame.

STARTING: Air or electric.

DIMENSIONS:

Length	158 in (401.3 cm)
Width	50 in (127 mc)
Height	54 in (140 cm)

WEIGHT: 6,800 lb (3,084 kg)

PERFORMANCE RATINGS: RM2D.

Max 5,800 bhp (5,880 cv) at max power turbine speed of 14,500 rev/min (primary gearbox output speed as required).

SPECIFIC FUEL CONSUMPTION:

Max	0.461 lb (209 gr)/bhp/hr

MARINE SPEY

The Marine Spey is based on the TF41 aero engine, largest of the spey family of gas turbines. The TF41 was developed jointly by Rolls-Royce and the Detroit Diesel Allison Division of General Motors Corporation under a joint $200 million contract awarded by USAF Systems Command in August 1966 for an advanced version of the RB168-25 Spey turbofan to power the LTV A-70 Corsair 11 fighter bomber for the USAF.

By May 1974 more than 1,000 TF41s had been delivered and the production of the TF41 for the Corsair 11 fighter bomber was expected to continue into the 1980s.

The Marine Spey has been under development since 1972 under a programme sponsored by the British Ministry of Defence.

DIMENSIONS:

Complete unit (including mounting frame):

BOEING PCH-1 HIGH POINT

GRUMMAN PGH-1 FLAGSTAFF

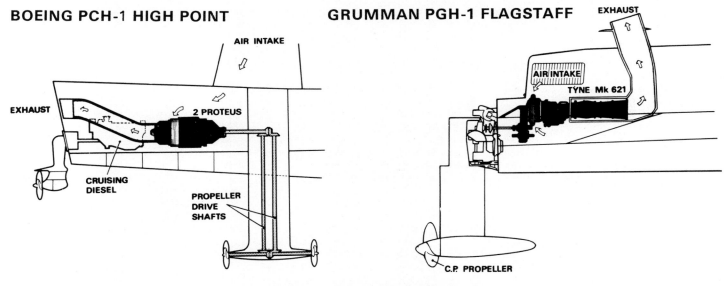

ITALIAN NAVY SWORDFISH

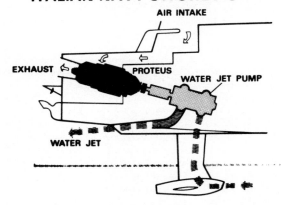

Rolls-Royce marine gas-turbines are employed on the PCH-1 High Point, the PGH-1 Flagstaff and the Swordfish Hydrofoils

Length (air intake flare to drive coupling)
223·6 in (5,680 mm)
Width   77·95 in (1,980 mm)
Height   95·27 in (2,420 mm)
Dimensions of gas generator change unit
only:
Length   105·0 in (2,677 mm)
Max diameter   35·82 in (910 mm)
WEIGHT:
Estimated weight of complete unit
17,150 lb (7,800 kg)
Estimated dry weight of gas generator
change unit   3,250 lb (1,474 kg)
NOMINAL PERFORMANCE:
*Maximum power   18,770 bhp
*Specific fuel consumption
0·415 lb/bhp/hr (0·250 kg/kWh)
*Based on L.C.V. of fuel of 18540 btu/lb
(43,125 kJ/kg)
No power off-takes
No intake or exhaust duct losses
Ambient air temperature of 15°C (59°F) and
a pressure of 14·7 lbf/in² (101·3 kPa)
TYPE: Marine gas-turbine, incorporating
two independently driven compressors, an
axial-flow free-power turbine and exhaust
volute, all on a lightweight mounting frame.
GAS GENERATOR CHARACTERISTICS
AIR INTAKE: Direct entry, fixed, without

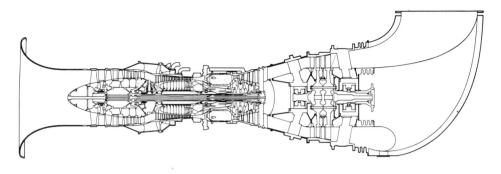

Rolls-Royce Marine Spey

intake guides.
L.P. COMPRESSOR: 5 axial stages.
H.P. COMPRESSOR: 11 axial stages.

COMBUSTION SYSTEM: Tubo-annular type
with ten interconnected straight flow flame
tubes.

TURBINES: Impulse reaction, axial-type.
Two H.P. and two L.P. stages.
EXHAUST: Fixed volume.

STARTING: Air/gas starter motor.
FUEL SYSTEM: Hydromechanical high
pressure system with automatic acceleration
and speed control.
FUEL GRADE: Diesel fuel Grade 'A',
Def 2402 or NATO F-75.
LUBRICATION SYSTEM: Self-contained
gear pump filters and chip detectors.
POWER TURBINE: 2-stage free axial-flow
turbine.

THE UNITED STATES OF AMERICA

**AIRESEARCH MANUFACTURING COM-
PANY, a division of the Garrett Corporation**
402 South 36th Street, Phoenix, Arizona
85034
TELEPHONE:
(602) 267-3011
EXECUTIVES:
Jack Teske, Vice-President and Manager
Donald L. Cauble, Assistant Manager
Robert A. Trusela, Sales Manager
AiResearch Manufacturing Company,
Phoenix, Arizona, is the world's largest
manufacturer of small gas turbine engines
for commercial, military, marine and industrial application, as well as a leading producer
of air turbine starters, air motors, pneumatic
valves and control systems for aircraft and
aerospace applications. The company occupies approximately 1 million sq ft of facilities
on 220 acres of land with its main facilities
adjoining Phoenix Sky Harbor International

Airport. Its employees number approximately 4,800.

GTP/GTPF990
Currently under development is a fully
marinized 5,000 hp advanced gas-turbine
scheduled to be available in the mid-1970s.
The engine is designed in two configurations,
a free turbine (GTPF990) for propulsion,
pump and compressor drive, and a coupled
turbine (GTP990) for applications such as
generator sets for primary and secondary
power. The engine is being designed specifically for ease of maintenance and long
TBO, and is expected to commence service
with a TBO of 6,000 hours.
Specification details available are as
follows:
TYPE: Simple-cycle, single-shaft (GTPF990)
or twin-shaft (GTP990).
COMPRESSOR: Two-stage centrifugal.
COMBUSTION CHAMBER: Single, annular.

TURBINE: Two-stage axial gas generator.
FUEL GRADE: DF-2.
DIMENSIONS:
Length   108 in (274·3 cm)
WEIGHT, Dry:
Fitted with lightweight gearbox
4,000 lb (1,814 kg)
Fitted with heavy-duty gearbox
5,000 lb (2,449 kg)
PERFORMANCE RATING:
Continuous S.L. 100°F: 5,000 shp at 18,000
rpm gas generator speed and 16,400
rpm power turbine speed.
System output speed   3,600 rpm

ME 831-800
A further development by AiResearch is a
fully marinized turbomarine power system,
having a continuous power rating of 380 shp
and an intermittant rating of 610 shp. This
unit, designated ME831-800, is under devel-

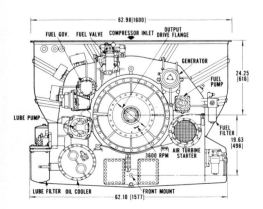

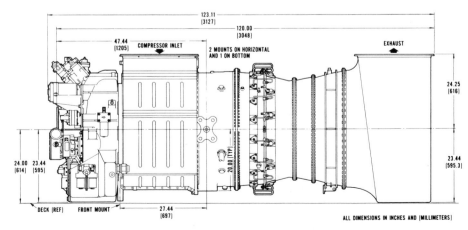

The Garrett GTPF 990, 5,000 shp heavy duty gas-turbine for marine applications

opment for the Boeing NATO PHM hydrofoil secondary power system, which uses two
units per ship.

Specification details available are as
follows:

TYPE: Simple-cycle, single-shaft.
COMPRESSOR: Two-stage centrifugal.
COMBUSTION CHAMBER: Single, reverse-
flow.

TURBINE: Three-stage axial.
FUEL GRADES: DF-1 and DF-2 per ASTM.
D975, VV-F-800, MIL-F-16884 and MIL-
R-46005, Jet A, A-1 and B per ASTM D1665.
JP-4 and JP-5 per MIL-F-5624 and VV-K-
211.
DIMENSIONS:

Length	72 in (182·9 cm)
Width	39 in (99·1 cm)

Height	34 in (86·4 cm)
WEIGHT, Dry:	1,500 lb (680·4 kg)
POWER RATING:	
Continuous S.L. 100°F	380 shp
Intermittent	610 shp
Rated rotor speed	41,730 rpm (max)

System output speed constant speed,
two output pad speeds of 8,000 rpm
and two at 3,600 rpm

AVCO LYCOMING
Avco Lycoming Division of Avco Corporation
HEAD OFFICE:
550 South Main Street, Stratford, Connecti-
cut 06497
WORKS:
Stratford, Connecticut
PRESIDENT OF AVCO CORPORATION:
George L. Hogeman
VICE-PRESIDENTS—LYCOMING DIVISION:
Joseph S. Bartos (General Manager)
Dr. H. K. Adenstedt (Senior Vice-President)
Seymour L. Rosenberg (Controller)
James F. Shanley (Administration)
E. Louis Wilkinson (Factory Operations)
Michael S. Saboe (Engineering and Develop-
ment)
Martine J. Leff (Product Support and
Marketing)
Dr. Fritz Haber, International Operations
T. B. Lauriat, Chief, Marine Industrial
Applications, Avco Lycoming
K. M. Austin, Manager, Avco International
Overseas Corporation

The Avco Lycoming Division, Stratford, is
the turbine engine manufacturing division of
the Avco Corporation.

Avco Lycoming is producing two families
of gas-turbine engines. Designated T53 and
T55, these are both of the free-turbine type
and are available in turboshaft, turbofan and
turboprop form. The T53 in particular has
been built in large numbers to power US
Army helicopters. Industrial and marine
versions of the T53 and T55 are designated
TF12A and 14B, and TF25A and 35 respectively.

TF12A and TF14B
The TF12 and TF14 engines are developments of the T53 aircraft engine. The T53
is a turboshaft with a free power turbine,
which was developed under a joint, USAF/
US Army contract. It has logged over 22
million hours of operation with the US
armed services and operators in 28 other
countries.

The TF14B is an uprated version of the
TF12B. Redesigned "hot end" and initial
stages of compressor section provide
substantially increased power for hot day
performance. Four turbine stages, compared with two in earlier models, and variable-
incidence inlet guide vanes combined with
redesigned first two compressor stages, permit greater airflow and lower turbine temperatures. This version has atomising
combustor to facilitate operation on a wider
range of fuels. Applications include US
Navy ATC/CCB and ASPBs (Assault Support
Patrol Boats).
TYPE: Free turbine turboshaft engine.
AIR INTAKE: Side inlet castings of aluminium alloy, supporting gearbox and front
main bearings.
COMPRESSOR: Five axial stages followed
by a single centrifugal stage. Four-piece
aluminium alloy casing with one row of

Avco Lycoming TF12B marine gas turbine engine of 1,150 shp

Avco Lycoming TF25C marine gas turbine engine of 2,500 shp

variable-incidence inlet guide vanes and
five rows of steel stator blades, bolted to one-
piece steel alloy diffuser casing with tangen-
tial outlet to combustion chamber. Rotor
comprises one stainless steel and four aluminium alloy discs with stainless steel blades,
and one titanium impeller mounted on shaft
supported in forward ball thrust and rear
roller bearings. Pressure ratio 6·5 : 1. Air
mass flow 9·98 lb/sec (4·85 kg/sec) at 25,240
gas producer rpm.
COMBUSTION CHAMBER: Annular
reverse-flow type, with one-piece sheet steel
outer shell and annular liner. Twenty-two
atomising fuel injectors.

FUEL CONTROL SYSTEM: Hydro-mechanical controls for gas generator and for power
sections. Woodward system with one fuel
pump. Pump pressure 600 lb/sq in (42
kg/cm²). Main and emergency flow controls.
Separate interstage air-bleed control.
FUEL GRADE: MIL-F-16884F, JP-4,
JP-5, CITE, marine diesel.
TURBINE: Four axial-flow turbine stages.
Casing fabricated from sheet steel. First
two stages, driving compressor, use hollow-
air-cooler stator vanes and cored-out cast
steel rotor blades, and are mounted on outer
co-axial shaft to gas producer. Second
stages, driving reduction gearing, have solid

steel blades, and are spline-mounted to shaft,
EXHAUST UNIT: Fixed-area nozzle.
Stainless steel outer casing and inner cone,
supported by four radial struts.
ACCESSORIES: Electric starter, Bendix-
Scintilla TGLN high-energy ignition unit.
Four ignitor plugs.
LUBRICATION: Recirculating system with
gear pump. Filter. Pump pressure 70 lb/sq
in (4·9 kg/cm²).
OIL GRADE: MIL-L 23699.
DIMENSIONS:

Length overall	51·4 in (1·30 m)
Width	30·4 in (0·72 m)
Height	42·6 in (1·08 m)

WEIGHT (Dry):

Less tailpipe	1,270 lb (576 kg)

POWER RATINGS:

Max intermittent (peak)*	
TF12B (at 59°F)	1,275 shp
TF14C (at 59°F)	1,600 shp
Max continuous (normal)*	
TF12B (at 59°F)	1,150 shp
TF14C (at 59°F)	1,400 shp

*All ratings based on no inlet pressure loss
and no exhaust pressure loss.
FUEL CONSUMPTION:
At max continuous rating:

TF12B	99 US gall/hr
TF14C	118 US gall/hr

OIL CONSUMPTION: 1·0 lb (450 gr)/hr

TF25C AND TF35C

These engines are developments of the T55
aircraft engine.
Current production and development versions are as follows:

TF25C. High-speed shaft-turbine engine,
with output shaft speed equal to power
turbine speed. Integral oil tank and cooling
system. The TF25 powers the Vosper
Thornycroft VT1, the Coastal Patrol Interdiction Craft (CPIC-X) and the Mitsui
MV-PP15 155-seat hoverferry.

TF35C. Uprated, redesigned version of
the TF25. New turbine section with four
stages and variable-incidence inlet guide
vanes. First two compressor stages transonic. New atomising fuel nozzles. TF35s
power a number of six-engined Patrol Ship
Multi-Mission craft (PSMM); a more powerful
production model of the 95-ft, high-speed
CPIC patrol boat; a number of tri-engine
waterjet ferries for the San Francisco Bridge
and Highway Authority off the coast of
California and the Aerojet-General SES-100A
surface effect test craft. This 100-ton vessel
employs four TF35 engines, each rated at
3,300 shp (maximum).
AIR INTAKE: Side inlet casting of aluminium alloy supporting optional reduction gearbox and front main bearings. Provision for
intake screens.
COMPRESSOR: Seven axial stages followed
by a single centrifugal stage. Two-piece
aluminium alloy stator casing with one row
of inlet guide vanes, fixed on TF25, variable
on TF35, and seven rows of steel stator
blades, bolted to steel alloy diffuser casing
to which combustion chamber casing is
attached. Rotor comprises seven stainless
steel discs and one titanium impeller mounted
on shaft supported in forward thrust ball
bearings and rear roller bearing. TF25C
pressure ratio 6 : 1 and 6·5 : 1 for TF35C.
COMBUSTION CHAMBER: Annular reverse
flow type. Steel outer shell and inner liner.
Twenty-eight fuel burners with downstream
injection.

Avco Lycoming TF35 C marine gas turbine engine of 3,000 shp

Avco Lycoming TF40 marine gas turbine engine of 3,500 shp

Avco Lycoming TF25C marine gas turbine engine of 2,500 shp

FUEL SYSTEM: Woodward fuel control system. Gear-type fuel pump, with gas producer and power shaft governors, flow control and shut-off valve,

FUEL GRADE: MIL: J-5624 grade JP-4, JP-5, MIL-F-46005 or marine diesel standard and wide-cut kerosene.

TURBINE: Two mechanically-independent axial-flow turbines. First turbine with single-stage on TF25C and two-stages of TF35C drives compressor. Has cored-out cast steel blades and is flange-bolted to outer co-axial drive shaft. Hollow stator vanes. Second, two-stage turbine drives output shaft. Has solid steel blades and is mounted on inner co-axial drive shaft.

EXHAUST UNIT: Fixed area nozzle, with inner cone, supported by six radial struts.

ACCESSORIES: Electric, air or hydraulic starter. Bendix-Scintilla TGLN high-energy ignition unit. Four igniter plugs.

LUBRICATION: Recirculating type. Integral oil tank and cooler.

OIL GRADE: MIL-L-17808, MIL-L-23699.

DIMENSIONS:

Length:	
TF25C	49·5 in (1·26 m)
TF35C	51·7 in (1·31 m)
Width:	
TF25C, TF35C	30·4 in (770 mm)
Height:	
TF25C, TF35C	42·6 in (1·08 m)

WEIGHT (Dry):

TF25C	1,270 lb (576 kg)
TF35C	1,700 lb (771 kg)

PERFORMANCE RATINGS:

Max intermittent (peak):	
TF25C	2,650 shp
TF35C	3,300 shp
Max continuous (normal):	
TF25C	2,500 shp
TF35C	3,000 shp

FUEL CONSUMPTION:

At max continuous rating:	
TF25C	198 US gall/hr
TF35C	223 US gall/hr

TF40

The TF40 engine is a scaled-up TF35 with higher mass flow. It has a four stage turbine section and variable-incidence inlet guide vanes. The first two compressor stages are transonic, and new atomising fuel nozzles are fitted.

Both the Jeff A (Aerojet General) and Jeff B (Bell Aerospace) AALCs employ TF40s. Jeff A employs six, each developing 3,350 shp continuous four drive individual, steerable ducted propellers, and the remaining two drive separate centrifugal lift fans. In the case of Jeff B, the six engines are arranged in two groups of three, located port and starboard. Each trio drives a single propeller and lift system through integrated gears.

Other craft due to be powered by TF40s include the SEDAM N.500, which employs two for lift and three, mounted in separate nacelles, for propulsion, and a twin engine waterjet ferry, currently being built in Scandinavia.

AIR INTAKE: Side inlet casting of aluminium alloy housing internal gearing and supporting power producer section and output drive shaft. Integral or separately mounted gears are operational. Provision for intake filters and/or silencers.

COMPRESSOR: Seven axial stages followed by a single centrifugal stage. Two-piece aluminium alloy stator casing, with one row of variable inlet guide vanes, and seven rows of steel stator blades bolted to steel alloy casing diffuser, to which combustion chamber casing is attached. Rotor comprises seven stainless steel discs and one titanium impeller mounted on shaft supported in forward thrust ball bearing and rear roller bearing. TF40 pressure ratio is 7·2 : 1.

COMBUSTION CHAMBER: Annular reverse flow type. Steel outer shell and inner liner. Twenty-eight fuel burners with downstream injection.

FUEL SYSTEM: Woodward fuel control system. Gear-type fuel pump, with gas producer and power shaft governors, flow control and shut-off valve.

FUEL GRADE: MIL-T-5624, JP-4, JP-5; MIL-F-16884 diesel, standard and wide-cut kerosene.

TURBINE: Two mechanically-independent axial-flow turbines. First turbine, with two stages, drives compressor. It has cored-out cast steel blades and is flange-bolted to outer co-axial drive shaft. Hollow stator vanes. Second two-stage turbine drives output shaft. It has solid steel blades and is mounted on inner co-axial drive shaft. (Other features include: integral cast first turbine nozzle, cooled first turbine blades in both first and second stages, second turbine vane cooling, second turbine disc and blade cooling, and a modified third stage nozzle shroud).

EXHAUST UNIT: Fixed area nozzle, with inner cone, supported by six radial struts.

ACCESSORIES: Electric, air or hydraulic starter. Bendix-Scintilla TGLN high-energy ignition unit. Four igniter plugs.

LUBRICATION: Recirculating type. Integral oil tank and cooler.

OIL GRADE: Synthetic base oils.

DIMENSIONS:

Length	51·7 in (1·31 m)
Width	30·4 in (0·77 m)
Height	42·6 in (1·08 m)

PERFORMANCE RATINGS:

Max intermittent (at 59° F sea level)—	3,650 shp
Max continuous (at 59°F—sea level)	3,350 shp

FUEL CONSUMPTION:

At max continuous rating	255 US gall/hr

OIL CONSUMPTION: 1·0 lb (454 gr/hr)

BRIGGS & STRATTON CORPORATION

HEADQUARTERS AND WORKS:
Milwaukee, Wisconsin 53201

CENTRAL SERVICE DISTRIBUTORS FOR GREAT BRITAIN AND IRELAND:
Autocar Electrical Equipment Co Ltd., 16 Rippleside Commercial Estate, Ripple Road, Barking, Essex

Briggs & Stratton is a major American supplier of low-power four-stroke gasoline engines, an important application of which is in motor lawn mowers of both US and European manufacture. Several installations of Briggs & Stratton in ACVs have been made. These include the American Bartlett M-8 Flying Saucer, a small lightweight

craft powered by a single 3 hp Briggs & Stratton engine mounted above a central plenum chamber driving a two-bladed Banks-Maxwell Mod 30-14 30 in diameter pusher propeller; and Coelacanth Gemco's Pluto two-seat test vehicle which has two 7 hp Briggs & Stratton engines each driving 42 in fans, one for lift and a second for propulsion.

CUMMINS ENGINE COMPANY INC

OFFICES:
Cummins Engine Company Inc, 1000 Fifth Street, Columbus, Indiana, 47201.
Cummins Engine Company Ltd, Coombe House, St Georges Square, Maldon Road, New Maldon, Surrey

The Cummins Engine Company was formed in 1919 in Columbus, Indiana. It produces a wide range of marine diesel engines which are now manufactured and distributed internationally. In addition to manufacturing plants in the United States, the company also produces diesel engines in Brazil, India, Japan, Mexico and the United Kingdom. All these plants build engines to the same specifications thus ensuring interchangeability of parts and the same quality standards.

Cummins marine diesels power the Seaflight 46 (two VT8N-370-M) hydrofoil, and the Hovermarine HM.2 sidewall hovercraft.

On the latter, two VT8-370-Ms, each derated to 320 bhp, supply propulsive power, and a single V-504-M , derated to 185 bhp, drives the lift fans.

MODEL V-555-M

Horsepower	240
Governed RPM	3,300
Number of cylinders	8
Bore and stroke	$4\frac{5}{8} \times 4\frac{1}{8}$ in
Piston displacement	555 cu in
Operating cycles	4
Crankcase oil capacity	5 gals
Coolant capacity	9·5 gals
Net weight (engine less gear)	1,850 lbs

BEARINGS: Precision type, steel backed

inserts.

CAMSHAFT: Single camshaft controls all valve and injector movement. Induction hardened alloy steel with gear drive.

CAMSHAFT FOLLOWERS: Roller type for long cam and follower life.

CONNECTING RODS: Drop forged, 6·72 in centre to centre length. Taper piston pin end reduces unit pressures.

COOLER, LUBRICATING OIL: Tubular type, jacket water cooled.

CRANKSHAFT: High tensile strength steel forging. Bearing journals are induction hardened.

CYLINDER BLOCK: Alloy cast iron with removable, wet liners. Cross bolt support to main bearing cap.

CYLINDER HEADS: Two, one each bank. All fuel lines are drilled passages. Individual intake and exhaust porting for each cylinder. Corrosion resistant inserts on intake and exhaust valve seats.

DAMPER, VIBRATION: Compressed rubber type.

FUEL SYSTEM: Cummins self adjusting system with integral flyball type governer. Camshaft actuated injectors.

GEAR TRAIN: Heavy duty, located rear of cylinder block.

LUBRICATION: Force feed to all bearings. Gear type pump.

PISTONS: Aluminium, cam ground, with two compression and one oil ring.

PISTON PINS: 1½ in diameter, full floating.

THERMOSTAT: Dual, modulating by-pass type.

VALVES: Dual intake and exhaust each cylinder. Each valve 1⅝ in diameter.

STANDARD EQUIPMENT:

CORROSION RESISTOR: Mounted, Cummins spin on type, checks rust and corrosion, controls acidity, and removes impurities from coolant.

DIPSTICK, OIL: Port side when viewing engine from drive end.

ELECTRICAL EQUIPMENT: 12 volt, 58 ampere ac system. Includes starting motor, alternator, regulator, magnetic switch and starting switch.

EXCHANGER, HEAT: Tubular type, mounted.

FILTERS: Cummins. Lubricating oil full flow paper element type, mounted. Fuel, spin on, mounted.

FLYWHEEL: For reverse and reduction gear.

GOVERNOR: Mechanical variable speed type.

HOUSING, FLYWHEEL: S.A.E. No. 3.

INTAKE AIR: Silenced.

MANIFOLD, EXHAUST: Two, fresh water cooled.

PAN, OIL: Aluminium, rear sump type, 5 U.S. gallon capacity.

PUMP, COOLANT: Belt driven, centrifugal type, 80 gpm at 3,300 rpm.

PUMP, EAW WATER: Belt driven rubber impeller type, 48 gpm at 3,300 rpm.

SUPPORT, ENGINE: Marine type, front and rear.

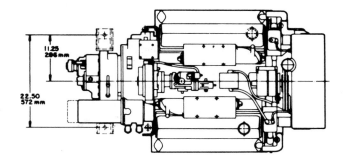

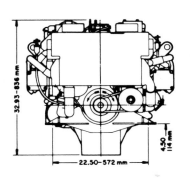

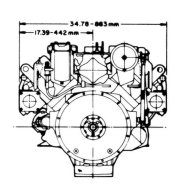

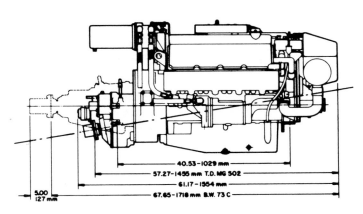

Cummins 8-cylinder V-555-M diesel, rated at 240 hp

MODEL V-903-M

Horsepower	320
Governed RPM	2,600
Number of cylinders	8
Bore and stroke	5½ × 4¾ in
Piston displacement	903 cu in
Operating cycles	4
Oil pan capacity	5 U.S. gals
Engine coolant capacity	12 gals
Net weight with standard accessories	2,800 lbs.

BEARINGS: Precision type, steel backed inserts. 5 main bearings, 3¾ in diameter. Connecting rod—3⅛ in diameter.

CAMSHAFT: Single camshaft controls all valve and injector movement. Induction hardened alloy steel with gear drive.

CAMSHAFT FOLLOWERS: Roller type for long cam and follower life.

CONNECTING RODS: Drop forged. Taper piston pin end provides superior load distribution and maximum piston crown material.

COOLER, LUBRICATING OIL: Tubular type, jacket water cooled.

CRANKSHAFT: High tensile strength steel forging. Bearing journals are induction hardened. Fully counterweighted.

CYLINDER BLOCK: Alloy cast iron with removable, wet liners.

CYLINDER HEADS: Two, one each bank. All fuel lines are drilled passages. Individual intake and exhaust porting for each cylinder.

DAMPER, VIBRATION: Compressed rubber type.

FUEL SYSTEM: Cummins wear-compensating system with integral, flyball type, mechanical variable speed governor. Camshaft actuated injectors.

LUBRICATION: Force feed to all bearings. Gear type pump.

MAIN BEARING CAPS: Cross bolted for rigidity.

PISTONS: Aluminium, cam ground, with two compression and one oil ring.

PISTON PINS: 1¾ in diameter, full floating.

THERMOSTAT: Single unit, modulating by-pass type.

VALVES: Dual intake and exhaust each cylinder. Each valve 1⅞ in diameter. Heat and corrosion resistant face on all valves.

STANDARD EQUIPMENT:

CLEANER, AIR: Silencer type.

CORROSION RESISTOR: Cummins, Mounted. Throw-away unit. Checks rust and corrosion, controls acidity, and removes impurities from coolant.

DIPSTICK, OIL: Port side when viewing engine from drive end.

ELECTRICAL EQUIPMENT: 12 volt, 55 ampere a.c. system. Includes starting motor alternator, regulator, and starting switch.

EXCHANGER, HEAT: Tubular type, mounted.

FILTERS: Cummins. Lubricating oil, full flow replaceable paper element type, mounted. Fuel, paper element throw-away type, mounted.

FLYWHEEL: For reverse and reduction gear.

GEAR, MARINE: Capitol 4HE-10200, 2·00:1 reverse and reduction gear with propeller shaft companion flange.
GOVERNOR: Mechanical variable speed type.
HOUSING, FLYWHEEL: S.A.E. No. 2.

MANIFOLD, AIR INTAKE: Two, located on inside of engine Vee.
MANIFOLD, EXHAUST: Two, fresh water cooled, with outlet to rear.
PAN, OIL: Aluminium, front sump type, 5 U.S. gallon capacity.

PUMP: COOLANT: Gear driven, centrifugal type, 78 GPM at 2,600 rpm.
PUMP, RAW WATER: Gear driven, 61 GPM at 2,600 rpm.
SUPPORT, ENGINE: Marine type, 22½ in centres.

DETROIT DIESEL ALLISON
(Division of General Motors Corporation)
GENERAL OFFICES:
13400 West Outer Drive, Detroit, Michigan 48228
TELEPHONE:
(313) 592-5000

DETROIT DIESEL ALLISON INTERNATIONAL OPERATIONS
(Division of General Motors Corporation)
25200 Telegraph Road, Southfield, Michigan 48075

GENERAL MOTORS POWER PRODUCTS—EUROPE
(Division of General Motors Corporation)
PO Box 6, London Road, Wellingborough, Northamptonshire, England NN8 2DL

Detroit Diesel Allison has been active in the development of gas-turbines for aircraft, industrial and marine use for many years. Production of the first Allison gas-turbine began in the 1940s, when the company built the power plant for the P-59, the first jet-powered aircraft to fly in the United States.

Later, the Allison T56 turboprop aircraft engine was developed. It demonstrated outstanding reliability and the same basic design has been adapted for industrial and marine applications. In the early 1960s, the first Allison gas-turbine powered 501-K electric powerplant went into service. Today, the 501-K industrial series engines are not only used in electric powerplants but also in industrial and marine applications.

ALLISON 501-K SERIES
The Allison 501-K series industrial gas-turbine incorporates a 14-stage axial-flow compressor, with bleed valves to compensate for compressor surge.

Of modular design, in comprises three main sections; the compressor, combustor and turbine. Each section can be readily separated from the other. Modular design provides ease in handling and servicing of the engine.

The first two stages of the four-stage turbine section are air-cooled, permitting the engine to be operated at higher than normal turbine inlet temperatures.

The combustor section of the 501-K consists of six combustion chambers of the through-flow type, assembled within a single annular chamber. This multiple provides even temperature distribution at the turbine inlet, thus eliminating the danger of hot spots.

The 501-K Series engines are available in either single-shaft or free turbine design.

The lightweight, compact size of the 501-K lends itself to multiple engines driving a single shaft through a common gearbox, or as a gas generator driving a customer-furnished power turbine.

Detroit Diesel Allison 501-KF two-shaft marine gas turbine (4,700 shp; 3,506 kw)

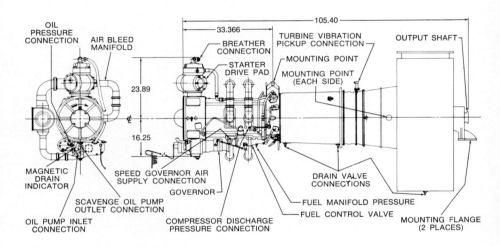

General arrangement of the Allison 501-KF two-shaft marine gas-turbine

The engine can be operated on a wide range of liquid fuels. Designation of the marine model is 501 KF, a brief specification for which follows. Dimensions are shown on the accompanying general arrangement drawing.

Exhaust gas temperature	930°F
Inlet air flow	26,000 cfm
Exhaust air flow	81,000 cfm
Engine jacket heat rejection	6,000 BTU/min
Lube heat rejection	1,200 BTU/min
Maximum liquid fuel flow	360 gph
Liquid fuel DF-1, DF-2 per Allison EMS66	
Lubricant	

Synthetic oil per Allison EMS 35 and 53
Specific fuel consumption: 0·54 lb/hp/hr
Required Auxiliaries:
25 hp starter;
20-29DC volt electrical power;
Power take-off shaft and couplings;
Temperature and speed controls from engine-furnished signals;
Oil cooler;
Auxiliary lube pump;
Compressor inlet sensor;
Gauge panel, meters and associated components;
Engine exhaust diffusing tailpipe.

DOBSON PRODUCTS CO.
HEAD OFFICE:
2241 South Ritchey, Santa Ana, California
92705
TELEPHONE:
(714) 557-2987
WORKS:
Santa Ana, California
DIRECTOR:
Franklin A. Dobson

Franklin Dobson has been building and marketing light ACVs in kit and factory-built form since 1963.

His company is now specialising in the design and construction of light ACV components evolved after a more thorough engineering approach. The components include reversible-pitch propellers and fans—the main purpose of which is to provide light craft with adequate braking—and suitable ducts, screens, etc.

Preliminary details of the company's first 3 ft (0.91 m) diameter, variable-pitch two-bladed propeller are given below.

DIMENSIONS:

Diameter	36 in (0.91 m)
Chord	4.25 in (104 mm)
Blades	2
Solidity (at 0.6 rad)	.125
Pitch range	60 deg (nom. +40, —20)
Max shaft dia.	1.25 in (28 mm)
Total weight	5 lb (approx) (0.45 gr)
Design rpm	3,000
Max rpm	3,250
Horsepower req.	7 to 10

Max static thrust (with shroud)
75 lb (forward or reverse) (34.01 kg)
Max thrust at 60 mph 50 lb (22.67 kg)
A duct with integral screen, suitable for use with this propeller, is also under development.

GENERAL ELECTRIC COMPANY AIRCRAFT ENGINE GROUP
HEADQUARTERS:
1000 Western Avenue, West Lynn, Massachusetts 01910
VICE PRESIDENT AND GROUP EXECUTIVE
Gerhard Neumann
COUNSEL:
J. W. Sack

The General Electric Company entered the gas-turbine field in about 1895. Years of pioneering effort by the late Dr Sanford A. Moss produced the aircraft turbosupercharger, successfully tested at height in 1918 and mass-produced in World War II for US fighters and bombers.

The company built its first aircraft gas-turbine in 1941, when it began development of Whittle-type turbojets, under an arrangement between the British and American Governments.

Since that time, General Electric has produced a series of successful designs, from the J47, which powered the Boeing B47 and the North American F 86 series of aircraft, to the big CF6 turbofan powering the new McDonnell Douglas DC-10 wide-body transport.

Three General Electric marinized gas-turbines are in marine service, the LM-100, the LM1500 and the new LM2500. The LM100 powers the Bell SK-5 air cushion vehicle and the Avalon high-speed ferry and the LM1500 powers the AGEH-1 Plainview and seventeen US Navy patrol gunboats.

GE LM100 gas-turbine

GE LM1500 gas-turbine

LM100
Earliest marine application of the LM100 was in the 24-foot experimental hydrofoil vessel Sea Wings developed for the Office of Naval Research. The craft was propelled at high speeds by a single LM100 gas turbine to explore the validity of supercavitation principles. Later, it was selected as the docking and harbour manoeuvring engine for the Maritime Administration's hydrofoil ship Denison. A version of this turbine, IM100, supplied by Ishikawajima-Harima Heavy Industries, a licencee of GE in Japan, powers the Mitsui MV-PP5 hovercraft.

The LM100 is an outgrowth of the GE T58 helicopter engine, which underwent some six years of development and has amassed more than seven million hours of operation. Rolls-Royce is manufacturing the T58 under licence in the United Kingdom as the Gnome, and the T58 is also being built under licence in Italy and Japan.
TYPE: Free turbine, axial flow, simple cycle.
AIR INTAKE: Axial, inlet bellmouth on duct can be customised to installation.

COMBUSTION CHAMBER: Annular.
FUEL: Kerosene, JP-4, JP-5, diesel, natural gas.
TURBINE: 2-stage gas generator, 1-stage power turbine.
JET PIPE: Customised to fit installation.
OIL SPECIFICATION: MIL-L-23699, MIL-L7808F and commercial equivalents.
MOUNTING: At power turbine and compressor front frame.
STARTING: Normally electric.
DIMENSIONS:

Length overall	6 ft 4 in (1.924 m)
Width overall	1 ft 8 in (0.508 m)
Height overall	2 ft 10 in (0.864 m)

Performance rating 1,100 shp at 80°F SLS
Specific Fuel Consumption:
0.61 lb (0.277 kg)/shp/hr
Oil Consumption 0.5 pint (0.29 litre)/hr

LM1500
The GE LM1500 turboshaft engine is the result of a company investment in a programme to adapt the J79 jet engine to a free power turbine for industrial and marine use.

On the US Navy's aluminium-hulled PG84 class gunboats an LM1500 gas turbine is used to supplement two cruise diesels whenever high speed operation is desired. By combining reduction gears, the LM1500 is used to drive two propellers.

Twin LM1500s supply foilborne propulsion power for the USS Plainview (AGEH).
TYPE: 2-shaft, axial flow, simple cycle.
AIR INTAKE: Axial, inlet bellmouth on duct can be customised to installation.
COMBUSTION CHAMBER: Annular.

FUEL GRADE: JP, aviation kerosene, diesel,
TURBINE: 3-stage gas generator, 1-stage power turbine.
JET PIPE: Customised to fit installation.
OIL SPECIFICATION: MIL-L-23699, MIL L-7808F and commercial equivalent.
MOUNTING: At power turbine and compressor front frame.
STARTING: Pneumatic, hydraulic.
DIMENSIONS:

Length overall	25 ft 0 in (7.62 m)
Width overall	6 ft 6½ in (2.0 m)
Height overall	6 ft 11 in (2.11 m)

Performance rating

15,400 shp at 59°F (15°C) at sea level

Specific fuel consumption

5 lb (0·25 kg)/shp/hr

LM2500

The LM2500 marine gas turbine is a 2-shaft, simple cycle, high efficiency engine. Derived from the GE TF39 CF-6 high-bypass turbo-fan engines for the US Air Force C-5 transport and DC-10 and A300B commercial jets. The engine incorporates the latest features of compressor, combustor, and turbine design to provide maximum progression in reliability parts life, and time between overhaul. The engine has a fuel rate 25% lower than that of current production marine gas turbines in its power range. This is made possible by high compressor pressure ratio, high turbine inlet temperature and improved cycle efficiency.

The LM2500 marine gas turbine has been specified for the foilborne power of the joint U.S. Navy/NATO Patrol Hydrofoil Missile ship (PHM) being built by the Boeing Company, Seattle, Washington.

This engine is in production for the U.S. Navy's new Spruance class destroyer fleet, the first major warships in the U.S. Navy to employ marine gas turbines for propulsion, and it will also power the U.S. Navy's new class of Patrol Frigates and the new Fast Frigates for the Italian and Peruvian navies.

Two LM2500s have completed more than 30,000 hours of operation aboard the GTS Admiral William M. Callaghan, a gas-turbine powered roll-on/roll-off cargo vessel operated for the U.S. Navy's Military Sealift Command by American Export Isbrandtsen Lines, Inc.

TYPE: 2-shaft, axial flow, simple cycle.

AIR INTAKE: Axial, inlet bellmouth on duct can be customised to installation.

COMBUSTION CHAMBER: Annular.

FUEL GRADE: Kerosene, JP4, JP5. Diesel, heavy distillate fuels and natural gas.

TURBINE: 2-stage gas generator, 6-stage power.

JET PIPE: Customised to fit installation.

OIL SPECIFICATION: Synthetic Turbine Oil (MIL-L-23699) or equal.

MOUNTING: At power turbine and compressor front frame.

STARTING: Pneumatic, hydraulic.

DIMENSIONS:

Length	20 ft 6 in (6·24 m)
Width	7 ft 7¼ in (2·3 m)
Height	7 ft 6¼ in (2·6 m)

GE LM 2500 gas turbine

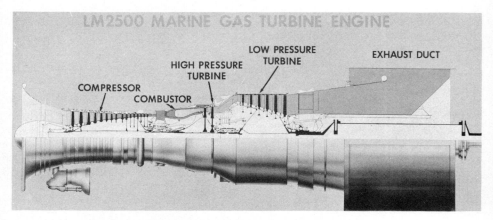

Internal arrangements of the GE LM2500 marine gas-turbine

PERFORMANCE RATINGS:
27,500 shp at 59°F (15°C) at sea level

SPECIFIC FUEL CONSUMPTION:
0·39 to 0·41 lb (0·177 to 0·186 kg)/hp/hr

McCULLOCH CORPORATION

ADMINISTRATION OFFICES:

5400 Alla Rd., Los Angeles, CA 90066

ASSEMBLY PLANT:

6151 W. 98th St., Los Angeles, CA 90045

MAIN MANUFACTURING PLANT:

648 Lake Havasu Dr., Lake Havasu, Ariz. 86403

AFFILIATES:

Malton, Ontario, Canada; Mechelen, Belgium; Singapore; Seven Hills N.S.W., Australia; Sao Paulo, Brazil.

PRESIDENT:

Richard V. Dempster

VICE-PRESIDENTS:

G. E. Maffey, Jr., Engineering

P. F. Masterson, Treasurer-Finance V.P.

M. V. Nodar, Administration

S. E. Page, Secretary-General Counsel

S. J. Stephenson, Marketing

R. D. VanderLeek, International Operations

DIRECTORS:

J. C. Babbitt, Customer Service

J. C. Carroll, Product Service

S. A. Cole, Professional Products

V. M. Gardner, Consumer Products

C. L. Hammond, Special Products

R. K. Orser, Communications

L. L. Tess, Purchasing

McCulloch Corporation produces a variety of small gasoline engines making extensive use of aluminium and magnesium high-pressure die castings. Over the past 25 years it has supplied more than 60,000 engines to the US armed services for use in radio-controlled target aircraft and helicopters.

Amateur builders have made extensive use of McCulloch target drone engines in light aircraft and autogyros, and air cushion vehicles. Current models include improved versions of the MC49, MC91 and MC101 single-cylinder, two-stroke series and details are given hereunder. New engines planned cover 12 to 34 hp in single or twin-cylinder versions.

McCulloch MC 49M/C, 6·5 HP

DISPLACEMENT: 4·9 cu. in. (80·3 cc)

BORE: 2·125″ (54 mm)

STROKE: 1·375″ (35 mm)

COMPRESSION RATIO: 9·4:1

WEIGHT: 12 lbs. (5·4 kg)

INLET VALVE: Dual petal, high flow reeds on vee block for full power at all speeds, and sensitivity towards unlet and exhaust tuning.

CARBURETTOR: BDC 22 1⅜ in (35 mm) bore with 1⅛ in (29 mm) venturi assures high flow air delivery. Adjustable high and low mixture needles. Standard equipped with choke for air filter installations. Multiple throttle cable connections. Special chrome throttle shaft. Steel bushings and dirt seals to protect carburettor against dirt.

AIR FILTER: Conventional types adaptable.

PISTON: Heat resistant aluminium alloy. Oversize available. ·010 in, ·020 in, ·030 in.

PISTON RINGS: Two narrow tool steel type with wear face for quick sealing, low friction and long life. Super abrasive resistant. Unpinned.

BEARINGS—

CONN ROD: Full complement M-50 tool steel needle rollers, hardened shaft and rod ends.

WRIST PIN: Two needle roller bearings in piston.

MAIN: Two caged ball bearings.

CRANKSHAFT: Engine equipped with SAE J609 ¾ in diameter P.T.O. shaft. Counterbalanced, hot forged steel hardening and ground.

ENGINE: Single cylinder, two-cycle, air-cooled. Loop scavenged.

CYLINDER-CRANKCASE: Die cast aluminium alloy with precision honed cast iron reborable liner. Deep finned integral head.

DIRECTION OF ROTATION: Clockwise (facing power take-off shaft).

IGNITION: Waterproof high tension extra high output magneto. Heat resistant, moistureproof coil bonded to lamination.

SPARK PLUG: Champion J8J.

FUEL OIL MIXTURE: 40:1 with McCulloch oil and automotive regular grade gasoline.

FLYWHEEL: High pressure die cast aluminium alloy with integral magneto magnets, steel hub.

STARTER: McCulloch, six position, automatic rewind starter is standard.

COMPRESSION RELEASE: Button type for easy starting, button locks out when engine starts.

KILL SWITCH WIRE: Standard.

CLUTCH: Conventional types adaptable.

MOUNTING: Four bolt holes provided on the P.T.O. side and four bolt holes on the bottom of crankcase. Engine operates in any position.

List price, USA, $99·95.

McCULLOCH MC 91M/C, 10 HP.

DISPLACEMENT: 6·05 cu. in. (99·3 cc).
BORE: 2·165 in (55 mm).
STROKE: 1·635 in (41·5 mm).
COMPRESSION RATIO: 9·4:1.
WEIGHT: 13 lbs. (5·9 kg).

INLET VALVE: Dual petal, high flow reeds on vee block for full power at all speeds, and sensitivity towards inlet and exhaust tuning.

CARBURETTOR: BDC 22 1⅜ in (35 mm) bore with 1⅛ in (29 mm) venturi assures high flow air delivery. Adjustable high and low mixture needles. Standard equipped with choke for air filter installations. Multiple throttle cable connections. Special chrome throttle shaft. Steel bushings and dirt seals to protect carburettor against dirt.

AIR FILTER: Conventional types adaptable.

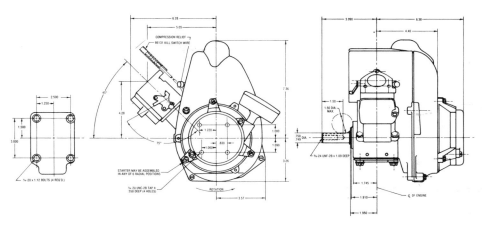

General arrangement of the MC101M/C giving dimensions

PISTON: Heat resistant aluminium alloy. Oversize available: ·005 in, ·010 in, ·020 in, ·030 in.

PISTON RINGS: Two narrow tool steel type with wear face for quick sealing, low friction and long life. Super abrasive resistant. Pinned.

BEARINGS—

CONN ROD: Full complement M-50 tool steel needle rollers, hardened shaft and rod ends.

WRIST PIN: Two needle roller bearings in piston. Extra length for additional lubrication and cooling.

MAIN: Two caged ball bearings.

CRANKSHAFT: Engine equipped with SAE J609 ¾ in diameter P.T.O. shaft. Counter-balanced, hot forged steel hardened and ground. Extensively shot peened. Super finished throw.

ENGINE: Single cylinder, two-cycle, air-cooled. Loop scavenged.

CYLINDER-CRANKCASE: Die cast aluminium alloy with precision honed cast iron reborable liner. Deep finned detachable head.

DIRECTION OF ROTATION: Clockwise (facing power take-off-shaft).

DIRECTION OF ROTATION: Clockwise (facing power take off shaft).

IGNITION: Waterproof high tension extra high output magneto. Heat resistant, moistureproof coil bonded to lamination.

SPARK PLUG: Champion L-88.

FUEL OIL MIXTURE: 40:1 with McCulloch oil and automotive regular grade gasoline.

FLYWHEEL: High pressure die cast aluminium alloy with integral magneto magnets, steel hub.

STARTER: McCulloch, six position, automatic rewind starter is standard.

COMPRESSION RELEASE: Button type for easy starting, button locks out when engine starts.

KILL SWITCH WIRE: Standard.

CLUTCH: Conventional types adaptable.

MOUNTING: Four bolt holes provided on the P.T.O. side and four bolt holes on the bottom of crankcase. Engine operates in any position.

List price, USA, /109·95.

McCULLOCH MC 101MC 11.5H.P.

DISPLACEMENT: 7·5 cu. in. (123 cc).
BORE: 2·280 in (58 mm).
STROKE: 1·835 in (46·6 mm).

Top: MC101B; Centre: MC92; Bottom: MC49E

COMPRESSION RATIO: 9·4:1.
WEIGHT: 13·5 lbs (6·1 kg).

INLET VALVE: Dual petal, high flow reeds on vee block for full power at all speeds, and sinsitivity towards inlet and exhaust tuning.

CARBURETTOR: BDC 22 1⅜ in (35 mm) bore with 1⅛ in (29 mm) venturi assures high flow air delivery. Adjustable high and low mixture needles. Standard equipped with choke for air filter installations. Multiple throttle cable connections. Special chrome throttle shaft. Steel bushings and dirt deals to protect carburetor against dirt.

AIR FILTER: Conventional types adaptable.

PISTON: Heat resistant aluminium alloy. Oversize available: ·010 in, ·020 in, ·030 in, ·050 in.

PISTON RINGS: Two narrow tool steel type with wear face for quick sealing, low friction and long life. Super abrasive resistant. Pinned.

BEARINGS—

CONN ROD: Full complement M-50 tool steel needle rollers, hardened shaft and rod ends.

WRIST PIN: Two needle roller bearings in piston. Extra length for additional lubrication and cooling.

MAIN: Two caged ball bearings.

CRANKSHAFT: Engine equipped with SAE J609 ½ in diameter P.T.O. shaft.

Counter-balanced, hot forged steel hardened and ground.

Extensively shot peened and tungsten counterweights. Super finished throw.

ENGINE: Single cylinder, two-cycle, air-cooled. Loop scavenged.

CYLINDER-CRANKCASE: Die cast aluminium alloy with precision honed cast iron reborable liner. Deep finned detachable head.

DIRECTION OF ROTATION: Clockwise (facing power take-off shaft).

IGNITION: Waterproof high tension extra high output magneto. Heat resistant, moistureproof coil bonded to lamination.

SPARK PLUG: Champion L-88.

FUEL OIL MIXTURE: 40:1 with McCulloch

oil and automotive regular grade gasoline.

FLYWHEEL: High pressure die cast aluminium alloy with integral magneto magnets, steel hub.

STARTER: McCulloch, six position, automatic rewind starter is standard.

COMPRESSION RELEASE: Button type for easy starting, button locks out when engine starts.

KILL SWITCH WIRE: Standard.

CLUTCH: Conventional types adaptable.

MOUNTING: Four bolt holes provided on the P.T.O. side and four bolt holes on the bottom of crankcase. Engine operates in any position.

List price, USA, $124·95.

NORTHROP CORPORATION

HEAD OFFICE:

1515 Rancho Conejo Blvd, Newbury Park, California 91320.

Northrop Corp. has purchased the corporate rights of the 4300 series engines from Mc-Culloch Corp.

Tooling has been acquired from McCulloch for the Model 4318, which is built in various versions covering 72 to 92 hp. Details of these engines are as follows:

Model 4318

This is a series of four-cylinder, horizontally-opposed air-cooled two-stroke piston engines covering the power range 72 hp (73 cv) to 92 hp (93 cv). The Bertelsen Aeromobile 13 light amphibious air cushion vehicle is powered by two 72 hp (73 cv) 4318AX or two 90 hp (91 cv) 4318G engines providing lift and thrust through 48 in (1,219 mm) diameter 8-bladed lift fan/propellers.

Model 4318A. Basic 72 hp (73 cv) model of the series, with "free roll" silver-plated bearings on the big-end of the connecting rods.

Model 4318E. Similar to the Model 4318A except that it is intended to drive a pusher airscrew. No carburettor is supplied with the engine.

Model 4318F. This is the same as the Model 4318A except that it has a power rating of 92 hp (93 cv) at 4,100 rpm, achieved by enlarged inlet and exhaust ports in the cylinders, together with a modified piston and ring configuration.

Model 4318G. Rated at 90 hp (91 cv).

The following data relates to the Model 4318A.

TYPE: Four-cylinder horizontally-opposed air-cooled two-stroke.

CYLINDERS: Bore 3 3/16 in (80·8 mm). Stroke 3 3/8 in (79·4 mm). Displacement 100 cu in (1·6 litres). Compression ratio 7·8 : 1. Heat-treated die-cast aluminium cylinders with integral heads, having hard chrome plated cylinder walls. Self-locking nuts secure cylinders to crankcase studs.

PISTONS: Heat-treated cast aluminium. Two rings above pins. Piston pins of case-hardened steel.

CONNECTING RODS: Forged steel. "Free-roll" silver-plated bearings at big end. Small end carries one needle bearing. Lateral

Model 4318A two-stroke piston engine of 72 bhp

position of rod controlled by thrust washers between piston pin bosses and end of rod.

CRANKSHAFT: Four-throw one-piece steel forging on four anti-friction bearings, two ball and two needle, one with split race for centre main bearing.

CRANKCASE: One-piece heat-treated permanent-mould aluminium casting closed at rear end with cast aluminium cover which provides mounting for magneto.

VALVE GEAR: Fuel mixture for scavenging and power stroke introduced to cylinders through crankshaft-driven rotary valves and ported cylinders.

INDUCTION: Crankcase pumping type. McCulloch diaphragm-type carburettor with adjustable jet.

FUEL SPECIFICATION: Grade 100/130 aviation fuel.

IGNITION: McCulloch single magneto and distributor. Directly connected to crankshaft through impulse coupling for easy starting. Radio noise-suppressor included.

BG type RB 916S spark plugs. Complete radio shielding.

LUBRICATION: Oil mixed with fuel as in conventional two-stroke engines.

PROPELLER DRIVE: RH tractor. Keyed taper shaft.

STARTING: By separate portable gasoline or electric motor with suitable reduction-gear and clutch. Can be started manually by hand-cranking propeller.

MOUNTING: Three mounting lugs provided with socket for rubber mounting bushings.

DIMENSIONS:

Length	27·0 in (686 mm)
Width	28·0 in (711 mm)
Height	15·0 in (381 mm)

WEIGHT (Dry)

Less propeller hub	77 lb (34·9 kg)

POWER RATING:

Rated output	72 hp at 4,100 rpm

CONSUMPTION:

Fuel/oil mixture	0·90 lb (0·408 kg) bhp/hr

ROCKETDYNE DIVISION
ROCKWELL INTERNATIONAL

HEAD OFFICE:

Canoga Avenue, Canoga Park, California 91304

EXECUTIVES:

Hal Oquist, Director of Waterjet Propulsion Programmes

Joe Stangelard, Programme Manager, SES Project

The technology gained in the design and manufacture of high-performance pumps for the US space programme has enabled Rocketdyne to develop a new family of waterjet propulsion systems, called Powerjet 16, 20 and 24. These propulsion systems employ advanced-design, axial-flow pumping elements to produce a compact, lightweight waterjet propulsor. Simplicity of design minimises the number of components necessary in the units, while allowing accessibility for servicing or replacement of seals and bearings. All system components, which are designed to meet American Bureau of Shipping requirements, have been built in materials selected for their resistance to cavitation damage, and seawater and galvanic corrosion.

In January 1975, the Division was awarded a contract by Bell Aerospace for the design of a 40,000 hp waterjet propulsion system for the projected 2,000-ton 2KSES. The vessel will be powered by four 40,000 hp waterjet units powered by gas-turbines. The contract calls for the completion of the detailed design of a full-scale waterjet propulsor, including the pump, steering sleeve and gearbox.

The Division's Powerjet 20 is installed in the Boeing Jetfoil hydrofoil series.

The Powerjet series of waterjets incorporate single-stage, axial-flow inducers. The impellers are one-piece titanium castings, keyed to corrosion-resistant steel shafts. Power absorption characteristics at low craft speeds are considered exceptional due to the high suction specific speeds attainable by Powerjet inducer designs.

POWERJET 24

TYPE: Single-stage, axial-flow.

APPLICATION: Designed for high-propulsive efficiency at moderate speeds.

PRIME MOVERS: Diesels and gas turbines developing up to 5,000 hp.

LUBRICATION SYSTEM: External recirculating supply requiring 3·8 to 4·2 gpm flow at 55 to 70 psi.

Lube oil grade:

MIL-L-23699

MIL-L-2105

Diesel crankcase oil—API (D Series)

Automobile differential oil—API (M Series)

SPECIFICATION:

Operating range:

Input horsepower	4,000*
Input shaft speed	1,640 rpm
Total inlet head	43 feet at 1,640 rpm
Pump flowrate (at 30 knots)	45,000 gpm
Propulsion pump weight	
Dry	3,900 lb
Wet	4,800 lg
Steering vector	±22 degrees
Reverse thrust	50% of forward gross thrust to a maximum of 1,330 hp

* 5,000 hp also available

POWERJET 16

TYPE: Single-stage, axial-flow.

APPLICATION: Designed for high propulsive efficiency at moderate speeds in all types

Above and below: The Powerjet 20 axial-flow waterjet pump employed in the Boeing Jetfoil. Lower illustration shows the complete foilborne propulsion system and rear foil assembly

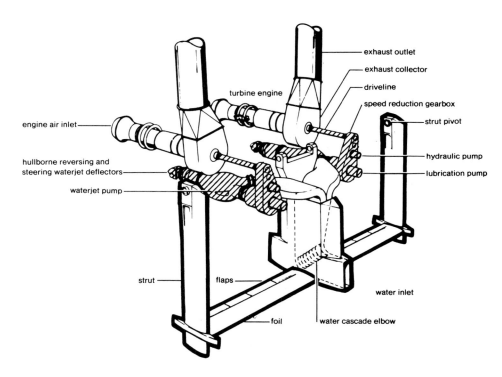

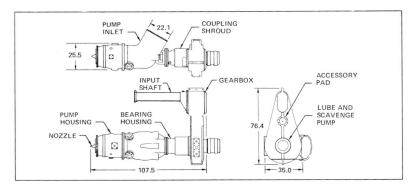

Mounting of the Powerjet 20, two of which are installed on the Boeing Jetfoil

of hull configurations.

PRIME MOVERS: Diesels and gas-turbines developing between 700 and 1,500 hp. Three inducer trims are available for direct coupling to most marine diesels.

LUBRICATION SYSTEM: Integrated recirculating system.

LUBE OIL GRADE:

  MIL-L-23699

  MIL-L-2105

  Diesel crankcase oil—API (D Series)

  Automobile differential oil—API (M Series)

SPECIFICATION:

  Operating Range:

	Trim Number		
	1	2	3
Maximum horse-power, up to	1,500	1,137	1,010
Input horsepower*	1,025	900	800
Input shaft speed, rpm	2,000	2,100	2,100
Total inlet head, feet, as low as	35	31	28
Pump flowrate (at 30 knots), gpm	17,800	16,200	15,300

  Propulsion pump weight:

Dry	1,950 lb
Wet	2,200 lb

  Steering vector   ±22 degrees

  Reverse thrust   50% of forward gross thrust to a maximum of 1,025 hp

*Direct drive

POWERJET 20

TYPE: Single-stage, axial-flow

APPLICATION: Designed for hydrofoils and high-speed craft at 3,500 hp and medium- to high-speed craft at lower horsepower. Two Powerjet 20 propulsion units, each of which is driven by an Allison 501-K20A gas-turbine through a 6·37:1 reduction gearbox, power the Boeing 929 Jetfoil, 106-ton, 45-knot passenger-carrying hydrofoil. In this application, the gearbox is used in conjunction with an over/under configuration, which results in a compact installation. Input horsepower to the gearbox is 3,700 at 13,250 rpm.

ACCESSORY DRIVE: For the Boeing Jetfoil, Powerjet 20 is coupled to a gearbox that provides two pads for accessory drive. The first pad supplies power for the boat's hydraulic system, while the second directs power to gearbox, pump, and turbine lubrication and scavenge pump.

PRIME MOVERS: Diesels and gas-turbines up to 3,700 horsepower.

LUBRICATION SYSTEM: External recirculating supply, with 2·5- to 3·5-gpm flow at 55 to 70 psi provided by a gerotor-type pump that contains both pressure and scavenge cavities.

LUBE OIL GRADE:

  MIL-L-23699

  MIL-L-2106

  Diesel crankcase oil—API (D Series)

  Automobile differential oil—API (M Series)

SPECIFICATION:

  Operating range

Input horsepower	3,500
Input shaft speed	2,080 rpm
Total inlet head	26 feet at 2,080 rpm
Pump flowrate	23,150 gpm

  Propulsion pump weight:

Dry	1,712 lb
Wet	2,326 lb

*4,300 horsepower also available.

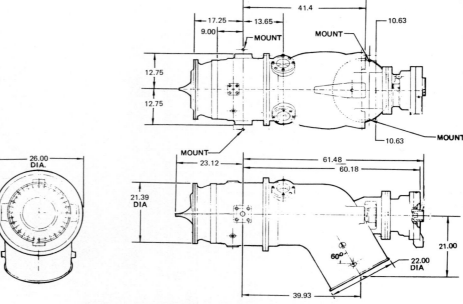

General arrangement of the Powerjet 20, two of which are installed on the Boeing Jetfoil

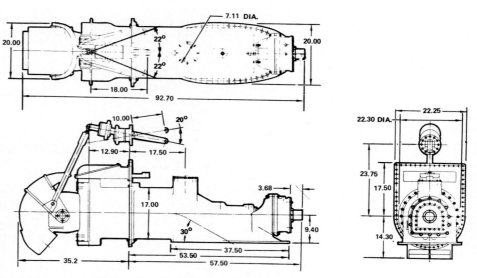

The Powerjet PJ16, for diesels and gas-turbines delivering between 700 and 1,500 shp

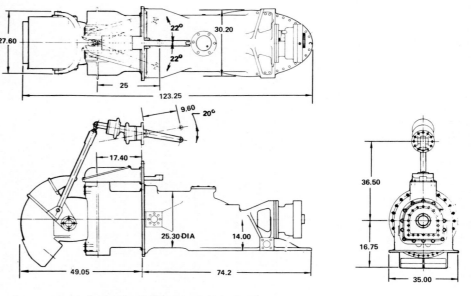

The Powerjet PJ 24 for diesels and gas-turbines developing up to 5,000 shp

SCORPION INC.

HEAD OFFICE:

Crosby, Minnesota 56441

TELEPHONE:

(218) 546-5123

PROJECT ENGINEER: Chuck Srock

Scorpion Inc. has purchased the JLO Division of Rockwell Manufacturing. The Company is now manufacturing and marketing the Cuyuna range of axial-fan cooled twin-cylinder engines, developing 29 hp-40 hp.

The engines are serviced through a network of 2,000 independent service outlets and central distributors throughout the US and Canada.

CUYUNA AXIAL-FAN TWIN-CYLINDER ENGINES

Models 295, 340, 400 and 440

Features of this range include a standard mounting for all models to ease installation; low engine profile with built-in shrouding; lightweight construction to reduce overall vehicle weight and high interchangeability of all parts. Crankshafts, crank cases, blower assemblies, magnetos, recoil starters and hardware items are fully interchangeable, thus reducing spare parts inventory requirements and lowering maintenance costs. Specifications for the four standard productions are given in the accompanying table.

Type	Twin Cylinder Axial-Fan Cooled			
Model	295	340	400	440
Bore	2.185″	2.362″	2.559″	2.658″
Stroke	2.362″	2.362″	2.362″	2.362″
Displacement	290 cc	339 cc	389 cc	428 cc
Compression Ratio	12.5:1			
Maximum Torque	6500 R.P.M.			
Brake HP/rpm	29 HP	32 HP	38 HP	40 HP
	6500/7000 rpm	6500/7000 rpm	6500/7000 rpm	6500/7000 rpm
Base Mounting Hole Thread	$\frac{7}{16}$—14 UNC			
Cylinder	Aluminium with Cast Iron Sleeve			
Connecting Rod Bearing Upper	Needle			
Connecting Rod Bearing Lower	Needle			
Connecting Rod. Matl.	Forged Steel			
Main Bearing	4 Heavy Duty Ball Bearings (1 Dual Row Bearing, P.T.O.)			
Ignition	Bosch			
Lighting Coil	12 Volt, 150 Watt			
Contact Breaker Gap	.014″ to .018″			
Ignition Setting Before TDC	.102″ to .112″ (Cam Fully Advanced)			
Spark Plug Thread	14 × 1.25 mm $\frac{3}{4}$″ Reach			
Gap	.016″ to .020″			
Type	Bosch W-260-T-2			
	(or) Champion N-3			
Rotation	Counter-Clockwise Viewed From P.T.O. End			
Fuel-Oil Mixture	40:1 (1 pt to 5 gal)			
Lubrication	Premium Gasoline & CUYUNA 2 Cycle Engine Oil			
Carburettor Type	2 $\frac{15}{16}$″ Center to Center Bolt Dimension			
Starter	Rewind Type, Standard; Electric, Optional			
Rope Material	Nylon			
Weight	62 lbs.			

Horsepower ratings established in accordance with specification SAE-J 607. Engines will produce no more than 78db. A when used with Cuyuna approved carburettor/muffler/intake silencer systems, according to SAE-J192 specification.

TURBO POWER AND MARINE SYSTEMS. INC.

(subsidiary of United Technologies Corporation)

HEADQUARTERS:

1690 New Britain Avenue,

Farmington, Connecticut USA 06032

TELEPHONE:

(203) 677-4081

EXECUTIVES:

R. L. Cole, President, Power Systems Division

W. J. Closs, President, TPM

A. B. Crouchley, Marketing Manager

R. F. Nordin, Sales Manager

A. Hart, Manager, Industrial & Commercial Marine Sales

R. Gill, Manager, Government Sales

D. G. Assard, Manager, Engineering Programmes

K. H. Truesdell, Manager, Systems Installation & Service

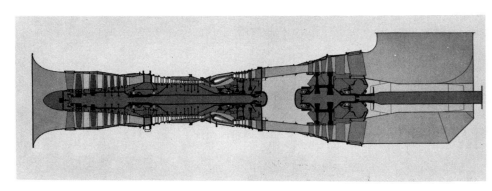

Cross-section of the TPM FT9 marine gas-turbine, rated at 33,000 shp at 100 deg F

Turbo Power and Marine Systems, Inc. (TPM), a wholly owned subsidiary of United Technologies Corporation in the Power Systems Division, designs and builds industrial and marine gas-turbine power plants and power plant systems. It also provides a continuing systems support for each of its installations.

Canadian sales of TPM gas-turbines are handled by Pratt & Whitney Aircraft of Canada Limited, Post Office Box 10, Longueuil, Quebec, Canada, which also manufactures and handles the sales of the PWA of Canada ST6 marine gas-turbine.

Over 1,000 TPM gas-turbines have been delivered for electric power generation, gas transmission and industrial drives as well as for marine propulsion.

TPM MARINE GAS-TURBINES

Turbo Power and Marine Systems offers the 46,000 shp FT4C-3F gas-turbines for marine propulsion.

TPM is also developing a new marine gas-turbine under a US Navy contract. The design of the new gas-turbine is based on the extensive operating experience of the TPM FT4 marine gas-turbine and the Pratt & Whitney Aircraft JT9D fan jet engine. Designated the FT9, the new gas-turbine will have an initial marine rating of 33,000 shp at 100°F with inlet and exhaust duct losses of 4 and 6 inches of water. Advantages of the new FT9 gas-turbine will include modular construction for maintainability and low fuel consumption. Details of the FT9 are shown in the cross section illustration.

MARINE INSTALLATIONS

TPM FT4 marine gas-turbines were first used for boost power in military vessels, including two Royal Danish Navy frigates, twelve U.S. Coast Guard Hamilton Class high endurance cutters and four Canadian Armed Forces DDH-280 Iroquois Class destroyers. Another boost power application of the FT4 is in the Fast Escort and ASW vessel *Bras d'Or* also built for the Canadian Armed Forces. A later application is for two new 12,000 ton Arctic ice breakers under construction for U.S. Coast Guard. With three TPM FT4 marine gas-turbines, these vessels will be capable of maintaining a continuous speed of three knots through ice six feet thick, and will be able to ram through ice 21 feet thick.

TPM marine gas-turbines are used for both the main and boost propulsion in the four new Canadian DDH-280 destroyers. These are the first military combatant vessels to be designed for complete reliance on gas-turbine power. TPM marine gas-turbines are also used in a military surface effect ship programme.

Four 32,000 ton container ships with TPM marine gas-turbines are in trans-Atlantic service with Seatrain Lines. These vessels are *Euroliner, Eurofreighter, Asialiner* and *Asiafreighter*.

Another commercial vessel where TPM FT4 gas-turbines will be used as the main propulsion unit is the *Finnjet*, a high speed Finnlines passenger liner being built by the Wartsila Shipyard in Helsinki for service in the Baltic Sea.

TPM MARINE POWER PAC

The photograph shows a TPM FT4 marine gas-turbine completely packaged as a marine power pacs ready for installation, with the minimum of interface connections to be made. Each is built upon a rigid mounting frame and includes a housing and engine mounting system, together with controls, accessory equipment, wiring and piping. A remote control system is also provided. Installation is simple and since all the equipment is pre-tested in the factory before shipment, the time required for checkout after installation is minimised.

The gas generator portion of the gas-turbine

TPM Marine Power Pac with an FT4 gas turbine

PERFORMANCE DATA: FT4C-1D MARINE GAS TURBINE

Rating	Power Output (1)	Special Fuel Consumption (2)
Max Intermittent	46,000 shp	0·46 lb (208 gr) /shp-hr
Max Continuous	42,000 shp	0·46 lb (208 gr)/shp-hr
Normal	36,900 shp	0·46 lb (208 gr)/shp-hr

(1) All ratings at 3,600 rpm shaft speed, 59°F and sea level.
(2) Based on fuel with LHV of 18,500 Btu/lb.
Oil Consumption: 0·4 gal. (1·82 litres)/hr. max. as measured over a 10 hour period.
0·1 gal. (0·45 litres)/hr service operation avg.

is easily removed for servicing. With a spare gas generator to replace the one removed for servicing, the ship's power plant can undergo even a major overhaul without tieing longer than necessary for a normal turn-around at dock.

TPM FT4 marine gas-turbines are manufactured by the Pratt & Whitney Aircraft Division of United Aircraft Corporation. Details are given below:

TYPE: Simple cycle two spool free turbine engine. A low pressure compressor is driven by a two stage turbine and a high pressure compressor is driven by a single turbine. The burner section has eight burner cans which are equipped with duplex fuel nozzles. An independent or free power turbine drives the load through a shaft which extends through the exhaust duct elbow.

AIR INTAKE: Fabricated steel casing with 18 radial struts supporting the front compressor bearing and equipped with a hot bleed air anti-icing system.

LP COMPRESSOR: Nine stage axial flow on inner of two concentric shafts driven by

two stage turbine and supported on ball and roller bearings.

HP COMPRESSOR: Seven stage axial flow on outer hollow shaft driven by single stage turbine and running on ball and roller bearings.

COMBUSTION CHAMBER: Eight burner cans located in an annular arrangement and enclosed in a one piece steel casing. Each burner has six duplex fuel nozzles.

GAS GENERATOR: Steel casing with hollow guide vanes. Turbine wheels are bolted to the compressor shafts and are supported on ball and roller bearings. A single stage turbine drives the high compressor and a two stage turbine drives the low compressor.

POWER TURBINE: The engine is available with either clockwise or counter clockwise rotation of the power turbine. Desired direction of rotation specified by customer. Power turbine housing is bolted to gas generator turbine housing. The two stage turbine shaft assembly is straddle mounted and supported on ball and roller bearings. The output shaft is bolted to the hub of the power turbine rotor and extends through the exhaust duct.

BEARINGS: Anti-friction ball and roller bearings.

ACCESSORY DRIVE: Starter, fluid power pump, tachometer drives for low compressor, high compressor and free turbine.

LUBRICATION SYSTEM: Return system and scavange pumps with internal pressure (45 psi).

LUBRICATING OIL SPECIFICATIONS: Type 2 synthetic lube oil PWA-521 MIL-L-23699.

MOUNTING: Horizontal 5 degrees nose up or nose down. 15 degrees either side of vertical. Momentary inclination for periods of 10 seconds; pitch 10 degrees nose up or down and up to a 45 degrees either side of vertical.

STARTING: Pneumatic or hydraulic.

DIMENSIONS: Length 328 in, width 76 in, height 85 ins.

FUEL SPECIFICATIONS:

Light Distillate (Naphtha)

PWA-532(1)		
Aviation Grade Kerosene		
PWA-522(1)	MIL-T-5624	
Marine Diesel		
PWA-527(1)	MIL-F-16884	
Heavy Distillate		
PWA-539	MIL-F-24376(2)	
	or	
	MIL-F-24397(3)	

(1) Covered by TPM-FR-1 for series engine
(2) Navy distillate fuel, referee
(3) Navy distillate fuel

UNION OF SOVIET SOCIALIST REPUBLICS

A. IVCHENKO

The design team headed by the late general designer Ivchenko is based in a factory at Zaporojie in the Ukraine, where all prototypes and pre-production engines bearing the "AI" prefix are developed and built. Chief designer is Lotarev and chief engineer Tichienko. The production director is M. Omeltchenko.

First engine with which Ivchenko was associated officially was the 55 hp AI-4G piston-engine used in the Kamov Ka-10 ultra-light helicopter. He later progressed via the widely used AI-14 and AI-26 piston-engines, to become one of the Soviet Union's leading designers of gas-turbines engines.

Two AI-20s in de-rated, marinised form and driving two 3-stage waterjets power the Burevestink, the first Soviet gas-turbine hydrofoil to go into series production, and a single AI-24 drives the integrated lift/propulsion system of the Sormovich 50 passenger ACV.

IVCHENKO

AI-20

Ivchenko's design bureau is responsible for the AI-20 turboprop engine which powers the Antonov An-10, An-12 and Iluyshin Il-18 airliners and the Beriev M-12 Tchaika amphibian.

Six production series of this engine had been built by the Spring of 1966. The first four series, of which manufacture started in 1957 were variants of the basic AI-20 version. They were followed by two major production versions, as follows.

AI-20K. Rated at 3,945 ehp. Used in Il-18V, An-10A and An-12.

AI-20M. Uprated version with T-O rating of 4,190 ehp (4,250 ch e). Used in Il-18D/E, An-10A and An-12.

Conversion of the turboprop as a marine power unit for hydrofoil waterjet propulsion (as on the Burevestink) involved a number of changes to the engine. In particular it was necessary to hold engine rpm at a constant level during conditions of varying load from the waterjet pump—and it was also necessary to be able to vary the thrust from the waterjet unit from zero to forward or rearwards thrust to facilitate engine starting and vessel manoeuvring.

Constant speed under variable load was achieved by replacing the engine's normal high pressure fuel pump with a special fuel regulator pump—and the waterjet pump was modified to have a variable exit area and was fitted with an air valve enabling a variable amount of air to be passed into the

A 1,750 hp Ivchenko AI-23-CI marine gas-turbine

intake just ahead of the pump rotor. With less air passing through the waterjet, unit load on the engine increased, and vice versa if the air flow was increased by opening the air valve.

The fuel regulator pump was designed to maintain engine rpm constant and to regulate output while the AI-20 was driving the waterjet unit. Steady running conditions were shown to be satisfactorily maintained by the engine under all operating conditions—and rpm and turbine temperature were held within the limits laid down for the aircraft turboprop version: engine rpm did not fluctuate outside ±2·5 per cent of its set speed when loading or unloading the waterjet unit.

During development of the marinised AI-20, the normal aircraft propeller and speed governor were removed and the turboprop was bench tested over the full range of its operating conditions. This demonstrated that the engine performed in a stable manner throughout, from slow running to normal rpm. These tests were run initially using aviation kerosene Type TS-1 fuel, and then diesel fuels Types L and DS.

Following satisfactory results on the bench, the test engine was mounted on a self-propelled floating test bed equipped with a waterjet propulsion unit. Further tests with this configuration were also satisfactorily concluded, including starting checks with varying degrees of submersion of the pump section of the waterjet unit.

Electrical starting of the engine up to slow running speed (equal to approximately 25 per cent of rated rpm) was shown to take 70 to 85 seconds. For starting and ignition at ambient conditions below 10°C, fuel pre-heating is employed, and modified igniters

are fitted. With this equipment, starts have been achieved down to —12°C.

Based on this experience, the marinised AI-20 for the twin-engined Burevestink was rated at 2,700 hp at 12,300 rpm. At this power output, the hydrofoil achieved speeds of up to 60 mph (97 km/hr). Specific fuel consumption was 0·71 to 0·73 lb (320-330 gr)/hp/hr.

Testing with the Burevestink exposed a number of operating characteristics of the vessel: when the two AI-20s were running while the vessel was moored or manoeuvring, residual exhaust thrust from the turbines occurred and this is required to be balanced by a negative, or reverse thrust from the waterjet by partially closing the unit's nozzle flaps. This increased the load on the engine however, and caused a rise in fuel consumption.

Also, experience showed that with a normal start following a series of wet starts, any fuel which had accumulated in the jet pipe became ignited. This resulted in a sharp rise in turbine temperature and back pressure, and flame emerged from the ejection apertures into the engine compartment and exhaust nozzle. To circumvent this, the ejection apertures were covered with a metal grid, and a spray of water is provided at the exhaust nozzle prior to starting.

Based on an overhaul life for the turboprop AI-25 of several thousand hours, special techniques have been applied to the marinised version to increase its service life. These include the use of high quality assembly procedures for the engine, efficient design of the air intake and exhaust duct, adoption of appropriate procedures for starting and on-loading of the main and auxiliary turbines at all ambient temperature conditions—and by the utilisation of highly-skilled servicing methods of the installation during operation.

The AI-20 is a single-spool turboprop, with a 10-stage axial-flow compressor, cannular combustion chamber with ten flame tubes, and a three-stage turbine, of which the first two stages are cooled. Planetary reduction gearing, with a ratio of 0·08732 : 1, is mounted forward of the annular air intake. The fixed nozzle contains a central bullet fairing. All engine-driven accessories are mounted on the forward part of the compressor casing, which is of magnesium alloy.

The AI-20 was designed to operate reliably in all temperatures from —60°C to +55°C at heights up to 33,000 ft (10,000 m). It is a constant speed engine, the rotor speed being maintained at 21,300 rpm by automatic variation of propeller pitch. Gas temperature after turbine is 560°C in both current versions. TBO of the AI-20K was 4,000 hours in the Spring of 1966.

WEIGHT (Dry):
AI-20K   2,380 lb (1,080 kg)
AI-20M   2,290 lb (1,039 kg)

PERFORMANCE RATINGS:
  Max T-O:
  AI-20K   3,945 ehp (4,000 ch e)
  AI-20M   4,190 ehp (4,250 ch e)
  Cruise rating at 390 mph (630 kmh) at 26,000 ft (8,000 m):
  AI-20K   2,220 ehp (2,250 ch e)
  AI-20M   2,663 ehp (2,700 ch e)
SPECIFIC FUEL CONSUMPTION:
  At cruise rating:
  AI-20K   0·472 lb (215 gr) hp/hr
  AI-20M   0·434 lb (197 gr) hp/hr
OIL CONSUMPTION:
  Normal   1·75 Imp pints 1 litre/hr

IVCHENKO
AI-24

In general configuration, this single-spool turboprop engine, which powers the An-24 transport aircraft, is very similar to the earlier and larger AI-20. Production in 1960 and the following data refer to engines of the second series, which were in production in the Spring of 1966.

A single marinized version, developing 1,800 shp, drives the integrated lift/propulsion system of the Sormovich 50-passenger ACV.

An annular ram air intake surrounds the cast light alloy casing for the planetary reduction gear, which has a ratio of 0·08255 : 1. The cast magnesium alloy compressor casing carries a row of inlet guide vanes and the compressor stator vanes and provides mountings for the engine-driven accessories. These include fuel, hydraulic and oil pumps, tacho-generator and propeller governor.

The 10-stage axial-flow compressor is driven by a three-stage axial-flow turbine, of which the first two stages are cooled. An annular combustion chamber is used, with eight injectors and two igniters.

The engine is flat-rated to maintain its nominal output to 11,500 ft (3,500 m). TBO was 3,000 hours in the Spring of 1966.
DIMENSIONS:
  Length overall   95·87 in (2,435 mm)
WEIGHT, Dry: 1,100 lb (499 kg)
PERFORMANCE RATING:
  Max T-O with water injection
                      2,820 ehp (2,859 ch e)

SUDOIMPORT
ADDRESS:
  ul. Kaliaevskaja, 5, Moscow K-6, USSR
Russian industry has developed a variety of marine diesel engines, selected models of which have been installed in the Krasnoye Sormovo series of hydrofoil craft. Most popular of these are the 1,100 hp M401 powering the Kometa hydrofoil, and the 1,200 hp M50 powering the Byelorus, Chaika, Meteor, Mir, Raketa, Sputnik, Strela and Vikhr hydrofoils. A third marine diesel engine is the 3D12 with a continuous rating of 300 hp. A version of this engine is installed in the Nevka hydrofoil, now in series production in Leningrad.

These and other marine diesels are available through Sudoimport, USSR marine export, import and repair organisation.

TYPE M 400
TYPE: Water-cooled, 12-cylinder, V-type four-stroke supercharged marine diesel engine.
CYLINDERS: Two banks of six cylinders set at 30°, each bank comprising cast aluminium alloy monobloc with integral head. Pressed-in liner with spiral cooling passages comprises inner alloy steel sleeve with nitrided working surface, and outer carbon steel sleeve. Each monobloc retained on crankcase by 14 holding-down studs. Bore 7·09 in. (180 mm). Stroke 7·87 in (200 mm). Cubic capacity 381 cu in (62·4 litres). Compression ratio 13·5 : 1.
CRANKCASE: Two-part cast aluminium alloy case with upper half carrying cylinder monoblocs, and transmitting all engine loads.
CYLINDER HEADS: Integral with cylinder monoblocs.
CRANKSHAFT: Six-crank seven-bearing crankshaft in nitrided alloy steel with split steel shells, lead bronze lined with lead-tin alloy bearing surface. Spring damper at rear end reduces torsional vibrations.
CONNECTING RODS: Master and articulated rods, with master connected to crankshaft by split big end with lead bronze lining.

Sudoimport M400

Articulated rods connected by pin pressed into eye of master rods.
PISTONS: Forged aluminium alloy with four rings, upper two of which are of trapeziform cross-section. Alloy steel floating gudgeon pin. Piston head specially shaped to form combustion chamber with spherical cylinder head.
CAMSHAFTS: Two camshafts acting direct on valve stems.
VALVES: Four valves in each cylinder, two inlet and two exhaust. Each valve retained on seat by three coil springs.
COOLING: Forced circulation system using fresh water with 1·0 to 1·1 per cent potassium bichromate added. Fresh water pump mounted on forward part of engine.

Fresh water, and lubricating oil leaving the engine are cooled by water-to-water and water-to-oil coolers, in turn cooled by sea water circulated by engine-mounted sea water pump.
SUPERCHARGING: Single-stage centrifugal supercharger, mechanically driven and providing supercharging pressure of at least 22 lb/sq in (1·55 kg/cm²) at rated power.
LUBRICATION: Comprises delivery pump together with full-flow centrifuge; twin-suction scavenge pump, double gauze-type strainers at inlet and outlet to oil system; and electrically-driven priming pump to prime engine with oil and fuel.
FUEL INJECTION: Closed-type fuel injection with hydraulically-operated valves,

giving initial pressure of 2,845 lb/sq in (200 kg/cm²). Each injector has eight spray orifices forming 140° conical spray. High pressure 12-plunger fuel injection pump with primary gear pump. Two filters in parallel filter oil to HP pump.

STARTING: Compressed air system with starting cylinder operating at 1,067 to 2,134 lb/sq in (75 to 150 kg/cm²), two disc-type air distributors and 12 starting valves.

GOVERNOR: Multi-range indirect-action engine speed governor with resilient gear drive from pump camshaft. Governor designed to maintain pre-set rpm throughout full speed range from minimum to maximum.

EXHAUST SYSTEM: Fresh water-cooled exhaust manifolds fastened to exterior of cylinder blocs. Provision made for fitting thermocouple or piezometer.

REVERSING: Hydraulically-operated reversing clutch fitted to enable prop shaft to run forwards, idle or reverse with constant direction of crankshaft rotation.

MOUNTING: Supports fitted to upper half of crankcase for attaching engine to bedplate.

DIMENSIONS:

Width	48·03 in (1,220 mm)
Height	49·21 in (1,250 mm)
Length	102·36 in (2,600 mm)

PERFORMANCE RATINGS:

Max	1,100 hp at 1,800 rpm
Continuous	1,000 hp at 1,700 rpm

FUEL CONSUMPTION:
At continuous rating
Not over 0·425 lb (193 gr)/hp/hr

OIL CONSUMPTION:
At continuous rating
Not over 0·013 lb (6 gr)/hp/hr

TYPE 3D12

TYPE: Water-cooled, 12-cylinder, V-type, four-stroke marine diesel engine.

CYLINDERS: Two banks of six cylinders in jacketed blocks with pressed-in steel liners. Bore 5·9 in (150 mm). Stroke 7·09 in (180 mm). Cubic capacity 237 cu in (38·8 litres). Compression ratio 14 to 15 : 1.

CRANKCASE: Two-part cast aluminium alloy case with upper half accommodating seven main bearings of steel shell, lead bronze lined type. Lower half carries oil pump, water circulating pump and fuel feed pump.

CYLINDER HEADS: Provided with six recesses to accommodate combustion chambers. Each chamber is connected via channels to inlet and outlet ports of cylinder bloc.

CRANKSHAFT: Alloy steel forging with seven journals and six crankpins. Pendulum anti-vibration dampers fitted on first two webs to reduce torsional vibration.

CONNECTING RODS: Master and articulated rods of double-T section forged in alloy steel. Master rod big-end bearings have steel shells, lead bronze lined. Small end bearings of master rods and both bearings of articulated rods have bronze bushes.

PISTONS: Aluminium alloy.

CAMSHAFTS: Carbon steel camshafts with cams and journals hardened by high frequency electrical current.

COOLING: Closed water, forced circulation type incorporating centrifugal pump, self-suction sea water pump and tubular water cooler.

Sudoimport 3D12

LUBRICATION: Forced circulation type with dry sump, incorporating three-section gear pump, oil feed pump, wire-mesh strainer with fine cardboard filtering element and tubular oil cooler.

FUEL INJECTION: Rotary fuel feed pump, twin felt filter, plunger fuel pump with device to stop engine in event of oil pressure drop in main line. Closed-type fuel injectors with slotted filters. Plunger pump carries variable-speed centrifugal governor for crankshaft rpm.

STARTING: Main electrical starting system, with compressed air reserve system.

REVERSE-REDUCTION GEAR: Non-co-axial type with twin-disc friction clutch; and gear-type reduction gear giving optional ratios, forwards, of 2·95 : 1, 2·04 : 1 or 1·33 : 1, and 2·18 : 1 astern.

DIMENSIONS:

Width	41·42 in (1,052 mm)
Height	45·63 in (1,159 mm)
Length	97·01 in (2,464 mm)

WEIGHT, Dry:

Fully equipped	4,189 lb (1,900 kg)

PERFORMANCE RATING:

Continuous	300 hp at 1,500 rpm

FUEL CONSUMPTION:
At continuous rated power
0·388 lb (176 gr)/hp/hr

OIL CONSUMPTION:
At continuous rated power
Not over 0·02 lb (9 gr)/hp/hr

M401A

The M401A, fitted to the new Voskhod and the latest variants of the Kometa and Raketa, is based on the M50. The new engine is more reliable than its predecessor and its development involved the redesigning of a number of units and parts, as well as the manufacturing of components with a higher degree of accuracy, which necessitated the employment of the latest engineering technique.

The engine is manufactured in left hand and right hand models. These differ by the arrangement on the engine housing of the fresh water pump drive and the power take-off drive for the shipboard compressor.

TYPE: Water-cooled, 12-cylinder, V-type four-stroke supercharged marine diesel.

CYLINDERS: Two banks of six cylinders set at 60°. Monobloc is a solid aluminium casting. Pressed into monobloc are six steel sleeves with spiral grooves on the outer surface for the circulation of cooling water. Bore, 7·09 in (180 mm), Stroke, 7·87 in (200 mm). Compression ratio: 13·5 : 0·5.

CRANKCASE: Two piece cast aluminium alloy case with upper half carrying cylinder monoblocs and transmitting all engine loads.

CYLINDER HEADS: Integral with cylinder monobloc.

CRANKSHAFT: Six-crank, seven bearing crankshaft in nitrided alloy steel with split

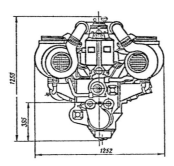

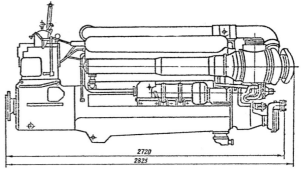

M401A water cooled 12-cylinder, V-type four-stroke supercharged marine diesel

steel shells, lead-tin bronze lined with lead-tin alloy bearing surface.

CONNECTING RODS: Master and articulated rods, with master connected to the crankshaft by split big end, lined with lead tin bronze. Articulated rod connected to crankshaft by a pin pressed into its eye ring.

PISTONS: Forged aluminium alloy with five rings. Top two steel rings, one cast iron of rectangular section and the two bottom rings, in cast iron and steel, are oil control rings fitted in a common groove.

CAMSHAFTS: Two, acting directly on valve stems.

VALVES: Four in each cylinder, two inlet and two exhaust. Each retained on seat by three coil springs.

SUPERCHARGING: Two, Type TK-18H superchargers, each comprising an axial-flow turbine and a centrifugal compressor mounted on a common shaft with a vane diffuser and volute. A silencer can be installed on the compressor air inlet. Turbine casing cooled with fresh water from the diesel engine cooling system.

GOVERNOR: Multi-range indirect action engine speed governor with resilient gear drive from pump camshaft. Designed to maintain pre-set rpm throughout full speed range.

LUBRICATION: Delivery pump with full-flow centrifuge, scavenge pump, double gauge strainers and electrically driven priming pump to power engine with oil and fuel.

COOLING: Double-circuit forced circulation system using fresh water with 1·0 to 1·1% potassium bichromate to GOST2652-71. Fresh water pump mounted on engine. Fresh water and lubricating oil leaving engine are cooled by water-to-water and water-to-oil coolers in turn cooled by sea water circulated by engine-mounted sea water pump.

STARTING: Compressed air system with two disc-type air distributors and twelve starting valves.

REVERSING: Hydraulically operated reversing clutch to enable propeller shaft to run forwards, idle or reverse. Manual control available in emergency.

Rated power at ahead running under normal atmospheric conditions and at rated rpm, hp	1,000
Rated rpm at ahead running	1,550
Maximum hourly power at maximum rpm, hp	1,100
Maximum rpm at ahead running	1,600
Maximum power at astern running	250
Minimum rpm at astern running (with the diesel engine control lever at reverse stop)	750
Maximum specific fuel consumption at rated power (with operating generator, hydraulic pump and the power take-off for compressor), g/e.h.p.hr	172+5%
Maximum specific oil burning losses at rated power, g/e.h.p.hr	5

Fuel

Diesel fuel Grade (GOST 4749—49) Oil MC-20 (GOST 4749—49) with additive (GOST 8312-57) 3% in weight

Sense of power take-off flange rotation (if viewed from turbo-supercharger):

of R.H. diesel engine	clockwise
of L.H. diesel engine	counter-clockwise
Operating life (until major overhaul) hrs.	2,500

Diesel engine dimensions, mm

Length	2,825*/2,720**
Width	1,252
Height	1,250
Weight (dry) with all units and pipe lines mounted, kg	2,000

*With muffler at intake
**Without muffler at intake

A SELECTED
BIBLIOGRAPHY

A SELECTED BIBLIOGRAPHY

AIR CUSHION VEHICLES

ACVs IN NORTH AMERICA

ACV Icing Problems, J. R. Stallabras and T. R. Ringer, National Research Council, Seventh Canadian Symposium on Air Cushion Technology, June 1973.

ACV potential in New York. Leedham, C. (New York City Commissioner for Marine and Aviation) Hoverfoil News, Vol. 5, No.6 March 14th 1974.

Air Cushion Technology: the Prospects for Canadian Industry, Dr P. A. Sullivan, Institute for Aerospace Studies, University of Toronto. Sixth CASI Symposium on Air Cushion Technology, Ontario, June 1972.

Air-Cushion Vehicles, Operational use in the Arctic, Ives, G, Petroleum Eng., Vol, 46 No. 1, January 1974.

Air Cushion Vehicles and Soil Erosion, P. Abeels., International Society for Terrain-Vehicle Systems 5th International Conference, Detroit, Houghton, Michigan, 2-6 June, 1975.

Arctic Development Using Very Large ACVs, J. L. Anderson, NASA Lewis Laboratories. Seventh Canadian Symposium on Air Cushion Technology, June 1973.

Arctic Operational Experience with SR.N6 engaged in Hydrographic Survey and Cushioncraft CC-7, L. R. Colby and G. M. Yeaton, Polar Continental Shelf Project, DEMR. Fourth Canadian Symposium on Air Cushion Technology, 1970. Canadian Aeronautics and Space Institute.

Dynamic Performance of an Air-Cushion Vehicle in a Marine Environment Fein, J. A. Magnuson, A. H. and Moran, D. D. (Naval Ship Research and Development Center, Bethesda, Md,) AIAA/ SNAME Advanced Marine Vehicle Conference, San Diego, California, February 25-28 1974.

Development of the Canadian Air-Cushion Vehicle Industry, Wade, R. G. (Ministry of Transport, Ottawa). AIAA/SNAME Advanced Marine Vehicle Conference, San Diego, California, 25-28 February 1974.

Heavy Goods Transport by Air-Cushion Vehicles. Eastman, C. A. R. The Society of Engineers Journal (U.K.) Vol. LXIV Nos. 2 and 3, Apr/June and July/Sept. 1973.

Effects of Hovercraft Operation on Organic Terrain in the Arctic, Gunars Abele, US Army Cold Regions Research and Engineering Laboratory, Hovering Craft, Hydrofoil and Advanced Transit Systems Conference, Brighton May 1974.

Environmental Effects of ACV and other Off-Road Vehicle Operations on Tundra, G. Abele and W. E. Rickard, U.S. Army Cold Region Research and Engineering Laboratory. Seventh Canadian Symposium on Air Cushion Technology, June 1973.

Improvements in Ice-breaking by the use of Air Cushion Technology, Wade, R. G., Edwards, R. Y. and Kim, J. K. Eastern Canada Section of S.N.A.M.E. Symposium Ice Tech 75, Montreal, 9-11 April 1975.

Marine Transportation and Air-Cushion Vehicles North of 60, Montpetit, L. R. Canadian Min. & Met. Bulletin. 68, January 1975. p. 78-81.

Model Tests of an Arctic Surface Effect Vehicle over Model Ice, Lecourt, E. J., Kotras, T. and Kordenbrock, J. Eastern Canadian Section of S.N.A.M.E. Ice Tech 75 Symposium, Montreal, 9-11 April 1975.

Arctic Surface Effect Vehicles, Vol 1, An Overview of SEV Developments, Final Report, by N. Ray Sumner Jr., Raymond D. Manners, Robert B. Ryan. Sponsored by Defense Advanced Research Projects Agency (ARPA). Science Applications, Inc, 1651 Old Meadow Road, McLean, Virginia 22101, USA

Hovercraft Operations in the Arctic, the Activities of Voyageur 003 Between Hay River, Northwest Territories, Canada and Umiat, Alaska, by N. Ray Sumner Jr, November 1974. Science Applications, Inc., 1651 Old Meadow Road, McLean, Virginia 22101, USA

NCTL's Voyageur Experience, B. Meade, Northern Transportation Co. Seventh Canadian Symposium on Air Cushion Technology, June 1973.

Operational Evaluation of the SK-5 in Alaska, R. A. Liston and B. Hanamoto, US Army Cold Region Research and Engineering Laboratory. Seventh Canadian Symposium on Air Cushion Technology, June 1973.

Requirements for a Canadian ACV Industry, R. G. Wade, Hovermarine (Canada) Ltd, June 1969. Third Canadian Symposium on Air Cushion Technology, Canadian Aeronautics and Space Institute, SC 2.00.

Review of Canadian Government Options for Future Action in the Development of Air Cushion Technology, I. G. Lochead, Dept of Industry, Trade and Commerce. Third Canadian Symposium on Air Cushion Technology, Canadian Aeronautics and Space Institute, June 1969. SC 2.00.

Some Air Cushion Technology Research in Canada, H. S. Fowler, National Research Council, Canada. Hovering Craft, Hydrofoil and Advanced Transit Systems Conference, Brighton, May 1974.

Small Air Cushion Vehicle Operation on Floating Ice under Winter Conditions, R. J. Weaver and R. O. Ramseier, Dept. of the Environment. Seventh Canadian Symposium on Air Cushion Technology, June 1973.

AIR CUSHION LANDING SYSTEMS

Further Developments in Surface Effect Take-Off and Landing System Concepts, A. E. Johnson, F. W. Wilson and W. B. Maguire, NSRDC. Sixth CASI Symposium on Air Cushion Technology, Ontario, June 1972

Elastically Retracting ACLS Trunks, Earl, T. D. (Textron Bell Aerospace). Canadian Aeronautics and Space Journal, Vol. 21 No. 5, May 1975. p. 169-173

ACLS for a commercial transport, Earl, T. D. (Textron Bell Aerospace). Society of Automotive Engineers Meeting, 30 April-2 May 1974.

Air-Cushion Landing Systems Development on a Buffalo Aircraft, Austin, C. J. (The De Havilland Aircraft Co. of Canada Ltd.) C.A.S.I. Flight Test Symposium, Edmonton, Alberta, 12-13 March 1975.

AIR CUSHION LOAD CARRIERS

Aircraft Recovery, G. M. Parkes, Hovertrailers International Ltd., Hovering Craft, Hydrofoil and Advanced Transit Systems Conference, Brighton, May 1974.

Movement of Heavy Loads, L. A. Hopkins, Air Cushion Equipment Ltd, Seventh Canadian Symposium on Air Cushion Technology, June 1973.

On the Applications of Air Cushion Technology to Off-Road Transport, Dr J. Y. Wong, Carleton University. Sixth CASI Symposium on Air Cushion Technology, Ontario, June 1972.

River Crossing Problems Posed by the Mackenzie Highway and a Possible Solution, R. G. Wade, Canadian Ministry of Transport. Seventh Canadian Symposium on Air Cushion Technology, June 1973.

Development of a Track Laying Air Cushion Vehicle, J. R. Goulburn and R. B. Steven, University of Belfast. Hovering Craft, Hydrofoil and Advanced Transit Systems Conference, Brighton ,May 1974.

The Role of the Non-Self-Propelled Air Cushion Vehicle, L. A. Hopkins, Air Cushion Equipment Ltd. Sixth CASI Symposium on Air Cushion Technology, Ontario, June 1972.

Air Cushion Towed Raft Evaluation Project—Current Trials, J. E. Laframboise, Transportation Development Agency. Seventh Canadian Symposium on Air Cushion Technology, June 1973.

An Amphibious Hover Platform for Civil Engineering uses, D. G. W. Turner, Mackace Ltd. Hovering Craft, Hydrofoil and Advanced Transit Systems Conference, Brighton, May, 1974.

Movement of Drill Rigs Using an Air Cushion Platform, R. L. Wheeler, British Hovercraft Corporation. Fourth Canadian Symposium on Air Cushion Technology, June 1970. Canadian Aeronautics and Space Institute.

A 1,000-ton River Hovercraft, R. A. Shaw, V. E. Barker and D. M. Waters, Hoverprojects Ltd., Hovering Craft, Hydrofoil and Advanced Transit Systems Conference, May, 1974.

AIR LUBRICATED HULLS

The Application of the Air Cushion Principle to Very Large Vessels —A Case for Further Research, J. W. Grundy, Naval Architect. Hovering Craft, Hydrofoil and Advanced Transit Systems Conference, Brighton, May 1974.

COMMERCIAL OPERATION

Air-Cushion Vehicles in the Gulf Offshore Oil Industry: A Feasibility Study, Pruett, J. M. (Louisiana State University, Baton Rouge). Final Report on Sea Grant Project (NOAA Contract 04-3-158-19), December 1973.

Air Cushion Vehicles in the Search and Rescue Role, Commander B. W. Mead, Canadian Coast Guard, June 1969. Third Canadian Symposium on Air Cushion Technology, Canadian Aeronautics and Space Institute, SC 2.00.

Air Cushion Vehicles in Support of the Petroleum Industry, Wilfrid J. Eggington, Donald J. Iddins, Aerojet-General Corporation. American Petroleum Institute Meeting: Shreveport, Louisiana.

March 1969.

Domain of the Air Cushion Craft, Peter J. Mantle and David R. Lavis, Bell Aerosystems Corporation, Society of Automative Engineers, Air Transportation Meeting, New York, May 1968.

Experience of Design and Operating the Naviplane, A. Thomas, SEDAM and J. Bertin, Bertin et Cie Institution of Production Engineers, Second International Hovercraft Conference, April 1971.

Current User Experience, E. W. H. Gifford, Hovertravel Ltd, Institution of Production Engineers, Second International Hovercraft Conference, April 1971.

The Contribution of Sidewall Hovercraft to the Evolution of the Marine Ferry, E. G. Tattersall, Hovermarine Ltd. International Hovercraft Conference (Southampton Section), April 1968.

Cross-Channel Hovercraft Operations. L. R. Colquhoun, Hoverlloyd Ltd. Fourth Canadian Symposium on Air Cushion Technology, June 1970. Canadian Aeronautics and Space Institute.

Operational and Technical Problems of Commercial Hovercraft L. R. Colquhoun, (Leslie Colquhoun & Associates, Ramsgate, England.) AIAA/SNAME Advanced Marine Vehicle Conference, San Diego, California, 25-28 February 1974.

Operational Engineering Reliability in Commercial Hovercraft, Cdr. J. M. Lefeaux, British Rail Hovercraft, Institution of Production Engineers, Second International Hovercraft Conference, April 1971.

ACV PROJECTS

ACV Technology Programs at Aerojet-General, R. W. Muir, Aerojet-General Corporation, June 1969. Third Canadian Symposium on Air Cushion Technology, Canadian Aeronautics and Space Institute, $C 2.00.

Development of Surface Effect Technology in the US Industry, John B. Chaplin, Bell Aerospace Company. AIAA/SNAME/USN Advanced Marine Vehicles Meeting, Annapolis, Maryland, July 17-19, 1972.

Control of a Single Propeller Hovercraft, with Particular Reference to BH7, R. L. Wheeler, British Hovercraft Corporation Ltd. Fourth Canadian Symposium on Air Cushion Technology, June 1970. Canadian Aeronautics and Space Institute.

New Advanced Design ACVs, Jean Bertin, Bertin et Cie. Third Canadian Symposium on Air Cushion Technology, June 1969. Canadian Aeronautics and Space Institute, $C 2.00.

Voyageur Trials and Operating Experience, T. F. Melhuish, Bell Aerospace, Canada. Seventh Canadian Symposium on Air Cushion Technology, June 1973.

Operational Experience on VT1s, R. D. Hunt, Hovercraft Division, Vosper Thornycroft Ltd. Institute of Production Engineers, Second International Hovercraft Conference, April 1971.

DESIGN

A method for the preliminary sizing of lift fan systems applicable to large hovercraft, Wilson, W. B. (Webb Institute of Naval Architecture, Glen Cove, New York). Naval Ship Engineering Center of the U.S. Navy, Propulsion Systems Analysis Branch, Technical Report no. 6144E-75-126. February 1975.

A Theoretical Note on the Lift Distribution of a Non-Planar Ground Effect Wing, Kida, T. and Miyai, Y. (University of Osaka Prefecture, Japan). The Aeronautical Quarterly, Vol. 24. August 1973. Part 3.

A Linearized Potential Flow Theory for the Motions of Air-Cushion Vehicles in a Seaway, T. K. S. Murthy, Portsmouth Polytechnic. Ninth Symposium on Naval Hydrodynamics, Paris, August 1972.

A Comparison of Some Features of High-Speed Marine Craft, A. Silverleaf and F. G. R. Cook, National Physical Laboratory. Royal Institution of Naval Architects, March 1969.

Development of the Axial-flow Surface Effect Vehicle, A. M. Jackes, AirSeamobile Co, Santa Ana, Calif. Advanced Marine Vehicle meeting AIAA/SNAME/USN, Annapolis, July 1972.

FANS: Design and operation of centrifugal, axial-flow and cross-flow fans. Translated from German, Edited by R. S. Azad and D. R. Scott, Pergamon Press 1973.

Some Design Aspects of Air Cushion Craft, Peter J. Mantle, International Congress of Subsonic Aeronautics, New York Academy of Sciences, April 1967.

Lateral Stability of a Dynamic Ram Air Cushion Vehicle, Aidala, P. V. (Transportation Systems Center, Cambridge, Mass.) DOT-TSC-FRA-74-6. FRA-ORD/D-75-6. PB-236-516/1WT. August 1974. 72p.

The Design of a Ram Wing Vehicle for high speed ground Transportation, Tan, E. A. (E. I. Dupont Co.), Goss W. P. and Cromack, D. E. (University of Massachusetts, Amherst). International Conference on High Speed Ground Transportation, Arizona State University, 7-10 January 1975, Tempe, Arizona.

On the Determination of the Hydrodynamic Performance of Air-Cushion Vehicles, S. D. Prokhorov, V. N. Treshchevski, L. D. Volkov, Kryloff Research Institute, Leningrad. Ninth Symposium on Naval Hydrodynamics, Paris, August 1972.

On the Prediction of Acceleration Response of Air-Cushion Vehicles to Random Seaways and the Distortion Effects of Cushion Inherent in Scale Models, D. R. Lavis and R. V. Bartholemew, Aerojet-General Corporation Advanced Marine Vehicle meeting, AIAA/SNAME/USN, Annapolis, July 1972.

Ram-Wing Surface Effect Boat, Capt R. W. Gallington, USAF, US Air Force Academy, Colorado, Advanced Marine Vehicle Meeting AIAA/SNAME/USN Annapolis, July 1972.

Resultats d'Exploitation des Aeroglisseurs Marins "Naviplane", M. P. Guienne, Bertin et Cie. Seventh Canadian Symposium on Air Cushion Technology, June 1973.

The Design, Fabrication and Initial Trials of a Light Amphibious Arctic Transporter, J. H. Kennedy and A. M. Garner, Jr, Transportation Technology Inc. Fourth Canadian Symposium on Air Cushion Technology, 1970. Canadian Aeronautics and Space Institute.

Some Design Aspects of an Integrated Lift/Propulsion System, D. Jones, Jones, Kirwan and Associates. Sixth CASI Symposium on Air Cushion Technology, Ontario, June 1972.

Some Aspects of Optimum Design of Lift Fans, T. G. Csaky, NSRDC. Sixth CASI Symposium on Air Cushion Technology, Ontario, June 1972.

Trade-Off Methodology for Evaluation of Design Alternatives of Air Cushion Vehicles, O. Gokcek and J. H. Madden, Aerojet General Corporation. Sixth CASI Symposium on Air Cushion Technology, Ontario, June 1972.

Aerodynamic Challenges for the Faster Interface Vehicles, P. R. Shipps, Rohr Corporation. Sixth CASI Symposium on Air Cushion Technology, Ontario, June 1972.

A Method for Generating Aerodynamic Sideforces on ACV Hulls, Dr R. J. Kind, Carleton University. Sixth CASI Symposium on Air Cushion Technology, Ontario, June 1972.

Vortex Shedding from the Ram Wing Vehicle, Technical Progress Report, Gallington, R. (Air Force Acadamy, Colorado) Jan-July 1973. AD-767234. August 1973. Available N. T. I. S.

EXTERNAL AERODYNAMICS

The External Aerodynamics of Hovercraft, Professor E. J. Andrews College of Aeronautics, Cranfield. Royal Aeronautical Society Rotorcraft Section, April 1969.

INDUSTRIAL APPLICATIONS

Hoverpallets for Material Handling, A. J. I. Poynder, British Hovercraft Corporation. Institution of Production Engineers, International Hovercraft Conference, April 1968.

Industrial Applications of Air Cushion Technology, P. H. Winter, Air Vehicle Developments Ltd, June 1969. Third Canadian Symposium on Air Cushion Technology, Canadian Aeronautics and Space Institute, C 2.00.

LIGHTWEIGHT ACVs

Control and Guidance of Light Amphibious Hovercraft up to a Gross Weight of 5,000 lbs, R. L. Trillo, Robert Trillo Ltd. Seventh Canadian Symposium on Air Cushion Technology, June 1973.

Small Hovercraft Design, P. H. Winter, Air Vehicle Developments. International Hovercraft Conference, 1968, the Institution of Production Engineers (Southampton Section).

Small Hovercraft Structure, A. J. English, Sealand Hovercraft Ltd, Hovering Craft, Hydrofoil and Advanced Transit Systems Conference, Brighton, May 1974.

MILITARY APPLICATIONS and OPERATING EXPERIENCE

A Review of British Army Hovercraft Activity 1967-72, Major G. G. Blakey, Royal Corps of Transport. Sixth CASI Symposium on Air Cushion Technology, Ontario, 1972.

Development of the SR.N6 Mk 5 Vehicle-carrying Hovercraft, Major M. H. Burton, Dept of Trade and Industry, UK. Seventh Canadian Symposium on Air Cushion Technology, June 1973.

ACV Military Applications—Experience and Potential, J. B. Chaplin. Bell Aerosystems Company, June 1969. Third Canadian Symposium on Air Cushion Technology, Canadian Aeronautics and Space Institute, $C 2.00.

Air Cushion Vehicles in a Logistical Role, Col H. N. Wood (Ret), US Army Combat Development Command Transportation Agency. Fourth Canadian Symposium on Air Cushion Technology, 1970. Canadian Aeronautics and Space Institute.

BH.7 Mk 2—Experience during the first 2,000 hours of Operation, Cdr L. G. Scovell, Dept of Trade and Industry, UK. Seventh Canadian Symposium on Air Cushion Technology, June 1973.

Military Experience, Commander D. F. Robbins, RN, Interservice Hovercraft Unit. International Hovercraft Conference, April 1968. The Institution of Production Engineers (Southampton Section).

US Army ACV Operations, Major D. G. Moore, US Army Air Cushion Vehicle Unit, June 1969. Third Canadian Symposium on Air Cushion Technology, Canadian Aeronautics and Space Institute, $C 2.00.

UK Military Hovercraft, Commander N. T. Bennett, AFC, RN, Interservice Hovercraft Unit. Second International Hovercraft Conference, Institute of Production Engineers, April 1971.

LEGISLATION and REGULATIONS

Lloyd's Register's Requirements for ACVs, A. K. Buckle, Lloyd's Register of Shipping. Second Canadian Symposium on Air Cushion Technology, June 1968. Canadian Aeronautics and Space Institute, $C 2.00.

Operating Legislation for ACVs, Captain J. Doherty, Department of Transport, June 1968. Second Canadian Symposium on Air Cushion Technology. Canadian Aeronautics and Space Institute, $C 2.00.

The Air Registration Board and Hovercraft, S. Gardner, Air Registration Board, June 1968, Second Canadian Symposium on Air Cushion Technology, Canadian Aeronautics and Space Institute, $C 2.00.

United States Requirements for Commercial Surface Effect Ships, W. A. Cleary Jr and Lt D. H. Whitten, US Coast Guard. Second Canadian Symposium on Air Cushion Technology, June 1968. Canadian Aeronautics and Space Institute, $C 2.00.

POWERPLANTS

Some Aspects of Free Turbine Engine Hovercraft Control, W. Bloomfield, T. B. Lauriat, AVCO Corporation Lycoming Division. Institute of Production Engineers, Second International Hovercraft Conference, April 1971.

The Selection of the Optimum Powerplant for the Air Cushion Vehicle, R. Messet, United Aircraft of Canada Ltd. Fourth Canadian Symposium on Air Cushion Technology, June 1970. Canadian Aeronautics and Space Institute.

PRODUCTION

The Production of Air Cushion Vehicles, E. F. Gilberthorpe, British Hovercraft Corporation. Institution of Production Engineers (Southampton Section), International Hovercraft Conference, April 1968.

Hovercraft from a Shipbuilder, A. E. Bingham, Vosper Thornycroft Ltd., Hovering Craft, Hydrofoil and Advanced Transit Systems Conference, Brighton, May 1974.

RESEARCH and DEVELOPMENT

A Decade of Development—The SR.N6 Family of Hovercraft, R. L. Wheeler, British Hovercraft Corporation, Hovering Craft, Hydrofoil & Advanced Transit Systems Conference, Brighton, May 1974.

Development of Hovermarine Transport Vehicles, E. G. Tattersall, Hovermarine Transport Ltd. Institute of Production Engineers, Second International Hovercraft Conference, April 1971.

Minimum Induced Drag of a Semi-Circular Ground Effect Wing, Mamada, H. (Aichi University of Education) and Ando, S. (Nagoya University) (Japan). Journal of Aircraft, Vol. 10 No. 11, November 1973.

Conceptual Study for a new Winged Surface Effect Vehicle System, McMasters, J. H. and Greeer, R. R. Naval Engineers Journal, 86 April 1974. p. 41-51.

Investigation of the static lift capability of a Low-Aspect-Ratio Wing Operating in a powered ground-effect mode, Huffman, J. K. and Jackson, C. M. NASA TM X-3031. July 1974. 32p.

Study of Materials and Nonmetallic coatings for erosion and wear resistance, Sertour, G., Armbruster, M., Bernard, H. and Renard, P. (Soc. Nationale Industrielle Aerospatiale, Paris). (In French). Association Technique Maritime et Aeronautique Bulletin No. 74, 1974. p. 357-367.

The Development of Marine Hovercraft with special reference to the Construction of the N500., Guienne, M. (SEDAM). 2nd International Conference Transport-Expo, Paris, 15-20 April 1975.

Response of Air-Cushion Vehicles to random seaways and the inherant distortion in scale models., Lavis, D. R., Bartholomew, R. J. and Jones, J. C. Journal of Hydronautics, Vol. 8, July 1974. p.83.

Hovercraft Research and Development, R. L. Wheeler, British Hovercraft Corporation Ltd. Institute of Production Engineers, Second International Hovercraft Conference, April 1971.

Development of the Hovergem Range of Commercial Air Cushion Vehicles, G. L. Green, Hovergem Australasia Pty Ltd, Institute of Production Engineers, Second International Hovercraft Conference, April 1971.

Some Aspects of Hovercraft Dynamics, J. R. Richardson, NPL Hovercraft Unit, Institution of Production Engineers, Second International Hovercraft Conference, April 1971.

Recent Developments in Hovercraft Performance Testing, B. J. Russell, Interservice Hovercraft Unit, HMS Daedalus. Hovering Craft, Hydrofoil & Advanced Transit Systems Conference, Brighton, May 1974.

Research and Development Work Associated with the Lift and Propulsion of Air Cushion Vehicles, J. G. Russell, Dowty Rotol Ltd, Hovering Craft, Hydrofoil & Advanced Transit Systems Conference, Brighton, May 1974.

STRUCTURAL DESIGN

A Method of Testing Models of Hovercraft in Open Waters, Prof. L. Koblinski and Dr. M. Krezelewski, Ship Research Institute, Technical University of Gdansk. Institution of Production Engineres, Second International Hovercraft Conference, April 1971.

SYSTEMS

Airscrews for Hovercraft, G. K. Ketley, Hawker Siddeley Dynamics Ltd. Second Canadian Symposium on Air Cushion Technology, 1968. Canadian Aeronautics and Space Institute, $C 2.00.

Ducted Propeller Installation for An Amphibious Hovercraft, R. Trillo & P. H. Winter, Hovering Craft, Hydrofoil and Advanced Transit Systems Conference, May 1974.

ACV Design Technology, J. B. Chaplin. Bell Aerosystems Co. Second Canadian Symposium on Air Cushion Technology, 1968 Canadian Aeronautics and Space Institute, $C 2,00.

An Accumulator Control System for Alleviating SES Craft Heave motions in waves, P. Kaplan and T. P. Sargent, Oceanics Inc, and James L. Decker, US Navy Surface Effect Ships Project Office, Washington DC. Advanced Marine Vehicle meeting AIAA/SNAME/USN. Annapolis, July 1972.

Deterioration of Hovercraft Skirt Components on Craft Operating over Water, M. D. Kelly, J. Morris & E. R. Gardner, Avon Rubber Co. Ltd., Hovering Craft, Hydrofoil and Advanced Transit Systems Conference, Brighton, May 1974.

Evolution of Integrated Lift, Propulsion and Control in the Aeromobile ACV, Dr W. R. Bertelsen, Bertelsen Manufacturing Co, June 1969. Third Canadian Symposium on Air Cushion Technology. Canadian Aeronautics and Space Institute, $C 2.00.

Experience of Using the Gas Turbine Engine for the Propulsion of the Fully Amphibious Air Cushion Vehicle, M. L. Woodward, Rolls-Royce (1971) Ltd. Sixth Canadian Symposium on Air Cushion Technology, Ontario, June 1972.

Hovercraft Skirts, R. L. Wheeler, British Hovercraft Corporation, Hovering Craft, Hydrofoil and Advanced Transit Systems Conference, Brighton, May 1974.

Jets, Props and Air Cushions, Propulsion Technology and Surfaces Effect Ships, Alfred Skolnick. Z. G. Wachnik, Joint Surface Effect Ships Program Office. Gas Turbine Conference and Products Show. The American Society of Mechanical Engineers, March 1968.

Pneumatic Power Transmission Applied to Hovercraft, J. F. Sladey Jnr. and R. K. Muench, United States Naval Academy and Naval Ship Research and Development Centre. Sixth CASI Symposium on Air Cushion Technology, Ontario, June 1972.

Power Transmission System of Hovercraft MV-PP1, MV-PP5 and MV-PP15, Yamada, T. Tamano, O., Morita, T., Horikiri, K,. Hirasawa, H. and Fujiwasa, M. (Mitsui Shipbuilding & Engineering Co.) Proc. International Symposium on Marine Engineering, Tokyo, Japan, 12-15 November 1973. Tech. Paper Vol. Ser. 2-4. p. 13-23. Pub: Marine Engineers Society in Japan, Tokyo, 1973.

Skirt Design for Small Hovercraft, J. A. Eglen, National Association of ACV Enthusiasts, June 1969. Third Canadian Symposium on Air Cushion Technology. Canadian Aeronautics and Space Institute, $C 2.00.

Characterisation and Testing of Skirt Materials, Dr R. C. Tennyson and J. R. McCullough, University of Toronto, Institute for Aerospace Studies. Seventh Canadian Symposium on Air Cushion Technology, June 1973.

Study of the Performance of a Partially Submerged Propeller, W. T. Lindemuth and R. A. Barr, Hydronautics Inc. Technical Report 760-1, July 1967.

Surface Effect Vehicle Propulsion: A Review of the State of the Art, J. B. Chaplin, R. G. Moore and J. L. Allison, Bell Aerospace. Sixth Canadian Symposium on Air Cushion Technology, Ontario, June 1972.

The French Technique of Aeroglisseurs Marins, C. Marchetti, SEDAM. Second Canadian Symposium on Air Cushion Technology, June 1968, Canadian Aeronautics and Space Institute, $C 2.00.

The Influence of Plenum Chamber Obstructions on the Performance of a Hovercraft Lift Fan, G. Wilson, Dr D. J. Myles and G. Gallacher, National Engineering Laboratory, June 1969. Third Canadian Symposium on Air Cushion Technology. Canadian Aeronautics and Space Institute, $C 2.00.

The Potential of an Air Cushion Landing Gear in Civil Air Transport, T. D. Earl, Bell Aer. stems Co. Second Canadian Symposium on Air Cushion Technology, 1968. Canadian Aeronautics and Space Institute, SC 2.00.

Water-Jet Propulsion, S. Kuether and F. X. Stora, Tamco Ltd US Army Mobility Equipment, R & D Center. Second Canadian Symposium on Air Cushion Technology, 1968. Canadian Aeronautics and Space Institute, SC 2.00.

Waterjet Propulsion for High Speed Surface Ships, P. Duport M. Visconte, J. Merle, SOGREAH. Ninth Symposium on Naval Hydrodynamics, Paris, August 1972.

SURFACE EFFECT SHIPS

An Analysis of Desired Manoeuvring Characteristics of Large SEVs, W. Zeitfuss Jr and E. N. Brooks Jr, Naval Ship Research and Development Centre, Washington DC. Advanced Marine vehicle meeting, AIAA/SNAME/USN. Annapolis, July 1972.

American Surface Effect Ship Activities, E. K. Liberatore, Aeromar Corporation. Jane's Surface Skimmer Systems, Second Edition 1968-69. Pages 210-212.

Crew/Combat System Performance Requirements in the Operational Environment of Surface Effect Ships, Skolnick, A. Naval Engineers Journal, Vol. 86 no. 6, December 1974. p. 15-32.

Current State-of-the-Art of Waterjet Inlet Systems for High Performance Naval Ships, Barr, R. A. and Stark, N. R. Hydronautics Inc., Tech. Rep. 7224-5, December 1973.

Some Special Problems in Surface Effect Ships, Robert D. Waldo, Aerojet-General Corporation. Journal of Hydronautics. July 1968. American Institute of Aeronautics and Astronautics.

Surface Effect Ships for Ocean Commerce (SESOC), Final Report, February 1966. The SESOC Advisory Committee, Commerce Technical Advisory Board, US Department of Commerce, Washington D.C.

Large High Speed Surface Effect Ship Technology. P. J. Mantle Aerojet-General Corporation, Hovering Craft, Hydrofoil & Advanced Transit Systems Conference, Brighton, May 1974.

Surface Effect Ship Habitability Familiarization, Clement, W. F. and Shanahan, J. J. Systems Technology Inc., Interim Tech. Rep. STI-1041-1. November 1973.

Surface Effect Ships in the Surface Navy, Truax, R. C. U.S. Navy Institute Proceedings, Vol. 99 no. 12/850. December 1973. p.50-54.

Ocean-Going Surface Effect Ships, Perkins, W. F. (Ocean Systems Div., Lockheed Missiles & Space Co., Sunnyvale, Ca.). Northern California Section of S.N.A.M.E. and Golden Gate Section of A.S.N.E., Meeting at Treasure Island Naval Station, 1974.

Study of Heave Acceleration/Velocity Control for the Surface Effect Ship AD-009 302/1WT. Grant, U. S. Jr. Naval Postgraduate School, Montery, Cal.) December 1974. 222p.

The Surface Effect Ship in the American Merchant Marine, Final Report for the US Department of Commerce, Maritime Administration, Booz-Allen Applied Research Inc.

The Nuclear Powered Ocean-Going SES. E. K. Liberatore, Aeromar Corporation, Jane's Surface Skimmers, 1971-72.

Transocean Surface Effect Ships, Dr A. Skolnik, Director of Technology, Surface Effect Ships Program Office. Proceedings of the IEEE Vol 56, No 4, 1968. Institute of Electrical and Electronics Engineers Inc.

TRACKED AIR CUSHION VEHICLES

Aerotrain Tridim for Urban Transportation, Jean Bertin and Jean Berthelot (Bertin & Cie and Soc. Aerotrain), Hovering Craft, Hydrofoil & Advanced Transit Systems Conference, Brighton, May 1974.

A New Linear Air Turbine Vehicle—TACV, Dr Yau Wu, Virginia Polytechnic Institute and State University. Sixth CASI Symposium on Air Cushion Technology, Ontario, June 1972.

Applications du Coussin d'Air Aux Transports en Zones Urbaines, André Garnault, Société d l'Aérotrain, June 1973.

The Operational Performance and Economics of URBA, M. E. Barthalon and L. Pascual, Seturba, Hovering Craft, Hydrofoil and Advanced Transit Systems Conference, Brighton, May 1974.

Canadian Research Activities Applicable to Tracked Levitated Vehicle Systems, P. L. Eggleton, Transportation Development Agency. Seventh Canadian Symposium on Air Cushion Technology, June 1973.

High Speed Ground Transportation, Documentation of Preliminary Engineering, Los Angeles International Airport and the San Fernando Valley, Kaiser Engineers, Los Angeles, California, April 1972.

Metrotran - 2,000, a study of future concepts in Metropolitan Transportation for the year 2,000, by Robert A. Wolf. Final Report CAL Internally Supported Project, October 1967. Cornell Aeronautical Laboratory Inc, Cornell University, Buffalo, NY 14221.

Problems Posés à Propos des Technologies non Conventionnelles de Transports Rapide au Sol, Jean Bertin, President Directeur Général de la Société de l'Aérotrain, June 1973.

Linear Propulsion by Electromagnetic River, Prof. E. R. Laithwaite, Imperial College of Science and Technology, Hovering Craft, Hydrofoil & Advanced Transit Systems Conference, Brighton, May 1974.

The Air-Cushion at High Speeds, Steiner, F. (Societe de l'Aerotrain) 2nd International Conference Transport-Expo, Paris, 15-20 April 1975.

The Invention and Development of a Suspended Air Cushion Passenger Transport System in France, Maurice Barthalon, ScM, MIT. The Inventor, Journal of the Institute of Patentees and Inventors, Vol 9, No 1, March 1969.

The Pendair Suspension System, D. S. Bliss, Pendair Ltd, Hovering Craft, Hydrofoil and Advanced Transit Systems Conference, Brighton, May 1974.

Tracked Air-Cushion Research Vehicle Dynamics Simulation Program User's Manual Final Report, Magnani, E., Lee, R. and Coppolino, R. (Grumman Aerospace Corp., Bethpage, N. Y.) PB-219 984/2. October 1972.

Tracked Air-Cushion Vehicle Suspension Models: Analysis and Comparison, Garg, D. P. (Duke University, North Carolina) and Platin, B. E. (M.I.T., Cambridge.) Vehicle System Dynamics (Holland) Vol. 2 No. 3, November 1973.

Tracked ACVs for Urban Applications, N. McQueen and H. R. Ross, Sverdrup & Parcel & Associates Inc, June 1969. Third Canadian Symposium on Air Cushion Technology. Canadian Aeronautics and Space Institute, $C 2.00.

Tracked Air Cushion Vehicle Research and Development by the US Department of Transportation, A. F. Lampros and C. G. Swanson, Mitre Corporation. Hovering Craft, Hydrofoil and Advanced Transit Systems Conference, Brighton, May 1974.

Status of "Transrapid" Development Programme. G. Winkel (Krauss-Maffei, Augsburg), Second Intercity Conference on Transportation, Denver, Colorado, September, 1973.

LIM—Suspension Interaction, Parker, J. H. and Charles R. J. (Ministry of Transportation & Communications, Ontario), Second Intersociety Conference on Transportation, Denver, Colorado, September 23-27, 1973. ASME Paper No. 73-ICT-116.

ACV PUBLICATIONS, BOOKS and GENERAL LITERATURE

GENERAL INTEREST

This is the Hovercraft, by Hugh Colver, Published by Hamish Hamilton.

Hovercraft & Hydrofoils Work Like This, by Egon Larsen, Published by J. M. Dent.

Hydrofoils and Hovercraft, by Bill Gunston, Published by Aldus Books.

The Hovercraft Story, by Garry Hogg, Published by Abelard-Schuman.

Hover Craft, by Angela Croome, Published by Brockhampton Press.

Hovercraft and Hydrofoils, by Roy McLeavy, Blandford Press Ltd, Link House, West Street, Poole, Dorset, BH15 1LL, 80pp col. £2·75.

Jane's Surface Skimmers (Annual) edited by Roy McLeavy, Published by MacDonald & Jane's.

TECHNICAL

Hovercraft Design and Construction, by Elsley & Devereux, Published by David & Charles.

Helicopter & Hovercraft Design, by Basil Arkell, Published by Weidenfeld & Nicholson.

Marine Hovercraft Technology, by Robert Trillo, Published by Leonard Hill Books.

Light Hovercraft Design Handbook, edited by Dave Waters, Published by Loughborough University.

Light Hovercraft Handbook, edited by Keith Oakley, Published by The Hover Club of Great Britain (available from G. Porter, 15 Watling Street, Dartford, Kent).

An Introduction to Hovercraft and Hoverports, by Cross & O'Flaherty, Published by Pitman Publishing/Juanita Kalerghi.

HOVERCRAFT PERIODICALS
Hoverfoil News, (fortnightly) Published by Horizon Publications Ltd., Shoemaker's House, Montacute, Somerset TA15 6XQ.
Hovering Craft & Hydrofoil, (monthly) Published by Kalerghi Publications, 51 Welbeck Street, London W1M 7HE.
Air Cushion Review, (monthly) Published by Aristos Publications, 25 Beatrice Road, Southsea, Hants PO4 0JY.
Light Hovercraft, (monthly) Published by The Hover Club of Great Britain Ltd., 128 Queens Road, Portsmouth, Hants PO2 7NE.
UKHS Newsletter, (monthly) Published by The United Kingdom Hovercraft Society, Rochester House, 66 Little Ealing Lane, London W5 4XX.
Air-Cushion and Hydrofoil Systems Bibliography Service, (bi-monthly) Published by Robert Trillo Ltd., Broadlands, Brockenhurst, Hants. SO4 7SX.

SPECIAL INTEREST
The Law of Hovercraft, by L. J. Kovats, Published by Lloyd's of London Press Ltd. 1975.

HYDROFOILS
BOOKS
Hydrofoils, Christopher Hook and A. C. Kermode. Sir Isaac Pitman & Sons Ltd, London, £ 1 12 6.
Hydrofoil Sailing, A. J. Alexander, J. L. Grogono, Donald J. Nigg. 96 pages. Price £3·00. Kalerghi Publications, 51 Welbeck Street, London WIM 7HE.
PAPERS, ETC.
COMMERCIAL OPERATION
Future of the Commercial Hydrofoil, Baron H. von Schertel, Supramar. Meeting, Business Aspects of Hovercraft and Hydrofoils, London. May 1968.
Running and Maintenance of Supramar Hydrofoils in Hong Kong, D. Hay and N. J. Matthew, Institute of Marine Engineers, April 1970.
The U.S. Gets Serious about Hydrofoils, Aronson, R. B., Machine Design, Vol 45 No. 25, 18th October 1973.
Safety, Reliability and Maintainability of Supramar Commercial Hydrofoils, Baron H. von Schertel, Supramar, 7th Reliability and Maintainability Conference, San Francisco, July 1968.
Die Antriebsanlagen von Schnellen Marinefahrzeugen und die Muglichkeit iher Verwendung auf Passágier-Tragflugelbooten, E. Faber, Supramar, Sonderdruck MTZ Motor-technische Zietschrift, published June 1968.
DESIGN
A High-Speed Hydrofoil Strut and Foil Study, Wermter, R. and Shen, Y. T. (Naval Ship Research & Development Center, Bethesda, Md.). AIAA/SNAME Advanced Marine Vehicle Conference, San Diego, California, 25-28 February 1974. Paper 74-310.
A Universal Digital Autopilot for a Hydrofoil Craft, Pierre Dogan and Frederick Gamber, M.I.T. Advanced Marine Vehicle meeting, AIAA/SNAME/USN, Annapolis, July 1972.
Design Optimization of Waterjet Propulsion Systems for Hydrofoils, Gill, R. P. M. S. Theseis, Massachusetts Institute of Technology, Cambridge, Mass., May 1972.
Hydrofoil Craft Designers Guide, R. Altmann, Hydronautics Inc, Technical Report 744-1, March 1968.
Laminar Boundary-Layer Induced Wave Forces on a Submerged Flat-Plate Hydrofoil, Journal of Hydronautics, Vol. 8 no. 2. April 1974. p. 47-53.
Bending Flutter and Torsional Flutter of Flexible Hydrofoil Struts, P. K. Beach, Y. N. Liu (U.S. Naval Ship Research and Development Centre). Ninth Symposium on Naval Hydrodynamics, Paris, August 1972.
Canadian Advances in Surface Piercing Hydrofoils, N. E. Jeffrey and M. C. Eames, Defence Research Establishment, Atlantic, Dartmouth, Nova Scotia. Advanced Marine Vehicle Meeting, AIAA/SNAME/USN, Annapolis, July 1972.
Flow Separation, Re-attachment and Ventilation of Foils with Sharp Leading Edge at Low Reynolds Number, Hecker, R. and Ober, G. Naval Ship Research & Development Center Report 4390, III. May 1974. 20p.
Hydroelastic Design of Sub-Cavitating and Cavitating Hydrofoil Strut Systems, Naval Ship Research & Development Center, Maryland, U.S.A. NSRDC Report 4257. April 1974.
Hydrodynamics and Simulation in the Canadian Hydrofoil Program, R. T. Schmitke and E. A. Jones Defence Research Establishment Atlantic, (Canada). Ninth Symposium on Naval Hydrodynamics, Paris, August 1972.

Large Hydrofoil Ships Feasability Level Characteristics, James R. Greco, Naval Ship Engineering Center, Hyattsville, Md. Advanced marine Vehicle meeting, AIAA/SNAME/USN, Annapolis, July 1972.
Prospects for very High Speed Hydrofoils, Conolly, A. San Diego Section of the Society of Naval Architects and Marine Engineers/ The American Society of Naval Engineers joint meeting, 20 November 1974. Avail: Section Librarian, Cder, R. Bernhardt, U.S. Coast Guard, Code 240, Box 119, U.S. Naval Station, San Diego, Ca. 92136.
Special Problems in the Design of Supercavitating Hydrofoils, Dobay, G. F. and Baker, E. S. (Naval Ship Research & Development Center, Bethesda, Md). AIAA/SNAME Advanced Marine Vehicle Conference, San Diego, California, 25-28 February 1974. Paper 74-309.
Tragflugelschiff Supramar PT 150 DC, V. Jost (Schiff); E. Faber (Maschine); D. Cebulla (Tragflugel), Supramar. Sonderdruck aus Fachzeitschrift, "Schiff und Hafen", published May 1968.
Typhoon—A Seagoing Vessel on Automatically Controlled Submerged Foils, I. I. Baskalov and V. M. Burlakov, Sudostroyeniye. Hovering Craft & Hydrofoil. October 1972.
100 Passagier-Tragflugelboote mit schnellaufenden Dieselmotoren im Verkehr, E. Faber, Supramar, Sonderdruck MTZ Motortechnische Zeitschrift, published November 1967.
Bau und Erprobung von Tragflugelbooten, A. Mattl, Supramar, Schweizerischer Technischer Verband, Uzwil, Aarau, 1968.
A Comparison of Some Features of High-Speed Marine Craft, A. Silverleaf and F. G. R. Cook, National Physical Laboratory Royal Institute of Naval Architects, March 1969.
NAVAL CRAFT
The NATO PHM Programme, Cdr Karl M. Duff, USN, Naval Ship Systems Command, Washington D.C. Advanced Marine Vehicle Meeting, AIAA/SNAME/USN, Annapolis, July 1972.
High Speed and U.S. Navy Hydrofoil Development, Jewell, D. A. (Naval Ship Research & Development Center, Bethesda, Md). AIAA/SNAME Advanced Marine Vehicle Conference, San Diego, California, 25-28 February 1974. Paper 74-307.
HMCS Bras d'Or—Sea Trials and Future Prospects, M. C. Eames and T. G. Drummond, Defence Research Establishment Atlantic, Canada. Royal Institution of Naval Architects, April 1972.
Operational and Development Experience on the US Navy Hydrofoil High Point, D. M. Petrie, The Boeing Company. AIAA/USN Marine Systems and ASW Conference. March 1965.
Military Hydrofoils, Baron H. Von Schertel, Dipl. Ing. Egon Faber, Dipl. Ing. Eugen Schatte, Supramar AG. Jane's Surface Skimmers, 1972-73.
PHM Hullborne Wave Tests, Stevens C. J. (Institute of Technology, Hoboken, New Jersey). Stevens Institute of Technology, Davidson Lab. Rep. R-1759, June 1974. 44p.
Research on Hydrofoil Craft, Prof. Dr. Siegfried Schuster, Director Berlin Towing Tank. International Hydrofoil Society Winter Meeting, 1971. Hovering Craft and Hydrofoil, December ,1971.
SEAKEEPING CHARACTERISTICS
Prediction of the Seakeeping Characteristics of Hydrofoil Ships, Irving A. Hirsch, The Boeing Company. Paper 67-352 at the AIAA/ SNAME Advanced Marine Vehicles Meeting, Norfolk Va, May 1967.
SYSTEMS
Heaving Motions of Ventilated Trapezoidal Hydrofoils, Tsen, L. F. and Guilbaud, M. (University of Poitiers, France). 4th Canadian Congress of Applied Mechanics, CANCAM '73, 28 May—1 June 1973. Ecole Polytechnique, Montreal.
The Longitudinal Behaviour of a Hydrofoil Craft in Rough Seas, M. Krezelewski, Institute of Ship Research, Gdank University, Hovering Craft, Hydrofoil and Advanced Transit Systems Conference, Brighton, May 1974.
On the Design of Propulsion Systems with Z-Drives for Hydrofoils Ships, A. A. Rousetsky, Kryloff Research Institute, Leningrad. Ninth Symposium on Naval Hydrodynamics, Paris, August 1972.
RESEARCH AND DEVELOPMENT
Key Problems Associated with Developing the Boeing Model 929-100 Commercial Passenger Hydrofoil, William Shultz, Boeing International Corporation. Hovering Craft, Hydrofoil and Advanced Transit Systems Conference, Brighton, May 1974.
Waterjet Propulsion for Marine Vehicles, V. E. Johnson, Jr. AIAA Paper 64-306, 1964. American Institute of Aeronautics and Astronautics.
Waterjet Propulsion for Marine Vehicles, J. Traksel and W. E. Beck. AIAA Paper 65-245, 1965. American Institute of Aeronautics and Astronautics.
The Design of Waterjet Propulsion Systems for Hydrofoil Craft, J. Levy, Soc Naval Architects and Marine Engineers, Marine Tech-

nology, 2, 15-25 41, January 1965.

Selection of Hydrofoil Waterjet Propulsion Systems, Ross Hatte and Hugh J. Davis, The Boeing Company. Journal of Hydronautics, Vol 1, No. 1, 1967. American Institute of Aeronautics and Astronautics.

The Development of Automatic Control Systems for Hydrofoil Craft, R. L. Johnston & W. C. O'Neill, Naval Ship Research & Development Centre, Bethesda, Maryland. Hovering Craft, Hydrofoil and Advanced Transit Systems Conference, Brighton, May 1974.

Hydrodynamic Study on Fully Submerged Foils of Hydrofoil Ships in a Sea Way up to 140 kt at Constant Froude Number. Dr de Witt. Supramar. Hovering Craft and Hydrofoil, Vol 8, No. 5, February 1969.

Machinery of the PT 150 DC Hydrofoil, E. Faber, Supramar, Marine Engineer and Naval Architect, January 1968.

Control of the Hydrofoil Ship, Dr P. Magini and Dr J. Burroughs, Advanced Marine Systems—Alinavi SpA. Journal of the Institute of Navigation, July 1967.

Controls Technology in Hydrofoil Ship Design, J. J. Jamieson, The Boeing Company. Ship Control Systems Symposium, November 1966.

Model Resistance Data of Series 65 Hull Forms Applicable to Hydrofoils and Planing Craft. Holling, H. D. and Hubble, E. N. Naval Ship Research & Development Center Report 4121, V. May 1974. 431p.

Nine Year's History of the Hitachi-Supramar Hydrofoil Boat, Hovering craft & Hydrofoil, November 1970.

The Economics of an Advanced Hydrofoil System, A. M. Gonnella, W. M. Schultz, Hydrofoil Systems Organisation, The Boeing Company, Hovering Craft & Hydrofoil, November 1970.

Air-Feed Stabilisation of Hydrofoil Craft, Baron H. von Schertel. Supramar. NATO, Brussels, September 1968.

The Effect of Nose Radius on the Cavitation Inception Characteristics of Two-Dimensional Hydrofoils, Valentine, D. T. Naval Ship Research & Development Center Report 3813, VI. July 1974. 46 p.

Stabilisierung von Tragflugelbooten durch Luftspeisung der Flugel, Baron H. von Schertel, Supramar. Tagung der Schiff bautechnischen Gesellschaft, Lucerne, June 5, 1968.

Betriebserfahrungen mit der Antriebsanlage des Tragflugalschiffes PT 150, E. Faber, Supramar. Sounderdrunk aus MTZ Motortechnische Zeitschrift, published October 1968.

An Examination of the Hazards to Hydrofoil Craft from Floating Objects. Christopher Hook. Society of Environmental Engineers Symposium, The Transport Environment, April 1969.

Survey of French Hydrofoil Programs (in French), Vollot, J. L. Bulletin de l'Association Technique Maritime et Aeronautique, No. 72, 1972. p. 229-248.

PGH Tucumcari: Successful Application of Performance Specification, Gene R. Myers, The Boeing Company, Naval Engineers Journal, June 1970.

50-knot Hydrofoils We Could Start Building Today, Gene R. Myers The Boeing Company, Aeronautics & Astronautics, June 1970.

SAILING SKIMMERS

A Self-Tending Rig with Feedback and Compass Course, Hook, C. Hovering Craft & Hydrofoil, Vol. 14 no. 10, July 1975. p. 26-31.

The Basic Mechanics of Sailing Surface Skimmers and their Future Prospects, Dr Jerzy Wolf, Aviation Institute, Warsaw. Hovering Craft & Hydrofoil, March 1972.

Hydrofoil Ocean Voyager "Williwaw", David A. Keiper, PhD, Hydrofoil Sailing Craft. Third AIAA Symposium on the Aero/Hydronautics of Sailing, November, 1971.

Why Sailing Hydrofoils?—Christopher Hook, "Ancient Interface IV" Symposium, American Institute of Aeronautics and Astronautics, January 1973.

Hydrofoil Sailing, James Grogono, Hovering Craft, Hydrofoil and Advanced Transit Systems Conference, Brighton, May 1974.

ACV AND HYDROFOIL LICENSING AUTHORITIES

ACV and HYDROFOIL LICENSING AUTHORITIES

ARGENTINA
ACVs and Hydrofoils
Prefectura Naval MaMaritiṇ
Paseo Colón 533
Buenos Aires.

AUSTRALIA
ACVs and Hydrofoils
Department of Transport
Childers Street,
Turner,
Australian Capital Territory,
Australia

AUSTRIA
ACVs and Hydrofoils
Bundesministerium für Handel,
Gewerbe und Industrie,
Stubenring 1,
Vienna 1.
Telephone 575655

BELGIUM
ACVs and Hydrofoils
Administration de la Marine et de la
Navigation Interieuré,
30, Rue Belliard,
B-1040 Bruxelles.
Tel: (02) 511 58 90

CANADA
ACVs and Hydrofoils
Chief of Air Cushion Vehicles, Marine Safety
Division, Ministry of Transport
Sir Richard Scott Building
191 Laurier Avenue W, Ottawa, Canada

DENMARK
ACVs
Handelsministeriet,
3 Atdeling,
Slotsholmsgade 12,
1216 Copenhagen K.
Hydrofoils
Generaldirektoratet for Statsbanerne,
Solvgade 40
1307 Copenhagen K.

EIRE
ACVs and Hydrofoils
Department of Transport and Power,
Kildare Street,
Dublin 2.

FIJI
ACVs and Hydrofoils
Director of Marine,
Marine Department,
Suva,
Fiji.

FINLAND
Board of Navigation,
Vuorimiehenkatu 1,
POB 158,
SF-00141 Helsinki 14

FRANCE
ACVs and Hydrofoils
Secrétariat Général de la Marine Marchande
3 Place de Fontenoy,
75700 Paris
Tel: (1) 783 4090
Telex: 25 823 Minimar Paris

GAMBIA
ACVs and Hydrofoils
Ministry of Works and Communications.
Bathurst,
Gambia

GERMANY
Hydrofoils (safety authority)
See-Berufsgenossenschaft,
D-2000 Hamburg 11,
Reimertswiete 2.

GHANA
The Shipping Commissioner
c/o Ministry of Transport and Communication
P.O. Box M.38, Accra, Ghana

GREECE
ACVs and Hydrofoils
Ministry of Mercantile Marine,
Marine Inspectorate,

HUNGARY
ACVs only
Ministry of Foreign Trade,
1880 Budapest,
Honvéd u. 13-15

ICELAND
Directorate of Shipping,
PO Box 484,
Reykjavik,
Iceland

INDIA
ACVs and Hydrofoils
Directorate-General of Shipping,
Bombay,
India

INDONESIA
ACVs and Hydrofoils
Departemen Perhubungan
Medan Merdeka, Barat 8,
Jakarta,
Indonesia

ISRAEL
ACVs and Hydrofoils
Ministry of Transport,
Division of Shipping and Ports
102, Ha'atzmauth Road,
Haifa,
Israel

ITALY
ACVs and Hydrofoils
Ministero Della Marina Mercantile,
Ispettorato Tecnico,
Viale Asia,
00100 Roma.

IVORY COAST
ACVs and Hydrofoils
Ministère des Travaux Publics et des Transports,
B.P. V6,
Abidjan,
Republic of the Ivory Coast

JAMAICA
The Collector General's Department,
Newport East.
Kingston,
Jamaica

JAPAN
ACVs and Hydrofoils
Japanese Ministry of Transportation,
2-1 Kaoumigaseki,
Chiyoda-ku,
Tokyo

KHMER REPUBLIC
(Formerly Cambodia)
ACVs and Hydrofoils
Ministère des Travaux Publics,
Phnom-Penh,
Khmer Republic

KUWAIT
ACVs and Hydrofoils
Department of Customs and Ports,
PO Box 9, Kuwait,
Arabian Gulf.

LEBANON
ACVs and Hydrofoils
Ministère des Travaux Publics,
Direction des Transports,
Beiruit, Lebanon.

LUXEMBOURG
ACVs
Ministère des Transports,
4 Boulevard Roosevelt,
Luxembourg.

MALAGASY REPUBLIC
ACVs and Hydrofoils
Ministère de l'Amina,
Jement du Territoire,
Anosy,
Tananarive,
Madagascar

MALAWI
The Ministry of Transport and Communication,
PO Box 30200,
Chichin,
Blantyre 3,
Malawi

MALAYSIA
The Ministry of Communications,
Jalan Gurney,
Kuala Lumpur,
Malaysia
Tel: 20 4044
Cables: Transport

MEXICO
ACVs and Hydrofoils
Departamento de Licencias,
Direccion de Marina Mercante,
Dr Mora No 15, 3er Piso,
Mexico 1, DF

MOROCCO
Ministère des Travaux Publics
Rabat,
Morocco

NETHERLANDS
ACVs and Hydrofoils
Directoraat-Generaal van Scheepvaart,
Afdeling Scheepvaartinspectie,
Noord-West Buitensingel 2,
's-Gravenhage (The Hague)

NEW ZEALAND
ACVs and Hydrofoils (Certificates of Construction and Performance)
Operating approval and licences:
Ministry of Transport,
Marine Division,
Private Bag,
Wellington,
New Zealand

NORWAY
ACVs and Hydrofoils
The Maritime Directorate,
Thv. Meyersgt 7,
Oslo-Dep,
Norway

SOUTH AFRICA
Department of Transport,
Private Bag X193,
Pretoria 0001,
South Africa

SOUTH KOREA
Ministry of Transportation,
1-3 Do-dong,
Choong-ku,
Seoul,
Republic of Korea

SPAIN
ACVs and Hydrofoils
The Subsecretaria de la Marina Mercante,
  Ruiz de Alarcon No. 1,
  Madrid 14.

SWEDEN
ACVs and Hydrofoils
The National Board of Shipping and Navigation,
  Fack S-102 50,
  Stockholm 27
  Sweden

SWITZERLAND
Cantonal licensing authorities for ACVs and Hydrofoils

Lake Zurich
Kantonale Seepolizei,
Werkhof Wädenswil.
Städtische Seepolizei,
Diemstgebaude,
Bellerivestrasse 260,
8008 Zürich.

Lake Constance
Polizeidepartement des Kantons Thurgau,
Regierungsgebaude,
8500 Frauenfeld.
Polizeidepartement des Kantons St Gallen
Schiffahrts- und Hafenverwaltung,
9400 Rorschach

Lake Lucerne
Polizeidepartement des Kantons, Luzern,
Bahnhofstrasse 17,
6000 Luzern.

Lake Geneva
Departement de Justice et Police Service de
  la Navigation
Place Bourg-de-Four 1,
1200 Geneva
Departement de la Justice,
de la Police et des affaires militaire,
Service de la police administrative,
Place Chateau 6,
1000 Lausanne

Lake Lugano
Ufficio cantonale de polizia,
VC Ghiringhelli 27b
6500 Bellinzona

Lake Thoune and Lake Brienz
Polizeidirektion des Kantons Bern,
Kramgasse 20,
3000 Bern

Lake Neuchatel
Departement de Police,
2000 Neuchatel

TURKEY
ACVs and Hydrofoils
T.C. Ulastirma Bakanligi,
  Liman ve Deniz Isleri Dairesi Baskanligi,
  Ankara,
  Turkey

UNITED ARAB REPUBLIC
ACVs
The Arab General Organisation for Air
Transport,
11 Emad El Din Street,
Cairo.

UNITED KINGDOM
Hovercraft
Safety and Experimental Certificates; Certificates of Construction and Performance:
Civil Aviation Authority,
Hovercraft Department,
Airworthiness Division,
Brabazon House,
Redhill, Surrey RH1 1SQ
Hovercraft and Hydrofoils
  Hovercraft Operating Permits and Hydrofoil
  Passenger Certificates,
Department of Trade,
Marine Division,
Sunley House,
90-93 High Holborn,
London WC1V 6LP

ACVs and Hydrofoils
Operating approval and licences:
  Department of Trade,
  Marine Division,
  Sunley House,
  90-93 High Holborn,
  London WC1V 6LP
  Telephone: 01 405 6911
  Telex: 264084

UNITED STATES OF AMERICA
ACVs and Hydrofoils
Department of Transportation,
Commandant (G-MMT-4),
U.S. Coast Guard,
Washington, DC 20590

VENEZUELA
Ministerio de Comunicaciones,
  Direccion de Marina Mercante,
  Esquina Carmelitas, Edificio Ramia,
  Caracas, Venezuela.

YUGOSLAVIA
Yugoslav Federal Economic Secretariat,
Transport Department,
Bulevar AVNOJ-a 104,
Belgrade,
Yugoslavia

UK CIVIL ACV
REGISTRATIONS

U.K. HOVERCRAFT REGISTRATIONS —1975

Registration Mark	Craft Type and No.	Constructor	Operator, Owner or Charterer
GH-2002	VT1-002	Vosper Thornycroft Ltd.	Lombard North Central Ltd.
GH-2003	VT1-003	Vosper Thornycroft Ltd.	Lombard North Central Ltd.
GH-2004	SR.N4-002	British Hovercraft Corporation Ltd.	Hoverlloyd Ltd.
GH-2005	SR.N4-003	British Hovercraft Corporation Ltd.	Hoverlloyd Ltd.
GH-2006	SR.N4-001	British Hovercraft Corporation Ltd.	British Rail Hovercraft Ltd.
GH-2007	SR.N4-004	British Hovercraft Corporation Ltd.	British Rail Hovercraft Ltd.
GH-2008	SR.N4-005	British Hovercraft Corporation Ltd.	Hoverlloyd Ltd.
GH-2009	SR.N5/A-001	British Hovercraft Corporation Ltd.	Air Vehicles Ltd.
GH-2010	SR.N6-022	British Hovercraft Corporation Ltd.	Hovertravel Ltd.
GH-2011	SR.N6-024	British Hovercraft Corporation Ltd.	Hovertravel Ltd.
GH-2012	SR.N6-026	British Hovercraft Corporation Ltd.	Hovertravel Ltd.
GH-2013	SR.N6-130	British Hovercraft Corporation Ltd.	Hovertravel Ltd.
GH-2014	SR.N6-009	British Hovercraft Corporation Ltd.	British Rail Hovercraft Ltd.
GH-2015	SR.N6-011	British Hovercraft Corporation Ltd.	British Rail Hovercraft Ltd.
GH-2016 (lapsed)	HM2-004	Hovermarine Transport Ltd.	Hellenic Hoverlines
GH-2017 (lapsed)	HM2-007	Hovermarine Transport Ltd.	Hellenic Hoverlines
GH-2018	HM2-005	Hovermarine Transport Ltd.	International Hoverservices Ltd.
GH-2019	HM2-012	Hovermarine Transport Ltd.	International Hoverservices Ltd.
GH-2020	HA5 Mk IIIW-101	Hover Air Ltd.	Lord Hotham (Contract Hover Ltd.)
GH-2021	SR.N6-016	British Hovercraft Corporation Ltd.	British Hovercraft Corporation Ltd.
GH-2022 (lapsed)	SR.N6-028	British Hovercraft Corporation Ltd.	British Hovercraft Corporation Ltd.
GH-2023	HC2-002	Hovermarine Transport Ltd.	Hovermarine Transport Ltd.
GH-2024	HM2-303	Hovermarine Transport Ltd.	International Hoverservices Ltd.
GH-2025	HQ-007	Mr. R. Parkhouse	Messrs. R. D. Warman & R. B. Pott
GH-2026	SH2-004	Sealand Hovercraft Ltd.	Sealand Hovercraft Ltd.
GH-2027 (lapsed)	SH2-005	Sealand Hovercraft Ltd.	
GH-2028 (lapsed)	HM2-304	Hovermarine Transport Ltd.	Hellenic Hovercraft Lines, Greece
GH-2029	SH2-008	Sealand Hovercraft Ltd.	Sealand Hovercraft Ltd.
GH-2030 (lapsed)	HM2-319	Hovermarine Transport Ltd.	Dolphin Ferries Ltd, Australia
GH-2031	SR.N6-025*	British Hovercraft Corporation Ltd.	British Hovercraft Corporation Ltd.
GH-2032	SH2-006	Sealand Hovercraft Ltd.	Sealand Hovercraft Ltd.
GH-2033	HM2-320	Hovermarine Transport Ltd.	Greater London Council
GH-3034	SH2-013	Sealand Hovercraft Ltd.	Airgo Ltd., Scotland
GH-2035	SR.N6-055**	British Hovercraft Corporation Ltd.	Hovertravel Ltd.
GH-2036	SH2-001	Sealand Hovercraft Ltd.	Sealand Hovercraft Ltd.
GH-2037	SH2-014	Sealand Hovercraft Ltd.	Sealand Hovercraft Ltd.
GH-2038	SH2-016	Sealand Hovercraft Ltd.	Sealand Hovercraft Ltd.
GH-2039	SH2-017	Sealand Hovercraft Ltd·	Sealand Hovercraft Ltd.
GH-2040	SH2-020	Sealand Hovercraft Ltd.	Sealand Hovercraft Ltd,
GH-2041	SR.N5-006	British Hovercraft Corp.	Hoverwork Ltd.
GH-2042	SH2/3-025	Sealand Hovercraft Ltd	Sealand Hovercraft Ltd.
GH-2043	SH2/4-035	Sealand Hovercraft Ltd.	Sealand Hovercraft Ltd.
GH-2049 (lapsed)	HM2-324	Hovermarine Transport Ltd.	Hovermarine Transport Ltd.
GH-2045	HM2-325	Hovermarine Transport Ltd.	Hovermarine Transport Ltd.
GH-2046	SR.N6	British Hovercraft Corp.	British Hovercraft Corp.

Notes

A Although originally built by BHC this craft (GH-2009) was re-built by Air Vehicles Ltd.

* This craft has been modified and is now in an SR.N6 Mk 6 configuration with twin-props.

** This craft has been constructed from components from other SR.N6 hovercraft by Hovertravel, Hoverwork and Air Vehicles Ltd.

Block of numbers issued to manufacturers for use with hovercraft subject to Test and Experimental Certificates. Each number is used only once.

British Hovercraft Corporation Ltd.
East Cowes
Isle of Wight — GH-9001 to GH-9050 inclusive

Hovermarine Transport Ltd
Hazel Wharf
Hazel Road
Woolston
Southampton
SO2 7GB — GH-9051 to GH-9100 inclusive

Vosper Thornycroft Ltd
Paulsgrove
Portsmouth
PO6 4QA — GH-9101 to GH-9150 inclusive

Cushioncraft Ltd
The Duver
St. Helens
Isle of Wight — GH-9151 to GH-9200 inclusive

Sealand Hovercraft Ltd.
Millom
Cumberland — GH-9251 to GH-9300 inclusive

SELECTED AMATEUR BUILT HOVERCRAFT

B. BAKER

ADDRESS:

1 Stud Farm Cottage, Adderbury, Oxon.

GREENFLY

This craft was completed in June 1974 and is one of the fastest and most promising light hovercraft in the UK. Bill Baker constructed the craft at an estimated cost of £400, although he is constantly modifying it in minor ways to further improve its performance.

LIFT AND PROPULSION: A Rowena Stihl 137 cc engine, rated at 9 bhp at 6,000 rpm, drives a single 22 in diameter, five-bladed, 30° pitch axial fan for lift. Propulsion is supplied by a Rotax 636 cc engine, rated at 45 bhp at 5,500 rpm. This drives via vee-belts two 21½ in diameter, five-bladed, 45° pitch, ducted fan units producing a static thrust of 135 lb. A further ducted thrust fan unit of 19 in diameter has been recently installed, run from the same thrust engine. Provision is made for 3 gallons of fuel to be carried. Cushion pressure is 10 lb/ft².

HULL: Hull and superstructure is made from ¼ in thick sheets of exterior grade plywood laid over a framework. Plastic drums, each sealed and airtight, are secured in nine chambers inside the hull for buoyancy. A bag skirt made from 4 oz/yd² polyurethane-coated nylon material is fitted to the craft.

ACCOMMODATION: Provision is made for one person to be carried in an open cockpit.

Bill Baker at the controls of "Greenfly" during the Hover Club's Easter Race meeting at Southport, Lancs

CONTROLS: A twist-grip throttle controls the thrust engine and a quadrant lever acts as throttle lever for the lift engine. Directional control is by twin rudders, one at the rear of each thrust duct.

DIMENSIONS:

Length overall	10 ft 0 in (3·05 m)
Width overall	5 ft 6 in (1·68 m)
Height, hovering	4 ft 6 in (1·37 m)
at rest	3 ft 11 in (1·19 m)

WEIGHTS:

Empty weight	330 lb (149·68 kg)
All-up weight	495 lb (224·52 kg)

PERFORMANCE:

Maximum speed, land	50 mph (8·47 km/h)
water	45 knots

BOURNE VALLEY SCHOOL

ADDRESS:

The Bourne Valley School, Oldfield Road, Hemel Hempstead, Herts.

SWIFT

This craft, completed at a cost of £450 in June 1974, was the winner of the 1974 Hertfordshire Schools Hovercraft Competition and the 1975 BP Schools Hovercraft Competition.

LIFT AND PROPULSION: A Rowena Stihl 137 cc engine, rated at 9 bhp at 6,600 rpm, drives direct a single 19 in diameter, three-bladed, 30° pitch axial fan. Propulsion is supplied by a JLO 440 cc engine rated at 40 bhp at 6,500 rpm which, via a toothed belt, drives a single 30 in diameter, ten-bladed, 45° pitch ducted fan. Two gallons of fuel are carried. The craft has an estimated cushion pressure of 9 lb/ft.

HULL: The hull is constructed from 3 mm and 6 mm marine grade plywood, with additional marine plywood used for the superstructure. Air tight chambers along the sides and front of the craft provide it with buoyancy. A skirt composed of extended segments made from 4 oz/yd² polyurethane-coated nylon material is fitted.

ACCOMMODATION: Seating for two persons on a longitudinal bench.

CONTROLS: A hand throttle lever controls the thrust engine with a friction lever for lift control. Directional control is provided

Bourne Valley School's hovercraft ,"Swift", at speed while racing at Southport, Lancs.

by a single split rudder placed in the slipstream from the thrust duct. The rudder is activated by movement of the handlebars.

DIMENSIONS:

Length overall	11 ft 0 in (3·35 m)
Width overall	7 ft 0 in (2·13 m)
Height, hovering	4 ft 6 in (1·37 m)
at rest	4 ft 0 in (1·22 m)

WEIGHTS:

Empty weight, approx	300 lb (136·07 kg)
All-up weight (two persons carried)	620 lb (281·21 kg)

PERFORMANCE:

Maximum speed, land	35 mph (56·33 km/h)
water	30 knots
Endurance	1 hour
Obstacle clearance	6 in (152·4 mm)

R. CRESSWELL

ADDRESS:

184 St. Bernards Road, Solihull, Warwickshire

BLUEBOTTLE

This is the second craft constructed by

Richard Cresswell and was completed in May 1975 at a cost of about £480. Already the craft has shown great potential at the first two Hover Club Race Meetings which it has attended, and came second in recent water speed trials in Scotland.

LIFT AND PROPULSION: A JLO 250 cc engine, rated at 15 bhp at 6,500 rpm, drives direct a 22 in diameter, five-bladed, 30° pitch axial fan for lift. Thrust is provided by a Kohler 440 cc engine rated at 42 bhp at 7,200 rpm. This drives via toothed belts,

a pair of 24 in diameter, five-bladed, 45°
pitch ducted thrust fans. The craft carries
eight gallons of fuel and has a cushion pressure of 8 lb/ft² with one person carried and
13 lb/ft² when three persons are carried.

HULL: Constructed from glass-reinforced
plastics (grp) and has ten sealed air chambers
for buoyancy. An extended segment skirt
system using 4 oz/yd² polyurethane-coated
terylene material is fitted.

ACCOMMODATION: Seating for up to three
persons is provided on a longitudinal central
bench seat.

CONTROLS: A twist-grip throttle lever
is used for the thrust unit and a quadrant
lever for the lift engine. Handlebars acti-
vate single rudders in the slipstream from
each thrust duct, providing the craft with
directional control.

Richard Creswells Bluebottle, a 50 mph 3-seater

DIMENSIONS:

Length overall	12 ft 0 in (3·66 m)
Width overall	6 ft 10 in (2·08 m)
Height, hovering	4 ft 1 in (1·24 m)
at rest	3 ft 4 in (1·02 m)

WEIGHTS:

Empty weight	340 lb (154·21 kg)
All-up weight (three persons plus fuel)	610 lb (276·68 kg)

PERFORMANCE:

Estimated max. speed,	land	50 mph (80·47 km/h)	Endurance	2½ hours
	water	45 mph (72·42 km/h)	Obstacle clearance	9 in (228·6 m)

R. DEE
ADDRESS:
Sweilandstraat 7, Warmond, The Nether-
lands

SOMETHING BLUE
This craft is the second to have been built
by Robert Dee, a keen Dutch hovercraft
builder. The craft shows great promise
and took part in the 1974 International Light
Hovercraft Rally at Calais. It was completed in February 1973 and cost in the region
of £200 to construct.

LIFT AND PROPULSION: A single JLO
99cc two-stroke engine, rated at 3 bhp at
3,500 rpm, drives direct an 18 in diameter,
six-bladed, axial fan fitted with 30° pitch
blades of Multi-wing design. Propulsion is
provided by a JLO 223cc engine rated at
15½ bhp at 5,300 rpm. This drives via
vee-belts, a single 24 in diameter, five-
bladed 45° pitch ducted fan. A static
thrust figure of 80 lb has been achieved with
this unit. Fuel capacity of the craft is
2½ gallons. Cushion pressure is 6 lb/ft².

HULL: The hull and superstructure of the
craft are constructed from glass-reinforced
plastic (grp), with polyurethane foam filling
the hull structure to provide buoyancy. A
bag skirt system made from 5 oz/yd² polyurethane-coated nylon material is fitted.

ACCOMMODATION: The craft is a single-
seater with an enclosed cockpit.

CONTROLS: For both lift and propulsion
engines there are simple throttle levers,
and for directional control, a single rudder

"Something Blue", a 35 mph single-seater built in the Netherlands by R. Dee

is fitted in the thrust duct at the rear of
the craft. This is activated by a lever in
the cockpit.

DIMENSIONS:

Length overall	10 ft 2 in (3·10 m)
Width overall	5 ft 6 in (1·68 m)
Height, hovering	3 ft 8 in (1·12 m)
at rest	3 ft 0 in (0·914 m)

WEIGHTS:

Empty weight	200 lb (90·71 kg)
All-up weight	350 lb (158·75 kg)

PERFORMANCE:

Maximum speed	
land	35 mph (56·33 km/h)
water	30 knots
Obstacle clearance	8 in (203·2 mm)

G. G. HARDING
ADDRESS:
Wood End Farm, Barnshaw, Nr. Knutsford,
Cheshire

WOTSIT 6
This is the latest craft to be built by Mr
Geoffrey Harding, who is the chairman of

the Hover Club of Great Britain. It was
completed in March 1974 at a cost of £100.
Mr Harding has built over thirty light hovercraft since he first became involved in the
hobby in the early 1960s.

LIFT AND PROPULSION: Lift power is
supplied by a Rowena Stihl 137 cc two-stroke

engine rated at 9 bhp at 6,000 rpm, which
drives direct a 19 in diameter, three-bladed
axial fan fitted with 30° pitch blades. A Reliant 600 cc automotive engine, rated at 23½ bhp
at 5,250 rpm, powers via two chain-drives, a
pair of 27½ in diameter, six-bladed, ducted
propulsion fans fitted with 45° pitch blades

and giving a static thrust of over 100 lb. Fuel capacity is 3 gallons. A low cushion pressure of 5 lb/ft² is claimed for the craft.

HULL: The whole of the craft structure is designed to be strong yet lightweight, and has a Parana pine framework covered in doped nylon material for the upper superstructure. Sections of the structure over and around the thrust engine compartment are covered with light alloy sheet. Buoyancy is provided by large blocks of expanded polystyrene foam along the sides of the craft and built into the hull. This gives some 600 lb of buoyancy. The skirt system employed is a novel one featuring an inflated bag from which is hung a loop and segment skirt. The skirt is made from 4 oz/yd² polyurethane-coated nylon material.

ACCOMMODATION: Seating is available for two persons in an open cockpit.

CONTROLS: Motor-cycle type levers are used for throttle controls on both thrust and lift units. Directional control is achieved by twin rudders in the rear of the thrust ducts, these being operated by a joystick arrangement in the cockpit.

Geoff Harding, Chairman of the Hover Club, driving "Wotsit 6", The hovercraft has a Reliant 600 cc engine for thrust and a lightweight hull structure

DIMENSIONS:

Length overall	14 ft 0 in (4·27 m)
Width overall	7 ft 0 in (2·13 m)
Height, hovering	4 ft 10 in (1·47 m)
at rest	4 ft 0 in (1·22 m)

WEIGHTS: Not known

PERFORMANCE:

Estimated,	
land	30-35 mph (48·28-56·33 km/h)
water	25-30 knots
Endurance	
	about 1 hour on normal fuel tanks

G. HARKER

ADDRESS:

38 Lyndon Avenue, Blackfen, Sidcup, Kent

GO-TUNE-ONE

This craft, the owner's first, was completed in October 1974 at an estimated cost of £400, It has been entered in a number of National Race Meetings organised by the Hover Club.

LIFT AND PROPULSION: A Villiers 250 cc engine, fitted with a Dynastart and rated at 15 bhp at 3,200 rpm, drives a single 24 in diameter axial fan fitted with ten blades at 30° pitch. The 30½ in diameter, ten-bladed ducted propulsion fan which is fitted with 45° pitch blades, is driven by a Hillman Imp 875 cc automotive engine rated at 45 bhp at 5,000 rpm. Transmission is via a chain-

drive system. Cushion pressure is about 10 lb/ft². No static thrust figure is yet known. The craft has capacity for 5¼ gallons.

HULL: A frame of Oregon pine is covered with sheets of marine ply, and eight sealed buoyancy tanks filled with expanded polystyrene foam are contained within this structure. A simple bag skirt system is fitted, fabricated in 4 oz/yd² neoprene-coated nylon material.

ACCOMMODATION: Seating is provided for two persons in an open cockpit, side-by-side, bench-style.

CONTROLS: To control the propulsion engine, a foot throttle lever is fitted. A simple hand lever provides variable lift throttle settings. Directional control is

maintained by use of a large single rudder mounted on the rear of the propulsion thrust duct.

DIMENSIONS:

Length overall	12 ft 0 in (3·66 m)
Width overall	6 ft 0 in (1·83 m)
Height overall	
hovering	5 ft 2 in (1·57 m)
at rest	4 ft 3 in (1·30 m)

WEIGHTS:

Empty weight	520 lb (235·86 kg)
All-up weight	700 lb (317·5 kg)

PERFORMANCE:

Maximum speed (estimated)	
	35 mph (56·33 km/h)
Hard structure clearance (approx)	
	9 in (0·228 mm)
Endurance	3 hours

N. LOW

ADDRESS:

7 Cattle End, Silverstone, Northants.

MISTRALE 1

This craft was completed at the end of May 1975 and was placed third in speed trials over the measured mile on water during its first day of hovering. Its owner, Nick Low, was assisted in the craft construction by two colleagues, Malcolm Saunders and David Council.

LIFT AND PROPULSION: A single JLO 295 cc engine, rated at 20 bhp at 5,000 rpm, drives direct a 24 in diameter, ten-bladed, 30° pitch axial fan. Propulsion is supplied by a Porsche Super 75 automotive engine of 1,600 cc and rated at 90 bhp at 5,500 rpm.

This drives via toothed belts, a pair of 36 in diameter, twelve-bladed, 45° pitch ducted thrust fans. Static thrust is 350 lbs. The craft carries 4 gallons of fuel.

HULL: Monocoque construction with fibreglass and foam laminates. The superstructure is made from glass-reinforced plastics. Inside sections of the hull structure are filled with expanded polystyrene foam for buoyancy. A bag skirt design of a modified Fishlock-type is fitted and uses Topsan 2 pvc material.

ACCOMMODATION: An open cockpit allows two persons plus equipment to be carried.

CONTROLS: Twist-grip throttle levers are fitted for engine control. Directional control is achieved through twin rudders in each of the ducted thrust units, activated by the movement of handlebars.

DIMENSIONS:

Length overall	16 ft 0 in (4·88 m)
Width overall	7 ft 6 in (2·29 m)
Height, hovering	5 ft 6 in (1·68 m)
at rest	4 ft 6 in (1·37 m)

WEIGHTS:

Empty weight	850 lb (385·54 kg)
All-up weight (two persons plus equipment and fuel)	1,500 lb (680·36 kg)

PERFORMANCE:

Maximum speed, land 45 mph (72·42 km/h)	
water	40 knots
Endurance	2 hours
Obstacle clearance	10 in (254 mm)

M. SCOTT

ADDRESS:

Beaupre Farm, Outwell, Wisbech, Cambs.

VIKING

This new craft was completed in July 1975 at an estimated cost of £300 and made its first over-water runs at Danson Park in August 1975.

LIFT AND PROPULSION: A Villiers 11E 197 cc engine, rated at 8 bhp at 4,500 rpm, drives a single 24 in diameter, ten-bladed, 30° pitch axial fan for lift. For propulsion a Hillman Imp engine of 875 cc, rated at 40 bhp at 5,000 rpm drives via toothed belts a pair of 30 in diameter, ten-bladed, 45° pitch ducted thrust fans. The craft carries two

gallons of fuel, and has a cushion pressure of 10 lb/ft².

HULL: A spruce frame forms the hull and is overlaid with exterior grade plywood. In the four corners of the craft are blocks of polyurethane foam and there are sealed containers in the craft sidebodies. This is estimated to provide in the region of 1,000 lb buoyancy. A deep bag skirt made from 4 oz/yd² polyurethane-coated nylon material is fitted to the craft.

ACCOMMODATION: Side-by-side seating for two persons in an open cockpit.
CONTROLS: A foot throttle is used for the thrust engine and a simple hand lever for the lift unit. Single rudders in each of the thrust ducts provide the craft with directional control.

DIMENSIONS:

Length overall	13 ft 0 in	(3·96 m)
Width overall	6 ft 6 in	(1·98 m)
Height, hovering	4 ft 2 in	(1·27 m)
at rest	3 ft 6 in	(1·07 m)

WEIGHTS:

Empty weight	550 lb	(249·46 kg)
All-up weight (one person carried)		
	710 lb	(322·04 kg)

PERFORMANCE:

Not yet known		
Obstacle clearance	8 in	(203·2 mm)

B. SHERLOCK
ADDRESS:
35 Combewell Close, Garsington, Oxford

SATURN 1
Completed in March 1975 at an estimated cost of £160, this craft has shown great promise during the early events of the Hover Club's 1975 Racing Programme.

LIFT AND PROPULSION: A JLO 98 cc engine, rated at 5 bhp at 3,500 rpm, drives direct a 19 in diameter, five-bladed, 35° pitch axial fan. Propulsion is supplied by a Triumph T100A engine of 500 cc, rated at 40 bhp at 6,000 rpm. This drives via toothed belts, a pair of 24 in diameter, five-bladed, 45° pitch ducted thrust fans. A static thrust of 170 lbs is obtained with this arrangement. The craft carries three gallons of fuel. Cushion pressure is estimated at 7 lb/ft².

HULL: Construction of the hull and superstructure is of glass-reinforced plastic with eight buoyancy chambers built into the hull. A deep bag skirt system is made from 5 oz/yd² coated nylon material.

ACCOMMODATION: Side-by-side seating for two persons is provided in an open cockpit.
CONTROLS: Movement of the control joystick backwards regulates the thrust engine and a twist grip operates the lift engine throttle. A single rudder in each thrust duct provides the craft with directional control.

"Saturn I", driven by Bill Sherlock, has a Triumph 500 cc thrust engine and a ILO lift unit

DIMENSIONS:

Length overall	11 ft 0 in	(3·35 m)
Width overall	5 ft 6 in	(1·68 m)
Height, hovering	3 ft 9 in	(1·14 m)
at rest	3 ft 0 in	(0·914 m)

WEIGHTS:

Empty weight	290 lb	(131·54 kg)
All-up weight (with two persons)		
	610 lb	(276·68 kg)

PERFORMANCE:

Max. speed, estimated		
land	35 mph	(56·33 km/h)
water		30 knots
Endurance		2 hours
Obstacle clearance	9 in	(228·6 mm)

A. STANLEY
ADDRESS:
12 Selwood Park, Weymans Avenue, Kinson, Bournemouth

TORNADO
This craft is the second one built by Alan Stanley and was completed in August 1974 at a cost of £250.

LIFT AND PROPULSION: A single Aspera 93 cc engine rated at 3 bhp at 2,500 rpm drives direct a single 19 in diameter, five-bladed, axial fan fitted with 30° pitch blades. Propulsion is achieved with a JLO 440 cc two-stroke engine, rated at 38 bhp at 6,500 rpm, with a belt drive to a pair of 24 in diameter, five-bladed, 45° pitch ducted thrust fans. Fuel capacity is 5 gallons.

HULL: The hull is constructed from glass-reinforced plastics with a superstructure of plywood. Polyurethane foam blocks in the craft corners and beneath the cockpit, provide some 200% buoyancy. The craft has a loop and segment skirt system using 4 oz/yd² pvc-coated nylon material.

ACCOMMODATION: The open cockpit accommodates two persons sitting side-by-side on a single bench seat.
CONTROLS: Cable controls connect separate throttle levers for lift and thrust units. A single rudder in the rear of each thrust duct provides directional control for the craft.

"Tornado", owned and built by Alan Stanley of Bournemouth. *Photo: Neil MacDonald*

DIMENSIONS:

Length overall	12 ft 6 in	(3·81 m)
Width overall	6 ft 4 in	(1·93 m)
Height overall,		
Hovering	4 ft 8 in	(1·42 m)
at rest	4 ft 0 in	(1·22 m)

WEIGHTS:

Empty weight	300 lb	(136·07 kg)
All-up weight	500 lb	(226·79 kg)

PERFORMANCE:

Estimated, land	35 mph	(56·33 km/h)
water		30 knots

G. WICKINGTON

ADDRESS:

8 Hardwicke Way, Hamble, Herts

GP Too

This is the third hovercraft built by Grant Wickington, the well-known light hovercraft enthusiast, and was completed in May 1975. The cost was about £50 since the main engine and the fan unit were taken from his first hovercraft, Guinea Pig, (see JSS 72/73) which has now been scrapped.

LIFT AND PROPULSION: A Hillman Imp 875 cc, rated at 40 bhp, supplies power for lift and thrust. The engine, through a centrifugal fan clutch and 4·8:1 reduction gearbox, drives a 3 ft 6½ in diameter centrifugal fan made of light alloy. A proportion of the air flow from the fan is ducted into the cushion system and the remainder is channelled aft to escape through louvres at the stern of the craft. The craft carries three gallons of fuel and has a cushion pressure of about 9 lb/ft².

HULL: The entire hull and superstructure is in light alloy, with 36 airtight buoyancy tanks included in the structure. A simple bag skirt system is employed, made from 4 oz/yd² pvc coated nylon material.

ACCOMMODATION: Open cockpit with side-by-side bench seating for two.

CONTROLS: A hand throttle lever controls the Imp engine and for directional control

"GP Too", built in light alloy by Grant Wickington of Hamble and powered by a Hillman Imp 875 cc car engine

the craft is equipped with a 'Butterfly'-type steering column. This activates three vanes in the rear section of the thrust duct.

DIMENSIONS:

Length overall	13 ft 0 in (3·96 m)
Width overall	6 ft 2 in (1·88 m)
Height overall, hovering	3 ft 0 in (0·914 m)

WEIGHTS:

Empty weight	550 lb (249·46 kg)
All-up weight (one person carried)	710 lb (322·94 kg)

PERFORMANCE:

Max. speed (estimated)-	
land	30 mph (48·28 km/h)
water	25-30 knots

T. WILCOX

ADDRESS:

15 Verney Close, East Howe, Bournemouth

AGGRO 11

This is the second craft built by Mr. Wilcox and his family. It was completed in May 1975.

LIFT AND PROPULSION: A Briggs & Stratton 150 cc engine, rated at 5 bhp at 3,600 rpm, drives direct a single 22 in diameter, five-bladed, 30° pitch axial fan. For propulsion, a JLO 440 cc engine, rated at 37 bhp at 6,000 rpm, drives via vee-belts, a pair of 24 in diameter, five-bladed, 45° pitch ducted fans.

HULL: The craft has a hull frame of Parana pine covered with sheets of plywood. Nine sealed compartments provide buoyancy. A bag skirt made from polyurethane-coated nylon material of 6 oz/yd² is fitted.

ACCOMMODATION: Side-by-side for two in an open cockpit.

CONTROLS: A twist-grip throttle on the craft control joystick operates the thrust engine and a simple friction lever operates the lift unit. Single rudders in the rear of both ducted fans provide directional con-

T.Wilcox in Aggro II during a national race meeting at Stamford Hall, nr Rugby

trol.

DIMENSIONS:

Length overall	11 ft 6 in (3·51 m)
Width overall	6 ft 0 in (1·83 m)
Height overall,	
hovering	4 ft 2 in (1·27 m)
at rest	3 ft 6 in (1·07 m)

WEIGHTS:

Not known

PERFORMANCE:

Maximum speed,	
land	35 mph (56·33 km/h)
water	25 knots
Obstacle clearance, approx.	8 in (203·2 mm)

D. L. WILSON

ADDRESS:

Furnace Garage, Crowhurst, Nr. Battle, Sussex.

UN-NAMED CRAFT

This interesting craft was completed in August 1975 and has yet to fully participate in Hover Club events. It cost about £220 to build.

LIFT AND PROPULSION: A Villiers 250 cc engine, fitted with a Dynastart and rated at 12 bhp at 3,800 rpm, drives a single 19½ in diameter ten-bladed 35° pitch axial fan.

A Fiat 600 automotive engine of 767 cc, rated at 30 bhp at 4,300 rpm, drives via vee-belts a pair of 24 in diameter, five-bladed, 45° pitch ducted thrust fans. Cushion pressure is about 10·5 lb/ft². The craft carries three gallons of fuel.

HULL: The hull is based upon a tubular steel frame on which has been built a superstructure of exterior grade plywood. Two large sealed air tanks, one placed along each side of the craft, provide substantial buoyancy. A segmented skirt system is fitted, made from 4 oz/yd² polyurethane-coated nylon material.

ACCOMMODATION: Seating is provided for two or three persons on a longitudinal bench seat.

CONTROLS: Hand throttles are provided for both lift and thrust engines. A single rudder in the rear of the thrust ducts provides directional control.

DIMENSIONS:

Length overall	12 ft 0 in (3·66 m)
Width overall	6 ft 4 in (1·93 m)
Height overall,	
hovering	4 ft 3 in (1·29 m)
at rest	3 ft 6 in (1·07 m)

		WEIGHTS:		
WEIGHTS:		All-up weight (with one person)		PERFORMANCE:
Empty weight	600 lb (272·14 kg)		800 lb (362·86 kg)	Unknown at the time of going to press.

WROCKWARDINE WOOD SCHOOL

Address: The Wrockwardine Wood School, New Road, Wrockwardine Wood, Telford, Salop.

NRS 4

This craft has been built by pupils of Wrockwardine Wood School as a project and was completed in July 1975 at a cost of £100. It took part in the 1975 National Schools Hovercraft Competion.

LIFT AND PROPULSION: Integrated lift/thrust system with a JLO 250 cc engine, rated at 15 bhp at 6,600 rpm, driving a 24 in diameter, ten-bladed, 30° pitch, ducted multiwing fan. 30% of the airflow from the ducted fan unit is bled off for lift. Drive from the engine to the fan unit is by toothed belts.

HULL: Hull and superstructure of the craft is in aluminium alloy sheet, with buoyancy bags fitted for craft safety when operated over water. The skirt system is of loop-and-segment type, made from 4 oz/yd² polyurethane-impregnated nylon material.

ACCOMMODATION: Seating is for one person astride a central bench seat in an open cockpit.

CONTROLS: A simple twist-grip throttle controls the single engine. Directional control is by a single rudder activated by movement of a handlebar control column.

NSR.4, a 15 hp, all-metal single-seater built by pupils of Wrockwardine Wood School, Telford, Salop

DIMENSIONS:		WEIGHTS:	
Length overall	9 ft 6 in (2·89 m)	Empty weight	110 lb (48·99 kg)
Width overall	4 ft 6 in (1·37 m)	All-up weight	260 lb (117·93 kg)
Height overall,			
hovering	3 ft 6 in (1·07 m)	PERFORMANCE:	
at rest	3 ft 0 in (0·914 m)	Not yet verified.	

ACV CLUBS AND ASSOCIATIONS

ACV CLUBS AND ASSOCIATIONS

ACV CLUBS AND ASSOCIATIONS
THE UNITED KINGDOM HOVERCRAFT SOCIETY

The UK Hovercraft Society was formed in 1971 as the United Kingdom constituent member of the 'International Air Cushion Engineering Society'. Its membership is drawn from ACV manufacturers, ferry operators, design groups, government departments and agencies, financial and insurance organisations, consultants and universities. Membership is also open to persons engaged in hovercraft related fields overseas.

In addition to a programme of regular meetings for the presentation of papers on the technical, design, operating and military aspects of hovercraft, the Society also produces a regular monthly "UKHS Newsletter", containing up-to-date information on hovercraft activities throughout the world. The Society also, from time to time, organises visits to hovercraft manufacturing or component factories for its members. A library of books, periodicals, papers and reports relating to hovercraft matters is held by the Society which also has a collection of films on the subject.

1975 UKHS COUNCIL
Sir Christopher Cockerell, President
L. A. Hopkins, Chairman
R. L. Wheeler, Vice-Chairman
J. Bentley, Hon. Treasurer
W. F. S. Woodford, OBE, Hon. Secretary
A. E. Bingham

P. S. Chennell
L. R. Colquhoun
A. G. Course
E. F. Davison
G. G. Harding
Miss J. Kalerghi
F. Lane
A. Latham
Dr. T. K. S. Murthy
M. A. Pinder
J. E. Rapson
R. A. Shaw, OBE
M. Thornton
P. H. Winter
P. A. Yerbury
Asst. Secretary: P. A. Bartlett

All correspondence for the UK Hovercraft Society should be addressed to:-
Rochester House, 66 Little Ealing Lane, London W5 4XX
Telephone: 01-579 9411

THE HOVER CLUB OF GREAT BRITAIN LTD.

The Hover Club of Great Britain is the National organisation for light hovercraft and exists to encourage the participation by private individuals, schools, colleges and youth groups in the construction and safe operation of light hovercraft for recreational purposes. Using the vast experience and information gathered by Club members during the course of the past ten years, the Hover Club occasionally publishes booklets advising upon different areas of light hovercraft design and practice and has its own technical enquiries officer to deal with members' problems.

One of the major activities of the Hover Club is the organisation through its branches in the British Isles of National Race Meetings and other events at which light hovercraft can compete or engage in hover-cruising. Each year the Club has between six and eight national meetings at different locations in Britain. These events frequently attract twenty or thirty light hovercraft and points gained by competitors count towards the annual Hovercraft Championships

Each month the Hover Club publishes a magazine entitled "Light Hovercraft" which deals with light hovercraft matters, particularly the technical aspects and reports of national meetings. The Hover Club also produces the "Light Hovercraft Handbook", a publication usually up-dated and amended each year which sets out in a fairly simple and straightforward way how to construct and operate light hovercraft.

HOVER CLUB COUNCIL:
Michael Bentine, President
G. G. Harding, Chairman
K. Oakley, Vice-Chairman
G. K. Porter, Hon. Treasurer
J. E. C. Bliault, Hon. Secretary
N. Beale
C. Curtis
D. Ison
P. Mayer

Some of the twenty-five entrants in the 1974 International Light Hovercraft Rally held in Calais, pose in front of Seaspeed's 190-ton SR.N4, "Princess Anne"

M. Pinder
N. Smith
D. M. Waters
G. Wickington

In addition the Hover Club has an Initial Enquiries Officer (K. Waddon, 45 St. Andrews Rd, Lower Bremerton, Salisbury, Wiltshire), a Technical Enquiries Officer (D. Ison, 28 Brunwins Close, Wickford, Essex) and an Executive Committee Secretary (D. Council, 4 Hunt Road, High Wycombe, Bucks).

The Hover Club's main address is 128 Queen's Road, Portsmouth, Hants PO2 7NE.

ADDRESSES OF THE HOVERCLUB'S BRANCHES:

BIRMINGHAM & DISTRICT
Mrs I. Mantell,
24 Bourne Avenue, Fazely, nr. Tamworth, Staffs.

CHILTERNS
J. Lyne,
Berkshire College of Agriculture, Hall Place, Burchetts Green, nr Maidenhead, Berks.

EAST ANGLIAN
C. Seager,
33 Acacia Road, Thorpe St Andrews, Norfolk.

ESSEX
E. Sangster,
53 Elm View Road, Benfleet, Essex.

ISLE OF WIGHT
M. Prentice,
South Lodge, Lushington Hill, Wootton Bridge IoW.

LONDON
K. Oakley,
7 Charles Close, Snodland, Kent.

MIDLANDS
D. M. Waters,
30 Shepherds Close, Loughborough, Leics.

NORTH WESTERN
Rev W. G. Spedding,
14 Avondale Road, Farnworth, nr. Bolton, Lancs.

SCOTTISH
W. S. Sharp,
1 Coates Place, Edinburgh, Scotland.

SOUTHERN
P. Hampson,
1 Rednal House, Greetham Street, Portsmouth, Hants.

SOUTH WESTERN
Mrs. G. Jacobs,
Mudford Manor, Up-Mudford, Yeovil, Somerset.

HOVERMAIL COLLECTORS CLUB
Honorary Secretary: C. J. Richards
93 Aldershot Road, Fleet, Hants
GU13 9NW, United Kingdom

INTERNATIONAL FEDERATION OF HOVER CLUBS
Honorary Secretary: J. E. C. Bliault
128 Queens Road, Portsmouth, Hants PO2 7NE
Telephone: 0705-61211

AUSTRALIA
Hover Club of Australia, 34 Gaven Avenue, Mermaid Beach 4218, Australia

FRANCE
Club Francais des Aergolisseurs, 85, Rue de la Republique, Suresnes 92, France

UNITED STATES
National Association of Air Cushion Vehicles, 801 Poplar Street, Terre Haute, Indiana 47807, USA

TRINIDAD AND TOBAGO
Hover Club of Trinidad and Tobago, 1 Richardson Street, Point Fortin, Trinidad, West Indies

NATIONAL SCHOOLS' HOVERCRAFT ASSOCIATION
CHAIRMAN AND TREASURER:
N. R. Smith
SECRETARY:
D. Hale,
Brookmead,
Rimpton,
Nr. Yeovil,
Somerset
TELEPHONE:
Marston Magna 241

This body was formed in 1975 to provide a focal point for the growing interest in building and operating recreational hovercraft shown by schools and colleges. Already over 170 schools have registered hovercraft either completed or in course of construction with the NSHA. Each year the Association, in conjunction with British Petroleum Ltd. and the Hover Club of Great Britain organises a National Schools Hovercraft Competition to enable school-built hovercraft to be judged and raced.

ACV CONSULTANTS

CONSULTANTS IN AIR-CUSHION VEHICLE TECHNOLOGY AND OPERATION

UNITED KINGDOM

AIR CUSHION EQUIPMENT LTD.
HEAD OFFICE:
360 Shirley Road, Southampton
TELEPHONE: Southampton 776468
TELEX: 47106
CABLES: HOVERACE SOTON
WORKS:
35 Randolph Street, Shirley, Southampton
DIRECTORS:
L. A. Hopkins
T. C. A. Horn
W. A. Melhiush
O. J. Coleman
J. M. Horn
P. B. A. Hopkins
B. H. Wright
G. Parkes
A. Latham
P. Stevens
EXECUTIVES:
R. Gilbert, Chief Designer
G. Parkes, Chief Engineer
A. Latham, Marketing Manager

The company, besides developing products and systems for its own benefit and that of its associate companies, also offers a comprehensive design and technical consulting service to any organisation with a load-moving problem. Many such problems have been considered and air cushion systems designed and built to cope with them. New products are under development for the mechanical handling industry and also for the civil engineering and construction industries specialising in very heavy and awkward steel and concrete erection projects..

Over the last two years the company has also been investigating new methods of adapting skirt systems for the dense load movement sector of the market and to reduce both the capital and operating costs. The latest product to emerge is known as the ACE Water Skate which uses water as the cushion fluid and has been tested up to 100 psi.

AIR VEHICLES LTD.
HEAD OFFICE
1, Sun Hill, Cowes, Isle of Wight
TELEPHONE: Cowes 3194 & 4439
OFFICERS AND DIRECTORS:
P. H. Winter, Msc., Director
C. D. J. Bland, Director
C. B. Eden, Director

Formed in 1968, Air Vehicles Ltd has specialised in the design and manufacture of small hovercraft, mainly in the 5-6 seater range, and also in the development of ducted propellers for hovercraft. The largest installation is a quiet ducted propeller for the N6 craft designed and built by Air Vehicles in early 1974. The company acts as consultants and designers for a wide range of hovercraft applications, from fan testing to large 350 ton hoverbarges. The company has also developed over several years, large soft wheels especially designed for swampy or rugged ground and proposals are available for a range of towing vehicles, trailers and lifting devices, all based on these wheels. The design and fitting out of hovercraft for special duties such as cargo carrying and survey work is also undertaken. With unrivalled experience in the operation of 5-6 seater hovercraft under working charter conditions Air Vehicles is able to advise on and evaluate a wide range of applications and routes. It can also call on the world-wide experience of its associated companies, Hoverwork Ltd and Hovertravel Ltd. Air Vehicles Ltd offer its N5 Hoverfreighter for charter.

C. A. BRINDLE & ASSOCIATES
ADDRESS:
10 Cliff Road, Cowes, Isle of Wight, PO31 8BN, England
TELEPHONE: (098 382)2218
C. A. Brindle & Associates provides a consultancy service special-

ising in marine transport and transportation economics, hydrofoil and hovercraft operation in all parts of the world.
Contractors to British and other Governments.

Work undertaken has included world-wide surveys for potential hovercraft and hydrofoil operation and the technical assessment of specific craft.

Detailed application studies have been carried out in the United Kingdom, United States of America, Canada, Mediterranean, Africa, France, Holland, Scandinavia and the Caribbean.

Practical experience with scheduled commercial services and specialised operations and maintenance in domestic and international fields. Adviser to United Nations Organisation and OECD on maritime operations in developing countries.

BRITISH RAIL HOVERCRAFT LIMITED
HEAD OFFICE
Royal London House, 22/25 Finsbury Square, London EC2P 2BQ
TELEPHONE: (01) 628 3050
Managing Director: J. M. Lefeaux
Commercial and Planning Manager: A. J. Tame
Chief Engineer: P. A. Yerbury

British Rail Hovercraft Limited is the most experienced commercial hovercraft in operation the world. It is the only company to have operated commercially both amphibious and non-amphibious craft on estuarial and open water services.

Studies have been conducted on behalf of clients in many parts of the world and the Company is able to provide a route costing and viability appraisal service based on "real time" operating experience.

LESLIE COLQUHOUN AND ASSOCIATES
HEAD OFFICE:
The Oast House, Way Hill, Minster, Ramsgate, Kent CT12 4HS
Telephone: Minster Thanet 357 STD 0843-88-357

Leslie Colquhoun and Associates was formed in 1973 to provide a hovercraft transport consultancy service using the unique experience of L. R. Colquhoun who has been closely associated with the hovercraft industry since 1959. This experience involved the testing, development and marketing of Vickers Ltd. hovercraft projects from 1959-1965, and from 1966-1973 the setting up and running of Hoverlloyd's Ramsgate to Calais hovercraft service with the SR.N6 and SR.N4. Mr Colquhoun was Managing Director of the Company when he resigned in December 1972 to set up the Consultancy.

The Consultancy is contracted to Hoverlloyd and has completed on their behalf a report on the Company's SR.N4 cross channel operations for the S.E.S.P.O. P.M.17 office of the Department of the US Navy.

Further work has been contracted in U.K., France, Hungary, America, Iran and Malaysia.

The Consultancy also provides assistance to International Hoverservices Ltd.

Through a close association with Comasco International Ltd. the Consultancy is involved in pollution and waste disposal schemes using both chemical and incineration processes.

PETER G. FIELDING, CEng, FRAeS
OFFICES:
UNITED KINGDOM:
30 Warmdene Road, Brighton, Sussex, BN1 8NL
TELEPHONE: Brighton 501212
Dock House, Niton Undercliff , Ventnor, Isle of Wight, PO38 2NE
Telephone: Niton 730 252
USA:
1701 North Fort Myer Drive, Suite 908 Arlington, Virginia 22209
Telephone: (703) 528-1092
7910 Woodmont Avenue, Suite 1103, Bethesda, Maryland 20014
Telephone: (301) 656-5991
Consultant in air cushion systems, air cushion operations, and

air cushion technology since 1959 to the US Army, the US Navy, US Department of Defense, the Advanced Research Projects Agency-DOD, US Department of Commerce-Maritime Administration, the Office of Naval Research, the US Naval Ships Research and Development Center, the US Army TRECOM, the Executive Office of the President USA, the US Navy-Chief of Naval Operations, the US Marine Corp, the Institute for Defense Analysis, the Center for Naval Analysis, the Bell Aerosystems Corporation, the Aerojet Corporation, the Research Analysis Corporation, Science Applications Incorporated, Hoverlift Applications Incorporated, Booz-Allen Applied Research Incorporated, Associated Consultants International Inc, and SeaSpan Inc. Services for the above organizations have included state of the art reports, technical and economic analysis, route surveys, environmental impact studies, sub-system analysis, operational plans, test plans, mission studies, advanced technology estimates, test site selection, cost analysis, structural and materials analysis and market research.

RECENTLY COMPLETED ASSIGNMENTS INCLUDE:

1. Review and assessment of the Arctic SEV advanced technology programme for the Advanced Research Projects Agency US Dept of Defence.
2. Analysis of "paddle wheel" propulsion and sealing systems for SES, for S.A. Inc. McLean, Va, U.S.A.
3. "The Surface Effect Vehicle (SEV) in Search and Rescue Missions in Alaska"—for the Research Analysis Corporation, McLean, Va.
4. "An Assessment of the Technological Risk and Uncertainty of Advanced Surface Effect Vehicles (SEV) for the Arctic"—for the US Naval Ships Research and Development Center, Carderock, Md.
5. "An Evaluation of Advanced Surface Effect Vehicle Platforms Performing Military Missions in the Arctic"—for Science Applications Inc, La Jolla, California, and Arlington, Virginia.
6. "An Exhaustive Bibliography of Air Cushion Subjects" for the Research Analysis Corporation, McLean, Virginia.
7. "Preliminary Findings of the Economic Suitabilities of the Surface Effect Ship to Various Routes in the US"—for SEASPAN Inc, Washington, D.C.
8. "Appraisal of Heavy Lift Systems for Commercial Applications"—for Hoverlift Applications Inc, Arlington, Virginia.
9. Results and Implications of the Advanced Projects Agency, US Department of Defence, Surface Effect Vehicles Programme—for Science Applications Inc, Arlington, VA, USA.

S. GARDNER

HEAD OFFICE:
Hurlands, The Haven, Billinghurst, Sussex
Telephone: Rudgwick 2646
ASSOCIATES:
S. Gardner, CEng, AFRAeS, Project Engineer (ACV)
A. Marchant, CEng, MICE, MIMechE, AFRAeS, Project Engineer (Structural).
Consultants in Air Cushion Vehicle and related Civil and Structural Engineering.
S. Gardner:
1969 Project design mechanical, structural and systems engineering of Enfield Marine Freight Hovercraft.
1964-69 Senior Hovercraft Surveyor to UK Air Registration Board.
1959-64. Project Engineer, Hovercraft Development Ltd. Supervision of Design and Construction of H.D.1 experimental ACV.
A. Marchant:
1966-69. Design specialist in ACV structures including HM.2 Hovercat, F.M.1 and E.M.2

HOVERCRAFT DEVELOPMENT LTD.

HEAD OFFICE:
Kingsgate House, 66-74 Victoria Street, London, SWIE 6SL
TELEPHONE: 01-828-3400
TELEX: 23580
TECHNICAL OFFICE:
Forest Lodge West, Fawley Road, Hythe, Hants SO4 6ZZ
TELEPHONE: Hythe (Hants) 84 3178 STD Code 84 0703
DIRECTORS:
T. G. Fellows (Chairman)
M. W. Innes

Prof. W. A. Mair
J. E. Rapson
T. A. Coombs
SECRETARY:
P. N. Randell

Hovercraft Development Ltd, was established by the National Research Development Corporation in 1959 to develop and exploit the hovercraft patents of Christopher Cockerell. The Technical Group of the Company was set up in 1960. It provided technical services for the Company's hovercraft manufacturing licensees until that part of HDL was taken over by Mintech (now the Department of Trade and Industry) to become a unit of the National Physical Laboratory. The office at Hythe continues to provide technical information for interested parties and particularly for the Company's licensees and for hovercraft operators. It also advises HDL on technical matters associated with development projects and the craft designs of prospective licensees.

HOVERWORK LIMITED

HEAD OFFICE:
12 Lind Street, Ryde, Isle of Wight. PO33 2NR
TELEPHONE: Ryde 5181
CABLES: Hoverwork Ryde
TELEX: 86513 (A/B Hoverwork Ryde)
DIRECTORS:
C. D. J. Bland (Managing)
D. R. Robertson
E. W. H. Gifford
A. C. Smith
R. G. Clarke

Hoverwork Limited is a subsidiary of Hovertravel Limited and was formed in 1966. The company provides crew training and charter facilities for all available types of ACVs, thus bridging the gap between the operators and manufacturers.

Hoverwork and its parent, Hovertravel, own the largest fleet of hovercraft available for charter in the world. Types include the SR.N6, the SR.6N freighter, SR.N5 passenger/freighter and AV.2. In recent years the company has concentrated on providing craft for seismic, gravity and hydrographic survey work in shallow water areas and terrain impossible to other forms of transport.

The company, jointly with Hovertravel Limited, offers a route feasibility investigation service.

PELLINKHOF CONSULTANCY

Th. Pellinkhof, C.Eng., F.I.Mar.E
ADDRESS: The Netherlands-British Chamber of Commerce,
The Dutch House, 307/308 High Holborn, London, WC1V 7LS
TELEX: NEDHAM LDN 23211—att. PELLINKHOF
TELEPHONE: 01-405 1358

Consultancy in the fields of rapid transit systems, amphibious vehicles and air-cushion applications.

Selection and indication of solutions for various transport problems in developing areas. Also the selection of air-cushion vehicles and hydrofoils to meet specific high-performance and amphibious requirements. Assistance in selection of air-cushion platforms and Air-Cushion Conveyor Belts to facilitate cost-saving load moving.

The Netherlands-British foundation of the enterprise ensures a wide area of industrial and technological resources.

R. A. SHAW

(Managing Director Hoverprojects Limited)
ADDRESS:
Fell Brow, Silecroft, Millom, Cumbria, LA18 5LS
Telephone: 0657 2022

Consultancy services to governments, local authorities and private enterprise on all aspects of fast transport with special emphasis on hovercraft and hydrofoils. Services include financial, economic and operational assessments in all conditions and new designs to meet particular requirements.

Contracts have included:

1. A study for the State of Washington to assess the feasibility of introducing hovercraft and hydrofoils into the Puget Sound ferry system.
2. A feasibility appraisal of proposed hovercraft operations in British Columbia.

3. Reporting to a local authority on prospects of establishing a hoverport within their borough.
4. A study for the Greater London Council on fast passenger services on the Thames.
5. Three independent studies on the potential for hovercraft in the Venetian lagoon.
6. Examination of world potential market for hovercraft.
7. Design and Economics of 1000 ton River Hovercraft.
8. Planning and operating consultancy for Airavia Ltd. and Speed Hydrofoils Ltd. for hydrofoils on the River Thames.

ROBERT TRILLO LIMITED

HEAD OFFICE:
Broadlands, Brockenhurst, Hampshire, SO4 7SX.
Telephone: Brockenhurst (05902) 2220.
MANAGING DIRECTOR:
R. L. Trillo, CEng., FIMechE, FRAeS, AFAIAA, AFCASI
Author "Marine Hovercraft Technology" (ISBN 0 249 44036 9) and Editor "Jane's Ocean Technology Yearbook' (ISBN 0 354 00500 6).

Operating since 1969 as a consultancy engaging principally in air-cushion vehicle technology and economics, the firm has worked for industry and government departments in a number of countries and has undertaken transport feasibility studies, preliminary design investigations and experimental investigations. Other work has been concerned with the design of three ducted propeller installations and two inflatable hovercraft, one of which is the largest built to date; research into skirt wear and the design of skirts has also been undertaken. Recent commissions have included work in Canada for the National Research Council, Ottawa, and in Australia for the Department of Aboriginal Affairs; in this context a feasibility study was carried out on the practicality of operating hovercraft between the islands in the coral reef areas in the Torres Strait between Papua New Guinea and Northern Queensland and as a result a successful SR. N5 operation has now been established. The firm publishes bi-monthly bibliography services on air-cushion and hydrofoil systems and on high-speed ground transportation and urban rapid transit systems.

REPRESENTATIVES:
CANADA:
Vice-Admiral K. L. Dyer, RCN Rtd.,
Dodwell, Dyer & Associates,
1177 St. Laurent Boulevard,
Ottawa,
Ontario KIK 3B7
DENMARK:
Mr. Leif Hansen,
A. B. C. Hansen Comp, A/S,
Hauchsvej 14,
DK-1825 Copenhagen V.
Affiliate member of Northern Associates Reg'd., Canada, Canadian. Arctic consulting group.

JOHN VASS

ADDRESS:
Beaverbrook Newspapers, Fleet Street, London E.C.4
Telephone: 353-8000
Home: Rosehaugh Farm, Newbarn Lane, Cudham, Kent
Telephone: Biggin Hill 2718

Received first official light hovercraft licence issued by Air Registration Board 1968. Elected first Life Member of Hoverclub of Gt. Britain, 1974. Author "Hovercraft" and "Express Air Rider Handbook" Hovercraft Correspondent, Daily Express. Light Hovercraft consultant, British Petroleum, Air Rider Research Ltd, and McCulloch & Associates, Ontario, Originator of National Schools Hovercraft Contest, (first held 1968).

UNITED STATES
AEROPHYSICS COMPANY

ADDRESS:
3500 Connecticut Avenue, N.W., Washington D.C. 20008
TELEPHONE: (202) 244-1926
OFFICERS:
Dr. Gabriel D. Boehler, President
Mr. William F. Foshag, Chief Engineer

Aerophysics Company was formed in 1957 to conduct fundamental research of the ground effect principle. Dr. Boehler had previously performed private feasibility work with Mr. M. Beardsley. Since then, Aerophysics has undertaken work in various areas of ACV design, including, skirt design, control techniques, parametric analysis, conceptual and design studies, studies of ACV lift air systems including various types of blowers and propulsion systems.

BOOZ-ALLEN & HAMILTON INC.

135 South La Salle Street, Chicago, Illinois 60603
ACTIVITIES:
General Management Consulting,
Computer Systems and Software
Market and Social Science Research
Industrial Engineering Systems
Pollution and Environmental Resources Management
Defence and Space Research
Product, Process and Equipment Development
Transportation and Airport Planning and Engineering

DAVIDSON LABORATORY
STEVENS INSTITUTE OF TECHNOLOGY

HEAD OFFICE:
Castle Point Station Hoboken, New Jersey 07030
Telephone: 201-792-2700
OFFICERS:
Dr. J. P. Breslin, Director
Daniel Savitsky, Assistant Director

Organised in 1935 as the Experimental Towing Tank, the Laboratory is active in basic and applied hydrodynamic research, including smooth water performance and manouvrability; seakeeping, propulsion and control of marine vehicles including ACV and hydrofoil craft. Special model test facilities are available to investigate the dynamic behaviour of ACV and hydrofoil craft in smooth water and waves.

FORRESTAL LABORATORY

ADDRESS:
Princeton University, Princeton, N.J.
OFFICERS:
T. E. Sweeney
ACTIVITIES:
Research prototypes (ACVs)

GIBBS & COX

ADDRESS:
40 Rector Street, New York, N. Y. 10006 Ph: (212) 487-2800
ACTIVITIES:
Project coordination, consultation, conceptual and preliminary designs contract drawings and specifications and "working" drawing efforts for commercial or naval vessels of the SES/ACV, or submerged system hydrofoils of the destroyer, escort, frigate and corvette types.

GLOBAL MARINE INC

HEAD OFFICE:
811 West 7th Street, Los Angeles, California 90017
Telephone: 213-680-9550
OFFICERS:
A. J. Field, President
R. B. Thornburg, Senior Vice-President
R. G. Longaker, General Manager
Arctic Engineers & Constructors
1770 St James Place, Suite 504, Houston, Texas 77027
Telephone: 713-626-9773

Global Marine Inc was incorporated in 1959, and is engaged primarily in offshore drilling and engineering. However, in 1968 the company undertook an engineering feasibility study directed towards developing equipment and techniques for drilling in Arctic areas. This engineering study led to the selection of ACT (Air Cushion Transport) units as the most feasible for operating in the area, and it has a continuing design programme directed towards various size ACT (Air Cushion Transport) drilling rigs with various drilling capabilities. This design work is handled by Global Marine Inc (Los Angeles), and the sales and operational aspects, with respect to the Arctic, are handled by Arctic Engineers & Constructors (see above). Arctic Engineers & Constructors is a joint venture between **Global Marine** and **Raymond International, Houston, Texas.**

AEC constructed the ACT-100 in Canada in 1971. This unit was test operated in the Arctic during 1971, and was test operated by the Canadian government in connection with the Mackenzie River Highway and by Imperial Oil Ltd. in connection with its offshore winter drilling operations in 1973-74. Design work on larger ACV drilling rigs continues.

HOVERLIFT APPLICATIONS INCORPORATED

HEAD OFFICE:

1651 Old Meadow Road, McLean, Virginia 22101 USA

TELEPHONE: (703) 790-9494

Hoverlift Applications Incorporated is a subsidiary of Science Applications, Inc. and provides wide ranging engineering consulting services, applications studies, economic analyses and operation of air cushion vehicles. The company also has concentrated expertise and experience in the design and application of air casters, hover-trailers and hoverpallets, tank moving systems, hoverbarges, lighter-than-air vehicles and heavy lift helicopters. Recent work has included participation in the ARPA Arctic SEV Program and feasibility studies for various municipalities in the United States.

HYDRONAUTICS, INCORPORATED

HEAD OFFICE:

7210 Pindell School Road, Howard County, Laurel, Maryland 20810

TELEPHONE: 301-776-7454

OFFICERS:

Marshall P. Tulin, Chairman of the Board

Phillip Eisenberg, Chairman of the Executive Committee

Virgil E. Johnson, Jr., President

Alex Goodman, Senior Vice-President

Bennett L. Silverstein, Senior Vice-President

Philip A. Weiner, Vice-President and Secretary

Harvey Post, Treasurer

The company was founded in July, 1959, and has undertaken research, development and design of air cushion vehicles, hydrofoil craft and other high speed marine vehicles as well as advanced propulsion systems, under United States Government and industrial contracts. Hydronautics has its own ship model basin and high speed water channel suitable for the evaluation of air cushion vehicles and hydrofoils.

INSTITUTE FOR DEFENSE ANALYSES (IDA)

HEAD OFFICE:

400 Army-Navy Drive, Arlington, Virginia 22202

Telephone: (703) 558-1000

ACTIVITIES:

Systems analysis, policy analysis, economics, military operational studies. Study of technology and applications.

E. K. LIBERATORE COMPANY

ADDRESS:

567 Fairway Road, Ridgewood, N.J. 07450

PERSONNEL:

E. K. Liberatore, Head

John Eller

Formed in 1964, the company specialises in systems engineering, vehicle design and in operations in the fields of ACVs, SESs, and VTOL aircraft. Work includes requirements, integration, analysis, design, costing, FAA and other certification, route and market surveys and methodology. Current projects in the areas of helicopter development, steam propulsion and non-expendable energy systems.

LIPPISCH RESEARCH CORPORATION
Consultants Ram-Wing Vehicles

HEAD OFFICE:

3450 Cottage Grove Avenue, S.E., Cedar Rapids, Iowa 52403

Telephone: 319, 365-0175

DESIGN FACILITIES:

Cedar Rapids, Iowa; Friedrichshafen, West Germany (In co-operation with Dornier GmbH), and Mönchengladbach (In co-operation with VFW-Rhein-Flugzeugbau GmbH)

SALES OFFICE:

Ten Old Post Office Road, Silver Spring, Maryland 20910

Telephone: 301, 588-3311

STAFF PERSONNEL:

Dr. Alexander M. Lippisch, President

George G. Lippisch, Vice-President

Gertrude L. Lippisch, Treasurer

Dr. Herschel Shosteck, Director of Marketing

Lippisch Research Corporation was organised by Dr. Alexander M. Lippisch in 1966 to continue development of high lift-drag ratio free-flying ram-wing and STOL vehicles. Building on the research concepts originated by Dr. Lippisch, the company, singly and in co-operation with airframe manufacturers, has designed, constructed and successfully test-flown an increasing number of advanced ram-wing craft as well as the "aerodyne" wingless STOL.

The major research work on ram-wing craft has been executed under contracts with VFW-Rhein-Flugzeugbau GmbH.

As a result of this work, Lippisch Research Corporation has successfully overcome the fundamental problems of pitch instability which had previously precluded development of successful ram-wing vehicles. The "aerofoil boat" class of vehicles operates from surface effect to free-flight and back again without difficulty. Their free-flight capabilities permit successful operation in high to precipitous sea states.

Current experimental prototypes achieve lift-drag ratios of approximately 35:1. Larger vehicles in the concept stage are designed for over double these efficiencies.

The "aero-skimmer" is an over-water class vehicle designed to operate in the immediate proximity of the surface. Vessels of this type are powered by standard outboard motors, with only the propeller in contact with the water. This design eliminates all super-cavitation-induced drag on the hull of the craft. Test vehicles readily exceed 100 knots while maintaining high stability and manouvrability. To date, craft performance has been limited only by the capacity of the power plant.

Lippisch concepts include ram-wing vehicles designed as ASW craft, military launch, assault craft, ocean transports, inland river boats, and arctic transportation vehicles.

Lippisch Research Corporation supplies engineering design and consulting services to other design organisations and airframe manufacturers.

GEORGE E. MEESE

ADDRESS:

194 Acton Road, Annapolis, Md USA 21403

Telephone: 301 263-4054

Cable: Meesmarine Annapolis

ACTIVITIES:

SES structures.

M. ROSENBLATT & SON, INC

HEAD OFFICE:

350 Broadway, New York, 10013 New York

Telephone: (212) 431-6900

OFFICERS:

Lester Rosenblatt, President

E. F. Kaufman, Vice-President and Manager, Western Division

N. M. Maniar, Vice-President and Technical Director

L. M. Schlosberg, Vice-President and Design Manager

F. K. Serim, Vice-President and Manager, Washington Area Branch

BRIEF HISTORY:

The firm was founded in 1947 and has since grown to be one of the largest engineering design firms of its type, specialising in naval architecture and marine engineering. An organisation of experienced engineers, designers and draftsmen has been assembled which is fully capable of providing the engineering, design and research and development services associated with ship and marine vehicle design.

Since its establishment, the company has successfully completed approximately three thousand ship design and related assignments for government and private customers. These assignments embrace work on commercial and naval ships and on almost every type of floating vessel. Merchant vessels include: passenger ships, containerships, oceanographic ships, general cargo ships, bulk carriers, tankers, surface effect ships, drilling platforms, survey vessels, tugs, etc. Naval vessels include: carriers, cruisers, destroyers, frigates, destroyer-escorts, tenders and auxiliaries of all kinds, submarines, LPDs, LPHs, LSTs, LSDs, hydrofoils and

patrol craft.
Typical ACV assignments include:

1. ARPA Advanced Surface Effect Vehicles
Conceptual studies, parametric studies and propulsion machinery analysis for phase "O" studies of Advanced Surface Effect Vehicles for Advanced Research Project Agency. Work performed for American Machine and Foundry Company.

2. JSESPO Surface Effect Ship Testcraft
Conceptual and feasibility design studies of candidate SES vehicles for the JSESPO sizing study for second generation SES testcraft in the 1,000 to 3,000-ton range. The work included studies of various candidate versions of SES to identify and evaluate their unique operational and design capabilities; technological assessment of various structural materials and systems; preparation of a proposed development programme with required supporting R&D. Work performed for Joint Surface Effect Ship Program Office.

3. Amphibious Fleet Conceptual Studies
Conceptual design studies of various types of ships for future amphibious fleets, including submarine, displacement, planing hydrofoil and ACV type ships. Studies included technological assessment of performance of the concepts, taking into account various operational capabilities, including speed, propulsion systems, manning, weapons, materials, payloads and costs. Work performed for Stanford Research Institute under basic contract with ONR.

4. The Surface Effect Ship, Advanced Design and Technology
A 283 page text book covering drag, structure, propulsion, transmission, propulsors, stability, lift systems, seals, auxiliaries, weights, parametric analysis, and sample problems. Each topic is discussed including design procedures and equations. The book was prepared for the U.S. Navy Surface Effect Ships Project Office.

5. 2000-ton Surface Effect Ship
Trade-off studies, system design parameters, equipment selection, system diagrams, hull-borne stability in connection with a complete design proposal. The scope of work included hullborne structural design criteria, electrical power generating and distribution, heating, ventilating, air conditioning, hull appurtenances, piping systems, hotel and auxiliary machinery arrangements. Work performed for the Lockheed Missiles and Space Co., and the Surface Effect Ships Project Office.

STANFORD RESEARCH INSTITUTE
ADDRESS:
Menlo Park, California 94025
Telephone: (415) 326-6200

EXECUTIVES:
Clark Henderson, Staff Scientist, Transportation

ACTIVITIES:
Operational tradeoff studies; optimising vehicles with missions; demand studies; economic evaluations; hydrofoils; ACVs.

SYSTEMS EXPLORATION INC.
HEAD OFFICE:
3687 Voltaire Street, San Diego, California
Telephone: (714) 223 8141
REPRESENTATIVES:
Richard E. Stedd
Sam W. Braly
Dale K. Beresford
Erwin J. Hauber
ACTIVITIES:
Consultants to the US Navy on ACV and hydrofoil development programmes. Developed high-speed aspect ratio displacement (HARD) hydrofoil concept.

MARTIN STEVENS
ADDRESS:
Woodhull Cove, Oldfield Village, Setauket, Long Island, N.Y.
ACTIVITIES:
Mechanical design, drive systems.

WATER RESEARCH COMPANY
HEAD OFFICE:
3003 North Central Avenue, Suite 600, Phoenix, Arizona 85012
Telephone: (602) 265-7722
EXECUTIVES:
Richard R. Greer, President
Dr. John H. McMasters, Chief Engineers

The Water Research Company was formed in 1972 to consolidate activities surrounding the patents held or applied for by Mr. Richard R. Greer relating to various aspects of water-borne vehicles. The company has subsequently prepared conceptual studies on a class of winged surface effect vessels (WSEV) intended to fill a variety of missions for the US Navy. An article on this subject was published in the Naval Engineer's Journal, April 1974. The company presently has the capability of performing analytical studies on hydrofoil, SES and WIG systems, and can provide contract co-ordinating services for such systems. The company has no immediate plans for acquiring hardware development facilities.

HYDROFOIL CONSULTANTS

CONSULTANTS IN HYDROFOIL TECHNOLOGY AND OPERATION

SWITZERLAND
Dr. Ing. E. G. Faber
HEAD OFFICE:
Weinberglistrasse 60, CH-Luzern Switzerland
Telephone: national (CH) 04/44 33 20
International +41/44 33 20
Telex: 78 670 DATAG-CH
Consultant in marine engine plant planning, marine engineering and marine technology; with special emphasis on high-speed and hydrofoil craft.
GENERAL: Feasibility Studies, Cost Estimates, Specifications, Plant Descriptions, Project Co-ordination.
CONCEPTUAL AND PRELIMINARY DESIGNS: Engine and Auxiliary Plants, Piping Systems and Hydraulics, Electrical and Monitoring Systems, Ventilation and Air Conditioning Systems, Noise Insulation.
TECHNICAL EXPERTISE: Speed Estimates and Hydrodynamic Problems, Waterjet Propulsion, Analysis of Ship Structure, Vibration and Shock Isolation, Acceptance Tests and Damage Survey.

Supramar AG
HEAD OFFICE:
Denkmalstrasse 2
6006 Lucerne, Switzerland
Telephone: (041) 36 96 36
Telex: 78228
MARKETING DEPARTMENT:
Supramar Trade Ltd.,
Address as above
MANAGEMENT:
Hussain Najadi, Chairman and Managing Director
Volker Jost, Ing., Technical Director and Assistant Managing Director
Baron Hanns von Schertel, Technical Director
DESIGN:
Dipl Ing Ernst Jaksch, Chief
SECTION HEADS:
Dipl-Ing Georg Chojka, Marine Engineering
Dipl-Ing Ernst Jaksch, Foil Design
Ing Volker Jost, Hull Design
RESEARCH AND DEVELOPMENT:
Baron Hanns von Schertel, Head of Development
SECTION HEADS:
Dipl Ing Eugen Schatté, Propulsion and Tests
Dr Ing Hermann de Witt, Hydrodynamics
Supramar was founded in Switzerland in 1952 to develop on a commercial basis the hydrofoil system introduced by the Schertel-Sachsenberg Hydrofoil Syndicate and its licensee, the Gebrüder Sachsenberg Shipyard.
From this early date Supramar have provided a consultancy service on a world-wide basis covering not only their hydrofoil vessels but also other aspects of fast marine transportation. Their scientists have delivered papers to most of the world's leading professional bodies.
The company has been under contract to many Governments and military services.

C. A. BRINDLE & PARTNERS
See main entry under ACV consultants.

CHRISTOPHER HOOK
ADDRESS:
Burfield Flat, Bosham Lane, Bosham, Sussex
Christopher Hook was responsible for the conception, design and development of the fully submerged hydrofoil which he demonstrated in the USA in 1951 with his Red Bug, and later with Miami-built conversion sets. He became a partner of the late Herr G. Sachsenberg, the pioneer hydrofoil builder and has completed hydrofoil design and consultancy contracts in the USA, Israel, Holland, France, Norway, Italy as well as with Strathclyde University. He is currently developing a self-tending sail rig for sailing hydrofoil craft, comprising sails that tilt to windward and have reefing. In the 1975 version a small wind vane ahead of the sails is coupled to the balanced air rudder with pilot differential interference so that the sail system will be constantly and automatically adjusted to any shift in the apparent wind. The four sail system was inspired by the hang glider. He is the holder of two gold and one silver medal for invention, President of the Republic Prize, France and an Inventaway award.

H. H. SNOWBALL
ADDRESS:
The Tower Hotel,
81 Katherine's Way,
London E1
TELEPHONE: 481 2575
Founder, in 1968, of Airavia Ltd, the first company to represent Sudoimport hydrofoils in the West. Founder, Speed Hydrofoils Ltd, which introduced Raketa hydrofoil's on scheduled services on the River Thames in 1974. Consultant Bataan-Manila Ferry Services, Hydrofoil Exploration Services, etc. Prime negotiator 1968-1975 in conversion of Raketa and Kometa to British Passenger Certificate standards for re-export. Crew training arranged also feasibility studies of projected hydrofoil routes.

T. PELLINKHOF See main entry under ACV consultants.

UNITED STATES
ATLANTIC HYDROFOILS INC
HEAD OFFICE:
Hancock, New Hampshire 03449
Telephone: 605 525-4403
DIRECTORS:
John K. Roper
Atlantic Hydrofoils' mechanically-controlled submerged foil system was the first to be approved for use on hydrofoil passenger ferries. The company has completed a number of Technical Reports for the United States Government on hydrofoil design and testing.

DAVIDSON LABORATORY
STEVENS INSTITUTE OF TECHNOLOGY
HEAD OFFICE:
Castle Point Station Hoboken, New Jersey 07030
Telephone: 201-792-2700
OFFICERS:
J. P. Breslin, Director
Daniel Savitsky, Assistant Director
Organised in 1935 as the Experimental Towing Tank, the Laboratory is active in basic and applied hydrodynamic research, including smooth water performance and manoeuvrability; seakeeping, propulsion and control of marine vehicles including ACV and hydrofoil craft. Special model test facilities are avilable to investigate the dynamic behaviour of ACV and hydrofoil craft in smooth water and waves.

GIBBS & COX
ADDRESS:
40 Rector Street, New York, N.Y. 10006 Ph: (212) 487-2800
6525 Belcrest Road, Hyattsville, Md. 20782 Ph: (301) 277-1919
ACTIVITIES:
Project coordination, consultation, conceptual and preliminary designs, contract drawings and specifications, and "working" drawing efforts for commercial or Naval vessels of the SES/ACV, submerged system hydrofoils, destroyer, escort, frigate and corvette types.

W. A. GRAIG

ADDRESS:

307 Troy Towers, Union City, N. J. 07087, USA

Telephone: (201) 864-3993

W. A. Graig, Mast.Eng'g (Ecole Nationale Superieure de l'Aeronautique, France). Registered Prof. Engineer (Ohio, U.S.A.).

W. A. Graig (formerly Grunberg) is the inventor of the Grunberg foil system, first patented in 1936. His approach provided the basis for the Aquavion series and many other designs, and his influence is still to be found in vessels in production today.

The Grunberg principle of inherent angle of attack variation is fully compatible with Forlanini's concept of area variation. Both can be incorporated in the same structure and in a number of modern hydrofoils the two principles work in association.

Among Mr Graig's recent developments are several foil systems which provide lateral stability without impinging on the original Grunberg concept. Directional control ensures co-ordinated turns.

HOERNER

ADDRESS: Hoerner Fluid Dynamics

P.O. Box 342

Brick Town, New Jersey 08723, USA

S. F. Hoerner, Dr-Ing habilitatus

Hydrodynamicist of hydrofoils "Sea Legs" and "Victoria", since 1951.

Author of **"Fluid-Dynamic Drag"** (1965) and **"Fluid-Dynamic Lift"** (to be published September, 1975)

HELMUT KOCK

ADDRESS:

3132 Carleton Street, San Diego, California 92106

Helmut Kock designed the Albatross, first hydrofoil in the United States to certificated by the US Coast Guard for passenger services in lakes, bays and sounds. Twenty of these craft were built. A 72 passenger hydrofoil ferry designed by Helmut Kock is to be built for International Hydrolines Inc.

HYDRONAUTICS INCORPORATED

ADDRESS, TELEPHONE AND COMPANY OFFICERS:

See main entry under ACVs in this section.

M. ROSENBLATT & SON. INC

HEAD OFFICE:

350 Broadway, New York, 10013 New York

Telephone: (212) 431-6900

OFFICERS:

Lester Rosenblatt, President

E. F. Kaufman, Vice-President and Manager, Western Division

N. M. Maniar, Vice-President and Technical Director

L. M. Schlosberg, Vice-President and Design Manager

F. K. Serim, Vice-President and Manager, Washington Area Branch

BRIEF HISTORY:

The firm was founded in 1947 and has since grown to be one of the largest engineering design firms of its type, specialising in naval architecture and marine engineering. An organisation of experienced engineers, designers and draftsmen has been assembled which is fully capable of providing the engineering, design and research and development services associated with ship and marine vehicle design.

Since its establishment, the company has successfully completed approximately three thousand ship design and related assignments for government and private customers. These assignments embrace work on commercial and naval ships and on almost every type of floating vessel. Merchant vessels include; passenger ships, containerships, oceanographic ships, general cargo ships, bulk carriers, tankers, surface effect ships, drilling platforms, survey vessels, tugs, etc. Naval vessels include: carriers, cruisers, destroyers, frigates, destroyer-escorts, tenders and auxiliaries of all kinds, submarines, LPDs, LPHs, LSTs LSDs hydrofoils and patrol craft.

Typical hydrofoil assignments include:

AGEH

Preliminary design and naval architectural services for preparation of proposal for design and construction of 300-ton AG(EH) Hydrofoil Research Vessel—for Lockheed Aircraft Corp.

HYDROFOIL (LVH)

Provided naval architectural services, including development of lines, powering predictions, stability curves and loading criteria for design and development of a 37-foot Landing Force Amphibious Support Vehicle Hydrofoil (LVH)—for Lycoming Division, Avco Corporation.

STANFORD RESEARCH INSTITUTE

ADDRESS:

Menlo Park, California 94025

Telephone: (415) 326-6200

EXECUTIVES:

Clark Henderson, Staff Scientist, Transportation

ACTIVITIES:

Operational tradeoff studies; optimising vehicles with missions; demand studies; economic evaluations; hydrofoils; ACVs.

SYSTEMS EXPLORATION INC.

HEAD OFFICE:

3687 Voltaire Street, San Diego, California

Telephone: (714) 223 8141

REPRESENTATIVES:

Richard E. Stedd

Sam W. Braly

Dale K. Beresford

Erwin J. Hauber

ACTIVITIES:

Consultants to the US Navy on ACV and hydrofoil development programmes. Developed high-speed aspect ratio displacement (HARD) hydrofoil concept.

WATER RESEARCH COMPANY

HEAD OFFICE:

3003 North Central Avenue, Suite 600, Phoenix, Arizona 85012

Telephone: (602) 265-7722

EXECUTIVES:

Richard R. Greer, President

Dr. John H. McMasters, Chief Engineer

The Water Research Company was formed in 1972 to consolidate activities surrounding the patents held or applied for by Mr. Richard R. Greer relating to various aspects of water-borne vehicles. The company has subsequently prepared conceptual studies on a class of winged surface effect vessels (WSEV) intended to fill a variety of missions for the US Navy. An article on this subject was published in the Naval Engineers Journal, April 1974. The company presently has the capability of performing analytical studies on hydrofoil, SES and WIG systems, and can provide contract co-ordinating services for such systems. The company has no immediate plans for acquiring hardware development facilities.

LARGE WINGED SURFACE EFFECT VEHICLES

Dr. John H. McMasters
and
Richard R. Greer

LARGE WINGED SURFACE EFFECT VEHICLES

by

Dr. John H. McMasters*

and

Richard R. Greer**

* Visiting Assistant Professor, School of Aeronautics and Astronautics, Purdue University, W. Lafayette, Indiana
** Chief Executive Officer, Water Research Company

THE AUTHORS

*John H. McMasters is Chief Design Engineer for Water Research
Company and a Visiting Assistant Professor in the School of Aero-
nautics and Astronautics at Purdue University. He has B.S. and
M.S. degrees in Aeronautical Engineering from the University of
Colorado and received his Ph.D. from Purdue. In addition to
work in transonic gas dynamics and aircraft design optimisation,
he served as a Project Officer on various missile systems at the Air
Force Weapons Laboratory (AFWL), Kirtland AFB, New Mexico;
and has held industrial and university teaching positions in design.
While at the AFWL he was awarded the Air Force Commendation
Medal for his work in conceiving and developing the XAIM-68
air-to-air missile. He is a member of the American Society of Naval
Engineers (ASNE) and the Soaring Society of America (SSA).
His primary interests are aerospace vehicle design optimisation,
and ultra-low speed and motorless flight. Much of the impetus for
the present study comes from extensive work on the problem of man-
powered flight, a topic on which he has published several articles and
technical papers.*

*Richard R. Greer is Chief Executive of Water Research Company,
Phoenix, Arizona and holds several U.S. and foreign patents on
various aspects of hydrofoil and SEV systems. He received his
B.S. degree from UCLA, and is actively engaged in practice as a
Certified Public Accountant as well as instructing at Phoenix College
and Arizona State University. He is a member of the American
Institute of Certified Public Accountants, the Arizona Society of
Certified Public Accountants, the Navy League and the American
Society of Naval Engineers.*

ABSTRACT

This article describes the results of a feasibility study of a class of
large winged surface effect vehicles (WSEVs) intended for naval use.
The objective of the study was to define a basic system which would:
(1) possess speed and operational capabilities substantially greater
than existing ACV and CAB surface effect vessels, (2) circumvent
size limitations inherent in conventional aircraft designs, and
(3) offer an economically and operationally viable alternative to
existing water-based and/or airborne naval systems for a variety of
military and commercial missions. The resulting proposed WSEVs
are a family of low aspect ratio channel shaped vessels operating on
the principle of an aerodynamic lifting wing in ground effect during
cruise. The baseline configuration is shown to be suitable for a
number of missions including low density cargo transport; highly
mobile ASW, air defence and missile launch; and quick response,
long range "carrier"/support for helicopters, coastal patrol craft,
and SEV patrol and landing craft. Two of the benefits of the basic
design are that the configuration is well suited to propulsion by
non-hydrocarbon fuel systems (e.g. hydrogen) and use of extensive
laminar boundary layer control.

INTRODUCTION

To a very large extent, the general trend in transportation system
development has been towards ever increasing productivity—or
simply increased speed. Nowhere is this trend more obvious than
in aviation where cruise speeds for commercial transport aircraft
have increased almost exponentially from the start of regular
passenger service in the 1920s, through the advent of supersonic
designs and culminating in hypersonic transport during the past
decade. All this has tended to ignore the finite supply of conventional hydrocarbon fuel—a resource which now appears to be
dwindling at a frighteningly rapid rate.

The "energy crisis" can be confronted in at least two ways by the transport system designer: 1) he can seek to improve the efficiency of conventionally fuelled systems, perhaps even at the expense of degrading productivity, and 2) he can seek alternative fuel sources. Both approaches appear viable and are probably complementary. The reasonable near-term approach is to increase the economy of conventional fuelled devices, a longer range goal being to gradually move to alternative energy sources as the technology and experience with the use of, say, liquid hydrogen becomes better established.

The basic purpose of this article is to describe a specific type of vehicle (the winged surface effect vehicle or WSEV) intended for both commercial and military naval use which is both economical and has the growth potential to utilise effectively non-hydrocarbon fuels. The discussion presented is an extension of the authors' previous study (1) of various surface effect vehicle systems intended to: 1) have substantially higher speed capability than existing hydrofoil and SES vehicles; 2) be simpler mechanically than existing SES vehicles, thus reducing both initial and maintenance costs; and 3) circumvent size and operational limitations of conventional aircraft, particularly those intended for naval or transoceanic cargo missions.

A number of methods for increasing the speed capability of waterborne vehicles have been the subject of very active research and development effort for the past decade. Principal among these are (1) hydrofoils, (2) air cushion vehicles (ACVs),(3) captured air bubble (CAB) systems, (4) ram wings, and (5) wing-in-ground-effect systems (WIGS).

The hydrofoil offers the possibility of substantial speed increases over conventional ships. However, it appears that the maximum feasible speed for such a vehicle is about 80 to 100 knots. Structural problems also place definite limits on the size and weight of such vehicles. The largest hydrofoil craft built to date is the USS Plainview (AGEH-1) with a weight of 320 tons. At the speed specified above, the specific power requirement (HP/ton) appears to be excessive.

Air cushion and other aerostatically supported vehicles appear to offer substantial increases in speed and efficiency compared with hydrofoil supported vehicles. However, they are mechanically complex and consequently expensive, both initially and from a maintenance point of view. In addition, for this type of vehicle to operate efficiently, it must remain in very close proximity to the water surface; this latter factor imposing fairly severe limits on speed and rough sea operations.

The captured air bubble (CAB) system seeks to improve the efficiency of an aerostatically supported vehicle by fitting what amounts to an ACV with rigid sidewalls and flexible seals at each end of the resulting channel to minimise lateral support cushion air spillage. The penalty here is the added hydrodynamic drag of the submerged side walls. The ram wing (2) seeks to reduce mechanical complexity of the ACV and CAB by generating the supporting cushion by aerodynamic means rather than by auxiliary powered "blowers". The major limitations of the ram wing are that it must again operate in very close proximity to the water surface and must have sufficient forward speed to establish a supporting air cushion.

To increase a vehicle's speed and operational capability much beyond that possible with an ACV or hydrofoil system, it appears necessary to physically remove the vehicle as far as possible from the water surface. This has led to the concept of the wing-in-ground-effect system (WIGS), based on the well-known aerodynamic principle that an airplane wing, when operated in close proximity to a solid surface, experiences a substantial reduction in drag due to lift (induced drag). Most pure WIG systems proposed so far have resembled conventional aircraft with fairly high aspect ratio wings and some sort of "boat" hull for flotation at rest and during take-off run. A typical WIG vehicle in the same size and weight category as the present C-5A jet transport is compared in Figure 1 to the 500-ton version of the winged surface effect vehicle (WSEV) proposed in this study. The use of "conventional" high aspect ratio (greater than 3 or 4) wings in close proximity (heights less than half the wing span) to a rough sea surface creates severe operational problems and the usual structural considerations in any aircraft design place upper bounds on the size of such vehicles, given the present state-of-the-art in material and structural technology. The largest aircraft built to date is the 382-ton C-5A, and at present it is difficult to contemplate conventional aircraft weighing in excess of 500 or 600 tons.

An extremely important alternative scheme to the "conventional" (i.e. high aspect ratio) WIG type vehicle is the *aerofoil boat* developed by Lippisch (3) and his associates. Lippisch's design is basically a very low aspect ratio WIG with heavy overtones of the ram wing. The great contribution of this extensive development and testing

TABLE 1.—VEHICLE CHARACTERISTICS

AIRCRAFT

Type	Wing Span (ft.)	Wing Area (ft².)	Weights Empty (tons)	Weights Loaded (tons)	Power or Thrust BHP or LBs.	Max. Speed (kt.)
1. Martin JRM-1 flying boat	200	3686	37·5	72·5	9,000 BHP	180
2. Lockheed 89 piston transport.	189	3610	57	92	12,000 BHP	225
3. Convair C-99 piston transport.	230	4772	70	132·5	18,000 BHP	260
4. Boeing B-52G jet bomber	185	4000	85	244	110,000 LBs.	550
5. Boeing 707-320 jet transport	154·7	2942	69	156	68,000 LBs.	520
6. Lockheed C-5A jet transport	222·7	6200	160	382	164,000 LBs.	500

HYDROFOILS:

Type:	Length (ft)	Gross Wt. (tons)	Power (SHP)	Max. Speed (kts)
1. AGEH-1 Plainview	212	320	28,000	50
2. Typhoon (USSR)	103	65	3,500	43
3. Vikhr (USSR)	156	117·5	4,800	43
4. FHE-400 (Canada)	151	212	22,000	60

AIR CUSHION VEHICLES

Type	Length (ft)	Gross Wt. (tons)	Power (SHP)	Max. Speed (kts)
1. SR.N 4 (U.K.)	130	180	17,000	70
2. Bell JEFF (B)	87	162·5	16,800	50
3. Sormovich (USSR)	96	30	2,500	75

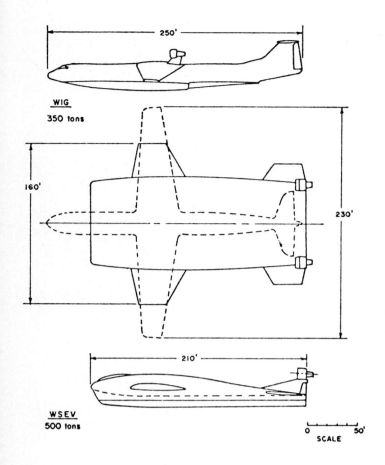

Fig I. WIG-WSEV size and configuration comparison

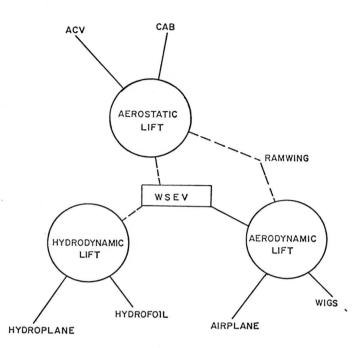

Fig. 2. System relations

effort is the apparent solution of the difficult stability and control problem inherent in operating a wing at various heights above the water—a difficulty also encountered in the basic ram wing and solved, in model form, by Gallington (2).

The characteristics of several existing hydrofoil boats, air cushion vehicles and a number of very large transport aircraft are listed in TABLE 1. It appears that on the basis of this data, and the previous discussion on the limitations of various types of surface effect vehicles, the most favourable means for producing very large vehicles with substantially higher speed capability is some variation on the wing-in-ground-effect scheme.

The goal of the work reported here was to investigate the feasibility of combining certain desirable features of the hydrofoil, surface effect, and WIG systems into a single type of vehicle suitable for a variety of potential naval missions. The inter-relationship between the types of vehicles suitable for these missions is summarised diagramatically in Figure 2. The resulting WSEV described in this article differs from the Lippisch scheme in both configuration and, more importantly, in anticipated size.

BASIC DESIGN FACTORS

Several fundamental design factors influence the selection of any specific vehicle configuration. Among these are power or thrust requirements, propulsive efficiency, and lift/drag characteristics Due to the unconventional nature of the proposed winged surface effect vehicle, a brief review of some design factors is in order.

POWER REQUIREMENTS AND PROPULSIVE EFFICIENCY

For a vehicle in steady (constant velocity) motion, the lift force (L) must equal the weight (W), and the thrust (T) must equal the resistance force or drag (D). The power required to propel the vehicle is:

$$\text{Engine Horsepower} = \text{SHP} = \frac{TV}{Cn} = \frac{WV}{Cn L/D} \qquad (1)$$

where

$$C = 550 \text{ if V in ft./sec.}$$
$$326 \text{ if V in kt.}$$
$$n = \text{propulsive efficiency}$$
$$V = \text{velocity}$$

and thrust required is:

$$\text{Thrust} = \text{Drag} = \frac{W}{(L/D)} \qquad (2)$$

Equation (1) may be rearranged to show the influence of aerodynamic efficiency (L/D) and speed on the specific thrust horsepower (SHP/W) required. Figure 3 illustrates the magnitude of this quantity for general values of L/D and for the specific case of current technology hydrofoil boats. Typical values of propulsive efficiency are 60% at 50 knots for a supercavitating propeller and 85% for a ducted fan from 150 to 300 knots. Figure 3 indicates that a vehicle with sufficiently high values of lift-to-drag ratio and propulsive efficiency could operate much more economically than a hydrofoil vehicle even at speeds in the order of 200 knots.

LIFT FORCES

The usual expression for the fluid-dynamic lift force on a vehicle is:

$$L = \text{lift force} = qC_L S \qquad (3)$$

where

$$C_L = \text{lift coefficiency}$$
$$q = 1/2pV^2$$
$$p = \text{mass density}$$

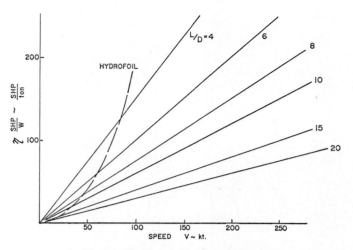

Fig. 3. Specific power required versus speed

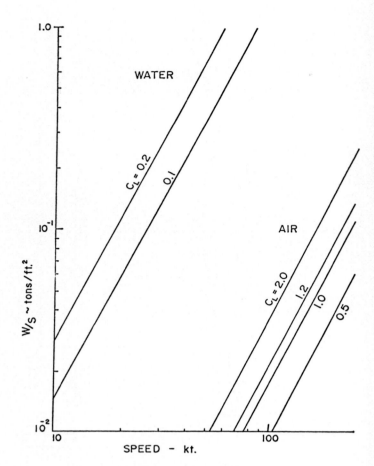

Fig. 4. Wing sizing relations

The very large difference between the density of water and that of air is one of the key elements in the design problem. High values of "q" can be obtained in water at even moderate velocities, while the "q" in air at the same speed is about 840 times less. In consequence, if the vehicle is to be sustained largely by aerodynamic rather than hydrodynamic lift (e.g. hydrofoils), the lifting area and/or lift coefficient would have to be correspondingly higher than those required in a water supported vehicle. Values of the weight per unit area of "wing" required for support in water and air are shown in Figure 4 as a function of speed and C_L.

DRAG FORCES

The resistance (drag) force on a vehicle operating in a fluid (air or water) is usually written:

$$D = \text{drag force} = C_D q S \qquad (4)$$

where

C_D = total drag coefficient

The Drag Coefficient in Equation (4) for a vehicle like a hydrofoil boat or an airplane is generally a complicated function of vehicle shape and several scale factors (Reynolds, Froude, and Mach numbers).

In first order aerodynamic theory, it is customary to write:

$$C_D = C_{D_p} + C_{D_i} = C_{D_p} + \frac{K_w C_L^2}{\pi AR} \qquad (5)$$

where

$$AR = \frac{(\text{span})^2}{\text{area}} = \frac{b^2}{S}$$

K_w = Wing "span efficiency factor"

In Equation (5) C_{D_p} is the "parasite" Drag Coefficient of the total vehicle, and C_{D_i} is the wing induced Drag (drag due to lift) Coefficient. C_{D_p} may be a very complex function and is usually dependent on vehicle angle of attack (and thus C_L). However, for purposes of making preliminary performance estimates it is usually sufficient to write:

$$C_{D_p} = C_{D_0} + K_0 C_L^2 \qquad (6)$$

where: C_{D_0} and K_0 are approximately constant, and are simply curve fitting parameters. The quantity AR/K_w in Equation (5) is usually referred to as the effective aspect ratio of the lifting surface. In simple theory, only the factor K_w is modified when a wing operates in ground effect. The span efficiency factor K_w has a theoretical minimum value of unity for a wing with an elliptic lift distribution operating outside ground effect. It should be noted that the total "airplane" or "Oswald efficiency factor" K frequently used for preliminary design estimates can be expressed in terms of the above formulation as:

$$K = K_0 \pi AR + K_w \qquad (7)$$

which then allows Equation (5) to be written in the simple form:

$$C_D = C_{D_0} + \frac{K C_L^2}{\pi AR} \qquad (8)$$

GROUND EFFECT

It is well known that the aerodynamic characteristics of a lifting wing are strongly altered when the wing is operated in very close proximity to a "solid" surface (ground effect). The main effects are:

a) the induced drag of the wing is decreased with increasing proximity to the "ground plane" due to interference of the "ground" with the full development of the downwash flow field, b) the lift curve slope of the wing is increased with increasing ground proximity, and c) the aerodynamic centre of the wing may shift considerably, resulting in substantial changes in pitching moment with ground proximity. To a lesser extent, the lift force at a given angle of attack may increase slightly with decreasing ground clearance.

For a simple planar wing, first order aerodynamic theory predicts that the magnitude of the influence of ground effect is proportional to the ratio of the height of the aerodynamic centre of the wing above the ground (h) to the wing span (b). Thus the reduction in induced drag is directly proportional to the ratio h/b. If the wing is to operate at a fixed height above the surface, then increasing wing span will result in decreasing induced drag.

In the present application it is desired to limit wing span for structural and operational reasons; e.g., in turns, the wing tip of a high aspect ratio wing may come dangerously close to the water surface and when docking the vehicle for loading. Consequently, if a simple planar wing is to be used, there is a definite upper limit to possible performance improvement to be had from exploitation of ground effect. Ashill (4), however, has shown that fitting a wing with inverted "tip plates" can magnify significantly the possible reduction in induced drag of a wing, depending on plate geometry and ground plane proximity. Ashill's theoretical results have been partially verified by wind tunnel tests, and the general validity of the theory has been verified by both wind tunnel tests and actual flight test for the case of low aspect ratio wings (5,6). The results of Ashill's analysis are shown in Fig. 5. It should be noted that this analysis assumes a smooth, rigid ground plane. The influence of a more realistic wavy, flexible surface typical of even a relatively calm sea is very difficult to estimate, and should be the subject of additional research.

THE WING SURFACE EFFECT VEHICLE (WSEV)

The basic criteria for the selection of the WSEV configurations studied were:

1) A simple, aerodynamically clean shape was desired.

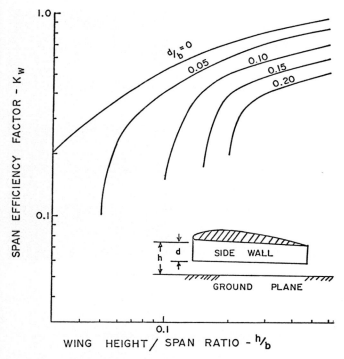

Fig. 5. Effect of wing height above ground on induced drag

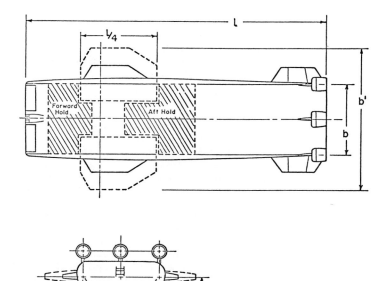

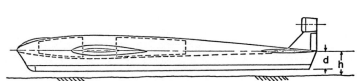

Fig. 6(a). Basic WSEV configuration

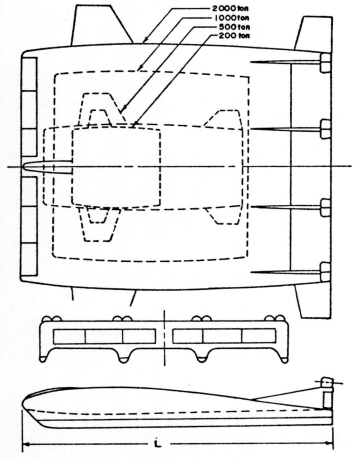

Fig. 6(b). WSEV size comparison

2) The overall system should be mechanically simple.

3) The viability of the system should not depend upon dramatic break-throughs in structural design, materials, or propulsion technology.

4) A shape which would provide maximum manoeuvrability in confined spaces was desired; and preferably one compatible with the Water Research Co. docking system (7).

In addition, the vehicle must possess adequate stability and flight handling characteristics throughout its entire operating envelope. As discussed thoroughly by Lippisch (3) and Gallington (2) this latter requirement is not so simple in the case of a vehicle with the capability of operating at wide variations in height about the ground plane.

The baseline WSEV configuration—Figure 6(a)—selected in a simple rectangular lifting surface with two or more (in the case of the larger vehicles studied) vertical sidewalls. The sidewalls produce the previously described increase in effective aspect ratio (decrease in drag due to lift) while the wing is in cruising flight, and provide flotation for the vehicle when it is at rest. WSEVs in four weight categories were analysed, and these are shown to the same scale in Figure 6(b). Their characteristics are summarised in TABLE 2.

The bridge is smoothly faired into the leading edge of the central wing, producing adequate visibility and minimum disruption of the airflow in this critical area. The ducted fans of the propulsion system are mounted on pylons at the rear of the vehicle so that: 1) the fans do not interfere with the airflow over the wing; 2) spray ingestion and flow distortion into the fan ducts is minimised; and 3) the fan ducts and pylons provide directional stability. The payload is carried in holds distributed around the vehicles' centre of gravity. For all the vehicles studied, even a very low centre-section airfoil thickness/chord ratio produced holds of very substantial depth.

TABLE 2.—SUMMARY OF BASELINE VEHICLE CHARACTERISTICS				
	V_{to} = 85 knots	C_{lto} = 2·0	n = 0·85	
	W = 200 tons	W = 500 tons	W = 1,000 tons	W = 2,000 tons
Channel Width (b)	80 ft	80 ft	200 ft	250 ft
Wing Span (b)	120 ft	160 ft	250 ft	300 ft
Wing Area (S)	8,200 ft²	20,400 ft²	40,800 ft²	81,600 ft²
Length (1)	93 ft	210 ft	204 ft	326 ft
Side-wall Depth (d)	10 ft	10 ft	15 ft	15 ft
Aspect Ratio (b²)	1·38	1·14	0·98	0·77
W empty (tons)	80	210	490	1,040

The major advantages of the proposed WSEV shape are: 1) the geometric aspect ratio (and hence wing span for a given lifting area) can be kept low enough to minimise stability problems during cruise, particularly over rough sea surfaces; 2) the width of the vehicle can be minimised to ease docking and loading.

The stability problems encountered while operating the simple channel shape at variable heights are resolved by fitting the basic centre section with two pairs of stub wings mounted fore and aft on the side walls. By proper sizing and incidence selection the pitching moments of the central channel can be altered to provide stability and/or control as the vehicle accelerates and cruises at the appropriate height above the water surface. It should be noted that the forward pair of stub wings act in much the same fashion as a canard empenage on more conventional aircraft. Tests of this scheme on a large radio controlled model shown in Figure 7 have yielded encouraging results. The stub wings also have the effect of increasing the *effective* aspect ratio of the machine in cruise.

The most difficult phase of WSEV operation is during transition from flotation to cruising flight. Substantial speed must be attained before a significant portion of the vehicle weight is supported by aerodynamic lift. Submerged surfaces operating at high speed lead to large resistance forces and excessive power (or thrust) requirements during acceleration to take-off. A realistic balance between wing size, power required, take-off speed and mechanical complexity can be achieved by proper selection of high lift devices. The baseline configuration assumes that the craft is fitted with a system of retractable leading edge slats and a simple single flap at the channel trailing edge. This system is simple, allows the basic wing to remain at a low geometric angle of attack even at high lift coefficients, and allows the vehicle to operate much like a ram wing during transition. A conservative value of CL = 2·0 at take-off was used for vehicle sizing assuming this high use lift system.

Two features of the proposed WSEV configuration make it particularly attractive:

1) The basic "airplane" nature of the vehicle allows it to fly out of ground effect for extended periods, thus allowing the WSEV to avoid obstacles and adverse weather or sea states. This capability cannot be matched by any hydrofoil or ACV system.
2) The basic channel shape of the vehicle is very favourable for the use of extensive laminar boundary layer control (BLC). While mechanically complex and suffering from problems of possible salt water corrosion of the BLC slots (unless a plastic outer wing skin is used), parasite drag reductions of at least 50% should be feasible. This drag reduction has not been applied in calculations for figures, tables or elsewhere in this article.

Structurally, the WSEV would most nearly resemble a large aircraft, although several factors tend to modify conventional aircraft design practice. Among these factors are:

1) The cargo area is within the wing itself, thus offering the possibility of distributing the load across the span. This results in a very significant relief in normal bending loads, with a consequent possible weight reduction.
2) The low aspect ratio inverted channel shape of the tip-plated (or sidewalled) wing is a much more favourable structural shape than that of a conventional aircraft, particularly in the case of vehicles with weights in excess of 500 tons.
3) The proposed WSEV operates in the speed range between 200 to 250 knots as compared with the 500 knot speed capability of jet transport aircraft. Thus, powerplant weight should be a smaller fraction of the total empty weight even accounting for the use of heavy duty marine turbine engines for propulsion.
4) There is no requirement for a pressurisation system or a wheeled landing gear.
5) The structural régime of the WSEV falls in the range classified as "ultra-low density" (8), wherein there is substantial advantage in the use of large composite material honeycomb panels for the skin and general use of "secondary spreading" of load carrying structural elements (e.g. spar caps are made hollow).

Several factors are important in selecting the propulsion system for the WSEV:

1) The anticipated speed of the vehicle allows the profitable use of ducted fans as the main thrust producer. Fans have substantially higher values of propulsive efficiency than hydrodynamic thrust devices such as supercavitating screw propellers and water jets.
2) The basic operating environment of the WSEV is at or near sea

Fig. 7. WSEV radio control test model

level, thus no compromises in engine design for altitude performance are required.
3) In cruise, all lift comes from aerodynamic forces, thus no power and associated ducting is required to maintain cushion pressure as in an ACV.

Two WSEV powerplant schemes appear promising. The first possibility is use of high by-pass ratio (8-10:1) turbofans. The technology of these engines is well established although specific fuel consumption is somewhat higher than desirable. The alternative is use of marine shaft turbines mounted in the aft portion of the wing centre section, and connected to the fans by extension shaft. The second scheme is mechanically more complex than the first, particularly if the turbines must be cross-shafted. However, this layout may be preferred for two reasons:

1) The marine shaft turbines are more robust and have lower specific fuel consumption than the turbofans.
2) The arrangement leads naturally to consideration of propelling the vehicle by non-hydrocarbon fuelled engines. There is adequate space and weight allowance in the larger WSEVs for a nuclear powerplant and its associated shielding, and there is space for the tankage required to use liquid hydrogen in an optimised engine.

WSEV PERFORMANCE AND ECONOMICS

The performance estimates made to date on the proposed WSEV relate basically to the vehicle in rectilinear cruise. Specifically, estimates have been made on: 1) vehicle size/power relations, 2) maximum and cruise speeds and 3) payload range relations. Basically, vehicles in four gross weight categories have been considered: 200, 500, 1,000 and 2,000 short tons. Performance characteristics for these baseline vehicles are summarised in Table 3. Predicted range/payload envelopes are shown in Figure 8.

The viability of this new scheme depends in large measure on obtaining maximum benefit from drag reduction through ground effect. In theory (4), large benefits can be gained even with the proposed vehicle configuration operating with substantial clearance between the vertical sidewalls and the water surface. This conclusion is, however, at variance with the views of Chaplin and Masters (9) which indicate that the clearance between sidewall and water surface must be kept very small. Operating a WSEV type vessel at high speed in close proximity to a rough sea surface raises major questions regarding structural strength and vehicle stability due to wave impact. This entire matter requires very careful experimental study and should be the subject of substantial future research.

It should be noted, however, that in the WSEV configuration, the lifting surface is well clear of the water surface, and the basic low aspect ratio shape of the WSEV reduces yawing moments produced by one sidewall impacting a wave compared to a WIG wing tip impacting at the same speed.

TABLE 3.—WSEV PERFORMANCE ESTIMATES

		W = 200 tons	W = 500 tons	W = 1,000 tons	W = 2,000 tons
CRUISE: (in ground effect)	CL*	0·35	0·40	0·32	0·27
	L/D*	16	16·5	15·5	14·0
	V*	200	195	215	230
	SHP req*	18,000	42,500	100,000	240,000
	T req*	25,000 lbs.	60,500 lbs.	130,000 lbs.	285,000 lbs.
CRUISE: (sea level, outside ground effect, 90%W)	L/D	10	9·5	9·0	8·4
	V	230 kt.	235 kt.	250 kt.	260 kt.
	SHP req	30,000	80,000	180,000	400,000
	T req.	36,000 lbs.	95,000 lbs.	200,000 lbs.	430,000 lbs.
RANGE/PAYLOAD: 1,000 n. mi.	+F (tons)	20	50	110	240
	U (tons)	100	240	400	720
3,000 n. mi.	F (tons)	55	140	290	640
	U (tons)	65	150	220	320

+F = Fuel load plus 10% reserves and U = Payload

A possible further means of reducing wave impact problems is to make the lower portion of the sidewalls flexible. A patent (10) for this kind of arrangement has recently been issued to the Water Research Company. The clearance problem and the influence of a "real" (i.e. flexible and wavy "ground" plane) sea surface on vehicle drag and stability would appear to be the major area of uncertainty in assessing the overall feasibility of the proposed system.

Due to the preliminary nature of the WSEV proposal, full economic analysis of the system has not been performed. Several simple indices for comparing the "direct operating economy" of transportation vehicles can, however, give a fair indication of relative merits of various schemes.

Three basic performance indices (figures of merit) have been used here. The first of these is simply:

$$Q_1 = \frac{\text{Payload weight (tons)}}{\text{gross weight (tons)}} = \frac{U}{W} \qquad (9)$$

The index Q_1 is meaningful if two competing vehicles are compared for trips of equal length, and it gives an indication of the percentage of the total vehicle weight which is "useful".

The second index used has been extensively studied by a number of authors, most notably GABRIELLI and VON KARMAN (11):

$$Q_2 = \frac{\text{Weight} \times \text{Distance travelled}}{\text{Unit of Energy Consumed}}$$

$$= \frac{\text{Weight} \times \text{Speed}}{\text{Power}} = \frac{WV}{P} \qquad (10)$$

The quantity Q_2 can be made dimensionless and can be defined in a variety of ways depending on whether the weight specified is the gross weight or the payload weight, the speed is maximum or cruise, etc. Q_2 is a meaningful comparison if the operating ranges used are equal.

The third index used is:

$$Q_3 = \frac{\text{Payload} \times \text{Speed}}{\text{Gross Weight}} = \frac{UV}{W} \qquad (11)$$

This is frequently referrred to as the "productivity index" of a vehicle.

Values of the three Q parameters for the C-5A aircraft, a typical ACV (12), and the four versions of the WSEV studied (W = 200, 500, 1,000 and 2,000 tons) are summarised in Table 4. This table, together with the range payload diagrams shown in Figure 8, gives a reasonably clear picture of the direct operating economics of the WSEV when compared to large aircraft and ACVs. Because of the large differences in cruise speed, the average productivity (Q_3) of the WSEV is about half that of the C-5A, but several times that of the ACV. On the basis of energy consumed per ton-mile travelled (Q_2), however, the WSEV is very much superior to the C-5A and the ACV. Payload/gross weight fractions (Q_1) for the WSEVs are very favourable compared to the aircraft and the ACV.

The above results are, admittedly, a very limited comparison of the overall economics of the systems considered. However, for a number of military missions, the WSEV may be attractive, particularly when consideration is given to the additional, less quantifiable characteristics of the WSEV:

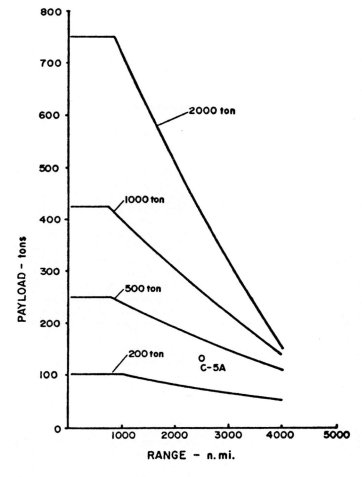

Assume 10% Fuel Reserves

Fig. 8. WSEV range/payload diagrams

1) The vehicle does not cruise in the water or at high altitude thus reducing vulnerability to both underwater and airborne detection and countermeasures.

2) The favourable geometric shape of the WSEV provides cargo holds of large size thus allowing bulky cargo to be carried more easily and with less penalty than in the basically round tubular fuselage of conventional aircraft.

TABLE 4.—ECONOMIC SUMMARY

	C-5A	ACV	WSEV A	B	C	D
W (tons)	382	300	200	500	1,000	2,000
Ver. (kt.)	457	60-80	200	195	215	230
$+Q_2=\dfrac{WV}{P}$ (at cruise)	9·1	5·8	16	16·5	15·5	14·0
* 1,000 n. mi. Range:						
$Q_1=\dfrac{U}{W}$	0·45	0·30-0·40++	0·51	0·49	0·41	0·37
$+Q_2=\dfrac{UV}{P}$	4·1	1·5-3++	8·2	8·1	6·4	5·2
$Q_3=\dfrac{UV}{W}$	205	20-30++	102	96	87	85
* 3,000 n. mi. Range:						
$Q_1=\dfrac{U}{W}$	0·36	—	0·35	0·33	0·24	0·19
$+Q_2=\dfrac{UV}{P}$	3·3	—	5·6	5·5	3·7	2·7
$Q_3=\dfrac{UV}{W}$	164	—	70	65	52	44

$$+Q_3 \text{(dimensionless)} = \frac{7\cdot2\ W\text{ (tons)} \times V\text{ (kt)}}{P\text{ (SHP)}} = \frac{W\text{ (ton)}}{T\text{ (ton)}}$$

++ Range of 100 n. mi.

*No reserves, cruise values of V (kt.), P (SHP), W (tons)

WSEV Applications

The initial mission envisioned for the larger WSEVs was low-density cargo transport over ranges from 1,000 to 3,000 nautical miles. In this case the basic configuration of the vehicle, sized to provide sufficient lifting surface area to "take-off" at speed and power settings consistent with hydrodynamically imposed "hump speed" and aerodynamically imposed cruise speed limits, results in cargo spaces inside the lifting surface capable of accommodating a wide variety of bulky low-density cargo. Further, the payload weight/space capacity of the larger vehicles is consistent with typical military cargoes such as troops, fully assembled helicopters, etc. Despite the previously assessed decrease in "productivity" compared to large aircraft like the C-5A, the increased "economy" and the favourable geometry of the WSEV which allows it to circumvent conventional aircraft size limits, plus the favourable operational characteristics such as use of water rather than land bases and decreased vulnerability to detection and interception make the WSEV attractive for "light-weight" (compared with ships) naval logistic missions.

The same features of the WSEV which benefit the logistics mission may offer potential advantages in other naval military missions. Specifically, the large "flat" catamaran type platform configuration of the vehicle and the high speed (compared to ships and SES vehicles) cruise capability give the WSEV substantial mobility.

High Mobility Platforms

For naval missions which require a rapid deployment capability with "light" payloads (but beyond the limits of conventional aircraft) and which require the existence of a relatively stable platform while stationary, the basic WSEV configuration may be promising. Three missions for such a capability can be initially envisioned: (1) ASW, (2) early warning and air-defence missile launching, and (3) short-to-intermediate range ballistic missile launching. All of these missions might be equally well served by other SEV types (e.g. the CAB); however, none possesses the high speed/range capability of the WSEV. Future loss of overseas bases and/or the need to establish well defended ports in unforseen locations make the air defence platform attractive. Similarly the need for a rapidly deployable "shore bombardment" platform may increase in future military scenarios.

Rapid Response "Carrier"/Support Vessels

Given the size and range/payload/speed characteristics of the WSEV, an intriguing set of "carrier" vehicle missions can be contemplated. The recent experience in Vietnam has shown the need for a class of very nimble, high speed patrol craft of relatively small size (13). Unfortunately, manoeuvrability and range are not

consistent design variables and to provide a limited number of these types of vessels with the range, let alone the required support (weapons replacement, maintenance, fuel) facilities, to cover the realistic operating areas is a very formidable task. Similarly, the same design conflict exists between range and nimbleness in helicopters, VTOL attack aircraft and ACV landing craft. Since all of these vehicles fall into the category of low-density cargoes when carried by a "mother" vessel, and none individually exceeds the size and payload capability of the WSEV, it is then natural to evaluate the possibility of configuring a WSEV as a carrier/support ship for each case. A typical WSEV, capable of carrying a pair of nominal 200 ton patrol hydrofoils together with required weapons support personnel and fuel, is shown in Figure 9. The catamaran type configuration of the basic WSEV is particularly well suited to the launch and retrieval of the patrol craft. The patrol craft would be carried in semi-submerged wells in the underside of the WSEV, there being adequate space inside the wing to completely enclose the above deck structure of the patrol boat and its retracted hydrofoil support struts, thus minimising the aerodynamic penalty to the WSEV in cruise flight. In the same way, ACV landing craft could be carried in underwing wells, with troops and their assault weapon housed inside the wing. For helicopter/VTOL missions, the large holds in the WSEV would serve as hangar space and an elevator would raise them to a take-off platform on the wing upper surface.

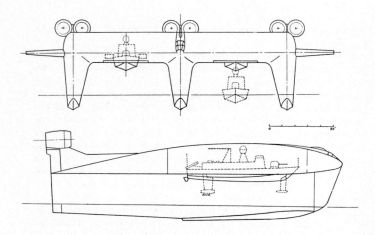

Fig. 9. WSEV—coastal patrol carrier/support configuration

Hydrogen Fuel Depot Vessel

The crisis both in cost and ultimate availability of hydrocarbon fuels has lead naturally to extensive considerations of alternative fuel sources. Strong cases have been made (14, 15) for the desirability and feasibility of using liquid hydrogen (LH$_2$) as a prime fuel—particularly in aircraft. The three main disadvantages to the use of LH$_2$ in military applications are:

1) On a unit energy content per unit weight basis LH$_2$ has about one fourth the weight density (weight per unit volume) of conventional hydrocarbon fuels. This is a severe penalty in volume limited vehicles.

2) LH$_2$ requires cryogenic storage, with a consequent fuel tankage weight penalty.

3) Some type of energy source (nuclear, solar, etc.) is required to "manufacture" the LH$_2$.

Again the WSEV may serve as a promising basis for a vehicle designer to exploit use of hydrogen fuel. The configuration of the WSEV, sized to fly at relatively low speeds on aerodynamic lift, is less limited in volume than either hydrodynamically supported vessels or high speed aircraft. Thus it possesses the internal capacity to carry the tankage required for LH$_2$ directly. In addition, one can easily contemplate a *fleet* of WSEVs, all hydrogen fuelled, *one* of which is configured to carry a nuclear reactor and associated storage tanks to serve as a "tanker". Thus the requisite LH$_2$ could be manufactured on site, with the tanker possessing the same range/mobility characteristics as the other elements of the fleet. To reduce vulnerability, the tanker WSEV could be configured to be externally indistinguishable from the other fleet elements (landing craft carrier/support vehicles, etc.).

Concluding Comments

A preliminary design description has been presented on a type of naval surface effect vehicle which holds promise of circumventing weight and size limits in conventional aircraft design, and speed and complexity limitations on existing SES vehicles (e.g. ACVs and CABs). The proposed WSEV design is based on well established aerodynamic principles and required no major breakthrough in aerodynamic or propulsion technology. The performance of the WSEV is significantly enhanced, however, if advances can be made in ultra low-density composite structural technology, and the practicality of extensive boundary layer control and LH$_2$ fuel can be demonstrated. A favourable trade-off exists between productivity and economy for the transport of low-density cargoes, even without the use of advanced technology refinements.

The ability of the WSEV to carry large bulky cargo over significant distances at relatively high speeds compared to competing naval SES systems, and its ability to actually fly at substantial heights to avoid high sea states and other surface obstructions make the WSEV concept attractive for both military and commercial applications. In addition a number of interesting purely military missions have been briefly described which would indicate a wide future use for WSEV type vehicles.

References

1. McMasters, J. H. and Greer, R. R., "A Conceptual Study for a New Winged Surface Effect Vehicle System", *Naval Eng. Jour.*, April 1974, pp. 41-51.

2. Gallington, R. W., "Ram Wing Surface Effect Boat", *J. Hydronautics*, Vol. 7, No. 3, July 1973, pp. 118-123.

3. Lippisch, A. M., *Jane's Surface Skimmers*, 1974-75 ed.

4. Ashill, P. R.; "On the Minimum Induced Drag of Ground Effect Wings", *Aero. Quarterly*, Aug. 1970. pp. 211-232.

5. Carter, A. W., "Effect of Ground Proximity on the Aerodynamic Characteristics of Aspect Ratio 1 Airfoils With and Without End Plates", NASA TN D-970.

6. Fink, M. P. and Lastinger, J. L.; "Aerodynamic Characteristics of Low-Aspect-Ratio Wings in Close Proximity to the Ground", NASA TN-D-962, 1961.

7. Greer, R. R., *Hydroplane Transport System*, U.S. Patent No. 3,653,035 (1972) and *Watercraft*, U.S. Patent No. 3,768,429 (1973).

8. Czerwinski, W.; "Dominant Factors in Light Weight Design", *Canadian Aero. Space Journ.*, Jan. 1967, pp. 9-22.

9. Chaplin, H. R. and Masters, L. W.; "Rheoelectric Measurements of Some Theoretical Effects of Ground Proximity on Wings", David Taylor Model Basin Aero. Rpt. 1068, Jan. 1964.

10. Greer, R. R., Wave Force Absorbing Device, U.S. Patent approved for issue, filed 1973.

11. Gabrielli, G. and von Karman, Th., "What Price Speed?" *Mech. Engineering*, October 1950, pp. 775-781.

12. Nakonechny, B. V., "A Synthesis of Design Data for Existing and Near-Future Air-Cushion Vehicles", *Naval Eng. Journal*, Dec. 1971, pp. 15-26.

13. Scharf, S.; "The Naval Special Warfare Craft Program", *Naval Engineers Jour.*, April 1975, pp. 93-7.

14. Brewer, G. D., "The Case for Hydrogen Fueled Transport Aircraft", AIAA Paper No. 73-1323, Nov. 1973.

15. Goodger, E. M.; "Alternative Fuels for Aviation", *Aero. Journ.*, May 1975, pp. 212-224.

BELL ACV AND SES DESIGNS 1959—1975

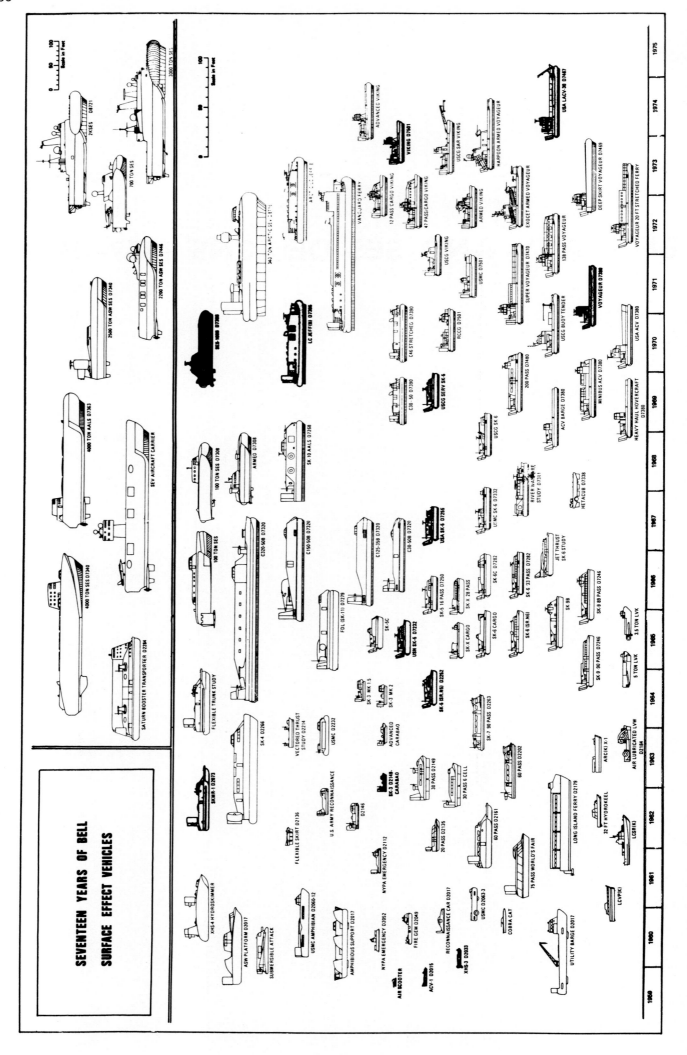

SEVENTEEN YEARS OF BELL
SURFACE EFFECT VEHICLES

BELL ACV AND SES DESIGNS 1959-1975

At no time in its relatively short history has the air cushion vehicle industry been better prepared to accept large commercial and military orders than at present. Technical advances and nearly one million hours of operating experience on practically every continent and in all climatic conditions have placed the reliability and performance of the ACV beyond doubt.

The astonishing pace at which the technology has advanced is dramatically illustrated by this drawing of the many vehicles and concepts created by the designers at Bell Aerospace between 1959 and 1975. Study of the drawing reveals, step-by-step, the evolution of the Voyageur and Viking from the SK-5, trends in skirt design and propulsion systems, and some of the lessons learned from the SES-100B test programme and incorporated in the 2KSES project.

From a variety of early research vehicles and small ACVs, Bell in the United States is now developing 2,200 ton surface effect ships and a 160-ton amphibious assault landing craft for the US Navy, in addition to which Bell Aerospace Canada is producing the Voyageur and Viking multi-purpose ACVs at a plant in Grand Bend, Ontario. Two "stretched" Voyageurs, designated LACV-30, have been ordered by the US Army, and there is a likelihood that it will require as many as thirty.

Produced at Bell's New Orleans (Louisiana) Operations, the SES-100B 100-ton surface effect ship test craft attained a speed of 82·3 knots, almost 95 miles per hour, on May 23rd, 1975. In addition, it has completed all its initial test objectives and has operated for considerable periods of time in high sea states in the Gulf of Mexico. Work is continuing under a $33 million contract to conduct an advanced development programme for the US Navy's proposed large SES, an ocean-going combat-capable ship.

Bell's research work on ACVs began seventeen years ago when it first built a tiny air cushion scooter, a one-ton ACV and a variety of other early test vehicles.

In 1963, the company completed the Carabao, a versatile operational research machine which weighed 1½ tons and featured a tri-cell concept in which a single fan fed air into three circular lift cells.

Also completed in 1963 was the 35-ton SKMR-1 research ACV for the US Navy. This vehicle, which reached speeds of up to 80 miles per hour, was a predecessor of the 160-ton JEFF(B) amphibious assault landing craft, due to be completed at Bell's New Orleans Operations in early 1976.

The combat capabilities of the ACV were proven in the 1960s by Army and Navy SK-5s in Vietnam. The three Navy craft were built by British Hovercraft Corp., with which Bell has a licensing agreement, and were extensively modified by Bell. Following two combat duty tours, the Navy ACVs were transferred to the US Coast Guard for evaluation as part of the operations unit in San Francisco, California. Built at Bell were the three SK-5s used by the US Army in Vietnam combat. These were armed and armoured craft delivered by Bell in 1968. Deployed in Vietnam, they operated in swamps, rice paddies and inland waterways, demonstrating a capability to perform a variety of special missions including amphibious assault, troop insertion, supply and search and rescue.

An outgrowth of SK-5 technology, employing an identical lift/propulsion system, is the Voyageur, which has performed a variety of tasks ranging from icebreaking in Montreal to cargo service on the Yukon River in Alaska. A Voyageur served under contract during the winter of 1974-75 to Alyeska Pipeline Service Company, the firm responsible for the design, construction and operation of the pipeline. It began work in Alaska in August 1974, and hauled pipes, drill casings, fuel and explosives to and from sites along the Beaufort Sea coastline, Colville and Killick Rivers.

The longest run was for the US Navy, transporting drill casing 200 miles from Umiat on the Colville River to an area near Pitt Point in Naval Petroleum Reserve No. 4. The craft then returned to Umiat by a more direct overland route—demonstrating its amphibious capability. With a payload capacity comparable to that of a Hercules aircraft, the Voyageur operates at speeds of up to 55 miles per hour in marginal terrain, water and ice, and in weather which stops other forms of transport.

Another Voyageur served with Kaps Transport Ltd. in Canada's Northwest Territories, and a third craft was used by Agence Maritime Inc., providing 1974-75 winter supplies to isolated communities along Quebec's Lower North Shore. The Quebec programme was being sponsored by the Federal Transportation Development Agency and the Quebec Ministry of Transport, Marine Branch. A regularly-scheduled freight service had never before been available to the communities during the winter. During the summer of 1975, Voyageur was put to work as a high-speed replacement for a disabled ferry, hauling trucks and cargo between the Quebec community of St. Joseph de la Rive and the St. Lawrence island, Ile aux Coudres.

The Voyageur in service with Agence Maritime is the fourth production Voyageur. Like its sister craft, Voyageur 004 is made of bolt-together modules that can be disassembled for ease of transportation between distant job sites. Since Voyageur is compatible with the hauling capacities of a range of other vehicles, the craft offers an economical extension of existing cargo haul operations.

Operating a Voyageur in Montreal, Quebec, the Canadian Coast Guard found the craft to be an unexpectedly effective icebreaker. The discovery had been made in 1974 by the federal government's air cushion vehicle personnel during tests with the Canadian Coast Guard Voyageur, then based at Parry Sound, Ontario. Initial trials were scheduled to check the low speed (four to seven knots) icebreaking capability of the self-propelled Voyageur against those of non-self-propelled ACVs tested earlier. Travelling at higher speeds over hard, unbroken ice, the crew noticed that a standing wave of ice developed behind the Voyageur. In this wave and in the diminishing waves which followed, the heavy ice was cracking and shattering with some violence. Recognising the implications of the unexpected phenomenon, officials immediately undertook an additional schedule of exploratory operations with the craft.

They found that at a speed of 15 knots and at a gross weight of about 45 tons, the Voyageur would break hard ice up to 15 inches thick continuously and effectively. In early 1975, the Canadian Coast Guard Voyageur opened a 3½-mile ice jam in the Riviere des Prairies north of Montreal, and kept the river clear of additional buildups. An estimated $3½ million in property damage along the river caused annually by spring flooding was avoided because of the Voyageur's ability to break up ice into small pieces that floated harmlessly downstream.

A participant in the US Navy's SES programme since 1966, Bell has accumulated a wealth of design and research data on ship-size ACVs unrivalled elsewhere in the industry. In the field of propulsion alone it is employing systems ranging from air propellers and waterjets to ducted propellers and semi-submerged marine propellers. As world requirements accelerate, Bell's experience across the whole ACV spectrum should enable it to cope effectively with a wide range of demands.

HOVERCRAFT—THE NEXT GENERATION

Leslie R. Colquhoun, DFC, GM, DFM,
Leslie Colquhoun & Associates

HOVERCRAFT—THE NEXT GENERATION

By Leslie R. Colquhoun, DFC, GM, DFM
Leslie Colquhoun & Associates

Impression of a BHC SR.N4 Mk 3 Mountbatten-class hovercraft

On the 25th July 1959 Commander 'Sheepy' Lamb and his crew, John Chaplin and Christopher Cockerell (now Sir Christopher Cockerell), set out from Calais in the early hours of the morning to attempt the first-ever crossing of the English Channel by hovercraft. Sometime later they landed safely, although earlier than expected, on the beach at Dover, thus establishing a unique first and providing a fitting tribute to another great pioneer, for it was on the same day 50 years earlier that M. Bleriot became the first man to fly the English Channel in an aeroplane.

To-day SR.N4 hovercraft make up to 60 crossings per day, providing a capability to carry nearly 2,000 cars and 15,000 passengers. A far cry from that epic pioneering trip in 1959, during which the only way Sir Christopher could be taken was clad in oilskins standing on the open deck.

It must therefore be a moment of pride for Sir Christopher Cockerell to know that the determination and sacrifice to get support for his ideas to use the air cushion principle during the 1950s has in part paid off; but it must also be a moment of sadness and frustration to know that only two companies are operating on the Channel and only five SRN4s are involved. Furthermore, the lead which Britain has held for so long now seems to be slipping to the French, Japanese and even the Americans.

The heady days of 1959, 1960, 1961 and 1962 gave great promise. The development of the flexible skirt, to contain the cushion and give greater obstacle and wave clearance height, enabled the lift power requirement to be reduced in relation to rise height. Thus, from the original concept of the SR.N1, when the cushion was contained by an air curtain, the distribution of power could be changed from two-thirds for lift and one-third for propulsion, to one-third for lift and two-thirds for propulsion, thus improving significantly the commercial prospects of developing air cushion transportation.

However, costs were also increasing significantly and it was becoming obvious that the application of the air cushion principle to modern transport methods was not going to prove so simple as had first been supposed.

Not least of the problems was the fact that the heavy spray generated by the air cushion was having a very adverse effect on the engines, and the degree of filtration originally provided was totally inadequate. During the operation of the world's first-ever hovercraft passenger service across the Dee Estuary from Rhyl to Wallasey in 1962, for example, thirteen engine changes were required during the ten weeks for which the service was scheduled to run.

The advent of the SR.N5, followed by the SR.N6, showed that some of these problems could be overcome, and regular passenger carrying operations were started on the Solent, on the Clyde, in Norway, in San Francisco, in Denmark and, in 1966, across the English Channel from Ramsgate to Calais. The latter was a prelude to the SR.N4, capable of carrying up to 30 cars and 250 passengers.

Unfortunately, operators soon found that without adequate maintenance facilities and competent engineers, the reliability of hovercraft fell far short of the requirement necessary for a scheduled service, and the provision of such facilities increased the cost of the operation. There was also over-confidence in the reaction of passengers to the hovercraft motion in rough seas. Most people thought that riding on a cushion of air meant a smooth crossing, and a welcome departure from the heaving and tossing experienced on conventional ships. This of course was not the case and although the SR.N6 can, and has been, operated in open seas of up to Force 7, it is quite another matter to ask passengers to pay for the experience. Quite apart from the fact that the motion is far from smooth, the normal journey time can be more than doubled, and whilst it is still probably shorter than the ship time, this is not much solace to the seasick passenger.

Consequently only three operators in the U.K. have succeeded in surviving. Hovertravel, whose history on the Solent goes back to 1964; Hoverlloyd, responsible for operating the Ramsgate-Calais SR.N4 passenger/vehicle service and Seaspeed, an offshoot of British Railways, which operates between Cowes and Southampton with SR.N6s and Dover-Calais/Boulogne with SR.N4.

Hovertravel and Hoverlloyd are private sector companies, which stand or fall on their commercial expertise and success. Not for them the soft cushion of the taxpayer when things are bad; on the contrary the hard and inescapable facts of liquidation and bankruptcy, a fate already experienced by some of the earlier operators.

It can be argued that the fate of the passenger-carrying hovercraft hinges upon the continued success of these two companies. The hovercraft industry must be thankful that its future is in good hands.

People who are keen to pour scorn on the future of the hovercraft in the passenger transport role say that the survival of Hoverlloyd and Hovertravel is due to the high fare structure on their particular routes. To some extent this is true, but it must also be remembered that both routes are subject to severe seasonal fluctuations and in order to have the capacity to service the peak demand the fleet size is such that during the off-peak season it is under utilised. The operators costs therefore are increased to cover this situation.

Nobody would deny that the relatively high operating costs of amphibious hovercraft require a high passenger throughput, but if this could be on a year round basis fares could be reduced. This argument equally applies to ships or any other form of transport faced with the same problem. Where hovercraft are at a disadvantage is that route length will determine the fare much more so than on ships. For this reason alone no attempt has been made to operate longer routes, and perhaps this is fortunate for there can be no doubt that the existing generation of hovercraft would not be equal to such routes in terms of passenger comfort and performance.

It must not be forgotten, however, that the hovercraft is a very diverse form of transportation. The comments made so far have been related to the amphibious type of hovercraft. The Hovermarine HM.2, using the sidewall principle which only requires flexible structures to contain the cushion at the bow and stern has had some success, after a disastrous start when the original Hovermarine Company were forced into liquidation. But, it is felt that much greater success was and is possible if the modest alterations that have been suggested by operators could be put into this craft to improve its performance and reliability. Some progress has been made, but it has been unnecessarily slow.

It is to be hoped that when the HM.5 comes on to the market some of these lessons will have been learned and the new hovercraft will benefit thereby.

Also to be considered is the industrial field. Here it can honestly be said that the new industry is growing in a healthy and encouraging way. Construction companies and the oil industry are becoming increasingly aware of the advantages of the air cushion principle, and it is a matter of some satisfaction that the British pioneers in this new technology are proving equal to the varied and unique demands being made upon them to produce acceptable air cushion concepts in order to solve the problems of moving equipment in difficult environmental conditions.

There can be no doubt, therefore, that application of air cushion technology will prosper, but those responsible for its advancement must keep foremost in their minds that the oil industry or the construction industry are adopting this technology for the advantages that it provides. If it is oversold, i.e., is not equal to the task required, or the standard of reliability is lacking, then the whole

business will backfire and the industrial application of air cushion technology will join the graveyard together with other bright ideas that have not proved equal to the customers' requirements.

What can be said then, regarding the future of the passenger-carrying hovercraft? As far as the sidewall concept is concerned the answer is relatively simple. The success of the HM.2 can be assured by relatively small modifications to increase performance and reliability. If this could be done it is not difficult to foresee HM.2s replacing the many similar-sized hydrofoils that are operating throughout the world and, what is more, doing a better job. This will need an agressive and sustained marketing policy.

For the future, the plans to build the HM.5, capable of carrying 200 passengers, would seem a logical next step. However, it will only be thus if the specification takes heed of the operators' requirements. These will relate to performance, payload, operating environment and operating costs. For example it would be no sense to produce a 200-seat craft which could only operate in limited areas. The great advantage of sidewall hovercraft is that, with its excellent manoeuvrability, it can safely operate at speed in relatively congested waters. Such areas would tend to be in sheltered or inland waters, or on the larger rivers and canals of the world. It would be essential therefore for the new craft to be environmentally acceptable. Low noise level, lack of wash, minimum spray and rapid acceleration would be firm requirements without which the craft would find the market severely limited.

One can only hope that these considerations are in hand, in which case the future for the HM.5 or a developed HM.2 will be assured, and one can only wish Hovermarine every success.

Amphibious hovercraft present a much more difficult problem. In the thirty-to fifty-seat range, only the BHC stretched SR.N6s are available. Regrettably the high capital and operating cost put these craft out of court in all but the most specialised routes.

It is suggested that BHC have not succeeded in selling an SR.N6 for commercial traffic for at least three and possibly four years. On the other hand the Japanese company Mitsui Shipbuilding and Engineering, has sold at least 12 MV-PP5s four of which, each capable of carrying 52 passengers, are reported to be successfully operating on the 37-mile route. The same company will be operating 3 MV-PP15s capable of carrying 155 passengers at the EXPO '75 Port on Okinawa. The British hovercraft industry has not produced such a craft.

Perhaps the nearest equivalent would be the Vosper Thornycroft VT1 which could carry up to 250 passengers or a combination of 10 cars and 146 passengers. Although this craft operated successfully between Malmo and Copenhagen in 1972 its operators were forced to take it off the route due to fierce price cutting from the rival operators who were running hydrofoils. This was unfortunate and did the VT 1 an injustice from which it has not yet recovered. Vosper Thornycroft now seems to be concentrating on military vehicles.

The SR.N4, however, has been more fortunate. Hoverlloyd operates three of these craft and runs a highly efficient and successful service from its purpose-built hoverport at Pegwell Bay, Ramsgate to the purpose-built hoverport at Calais. Seaspeed operate the other

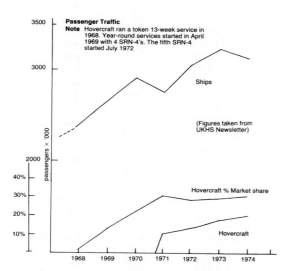

Figure 1. Dover/Folkestone/Ramsgate ferry services to Calais/Boulogne

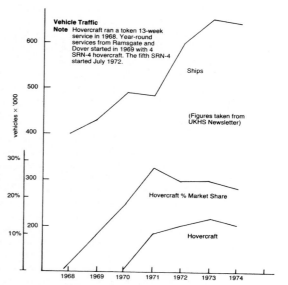

Figure 2. Dover/Folkestone/Ramsgate to Calais/Boulogne Ferry services

two SR.N4s on their routes, Dover to Calais Hoverport and Dover to Boulogne Hoverport. Jointly the two companies are now carrying nearly 30% of the short haul Channel passenger and car traffic. *Figures 1 and 2.*

This is a very significant achievement, especially as their share of the traffic seems to be increasing each year. This is contrary to predictions made by the shipping lines when the service started in 1968. They predicted a very short and painful life for both Hoverlloyd and Seaspeed.

Their forecasts have therefore been confounded, and it would seem that, for the future, the hovercraft companies will continue to increase their share of the channel traffic. However, to do so both companies will need new craft capable of higher performance in rough seas, providing greater comfort in terms of less vibration and noise, in addition to a smoother ride and the ability to carry a larger payload at lower cost. Such a craft could dramatically increase the popularity of hovercraft travel and cause a significant switch from traditional ships to the new form of transport.

More important, perhaps, is that such a craft would permit the operators to consider longer routes. For example Ramsgate to Ostend, 60 n. miles, or Ramsgate to Flushing, 85 n. miles. Ramsgate to Flushing would have considerable advantages in that Flushing could be described as the gateway to central Europe. Thus a completely new market would be opened up.

If this were so, more hovercraft would be required to operate the route, and this would have an escalating effect on the passenger-carrying hovercraft market. Ferry operators with routes elsewhere in the world would consider that the success of the channel operations would need a reappraisal of their own situation, and the new craft could well fulfil their needs.

The next generation of large hovercraft could therefore be important. If it is successful the dreams and aspirations of Sir Christopher Cockerell in 1959 could be realised and the hovercraft would take its rightful place in the transport scene. However, for this success to materialise, the right decisions must be taken regarding the new craft. Failure to do so could result in further setbacks for an already frail industry.

It is thought that the basis for any second generation hovercraft specification should be based upon the requirements of existing operators, since these will be the first users of such equipment. However, some thought should be given to the longer term objectives of operating on extended routes.

The basic headings for a new craft specification would be:

1. Payload
2. Passenger comfort.
3. Improved performance
4. Reliability.
5. Operating costs.
6. Range.
7. Environmental acceptability.

Regarding payload, the SR.N4 Mk.2 can carry 280 passenger and up to 35 cars. During the peak season this could be increased with advantage. However, there are some constraints to be considered. Firstly, the limitation of passenger handling facilities. It is of little use if the hovercraft provides comfortable and spacious conditions for 1,000 passengers, if prior to their departure, and after landing, they have been subjected to cramped accommodation, delays in passing through the customs and immigration procedures and problems in reclaiming luggage. These are the frustrations of existing forms of transport. The arrival of the Jumbo-jet has not always benefitted the traveller. The problems of 300-400 passengers trying to reclaim their luggage and get through customs can only be resolved by considerable improvements in ground handling facilities, for which there is not always the space nor the money.

It must also be remembered that the hovercraft has been successful because of its high work rate. This has been achieved by rapid turn-round time. The SR.N4 at the moment takes 20 minutes to load and unload 250 passengers and 30 cars. The Mk.2 version takes slightly longer due to the manoeuvring necessary to get the five extra car units stowed. Turn-round time is therefore an important consideration. Unless careful attention is paid to it, all advantages of any improved performance could be lost. It must be remembered that many people travel on the SR.N4 because of the convenience it provides as much as for the shorter journey time. This advantage must not be lost.

The seasonal nature of the route must also be taken into consideration. Despite the strong marketing efforts made both by the shipping companies and the hovercraft companies, there has

not been a significant increase in the winter passenger traffic across the Channel. The extent of this variation can be gauged by the fact that during July, August and the first two weeks of September, Hoverlloyd operate up to 20 schedules a day from Ramsgate, but from the middle of October to the middle of March this is reduced to four, and on many occasions the traffic only warrants three. Thus a new craft offering an improved payload would be operating at a very low load factor during the winter months, and the problems of under-utilisation become more difficult.

The possible argument that the larger craft, by operating fewer services could carry the traffic at a high load factor than at present would destroy one of the advantages of hovercraft travel, namely a frequent, fast and reliable service. In any event the need is for the hovercraft operators to increase their share of the market and expand their business. However there is room for compromise in this area since fewer schedules reduce the craft operating costs and enable possible reductions in crew requirements. Since larger craft will require more crew members the latter is not an insignificant saving.

Passenger comfort is of primary importance. The novelty of hovercraft travel is past and passengers are now critically comparing it with more conventional transport systems.

There can be no doubt that improvements must be made to reduce the internal noise and vibration levels. It is of little use comparing it to a tube train or an Argonaut aeroplane: the modern standard is a 747 or a Tristar airliner. This aspect is of considerable importance if longer routes are to be contemplated. It is essential, therefore, that the manufacturers of the next generation of hovercraft set themselves the highest possible standard.

Passenger cabin ventilation is another area where significant improvements are required. This is particularly so when crossings are made in rough sea conditions. Motion sickness is bound to occur in these conditions and adequate ventilation is essential.

Thought must also be given to cabin temperature control, and in addition to a heating system, it may be necessary to install air-conditioning. The latter would be essential if the operations were being carried out in a warmer climate than experienced in this country. Unfortunately, these requirements have tended to be treated as of secondary importance in the past but they are essential and must be designed into the hovercraft from the very beginning. It is very difficult and costly to improve these problem areas after the hovercraft has been built.

However, all these requirements are complementary to the basic need to provide the passenger with a smooth and comfortable ride. Excessive movement can be minimised by seating the passengers near the longitudinal and lateral c.g. of the hovercraft and providing comfortable and well-cushioned seats. In this way the motion of the craft as it contours the wave pattern will be considerably reduced as far as the passengers are concerned.

The actual motion of the craft will be reduced by making it longer so that it will tend to bridge the wave trough rather than ride down into it. But it should be remembered that the captain can in effect achieve the same result by intelligent handling of the hovercraft. This might put two or three minutes on the journey, but from the passengers' point of view the journey is a great deal more comfortable.

The vertical accelerations occurring in the craft due to wave impacts also tend to be minimised at the c.g., but the cushion characteristics will govern the general level of such accelerations. Much theoretical work has been carried out to establish how the cushion aerodynamics can be controlled to reduce craft motion and relieve the accelerations. So far no practical solution has been used successfully. On the SR.N6 the skirt lift system could be used as a form of control, not as a method of reducing craft motion. On the VT 1 a mechanical system was tried to shift the c.p. of the cushion by pulling in the skirt system on one side and letting it out the other. However, the mechanical problems of the system outweighed the advantages gained. In America the two companies responsible for the systems evaluation and design of the 2KSES are investigating heave alleviations systems. This is being achieved either by altering the cushion fan air flow by variable incidence blades, or choking the inlet, or by having vent gates in the sidewalls that operate to relieve the cushion pressure when it gets to a designed maximum. Model tests have given encouraging results and the system is being evaluated on the Bell SES-100B and Aerojet SES-100A sidewall hovercraft. Such systems have not been tried on British hovercraft to date. The tendency in the British hovercraft industry has been to achieve a reasonable compromise using the cushion stiffness characteristics.

On new designs it may well be advisable to consider heave alleviation systems, but to be effective they must be connected to electronic sensors registering either cushion pressure or wave trains so that the heave alleviation becomes an automatic process. This unfortunately introduces extra costs and further complexity adding to the maintenance problems. However, the beneficial results from a successful system would prove cost effective in that operations in rougher sea conditions would be possible without subjecting passengers to severe discomfort or even danger.

Improved performance must be achieved by any new design of hovercraft, not so much in terms of absolute speed in calm conditions, but the ability to go faster in rougher seas. It is a fact that up to the end of 1972 the average journey time between Ramsgate and Calais was 45 minutes. This took into account journeys on the roughest days when the actual journey time could be between 50 and 60 minutes. If the average journey time could be reduced by as much as 5 minutes, the savings in cost would be considerable measured over the full year's operations. On the basis of 4,000 crossings a year, some 335 hours could be saved which would represent a saving of well over £100,000.

Such an improvement could be obtained by improving the speed of the hovercraft in 1-2 metre waves. This represents the average sea state for the channel. It could be achieved not so much by increasing the propulsion power but by minimising the drag, particularly that caused by wave impacts. Although the method of achieving this may not result in a higher top speed there is no doubt that beneficial results would be obtained in rougher seas.

Skirt drag can only be reduced by changes to the aerodynamics of the cushion, and possibly by using lighter and more flexible materials. It is interesting to recall that when Saunders-Roe and Vickers were pursuing their separate paths in the hovercraft field, Vickers were working on much lower drag estimates. For example VA-4, which was designed to carry almost the same payload as the original SR.N4, was powered with only three Proteus engines, compared to the four engines used on the SR.N4. The difference in top speed was of the order 5 to 7 knots in favour of the SR.N4, but this difference was reduced in rougher sea states. Vickers' skirt concept was very much more flexible than that used for the SR.N4. In fact it was proposed to use an 8 ft. finger with no bag or loop in very much the same way as the skirt system on VA-3 which carried out some very successful trials in America in rough sea conditions. Vosper Thornycroft have also adopted this very flexible material approach, and it will be interesting to see how the VT 2 performs now that it is fully amphibious.

However, at the moment it would be unwise to criticise the Saunders-Roe/B.H.C. bag-and-finger concept as used on the SR.N6s and SR.N4s, and indeed on the hovercraft that Bell, their licensee in America, manufactures. These, after all, are the only passenger-carrying hovercraft that have stood the test of time, and to date there must be well over 30,000 hours experience with the SR.N4s and even more on the smaller craft. This is a tremendous achievement by any standard, but is it not to say that it is the only way. It has been highly successful in what may be termed the first generation hovercraft, but for the next generation it is conceivable that cushion technology will make a significant advance which will greatly benefit performance and general ride comfort.

Quite apart from the increased speed that advanced cushion technology might make possible, it opens up the possibility of operating on routes of greater length. For example, if the next generation of hovercraft is capable of 50 knots in seas of up to 2 metres, the Ramsgate-Flushing route would be accomplished in about 1½ hours. The existing ferry from Harwich to Flushing takes over 5 hours. Hovercraft could, therefore, make a very dramatic impression on this service. Since this improvement in journey time would also be accompanied by a more comfortable and quieter ride than on present day hovercraft, it is likely that it would have considerable passenger appeal. The fare structure would probably be slightly higher than the ship fare, but the advantage in time saved and the greater convenience would more than compensate for this. With such craft operating the route it would be possible to maintain an hourly service for most of the day.

Reliability has been significantly improved with the existing generation of hovercraft. All three operators have claimed that they have maintained at least a 99 per cent reliability record during periods of peak activity. In fact it can be fairly stated that weather and traffic factors represent the most frequent reasons for failure to operate a service.

The next generation of hovercraft will have the advantage that the areas of greatest engineering vulnerability will be well known from the experience gained from the present machines. Consequently, many of the troubled spots will have been designed out of the new craft. The problems of engine filtration, hydraulics and skirt wear, for example, will be considerably reduced by the new technology involved. Accessibility, which is vitally important, since it controls to a large extent the time taken to perform a particular maintenance task, must also be acknowledged. Items that are likely to cause trouble must be sited in areas where engineers can readily service them.

It can be safely predicted, therefore, that the operators should be able to maintain and even improve their excellent engineering performance, but perhaps of greater importance in these days of high manpower costs, they will be able to do so at less effort. This should represent a significant saving in maintenance costs.

There can be little doubt that the improved cushion technology allowing the hovercraft to operate safely and comfortably in rougher seas, will reduce the weather cancellations that are at present necessary. However, in this respect it must not be forgotten that slow speed manoeuvrability in the landing areas can be seriously affected by wind conditions. Although this can be alleviated by choosing a sheltered hoverport with uncluttered approaches, designers must ensure that the controllability of the hovercraft at slow speed in high wind conditions at the base must be sufficiently effective for the captain to handle his machine safely, and without fear of collision with other hovercraft or the port buildings. There would be little point in producing a hovercraft able to operate safely in Force 8 conditions at sea if it was not possible to enter or leave port in these conditions.

Inflation is a world wide problem and must be effectively controlled, but for the new hovercraft industry it has created special difficulties. When hovercraft were originally introduced to commercial passenger service, operators were extremely concerned that the estimates of operating costs were optimistic to say the least. In some cases the hard facts could not be met and operators were forced to close down.

The more determined and financially strong weathered the storm, and found ways in which the operation could be made profitable despite the higher costs involved. It would be unfair to place responsibility for the over-optimistic estimates on the manufacturer. Hovercraft were a completely new mode of transportation and as such there were many unknowns to be faced. For example, the effects of spray on rotating machinery and entering the engine intakes were more serious than was at first thought. The behaviour of skirt material was also completely unknown, particularly when operating in wave conditions. These problems were encountered the hard way and therefore costs increased, in some cases considerably.

The burden was shared between operator and manufacturer, although it would be true to say that the operator had a double concern. In the first place there was the cost of repair, or modification, which could be shared with the manufacturer, but secondly there was the loss of service with its attendant loss of direct revenue and the almost equally damaging blow to service reliability.

The costs were and are being brought under control. If one were to plot a graph using the manufacturer's operating cost estimate as the null it would be seen that in the first year there was an alarming increase, but with succeeding years, and ignoring the effect of inflation, the slope has flattened and in some areas has dropped. Unfortunately, the onset of rapid inflation has tended to mask this situation and to the uninitiated it would appear that costs have continued to soar.

This, is an extremely worrying situation for the industry, particularly at a time when the success of the three British operators and the cancellation of the Channel Tunnel project has shown that hovercraft could play an important part in the continuing growth of cross channel traffic. In these bleak economic times it is a difficult task to persuade investors to part with up to £6 million for a large passenger and vehicle carrying hovercraft, and since two would be required to run a service, a minimum total investment of some £12 million would be involved. Regrettably, as hovercraft are still viewed as a new industry such capital investment is deemed risky.

In fact, it is no worse than the decision taken by Swedish Lloyd and Swedish American Line, when in 1965 they ordered the first two SR.N4s. The sum of money involved then was in the region of £5 million and if one calculates the rate of inflation since then, £12 million is not extraordinary. It could be argued that the

Swedish companies took a much braver decision, for they were embarking on a venture where there was no previous experience. At least in 1975 there is a wealth of experience to call upon, and a great deal more confidence in the capability of the hovercraft to operate in the conditions necessary to ensure a reliable and commercially viable service.

But costs do matter and efforts must continue to reduce them as drastically as possible. Improved engine filtration arrangements have enabled engine hours between overhauls to be increased, thus reducing costs in the sense that the number of overhauls per given period has been reduced. Further reductions in costs have been achieved because the modifications have resulted in fewer engine failures.

New engines will also improve the situation since they are of modular construction and unit changes can be made faster with less disturbance to adjacent machinery and structure. The new engines will also have greatly improved specific fuel consumption. Since the quadrupling of oil prices in December 1973, this represents a significant saving, not only in terms of fuel cost, but also the need to carry less for a given range, thus allowing a payload increase.

The vast experience now available should ensure greater reliability for less cost than at present. But, with inflation at over 20% costs still appear to be spiralling upwards. This must have an adverse effect on the development of any new industry, particularly as with such high capital investment the interest on the money borrowed creates a significant burden.

The breakout from this vicious spiral can only be made by the use of more efficient craft, which despite their high first cost will enable a lower seat mile cost, thus giving the operator a better opportunity to recover the costs of financing. But first he must ensure the profitability of his existing fleet, for it will be upon performance in this field that the finance institutions will develop the confidence to provide the capital for the new hovercraft. Fortunately, the evidence available suggests that this situation prevails today and with the continuing growth of channel traffic assured by confirmation of our entry into the Common Market, and cancellation of the tunnel project, there is no reason to think that the situation will change other than for the better. *Figure 3.*

Two other factors that could materially affect the next generation of hovercraft are range and environmental acceptability. Range can be dealt with simply. Since one of the principal requirements needed of the new hovercraft will be the ability to operate on longer routes, greater range will be needed. However, it is suggested that this should be flexible in that operators working on short routes could reduce the fuel loading and increase the commercial payload. The extra fuel for the longer routes would thus require some sacrifice of commercial payload. The alternative to this would be a heavier hovercraft requiring more power to maintain performance. The overall effect of such an approach might result in a less viable operation than adopting the more flexible method of varying fuel load against commercial payload to alter range.

Environmental acceptance is a vitally important factor. Antinoise and nuisance lobbies are growing in power and influence; it would be foolish, therefore, to ignore the need to reduce noise or other nuisance to the lowest possible levels. For the future it may not be possible to site hoverports in quite such favourable positions as exist with those already in operation. The growing outcry concerning airport noise would certainly spin off to any new hoverport

Compete is the operative word. Hoverlloyd have shown that, using a lower fare structure for foot passengers than that used by ships and a car fare structure that is also lower than that used on the ships, provided that there are three or more passengers in the car they can operate at a profit. With improved hovercraft capable of faster speeds and lower seat mile costs, it is thought that they could considerably improve the situation, despite the high capital costs of the new hovercraft. They would also be able to offer a much higher capacity if the same number of flights were scheduled as at present thus improving the revenue earning potential and ensuring the opportunity for traffic growth.

The overall conclusion is that although the prospects for amphibious hovercraft larger than the SR.N4 are potentially good, those for the small and medium sized hovercraft, such as the SR.N6 Mk.6 are poor, except in highly specialised roles. The high capital cost and high running costs of this type of hovercraft are pushing the fare structure to the point where passenger resistance is experienced even on such favoured routes as exist in the Solent. Whether or not the existing operators can stay on the Solent routes appears to be dependent upon the supply of refurbished and modified SR.N6s. This can only be described as a tragic situation and one must look to Japan to see how they are managing to develop routes using similar-sized hovercraft. From reports it would seem that, contrary to British experience, they are in an expanding situation.

With regard to the larger amphibious craft it appears that there is a need for something a little larger than the SR.N4. Already a Mk.2 version, increasing the commercial payload by 30 passengers and 5 cars, is successfully operating on the channel route. A Mark 3 version is being projected capable of carrying 60 cars and 400 passengers. However, in competition with this is the French SEDAM N.500, also carrying 60 cars and 400 passengers. But because this is a new hovercraft with the advantage of incorporating the latest developments in ACV technology, it is likely to prove faster than the stretched SR.N4 and provide the passenger with a more comfortable ride. The N.500 is due to start operations on the Dover-Boulogne channel route in 1977.

The size of hovercraft that seems to have evolved either as the stretched SR.N4 or the SEDAM. N.500 does fulfil most of the requirements touched upon earlier. Both should provide the extra capacity required during the peak periods that would ensure op- projected and a public enquiry might well be required to satisfy the environmental lobby. The damaging delays, frustration and worry of such enquiries, quite apart from the cost, should be enough incentive for manufacturers to devote a great deal of time and effort to this problem.

Some time and attention has been given to this amphibious passenger application because it is felt that its success is basic to the needs of the new industry. Sidewall hovercraft are much more akin to the shipping world and indeed it is thought that they should be classified as such. The present somewhat ridiculous situation where, because of the existing Hovercraft Act, a sidewall hovercraft operator is penalised by higher costs and more arduous standards for crews when compared to a hydrofoil operator on the same route, is a serious problem for the hovercraft operator. Amphibious hovercraft are in a totally different category. In terms of speed, motion, manoeuvrability, stopping distance and their unique amphibious capability they are totally different from the conventional ship ferry with which they compete.

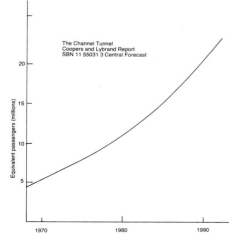

Figure 3. Predicted Cross-Channel Traffic Short Sea Route

Model of the SEDAM N 500, 240-tonne mixed-traffic hoverferry

erators a continuing opportunity for expanding their share of the market. As far as the off-season period is concerned it will probably mean that schedules will effectively be carried out at a lower load factor, but there should be no actual reduction in the numbers carried. In fact, because the new hovercraft will operate in rougher weather at faster speeds than are presently possible, more passengers would be attracted from the conventional ferries. New craft of the size proposed are, therefore, an attractive proposition and are becoming available when the existing SR.N4s are 10 years old, and their replacement would be a logical development of the company concerned

In addition to the finance required to purchase the new hovercraft, both British hoverports would need further investment. As far as the hoverport at Dover is concerned, a completely new facility would be required since the existing port is not large enough for use by large hovercraft. The passenger and car handling facilities are also too small. The privately owned hoverport at Pegwell Bay, Ramsgate, could easily accommodate up to four or even six of the new hovercraft from an operational point of view, but although the terminal facilities for both passengers and cars are better than at Dover, modifications would be required to make more space available. Fortunately this is physically possible but further investment would be required.

In France the hoverports at Calais and Boulogne would also need structural alterations to improve passenger amenities. This would apply particularly to Boulogne.

With building costs in Britain and France at their present level, considerable sums of money will be involved. As far as the operator is concerned he knows full well that he will have to foot the bill, either directly, as may be the case at Ramsgate, where Hoverlloyd own the port, or by guarantees and harbour dues as may prevail at Dover, Boulogne and Calais. Perhaps Dover has the most difficult decision of all since they have to provide a completely new facility. This is not only a sizeable investment decision to make but also carries an element of risk in that the return on the capital involved will be dependent upon the growth of the hovercraft industry. In choosing the site, therefore, consideration must be given to the possibility of development of the facility to accommodate an even greater number of hovercraft or even larger ones when the third generation arrives.

The manufacturers claim that both the N.500 and the stretched SR.N4 will be able to operate in rougher seas, and as far as the N.500 is concerned, the passenger cabins have been placed close to the longitudinal c.g. of the craft and they should therefore have a more comfortable ride. These facts enable consideration to be given to new routes, thus increasing the operators' scope for new markets and further expansion.

It would appear, therefore, that the industry could be entering a critical phase. If this new generation of hovercraft proves successful, Sir Christopher Cockerell's dreams and aspirations when he was making his early experiments will be fulfilled, and hovercraft will appear on ferry routes throughout the world. The stakes being played for by the French and British hovercraft industries are therefore significant.

Looking further into the future, the efforts the Americans are making to develop a ship capability of at least 80 knots for units of their Navy cannot be ignored. The target is to have at least an experimental version available for 1980. The actual and estimated spending on this project alone from 1974 until F.Y. 1977 is $230 million, over $100 million. This does not include the actual building programme of the ship which will emerge as a 2,000 ton vessel, capable of operating in Atlantic sea conditions and reaching speed in excess of 80 knots.

Such a device is clearly not for the commercial market, but it is inevitable that the technical knowledge the 2KSES programme will eventually accumulate, will spin off into commercial fields. For example, skirt material development will take place at a higher rate than could be achieved on the modest U.K. budgets. Since skirt wear is a source of high costs, developments that improve life and integrity will make a significant contribution to an increase in the use of hovercraft.

Similarly, the cushion aerodynamics are being investigated in considerable depth, although it must be admitted mostly by computer models to date. However, information on such things as stability stiffness, heave alleviation and associated control systems is being generated and will benefit all hovercraft development if the knowledge is made available.

Studies have also been carried out into the general feasibility of hovercraft up to 2,000 tons by the E.E.C. This is a group meeting in Brussels and to which B.H.C., Vosper, S.E.D.A.M. and Fiat have contributed. Its efforts have not had the same financial support as has been supplied by the American Government to its 2KSES project but nevertheless enough has been done to cause potential operators to become interested.

It is possible, therefore, that during the late 1980s hoverships will be in use on the major sea routes, not concerned with passenger traffic perhaps, but playing a major role as freight carriers. Whether or not this prediction will be fulfilled will depend upon the rate of progress achieved in America, the development of conventional ships (new merchant vessels are already being planned or in service that will cruise at 25-27 knots and have top speeds of 30 knots) and lastly cost. The latter will be the deciding factor. The requirement for faster movement of freight already exists, hence the development of faster freight ships. but there must be a limit to the price to be paid for speed.

For the hovercraft industry it will be essential that this factor is kept in mind. Technological progress is one thing but to be really successful it must be viable. It is certain that this lesson has now been learnt and for the future hovercraft transport will find its right place. The tragedy lies in the fact that after pioneering and leading the industry in the early and difficult years Britain is losing the initiative to the French, Americans and Japanese.

Although it could be viewed equally as an indictment of the frustrations of the present way of British life it is perhaps some consolation that much of the development taking place in the American air cushion industry is led by some of the original British pioneers.

GLOSSARY

GLOSSARY OF ACV AND HYDROFOIL TERMS

ACV. Air cushion vehicle.

AMPS. Abbrev. Arctic Marine Pipelaying System. Method of laying pipelines in ice-covered Arctic waters employing a skirted air-cushion barge as an icebreaker. System was devised after Arctic Engineers successfully and continuously broke ice up to 27 in (0·68 m) thick using the 250-ton ACT-100 platform. On contact with the ice sheet, the skirt rises above it, maintaining its seal. As the ice sheet enters the cushion zone, the water level beneath it is depressed by the air pressure. Having lost flotation support, the ice becomes a cantilevered ledge and when it reaches its critical length, it breaks off into the water below. The broken ice is then thrust aside by a plough-like deflector.

APU. Auxiliary power unit.

abeam. Another craft or object seen at the side or beam.

actuator. Unit designed to translate sensor information and/or computer instructions into mechanical action. Energy is transferred to control surfaces hydraulically, pneumatically or electrically.

A to N. Abbrev. Aids to navigation.

aeration. See **air entry.**

aerodynamic lift. Lifting forces generated by a vehicle's forward speed through the atmosphere due to the difference in pressure between upper and lower surfaces.

Aerofoil boat. Name given by Dr Alexander M. Lippisch, the inventor and aircraft designer, to his range of aerodynamic ram-wing machines.

aeroglisseur, (French, air-glider). Name given to range of passenger-carrying amphibious ACVs designed in France by Société Bertin & Cie in conjunction with Société D'Études et de Développement des Aéroglisseurs Marins (SEDAM). The name **Aerobac** is given to mixed passenger/car ferries and freighters designed by Bertin and SEDAM.

aeroplane foil system. Arrangement in which the main foil is located forward of the centre of gravity to support 75% to 85% of the load, and the auxiliary foil, supporting the remainder, is located aft as a tail assembly.

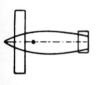

Aeroplane or conventional foil systems. The main foil may be divided into two to facilitate retraction

aerosuspendu (French, air-suspended). Form of suction-suspended monorail designed in France by Maurice Barthalon for mass public transportation on urban and suburban routes. The vehicle is suspended from its track by an air lift system in which the pressure is sub-atmospheric. Propulsion is by linear induction motor, q.v.

Aerotrain. Generic name for a range of tracked air cushion vehicles under development in France by Société de l'Aerotrain.

aft. At, near or towards the stern of the craft.

air bleed (hyd). See **air stabilisation.** Occasionally used instead of earation or air entry.

air bleed (ACV). One method of preventing "plough in" on a skirted ACV is to bleed air from the cushion through vent holes on the outer front of the skirt to reduce its water drag by air lubrication.

air cushion vehicle. A vehicle capable of being operated so that its weight, including its payload, is wholly or significantly supported on a continuously generated cushion or 'bubble' of air at higher than ambient pressure. The air bubble or cushion is put under pressure by a fan or fans and generally contained beneath the vehicle's structure by flexible skirts or sidewalls. In the United States large or ship size air-cushion vehicles are called **surface effect ships** or **surface**

Four aerostatic-type air cushion vehicles. Each is supported by air put under pressure by a fan or fans and contained beneath the vehicle by flexible skirts or sidewalls. *Left to right:* The projected 2,000-ton Bell 2KSES; the Mitsui MV PP5 50-seat hoverferry and, *below,* a BHC BH.7 Mk 4 of the Royal Navy's Naval Hovercraft Trials Unit, accompanied by one of the unit's SR.N6s.

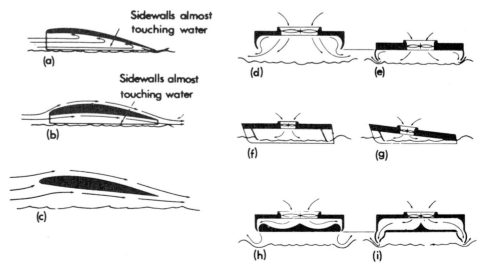

(a) ram wing; (b) channel-flow wing; (c) wing-in-ground effect; (d) plenum chamber; (e) plenum chamber with skirt; (f) captured air bubble; (g) hydrokeel; (h) annular jet; (i) trunked annular jet

effect vessels.

Broadly speaking, there are two main types of air-cushion vehicles, those supported by a self-generated cushion of air and those dependent upon forward speed to develop lift. The former are designated *aerostatic*, and the latter, *aerodynamic*.

Aerodynamic craft include the *ram-wing*, the *channel-flow wing* and the *wing-in-ground-effect*. The *ram-wing* (a) can be likened to a short-span wing with sidewalls attached to its tip. The wing trailing edge and the sidewalls almost touch the water surface. At speed, lifting forces are generated by both the wing and the ram pressure built up beneath. One of the first concepts utilising a *channel-flow* wing (b) was the Columbia, designed in the USA by Vehicle Research Corporation in 1961 (JSSS 1967-8 edition). The design featured a peripheral jet sidewall system for use at low speeds and an aerofoil shaped hull to provide lift at high speeds during forward flight. The side curtains of the peripheral jet were to be retained to seal the high pressure "channel" of air developed beneath from the low pressure airflow above and along the sides of the craft, down to the water surface. A 30 ft long manned model of the Columbia was successfully tested in 1964.

The *wing-in-ground-effect* (c) is essentially an aircraft designed to fly at all times in close proximity to the earth's surface, in order to take advantage of the so-called "image" flow that reduces induced drag by about 70%. In the Soviet Union this type of machine is known as an **Ekranoplan,**

Aerostatic-type air cushion vehicles can be divided into two categories—plenum chamber craft and peripheral or annular jet craft. *Plenum chamber craft* (d) employ the most simple of surface effect concepts. Air is forced from the lift fan directly into a recessed base where it forms a cushion which raises the craft. The volume of air pumped into the base is just sufficient to replace the air leaking out beneath the edges.

Variants of this category include the *skirted plenum craft* (e), in which a flexible fabric extension is hung between the metal structure and the surface to give increased obstacle and overwave clearance capability. The Naviplanes and Terraplanes designed by Bertin and SEDAM employ separately fed multiple plenum chambers, each surrounded by lightweight flexible skirts. Skirted plenum chamber types are also favoured by builders of light air cushion vehicles because of their relatively simple design and construction.

Another variant is the *sidewall* ACV (f), in which the cushion air is contained between solid sidewalls or skegs and deflectable seals, either solid or flexible, fore and aft. Stability is provided by the buoyancy of the sidewalls and their planing forces. Sidewall craft are also known as captured air bubble vessels (*CABs*) a term used widely in the United States. One of the derivatives of the sidewall type is the *hydrokeel* (g) which is designed to plane on the after section of its hull and benefit to some degree from air lubrication.

In *peripheral* or *annular jet craft* (h) the ground cushion is generated by a continuous jet of air channelled through ducts or nozzles around the outer periphery of the base. The flexible skirts fitted to this type can take the form either of an extension to the outer wall of the duct or nozzle only, or an extension to both outer and inner walls. In the latter form it is known as a *trunked annular jet* (i).

air entrainment. See **air entry.**

air entry. Entry of air from the atmosphere that raises the low pressures created by the flow due to a foil's cambered surface.

air gap; also daylight gap, daylight clearance and **hover gap.** Distance between the lowest component of the vehicle's understructure, e.g. skirt hem, and the surface when riding on its cushion. **air gap area**: area through which air is able to leak from a cushion.

air pad. Part of an air pallet assembly into which compressed air is introduced and allowed to escape in a continuous flow through communicating holes in the diaphragm.

air pallet, also **hoverpallet.** Air cushion supported, load-carrying structure, which bleeds a continuous low pressure volume of air between the structure and the reaction surface, creating an air film.

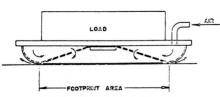

An air pad with a flexible plastic diaphragm

air-port system, also **thrust port.** See **puff-port.**

air-rider. Alternative generic name for air cushion vehicles or weight carrying structures lifted off the surface by a cushion or film of air.

air stabilised foils. See **foil systems.**

amidships. (1) Midway between the stem and stern of a hull. (2) abbreviated to **midships** and meaning the rudder or helm is in a mid-position.

angle of attack. The angle made by the mean chord line of an aero- or hydrofoil with the flow.

angle of incidence. The angle made by the mean chord line of a hydrofoil in relation to the fixed struts or hull.

Aquavion type foil. Adapted from the Grunberg system. About 85% of the load is carried by a mainfoil located slightly aft of the centre of gravity, 10% by a submerged aft stabiliser foil, and the remainder on a pair of planing sub-foils at the bow. The planing subfoils give variable lift in response to wave shapes, whether skimming over them or through them, and so trim the angle of the hull in order to correct the angle of attack of the main foil.

articulated air-cushion vehicle. A modular type load-carrying platform designed by Charles Burr of Bell Aerospace. A number of skirted platforms can be joined to form a variety of ACVs of different load carrying capacities. An application envisaged for craft of this type is the movement of containers and other heavy machinery in the American arctic and middle north.

aspect ratio. (1) the measure of the ratio of a foil's span to its chord. It is defined as

$$\frac{span^2}{total\ foil\ area}$$

(2) for ACVs it is defined as $\frac{cushion\ beam}{cushion\ length}$

athwart, athwartship. Across the hull in a transverse direction from one side of the craft to the other.

axial-flow lift fan. A fan generating an airflow for lift that is parallel to the axis of rotation.

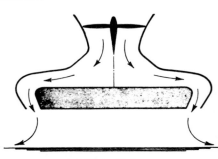

Axial flow lift fan

b.h.p. Brake horse power.

backstrap. A fabric strap used to secure a lift jet exit nozzle in a flexible skirt at the correct angle.

baffle plates. See **fences.**

ballast. Fuel, water or solids used to adjust the centre of gravity or trim of a craft.

ballast system. A method of transferring water or fuel between tanks to adjust fore and aft trim. In Mountbatten class ACVs, four groups of tanks, one at each corner of the craft, are located in the buoyancy tanks. A ring main facilitates the rapid transfer of fuel between the tanks as ballast and also serves as a refuelling line.

ballast tank or box. Box or tank containing the liquids or solids used to trim a craft.

base ventilated foil. A system of forced ventilation designed to overcome the reduction in lift/drag ratio of a foil at supercavitating speeds. Air is fed continuously to the upper surface of the foil un-wetting the surface and preventing the formation of critical areas of decreased pressure. Alternatively the air may be fed into the cavity formed behind a square trailing edge.

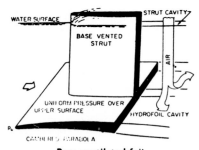

Base ventilated foil

beam. Measurement across a hull at a given point.

Beaufort Scale. A scale of wind forces described by name and range of velocity and classified as from force 0 to force 12, or in the case of strong hurricanes to force 17.

Three aerodynamic air cushion vehicles. Like aeroplanes, these craft depend upon forward speed to develop lift. A dynamic air cushion is formed between the vehicle and its supporting surface below. *Left to right:* The Soviet ESKA-1, two-seat river rescue craft; the Lippisch Rheinflugzeugbau X 113 Am and a large Soviet experimental wing-in-ground-effect machine said to have been built at Gorky, and which is undergoing tests

Named after Admiral Sir Frances Beaufort, 1774-1857, who was responsible for preparing the scale.

Beaufort Force Number	State of Air	Description	Wind Velocity in Knots
0	calm	Smoke ascends vertically. Sea mirror-like	Less than 1
1	light air	Wind direction shown by smoke. Scale-like ripples on surface but no crests	1-3
2	slight breeze	As force 1, but wavelets more pronounced	4-6
3	gentle breeze	Flags extended. Short pronounced wavelets; crests start to break, scattered white horses	7-10
4	moderate breeze	Small waves, lengthening. Frequent white horses	11-16
5	fresh breeze	Waves more pronounced and longer form. More white horses some spray	17-21
6	strong breeze	Larger waves and extensive white foam crests. Sea breaks with dull rolling noise. Spray	22-27
7	moderate gale	White foam blown in streaks in direction of wind Spindrift appears Noise increases	28-33
8	fresh gale	Moderately high waves breaking into spindrift: well marked foam	34-40
9	strong gale	High waves and dense streaks of foam along direction of wind. Sea begins to roll	41-47
10	whole gale	Sea surface becomes white. Very high waves with overhanging crests. Rolling of sea heavy. Visibility affected	48-55
11	storm	Waves exceptionally high, visibility affected	56-65
12	hurricane	Air full of foam and spray. Visibility seriously affected	above 65

bilge. Point of the hull where the side and the bottom meet. Also water or fuel accumulated in the bilges.

bilge system. A pumping system devised to dispose of water and other fluids which have accumulated in the bilges. In air-cushion vehicles bilge systems are installed to clear the buoyancy tanks. Small craft generally have a hand operated pump which connects directly to pipes in the tanks. In larger craft, like the 190-ton BHC Mountbatten, because of the large number of buoyancy compartments, four electrically driven pumps are provided, each of which can drain one compartment at a time.

block speed. Route distance divided by block time.

block time, also **trip time.** Journey time between lift off and touchdown.

boating. Expression used to describe an air cushion vehicle when operating in displacement condition. The boating or **semi-hover** mode is used in congested terminal areas, when lift power and spray generation is kept to a minimum. Some craft have water surface contact even at full hover for stability requirements.

bow. Forward part of a craft. The stem.

bow-up. Trim position or attitude when a craft is high at the bow. Can be measured by eye or attitude gyro.

breast, to. To take waves at 90° to their crests.

bridge. Elevated part of the superstructure, providing a clear all round view, from which a craft is navigated and steered.

broach, to. Sudden breaking of the water surface by a foil, or part of a foil, resulting in a loss of lift due to air flowing over the foil's upper surface.

to broach to. Nautical expression meaning to swing sideways in following seas under wave action.

bulkheads. Vertical partitions, either transverse or longitudinal, which divide or subdivide a hull. May be used to separate accommodation areas, strengthen the structure, form tanks or localise fires or flooding.

buoyancy. The reduction in weight of a floating object. If the object floats its weight is equal to (or less than) the weight of fluid displaced.

buoyancy chamber. A structure designed in such a way that the total of its own weight and all loads which it supports is equal to (or less than) the weight of the water it displaces.

buoyancy, reserve. Buoyancy in excess of that required to keep an undamaged craft afloat. See **buoyancy.**

buoyancy tubes. Inflatable tubular members providing reserve buoyancy. May be used as fenders if fitted to the outer periphery of a craft.

CAA (Abbrev.) Civil Aviation Authority.

CAB. Captured Air Bubble. See **air cushion vehicle.**

c.p. Centre of pressure.

CP shifter. A control system which moves the centre of pressure of an air cushion to augment a craft's natural stability in pitch and roll.

CWL. Calm water line.

camber. (1) A convexity on the upper surface of a deck to give it increased strength and/or facilitate draining. (2) The convex form on the upper surface of a foil. The high speed flow over the top surface causes a decrease in pressure and about two-thirds of the lift is provided by this surface.

canard foil system. A foil arrangement in which the main foil of wide span is located near the stern, aft of the centre of gravity, and bears about 65% of the weight, while a small central foil is placed at the bow.

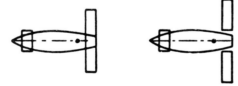

Canard foil configuration. The main foil area may be divided into two to facilitate retraction

captain. Senior crew member aboard a hovercraft. Defined as the person designated by the operator to be in charge of a hovercraft during any journey, under the UK government's "The Hovercraft (Application of Enactments) Order 1972". Equivalent in rank to airliner or ship's captain. Alternative terms: pilot, driver, helmsman, coxswain and ACV operator.

captured air bubble craft (see also **sidewall craft** and **surface effect ship**). Vessel in which the cushion (or air bubble) is contained by rigid sidewalls and flexible bow and stern skirts. Occasionally used for any air cushion craft in which the air cushion (or air bubble) is contained within the cushion periphery with minimal air leakage.

cavitation. Cavitation is the formation of vapour bubbles due to pressure decrease on the upper surface of a foil or the back of a propeller's blades at high speeds, and falls into two categories, unstable and stable. Non-stable cavities or cavitation bubbles of aqueous vapour form near the foil's leading edge and extend down stream expanding and collapsing. At the points of collapse positive pressure peaks may rise to as high as 20,000 psi These cause erosion and pitting of the metal. Cavitation causes an unstable water flow over the foils which results in abrupt changes in lift and therefore discomfort for those aboard the craft.

Foil sections are now being developed which either delay the onset of cavitation by reduced camber, thinner sections, or sweepback, or if the craft is required to operate at supercavitating speeds, stabilise cavitation to provide a smooth transition between sub-cavitating and super-cavitating speeds.

centrifugal flow lift fan. A cushion lift fan which generates an airflow at right angles to the axis of rotation.

chain ties. Chains used to maintain the correct shape of an air jet exit nozzle on a flexible skirt.

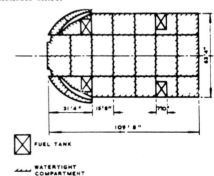

FUEL TANK

WATERTIGHT COMPARTMENT

Typical buoyancy tank unit on the SR.N4. The basic structure of the SR.N4 is the buoyancy chamber, built around a grid of logitudinal and transversal frames, which form twenty-four watertight sub-divisions for safety. Below, the SR.N4 buoyancy tank layout.

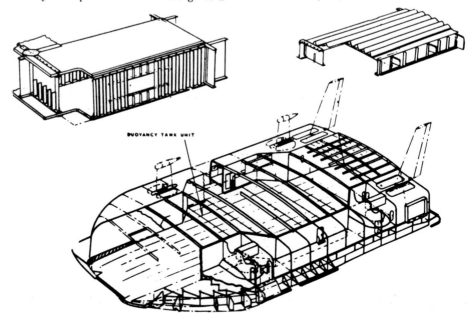

BUOYANCY TANK UNIT

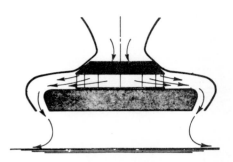

Centrifugal flow lift fan

chord. The distance between the leading and trailing edges of a foil section measured along the chord line.

chord-line. A straight line joining the leading and trailing edges of a foil or propeller blade section.

classification, also certification. Seagoing and amphibious craft for commercial application are classified by mode and place of construction, in the manner of the registration system started in the City of London by Edward Lloyd, and continued since 1760 by Lloyd's Register of Shipping. Outside the British Isles classification socities now include Registro Italiano Navale, Germanischer Lloyd, Det Norske Veritas, American Bureau of Shipping and the Japanese Ministry of Transport.

A classification society's surveyors make a detailed examination of craft certificated by them at regular intervals to ensure their condition complies with the particular society's requirements.

continuous nozzle skirt. See **skirt.**

contour, to. The motion of an air cushion vehicle or hydrofoil when more or less following a wave profile.

craft. Boats, ships, air cushion vehicles and hydrofoils of all types, regardless of size.

crew. Those responsible for manning a craft of either boat or ship size, including the officers. The company of an ACV or hydrofoil.

cross-flow. The flow of air, transversally or longidutinally within an air cushion.

cryogenics. Science of refrigeration, associated in particular with temperatures of —260 deg C and lower.

cushion. A volume of higher than ambient pressure air 'trapped beneath the structure of a vehicle and its supporting surface causing the vehicle to be supported at some distance from the ground.

cushion area. Area of a cushion contained within a skirt or sidewall.

cushion beam. Measurement across an air cushion at a given point.

cushion borne. A craft borne above the sea or land surface by its air cushion.

cushion length. Longitudinal cushion measurement.

cushion length, mean. Defined as:

$$\frac{\text{cushion area}}{\text{cushion beam}}$$

cushion seal. Air curtains, sidewalls, skirts, water-jets or other means employed to contain or seal an air cushion to reduce to a minimum the leakage of trapped air.

cushion thrust. Thrust obtained by the deflection of cushion air.

DWL. Displacement water line.

daylight clearance. See **air gap.**

daylight gap. See **air gap.**

deadrise. The angle with the horizontal made at the keel by the outboard rise of a vessel's hull form at each frame.

Delta wing. A triangular-shaped aircraft wing, as in fourth letter of Greek alphabet **Δ**, corresponding to D. Designed and developed by Dr. Alexander Lippisch and applied in supersonic configuration on the Me 163B rocket-propelled interceptor, the fastest military aircraft of World War II. More recently the delta wing has been employed by Dr. Lippisch in his series of Aerofoil Boats. Applied also in Soviet Union because of its high aerodynamic qualities and stability

for a range of Ekranoplan aerodynamic ram-wings.

Diesel engine. An internal combustion engine which burns a relatively inexpensive oil of similar consistency to light lubricating oil. Invented by Rudolf Diesel, 1858-1913. Fuel oil is pumped into the cylinder then compressed so highly that the heat generated is sufficient to ignite oil subsequently injected, without an electric spark.

diffuser-recirculation. See **recirculation system.**

direct operating cost. Cost of operating a craft, excluding company overheads and indirect costs.

displacement. The weight in tons of water displaced by a floating vessel. Light displacement is the craft weight exclusive of ballast.

ditch, to. An emergency landing on water while under way due to a local navigation hazard, loss of cushion air or failure of a powerplant.

Doppler, navigator An automatic dead reckoning device which gives a continuous indication of position by integrating the speed derived from measuring the Doppler effect of echoes from directed beams of radiant energy transmitted from the vessel.

down-by-the-head. Trim or sit of a craft with its bow more deeply immersed than the stern. The opposite expression is 'down by the stern'.

drag. (1) ACVs—aerodynamic and hydrodynamic resistances encountered by an air cushion vehicle resulting from aerodynamic profile, gain of momentum of air needed for cushion generation, wave making, wetting or skirt contact.

(2) hydrofoils—hydrodynamic resistances encountered by hydrofoils result from wave making, which is dependent on the craft shape and displacement, frictional drag due to the viscosity of the water, the total wetted surface and induced drag from the foils and transmission shafts and their supporting struts and structure, due to their motion through the water.

draught. Depth between the water surface and the bottom of a craft. Under the Ministry of Transport Merchant Shipping (Construction) rules, 1952, draught is defined as the vertical distance from the moulded base line amidships to the sub-division load waterline.

draught marks. (1) marks on the side of a craft showing the depth to which it can be loaded. (2) figures cut at the stern and stem to indicate draught and trim.

drift angle. Difference between the actual course made and the course steered.

ESKA (Russian). Abbrev. Name given to series of small wing-in-ground-effect machines developed by the Central Laboratory of Lifesaving Technology, Moscow. Shortened form of Ekranolytny Spasatyelny Kater Amphibiya (screen-effect amphibious lifeboat). Also known as **Ekranolyet** or **Nizkolet** (skimmer).

Ekranoplan. (USSR). Composite word based on *ekran*, a screen or curtain, and *plan*, the principal supporting surface of an aeroplane. Employed almost exclusively to describe types of ACVs in the Soviet Union raised above their supporting surfaces by dynamic lift. Western equivalent, wing-in-ground-effect machines (WIG) and aerodynamic ram-wing.

elevator. Moveable aerodynamic control surface used on small hovercraft to provide a

degree of fore and aft trim control. Elevator surfaces are normally located in the slipstream of the propulsive units in order to provide some control at low speed.

FWL. Foilborne water line.

fathom. A depth of 6 ft.

fences. Small partitions placed at short intervals down the upper and lower surfaces of a hydrofoil tending to prevent air ventilation passing down to destroy the lift. They are attached in the direction of the flow.

ferry. A craft designed to carry passengers across a channel, estuary, lake, river or strait.

fetch. The number of miles a given wind has been blowing over open water or the distance upwind to the nearest land.

finger skirt. See **skirts.**

fire zone. A compartment containing a full supply and ignition source which is walled with fire resisting material and fitted with an independent fire warning and extinguishing system.

fixed annual cost. Major component of a vehicle's direct operating cost. This comprises depreciation, craft insurance and operating and maintenance crew salaries, all of which are incurred regardless of whether the craft is operated or not.

flare. Upward and outward curvature of the freeboard at the bow, presenting additional, rising surface to oncoming waves.

flexible skirt. See **skirt.**

flying bridge. A navigating position atop the wheel or chart house.

foilborne. A hydrofoil is said to be foilborne when the hull is raised completely out of the water and wholly supported by lift from its foil system.

foil flaps. Foils are frequently fitted with (a) trailing edge flaps for lift augmentation during take-off and to provide control forces, (b) upper and lower flaps to raise the cavitation boundary.

foil systems. Foil systems in current use are generally either **surface piercing, submerged** or **semi-submerged.** There are a number of craft with hybrid systems with a combination of submerged and surface piercing foils, recent examples being the Supramar PT.150 and the De Havilland FHE-400.

surface piercing foils are more often than not vee-shaped, the upper parts of the foil forming the tips of the Vee and piercing the surface on either side of the craft. The

Fences on the bow foil of a Supramar hydrofoil

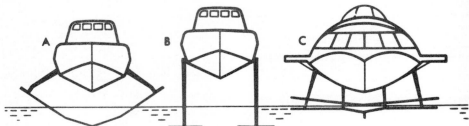

Foil systems in current use. A surface piercing: B submerged and C shallow draught submerged

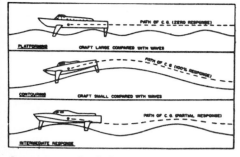

Comparison of platforming and contouring modes, and the intermediate response of a craft equipped with fully submerged, automatically controlled foil system

vee foil, with its marked dihedral is area stabilised and craft employing this configuration can be designed to be inherently stable, and, for stability, geometry dependent.

The forces restoring normal trim are provided by the area of the foil that is submerged. A roll to one side means the immersion of increased foil area, which results in the generation of extra lift to counter the roll and restore the craft to an even keel.

Equally, a downward pitching movement at the bow means an increase in the submerged area of the forward foil, and the generation of extra lift on this foil, which raises the bow once more. Should the bow foil rise above its normal water level the lift decreases in a similar way to restore normal trim. This type of foil is also known as an **emerging foil system.**

As the vee-foil craft increases its speed, so it generates greater lift and is raised further out of the water—at the same time reducing the wetted area and the lift. The lift must be equal to the weight of the craft, and as the lift depends on the speed and wetted foil area, the hull rides at a pre-determined height above the water level.

ladder foils. Also come under the heading surface piercing, but are rarely used at the present time. This is one of the earliest foil arrangements and was used by Forlanini in his 1905 hydro-aeroplane, which was probably the first really successful hydrofoil. In 1911 Alexander Graham Bell purchased Forlanini's patent specifications and used his ladder system on his Hydrodromes, one of which, the HD-4, set up a world speed record of 61·5 knots in 1919. Early ladder foils, with single sets of foils beneath the hull, fore and aft, lacked lateral stability, but this disadvantage was rectified later by the use of two sets of forward foils, one on each side of the hull. The foils were generally straight and set at right angles to their supporting struts, but were occasionally of vee configuration, the provision of dihedral preventing a sudden change of lift as the foils broke the surface. Both the vee foil and the ladder systems are self stabilising to a degree. The vee foil has the advantage of being a more rigid, lighter structure and is less expensive.

Primary disadvantages of the conventional surface-piercing systems in comparison with the submerged foil system are: (a) the inability of vee-foil craft without control surfaces to cope with downward orbital velocities at wave crests when overtaking waves in a following sea, a condition which

can decrease the foil's angle of attack, reducing lift and cause either wave contact or a stall; (b) on large craft the weight and size of the surface piercing system is considerably greater than that of a corresponding submerged foil system; (c) restoring forces to correct a roll have to pass above the centre of gravity of the craft, which necessitates the placing of the foils only a short distance beneath the hull. This means a relatively low wave clearance and therefore the vee foil is not suited to routes where really rough weather is encountered.

shallow-draught submerged foil system. This system which incorporates the Grunberg angle of attack variation approach, is employed almost exclusively on hydrofoils designed and built in the Soviet Union and is intended primarily for passenger carrying craft used on long, calm water rivers, canals and inland seas. The system, also known as the immersion depth effect system, was evolved by Dr. Rostislav Alexeyev. It generally comprises two main horizontal foils, one forward, one aft, each carrying approximately half the weight of the vessel. A submerged foil loses lift gradually as it approaches the surface from a depth of about one chord, which prevents it from rising completely to the surface. Means therefore have to be provided to assist take-off and prevent the vessel from sinking back into the displacement mode. Planing subfoils, port and starboard, are therefore provided in the vicinity of the forward struts, and are so located that when they are touching the water surface, the main foils are submerged at a depth of approximately one chord.

submerged foils have a greater potential for seakeeping than any other, but are not inherently stable to any degree. The foils are totally immersed and a sonic, mechanical or air stabilisation system has to be installed to maintain the foils at the required depth. The system has to stabilise the craft from take-off to touchdown in heave and all three axes—pitch, roll and yaw. It must also see that the craft makes co-ordinated banked turns in heavy seas to reduce the side loads on the foil struts; ensure that vertical and lateral accelerations are kept within limits in order to prevent excessive loads on the structure and finally, ensure a smooth ride for the passengers and crew.

The control forces are generated either by deflecting flaps at the trailing edge of the foil or varying the incidence angle of the entire foil surface. Incidence control provides better performance in a high sea state.

A typical sonic electronic autopilot control system is that devised for the Boeing PCH-1 High Point. The key element is an acoustic height sensor located at the bow. The time lag of the return signal is a measure of the distance of the sensor from the water.

Craft motion input is received from dual sonic ranging devices which sense the height above the water of the bow in relation to a fixed reference; from three rate gyros which measure yaw, pitch and roll; from forward and aft accelerometers which sense vertical acceleration fore and aft and from a vertical gyro which senses the angular position of the craft in both pitch and roll. This information is processed by an electronic computer and fed continuously to hydraulic

actuators of the foil control surfaces, which develop the necessary hydrodynamic forces for stability producing forces imposed by wave action manoeuvring and correct flight.

mechanical incidence control. The most successful purely mechanically operated incidence control system is the Hydrofin autopilot principle, designed by Christopher Hook, who pioneered the development of the submerged foil. A fixed, high-riding crash preventer plane is mounted ahead of and beneath the bow.

The fixed plane, which is only immersed when the craft is in a displacement mode, is also used as a platform for mounting a lightweight pitch control sensor which is hinged to the rear.

The sensor rides on the waves and continuously transmits their shape through a connecting linkage to vary the angle of incidence of the main foils as necessary to maintain them at the required depth. A filter system ensures that the craft ignores small waves and that the hull is flown over the crests of waves exceeding the height of the keel over the water.

Two additional sensors, trailing from port and starboard immediately aft of the main struts, provide roll control. The pilot has overriding control through a control column, operated in the same manner as that in an aircraft.

air stabilisation system. A system designed and developed by Baron Hanns von Schertel of Supramar AG, Lucerne. Air from the free atmosphere is fed through air exits to the foil upper surface and under certain conditions the lower surface also (i.e. into the low pressure regions). The airflow decreases the lift and the flow is deflected away from the foil section with an effect similar to that of a deflected flap, the air cavities extending out behind producing a virtual lengthening of the foil profile. Lift is reduced and varied by the quantity of air admitted, this being controlled by a valve actuated by signals from a damped pendulum and a rate gyro. The pendulum causes righting moments at static heeling angles. If exposed to a centrifugal force in turning, it causes a moment, which is directed towards the centre of the turning circle, thereby avoiding outside banking (co-ordinated banking). The rate gyro responds to angular velocity and acts dynamically to dampen rolling motions.

following sea. A sea following the same or similar course to that of the craft.

force time effectiveness. Time to land an effective landing force ashore.

fore peak. The space forward of the fore collision bulkhead, frequently used as storage space.

forward. Position towards the fore end of a craft.

frames. The structure of vertical ribs or girders to which a vessel's outside plates are attached. For identification purposes the frames are numbered consecutively, starting aft.

freeboard. Depth of the exposed or free side of a hull between the water level and the freeboard deck. The degree of freeboard permitted is marked by load lines.

freeboard deck. Deck used to measure or determine loadlines.

These military hydrofoil designs illustrate three different foil systems. *Left to right:* The De Havilland Canada MP-100, a 100-ton missile craft with its inherently stable 'canard' surface-piercing system, incorporating a trapeze configuration main foil aft; the 83·5 ton Super Flagstaff with incidence-controlled fully submerged foils in "aeroplane" configuration and the Boeing NATO/PHM. The latter has a fully submerged canard system with 32% of the dynamic lift provided by the bow foil and 68% by the aft foil. Lift control is provided by trailing edge flaps on each foil

free power turbine. A gas-turbine on which the power turbine is on a separate shaft from the compressor and its turbine.

full hover. Expression used to describe the condition of an ACV when it is at its design hoverheight.

g. Gravitational acceleration.

g.r.p. Glass-reinforced plastics.

gas-turbine engine. Engine in which expanding gases are employed to rotate a turbine. Its main elements are a rotary air compressor with an air intake, one or a series of combustion chambers, a turbine and an exhaust outlet.

GEM. Ground effect machine.

gross tonnage. Total tonnage of a vessel, including all enclosed spaces, estimated on the basis of 100 ft² = 1 ton.

ground effect machine. Early generic term for air cushion vehicles of all types.

ground crew and **ground staff.** Those responsible for craft servicing and maintenance. Also those responsible for operational administration.

Grunberg Foil System. First patented in 1936, the Grunberg principle of inherent angle of attack variations comprises a "stabiliser" attached to the bow or a forward projection from the latter, and behind this a 'foil'. Both foil and stabiliser can be "split" into several units. The lift curve of the stabiliser, plotted against its draft, is considerably steeper than its corresponding foil lift curve. Hence as the operational conditions (speed, weight, CG travel) change, the foil sinks or rises relative to the stabiliser, automatically adjusting its angle of attack. The "foil" is set at an appropriate angle of incidence in order to prevent it from approaching the interface. The system is fully compatible with Forlanini's concept of area variation and both can be incorporated in the same structure.

HDL. Hovercraft Development Ltd.

hp. Horsepower.

Hz (abbrev). Unit of wave frequency employed especially in acoustics and electronics. 1 hertz = 1 cycle per second. Named after Heinrich Hertz (1857-1894), German physicist.

hard chine. Hull design with the topsides and bottom meeting at an angle, rather than curving to a round bilge.

head sea. A sea approaching from the direction steered.

heave. Vertical motion of a craft in response to waves.

heel. (a) To incline or list in a transverse direction while under way. (b) Lower end of a mast or derrick. (c) Point where keel and stern post meet.

Helibarge. System devised by A Walter. Crowley (USA) combining a helicopter with an air-cushion barge. The downwash of the helicopter rotor pressurises the air-cushion.

hourly running cost. That part of the direct operating cost incurred when the craft is operated, i.e., fuel, maintenance and overhauls.

hoverbarge. Fully buoyant, shallow-draught hovercraft built for freight carrying. Either self-propelled or towed.

hovercraft. (a) Originally a name for craft using the patented peripheral jet principle invented by Sir Christopher Cockerell, in which the air cushion is generated and contained by a jet of air exhausted downward and inward from a nozzle at the periphery at the base of the vehicle. (b) Classification in the USA for skirted plenum chamber and annular jet-designs. (c) In the British Hovercraft Act 1968, a hovercraft is defined as a vehicle which is designed to be supported when in motion wholly or partly by air expelled from the vehicle to form a cushion of which the boundaries include the ground, water or other surface beneath the vehicle.

hoverplatform. Non self-propelled hovercraft designed primarily to convey heavy loads across terrain impassable to wheeled and tracked vehicles under load.

hoverport. Defined by the British Hovercraft Act, 1968 as any area, whether land or elsewhere, which is designed, equipped, set apart or commonly used for affording facilities for the arrival and departure of hovercraft.

hover gap. See **air gap.**

hover height. Vertical height between the hard structure of an ACV and the supporting surface when a vehicle is cushion-borne.

hover-listen. Expression covering ACVs employed for anti-submarine warfare while operating at low speeds to detect a target.

hover-pallet. See **air pallet.**

hoversled. Vehicle designed for northern latitudes combining features of an air cushion vehicle with skis or pontoons. The first vehicle of this type was designed in Finland by Mr. Erkki Peri. Because of the contact between the vehicle's skis and the supporting surface beneath, directional control is a great improvement on that of most conventional skirted ACVs while operating over ice and snow.

hover-time. Time logged by an air cushion vehicle when cushion borne. Often called **power hours.**

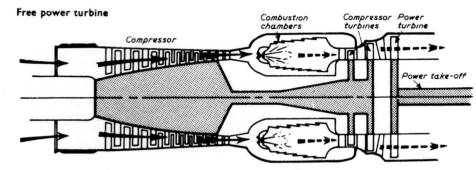

Free power turbine

A Mackace 50-ton hoverplatform

hovertrailer. A steel structure platform around which is fitted a flexible segmented skirt, cushion lift being provided by fans driven by petrol or diesel engines on the platform. The system devised by Air Cushion Equipment Ltd and Hovertrailers International Ltd is designed to increase the load capacity of tracked and wheeled vehicles many times. In cases where it is impossible for a tow vehicle to operate, the trailer can be winched.

A hovertrailer. Payload at 100 psf is 6.7 tons

hull cresting. Contact of a hydrofoil's hull with the waves in high seas. The term **hull slamming** q.v., or slamming, is used if the hull contact is preceeded by foil broaching.

hull slamming. Contact of a hydrofoil's hull with the water following a foil broach. See **broach, to.**

hump. The "hump" formed on the graph of resistance against the speed of a displacement vessel or ACV. The maximum of the "hump" corresponds to the speed of the wave generated by the hull or air depression.

hump speed. Critical speed at which the curve on a graph of wave making drag of an ACV tends to hump or peak. As speed is increased, the craft over-rides its bow wave; the wave making drag diminishes and the rate of acceleration rapidly increases.

hydrofoils. Small wings, almost identical in section to those of an aircraft, and designed to generate lift. Since water has a density some 815 times that of air, the same lift as an aeroplane wing is obtained for only $\frac{1}{815}$ of the area (at equal speeds).

hydroskimmer. Name given originally to experimental air cushion vehicles built under contract to the US Navy Bureau of Ships. Preference was given to this name since it gave the craft a sea-service identity.

inclined shaft. A marine drive shaft used in

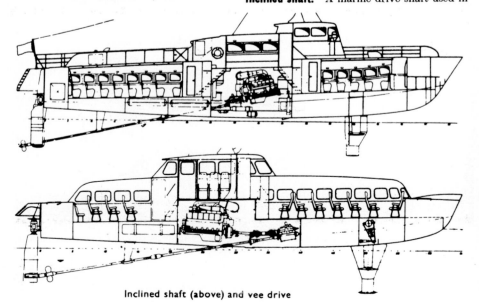

Inclined shaft (above) and vee drive

small vee foil and shallow-draught submerged foil craft, with keels only a limited height above the mean water level. The shaft is generally short and inclined at about 12°-14° to the horizontal. On larger craft, designed for operation in higher waves, the need to fly higher necessitates alternative drive arrangements such as the vee drive and Z-drive, the water jet system or even air propulsion.

Indirect operating cost. Costs incurred apart from running a craft. Includes advertising, buildings, rents, rates and salaries for terminal staff other than those employed for craft maintenance.

induced wave drag. Drag caused by the hollow depressed in the water by an ACV's air cushion. As the craft moves forward the depression follows along beneath it, building up a bow wave and causing wave drag as in a displacement craft until the hump speed has been passed.

integrated lift-propulsion system. An ACV lift and propulsion system operated by a common power source, the transmission and power-sharing system allowing variation in the division of power.

JP-4. Liquid fuel, based on kerosene, used widely in gas-turbines.

keel. (a) The "backbone" of a hull.
(b) An extension of an ACV's fore-and-aft stability air jet, similar in construction and shape to a skirt, and taking the form of an inflated bag.

knitmesh pads. Thick, loosely woven pads, in either metal or plastic wire fitted in the engines air intake to filter out water and solid particles from the engine air.

knot. A nautical mile per hour.

land to. At the end of a run hyfrodoils and ACVs are said to settle "down" or "land".

LIMRV. Abbrev. Linear Induction Motor Research Vehicle.

landing pads, also **hard points.** Strengthened areas of the hull on which an ACV is supported when at rest on land. These may also provide attachment points for towing equipment, lifts and jacks.

leading frequency of sea waves. See **significant wave height.** Sea waves are composed of different frequencies. The sea wave of greatest energy content is called the sea wave of leading frequency.

leakage rate. Rate at which air escapes from an air cushion, measured in cubic metres or cubic feet per second.

lift fan. See also **axial flow lift fan** and **centrifugal flow lift fan.** A fan used to supply air under pressure to an air cushion, and/or to form curtains.

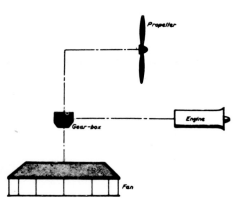
Integrated lift-propulsion system

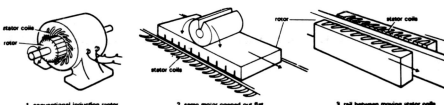
1 conventional induction motor   2 same motor opened out flat   3 rail between moving stator coils
Principle of the linear induction motor

lift off. An ACV is said to lift off when it rises from the ground on its air cushion.

linear induction motor. Linear induction motors show considerable promise as a means of propulsion for tracked skimmers, and are now under development in France, the United Kingdom, West Germany, Italy, Japan, the United States and USSR. An attractive feature of this method of electric traction is that it does not depend upon the vehicle having contact with the track or guideway.

The motor can be likened to a normal induction motor opened out flat. The "stator" coils are attached to the vehicle,

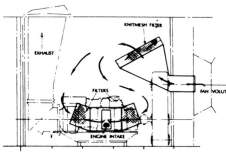
Gas turbine air filtration path on the Vosper Thornycroft VT 1, showing the knitmesh filter pad

while the "rotor" consists of a flat rail of conductive material which is straddled by the stator poles. The variable frequency multiphase AC current required for the linear motor can either be generated aboard the vehicle or collected from an electrified track.

Although the mounting of the stators on the vehicle appears to be preferred in Europe at present they can also be built into the guideway. In this case the rotor, in the form of a reaction rail, would be suspended from the vehicle. It would be of sufficient length to span several of the fixed stators simultaneously to avoid jerking.

load factor. Relationship between the payload capacity available, and the capacity filled.

logistics. Science of transporting, accommodating and supplying troops.

longitudinal framing. Method of hull construction employing frames set in a fore and aft direction or parallel to the keel.

maglev (abbrev). magnetic levitation.

multiple skirt. System devised by M. Jean Bertin, employing a number of separate flexible skirts for his system of individually fed, multiple air cushions.

nautical mile. A distance of 6,080 ft or one minute of latitude at the equator.

Naviplane. Name for the overwater or amphibious air cushion vehicles developed in France by SEDAM.

net tonnage. Total tonnage of a craft based on cubic capacity of all space available for carrying revenue-producing cargo less allowance for the engine room, crew quarters, water ballast, stores and other areas needed to operate the craft.

orbital motion. Orbital or circular motion of the water particles forming waves. The circular motion decreases in radius with increasing depth. It is the peculiar sequence of the motion that causes the illusion of wave translation. In reality the water moves very little in translation. The circular directions are: up at the wave front, forward at the crest, down at the wave back and back at the trough.

payload weight. Weight of revenue earning load, excluding crew and fuel.

PTO. See **power take-off unit.**

peripheral jet. See **air curtain** and **hovercraft.**

peripheral jet cushion system. A ground cushion generated by a continuous jet of air issued through ducts or nozzles around the outer periphery of the base of a craft. The cushion is maintained at above ambient pressure by the horizontal change of momentum of the curtain.

peripheral trunk. See **skirt.**

pitch. Rotation or oscillation of the hull about a transverse axis in a seaway. Also angle of air or water propeller blades.

pitch angle. Pitch angle a craft adopts relative to a horizontal datum.

platform, to. Approximately level flight of a hydrofoil over waves of a height less than the calm water hull clearance.

plenum. Space or air chamber beneath or surrounding a lift fan or fans through which air under pressure is distributed to a skirt system.

plenum chamber cushion system. The most simple of air cushion concepts. Cushion pressure is maintained by pumping air continuously into a recessed base without the use of a peripheral jet curtain.

"plough in". A bow down attitude resulting from the bow part of the skirt contacting the surface and progressively building up a drag. Unless controlled this can lead to a serious loss of stability and possibly an overturning moment.

With the skirt's front outer edge dragging on the water towards the centre of the craft (known as 'tuck under') there is a marked reduction in righting moment of the cushion pressure. As the downward pitch angle increases, the stern of the craft tends to rise from the surface and excessive yaw angles develop. Considerable deceleration takes place down to hump speed and the danger of a roll over in a small craft is accentuated by following waves which further increase the pitch angle.

Solutions include the provision of vent holes on a skirt's outer front to reduce its drag through air lubrication, and the development of a bag skirt which automatically bulges outwards on contact with the water, thereby delaying tuck under and providing a righting moment.

power take off unit. Unit for transmitting power from the main engine or engines, generally for auxiliary services required while a craft is under way, such as hydraulics, alternators and bilge pumps.

pvc. Polyvinylchloride.

puff ports. Controlled apertures in a skirt system or cushion supply ducting through which air can be expelled to assist control at low speeds.

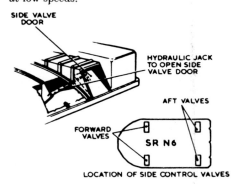
Puff port arrangement on the BHC SR.N6

ram wing. See **air cushion vehicles.**

recirculation system. An air curtain employing a recirculating air flow, which is maintained within and under the craft.

reliability factor. Percentage relationship between the number of trips scheduled and those achieved.

Ro-Ro. (abbrev USA). Roll-on roll-off. Applied to ships and air cushion vehicles with decks providing straight through loading facilities, i.e. with cargo ramps or loading doors fore and aft.

roll. Oscillation or rotation of a hull about a longitudinal axis.

roll attitude. Angle of roll craft adopts relative to a longitudinal datum.

running time. Time during which all machinery has been in operation, including idling time.

SAR. Abbrev. Search and rescue.

SES. See **surface effect ship.**

SEV. Surface effect vehicle. Currently used in the USA to describe air cushion vehicles of all types. In the Soviet Union, the term is employed to describe large sea- or ocean-going wing-in-ground-effect machines.

Savitsky Flap. Hinged vertical control flaps employed for foil lift variation, attached to the trailing edge of the foil struts, and canted out at an angle. The flaps are attached mechanically to the trailing-edge flaps on the foil. At the normal flying height only the lower part of the Savitsky flap is submerged.

As more of the flap becomes submerged due to increased wave height, the moment of the flap increases causing it to raise the the foil flap, thus increasing lift and restoring normal inflight attitude and flying height. The system can be adjusted to react only to lower-frequency layer waves. The system is employed on the Atlantic Hydrofoils Flying Cloud and Sea World. It was invented by Dr Daniel Savitsky of the Davidson laboratory.

seal. See **cushion seal.**

sea state. A scale of sea conditions classified from state 1, smooth, to state 8, precipitous, according to the wind duration, fetch and velocity, also wave length, period and velocity.

semi-submerged propeller. A concept for the installation of a partially submerged, supercavitating propeller on ship-size air cushion vehicles, driven through the sidewall transom. The advantages of this type of installation include considerable drag reduction due to the absence of inclined shafts and their supporting structures, and possibly the elimination of propeller erosion as a result of appendage cavity impingement.

service speed. Cruising speed obtained by an average crew in an average craft on a given route.

set down. To lower an air cushion vehicle onto its landing pads.

skirt. Flexible fabric extension hung between an ACV's metal structure and the surface to give increased obstacle and overwave clearance capability for a small air gap clearance and therefore reduced power requirement. The skirt deflects when encountering waves or solid obstacles, then returns to its normal position, the air gap being increased only momentarily. On peripheral jet ACV's the skirt is a flexible extension of the peripheral jet nozzle with

inner and outer skins hung from the inner and outer edges of the air duct and linked together by chain ties or diaphragms so that they form the correct nozzle profile at the hemline.

skirt, bag. Simple skirt design consisting of an inflated bag. Sometimes used as transverse and longitudinal stability skirts.

skirt, finger. Skirt system designed by British Hovercraft Corporation, consisting of a fringe of conically shaped nozzles attached to the base of a bag or loop skirt. Each nozzle or finger fits around an air exit hole and channels cushion air inwards towards the bottom centre of the craft.

skirt, segmented. Conceived by Hovercraft Development Ltd's Technical Group, this skirt system is employed on the HD.2, Vosper Thornycroft VT1, VT2 and many new craft either under design or construction. It is also being employed for industrial applications, including hoverpallets and hovertrailers.

The flexible segments are located around the craft periphery, each being attached to the lower edge of a sheet of light flexible material, which inflates to an arc shape, and also to the craft hard structure.

The system enables the craft to clear high waves and obstacles as the segments occupy a substantial part of the full cushion depth. No stability skirts or other forms of compartmentation are necessary. A smooth ride is provided as the skirt has good response due to low inertia.

The cushion area can be the same as the craft hard structure plan area. The skirt inner attachment points can be reached without jacking the craft up from its off-cushion position, simplifying maintenance.

skirt shifting. A control system in which movement of the centre of area of the cushion is achieved by shifting the skirt along one side, which has the effect of tilting the craft. Pitch and roll trim can be adjusted by this method.

sidewall vessel. An ACV with its cushion air contained between immersed sidewalls or skegs and transverse air curtains or skirts fore and aft. Stability is provided by the buoyancy of the sidewalls and their planing forces.

single shaft gas-turbine. A gas-turbine with a compressor and power turbine on a common shaft.

significant wave height. Sea waves are composed of different frequencies and have different wave heights (energy spectrum). A wave with the leading frequency of this spectrum and energy content is called the significant wave. It is from this wave that the significant wave height is measured.

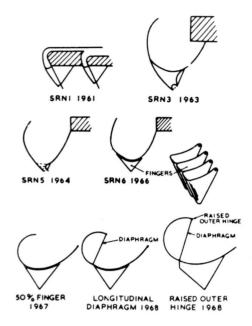

SRN1 1961 **SRN3 1963**

SRN5 1964 **SRN6 1966**

50% FINGER 1967 **LONGITUDINAL DIAPHRAGM 1968** **RAISED OUTER HINGE 1968**

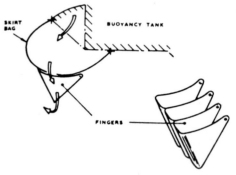

Types of finger skirts developed by British Hovercraft Corporation

split foil. A main foil system with the foil area divided into two, either to facilitate retraction, or to permit the location of the control surfaces well outboard, where foil control and large roll correcting moments can be applied for small changes in lift.

stability curtain. Transverse or longitudinal air curtains dividing an air cushion in order to restrict the cross flow of air within the cushion and increase pitch and roll stability.

stability skirt. A transverse or longitudinal skirt dividing an air cushion so as to restrict

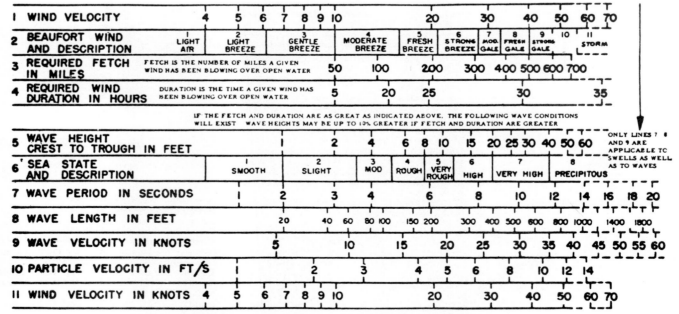

1	WIND VELOCITY				4	5	6	7	8	9	10		20		30		40	50	60	70
2	BEAUFORT WIND AND DESCRIPTION	1 LIGHT AIR	2 LIGHT BREEZE	3 GENTLE BREEZE			4 MODERATE BREEZE			5 FRESH BREEZE		6 STRONG BREEZE	7 MOD. GALE	8 FRESH GALE	9 STRONG GALE	10	11		STORM	
3	REQUIRED FETCH IN MILES	FETCH IS THE NUMBER OF MILES A GIVEN WIND HAS BEEN BLOWING OVER OPEN WATER					50		100		200		300	400	500	600	700			
4	REQUIRED WIND DURATION IN HOURS	DURATION IS THE TIME A GIVEN WIND HAS BEEN BLOWING OVER OPEN WATER					5		20		25			30			35			

IF THE FETCH AND DURATION ARE AS GREAT AS INDICATED ABOVE, THE FOLLOWING WAVE CONDITIONS WILL EXIST   WAVE HEIGHTS MAY BE UP TO 10% GREATER IF FETCH AND DURATION ARE GREATER

5	WAVE HEIGHT CREST TO TROUGH IN FEET					1		2		4		6	8	10	15	20	25	30	40	50	60
6	SEA STATE AND DESCRIPTION	1 SMOOTH		2 SLIGHT			3 MOD	4 ROUGH	5 VERY ROUGH		6 HIGH		7 VERY HIGH		8 PRECIPITOUS						
7	WAVE PERIOD IN SECONDS	1		2		3		4			6		8		10	12	14	16	18	20	
8	WAVE LENGTH IN FEET			20		40	60	80 100		150 200		300	400	500 600		800 1000		1400	1800		
9	WAVE VELOCITY IN KNOTS			5			10		15		20		25		30	35	40	45	50 55 60		
10	PARTICLE VELOCITY IN FT/S			1			2		3		4	5	6		8	10	12	14			
11	WIND VELOCITY IN KNOTS			4	5	6	7	8 9	10		20		30		40		50	60	70		

ONLY LINES 7 8 AND 9 ARE APPLICABLE TO SWELLS AS WELL AS TO WAVES

Chart of sea state conditions. Corresponding values lie on a vertical line

cross flow within the cushion and increase pitch or roll stability.

strake. (a) a permanent band of rubber or other hard wearing material along the sides of a craft to protect the structure from chafing against quays, piers and craft alongside. (b) lengths of material fitted externally to a flexible skirt and used to channel air downwards to reduce water drag.

submerged foil system. A foil system employing totally submerged lifting surfaces. The depth of submergence is controlled by mechanical, electronic or pneumatic systems which alter the angle of incidence of the foils or flaps attached to them to provide stability and control. See **foil systems.**

supercavitating foil. A general classification given to foils designed to operate efficiently at high speeds while fully cavitated. Since at very high speeds foils cannot avoid cavitation, sections are being designed which induce the onset of cavitation from the leading edge and cause the cavities to proceed downstream and beyond the trailing edge before collapsing. Lift and drag of these foils is determined by the shape of the leading edge and undersurface.

surf. The crests of waves that break in shallow water on a foreshore.

surface effect ship. Term implying a large ship-size ACV, regardless of specific type.

The various surface effect ship concepts are illustrated. For further definitions see **air cushion vehicles.**

surface piercing a.c.v. A craft with rigid sidewalls that penetrate the water surface. The air cushion is contained laterally by the sidewalls and at the bow and stern by flexible seals. (see sidewall air cushion vehicles or surface effect ships).

surf zone. Area from the outer waves breaking on the shore to the limit of their uprush on a beach.

TLACV. Abbrev. Track-laying air cushion vehicle. Air cushion vehicle employing looped caterpillar-like tracks for propulsion. The air cushion and its seals may be located between the flexible tracks, as in the case of the Soviet MVP-3 series, or it can take the form of a broad belt or track that loops round the complete air cushion. The latter approach is being developed by the Ashby Institute Belfast.

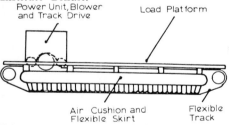

Track laying air cushion vehicle operating on a broad track that loops around the air cushion. This approach is being developed at the Ashby Institute, Belfast

TLRV. Abbrev. Tracked Levitated Research Vehicle.

take-off speed. Speed at which the hull of a hydrofoil craft is raised clear of the water, dynamic foil lift taking over from static displacement or planing of the hull proper.

tandem foils. Foil system in which the area of the forward foils is approximately equal to that of the aft foils, balancing the loading between them.

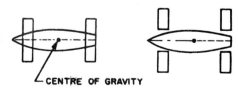

Tandem foil system. The foil areas can be "split" into two to facilitate retraction

terramechanics. Study of the general relationship between the performance of an off-road vehicle and its physical environment.

thickness-chord ratio. Maximum thickness of a foil section in relation to its chord.

Single shaft gas turbine

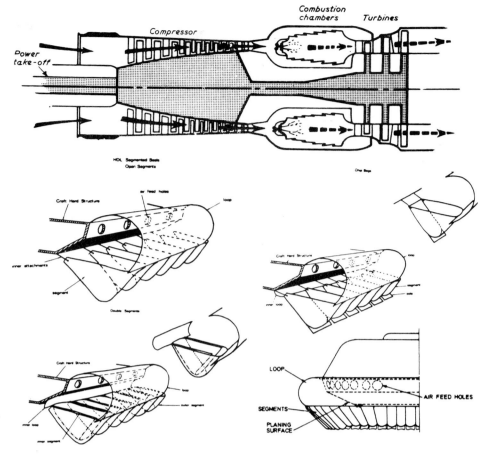

Segmented skirt developed by Hovercraft Development Ltd and employed on the HD.2. The separate segments occupy the full depth of the cushion between the hard structure and the supporting surface

Underside of the SR.N4 showing stability skirts

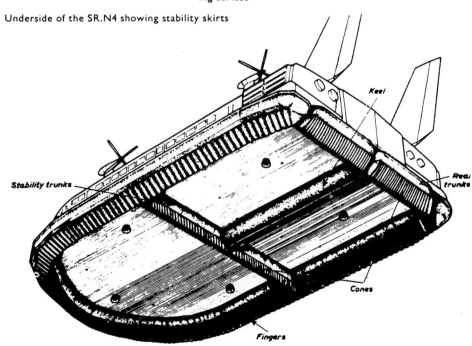

thruster. Controlled aperture through which air can be expelled to assist control at low speeds.

Tietjens-type foil. Named after Professor Tietjens, this system was based on a forward swept (surface piercing) main foil located almost amidships and slightly ahead of the centre of gravity. It was intended that the pronounced sweep of the vee foils would result in an increasing area of the foil further forward coming into use to increase the bow up trim of the craft when lift was lost. The considerable length of unsupported hull ahead of the centre of gravity meant the craft was constantly in danger of "digging in" in bad seas and it was highly sensitive to loading arrangements.

transcavitating foil. Thin section foil designed for smooth transition from fully wetted to supercavitating flow. By loading the tip more highly than the root, cavitation is first induced at the foil's tip, then extends spanwise over the foil to the roots as speed increases.

transisting foil. See **transcavitating foil.**

transit foil. See **transcavitating foil.**

transom. The last transverse frame of a ship's structure forming the stern board.

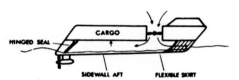

Transit foil operation

transverse framing. Steel frames running athwartships, from side to side, instead of in a fore and aft direction.

trapped air cushion vehicle. A concept for a skirt-type surface effect ship with 20 ft skirts separated from the water surface by a thin film of air lubrication.

trim. Difference between drafts forward and aft in a displacement vessel and by extension of the general idea. ACV and hydrofoil hull attitude relative to the line of flight.

turnround time. Time from doors open to doors closed between trips.

utilisation. Operating hours timed from doors closed to doors open, including man-oeuvring time.

utilisation, annual. Annual total of utilisation time.

variable-pitch propeller. A propeller with blades which can be rotated about their longitudinal axes to provide forward or reverse thrust.

ventilation. See **air entry.**

water wall ACV. A craft employing a curtain of water to retain its air cushion instead of an air curtain.

waterjet propulsion. A term now applied to a propulsion system devised as an alternative to supercavitating propellers for propelling high speed ship systems. Turbines drive pumps located in the hull, and water is pumped through high velocity jets above the water line and directed astern. The system weighs less than a comparable supercavitating propeller system and for craft with normal operating speeds above 45 knots it is thought to be competitive on an annual cost basis. First high speed applications include the Soviet Burevestnik and Chaika hydrofoils the Aerojet-General SES-100A testcraft and two products of the Boeing Company— the PGH-2 hydrofoil gunboat and the NATO PHM Fast Patrol Ship Guided Missile.

Waterjets are also being employed for propulsion at relatively low speeds. In the Soviet Union the Zarya shallow-draught waterbus (24 knots) and the Gorkovchanin sidewall ACV are propelled by waterjets. In the USA the PGH-1 and PGH-2 hydrofoils use waterjets for hullborne propulsion The jet can be turned easily to give side propulsion to facilitate docking which is not so easy for a normal propeller.

wave height. The vertical distance from wave trough to crest or twice the wave amplitude.

wave length. The horizontal distance between adjacent wave crests.

wave velocity. Speed at which a wave form travels along the sea surface. (The water itself remaining without forward movement).

weights. The subject of weights involves definition of format, nomenclature, and units. There are no generally accepted standards with respect to ACV and SES weights, except that small ACVs tend to follow aircraft practice and large types follow ship practice. The hydrofoil concepts are ship orientated. A consistently used format aids in evaluating the concept and permits usage on, or direct comparison with other designs. Format 1, below is according to US Naval practice and is suitable for all sizes of ACVs, SESs, and hydrofoils. The actual terminology used for the totals is optional, so that the nomenclature can be consistent with the size of the vessel. In presenting results, the units (short tons, long tons, metric tons, pounds, etc) should be clearly indicated.

SURFACE EFFECT SHIP CONFIGURATIONS

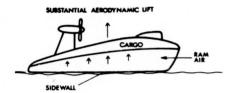

Ram wing SES

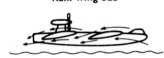

Wing-in-ground-effect SES

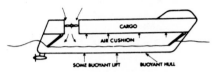

Aircat SES with wide buoyant hulls

Hybrid SES with rigid sidewalls and bow skirt

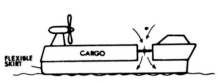

Air-propelled amphibious SES

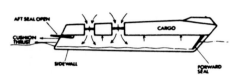

Airjet SES, propelled by cushion thrust

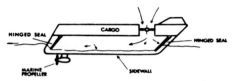

Sidewall SES. Also known as a captured air bubble or CAB type

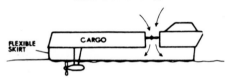

Water propelled, semi-amphibious SES

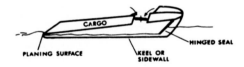

Air lubricated hull or hydrokeel SES

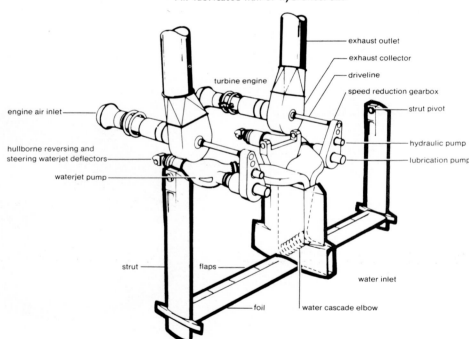

Waterjet propulsion system employed on the Boeing 929-100 Jetfoil, 106-ton, 190-250 passenger hydrofoil fast ferry

Format 2 is used by the Hovercraft industry in the United Kingdom. This emphasises equipment options, and by breaking down the expendable or useful load, the payload/range performance can be readily determined. It is also useful in defining first costs and operating costs.

winged hull. Alternative name given by Dr Alexander M. Lippisch to his range of aerodynamic ram-wing machines. See also **Aerofoil boat.**

wing-in-ground-effect. See **air cushion vehicle.** An aerodynamic-type air cushion vehicle which depends upon forward speed in order to develop lift. At speed lifting forces are generated both by the wing and a dynamic cushion of air built up beneath the vehicle and its supporting surface.

yaw angle. Rotation or oscillation of a craft about a vertical axis.

yaw-port. See **puff port.**

Z-drive. A drive system normally employed on hydrofoils to transmit power from the engine in the hull to the screw. Power is transmitted through a horizontal shaft leading to a bevel gear over the stern, then via a vertical shaft and a second bevel gear to a horizontal propeller shaft, thus forming a propeller "Z" shape.

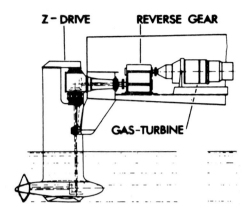

Z-Drive

HOVERCRAFT WEIGHT TERMS

Format 1

Group		Typical Items
1	Hull (or structure)	Basic structure, planting, frames, stringers, scantlings, decks, foundations, fittings, super-structure, doors and closures.
2	Propulsion	Engines, turbines, propellers, fans, gearboxes, shafting, drive systems, associated controls, nuclear plant, associated fluids.
3	Electrical	Power generation, switching. lighting, load canters, panels, cable
4	Communication and Control	Communications (internal, external) and navigation equipment, military electronics, computers, displays (note ship controls are in Group 5)
5	Auxiliary Systems	Fuel, heating, ventilation, fresh water, ship controls, rudder, cushion seal (flexible or articulated), plumbing, oil, fire extinguishing, drainage, ballast, mooring, anchoring, hydrofoils distilling plant.
6	Outfit and Furnishings	Hull fittings, marine hardware, ladders, furnishings, boats, rafts, preservers, stowages, lockers, painting, deck covering, hull insulation, commissary equipment, radiation shielding (other than at reactor area)
7	Armament	Weapons, mounts, ammunition stowage, handling systems, special plating
Total: Light Ship or Light Displacement or Empty Weight		(sum of the above items)
Variable Load or Useful Load		Operating personnel and effects, cargo, freight fuel, passengers, baggage, water, ammunition, aircraft, stores, troops, provisions.
Full Load Displacement or Load Displacement or Gross Weight or All Up Weight		(sum of empty weight and useful load)

Format 2

Standard Bare Weight

(1) Weight of structure, power plants & systems considered to be integral parts of the standard craft
(2) Oil (turbine engines only)
(3) Full hydraulic/pneumatic/cooling etc. systems
(4) Essential standard equipment common to all customer requirements
(5) Unusable fuel
(6) Other unconsumable liquids

Customer Equipment Weight

(1) Flight crew seats
(2) Flight crew emergency equipment
(3) Soundproofing, trim, partitions, floor covering etc. in payload areas
(4) Passenger seats, tables, lockers and other furnishings
(5) Heating, ventilating and air conditioning
(6) Toilet and washing facilities
(7) Galley facilities
(8) Domestic water supply (inc toilet)
(9) Fire precautions in payload areas
(10) Marine equipment
(11) Life rafts and containers
(12) Life jackets and stowages
(13) Emergency equipment (axes, first aid etc)
(14) Radio
(15) Radar
(16) Navaids
(17) Intercommunication and internal broadcasting
(18) Racking (for 14-17)
(19) Weapon and system installations
(20) Signalling equipment, distress flares etc
(21) Environmental equipment
(22) Long range tankage and system

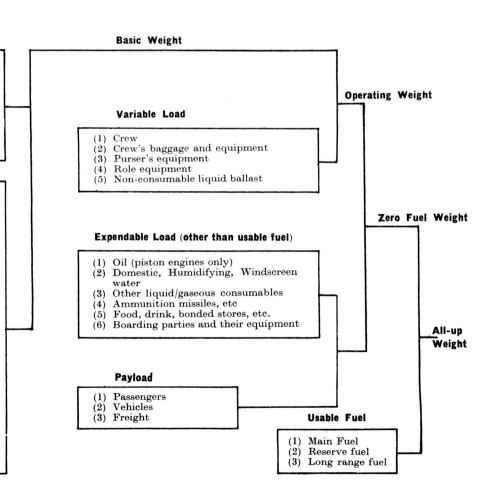

ADDENDA

AIR CUSHION VEHICLES

BRITISH HOVERCRAFT CORPORATION

HEAD OFFICE:
  East Cowes, Isle of Wight
TELEPHONE:
  Cowes 4121
TELEX:
  86190
TELEGRAMS:
  BRITHOVER COWES TELEX
DIRECTORS:
  See Main Entry

BHC MINE CLEARANCE HOVERCRAFT

Minesweeping is one of the most hazardous of all naval activities. Clearance techniques in the past have been very much on a hit or miss basis with craft operating in pairs, one sweeping and the other hunting and destroying the released mines as they surfaced by rifle and machinegun fire. Since the precise location of each mine was unknown, it was not unusual for a released mine to surface in the path of or beneath the hull of the hunter craft.

In the United States in recent years, efforts to reduce the tremendous wastage in lives and craft led to the introduction of the Edo 105 and 106 foil-equipped catamaran minesweeping systems. These not only speed up the process of mine clearance, but since they are towed by helicopter, reduce very considerably the risks to the crews involved.

In the United Kingdom, the Ministry of Defence (Navy) has stated that as hovercraft normally operate clear of the water, they are less vulnerable to possible mine explosions than conventional vessels, and with mine countermeasures equipment they have a potential for this type of work.

British Hovercraft Corporation has announced plans for both sweeper and hunter versions of the BH.7 and the SR.N4 Descriptions of these vessels are given below.

BH.7 Mk. 5A MINESWEEPER

Among the advantages offered by the use of this type of fully amphibious hovercraft for MCM, as opposed to a displacement vessel are four times the transit speed; very low acoustic and magnetic underwater signatures; and virtual immunity to underwatwr explosions. Additionally, the craft can be used for crew rescue in mined waters. Since the craft is based on the standard BH.7 Mk5A, and retains its bow landing door, it has logistic support capability when not being employed for minesweeping.

LIFT AND PROPULSION: Integrated lift/propulsion system powered by a single Rolls-Royce/BS Marine Proteus 15M/549 gas-turbine with a continuous output at 15°C of 3,800 hp at 10,000 turbine rpm. This drives via a light alloy drive shaft and bevel drive gearbox, a BHC 12-blade, centrifugal 11 ft 6 in (3·5 m) diameter, lift fan and an HSD 4-blade, variable-pitch 21 ft (6·40 m) diameter, pylon-mounted propeller.

ACCOMMODATION: Total crew complement is eight men. The raised control cabin accommodates a three-man operating crew, with the captain and navigator in front and the third crew member behind. An off-duty cabin is located immediately beneath, with bunks for four. Ahead of the off-duty cabin is a galley and aft, in the

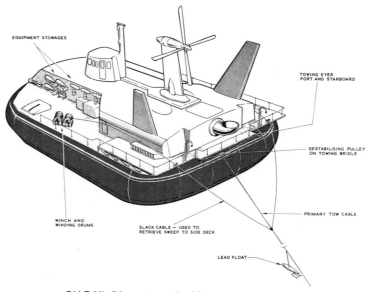

BH.7 Mk 5A equipped for Minesweeping

midship cabin, is the operations room with navigation, surface and under surface plotting tables, radar display and data processing equipment. The control cabin is air-conditioned and the rest areas are air-conditioned and soundproofed. Access from the off-duty cabin to the control cabin is via a ladder.

SYSTEMS, MCM EQUIPMENT: Minesweeping equipment, including winches and cable reels, are stowed on the side decks and sides of the superstructure forward. Equipment includes floats, depressors, otters and cutters, venturi acoustic sweeping gear, marker buoys and an inflatable dinghy.

SWEEP DEPLOYMENT: Sweeps are deployed from the port side deck and shackled to the primary tow cable which is permanently attached to the destabilising pulley running on the towing bridle.

DIMENSIONS, EXTERNAL:

Length overall	78 ft 4 in (23·9 m)
Beam overall	45 ft 6 in (13·9 m)
Height overall	
on cushion	38 ft 8 in (11·8 m)
on landing pads	34 ft 0 in (10·4 m)

DIMENSIONS, INTERNAL:
Cabin headroom, on centreline
    7 ft 10 in (2·4 m)
Bow door opening
  13 ft 9 in × 7 ft 3 in (4·1 m × 2·9 m)

WEIGHTS:

Starting all-up weight	53 tons app
Mean operating weight	48 ton app
MCM payload	3 tons app

PERFORMANCE:
Cruising speed, knots

Craft heading	Into wind	Beam wind
Calm water, still air	68	68
Significant wave height/wind speed		
1 ft/6 kt	57	59
2 ft/11 kt	47	52
3 ft/15 kt	38	44

ENDURANCE:
Total fuel consumption at max. continuous power (includes both APUs) 1·16 ton/hour
Endurance on a nominal 10 ton fuel load
    8·6 hours

Towing capability. A towing force of 3·5 tons is available at speeds of up to 10 knots in significant waveheights up to 3 ft.

BH.7 Mk 5A MINE HUNTER

This version is identical in practically every respect to the mine sweeper model and can be reconfigured readily to sweeping duties or logistic support roles. It differs from the sweeper only in the mine disposal equipment carried.

SYSTEMS: MCM EQUIPMENT: A 20 mm machine gun mount ahead of the control cabin is optional. Towed or dunking mine detection and classification sonars; remotely piloted mine disposal vehicles; sonar display units; recorders etc; navigation and communications gear.

DEPLOYMENT: Over the sidedecks via davits and swinging A frames. Towing lines are deployed and retrieved by winch and shackled to the primary tow cable which is permanently attached to the destabilising pulley running on the towing bridle.

PERFORMANCE:
Cruising and towing speed
    As for minesweeper
Endurance: In the case of a sonar being towed at a speed of 5 knots or less, but with the craft in full hover condition, the estimated fuel consumption (ton/hour) is:

Proteus	0·677 (ISA conditions)
2 Rover APU	
	0·111 (assumed requirement)
	0·778 Ton/hour total

On a nominal 10 ton fuel-load, endurance would be 12·9 hours

SR.N4 Mk 4 MINESWEEPER

The SR.N4 Mk 4 would have a transit speed of up to five times that of conventional minesweepers. It would also retain its logistic capability and operate as a support vessel when required. In most respects the craft would be similar to the SR.N4 Mk 2.

LIFT AND PROPULSION: Power is supplied by four Rolls-Royce Marine Proteus free turbine turboshaft engines located in pairs at the rear of the craft on either side of the working deck space. Each would operate at 3,800 shp when cruising. Each engine is connected to one of four identical propeller/fan units, two forward, two aft. The propellers, made by Hawker Siddely Dynamics, are of 4-bladed, variable and reversible pitch type, 21 ft (6·40 m) in diameter. The lift fans, made by BHC, are of 12-bladed centrifugal type, 11 ft 6 in (3·5 m) in diameter.

CONTROLS AND HULL: Similar to SR.N4 Mk 2.

ACCOMMODATION: Crew complement is up to twenty men, with 10-15 on watch. Rest areas and bunks are provided for 10 men.

A typical minesweeper interior places the operations room amidships, at the most advantageous position to minimise the effects of craft motion on the seated operators. Within the operator's room are navigation, surface and below-surface plotting tables and data processing equipment. The operators room and rest areas are ventilated by forced air and the noise level is 65-70 dbA.

Stowed on the works deck aft of the operations room are Oropesa sweeps, otters and floats, acoustic sweep equipment, side scan sonars, short scope buoys and an inflatable dighy. A pulse generator can be installed forward of the accomodation spaces. The entire work deck space is ventilated with forced air draught to prevent the ingress of spray and exhaust fumes.

EQUIPMENT DEPLOYMENT: All equipment is deployed over the stern via two destabilising carriages or davits. A main double warp winch is provided for wire sweeping. Space is available for a magnetic sweep reel.

WEAPONS: Two 20 mm, hand-operated machine guns can be fitted in recesses at main deck level in port and starboard forward quarters.

NAVIGATION:

Track: Pilot function, determined by limiting wind and sea conditions.

Position: Derived from external navigation datum.

Course to steer: Derived from navigation system computer.

DIMENSIONS, EXTERNAL:

Overall length	130 ft 2 in (39·68 m)
Beam	78 ft 0 in (23·77 m)
Height on landing pads	37 ft 8 in (11·48 m)

WEIGHTS:

Starting all-up weight	220 tons
Mean operating weight	200 tons
MCM equipment	35 tons

PERFORMANCE:

Cruising speed, knots.

Craft heading	Into wind	Beam and Downwind
Calm water, still air	69	69
Significant wave height/wind speed		
3 ft/15 kt	45	50
6 ft/25 kt	26	36
9 ft/30 kt	19	25

Endurance. Based on a nominal 40 ton fuel load, operation at 3,800 output hp/engine and continuous use of both APUs, endurance would be 9·3 hours.

Towing capability. A towing force of 8-20 tons is available at speeds of up to 10 knots in significant waveheights up to 9 ft.

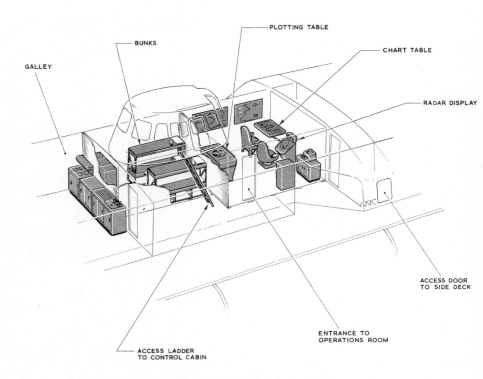

Interior layout of the BH.7 Mk 5A Minesweeper

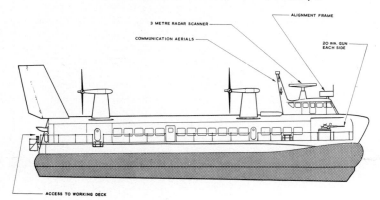

Above and below: Features of the SR.N4 Mk 4 Minesweeper •

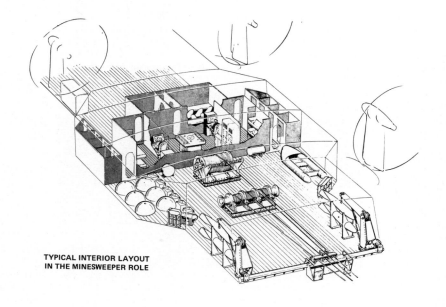

TYPICAL INTERIOR LAYOUT IN THE MINESWEEPER ROLE

SR.N4 Mk 4 MINEHUNTER

This variant of the SR.N4 is identical to the minesweeper model and can be converted readily to this configuration from the mine-sweeper role. It differs only in the mine disposal equipment carried.

The craft can operate in conjunction with conventional MCM vessels and does not need a separate remote platform for mine disposal equipment employment.

SYSTEMS, MCM EQUIPMENT: Towed or dunking sonar and mine disposal vehicles are deployed over the stern by means of stern davits. The craft can also deploy remote piloted vehicles. Two hand-operated 20 mm machine-guns mounts can be installed in the forward port and starboard quarters on the main deck.

BH.88

During the summer of 1975, BHC announced that it was developing a new generation hovercraft, designated BH.88, to replace the SR.N4. The new craft will be able to operate in winds of up to Force 9, have a higher cruising speed and use approximately one third of the fuel per passenger compared with that used the the SR.N4.

At present, BHC is awaiting a contract from British Rail Seaspeed for stretching its two standard SR.N4s. In lengthened form, the SR.N4 Mk 3 will provide much of the operational data for the projected BH.88, which will be of approximately the same size and carry a similar payload of 400 passengers and 50 cars—considered close to the optimum for cross-Channel routes. Improvements in the overall design will include a new propulsion system, employing either the latest large propellers or ducted fans, the installation of Rolls-Royce Marine Tyne gas-turbines to achieve a 25 per cent improvement in fuel consumption, lift fans of higher efficiency and a modified skirt and hull to reduce hydrodynamic resistance.

The new craft is expected to be about five knots faster than the SR.N4 and it will also show a 40 per cent reduction in power requirements and a 60 per cent saving in fuel. The fuel consumption is expected to be about 2·0 lb/payload ton-mile, some 15 per cent less than orthodox ships per unit of payload.

Estimated cost of the craft is about £6 million at today's prices, but at the same time an initial research and development investment of about £0·5 million is considered necessary. The craft will be suitable for many mixed ferry routes in the Pacific, North and Central America, Canada, Europe and the Mediterranean.

An artist's impression of one of the configurations under investigation accompanies this entry.

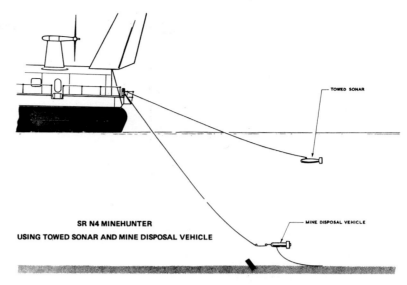

One of the sweeping techniques likely to be employed by the SR.N4 mine hunter.

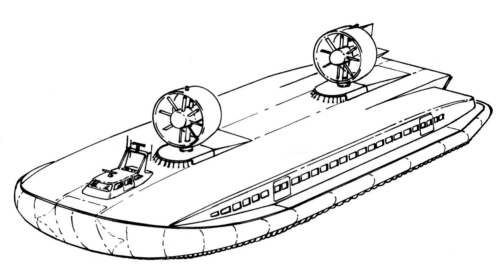

Features of the proposed 'aerodynamically clean' BH.88 will include ducted fans, a deeper cushion and an improved hull design.

PINDAIR LTD.

HEAD OFFICE:

Unit 11, Quay Lane, Hardway, Gosport, Hants, PO12 4LS

DIRECTORS, ETC:

See main entry.

GRIFFON

Production of the Griffon, a new inflatable-hulled 12-seater, designed by D. R. Robertson and E. W. H. Gifford, both directors of Hovertravel/Hoverwork, is to be undertaken by Pindair Ltd.

The craft is intended to fill the gap between a four-wheel-drive vehicle and a high speed ferry or workboat. It is fully amphibious and can operate in many places normally inaccessible to land vehicles and orthodox displacement boats. It is designed to carry up to 12 people or one ton of freight at speeds of up to 30 knots. Since it is inflatable, it is relatively light and can be folded to a small size for transport. Technical details will be made available once proving trials are completed.

Pindair Ltd. is a leading manufacturer of light hovercraft and examples of their two-seat Skima 2 and four-seat Skima 4 inflatable hovercraft are in use in more than twenty countries.

Griffon has a loop and segment skirt design, patented by Hovercraft Development Ltd which is providing Pindair with financial and technical assistance for the project.

VOSPER THORNYCROFT

HEAD OFFICE:
Vosper House, Southampton Road, Paulsgrove, Portsmouth PO6 4QA
TELEPHONE:
Cosham 79481
TELEX:
86115
DIRECTORS:
See main entry.

VOSPER VT 2 MINE COUNTERMEASURES

Vosper Thornycroft's VT 2 hovercraft, which is aimed primarily at the military market, underwent its first over water trials on September 2nd. From September 15-19th, the craft, which has a starting all-up weight of 105 tons, was displayed at the Royal Navy Equipment Exhibition at Greenwich. On the completion of manufacturer's trials it was due to be delivered to the Naval Hovercraft Trials Unit (formerly IHU), Lee-on-the-Solent, which is primarily concerned with the development of hovercraft for mine countermeasures duties.

Interest in amphibious hovercraft for this application stems from its relative invulnerability compared to displacement vessels, to underwater explosions and their low magnetic and underwater noise signatures. The accompanying drawing shows one possible arrangement of a VT 2 for this particular role.

As can be seen from the drawing, the VT 2 is of suitable size for this work. In the plan view the starboard propulsor is removed to show the sweepdeck space with sweepgear stowed. The gear illustrated is either in current use or readily available commercially.

The VT 2 prototype is powered by two 4,500 shp Rolls-Royce Proteus marine gas-turbines which gives it a maximum speed of approximately 60 knots. Alternative power-plants, such as the more powerful 5,800 shp Rolls-Royce Tyne RM2D, can be installed, if increased performance is required.

DIMENSIONS:

Length overall	98·5 ft (30·0 m)
Beam, hard structure	43·5 ft (13·25 m)
Height, on cushion, to top of propulsor	29·7 ft (9·0 m)

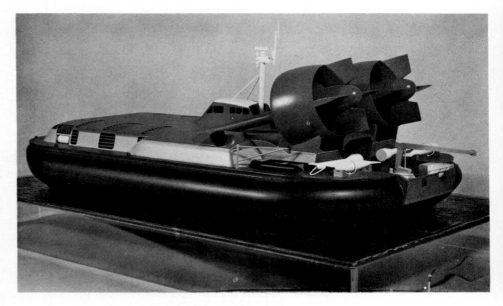

Model of the VT 2 in a possible MCM configuration

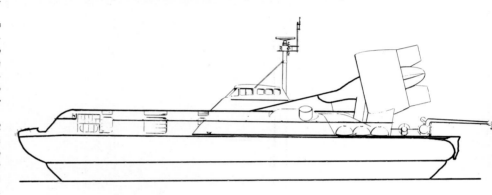

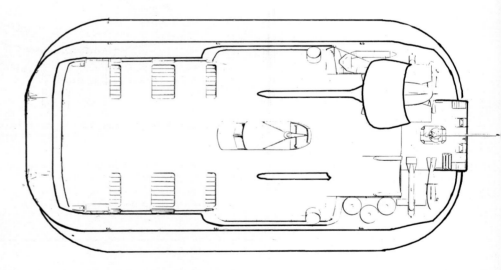

Vosper Thornycroft VT 2 in MCM configuration showing its sweepgear. The starboard propulsor is removed in the drawing to show the sweepdeck space with sweepgear stowed

BELL AEROSPACE

Bell Aerospace has received a $278,000 contract to participate as one of three industry teams in the design and model-testing high speed US Marine Corps combat vehicles to be known as the Landing Vehicles Assault (LVAs).

The project is being sponsored by the US Naval Sea Systems Command under a programme to examine vehicles to succeed the current LTVP-7, which is slow in water

operations. The LTVP-7 carries an assault force of twenty-five marines at 8 mph over-water toward the beach from the parent ship, then operates at 40 mph overland.

In contrast, the LVA will move at 35 to 70 mph over water and 40 to 55 mph overland with greatly improved rough ground performance.

The difference is the proposed Bell version has an air suspension system that in com-

bination with hydropneumatic track suspension gear will lift the LVA high in the water so it can skim the surface at high speed.

Several companies are participating with Bell in the project. General Motors Corp's Detroit Diesel Allison Division will design the transmission; National Water Lift Co. will design land running gear and the primary weapons system; Carborundum Corp., parasitic armour; and Alcoa, aluminium, armour. Rosenblatt & Sons, New York N.Y., will act as hydrodynamic consultants.

The initial 12-month phase of the programme involves building and testing a scale model of the LVA design. Preliminary model tests have already been conducted at Bell's Air Cushion Vehicle Laboratory.

The Bell LVA air suspension system is based on Bell's extensive background in air cushion vehicle technology. The system offers high overwater performance but yet does not degrade the land combat capabilities of the vehicle.

Impression of the projected Bell Landing Vehicle Assault, a Combat Vehicle for the US Marine Corps. It is designed to operate at 70 mph over water and 55 mph over land.

SOVIET UNION

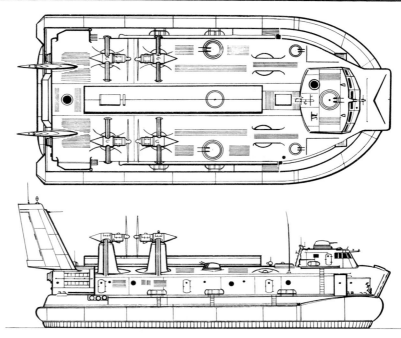

Provisional drawing of the 220-ton Aist armed logistic support hovercraft operated by the Soviet Navy

ACV OPERATORS

ACV OPERATORS
AUSTRALIA
DOLPHIN FERRIES PTY

Reports suggest that this craft is now operating HM.2 319 on the River Derwent, in Tasmania.

DEPARTMENT OF ABORIGINAL AFFAIRS

This Australian Government department has chartered SR.N5-001, which is being operated on medical and community support work in the Torres Strait region of Northern Australia. Operated by Hoverwork personnel, the craft has been in service since January 1975.

VENEZUELA
TOURISMO MARGARITA

On September 1st, 1975, Hovermarine Transport Ltd was awarded a £¾ million contract to supply three HM.2s to Venezuela. The purchaser, Tourisme Margarita will operate the craft between the Venuzuelan mainland and the duty-free Isle of Margarita.

HYDROFOIL OPERATORS

HYDROFOIL OPERATORS
JAPAN
ARIMURA LINE

Arimura Line is operating two Hitachi-built PT 50 Mk IIs, Kariyushi I and Kariyushi II. The two craft, both seating 125 passengers, are being employed to carry passengers to the Okinawa Ocean Exposition, which opened in July 1975 and will continue until mid-January 1976. The vessels are each operating five fifty-minute trips each way every day.

AUSTRALIA

ACVs and Hydrofoils
Department of Transport,
Civic Permanent Centre,
Allara Street,
Civic,
Australian Capital Territory,
Australia 2600.

Ministry of Motor Transport,
Rothchild Avenue,
Rosebery,
Sydney,
New South Wales,

Australia 2000.

Department of Harbours and Marine,
Edward Street,
Brisbane,
Queensland,
Australia 4000.

Department of Marine and Harbours,
211 Victoria Square West,
Adelaide,
South Australia,
Australia 5000.

Navigation and Survey Authority of
Tasmania,
1 Franklin Wharf,
Hobart,
Tasmania,
Australia 7000.

Harbour and Light Department,
Crane House,
185-187 High Street,
Fremantle,
West Australia,
Australia 6000.

INDEX

VT2
60 knots and
fully amphibious